McGRAW-HILL SERIES IN CHEMICAL ENGINEERING
SIDNEY D. KIRKPATRICK, *Consulting Editor*

THE CHEMICAL PROCESS INDUSTRIES

McGRAW-HILL SERIES IN CHEMICAL ENGINEERING
SIDNEY D. KIRKPATRICK, *Consulting Editor*

BUILDING FOR THE FUTURE OF A PROFESSION

Fifteen prominent chemical engineers first met in New York more than thirty years ago to plan a continuing literature for their rapidly growing profession. From industry came such pioneer practitioners as Leo H. Baekeland, Arthur D. Little, Charles L. Reese, John V. N. Dorr, M. C. Whitaker, and R. S. McBride. From the universities came such eminent educators as William H. Walker, Alfred H. White, D. D. Jackson, J. H. James, J. F. Norris, Warren K. Lewis, and Harry A. Curtis. H. C. Parmelee, then editor of *Chemical & Metallurgical Engineering*, served as chairman and was joined subsequently by S. D. Kirkpatrick as consulting editor.

After several meetings, this Editorial Advisory Committee submitted its report to the McGraw-Hill Book Company in September, 1925. In it were detailed specifications for a correlated series of more than a dozen text and reference books, including a chemical engineers' handbook and basic textbooks on the elements and principles of chemical engineering, on industrial applications of chemical synthesis, on materials of construction, on plant design, on chemical-engineering economics. Broadly outlined, too, were plans for monographs on unit operations and processes and on other industrial subjects to be developed as the need became apparent.

From this prophetic beginning has since come the McGraw-Hill Series in Chemical Engineering, which now numbers about thirty-five books. More are always in preparation to meet the ever-growing needs of chemical engineers in education and in industry. In the aggregate these books represent the work of literally hundreds of authors, editors, and collaborators. But no small measure of credit is due the pioneering members of the original committee and those engineering educators and industrialists who have succeeded them in the task of building a permanent literature for the classical engineering profession.

THE SERIES

The Chemical Process Industries

R. NORRIS SHREVE

Consulting Chemical Engineer
Professor of Chemical Engineering
Purdue University

SECOND EDITION

McGRAW-HILL BOOK COMPANY, INC.

New York   Toronto   London

1956

THE MAPLE PRESS COMPANY, YORK, PA.

This book represents a lifetime of experience in the chemical industry. As such it should be and is dedicated to him who helped to give the author his start in the chemical field

EDWARD MALLINCKRODT, JR.

PREFACE

Chemical engineering underlies the chemical process industries, and the emphasis on this has been the main objective in writing this book. Other objectives, and the ways in which they have been approached, are explained in detail in Chapter 1.

This second edition represents a checking of the literature and of the chemical industry since the first edition appeared. The literature covered is to January 1954, with a very few notable articles which have been added while the manuscript was being put into print. The statistics for the inorganic field cover generally through 1952 because of the very serious delay in getting out the recent statistics on the part of the U.S. Bureau of the Census. However, most of the industries that fall within the organic field actually have many figures through December, 1954, because of the very prompt and up-to-date publications of these statistics by the U.S. Tariff Commission.

The question of nomenclature is often a troublesome one, particularly for industrial usage. It is difficult to get people in industry to employ the scientific nomenclature such as has been adopted by *Chemical Abstracts*. In most cases this text follows the scientific nomenclature of *Chemical Abstracts* with the exception that for long, complicated organic names hyphens are inserted frequently to break these names into their component parts. This is much better than the writing of these names as separate words as is done so frequently in industry. An example is the writing of chloro-nitro-benzene rather than chloronitrobenzene or chloro nitro benzene. However, as a concession to wide industrial usage, glycerine is used rather than glycerol and gelatine rather than gelatin.

This book has as an important part—many flow sheets. These have all been gone over carefully by the author and by experts in the respective industries. Many have been corrected, some only in a minor way. Obsolete flow sheets have been discarded and new ones added.

Many of the older references appearing in the first edition have been dropped unless there was a special reason for such retention. Newer references have been added.

One of the most disputed points in the first edition, particularly from the point of view of teachers in chemical engineering, was concerned with the problems. The majority wanted these short problems dropped as not worthwhile; however, an influential group considered them very useful. After weighing the whole situation, these problems were removed from the ends of the chapters and placed in a special appendix arranged by chapter headings and supplemented very importantly by references to the book by Lewis, Radasch, and Lewis entitled "Industrial Stoichiometry." The book by Lewis, Radasch, and Lewis will be of very great service as a teaching aid particularly since the problems given by these authors have their principles fully discussed in this special problem book. Furthermore, comprehensive problems are included which are more useful than short special problems. The author in his teaching of this subject for over 25 years has found comprehensive problems particularly helpful.

This book has a dual purpose. It is a college text to integrate various courses and to give the young chemical engineer some comprehension of the various fields into which he will enter or with which he will be affiliated even if only indirectly. It is also a reference book for practicing chemical engineers and chemists. For them the various outline flow sheets are supplemented with references to pictured flow sheets in *Chemical Engineering* which will furnish the details a practicing engineer will need but which would be confusing to students. Also the many references in the footnotes and under "Selected References" at the end of each chapter will be of most value to the practicing chemical engineer and chemist. However, the students should always look up the references to Perry's third edition of "Chemical Engineers' Handbook." If it had not been for the good coverage in Perry's Handbook on equipment, many more pages would have needed to be added to this textbook.

As is true of a book of this nature, no one author can know the whole field. Therefore, the policy pursued in the first edition has been carried out in the second where chapters and parts of chapters have been submitted to experts for checking. Not only did many experienced teachers and practicing engineers help in the first edition but they have also cooperated in this, supplemented by many new ones. In particular, it is a pleasure to acknowledge the following who have aided materially: Raymond H. Ewell, Robert C. Forney, George T. Austin, Charles H. Prien, Donald F. Othmer, Kenneth A. Kobe, H. A. Lubs, Otto Stallmann, Brage Golding, Jacqueline Bailey, James D. Idol, H. M. Kurihara, Eskell Nordell, U. B. Yeager, H. S. Turner, H. J. Rose, A. R. Powell, H. A. Gollmar, Carl Ulmer, Currey E. Ford, George W. Feus, W. W. Palmquist, Stanley E. Zager, J. C. Radamaker, Paul D. V. Manning, R. W. Mumford, H. H. Bruhn, R. M. Hunter, R. C. Specht, W. M. Leaders, Charles D. Harrington, E. F. Richner, G. E. Matthews, T. H. James, E. K. Carver, R. M. Evans, Max Spencer, R. E. Hall, G. P. Halberstadt, Foster D. Snell, Sylvan B. Lee, Jerome Martin, R. J. Hickey, A. R. Miller, A. B. Welty, C. E. Springhorn, Gustav Egloff, Hans Z. Lecher, Walter M. Ralph, W. B. Hardy, W. D. Appel, and J. D. Fennesbresque.

The revision of this book could not have been done in this time without the meticulous and skilled help given by Marilyn G. Forney and Elizabeth Prentiss who have worked closely with me over the last few years. Mrs. Forney and Miss Prentiss have also prepared the indexes.

As it is impossible to catch every mistake, the author requests that any errors that are found be brought to his attention for correction in subsequent printings.

R. NORRIS SHREVE

CONTENTS

CHAPTER 1

OBJECTIVES[1]

Chemical engineering has been well defined for the American Institute of Chemical Engineers as follows:

Chemical engineering is that branch of engineering concerned with the development and application of manufacturing processes in which chemical or certain physical changes of materials are involved. These processes may usually be resolved into a coordinated series of unit physical operations and unit chemical processes. The work of the chemical engineer is concerned primarily with the design, construction, and operation of equipment and plants in which these unit operations and processes are applied. Chemistry, physics, and mathematics are the underlying sciences of chemical engineering, and economics its guide in practice.[2]

These unit operations or *physical* changes and these unit processes or *chemical* changes may be accepted as the units or blocks into which we can break down the manufacturing processes of the various chemical industries. Many now hold that these two concepts bring unifying principles into what was previously a large, diversified group of apparently unrelated industries. Beginning in Chap. 2, this book correlates these two concepts as they are applied to the various chemical process industries.

Chemical engineering has been defined more fundamentally and yet in more precise terms in the new Constitution, 1954, of the American Institute of Chemical Engineers as "the application of the principles of the physical sciences together with the principles of economics and human relations to fields that pertain directly to processes and process equipment in which matter is treated to effect a change in state, energy content or composition."

The objectives sought are to present a cross section of the manufacturing procedures employed by modern chemical industries, largely

[1] This short chapter is actually an introduction to this book, its aims and methods. The author would strongly urge that, when the book is employed as a text, the instructor assign this chapter to the students for study and discussion so that they may early gain a comprehension of the fundamental viewpoints as well as the objectives sought.

[2] NEWMAN, Development of Chemical Engineering Education, *Trans. Am. Inst. Chem. Engrs.*, Supplement to **34** (3a), 6 (July 25, 1938); see also *Trans. Am. Inst. Chem. Engrs.*, **32**, 568 (1936).

separated into their unit chemical processes and unit physical operations through the help of flow charts. The presentation is from the viewpoint of the fundamental chemistry involved in the changes necessary to make the processes operate and of the energy released or absorbed in the reactions, as well as the energy required for evaporation, fusion, and related operations. Because we must have a yardstick to evaluate these industries, domestic statistics of production and consumption are frequently cited with dollar values where available. Likewise costs and other phases of the economic picture are included. Because these are industrial processes, the equipment necessary to carry out the chemical reactions on an industrial scale is of paramount importance.

These chemical process industries not only involve the manufacture of chemicals as such, but they embrace many manufacturing processes based on important chemical changes. Such processes naturally include a considerable variety of operations based on data and principles from other branches of science and engineering. Therefore, it may well be maintained that the chemical process industries represent the summation or the integration of the contributions of many scientists, engineers, and technologists. Specifically, any description of these industries should show the reason why a chemical engineer or an industrial chemist should be interested in inorganic or organic chemistry, physical chemistry, analytical chemistry, physics, mathematics, as well as the modern concept of chemical engineering in its twofold application of unit operations and unit processes. Nor should we forget, of course, that all these activities are carried on to make money and hence exist under the enveloping mantle of sound economics and business principles. Included in this integration should be such other divisions of engineering as strength of materials and the fundamentals of electrical engineering. Hence, to the student, this book may well be the link, or tie, between many of his basic scientific and technical courses, on the one hand, and their industrial application, on the other.

Because of space limitations, very little has been included pertaining to the chemical industries of foreign countries. Their practice is available from the detailed presentations,[1] in many volumes, by Thorpe and Ullmann, to which references are given at the end of this chapter. Nor is any attempt made here to supply the names of companies in the various branches of chemical industry, although there is an occasional reference

---

[1] Reports on German and Japanese technology covering the period 1939–1945 are obtainable from the Office of Technical Services, U.S. Department of Commerce, Washington, D.C., and from the British Intelligence Objectives Sub-Committee (the BIOS reports), 32 Bryanston Square, London, W. I. Many foreign processes are also covered in KIRK and OTHMER, "Encyclopedia of Chemical Technology," 15 vols., The Interscience Encyclopedia, Inc., New York, 1947–1956. However, this most excellent encyclopedia deals mainly with United States technology. Hereafter, this will be referred to as KIRK and OTHMER, *op. cit.*

to a specific company. However, the full listing of such companies is obtainable from a number of trade directories and from the pages of various chemical publications, including the "Chemical Engineering Catalog."

Most chemical engineers do not have intimate contact with more than one industry. With this in mind, the text emphasizes not details but broad principles, or a distinguishing characteristic of a certain process or industry. These should be a part of the working knowledge of even the engineer who becomes a specialist, for he never knows when he can translate to his own field a principle that has been put into practice in another process. For the growing number of chemical engineers who enter sales, executive, or management positions, a broader acquaintance with the chemical industry in its entirety is essential. For all these, the specialist, the salesman, and the manager, the flow sheets will present in a connected logical manner an over-all viewpoint of many processes, from raw materials to salable products, such as has been developed so excellently by our competitive system under the economic stimulus and wise temporary protection of our patent laws.

The presentation of the chemical process industries around the flow sheets and the energy changes ought to lead to a logical following through of a connected series of unit operations and unit processes, rather than to the memorizing of purely descriptive matter. These will emphasize the *why* rather than the *how* of industrial procedures, or *thinking* rather than *memorizing*.

An engineer has to do with the direction and control of *energy*. This energy may be expended in the moving of raw materials by ship, rail, or pipe line, it may be employed in the form of heat or steam or electricity, or it may be the energy that is given out in exothermic reactions or that which is absorbed in endothermic chemical reactions. The chemical engineer works with chemical change involving chemical reactions but, on the other hand, in these modern competitive times serious consideration should be given to the other types of energy expenditure connected particularly with the process with which he is concerned. The unit processes consider the change in chemical energy and the resultant effects. Unit operations include the physical changes in energy or position, such as heat flow, liquid flow, or separation; these frequently are an essential part of the fundamental unit process. It is thoroughly believed that the chemical engineer should also consider other broad energy expenditures, such as those represented by the transportation of raw materials. All of these enter into the cost.

The cost of things must be always in the consciousness of the engineer, since he is a part of our industrial system. One of the primary objectives of the engineer's endeavor should be to deliver the best product or the most efficient service at the lowest cost to the consuming public. Therefore, we may well say, quoting from Dean Emeritus A. A. Potter of Purdue University, "No matter what the numerator may be in an equation one may place before the students in an engineering institution, the dollar sign should appear in the denominator, either apparent or latent."

Every chemical engineer should be familiar with the current selling prices of the principal chemicals with which he is concerned. There is no use in publishing such a list in a book of this nature; these costs change too much and too frequently. To be of any value, such quotations must be secured when the chemical engineer is interested in them. They can be readily obtained from such journals as the *Oil, Paint and Drug Reporter* and *Chemical and Engineering News.* Indeed, a corollary to the obtaining of a list of current market prices is the introduction of the chemical engineer to these essential periodicals.

Although this book is not a study in cost determination, there are included many data on the basis of which a cost estimate can be made. Particularly in the flow sheets and in a few other selected parts of the book, approximate figures are given leading to at least the material cost of the product considered, or to labor and material (the so-called *L. & M.*) costs. On the other hand, it is impossible adequately to present or understand the determination of costs without long experience in a particular industry, and too much emphasis cannot be placed upon the inadequacy of the labor and material costs without there being added the various so-called overhead costs, such as research and development expense, depreciation and obsolescence of plant and process, provision for taxes and insurance, and interest on invested capital. These overhead and fixed items often equal or exceed the direct labor and material charges. The cost of chemicals tends to drop as processes are perfected and as production rises.

This book contains no separate chapters on equipment. Specialized books on the subject are available. It was thought better to emphasize equipment in conjunction with the description of the various processes and with the flow sheets representing those processes. On the other hand, any chemical engineer should start early to familiarize himself with industrial equipment such as pumps, filter presses, nitrators, and sulfonators.

The "Chemical Engineering Catalog"[1] includes the most available and convenient information concerning the actual equipment that can be supplied by various manufacturers. In short, it is a yearly résumé of the different catalogs put out by these suppliers. It should be employed as the current apparatus supplement. When this book is used as a text, it is suggested that the instructor so conduct his course that, from time to time, the students are required to go through this catalog and select

[1] Reinhold Publishing Corporation, New York. Distributed annually to *practicing* chemical engineers.

therefrom the various pumps or filter presses or reactors that would be most suitable for the process or flow sheet being studied.

Every chemical engineer, whether in training or in practice, should have as his constant companion the current edition of Perry's "Chemical Engineers' Handbook."[1] Not only are its voluminous tables of data essential to the chemical engineer but also the descriptions and illustrations of apparatus present more about these tools than are contained in any other one volume. The collection of formulas with illustrations is also unexcelled elsewhere. Finally, each section starts with well-selected references for anyone desiring even more details. Because of the excellence of this handbook, particularly covering equipment, many specific references are given to it here when otherwise fuller presentation would have been necessary.

Because of the very considerable number of flow sheets included and the desire to conserve space, not many pictures or line drawings to illustrate the process industries are included in this text. On the other hand, as visual presentation of equipment is extremely helpful, it is advised that instructors, to supplement this text, gather appropriate photographs of plants and equipment from the industries being studied. Quite frequently pictures can be obtained of plants which the students have visited or are planning to visit on their inspection trips. By having all these pictures on lantern slides, they can be used in the appropriate places and in much greater number than would be possible in these pages.

The texts and advertising pages of such journals as *Industrial and Engineering Chemistry, Chemical Engineering, Chemical and Engineering News, Chemical Engineering Progress, Chemical Week*, together with the very many specialized journals such as *Modern Plastics, Sugar, Petroleum Refiner*, and many others, should be consulted by the chemical engineer for up-to-date information on equipment and fundamental data.

Usually a chapter is assigned to a given process industry like glass, paper, rubber, or sulfuric acid. Such a chapter has its contents arranged in somewhat the following order:

After a brief introduction, aimed to epitomize the industry, some aspect is given of the historical side or background of the particular process. This is followed by a consideration of Uses and Economics, including statistical tabulations by which the importance of the industry can be judged. It is well recognized that trends in production, whether on the increase or decrease, are found of more importance than the mere statement that so many pounds or so many dollars' worth of a given substance are being manufactured. This is shown by parallel columns for different years and by statistical curves. Under Manufacture, this

[1] PERRY, JOHN H., editor-in-chief, with a staff of specialists, "Chemical Engineers' Handbook," 3d ed., McGraw-Hill Book Company, Inc., New York, 1950, 1,942 pages of tabulated data and epitomized information. Hereafter this book will be referred to as Perry, *op. cit.*

being a book on chemical engineering, *energy change, unit operations,* and *unit processes* are particularly brought to the attention of the reader. For some of the important processes, the principal unit operations and unit processes are tabulated. Dividing the industries into these units helps greatly in the transference of information from one industry to another. Indeed, flow sheets do this same thing in a visual manner. It is felt that by this breakdown the reader will gain a clearer comprehension that filtration or evaporation or hydrogenation or nitration is employed in a considerable number of industries. The source of the *raw materials* and their relationship to the manufacturing procedures are discussed in their economic and chemical relationship. The product of one industry is frequently the raw material of another—indeed, it has been remarked frequently that the chemical industry is its own best customer.[1] Ultimately chemicals stem

TABLE 1. ULTIMATE GEOLOGIC RAW MATERIALS FOR 150 IMPORTANT
INDUSTRIAL CHEMICALS[a,b]

	Index number[c]		Index number[c]
1. Water	99	18. Iron ores	6
2. Air	96	19. Phosphate rock	6
3. Coal	91	20. Sea water	5
4. Sulfur	88	21. Copper ores	4
5. Mineral salt	75	22. Fluorine minerals	4
6. Limestone	63	23. Arsenic minerals	3
7. Sulfide ores	32	24. Magnesium minerals	3
8. Brines	24	25. Mercury ores	3
9. Petroleum	23	26. Zinc ores	3
10. Natural gas	16	27. Antimony minerals	2
11. Saltpeter	13	28. Barium minerals	2
12. Potassium minerals	11	29. Boron minerals	2
13. Gypsum	10	30. Manganese ores	2
14. Lead ores	9	31. Tin ores	2
15. Sand	9	32. Bismuth minerals	1
16. Aluminum minerals	8	33. Silver ores	1
17. Chromium ores	7	34. Titanium ores	1

[a] KELLER and QUIRKE, *Ind. Eng. Chem., News Ed.,* **17**, 444 (1939).

[b] Note that coal, petroleum, and natural gas combined equal 130; sulfur and sulfide ores combined equal 120; and salt, brines, and sea water combined equal 104.

[c] Index numbers indicate relative frequency in use. The names of the 150 chemicals are tabulated in the reference.

from the minerals as shown in Table 1 (see also Fig. 1 in Chap. 39). The actual *manufacturing procedures,* in the case of the principal industries, are woven in and around the various *flow sheets.* Here the raw materials entering into unit operations and unit processes, carried on in industrial equipment, are all connected together. This is the heart of each industry and, although the flow sheets

[1] EWELL, Past and Future Growth at the Chemical Industry, *Chem. Eng. News,* **29**, 5228 (1950).

show the general sequence of operations and processes, the text supplements this and refers to the literature for further details.

The order of chapters was determined very largely from a teaching viewpoint. When this book is used in college, the student will frequently be taking physical chemistry and organic chemistry simultaneously. Primarily because of this, it was thought wise to place first those chapters which would be easiest for the student to learn. Hence, such a chapter as that presenting sulfuric acid, involving applications of equilibriums and certain other phases of physical chemistry, is placed after the more purely descriptive chapters pertaining to water, fuels, distillation of coal, gases, and carbon. The sequence of presentation as used in this book has been employed in the classes at Purdue University for a number of years, with an increased ease of learning on the part of students. This seems much better than starting at the beginning of the year with a chapter on sulfuric acid and trying to get the student to comprehend the physical and chemical reasons for some of the procedures that have been applied industrially in the manufacture of this important acid. If an instructor wishes to vary the order of the chapters, it will be very simple for him to make a mimeographed sheet, giving the sequence he desires his students to use.

As the aim of a book such as this is to impress upon the reader the quantitative engineering aspects and to lead him to think from raw materials to salable products, the *working of problems*[1] is of great importance. They also disclose whether the reader has sufficiently mastered the given industry to make calculations concerning its procedures. Therefore, at the end of the book there are a few typical problems pertaining to many of the industries concerned. However, when this volume is used as a college text, each instructor should supplement these problems with some of his own devising which, for obvious reasons, should be changed from year to year. Since these problems are the so-called *simple* ones, it would be very helpful if each instructor toward the end of the course would devise comprehensive problems to be given to his class, involving one or more industries, such as are given out each year by the American Institute of Chemical Engineers.[2] In certain universities such comprehensive problems are included in a special problem course. Too much emphasis cannot be placed upon quantitative thinking whether in the practice of chemical engineering or in the living of life in general.

[1] PERRY, *op. cit.*, pp. 233–357; HOUGEN, WATSON, and RAGATZ, "Chemical Process Principles," Part 1, Material and Energy Balances, 2d ed., John Wiley & Sons, Inc., New York, 1954; LEWIS, RADASCH, and LEWIS, "Industrial Stoichiometry," 2d ed., McGraw-Hill Book Company, Inc., New York, 1954.

[2] "A.I.Ch.E. Student Contest Problems, and the Prize Winning Solutions," American Institute of Chemical Engineers, New York, 1950.

The objectives sought in this volume may be summarized by stating that it has been the endeavor to present the various chemical processes in a generalized form through the correlation into flow sheets and descriptive text of the following:[1]

1. Unit processes: chemical change.
2. Unit operations: physical change.
3. Physical chemistry: equilibriums and reaction rates.
4. Economics: costs, statistics, and consumption.
5. Energy and power: chemical as well as electrical and mechanical.

SELECTED REFERENCES

General:

Kirk, R. E., and D. F. Othmer, "Encyclopedia of Chemical Technology," 14 vols., The Interscience Encyclopedia, Inc., New York, 1947–.

Richter, Otto, "The German Chemical Industry," Badgandersheim, Hartz, 1954.

Ullmann, Fritz, "Enzyklopaedie der technischen Chemie," 3d ed., 13 vols., Urban & Schwarzenberg, Berlin and Vienna, 1950–.

Thorpe, T. E., "Dictionary of Applied Chemistry," 4th ed., Longmans, Green & Co., Inc., New York, 1937.

Turner, F. M., "The Condensed Chemical Dictionary," 4th ed., Reinhold Publishing Corporation, New York, 1950.

Haynes, Williams, "This Chemical Age, The Miracle of Man-made Materials," Alfred A. Knopf, Inc., New York, 1942.

Perry, John H., editor-in-chief, "Chemical Engineers' Handbook," 3d ed., McGraw-Hill Book Company, Inc., New York, 1950.

Costs and Economics:

"Chemical Economics Handbook," Stanford Research Institute, Stanford, Calif., 1950–. Revised yearly.

Perry, John H., editor-in-chief, "Chemical Business Handbook," McGraw-Hill Book Company, Inc., New York, 1954.

Perry, *op. cit.*, pp. 1827–1845, with other references on p. 1828.

[1] It is recognized that the limitations of one volume have restricted the full application of all these factors to every process. However, frequent references from text as well as in the Selected References at the end of each chapter will serve to supplement what has been given. The author will welcome criticism of what has been chosen as well as suggestions regarding what should be added.

CHAPTER 2

UNIT PROCESSES AND UNIT OPERATIONS

In an inexact but expressive manner we may define chemical engineering in its modern sense by the following equation:

Chemical engineering = unit processes   +   unit operations
(chemical changes)   (physical changes)

The unit process is a very useful concept for technical chemical change and has been described[1] as "*the commercialization of a chemical reaction under such conditions as to be economically profitable*. This naturally includes the machinery needed and the economics involved, as well as the physical and chemical phases." The unit operation is a physical change connected with the industrial handling of chemicals or allied materials; it frequently is tied in with the unit process as when heat flows into an endothermic chemical reaction or out of an exothermic reaction. The unit operation may also be distinctly separated from the chemical change as when, by "flow of fluid," a liquid is moved from one part of an industrial establishment to another.

Chemical engineering, if successfully practiced, requires that the respective unit processes and operations be applied to the various manufacturing procedures. The study of the unit operations on the one hand and of the unit processes on the other is the characteristic of the present stage of this branch of engineering. Indeed, the development of chemical manufacturing procedures is largely through *flow sheets* which are definitely constructed from a coordinated sequence of unit processes and operations that fabricate the raw materials into the finished product and by-products. In the actual technical application, both unit processes and unit operations are carried on either simultaneously or independently in suitable equipment under the guidance of skilled labor supervised by chemical engineers. This is often called a *chemical process*.

These unit processes and unit operations are the common bond between otherwise widely divergent chemical manufacturing procedures. They, of course, are applied differently under the necessarily varying conditions. Although we hope that we shall have formulas that will enable the

[1] SHREVE, Unit Processes, Background and Objects, *Ind. Eng. Chem.*, **32**, 145 (1940).

chemical engineer to *calculate* at his desk what is going to *happen* in the factory, this millennium has not arrived. There are many more formulations for the unit operations than for the unit processes, as the latter are more complicated and have only lately been receiving the attention of chemical engineers. Indeed, broad experience is still necessary to apply wisely and economically the formulas and knowledge that are available. In the words of the eminent chemical engineer, W. L. Badger,[1]

. . . the engineer is the man who must build equipment, assemble it into a process, and make it run, whether or not he has all the theoretical data necessary for its calculation. He must think of equipment in terms not of strictly solved differential equations but of actual chunks of cast iron and steel that somebody shall be able to fabricate, assemble, and operate in terms of a working, practical, economical process.

The characteristics of unit processes as applied to the manufacture of chemicals may be summarized as follows:

1. Each unit process points out the *unitary* or like aspects in a group of numerous individual reactions. This unitary aspect, apart from the

TABLE 1. PRINCIPAL UNIT PROCESSES AND UNIT OPERATIONS

Unit processes	*Unit operations*
1. Combustion	1. Fluid dynamics
2. Oxidation	2. Heat transfer vs. cooling
3. Neutralization	3. Evaporation vs. evaporative cooling
4. Silicate formation	4. Humidification
5. Causticization	5. Gas absorption
6. Electrolysis	6. Solvent extraction
7. Double decomposition	7. Adsorption
8. Calcination, dehydration	8. Distillation and sublimation
9. Nitration	9. Drying, high-vacuum distillation
10. Esterification (sulfation)	10. Mixing
11. Reduction	11. Classification or sedimentation vs.
12. Ammonolysis	fluidization
13. Halogenation	12. Filtration
14. Sulfonation	13. Screening
15. Hydrolysis, hydration	14. Crystallization vs. extraction
16. Hydrogenation, hydrogenolysis	15. Centrifugation
17. Alkylation	16. Size reduction vs. size enlargement
18. Condensation	17. Materials handling
19. Polymerization	
20. Diazotization and coupling	
21. Fermentation	
22. Pyrolysis, cracking	
23. Aromatization	
24. Isomerization	
25. Hydroformylation (oxo)	
26. Ion exchange	

[1] BADGER, Education, Experience and Engineers, *Ind. Eng. Chem.*, **33**, 1103 (1941).

basic chemical family, may be a similarity in energy change or corrosion or pressure or reaction time or equilibrium or raw materials.

2. Frequently there is a *factory segregation* by unit processes wherein a building or section of a building may be devoted to the making of many chemicals under a given unit process as diazotization and coupling or nitration or hydrogenation or esterification or fermentation or alkylation.

3. There frequently is a close relationship in the *equipment* used for making many examples under a unit process. For instance, the cast-iron well-agitated reactor, provided with cooling coils, called a *nitrator*, is used for conducting the nitration unit process in the manufacture of a number of chemicals such as nitro-benzene, nitro-naphthalene, or T.N.T.

4. Equipment may be conveniently transferred from the making of one chemical to that of another within the same unit process. It is the aim of a chemical superintendent to keep all his equipment constantly in use. To do this he frequently must make first one chemical then another in the same general reactor—a sulfonator, for example. This *multiple use of equipment* is most easily realized under the unit process arrangement.

5. The unit process classification enables a chemical engineer to think from group performance to that of a new individual chemical in the like class. He needs chiefly to remember *principles* rather than specific performances. This method of approach greatly facilitates the making of any chemical by having available past knowledge regarding the generalized data of this unit process. This procedure saves much memorizing of individual observations.

6. As the basis of unit process classification is a chemical one, this places stress upon the *chemical reaction*. Here, usually a slight increase in the chemical yield will materially affect the profit of the manufacturing sequence. Hence the unit process conception lays emphasis upon the necessity for an exhaustive study of the basic chemical change. The cost of raw materials[1] looms up in the cost distribution, being from 50 to 80 per cent of the manufacturing expense. Following the obtaining of the highest possible chemical yield or, if time is available, simultaneously with this study, should go the careful investigation of every unit operation involved, with the aim of saving power or heat or any other physical factor.

7. The *inorganic and the organic procedures* need not be set apart industrially. This, of course, involves no criticism of the traditional separation as a teaching aid. As the equipment and the manufacturing problems are frequently so similar in both organic and inorganic chemicals, it is industrially important to group them together. "The principles[2] involved in the physical chemistry of the basic reactions or the con-

---

[1] SHREVE, *op. cit.*, NEWTON and ARIES, Preliminary Estimation of Operating Costs, *Ind. Eng. Chem.*, **43**, 2304 (1951).

[2] SHREVE, Inorganic Aspects of Unit Processes, *Ind. Eng. Chem.*, **36**, 411 (1944).

TABLE 2. UNIT PROCESSES WITH EQUIPMENT

Unit process	Chapter number and industry or product	Equipment
1. Combustion (completed oxidation)	5. Fuel and power	Boilers (steel, firebrick)
2. Oxidation	4. Water and wastes	Tanks (concrete)
	7. Water gas	Generators (steel, brick)
	8. Industrial gases (CO_2, H_2)	Boilers (steel, brick), reactors (alloy steel)
	18. Phosphoric acid (from P)	Oxidizers (carbon, graphite)
	19. Sulfuric acid	Sulfur burners (steel), converters (steel, cast iron), chambers (lead lined)
	20. Nitric acid (from NH_3)	Oxidizers (steel)
	24. Paints and pigments	Reactors, kettles, mixers (steel)
	24. Linoleum	Oxidizing rooms (brick)
	27. Perfumes	Reactors (enamel steel)
	31. Fermentation: acetic, citric, and gluconic acids	Tanks (wood, stainless steel) trays (aluminum)
	38. Phthalic anhydride	Reactors (steel)
	39. Formaldehyde	Oxidizers (steel), catalyst (silver gauze)
	39. Acetic acid (from CH_3CHO)	Reactors and condensers (stainless steel)
	39. Camphor	Reactors (stainless steel)
3. Neutralization	4. Water treatment	Treaters (steel), settlers (steel or concrete), reservoirs (concrete)
	13. Ammoniated superphosphate	Reactors and bins (steel, concrete)
	14. Sodium salts	Kettles, crystallizers (mostly steel)
	18. Na and NH_4 phosphates	Reactors (mostly steel) (lead lined)
	6. Ammonium sulfate	Absorbers (heavy lead)
	20. Ammonium nitrate	Absorbers (ceramic lined)
	20. Urea	Reactors (silver-lined steel)
	21. Aluminum sulfate	Tanks (lead lined)
	26. Arsenites, arsenates	Tanks (wood)
	29. Soap from fatty acids	Tanks (stainless steel or Monel)

TABLE 2. UNIT PROCESSES WITH EQUIPMENT (*Continued*)

Unit process	Chapter number and industry or product	Equipment
4. Silicate formation	10. Ceramics	Molds (steel), kilns (ceramic brick)
	10. Sand-lime bricks	Presses (steel), retorts (steel)
	11. Cement	Kilns (mostly steel, brick lined)
	12. Glass	Glass furnaces (ceramic blocks)
5. Causticization	15. Caustic soda	Causticizers (steel)
6. Electrolysis	8. Industrial gases (H_2, O_2)	Electrolytic cells (steel)
	15. Caustic soda and chlorine	Electrolytic cells (concrete and steel)
	16. Aluminum	Electrolytic cells (steel)
	16. Magnesium	Electrolytic cells (steel)
	16. Sodium	Electrolytic cells (steel and brick)
7. Double decomposition	4. Water softening	Tanks (steel), settlers (concrete)
	11. Ca and Mg salts	Tanks (steel and concrete)
	13. Potassium salts	Reactors (steel)
	14. Sodium salts	Reactors (steel, etc.)
	15. Soda ash	Brine treaters (wood tanks), absorbers (cast iron)
	18. Phosphoric acid	Reactors (lead lined)
	18. Superphosphate	Mixers and bins (iron and concrete)
	21. Hydrochloric	Stills (cast iron), condensers (earthenware, tantalum, or carbon)
	21. Hydrofluoric	Stills (cast iron), condensers (lead)
	24. Pigments	Reactors (steel)
8. Calcination	11. Lime	Kilns (rotary, brick-lined steel, or upright of steel and brick)
	11. Gypsum	Driers (steel)
	15. Soda ash	Calciners, rotary (steel)
9. Nitration	22. Explosives	Nitrators (cast iron or stainless steel)

TABLE 2. UNIT PROCESSES WITH EQUIPMENT (*Continued*)

Unit process	Chapter number and industry or product	Equipment
	38. Intermediates for dyes, nitro-benzene, etc.	Nitrators (cast iron or stainless steel)
	39. Nitro-paraffins	Nitrators and separating columns, continuous (stainless steel)
	27. Perfumes	Reactors (copper)
10. Esterification	34. Rayon: xanthate or viscose	Steeping press, shredders, agers, barratte (steel)
	34. Rayon: acetate	Mixers, acetylators (aluminum)
	39. Ethyl and vinyl acetate	Reactors (copper or stainless steel)
11. Reduction	18. Phosphorus	Furnaces (steel, brick)
	19. Sulfur from SO_2	Reactors (steel)
	38. Aniline from nitro-benzene	Reducers (cast iron or wood)
	38. *p*-Phenylenediamine	Reducers (cast iron)
12. Amination by ammonolysis	38. Aniline from chloro-benzene	Autoclaves (steel)
	38. β-Naphthylamine	Autoclaves (steel)
	39. Ethanolamines	Autoclaves (steel)
13. Halogenation	22. Chemicals for warfare	Reactors (steel)
	26. Insecticides	Reactors (steel or ceramic)
	38. Intermediates for dyes	Reactors (steel or earthenware)
	38. Chloro-benzene	Halogenators (steel)
	39. Benzyl chloride, carbon tetrachloride	Chlorinators (ceramic), reactors (lead lined)
14. Sulfonation	22. Explosives	Sulfonators (cast iron or steel)
	33. Sulfite paper	Burners, sulfite towers, digesters, beaters (mostly steel with towers concrete)
	38. Intermediates for dyes	Sulfonators (cast iron or steel)
	38. Benzene-sulfonate for phenol	Sulfonators (cast iron or steel)

TABLE 2. UNIT PROCESSES WITH EQUIPMENT (*Continued*)

Unit process	Chapter number and industry or product	Equipment
15. Hydration and hydrolysis (saponification) (alkali fusion)	11. Slaked lime	Hydrators (steel)
	18. Phosphoric acid from phosphorus pentoxide	Hydrators (ceramic lining)
	19. Sulfuric acid from sulfur trioxide	Absorbers (steel tower), cooler coils (steel)
	25. Gelatine and glue	Extractors (steel), special driers
	29. Glycerine	Soap kettles (steel with top stainless), evaporators and stills (steel)
	29. Soap	Soap kettles (steel with Monel or stainless-steel top)
	30. Corn sugar	Acid-resistant low-pressure autoclaves (copper)
	30. Dextrin	Same as for corn sugar
	31. Sucrose to glucose and fructose	Fermenters (wood tanks or steel)
	32. Hydrolysis of wood	Acid-resistant low-pressure autoclaves (copper)
	38. Phenol	Fusion pots (cast iron)
	39. Acetaldehyde from acetylene	Reactors (Duriron)
	39. Alcohols from chlorides and sulfates	Hydrolyzers (steel or lead lined)
16. Hydrogenation and hydrogenolysis	20. Ammonia from nitrogen	Catalyst chambers (Cr alloy)
	21. Hydrochloric acid from chlorine	Reactors (steel), absorbers (earthenware, tantalum or carbon)
	28. Hydrogenated oils and fats	Hydrogenators (steel), catalyst (nickel)
	29. Detergents (Hymolal class)	Hydrogenating autoclaves (stainless steel lined)
	37. Petroleum industry	Catalyst chambers (steel or Cr alloy)
	39. Methanol from CO	Compressors, heat exchanger, catalyst chambers (steel or Cr alloy)
17. Alkylation	23. Photography	Autoclaves (steel)
	36. Styrene	Reactors (steel)

TABLE 2. UNIT PROCESSES WITH EQUIPMENT (*Continued*)

Unit process	Chapter number and industry or product	Equipment
	37. Petroleum industry	Alkylators (steel), bubble towers (steel)
	38. Intermediates	Reactors (steel), stills (copper)
	38. Dimethyl-aniline	Autoclaves (steel)
	39. Medicinals	Autoclaves (copper)
	39. Tetraethyl lead	Reactors (steel)
18. Condensation	24. Resinification	Reactors (steel, nickel, stainless steel)
	38. Benzoyl-benzoic acid for anthraquinone	Reactors (steel or enamel)
	39. Phenolphthalein	Reactors (steel)
19. Polymerization	36. Rubber	Polymerizers (steel)
	37. Petroleum industry	Polymerization reactors (steel)
20. Diazotization and coupling	38. Dyes	Vats (wood), filters (wood or cast iron)
21. Fermentation	8. Industrial gases (CO_2)	Fermenters (wood or steel)
	31. Alcohol and CO_2 from monosaccharides	Fermenters (wood or steel tanks)
	31. Alcohol, acetone, and butanol from carbohydrates	Fermenters (steel tanks)
	31. Wines, beers, and liquors	Fermenters (steel, wood, concrete)
	31. Lactic acid	Fermenters (wood tanks)
	31. Penicillin	Fermenters (steel tanks)
22. Pyrolysis or cracking (thermal decomposition)	6. Distillation of coal	Retorts (steel-braced firebrick with steel and cast-iron connections)
	7. Fuel (coal) gases	Retorts (steel-braced firebrick)
	7. Oil gas for carbureted water gas	Carburetors (brick-lined steel)
	9. Carbon black	Channel coolers (steel)
	9. Lampblack	Distillation chambers (steel, brick)
	32. Distillation of wood	Retorts (steel)
	37. Petroleum industry	Reaction chambers (steel)

TABLE 2. UNIT PROCESSES WITH EQUIPMENT (*Continued*)

Unit process	Chapter number and industry or product	Equipment
23. Aromatization	37. Petroleum industry	Reaction chambers (steel)
24. Isomerization	37. Petroleum industry	Isomerizers (steel)
25. Miscellaneous (ion exchange) (allo-tropic change), etc.	4. Water	Tanks (steel)
	9. Graphite	Electrothermal furnaces (steel and brick)
	17. Calcium carbide	Electrothermal furnaces (steel protected by charge)
	17. Silicon carbide	Electrothermal furnaces (steel protected by charge)
	17. Carbon disulfide	Electrothermal furnaces (steel and brick)
	23. Photographic industry	Tanks and special equipment (nickel, silver, ceramics, rubber)
	25. Leather	Tanks (wood)

struction and control of the equipment or the economics involved are the same whether organic or inorganic products are obtained." For example, there is surprisingly little differentiation in the conditions or equipment used to hydrogenate nitrogen to ammonia, or carbon monoxide to methanol, except in raw materials charged and catalyst employed.

8. The *design* of equipment is greatly aided by the generalizations arising from the unit process arrangement rather than by considering each reaction separately. What experience has indicated for a number of reactions allied under a unit process is an excellent guide for a new reaction in this same grouping.

In handling unit processes, the more that is understood about the underlying physical chemistry of the equilibriums and the reaction rates, the better will be the control, the higher the conversion, and the lower the costs. It is very important to know how fast a reaction will go and how far. Many times, as is pointed out in connection with the manufacture of sulfuric acid by the oleum process (Chap. 19), conditions that increase the rate decrease the equilibrium. Therefore, as is shown in the design of the sulfur trioxide converter, conditions are first secured to cause a high rate of reaction and then, toward the end, are changed to favor the equilibrium. The work that Hougen[1] and others are doing in

[1] HOUGEN and WATSON, "Chemical Process Principles," 3 vols., 2d ed., Vol. 1 with RAGATZ, 1954, John Wiley & Sons, Inc., New York, 1943–1954; LAIDLER, "Chemical Kinetics," McGraw-Hill Book Company, Inc., New York, 1950.

TABLE 3. UNIT OPERATIONS WITH EQUIPMENT

Unit operation	Chapter number and industry or product	Equipment
1. Fluid flow or fluid dynamics	4. Water and wastes	Pumps (steel), tanks (steel, concrete)
	28. Oils and fats	Pumps (steel)
	37. Petroleum industry	Pumps (steel)
2. Heat transfer	5. Fuels and power	Boilers and heat exchangers (steel)
	6. Distillation of coal	By-product ovens and regenerators (firebrick)
	7. Fuel gases	Generators (steel and brick), exchangers and coolers (steel)
	8. Industrial gases	Exchangers and liquefiers (steel)
	10. Ceramics	Kilns (steel and firebrick)
	11. Cement	Rotary kilns (steel, firebrick)
	12. Glass	Furnaces and regenerators (ceramic blocks and bricks)
	15. Soda ash	Calciners (steel)
	18. Phosphorus	Electrothermal or blast furnaces (steel, brick)
	19. Sulfuric acid	Burners and converters (steel)
	20. Ammonia	Converters and exchangers (steel)
	37. Petroleum industry	Pipe furnaces, exchangers, condensers (steel)
3. Evaporation	13. Potassium salts	Multiple evaporators (cast iron)
	14. Salt	Multiple evaporators (cast iron)
	15. Caustic soda	Multiple evaporators (nickel lined)
	18. Phosphoric acid	Evaporators (lead lined)
	29. Glycerine	Multiple evaporators (steel)
	30. Sugar	Multiple evaporators (steel)
4. Humidification	34. Textile fibers	Factories (brick, concrete, wood)
5. Gas absorption	6. Distillation of coal	Absorbing towers (steel)

TABLE 3. UNIT OPERATIONS WITH EQUIPMENT (*Continued*)

Unit operation	Chapter number and industry or product	Equipment
	7. Fuel gases	Absorbers or purifying towers (steel)
	8. Industrial gases	Absorbing towers (steel)
	15. Bleach	Shelves or rotary (concrete)
	20. Nitric acid	Absorbers and oxidizers (Cr-steel)
	21. Hydrochloric acid	Absorbers (ceramic, tantalum, or carbon)
	25. Leather	Vats (wood)
6. Solvent extraction	7. Coal gas	Towers (steel)
	26. Insecticides	Percolators (steel)
	27. Perfumes	Percolators (steel)
	28. Oils	Extractors (steel)
	32. Acetic acid	Extractors (copper or stainless steel)
	32. Rosin	Extractors (copper or stainless steel)
	37. Lubricating oils	Extractors (steel)
7. Adsorption	4. Water and wastes purification	Tanks (concrete) for carbon
	24. Artificial leather solvent recovery	Tanks (steel) for carbon
8. Distillation and sublimation	6. Distillation coal	By-product ovens (firebrick), stills (steel)
	8. Industrial gases (O_2, N_2)	Rectifiers for liquid air (steel)
	27. Perfumes	Stills (copper)
	29. Glycerine	Vacuum stills (steel)
	31. Alcohol, acetone	Stills (copper)
	37. Petroleum industry	Bubble towers, stills (steel)
	38. Intermediates	Stills (cast iron, steel)
9. Drying	10. Ceramics	Driers (steel or brick)
	14. Sodium salts	Rotary and pan driers (Monel, steel)
	24. Pigments	Box driers (steel)
	29. Soap	Drying rooms (brick and wood)
	30. Sugar	Rotary driers (steel)
	33. Pulp and paper	Steam-heated cylinders (steel)

TABLE 3. UNIT OPERATIONS WITH EQUIPMENT (*Continued*)

Unit operation	Chapter number and industry or product	Equipment
	36. Rubber	Driers (steel)
10. Mixing	13. Fertilizers	Mixers (steel)
	22. Dynamite	Mixers (wood)
	24. Paints, lacquers	Mixers (steel)
	38. Dyes	Mixing vats (wood)
11. Classification or sedimentation	11. Cement rock	Beneficiation equipment (steel)
	18. Phosphate rock	Beneficiation equipment (steel)
	13. Potassium salts	Thickeners (steel)
	15. Caustic soda	Thickeners (steel)
12. Filtration	10. Ceramics	Plate and frame filters (iron)
	11. Ca and Mg salts	Filters (iron and brass)
	13. Potassium salts	Filters (iron)
	14. Sodium salts	Filters (iron and wood)
	30. Sugar	Filters (iron)
	34. Rayon	Filters before fiber formation (brass)
	37. Paraffin	Filters (iron)
	38. Intermediates and dyes	Plate and frame filters (iron, wood)
	39. Organic chemicals	Plate and frame filters (iron, wood)
13. Screening	11. Cement	Screens (iron)
	15. Soda ash	Screens (iron and wood)
	17. Silicon carbide	Screens (iron and wood)
	30. Sugar	Screens (iron and wood)
14. Crystallization	11. Ca and Mg salts	Tanks (steel)
	13. Potassium salts	Vacuum and open crystallizers (steel)
	14, 18. Sodium salts	Crystallizers (steel)
	30. Sugar	Crystallizers (steel)
15. Centrifugation	6. NH_4 sulfate	Centrifuges (copper and iron)
	11. Ca and Mg salts	Centrifuges (copper and iron)
	13. Potassium salts	Centrifuges (copper and iron)

TABLE 3. UNIT OPERATIONS WITH EQUIPMENT (*Continued*)

Unit operation	Chapter number and industry or product	Equipment
	14. Sodium salts	Centrifuges (copper and iron)
	30. Sugars	Centrifuges (copper and iron)
16. Size reduction	10. Ceramics	Mills (steel)
	11. Cement	Mills, many types (steel)
	12. Glass raw materials	Mills (steel)
	12. Rock wool	Fiber making (steel and brick)
	24. Paints	Ball, cylinder, and disk mills (steel, stone)
	35. Resins	Mills (steel)
17. Materials handling	5. Fuels	Conveyers (rubber, canvas)
	7. Fuel gases	Pumps and pipes (steel)
	10. Ceramics	Screws, conveyers (steel, rubber)
	11. Cement	Conveyers (steel, rubber)
	12. Glass	Special conveyers (steel)
	15. Soda ash	Screw conveyers (steel)
	32. Wood	Trucks (steel)
	36. Rubber	Trucks, conveyers (steel)

NOTE: Table 3 is intended to point out only important or striking applications of the unit operation. Indeed it would be difficult to find a chemical industry in which such important unit operations as fluid flow, heat transfer, drying, mixing, and filtration are not used.

studying kinetics is of the utmost significance. It is to be hoped that more chemical engineers and physical chemists will direct their attention to the fundamental facts of the reaction rates and reaction equilibriums. All of this will aid in making the unit process conception more quantitative and bring into the unit process field more equations for calculating results.

The unit operations have been given very intensive and fruitful study by most of the college research laboratories in the field of chemical engineering. Since 1915 when Arthur D. Little called particular attention to the importance of these physical aspects and laid the foundation for the modern conception of chemical engineering, these principles have been so well presented by William H. Walker and his coworkers, Lewis, McAdams, and Gilliland[1] together with Badger and McCabe[2]

[1] WALKER, LEWIS, McADAMS, and GILLILAND, "Principles of Chemical Engineering," 3d ed., McGraw-Hill Book Company, Inc., New York, 1937.

[2] BADGER and McCABE, "Elements of Chemical Engineering," 2d ed., McGraw-Hill Book Company, Inc., New York, 1936.

that anyone desiring an understanding of the principles connected with unit operations need only refer to the writings by these authors and many others.[1]

Throughout this book, attention is constantly called to unit processes and unit operations since the numerous flow charts are broken down into a coordinated sequence of these units. However, at least a naming of both the principal unit processes and the principal unit operations is in order here and is given in Table 1. The unit processes are the basis of the classification of the various intermediates presented in Chap. 38 and of the miscellaneous organic chemicals included in Chap. 39. Under each unit process in these chapters is included much of a general nature pertaining to that particular unit process. In Table 2 is arranged a listing of the principal unit processes occurring in the various industries together with the main equipment as used in the different fields of the chemical process industries. Likewise, Table 3 presents this same aspect for unit operations.

SELECTED REFERENCES

Groggins, P. H., editor, "Unit Processes in Organic Synthesis," 4th ed., McGraw-Hill Book Company, Inc., New York, 1952.

Walker, William H., Warren K. Lewis, William H. McAdams, and Edwin R. Gilliland, "Principles of Chemical Engineering," 3d ed., McGraw-Hill Book Company, Inc., New York, 1937.

Badger, Walter L., and Warren L. McCabe, "Elements of Chemical Engineering," 2d ed., McGraw-Hill Book Company, Inc., New York, 1936.

Furnas, C. C., editor, "Rogers' Manual of Industrial Chemistry," vols. 1, 2, D. Van Nostrand Company, Inc., New York, 1942.

McCormack, Harry, editor, "The Applications of Chemical Engineering," D. Van Nostrand Company, Inc., New York, 1943.

Brown, G. G., "Unit Operations," John Wiley & Sons, Inc., New York, 1950.

Hougen, O. A., and K. M. Watson, "Chemical Process Principles," 3 vols., 2d ed., Vol. 1 with Ragatz, 1954, John Wiley & Sons, Inc., New York, 1943–1954.

Unit Process Symposia, *Ind. Eng. Chem.*, each year since 1937. Since 1955 published as "Chemical Processes."

Annual Unit Processes Review, *Ind. Eng. Chem.*, each year since 1948.

Annual Unit Operations Review, *Ind. Eng. Chem.*, each year since 1946.

Ind. Eng. Chem. Editorial Staff, "Modern Chemical Processes," Reinhold Publishing Corporation, New York, 1950 for vol. 1. Each volume includes the "Staff Industry" reports from 2 years' publication in *Ind. Eng. Chem.* References in *this text* to latter.

[1] *Cf.* Brown, *et al.*, "Unit Operations," John Wiley & Sons, Inc., New York, 1950; Lauer and Heckman, "Chemical Engineering Techniques," Reinhold Publishing Corporation, New York, 1952.

CHAPTER 3

GENERAL FUNDAMENTALS

To carry out commercially the *unit processes* and the *unit operations* in any chemical plant presupposes factory-scale equipment. To keep the factory itself from corroding away, proper materials of construction should have been selected by the designing chemical engineer. To regulate properly the chemical processes requires instruments for recording and controlling the procedures. To avoid harmful impurities in the raw materials, to follow the course of the chemical reactions, and to secure the requisite purity of products require careful chemical control by periodic analyses. To transmit goods in a clean and economical manner from the manufacturer to the customer, suitable containers must be provided. To effect the safety of the workman and the plant, all these procedures must be carried on in a nonhazardous manner. To secure the processes from unfair competition and to ensure an adequate return for the large sums spent on research, the chemical steps and the equipment in the factory must be protected for the limited period granted by the American patent laws. To guarantee progress, to continue profits, and to replace obsolescent processes and equipment, much attention and money must be spent upon appropriate research. To prevent contamination of streams and interference with the rights of neighbors, factories must avoid the discharge of waste materials either into the air or into the streams of their locality.

MATERIALS OF CONSTRUCTION[1]

In chemical factories the successful consummation of chemical reactions and the maintenance of equipment depend not so much upon the strength of the materials as upon their proper selection to resist corrosion and withstand the effects of elevated temperatures and pressures. Mechanical failures are seldom experienced unless there has been a previous corroding or a weakening by chemical attack on the material used for the construction of either the equipment or the building. Thus corrosion is a constant and continuing problem with the chemical engineer in industry.

[1] See the Materials of Construction reviews in *Ind. Eng. Chem.*, October issue during 1947–1954, September supplement since 1955.

In some cases corrosion cannot be prevented; it can only be minimized. In these instances the designing engineer must provide for periodic replacements. Fortunately, however, particularly since about 1920, the advance of chemical engineering has provided many corrosion-resisting materials. Among such relatively new materials are the following: rubber-covered steel, resin-bonded carbon, and tantalum—all to resist hydrochloric acid—stainless steel to resist the action of aqueous nitric acid even under pressure, and nickel or nickel-clad steel to resist caustic solutions, hot or cold.

Among construction materials used by chemical engineers are to be found many of the commonest products as well as some of the rarest—brick, iron, cement, and wood on the one hand and platinum, tantalum, and silver on the other. To choose the proper material, namely, one that will have the strength necessary and the chemical resistance needed, requires that the chemical engineer have an accurate knowledge of the chemical processes for which the materials of construction are needed. He must also know the corrosion resistance of the materials he thinks will be employed. Frequently actual testing will be in order. When any corrosion tests are made, they should not be carried out with pure laboratory chemicals but with the commercial grades not only of the chemicals to be used in the factory but also of the actual construction material to be tested. It frequently happens that a small amount of contaminant in a commercial raw material affects the corrosion very appreciably. An example of this is the attack upon aluminum by dilute nitric acid carrying a small quantity of halogen.

In recent years many data have been collected and added to the literature pertaining to corrosion, particularly about the properties of the structural materials employed in our chemical factories. For classified specific information reference should be made especially to the books by Speller,[1] Lee,[2] and Perry.[3] Also the current issues of our engineering journals should be consulted, especially the pages of *Chemical Engineering*[4] and *Industrial and Engineering Chemistry*.[5] Where metals are concerned, stress corrosion and corrosion fatigue may become very important in high-pressure vessels that are subject to vibration.

[1] SPELLER, "Corrosion: Causes and Prevention," 3d ed., McGraw-Hill Book Company, Inc., New York, 1951.

[2] LEE, "Materials of Construction for Chemical Process Industries," McGraw-Hill Book Company, Inc., New York, 1950.

[3] PERRY, *op. cit.*, pp. 1458–1558; here LEE, *et al.*, present directions for conducting corrosion tests. Many excellent tables of properties are given for recommended materials of construction for various uses.

[4] *Chemical Engineering* has published extensive tables on the properties and materials of construction and corrosion. Many of these tables are reprinted in PERRY, *op. cit.*, or have been published as separate pamphlets.

[5] *Cf.* the important Materials of Construction reviews in *Ind. Eng. Chem.*, October issue, published annually since 1947.

The following pages present a general outline of some of the chief materials of construction and their applications to the chemical industries:

Ferrous Materials. *Steel* is still our main structural material. It is the metal almost universally employed in the construction of most buildings and in the reinforcing of concrete. It is widely used in pipes, tanks, reaction vessels, pumps, valves, and other tools of the chemical process industries.

Under certain conditions its corrosion resistance is excellent, as, for example, in the handling of cool, concentrated sulfuric acid[1] or of mixed nitric and sulfuric acids containing not more than 25 per cent of water. In general, however, practically all dilute acids, even moisture of the air, will cause serious corrosion of unprotected steel surfaces.

Steel is employed extensively, together with cast and wrought iron, for handling dilute alkaline solutions or the neutral organic liquids met in the petroleum and coal-tar industries. When the concentration of alkalies is high or the temperature is raised, there is often some attack upon the ferrous metals, in which case a more costly material such as nickel, Monel metal, or even silver is substituted.

Wrought iron has behind it a long history of service in the chemical industries. Presumably its inclusions of chemically resistant slag provide an increased measure of protection against many corrosives. Wrought-iron pipe is often used in applications where steel or cast iron proves unsatisfactory.

Cast iron resists sulfuric acid and alkali a little better than does steel. Also, when it does corrode, this takes place much more slowly and evenly. Consequently, cast-iron pipe or vessels are preferable when their enhanced weight and greater brittleness do not prevent their use.

High-silicon irons, such as Duriron and Corrosiron containing 14 per cent of Si, are very resistant materials for use with nitric acid, even in low concentrations. They are also preferred for boiling nitric acid. The high-silicon irons cannot be forged or welded, and their castings are somewhat more brittle than ordinary cast iron.

The *stainless steels*[2] consist essentially of iron, chromium, and nickel, with minor but important other constituents. A typical formula is "18:8," containing 18 per cent chromium and 8 per cent nickel. Stainless steels, now among the most important of the construction materials used by the chemical engineer, can be fabricated and welded like other steels, can be forged or cast, and they resist organic acids and nitric acid of all concentrations.

---

[1] For details of corrosion resistance of various materials against different strength acids, see Furnas, "Rogers' Manual of Industrial Chemistry," 6th ed., pp. 243, 308–311, D. Van Nostrand Company, Inc., New York, 1942; SPELLER, *op. cit.*

[2] SANDS, Stainless Steel Developments in Process Industries, *Chem. & Met. Eng.,* **49** (4), 88; (5), 132 (1942).

Nonferrous Metals and Alloys. *Copper* for many decades has been a stand-by of the chemical engineer in multitudinous applications. It is relatively inexpensive and can be fabricated into complicated shapes and possesses fair strength. Its chemical resistance against ordinary atmospheric moisture and oxygen is excellent as there is formed an adherent protective coating usually of copper oxide. Copper resists alkali (except ammonia) better than does steel. It resists organic acids except in high concentrations. It should not be used, however, where any mercury will touch it because of the amalgams that are formed. Even a broken mercury thermometer in a copper vessel may give trouble. In the factory it is employed extensively as the material for the construction of kettles, stills, heat exchangers, tanks, and many reactors. It should not be used in contact with ammonia or amines. Copper alloys such as brass, bronze, and admiralty metals are often superior in corrosion resistance and possess better mechanical properties than the pure metal.

Aluminum is applicable to specialized situations where its lightness and relative ease of fabrication are advantageous. Chemically, it resists strong organic acids, nitric acid, and nitrates providing halogens are absent. Corrosion resistance of aluminum is due to the formation of an *adherent* film or hydrated aluminum oxide; the removal of this film by halogen acids or alkalies exposes the metal to what may be rapid corrosion. As in the case of copper, a wide range of special alloys is available for the chemical engineer's use.

Nickel[1] is widely employed for its excellent resistance to alkalies including ammonia. In the manufacture of iron-free caustic soda, nickel or nickel-clad steel is chosen for tanks, evaporator tubes, evaporator bodies, and even for tank cars. Nickel and its alloys also possess very superior mechanical properties. Most widely used of these is *Monel metal* which is a natural alloy of nickel (67 per cent) and copper (30 per cent). Monel is especially important in the food industries.

Lead[2] is another old stand-by in the chemical industries. Its use is particularly advantageous because of its high resistance to dilute sulfuric acid. It is almost universally used in the building of chamber plants for the making of sulfuric acid and for the lining of tanks for storage of dilute sulfuric acid. Its disadvantage is its lack of mechanical strength and its tendency to creep. Different lead sections are joined together by what is called *lead burning*, a reducing flame (hydrogen) being used for this purpose.

Silver,[3] particularly in its pure form, has excellent chemical resistance

---

[1] FRIEND and LA QUE, Corrosion-resisting Nickel Alloys and Chemical Progress, *Ind. Eng. Chem.*, **44**, 965 (1952).

[2] ROLL, Lead in Modern Chemical Construction, *Chem. Eng.*, **59** (1), 281 (1952).

[3] BUTTS and GIACOBBE, Silver Offers Resistance to Many Chemicals, *Chem. & Met. Eng.*, **48** (12), 76 (1941); ADDICKS, "Silver in Industry," extensive bibliography, Reinhold Publishing Corporation, New York, 1940.

to alkalies as well as to many organic acids, particularly when hot. Consequently in the preparation of the purest grade of alkali, silver is the metal used. The autoclaves for the manufacture of urea from carbon dioxide and ammonia are lined with silver. This metal is likewise used for the handling of acetic acid. The disadvantage of silver lies in its mechanical weakness. Consequently it is employed whenever possible as a liner to protect metals mechanically stronger.

Tantalum has a high resistance to hydrochloric acid and has consequently been used in such specialized equipment as immersion heaters and condensers designed for heat transfer involving hydrochloric acid solutions.

Platinum has long been employed in the chemical industry. At present its application is most essential as one of the catalysts for the contact sulfuric acid process and in the Ostwald ammonia oxidation procedure. In the latter application, to lessen volatilization loss, the platinum is alloyed with 10 per cent rhodium.

Inorganic Materials Other Than Metals. *Glass,* long the main material used in chemical laboratories, is rapidly moving out into industrial processing.[1] Glass is used in three forms in the plant: (1) in bulk, in fairly large pieces of equipment, such as pipe, towers, and pumps; (2) as a coating, over cast iron and steel, as in tanks, reactors, and pipe; and (3) as fibers, in insulation, fabrics, tower packing, and plastic laminates. The biggest plant use is in piping. It has the advantage of transparency, corrosion resistance, and ease of cleaning. The resistance of glass to almost everything except hydrofluoric acid, strong alkalies, and mechanical stress is very satisfactory. Special precautions should be observed for operations involving higher temperatures (around 200°C.) because of thermal shock. Tempered glass and high-silica glass are less vulnerable to this.

Silica equipment in a great variety of shapes has long been available and is used for particular applications where bad thermal shock is encountered. Silica is also hard and greatly resists erosion. It is, however, attacked by alkalies, is easily broken, and is expensive.

Ceramic materials, such as chemical stoneware and porcelain, are available for vessels, pipes, and valves of medium capacity and have been employed where acid conditions prevail. Even large tanks are made out of ceramic bricks[2] or tile held together by acid-resisting cements.

Concrete is cheap, easily fabricated, and widely employed where non-acid conditions prevail. Even where mild acid conditions occur, concrete

[1] SMITH, Glass—Its Place in Chemical Processing, *Chem. Eng.,* **58** (4), 117 (1951); *cf.* Chap. 12.

[2] KINGSBURY, Ceramic Linings for Chemical Equipment, *Ind. Eng. Chem.,* **29**, 402 (1937).

can be protected by various integrating compounds, such as oleic soaps, and by being coated on the outside with special asphalt paints.

Carbon is very resistant chemically. With the advent of acid-resisting resins, various shapes of carbon products held together by these resins are now on the market. Phenol-formaldehyde resin is one that seems quite suitable for the binding. These carbon[1] materials are supplied in the form of various bricks and building blocks as well as piping, valves, and fittings. Much of the construction material used in the newer hydrochloric acid plants is one of these carbon-resin materials sold under the name of Karbate.

Organic Materials of Construction. *Wood*, by virtue of its cheapness and ease of working, is widely used for equipment handling, neutral solutions, or even occasionally for weak acids such as dilute acetic acid. Wood also resists saline solutions, such as sodium chloride. Consequently wooden tanks, filter presses, and pipes have long been important factors in the construction of our chemical plants. The new synthetic fibers such as Orlon, Vinyon, nylon, and glass fibers are superseding the use of cotton as a filter medium for specialized applications because of their excellent chemical resistance and durability. Cloth made out of Monel or stainless steel is also used.

Rubber is assuming increasing importance as a material of construction for the chemical engineer as different varieties are manufactured and made available at reasonable costs. Natural rubber as a liner for steel tanks and pipes has greatly facilitated the handling of hydrochloric acid. Indeed, this acid is now shipped in rubber-lined tank cars. Several synthetic rubbers possess resistance against nonaqueous solvents such as the various products of the petroleum industry. Consequently they have found wide acceptance for the lining of hose to transport these solvents and also as gasket materials.

Some of the *plastics*[2] are sufficiently resistant to be very important materials for the chemical industries. Of the thermosetting plastics, asbestos-filled phenolic resins (Haveg) are used successfully with non-oxidizing acids, and equipment based on "filled" cast furfuryl alcohol resins are satisfactory against certain alkalies. The thermoplastics most acceptable for equipment fabrication are polymethyl methacrylate, polyethylene, Saran, and polyvinyl chloride.

The lack, at present, of corrosion-resistant alloys has stimulated further work on furan resin linings bonded to steel or concrete in the construction of acidproof chemical process equipment. Furan resin

---

[1] See Chap. 9, Industrial Carbon, where Karbate materials are described and pictured.

[2] Chap. 35; SEYMOUR and FRY, Plastic Processing Equipment Today, *Chem. Eng.*, **59** (3), 136 (1952).

cements, phenol-formaldehyde resin cements, and sulfur cements are meeting increased acceptance.

PROCESS INSTRUMENTATION

At one time labor was plentiful and chemical operations were carried out on a small scale in individual batches. The skilled chemical engineer now finds that very many of his manufacturing projects, particularly those operated on a large scale, proceed much more economically as *continuous* processes rather than as small-batch operations. These continuous processes have been and can be controlled by the workman, but they give much more uniform results if, after the best conditions are ascertained, these conditions are maintained throughout by the use of modern instruments for automatic control. The chemical engineer should not choose instruments simply to record temperatures or pressures but as reliable tools to control and maintain desired operating conditions. In these large-scale continuous operations, the function of the workman and the supervising chemical engineer is largely to maintain the plant in its proper running order. Under this maintenance, instruments play a very important part.

When chemical manufacturing is on a small scale or when it is not adaptable to continuous procedures, the *batch sequence* should be used. This requires more supervision on the part of the workman and the chemical engineer because usually the conditions of procedure differ from the start through to the finish. Even with this changing picture, instruments give a record which can be compared from batch to batch and which leads frequently to the choice of superior operating conditions.

Instrumentation[1] *for the indicating, recording, and control of process variables is an almost universal outstanding characteristic of modern chemical manufacture.* In many chemical plants the instrument expense amounts to 20 per cent of the total cost of the plant. Instrumentation has been forced to this position of eminence by the increase of continuous procedures, by the increase in the cost of labor and supervision, by the decrease in the cost of capital, by the increase in the scale of chemical procedures, and by the standardization of chemical procedures under *unit operations* and *unit processes*.

Instruments are available that furnish a wide variety of data and controls, such as,

---

[1] RHODES, "Industrial Instruments for Measurement and Control," McGraw-Hill Book Company, Inc., New York, 1941; PERRY, *op. cit.*, pp. 1265–1337 contains an up-to-date presentation of the principles and details of instrumentation; Symposium, Instrumentation, *Ind. Eng. Chem.*, **43**, 2694 (1951); Process Instrumentation, *Chem. Eng.*, **59** (5), 161 (1952), plus a most excellent chart.

1. *Instantaneous data* from mercury thermometers for temperature, ordinary scales for weighing, and pressure gages for pressure.

2. *Continuous records* from special instruments for recording temperature, pressure, weight, viscosity, flow of fluids, percentage of carbon dioxide, and many other physical and chemical data. In such cases clocks frequently move a chart so that various readings are correlated with time. Recording of electrical energy[1] required frequently indicates a certain state in carrying out a chemical procedure when a change ought to be made, as in "beating" pulp in a Jordan or crystallizing sugar in a vacuum pan.

3. *Automation or automatic control* of different variables through special instruments for maintaining a desired pressure or temperature or pH or flow of material. These are more or less complicated devices. The simple thermostat, used in almost every home as a necessary adjunct to a modern furnace, is a sample of a very simple controlling instrument. This division of instrumentation is a specialty in itself, but is growing rapidly.

CHEMICAL CONTROL

Chemical control has a threefold function in factory procedures: (1) analysis of incoming raw materials, (2) analysis of reaction products during manufacturing, *i.e.*, so-called "process control," and (3) analysis of the outgoing finished products.

The chemical manufacturer should not only know the character of the raw materials he is buying but should often set up strict quality specifications to assure the minimum or complete absence of certain undesirable impurities. For instance, the presence of arsenic in the acid employed would be deleterious for hydrolyzing starch to dextrose for food purposes although of lesser significance if the hydrolysis were to produce dextrin adhesives. Well over 90 per cent of the raw materials of the chemical process industries are probably purchased on the basis of *chemical analysis*.

Process control, the second of our functions, is an essential part of practically all manufacturing operations involving chemical change. Otherwise the reactions may occasionally get out of hand, with resulting losses of time and materials. To avoid this, many "in-process tests" should be made at various steps during the progress of manufacturing. This does not mean that an extensive laboratory should be provided in connection with every unit process or operation. Frequently the plant chemist in the control laboratory can devise fairly simple tests to indicate the progress of a given reaction, and these are sufficiently simple and reliable so that the nonchemical workman can be taught to carry them out. If chemical changes are at all complicated, check samples should be drawn and submitted to the control laboratory for a more

[1] SHREVE, Graphic Instruments in Chemical Processes, *Ind. Eng. Chem.*, **26**, 1021 (1934).

careful analysis than is possible by the workman in the factory. For proper operation of a plant, close cooperation between the manufacturing and control divisions is essential. They should, however, be independent of each other to the extent that the laboratory results are not subject to the influence of the man in charge of production.

Finally, to ensure that the customer gets material which meets his specifications and which does not vary beyond predetermined limits, a rather *complete analysis* should be made of the *finished product*. Most customers, if their purchases represent any considerable sum of money, maintain a laboratory for checking the purity of what they purchase. In case of any dispute between the seller and the purchaser, this is usually settled by referee analysis on the part of some well-recognized and accepted public analyst.

It is interesting to see the increasing importance of physical means for control of chemical procedures. Such instruments as refractometers, spectrophotometers, and photographing apparatus are now being used, often in the hands of specialists, to supplement the old readings of hydrometers and thermometers.

There is no use spending time and money in the careful making of an analysis unless the *sampling*[1] has been adequate. Too often the drawing of the sample is left to an untrained boy, and a highly skilled chemist will spend hours upon the analysis of the sample brought to him. *As much thought, care, and supervision should be placed upon the taking of a truly representative sample as are expended upon the chemical analysis.*

Sampling is a specific application of the unit operation of size separation and is so presented by Perry[2] where directions with diagrammatic representation of accepted operations are given in detail.

CONTAINERS

The most economical containers are the refillable bulk ones such as tank cars, boxcars, gondola cars, barges, or even tank steamers. Under this class might even come pipe lines for the transportation of petroleum products, acid, or brine, and many other liquid chemicals. Coal is shipped in bulk containers and stored in bins in houses or in stock piles in factories. The United States has been most progressive in the development of bulk means of transportation such as are now used not only for coal, oil, and gasoline but also for alcohol, molasses, sulfur, soda ash, nitric acid, sulfuric acid, hydrochloric acid, caustic soda, liquid ammonia, etc. Tank cars and boxcars or barges make many trips between seller and purchaser and afford a very low-cost container. The railroad car is low in its original capital cost as well as in its handling expense.

[1] DEMING, "Theory of Sampling," John Wiley & Sons, Inc., New York, 1954.
[2] PERRY, *op. cit.*, pp. 1095–1102.

Many chemicals are shipped in smaller containers which may be either of the returnable or of the one-trip variety. Among the *returnable* containers are

Metal drums, 55 and 100 gal., for acids, oil, solvents, and many liquids.
Steel cylinders, for compressed gas such as hydrogen and oxygen and for liquids such as ammonia and carbon dioxide.
Wooden barrels, 50 gal., for very many liquids and solids.
Wooden kegs, 1 to 10 gal., for very many liquids and solids.
Glass carboys, 12 gal., for acids and other liquids.
Glass demijohns, 1, 2, and 2½ gal., for liquids.
Glass-stoppered acid bottles, usually about 1 gal. or smaller.
Cotton bags for cement.

Among the nonreturnable or *one-trip* containers may be listed the following:

Thin steel drums, for caustic soda, asphalt, and tar.
Fiber drums, for solid chemicals.
Fiber[1] cans, for small amounts of solid chemicals.
Cotton bags, for soda ash, salt, and many bulk chemicals.
Light wooden barrels, for solid chemicals.
Light wooden boxes and crates, mostly for protecting other containers.
Paper sacks, lined or multiwalled, for even hydroscopic chemicals.
Tinned or other thin metal cans, for liquids or solids.
Small glass bottles of various sizes, for very many solid and liquid chemicals.

The choice of a suitable container is often one for a specialist.[2] Many containers are lined with paper, which may or may not be waterproofed, or with a plastic.

The cost of containers varies from 6 to 10 cents for paper bags, around $1 for wooden barrels for solids, $3 to $4 for iron drums, $4.50 for glass carboys, $11 for steel cylinders, up to around $3,000 to $4,000 for 10,000-gal. low-pressure tank cars, or $6,000 to $7,000 for high-pressure cars used in transporting such gases as helium. To reduce the cost of container and handling and to effect a saving of warehouse space, the use of multi-walled heavy-duty paper containers[3] is on the increase.

Under the unit operation of *movement and storage of materials* occurs the subdivision of *bulk-packing equipment* wherein the chemical engineer handles the equipment needed to put his product economically into a

---

[1] BIGGER, Fiber Cans, Alternates for Metal Containers, *Chem. Eng. News*, **21**, 1436 (1943).

[2] *Industrial Engineering Chemistry* conducts a department called "Materials Handling" under the leadership of T. W. Rhodes. This is devoted to the various phases of packaging, such as production, improvements, availability, new inventions, and governmental statistics and regulations.

[3] ANON., Bulk Packaging of Chemicals, *Chem. Eng.*, **55** (4), 127 (1948).

TABLE 1. METHODS OF TRANSPORTATION FOR THE CHEMICAL INDUSTRIES[a]

Inbound shipments				Outbound shipments			
Material	Tons	Per cent	Via	Product	Tons	Per cent	Via
Solid fuels and raw materials	230,000,000	77	Railway	Solids	180,000,000	82	Railway
Liquid fuels and raw materials..........	175,000,000	17	Waterway	Liquids...	125,000,000	12	Waterway
		6	Highway	Gases.....	1,000,000	6	Highway

[a] Chem. & Met. Eng., **44,** 557 (1937). In recent years, highway or truck transportation has increased proportionally.

barrel, drum, or sack. Perry[1] presents this with regard to the various laborsaving and automatic devices that are in use.

SAFETY AND FIRE PROTECTION

The superintendent of a chemical factory pays much attention to the safety of his men and to protection against fire. Safety measures not only keep an employee regularly on the job and the equipment working but actually save money in the reduction of the premiums paid by employers for liability and fire insurance. One of the principal jobs of the chemical engineer, if there is no safety engineer, is the establishment of adequate safety measures to protect workmen and also the chemical engineer himself. Too frequently, familiarity with chemicals breeds carelessness. To ensure against this attitude, well-run plants have safety committees in which men from other departments check up the safety devices and recommendations of those actually working with the given process. There is only one thing more disturbing than a bad accident and that is a conflagration. Although both can be insured against, it is cheaper and interrupts production less to prevent such accidents or fires.

Adequate safety and fire protection measures require expert guidance. Whereas much information[2] is available in the literature, more specific help can be obtained from the National Safety Council,[3] a cooperative organization for the purpose of disseminating information among its members and of promoting safety in all its aspects.

Table 2 summarizes the disabling injuries met with throughout the chemical industries. Certain companies by proper organization and

[1] Op. cit., pp. 1381–1414.

[2] PERRY, op. cit., pp. 1847–1884, excellent presentation with bibliography; ANON., Fire Prevention, Chem. Eng., **56** (12), 123 (1949).

[3] 425 North Michigan Drive, Chicago 22, Ill.

TABLE 2. DISABLING INJURIES, 1953, CHEMICAL INDUSTRY, BY GROUPS[a]

| Group | No. of units | Man-hours worked (1000's) | Avg. No. of employees | No. of disabling injuries | | | | Frequency rates | | | Severity rates | | |
				Death and permanent	Permanent partial	Temporary	Total	1951–1953	1953 Deaths and permanent disability	1953 All injuries	1951–1953	1953 Deaths and permanent disability	1953 All injuries
Entire industry	851	807,912	403,956	75	266	3,320	3,661	5.03	0.42	4.53	0.73	0.70	0.81
Synthetic fibers	21	88,669	44,335	2	10	89	101	1.36	0.14	1.14	0.32	0.21	0.24
Laboratories	59	41,027	20,514	1	10	84	95	1.89	0.27	2.32	0.20	0.22	0.25
Plastic materials	44	65,393	32,697	5	32	108	145	2.21	0.57	2.22	0.61	0.64	0.69
High explosives	29	44,862	22,431	23	28	75	126	2.85	1.14	2.81	3.57	3.53	3.63
Synthetic rubber	16	22,051	11,025	2	9	95	106	3.77	0.50	4.81	0.70	0.62	0.14
Fuses and powder	10	8,562	4,281	5	3	38	46	4.93	0.93	5.37	2.25	3.92	4.12
Chlorine and alkali	40	63,011	31,505	5	25	270	300	5.17	0.48	4.76	0.87	0.72	0.84
Photographic film	3	12,469	6,235	0	8	32	40	5.75	0.64	3.21	0.24	0.04	0.10
Paint and varnish	74	50,134	25,067	1	6	259	266	5.85	0.14	5.31	0.38	0.15	0.25
Acids	32	14,569	7,284	2	9	73	84	5.97	0.76	5.77	1.13	1.19	1.28
Soap and glycerine	22	25,726	12,863	0	12	130	142	6.38	0.47	5.52	0.45	0.27	0.48
Pharmaceuticals, fine chemicals, and cosmetics	95	103,662	51,831	2	23	544	569	6.49	0.24	5.49	0.30	0.16	0.26
Alcohol and wood distilling	13	6,508	3,254	0	3	42	45	7.28	0.46	6.91	0.74	0.06	0.21
Fats and oils	55	16,050	8,025	1	6	142	149	10.45	0.44	9.28	0.78	0.51	0.69
Coal-tar products	27	6,797	3,399	2	1	71	74	10.56	0.44	10.89	1.12	2.02	2.29
Industrial gases	118	25,258	12,629	4	6	230	240	11.04	0.40	9.50	1.45	1.18	1.42
Fertilizers	57	23,814	11,907	7	14	215	236	12.51	0.88	9.91	2.27	2.22	2.40
Salt	15	5,545	2,773	0	4	78	82	17.74	0.72	14.79	0.57	0.38	0.60
Not otherwise classified	121	183,806	91,903	13	57	745	815	4.29	0.38	4.43	0.58	0.53	0.64

[a] Courtesy of National Safety Council. The "No. of units" are the units reporting to the National Safety Council. If the exact number of hours worked for a unit is unknown, an arbitrary 2,000 man-hours per year per man is the man-hour figure used. The frequency rates are the number of disabling injuries per million man-hours. The severity rates are the total time charges, in days, per thousand man-hours.

training have greatly reduced the number and severity of harmful accidents to life, limb, and plant. This is true of even those industries which are inherently dangerous.

The National Safety Council, reporting on 400 accidents in 1942, tabulates the following causes:

Agency of injury	Number of injuries
Presses, rolls, and other machinery	139
Acids, alkalies, and other chemicals	44
Floors, ladders, and other working surfaces	34
Trucks, railroad cars, and other vehicles	33
Pipe lines, boilers, and other pressure apparatus	27
Elevators, cranes, and other hoisting apparatus	22
Hand tools	17
Conveyers	14
Mechanical power transmission apparatus	11
Other	59
Total	400

From this tabulation it is seen how very important it is to continue training men to protect themselves from moving machinery as well as from chemicals. Unsafe practices caused 85 per cent of these 400 injuries. Some of these unsafe practices are cleaning, adjusting, or repairing in the vicinity of moving machinery, using defective machinery or tools, starting or stopping machinery without signaling other workmen, standing under suspended loads or assuming unsafe positions, failure to wear protective devices such as goggles or safety shoes, entering dangerous areas, removing safety devices, mixing chemicals to cause explosion or fire.

Equipment should be tested initially and periodically to ensure safety and efficiency. The chemicals handled most frequently have certain hazardous aspects, which should be ascertained and guarded against. Flammable liquids[1] can be safely processed. Specific chemicals, such as ammonia and hydrofluoric acid and many others that are hazardous, can be so handled by the chemical engineers who are conversant with their properties that safety of plant and of workman can be secured. Among the large number of materials handled in the chemical industry, there are many that will cause illness to employees handling them unless adequate safeguards are provided and used. Materials that are toxic may enter the body in three ways: ingestion, inhalation, and skin absorption. The chemical engineer should be able to recommend precautionary measures which will eliminate or minimize these hazards and save not only health but man-hours and tend to increase production.

---

[1] "National Fire Codes," Vol. I, "Flammable Liquids, Gases, Chemicals, and Explosives," N.F.P.A., Boston, 1951.

PATENTS

In order to encourage new discoveries for the benefit of the nation the Constitution provides for patents. These are limited monopolies extending over 17 years and given in exchange for something new and beneficial. However, as it takes an average of about 7 years between the time an invention is patented until it is commercialized, the monopoly exists practically for only about 10 years. After this the public has a right to use the invention freely. Patents are necessary in this competitive system of free enterprise in order that research funds can be generously spent for improvements on old processes and for new and useful discoveries. The system of inventions enables a concern to reimburse itself for its large expenditure for research. The United States patent system also discourages secret processes by guaranteeing the limited monopoly only in case of an adequate disclosure. There is no quicker way to have a patent declared invalid than to show before an impartial court that an inventor has held back some essential step in the disclosure of his idea.

Dean A. A. Potter, when Executive Director of the National Patent Planning Commission, wrote the following about patents.[1]

A clear understanding is essential of the difference between an invention, a patent, and a marketable product. Invention is the act of finding something that is new. A patent is a grant of exclusive right to the inventor to his invention for a limited period of time. An invention is not a product, and the patent by itself does not produce a product. To produce a marketable product a new idea in the form of an invention must be developed and embodied in a form suitable for manufacture, and appropriate tools must be available so that the product can be manufactured at a cost acceptable to the public. The patent serves to protect the inventor and those who develop, manufacture, and sell the product from the uncontrolled competition of parties who have not shared the burden of invention and its commercialization.

Inventions, by bringing these new products to the commercial world, benefit the public at large and *for all time*. The inventor himself receives only a *limited* reward. The inventor, however, *creates* something that did not exist before. In the field of the chemical industries, the American patent system is accountable for much of the recent growth by encouraging the research upon which this growth is founded. The obtaining of a patent is a procedure requiring skilled and experienced guidance. The patent office does not require that an inventor proceed with the help of a patent attorney but sound business judgment does. The patent must be of something *new* and must be fully *disclosed*, and the essentials of the invention must be properly covered by the *claims*. There are

[1] POTTER, The Engineer and the American Patent System, *Mech. Eng.*, **66**, 15–20 (1944).

also a number of pitfalls that an inexperienced inventor might fall into, such as attempting to cover more than one invention in one patent or not keeping the necessary records of the conception of his invention or of its reduction to practice. All these requirements, and more too, are largely avoided by the association of reputable patent counsel with the inventor.

RESEARCH

It is certainly true that adequate and skilled research with patent protection guarantees future profits. In the chemical process industries some of the outstanding characteristics are changing procedures, new raw materials, new products, and continual increase from laboratory test tube to tank car shipments. Research creates or utilizes these changes. Without this forward-looking investigation or research, a company would be left behind in the competitive progress of the industry. A company might possibly have so fundamental a raw material and such a well-developed process that research could not improve the product. Though this latter statement is rarely true, it is a fact that the progress of industry opens up new markets for even the most fundamentally established products. The results and benefits of research[1] may be tabulated as follows:

1. New and improved processes.
2. Lower costs and lower prices of products.
3. New services and new products never before known.
4. Change of rarities to commercial supplies of practical usefulness.
5. Adequate supply of chemicals previously obtained only as by-products.
6. Freedom for American users from foreign monopoly control.
7. Stabilization of business and of industrial employment.
8. Products of greater purity.
9. Products of superior service, *e.g.*, light-fast dyes.
10. New medicines and other new health aids.
11. More efficient use of raw materials.
12. More efficient by-product recovery.

These results, just quoted, may also in their own words be summarized by the expression "creation of new industry and stabilization of old."

There has been a rapid growth in research in the chemical process industries. According to Perazich,[2] in 1927 these industries employed 3,500 researchers and their assistants. In 1940 the total was 15,000, a growth of about 330 per cent or something like 25 per cent per year. In the next decade this same group grew to nearly 33,000, or a net annual gain of about 12 per cent. Research personnel of all manufacturing industries, including the chemical and allied industries, has grown in

[1] *Chem. & Met. Eng.*, **44,** 545 (1937).
[2] PERAZICH, Research: Who, Where, How Much, *Chem. Week*, **69** (17), 17 (1951).

the period 1927–1950 from 17,000 to over 165,000; the number of laboratories themselves increased from 1,147 to 3,313. Another measurement of research growth is the ratio of research staffs to the total number of workers engaged in production. For the chemical process industries between 1927 and 1950 the ratio of total research staff personnel per 10,000 production workers increased from 137 to 657.

The cost of research varies widely between individual industries and between individual companies in the same field. One company[1] estimates that the average cost to maintain one technically trained man in research is $24,000 annually and involves an average investment of over $30,000 in laboratory facilities. Including salaries, equipment, and materials, the most recent estimates place the chemical process industries annual cost per laboratory worker at about $7,000, but 60 per cent of this one company's sales in 1950 came from products that were either unknown or in their commercial infancy in 1930. The country's total university, governmental, and industrial research and development expenditures amounted to almost 3 billion dollars for 1952,[2] with Federal funds supplying over half of this large sum.

Another way of evaluating research is as a percentage of each sales dollar. For the chemical field this varies from 1 to 5 per cent.

As a result of research, the characteristics of the chemical process industries are *change* and *improvement*. Finally it may be remarked that, in a business and financial sense, it would be unwise either to work for or to continue to hold the securities of any firm which, in these competitive days, is not research-minded.

The risks of research are high and success comes only when good judgment is coupled with research ability. Many companies spend large sums before the payoff arrives. The Du Pont company spent around 38 million dollars on their 1950 research budget. Looking back, this company *invested* 43 million dollars in dyes before the profits were large enough to offset the losses. Similarly for ammonia they invested at their Belle, W. Va., plant 27 million dollars before the process became a profitable one. In nylon they *invested* 27 million dollars before getting into satisfactory commercial production.

WASTE DISPOSAL

There was a time when any product that a manufacturer did not want was turned loose into the air or run into the nearest stream irrespective of odor, color, or toxicity. Fortunately those days are past.

However, it is not always an easy procedure to dispose of wastes. Sometimes a long-drawn-out study is required to ascertain how either to

[1] E. I. du Pont de Nemours and Company Annual Report, 1951.
[2] *Chem. Eng. News*, **31**, 228 (1953).

neutralize the waste, to destroy it, or to turn it to something useful. Chemical wastes are particularly bothersome because they are so variable in their properties. The colored liquor running from a dyeing establishment should be treated entirely differently from the acid liquors escaping from a coal mine. Hence, the treatment of chemical wastes is largely in the hands of the experienced chemical engineer who must first determine the exact chemical nature and properties of a waste product. He should then endeavor to prevent its formation or to turn it into something useful. When this is impossible, his efforts should be directed to neutralize economically the harmful effect of the waste so that neither the air nor the rivers are contaminated.

GROWTH AND STATISTICS

Statistics are available from a number of sources: the *U.S. Bureau of Mines* and its *"Mineral Resources"* as well as the *U.S. Bureau of the Census.* The monthly issues of *Chemical Engineering* and the weekly issues of *Chemical and Engineering News* are most helpful. For a comprehensive survey on economic data on individual chemicals and raw materials,

TABLE 3. POSTWAR GROWTH OF SOME CHEMICAL GROUPS[a]

Production	Millions of pounds		Ratio 1952 to 1945
	1952	1945	
Resins and plastics............................	2,333	818	2.8
Synthetic rubbers............................	1,889	1,904	1.0
Synthetic detergents.........................	741	184	4.0
Pesticides, etc................................	418	43	9.7
Synthetic fibers (excluding rayon and acetate)....	261	52	5.0
Drugs..	67	44	1.5

[a] U.S. Tariff Commission, "Synthetic Organic Chemicals, U.S. Production and Sales," except synthetic fibers from "Textile Organon."

TABLE 4. AMERICAN SYNTHETIC ORGANIC CHEMICAL INDUSTRY[a]

Growth rate..........................	4 Times average of all American industry
Employees............................	153,000
Research workers......................	12,203
Annual research bill...................	$204,000,000
Rate of production gain................	3 Times average of all American industry
Rate of sales increase.................	5 Times average of all American industry
Average hourly wages..................	$2.08
Annual payrolls.......................	$717,000,000
Value of products.....................	$4,500,000,000

[a] *Chem. Eng. News,* **32,** 3719, 3912 (1954).

on the principal chemical-consuming industries, and on financial aspects of the chemical industry, reference should be made to "Chemical Economics Handbook," instituted by Raymond H. Ewell and published and revised yearly by Stanford Research Institute, Stanford, Calif. This most excellent book utilizes a base period of 1910–1950 with emphasis on long-range trends.

Tables 3 and 4 indicate the high growth rate of the manufacture of organic chemicals in comparison with all industry.

MISCELLANEOUS ASPECTS

Whereas the first part of this chapter has considered in more or less outline the general fundamentals in connection with the operation of chemical plants, there are many other aspects of importance, among which are plant location, consideration of competing processes, the labor market, and the sales outlet. Furthermore, every growing concern should have a number of adjuncts to its manufacturing operations, among which may be mentioned an efficient pilot plant and a library.

Plant Location.[1] Naturally, the proper location for a chemical plant or a branch plant is conditioned largely by raw materials, transportation, and markets. Yet, many other factors appear, such as power, water, availability of efficient labor, cost of land, and ability to dispose of wastes. There is a very strong tendency on the part of chemical concerns to leave congested cities and to move out either into smaller towns or actually into the country.

Competing Processes. As change is almost the outstanding characteristic of chemical procedures, this phase of any process is not only of importance when the plant is first designed but should be always in the consciousness of any chemical executive. Indeed, one of the functions of a research organization is to keep abreast with the progress of the basic sciences and to make available for the organization any improvements or even fundamental changes leading to the making of any given product in which the organization is interested. The research organization should also keep informed regarding developments in other companies and be in a position to advise the executives of the relative competitive position of actual or contemplated processes or products.

Labor. The conduct of chemical plants requires, as a rule, rather skilled labor with a limited requirement for ordinary backbreaking work. Most of the help needed is for men who can repair, maintain, and control the various pieces of equipment necessary to carry out the *unit processes* and the *unit operations*. As each year passes, the chemical

---

[1] PERRY, *op. cit.*, pp. 1719–1730; *cf.* the most excellent Symposia on Resources for the Chemical Industry, *Ind. Eng. Chem.*, **43**, 1723, 2647 (1951).

industry by virtue of a wider use of instruments and a greater complexity of equipment requires more and more of the higher type of skilled labor.

Sales. There is no reason to manufacture anything unless it can be used or sold. In order to sell goods properly in these competitive times, "sales service" must frequently accompany the delivery of the manufactured article. A customer can be shown more appropriately how to use a given product by the salesman fully acquainted with its properties. An understanding of the customer's problems often helps in planning manufacturing operations. By reason of these sales aspects many chemically trained men are entering sales or sales service as their life work.

Pilot Plants. No new process should be moved from the laboratory into the plant without going through a pilot plant. A good principle is to insist that the product be made first on the small scale. It is much cheaper to make errors and quicker to correct them when operating in a pilot plant than in the factory. Furthermore, if a new venture is being undertaken, it is difficult to design the large-scale procedure effectively without having first run the process in a small pilot plant. There the equipment should be made out of the same materials as the best engineering judgment indicates should be chosen for the large plant. There, also, the corrosion, wear, and tear on these materials can actually be observed under small-scale manufacturing conditions. In the pilot plant the installation should be of *replica* equipment usually on the smallest scale available. The pilot plants also serve to train foremen for the factory procedures.

Library. Any plant of any size should have available present and past literature,[1] in its field as well as the records of its past experience. In the library there should be collected and made available statistics[1] pertaining to the domestic manufacture and imports of any products the company makes or is considering.

SELECTED REFERENCES

General:

Perry, John H., editor-in-chief, "Chemical Engineers' Handbook," 3d ed., McGraw-Hill Book Company, Inc., New York, 1950. This is the one absolutely essential reference book and constant technical companion for every chemical engineer.

"Chemical Engineering Catalog," Reinhold Publishing Corporation, New York. Annual compilation of manufacturers' catalogs.

Vilbrandt, Frank C., "Chemical Engineering Plant Design," 3d ed., McGraw-Hill Book Company, Inc., New York, 1949.

Riegel, Emil, "Chemical Process Machinery," 6th ed., Reinhold Publishing Corporation, New York, 1949.

[1] For exceptional articles on the Literature of Chemical Technology, see KIRK and OTHMER, *op. cit.*, Vol. 8, pp. 418–448; KOBE, "Inorganic Chemical Processes," Chap. 1, The Macmillan Company, New York, 1948.

Industrial and Engineering Chemistry, Literature Resources for Chemical Process Industries, Washington, D.C., 1954.

Chemical Processing, New Processes, Materials, Machinery, Putnam Publishing Co., Chicago.

Haynes, Williams, American Chemical Industry, 6 vols., D. Van Nostrand Company, Inc., New York, 1945–1954.

Materials of Construction and Corrosion:

Lee, J. A., "Materials of Construction for Chemical Process Industries," McGraw-Hill Book Company, Inc., New York, 1950.

Uhlig, H. H., "The Corrosion Handbook," John Wiley & Sons, Inc., New York, 1948.

Rabald, Erich, "Corrosion Guide," Elsevier Press, Inc., New York, 1951.

Speller, F. N., "Corrosion: Causes and Prevention," 3d ed., McGraw-Hill Book Company, Inc., New York, 1951.

Process Instrumentation:

Rhodes, Thomas J., "Industrial Instruments for Measurement and Control," McGraw-Hill Book Company, Inc., New York, 1941.

Eckman, D. P., "Industrial Instrumentation," John Wiley & Sons, Inc., New York, 1950.

Instrumentation for the Process Industries, *Bulls.* 100 and 103, Agricultural and Mechanical College of Texas, College Station, Tex., 1946–1947.

Chemical Control:

Griffin, Roger C., "Technical Methods of Analysis," 2d ed., McGraw-Hill Book Company, Inc., New York, 1927.

Allen, A. H., "Commercial Organic Analysis," 5th ed., 10 vols. covering years 1923–1933, Blakiston Division, McGraw-Hill Book Company, Inc., New York.

Containers:

Modern Packaging Magazine, Breskin Publishing Corporation, New York.

Safety and Fire Protection:

Manufacturing Chemists Association, various "Safety Data Sheets," Washington, D.C.

General Safety Committee of the Manufacturing Chemists Association, "Guide for Safety in the Chemical Laboratory," D. Van Nostrand Company, Inc., New York, 1954.

Perry, *op. cit.,* Sec. 30, pp. 1847–1884. Excellent bibliography.

National Safety Council, cooperative organization with publications and data available to members, 425 N. Michigan Ave., Chicago.

Henderson, Yandell, and H. W. Haggard, "Noxious Gases and the Principles of Respiration Influencing Their Action," 2d ed., Reinhold Publishing Corporation, New York, 1943.

National Fire Protection Association, Boston, excellent publications: "National Fire Codes," Vol. I; "Flammable Liquids, Gases, Chemicals, and Explosives," 1951; "N.F.P.A. Handbook of Fire Protection," 10th ed., 1948.

Sax, N. I., "Handbook of Dangerous Materials," Reinhold Publishing Corporation, New York, 1951.

Patty, F. A., editor, "Industrial Hygiene and Toxicology," 2 vols., Interscience Publishers, Inc., New York, 1948.

Patents:

Biesterfeld, Chester H., "Patent Law for Chemists, Engineers and Students," 2d ed., John Wiley & Sons, Inc., New York, 1949.

Rossman, Joseph, "Law of Patents for Chemists," 2d ed., The Williams & Wilkins Company, Baltimore, 1934.

Thomas, Edward, "Chemical Inventions and Chemical Patents," Matthew Bender and Company, Inc., Albany, 1950.

Symposium, Evolution of a Patent, *Ind. Eng. Chem.*, **43**, 2487 (1951). The second half of this symposium is published in *Chem. Eng. News*, **29** (43, 44), 1951.

Research:

Mees, C. E. K., and J. A. Leermakers, "The Organization of Industrial Scientific Research," 2d ed., McGraw-Hill Book Company, Inc., New York, 1950.

Furnas, C. C., "Research in Industry," D. Van Nostrand Company, Inc., New York, 1948.

Hertz, D. B., "The Theory and Practice of Industrial Research," McGraw-Hill Book Company, Inc., New York, 1950.

Waste:

Besselievre, E. B., "Industrial Waste Treatment," McGraw-Hill Book Company, Inc., New York, 1952.

Rudolfs, William, editor, "Industrial Wastes, Their Disposal and Treatment," A.C.S. Monograph 118, Reinhold Publishing Corporation, New York, 1953.

Lipsett, C. H., "Industrial Wastes," Atlas Publishing Company, Inc., New York, 1951.

Cost and Economics:

Corley, H. M., "Successful Commercial Development," 106 coauthors, John Wiley & Sons, Inc., New York, 1954.

Perry, J. H., editor, "Chemical Business Handbook," McGraw-Hill Book Company, Inc., New York, 1954.

Aries, R. S., and R. D. Newton, "Chemical Engineering Cost Estimation," Chemonomics, Inc., New York, 1950.

Tyler, Chaplin, "Chemical Engineering Economics," 3d ed., McGraw-Hill Book Company, Inc., New York, 1948.

Symposium, Plant Cost Estimation, *Ind. Eng. Chem.*, **43**, 2295–2311 (1951).

Sales and Uses:

Gregory, T. C., "Uses and Applications of Chemicals and Related Materials," Reinhold Publishing Corporation, New York, 1939.

Schoengold, M. D., "Encyclopedia of Substitutes or Synthetics," Philosophical Library, Inc., New York, 1943.

Statistics:

"Chemical Statistics Handbook," with semiannual summaries, 4th ed., Manufacturing Chemists' Association, Washington, 1955.

"Census of Manufactures," biennial publication, U.S. Bureau of the Census, 1947.

"Synthetic Organic Chemicals," U.S. Tariff Commission, annually since 1917.

"Minerals Yearbook," U.S. Bureau of Mines, annually.

"Chemical Economics Handbook," Stanford Research Institute, Stanford, Calif., annually.

CHAPTER 4

WATER CONDITIONING AND WASTE-WATER TREATMENT

Water conditioning and waste-water treatment have long been essential functions of municipalities. However, the importance of suitably preparing water for the chemical industry is sometimes underemphasized, although the chemical manufacturing processes consume large quantities of water ranging in quality from untreated to deionized. Industrial waste waters present a complex and challenging problem to the chemical engineer. Besides moral and publicity considerations, laws prohibiting and limiting the pollution of streams force this problem to be considered a necessary operating expense. While the solution is specific with each industry (indeed, almost with each plant or factory), a few general principles may be observed: reuse of waste waters, recovery of by-products to lessen the expense of treatment, and pooling of wastes to distribute pollution or to effect a saving in neutralization costs.

As is well known, the purity and the quantity of available water are very important in the location[1] of a chemical plant. Both the surface and the ground water should be considered. The latter is more suitable usually for cooling purposes because of its uniformly low summer and winter temperature, but such water is generally harder, may cause scale, and hence may interfere with heat transfer.

The impurities contained in water[2] vary greatly from one section of the country to another. Hard waters are those containing objectionable amounts of dissolved salts of calcium and magnesium. These are present as bicarbonates, chlorides, or sulfates. These salts give insoluble precipitates with soap and form clogging scales with low thermal conductivities when used in boilers.

[1] ANON., Water Supply, *Chem. Eng.*, **55** (1), 137 (1948), a most excellent report; *cf.* ANON., The Water Problem, *Chem. Eng.*, **56** (7), 119 (1949).

[2] Typical water analyses are tabulated in many books and articles. See CLARKE, Composition of River and Lake Waters of the U.S., *U.S. Geol. Survey, Profess. Paper* 135, Washington; CERNA, Industrial Water Conditioning Processes, *J. Chem. Educ.*, **20,** 108 (1943). Maps showing hardness of surface waters and of ground waters for the United States are given by OLSON, Benefits and Savings from Softened Water, *J. Am. Water Works Assoc.*, **31,** 609 (1939); MONTGOMERY, How Process Industries Are Meeting Their Water Supply Problems, *Chem. & Met. Eng.*, **47,** 622 (1940). See also MASON and BUSWELL, "Examination of Water," 6th ed., John Wiley & Sons, Inc., New York, 1936.

Hardness is usually expressed in terms of the dissolved calcium and magnesium salts calculated as calcium carbonate equivalent, $CaCO_3$; when these constituents are measured by titrating with a standard soap solution, this is frequently called *soap hardness*. The common units used in expressing water analyses are parts per million (p.p.m.) and grains per gallon. One grain per gallon is equivalent to 17.1 p.p.m. Water hardness may be divided into two classes: *carbonate* and *noncarbonate*, also frequently known as *temporary* and *permanent*. Temporary hardness can usually be greatly reduced by boiling; permanent hardness requires the use of chemical agents. Carbonate or temporary hardness is caused by bicarbonates of lime and magnesia; noncarbonate or permanent hardness is due to the sulfates and chlorides of lime and magnesia. In addition to hardness, there may also be present varying amounts of sodium salts, silica, alumina, iron, or manganese. The total dissolved solids may range from a few parts per million in snow water to several thousand parts per million in water from mineral springs. Other water impurities that may be present are suspended insoluble matter (classed usually as turbidity), organic matter, color, and dissolved gases. Such gases are carbon dioxide (largely as bicarbonate), oxygen, nitrogen, and, in sulfur waters, hydrogen sulfide.

WATER CONDITIONING

Water conditioning must be adapted to the particular use for which the water is designed. It is furthermore a complicated phase of chemical engineering practice, and problems should be referred to the experts in this field. The use of elevated pressures (1,400 lb. per sq. in. and higher for steam generation) requires the employment of more carefully purified boiler feed water. And each industry[1] has its special water-conditioning requirements, *e.g.*, laundries require zero hardness to prevent precipitation of calcium and magnesium soap on the clothes. Likewise calcium and magnesium salts cause undesirable precipitates with dyes in the textile industries or with the dyes in paper manufacture.

Historical. In this country an abundance of fairly soft water has long been available from surface supplies of the industrial Northeast. Cities such as New York and Boston obtain comparatively soft water from rural watersheds over igneous rocks. However, as the Middle West and the West were developed, it became necessary to use the harder water that prevails in these limestone areas. This hard water needs to be softened for many uses. Furthermore, as the advantages of really soft water are recognized, more and more even fairly soft waters are being

[1] FURNAS, "Rogers' Manual of Industrial Chemistry," pp. 199–205, D. Van Nostrand Company, Inc., New York, 1942.

completely softened for laundries, homes, textile mills, and certain chemical processes.

Thomas Clark of England, in 1841, patented the lime processes for the removal of carbonate or temporary hardness. A short time after Clark's patent, Porter developed the use of soda ash in removing the noncarbonate or permanent hardness of water. In spite of earlier work by Thompson, Way, and Eichhorn on zeolite base exchange, it was not until 1906 that Robert Gans, a German chemist, applied zeolites to actual commercial use for water-softening purposes. The two earliest softening plants for an entire city supply were installed at Canterbury and Southampton,

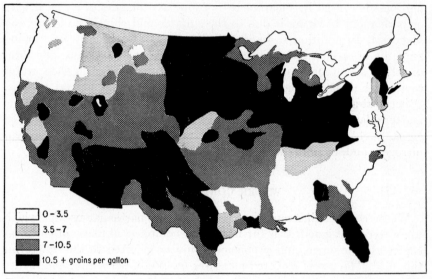

FIG. 1. A hard-water map of the United States shows few parts have soft water (white areas). Most of country has water of varying hardness (gray and black areas).

England, about 1888.[1] Only since the 1930's has softening been extended to municipal supplies to any appreciable extent. The explanation may be that many people, lacking in experience with water other than hard waters, were ignorant of the advantages of softened water. Figure 1 shows the varying hardness of waters in use in the United States.

METHODS OF CONDITIONING WATER

The purification and softening of water may be accomplished by different methods. Table 1 presents a summary of the principal water-softening processes. The use to which the water is to be put determines, frequently, the treatment chosen. *Softening* is the term applied to those processes which remove or reduce the hardness of the water. *Purification*,

[1] OLSON, *op. cit.*, **31** (4), 612 (1939).

as distinguished from softening, usually refers to the removal of organic matter and microorganisms from the water.

TABLE 1. SUMMARY OF WATER-SOFTENING INSTALLATIONS IN THE UNITED STATES FOR 1954[a]

Type and field	Number
Zeolite, household	1,750,000
Zeolite, industrial	50,000
Zeolite, municipal	300
Chemical precipitation, industrial	4,500
Chemical precipitation, municipal	700

[a] *Private communication*, Eskel Nordell of the Permutit Co. The chemical-precipitation type includes cold and hot lime-soda installations.

Ion Exchange. In 1852, Way discovered that the removal of ammonia from aqueous liquids on passing through certain soils was really an exchange with the calcium of a particular type of silicate occurring in the soils. Way's prime interest in ion exchange was in its possible application to agriculture. It required some 50 years after Way's discovery for ion exchange to assume any industrial importance. The first decade of the twentieth century marked the beginning of zeolite water softening, an industry which has grown to large proportions. The advent of sulfonated-coal cation-exchange materials initiated the modern era of ion exchange. The real stimulus for organic exchange resins came when Adams and Holmes[1] published their paper on purely synthetic organic exchange resins and described the anion exchange resins for the first time. From this humble beginning ion exchange has grown to be a valuable chemical engineering unit process. Its utilization on a large industrial scale has been widespread, including the commercial production and use of water having an electrical resistivity of conductivity and the recovery of antibiotics.[2]

Zeolite Exchange. The most important method for softening water is the cation-exchange system commonly referred to as the zeolite system. The present-day usage of the term "zeolite" loosely covers a variety of ion exchangers, such as processed greensand, bentonitic clay, synthetic gel-type minerals, and the new synthetic-resin exchangers.[3] As in the case of soils with base exchange properties, the "inorganic" zeolites are composed principally of hydrated alkali alumina-silicates that contain easily exchangeable ions such as sodium or potassium. Chemical treat-

[1] *J. Soc. Chem. Ind.*, **54**, 1–6T (1935).

[2] Ion Exchange section of Unit Operations Review, annual in the January issue of *Ind. Eng. Chem.*, since 1946; *cf.* ANON., Ion Exchange, *Chem. Eng.*, **54** (7), 123 (1947); Symposia, Ion Exchange, *Ind. Eng. Chem.*, **43**, 1062 (1951); **41**, 447 (1949).

[3] Chap. 18, Zeolite Water-softening Process, in Nordell, "Water Treatment for Industrial and Other Uses," Reinhold Publishing Corporation, New York, 1951.

ment of natural greensand improves its base exchange and physical properties. Research developed synthetic[1] inorganic materials similar to natural "zeolites" but with a higher base exchange.

During the softening process, the Ca and Mg ions are exchanged from the hard water by the zeolite for the Na ions. When the zeolite becomes almost all changed to calcium and magnesium compounds, it is regenerated to restore the sodium zeolite. This is usually done with salt solution and in the pH range between 6 and 8. Industry largely uses the sodium cycle for softening water.[2] Regeneration is with common salt, at a chemical efficiency which varies between the limits of 0.275 and 0.5 lb. of salt per 1000 grains of hardness removed as compared with the stoichiometric efficiency of 0.17 lb. of salt. Choice of exchanger is governed by cost and conditions of use.

The two most widely used hydrogen cation exchangers for water treatment are the polystyrene-base sulfonated-synthetic-resin type and the sulfonated-coal type. The former has only —SO_3H exchange groups. It is exceptionally stable at high temperatures and pH, and it is resistant to oxidizing conditions. The exchange capacity of the best of these is up to 40,000 grains of $CaCO_3$ per cubic foot of ion exchanger on a hydrogen cycle and up to about 35,000 grains of $CaCO_3$ per cubic foot on a sodium cycle. The usual practical operating capacities are not that high. For removing metal cations at low concentrations, the sulfonated-coal-type resin having —SO_3H and —$COOH$ exchange groups is very efficient. The exchange capacity of this type of resin will run about 8,000 grains of $CaCO_3$ per cubic foot. The equations for the exchange and regeneration of these resins will be found on the following pages. Both of the above exchangers may be regenerated with either acid or salt.

Using water containing calcium bicarbonate, for example, a typical equation for zeolite softeners follows, where Z represents the complex cation exchanger radical:

$$Ca(HCO_3)_2 + Na_2Z \rightarrow CaZ + 2NaHCO_3 \qquad (1)$$
$$CaCl_2 + Na_2Z \rightarrow CaZ + 2NaCl \qquad (2)$$

Similar reactions may be written for the other bicarbonates found in water such as magnesium. For regeneration the reaction is

$$CaZ + 2NaCl \text{ (excess)} \rightarrow Na_2Z + CaCl_2 + [\text{excess} - 2(NaCl)] \quad (3)$$

The equipment for the process, shown in Fig. 2, is a large closed cylindrical tank in which the zeolite is supported on graded gravel. The water to be softened may flow down through the tank. Auxiliary apparatus includes both brine- and salt-storage tanks. The washing and

[1] CALLAHAM, Synthetic Zeolite, Chem. Eng., 56 (9), 92 (1949), with a pictured flow sheet, p. 140.

[2] GUSTAFSON, Ion Exchange in Water Treatment, Ind. Eng. Chem., 41, 464 (1949).

regeneration may be carried out automatically as well as manually. These softeners are installed in the water lines and operated under whatever water pressure is necessary. As the zeolite bed also exerts a filtering action, any sediment from the water or from the salt must be washed off by an *efficient backwash*. This step suspends and hydraulically regrades the zeolite bed.

The water from zeolite treatment is usually practically zero in hardness. In cases where very hard water is encountered, it is often desirable to treat the water first by the lime process and follow this by a zeolite

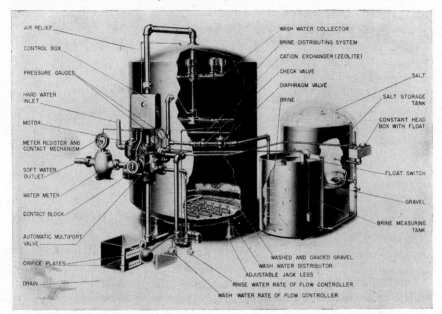

FIG. 2. Automatic zeolite softener. (*Courtesy of the Permutit Company.*)

unit. The lime process actually *removes* bicarbonate hardness from the water while the zeolite process *exchanges* Ca and Mg ions with Na ions.

The great advantage of the zeolite softeners is their convenience and the fact that they furnish a water of zero hardness *without attention* or *adjustment* until regeneration is required even though the raw water varies in hardness from one day to the next.

Organic Ion Exchange. Because of the development of the organic ion exchangers, this process is now used in many industries other than water treatment. Some of these industries are chemical, especially process liquor and waste treatment, biological, drug and pharmaceutical, glues and gelatine, insecticide, rare earth separations, and sugar. These ion exchangers may be divided into two classes: cation and anion.

The *cation organic exchangers* are employed to treat solutions in a relatively wide pH range. They may be roughly divided into

1. Synthetic organic resins such as sulfonated styrene resins (most widely used), sulfonated phenolic resins, and carboxylic acid resins.

2. Processed natural organic materials such as sulfonated coal, coke, charcoal, lignite, and wood shavings.

These contain an exchangeable *hydrogen ion* and can be employed to remove all cations according to the following reactions:

$$Ca(HCO_3)_2 + 2HSO_3R \rightarrow Ca(SO_3R)_2 + 2CO_2 + 2H_2O \qquad (4)$$

The acid formed, H_2CO_3 in this case, decomposes and can be removed

FIG. 3. Demineralization equipment in two steps. (*Courtesy of the Permutit Company.*)

easily. A similar reaction would be true for magnesium or sodium bicarbonates. Sulfates and chlorides react as follows:

$$CaSO_4 + 2HSO_3R \rightarrow Ca(SO_3R)_2 + H_2SO_4 \qquad (5)$$
$$NaCl + HSO_3R \rightarrow NaSO_3R + HCl \qquad (6)$$
$$CaCl_2 + 2HSO_3R \rightarrow Ca(SO_3R)_2 + 2HCl \qquad (7)$$

The regeneration is usually effected by sulfuric acid as follows:

$$Ca(SO_3R)_2 + H_2SO_4 \text{ (excess)} \rightarrow 2HSO_3R + CaSO_4 \qquad (8)$$
$$2NaSO_3R + H_2SO_4 \text{ (excess)} \rightarrow 2HSO_3R + Na_2SO_4 \qquad (9)$$

Such cation exchangers are naturally rugged and also possess considerable exchange capacity, up to 30,000 grains per cu. ft. Their application is shown in Fig. 3. If these cation exchangers are regenerated by sodium chloride instead of acid, they function like the ordinary zeolite softeners (Fig. 2).

Acidic water is not desirable for most purposes and, therefore, the effluent from the hydrogen cation-exchange treatment is either neutralized or, if demineralization is required, is passed through an anion-exchange material, as shown in Fig. 3.

Anion exchangers are of two types—highly basic type and weakly basic type. Such anion exchangers are for the most part basic resins.[1] Both types will remove strongly ionized acids such as sulfuric, hydrochloric, or nitric, but only the highly basic anion exchangers will remove weakly ionized acids such as silicic and carbonic as well as the strongly ionized acids. For the anion exchange of a strongly ionized acid, where R_4N represents the complex anion exchanger radical, the reactions follow (some of the R's may be hydrogen):

$$H_2SO_4 + 2R_4NOH \rightarrow (R_4N)_2SO_4 + 2H_2O \tag{10}$$

Regeneration:

$$(R_4N)_2SO_4 + 2NaOH \rightarrow 2R_4NOH + Na_2SO_4 \tag{11}$$

Highly basic anion exchangers are regenerated with caustic soda, while the weakly basic anion exchangers may be regenerated with caustic soda, soda ash, or sometimes ammonium hydroxide.

Generally speaking the complete deionization or demineralization of water is conducted in a two-bed process as shown in Fig. 3. Single mixed-bed demineralization units are available.[2] For complete deionization the monobed unit must consist of a strong base and strong acid resin combination. This produces water at approximately half the cost of distilled.

The only other process for removing all the ions in water is *distillation*. Both distilled water and deionized water should be handled in special pipes to keep the soft water from dissolving small amounts of the metal and thus becoming contaminated. Block tin has been employed for this purpose for many years but has the disadvantage of extreme softness. Aluminum and molded polyvinylidine chloride pipes are now satisfactory substitutes for conducting "pure" water.

Lime-soda Process. The use of slaked lime and of soda ash to remove hardness in water has long been important. The modern application has been divided into the cold lime process and the hot lime-soda process. The calcium ions in the hard water are removed as $CaCO_3$ and the magnesium ions as $Mg(OH)_2$. Typical equations for these reactions are

For carbonate hardness,

$$Ca(HCO_3)_2 + Ca(OH)_2 \rightarrow 2CaCO_3 + 2H_2O \tag{12}$$

$$Mg(HCO_3)_2 + Ca(OH)_2 \rightarrow MgCO_3 + CaCO_3 + 2H_2O \tag{13}$$

---

[1] WHEATON and BAUMAN, Properties of Strongly Basic Anion Exchange Resins, *Ind. Eng. Chem.*, **43**, 1088 (1951).

[2] KUNIN and McGARVEY, Monobed Deionization with Ion Exchange Resins, *Ind. Eng. Chem.*, **43**, 734 (1951).

Then, since the $MgCO_3$ is fairly soluble,

$$MgCO_3 + Ca(OH)_2 \rightarrow \underline{Mg(OH)_2} + \underline{CaCO_3} \tag{14}$$

For noncarbonate soluble calcium and magnesium salts,

$$MgCl_2 + Ca(OH)_2 \rightarrow \underline{Mg(OH)_2} + CaCl_2 \tag{15}$$

$$CaCl_2 + Na_2CO_3 \rightarrow \underline{CaCO_3} + 2NaCl \tag{16}$$

$$CaSO_4 + Na_2CO_3 \rightarrow \underline{CaCO_3} + Na_2SO_4 \tag{17}$$

$$MgSO_4 + Na_2CO_3 + Ca(OH)_2 \rightarrow \underline{Mg(OH)_2} + \underline{CaCO_3} + Na_2SO_4 \tag{18}$$

From these reactions it is apparent that, for carbonate hardness, each unit of calcium bicarbonate requires one mole of lime while for each unit of magnesium bicarbonate there is needed *two* moles of lime. For non-carbonate hardness, likewise, the magnesium salts require more reagents (one mole each of soda ash and lime) while the calcium salts require only one mole of soda ash.

Based on a price of $15 per ton for lime (quicklime of 90 per cent purity) and of $35 per ton of soda ash (98 per cent purity), the following material costs have been figured for removing 100 p.p.m. of hardness from 1,000,000 gal. of water.

Calcium bicarbonate hardness (expressed as $CaCO_3$), 520 lb. lime 3.90
Magnesium bicarbonate hardness (expressed as $CaCO_3$), 1,040 lb. lime 7.80
Calcium noncarbonate hardness (expressed as $CaCO_3$), 900 lb. soda ash 15.75
Magnesium noncarbonate hardness (expressed as $CaCO_3$), 900 lb. soda ash,
  520 lb. lime 19.65

The *cold lime* process is employed chiefly for partial softening and ordinarily uses only the cheaper lime for its reagent reactions (12) to (15) above. It reduces the calcium hardness to 35 p.p.m. if proper opportunity is given for precipitation of the hardness, thus discharging the "supersaturation" so frequently met with in this process. This cold lime process is particularly applicable to partial softening for municipal water (Figs. 5 and 6), to the conditioning of cooling water where calcium bicarbonate hardness may be the scale former, and to certain paper-mill waters where calcium bicarbonate is troublesome. The magnesium carbonate hardness can be removed to any desired or economical amount but, if a low residual is wanted, an excess of hydroxyl ions is needed to depress the solubility of the magnesium hydroxide. Usually to aid in the precipitations, a coagulant, aluminum sulfate or ferrous sulfate, is added to lessen afterdeposit.

A successful method of eliminating *supersaturation* in the cold lime-soda process is contacting previously precipitated sludge (see Fig. 5). When this material is exposed to the raw water and chemicals, the like surfaces or "seeds" accelerate the precipitation. The result is a more rapid and more complete reaction with larger and more easily settled particles in the newly formed precipitate.

The equipment developed for this contact by the International Filter Company is called the *Accelator*.[1] In this apparatus there is a special device for mixing the treating chemicals with the suspension of the previously precipitated sludge. Following this, the raw water is introduced into the mixture of chemically impregnated slurry whereupon the positive contact of solid particles and water to be softened with the softening chemicals affords an improved opportunity for precipitation of calcium carbonate and magnesium hydroxide, thus resulting in "desupersaturation."

The Permutit Spaulding Precipator[2] consists of two compartments: one for mixing and agitating the raw water with the softening chemicals and with the previously formed sludge, and the other for settling and filtering the softened water as it passes upward through the suspended blanket of sludge. Machines of these types reduce sedimentation time from 4 hr. to less than 1 hr. and usually effect savings in chemicals employed. A newer machine, the Spiractor, has a detention period of about 10 min. and also functions in the cold lime-soda process.[3] In the Spiractor the hard water plus the necessary softening chemicals travels upward and spirally around granules upon which the hardness precipitates.

The *hot lime-soda process* is employed almost entirely for conditioning boiler feed water. Since it is operated near the boiling point of the water, the reactions proceed faster, the coagulation and the precipitation are facilitated, and much of the dissolved gases such as carbon dioxide and air is driven out.

The hot lime-soda treatment for softening may consist of the following coordinated sequences of *unit operations* (Op.) and *unit processes* (Pr.) which are frequently carried out in such equipment, as illustrated by Fig. 4:

Analysis of the raw water (Pr.).

Heating of the raw water by exhaust steam (Op. and Pr.).

Mixing and proportioning of the lime and soda ash in conformance with the raw water analysis (Op.).

Pumping of the lime-soda mixture into the raw water (Op.).

Reacting of the lime soda, facilitated by mixing with or without previous heating (Pr. and Op.).

[1] BEHRMAN and GREEN, Accelerated Lime Soda Water Softening, *Ind. Eng. Chem.*, **31**, 128 (1939).

[2] SPAULDING, Conditioning of Water Softening Precipitates, *J. Am. Water Works Assoc.*, **29**, 1697 (1937); NORDELL, *op. cit.*, pp. 413–420 (1951).

[3] TIGER and GILWOOD, The New Sludgeless Cold Lime Soda Water Softener, *Paper Trade J.*, **113** (13), 27 (1942); NORDELL, *op. cit.*, pp. 421–425.

Coagulation or release of the "supersaturation" by various methods such as slow agitation or contact with "seeds" (Pr. and Op.).

Settling or removal of precipitate with or without final filtration (Op.).

Pumping away of softened water (Op.).

Periodic washing away of the sludge from the cone tank bottom (and from the clarifying filters) (Op.).

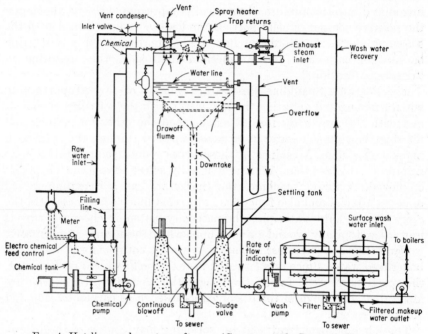

Fig. 4. Hot lime-soda water softener. (*Courtesy of the Permutit Company.*)

If the chemical reactions involved could be carried to completion, the hardness of the water would be reduced to the theoretical solubilities of the calcium carbonate and magnesium hydroxide. This would leave a hardness of approximately 20 to 25 p.p.m. in pure water and a little less at the pH of 10 to 11 involved in the lime-soda process. Frequently for feed water, a sodium phosphate treatment follows the lime soda in order to soften the water more completely. The newest development is the use of resinous ion exchangers for the more complete deionizing of the effluent of a hot-lime process.[1] This is particularly necessary when feeding high-pressure boilers.

Phosphate Conditioning. Various phosphates are employed, usually in conjunction with one of the previously described procedures. *Mono-*

[1] LINDSEY, *et al.*, Ion Exchange in High Temperature Industrial Applications, *Ind. Eng. Chem.*, **43**, 1062 (1951).

sodium, disodium, and *trisodium phosphates* are often added to water to precipitate the hardness ions in the form of easily removed soft phosphate sludges. Sodium hexametaphosphate, $(NaPO_3)_6$,[1] likewise softens water but instead of precipitating the hardness ions it forms soluble complexes with the Ca, Mg, Fe, and Al ions and sequesters them or prevents the formation of scale or insoluble soaps when the phosphate is present in excess and when the water is not too hot. This chemical also possesses the valuable property of dispersing previously formed insoluble soaps. These properties led to the so-called *threshold treatment*[2] of water with an addition of as little as one-half to 5 p.p.m. of this hexametaphosphate, resulting in prevention of the afterprecipitation of calcium carbonate from softening operations, which would cause scale formation in pipes with consequent reduction in fluid flow and in heat transfer. This is important in domestic hot-water heaters, in water pipes, in heat exchangers, and also in washing and laundering. The addition of the sodium hexametaphosphate also reduces corrosion, particularly in nondeaerated waters.

Silica Removal. Silica is not removed by hydrogen cation exchange or sodium zeolite exchange, and usually is only partially removed in the cold or hot lime-soda processes. It may be a very objectionable impurity, especially in boiler feed water, as it can form a tenacious scale. Its presence may be due to dissolved silica in the feed water, or it may be introduced by filtering hot alkaline waters through sand in preliminary softening treatments. In the latter case the use of a different filtering medium, such as anthracite, is indicated. Silica may be removed from the feed water by the use of dolomitic lime or activated magnesia. If preliminary coagulation and settling are carried out, the use of a ferric coagulant will remove some silica. These are especially suitable where the silica concentration of make-up water would be high. Such methods do not entirely take away the dissolved silica, but they do lower its concentration to a point where careful use of a blowdown will eliminate danger of scale. Silica may also be removed completely from the feed water when it is demineralized by hydrogen cation exchange plus anion exchange with a highly basic anion exchanger.

Deaeration. The removal of oxygen dissolved in water is often necessary to condition the water properly for industrial purposes, although this is unnecessary for municipal waters. Dissolved oxygen hastens

---

[1] The formula is sometimes given as $NaPO_3$, which is also called sodium phosphate glass or Calgon. See Chap. 18, under Sodium Phosphates.

[2] HATCH and RICE, Surface-active Properties of Hexametaphosphate, *Ind. Eng. Chem.*, **31**, 51 (1939); SCHWARTZ and MUNTER, Phosphates in Water Conditioning, *Ind. Eng. Chem.*, **34**, 32 (1942); PARTRIDGE and TENTER, Calgon, *Chem. Eng. News*, **27**, 840 (1949).

corrosion by a number of reactions,[1] depending on conditions. The following is a typical presentation of an important phase of iron water corrosion accelerated by oxygen in alkaline or neutral conditions. Iron in contact with water exerts a certain solution pressure and sets up the oxidation or anodic half reaction:

$$Fe(s) \rightarrow Fe^{++}(aq) + 2e$$

This would cease after a certain potential was reached. However, oxygen can react with water to give OH ions at cathode areas:

$$O_2(g) + 2H_2O(l) + 4e \rightarrow 4OH^-(aq)$$

The Fe^{++} and the OH^- ions would react and the electrons would neutralize by flow of current between the adjacent anode and cathode areas:

$$Fe^{++}(aq) + 2OH^-(aq) \rightarrow Fe(OH)_2(s)$$

The initial reactions would then proceed further. This electrochemical corrosion can be summarized:

$$2Fe(s) + O_2(g) + 2H_2O(l) \rightarrow 2Fe(OH)_2(s)$$

Naturally air and water can change the ferrous into the ferric hydroxide. Anything that stops the foregoing sequences will stop the corrosion. This may be by the removal of the dissolved oxygen, by electrode polarization, by organic inhibitors, or by protective salts. Such protective salts would be chromates, silicates, phosphates, or alkalies which probably act as anodic inhibitors by forming a film over the anodic or active areas and thus interrupting the electrochemical sequences.

Water ordinarily saturated with air at 50°F. contains about 8 cc oxygen per liter. Oxygen is removed by spraying or by cascading the water down over a series of trays contained in a tank. During the downward flow the water is scrubbed by uprising steam. An open feed-water heater of the spray type will usually lower the dissolved oxygen content to below 0.3 cc. per liter. Scrubbing devices will remove even this small amount, or it can be chemically combined using a scavenger like sodium sulfite:

$$O_2 + 2Na_2SO_3 \rightarrow 2Na_2SO_4$$

Such complete deoxygenation is necessary to avoid corrosion in the modern high-temperature high-pressure boiler.

Water Purification. This usually signifies the removal of organic material and harmful microorganisms from municipal supplies. Coagulation and filtration through sand or hard coal and oxidation by aeration

---

[1] An excellent summary with references to the various phases of the corrosion of metals, largely based on this electrochemical mechanism, is presented by J. C. Warren in Chap. 9 of LEIGHOU, "Chemistry of Engineering Materials," 4th ed., McGraw-Hill Book Company, Inc., New York, 1942.

are usually sufficient to remove organic matter. This treatment also removes some of the microorganisms. As a further decrease is usually considered necessary in order to produce safe or potable water, treatment with chlorine is indicated. Large quantities are consumed in this manner to protect the health of the nation. Chloramine and chlorine dioxide are also employed, and the former is made by feeding ammonia into the chlorinated water:

$$2NH_3 + Cl_2 \rightarrow NH_2Cl + NH_4Cl$$

This produces a better-tasting water in certain instances. Chlorine and glassy phosphates are applicable to cooling water to prevent the growth of organisms on the condenser interfaces with consequent increase therein in the fouling factor in the heat-transfer coefficient.

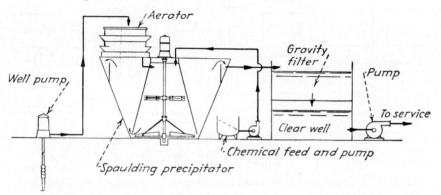

FIG. 5. Municipal cold-lime water softener and iron-removal plant. (*Courtesy of the Permutit Company.*)

Municipal Water Conditioning. Treatment of municipal water supplies is usually necessary to produce potable and safe water.[1] Prior to widespread municipal treatment, epidemics particularly of typhoid fever were caused by contaminated water. The requisites of a safe municipal water supply are freedom from pathogenic microorganisms and freedom from suspended solids. It is also desirable, but not necessary, that the water be soft.

Figures 5 and 6 show a flow sheet for a municipal water-treating plant in which both purification and softening are carried out. The raw water is aerated to remove iron, odor, and taste, partly softened with lime, and the precipitate coagulated and filtered. Chlorine may be added to destroy pathogenic microorganisms, and activated carbon may be employed to remove odors and to improve flavor.

More than 600 municipalities have adopted softening as part of their water treatment, but the public as yet does not realize the economic

[1] BUSWELL, Changes in Purity Standards for Drinking Water, *Ind. Eng. Chem.*, **43**, 594 (1951).

advantages of this process. The savings in soap alone are sufficient to more than pay for the cost. The many other advantages of soft water are therefore essentially free to the user.[1]

Industrial Water Conditioning. The necessary quality of water for industrial purposes depends upon the special use to which it is to be put. In most cases hard waters cannot be utilized without treatment. Many process industries employ several kinds of water, each of which serves a particular demand and is previously treated specially for this purpose.

One of the most important industrial applications of water is for boiler feed. Untreated water, even if reasonably low in hardness, is usually not completely adapted to that use. It is, therefore, common practice to treat all water for use in boilers. Among the damages that

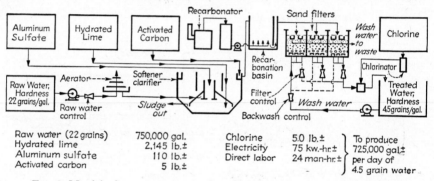

Raw water (22 grains)	750,000 gal.±	Chlorine	5.0 lb.±	To produce
Hydrated lime	2,145 lb.±	Electricity	75 kw.-hr.±	725,000 gal.±
Aluminum sulfate	110 lb.±	Direct labor	24 man-hr.±	per day of
Activated carbon	5 lb.±			4.5 grain water

FIG. 6. Municipal water-treatment flow diagram. (*Courtesy of Infllco, Inc.*)

untreated feed water may cause are rapid corrosion of boiler plates, tubes, and fittings, development of leaks caused by unequal expansion and contraction arising from overheating due to deposition of heat-insulating scale, bulging of tubes, loss of heat, and complete clogging of tubes due to scale deposits.[2] Silica and oxygen are not removed by ordinary softening and must be especially treated for high-pressure boilers as is outlined before.

The quality of the water required for various operations in the process industries varies widely. Untreated water can be utilized satisfactorily for many purposes, especially if it is not too hard. Many processes, however, require very soft water. The textile industry must have softened water to ensure level dyeing. Other industries require, or find it advantageous to use, deionized or distilled water. The deionized exchange process has reduced the cost of this pure water and has been installed in many process industries.

[1] OLSON, *op. cit.*, p. 607.

[2] DISTELHORST, Modern Methods of Feedwater Conditioning for High Pressure Boiler Plants, *Paper Trade J.*, July 31, 1947.

SEWAGE AND INDUSTRIAL WASTE-WATER TREATMENT

Municipal Waste Waters. Efficient *sewage disposal* is important to the health of any community. The easy method of disposal is by dilution, the waste being dumped into an available body of water such as a river or lake where the already present oxygen would in time destroy the organic sewage. This was the first method employed and is still used by many cities. However, public condemnation of this even temporary pollution of streams and lakes has led to the development of methods of treating the sewage so that it is no longer objectionable.

The present procedures may be divided into three main classes: mechanical treatments, chemical treatments, and activated sludge processes. Each of these classes entails the separation of the solids from the liquid followed by treatment of the two parts separately.

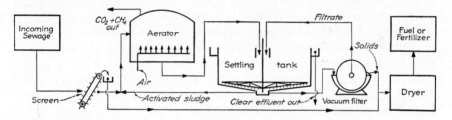

Average technical data: Air required, 0.35 to 1.94 cu. ft. per gal. sewage; detention in aeration tank, 4-6 hrs.; detention in settling tank, 1½-2 hr.; sludge return to aerator, 10-50 percent of total

Fig. 7. Activated-sludge sewage disposal.

The impurity in a particular sewage or, in other words, the amount of treatment required is usually measured on one of two bases: (1) The amount of suspended solids, needs no explanation. (2) The biological oxygen demand (B.O.D.), measures the amount of impurities by the amount of oxygen required to oxidize it.

Mechanical methods of removing solids are passing the sewage through screens, or filters, grit chambers (shallow rectangular tanks in which the velocity of flow is checked so as to cause the grit to settle out, carrying some of the organic material with it), sedimentation basins, and trickling filters. In some installations, the various methods are employed in series. The procedures of Fig. 7 depict mechanical screening, followed by activated sludge treatment, thickening, and filtering.[1]

Chemical treatment precipitates the solids by coagulation. The coagulated materials are removed by sedimentation or filtration. Coagulants of importance are ferric sulfate or chloride or aluminum sulfate with lime.

---

[1] PERRY, *op. cit.*, p. 986, presents sewage dewatering after sludge conditioning. Such cake moistures are high (65 to 85 per cent water). *Cf.* p. 1012 for centrifugating of sewage sludges.

Activated sludge provides one of the most effective methods for removing both suspended and dissolved substances from sewage. The activated sludge contains aerobic microorganisms which digest the raw sewage. Some activated sludge from the previous run is introduced into the raw sewage and air blown in, not in excess but only in the amount needed (see Fig. 7).

The disposal of the solids removed by any of these processes depends upon the local conditions. In some cases they are buried, burned, or sold as fertilizer material after filtering and drying.[1] The liquids remaining after the removal of the solids are usually chlorinated to destroy harmful microorganisms and then discharged into near-by streams.

Industrial Waste Waters. The disposal of waste waters is of widespread national concern. In the chemical field alone there is a large volume[2] of literature. The problem of adequately handling industrial waste waters is more complex and much more difficult than sewage. Increasingly stringent Federal, state, and other laws have been enacted prohibiting or limiting the pollution of streams, lakes, and rivers. Economic and technical studies are necessary to determine the least expensive way to comply with legal requirements and to reduce expenses or to show a profit through the recovery of salable materials. Other factors, such as reduction of real estate values, danger to the inhabitants, and destruction of wildlife are present.

The great variety of chemical wastes produced in the nation's factories forces a specific treatment in many instances. A few general practices are in use in many fields. One such is that of storing or "lagooning" wastes. This may serve many different purposes. In factories having both acid and basic wastes it reduces the cost of neutralization. In plants having waste water containing large amounts of organic material (*e.g.*, some paper mills) this results in a decrease in suspended matter and a reduction of the B.O.D. Dow Chemical Company stores its salt waste water (concentration eight times that of sea water) until the river nearby is at high water, when the brine may be discharged slowly without increasing unduly the salinity of the river.[3] The use of flocculating agents (alum or $FeSO_4$) to remove suspended solids, and aeration to improve the B.O.D. is also common to many industries.

A general problem in all industries is the disposal of wastes obtained as a result of water-softening treatment. Lime sludges may be lagooned

[1] ANON., Flash Drying of Sludge, *Chem. & Met. Eng.*, **48** (1), 108 (1941). This article gives a detailed pictured flow sheet for disposal of activated sludge from Chicago's large Southwest Works treating 400,000,000 gal. daily.

[2] For various symposia and reports on Industrial Waste Disposal, see *Chem. Eng.*, **52** (8), 117 (1945); **56** (3), 96 (1949); **58** (5), 111 (1951); *Ind. Eng. Chem.*, **39**, 539 (1947); **41**, 2434 (1949); **42**, 594 (1950); *Chem. Eng. Progr.*, **46**, 377 (1950).

[3] HARLOW and POWERS, Pollution Control at a Large Chemical Works, *Ind. Eng. Chem.*, **39**, 572 (1947).

and settled, or they may be dewatered and calcined for reuse. This sludge also finds some application in absorbing oil from other wastes. Brine used in regenerating zeolite plants is best stored and then added to streams by controlled dilution at high water.

When the industry uses raw materials of complicated organic nature an activated sludge process may work to treat the wastes. This process can be adapted to wastes from canneries, meat-packing plants, milk-processing plants, rendering plants, and others.

Tannery wastes may be treated by flocculation and sedimentation or filtration. Brewery wastes are subjected to trickling filters to reduce the B.O.D. and remove most of the suspended solids. Paper mills have a serious problem, especially in treating sulfite wastes (see Chap. 33). Processing of wastes from large chemical plants is exceedingly complex because of the variety of chemicals produced. Dow Chemical Company at Midland, Mich., for example, manufactures 400 chemicals in 500 buildings, with a total of 200,000,000 gal. per day of waste waters.[1] Equalization of acid and basic wastes, storage of brine for high-water disposal, and other general practices are followed, but many of the wastes are given treatment at the source, with an eye to recovery of valuable materials and by-products. Calco Chemical Division[2] also institutes recovery treatment at the source. Here acid wastes are reacted in a settling basin with waste lime from the near-by Johns Mansville factory to a pH of 4.0 and lagooned. Ten tons of solids per day settle in the basin and lagoon.

Increasing emphasis in industrial waste treatment is being placed on the recovery of useful materials. Phenol extraction from coal wastes is practiced. Fermentation wastes ("slop") after evaporation and drying are being sold as animal food. The use of ion exchangers promises the recovery of chromium and other metals from plating procedures. Ferrous sulfate is being obtained from pickling operations to a limited extent.

Air pollution[3] or atmospheric contamination is an acute problem in many areas. There are many contributors, ranging from industrial operations and the transport vehicles to the incineration of rubbish and waste by individuals. If the contaminant is an air-borne solid, it is much easier to collect at the point of production. For this purpose filters take most of the load, but many other types of dust- or mist-collection equipment are needed. Electrostatic precipitators are widely used for dust collecting in cement plants, fly ash in coal-fired powerhouses, salt-cake fumes from black-ash furnaces in paper mills, and acid mist from chemical plants.

[1] HARLOW and POWERS, *op. cit.*

[2] KING, *et al.*, Relation of Stream Characteristics to Disposal of Chemical Manufacturing Effluent, *Sewage Works J.*, **21**, 534 (1949).

[3] Symposium, Atmospheric Contamination and Purification, *Ind. Eng. Chem.*, **41**, 2434 (1949); Symposium, Pollution Control, *Chem. Eng.*, **58** (5), 111 (1951).

Centrifugal separators, packed beds, scrubbers, and sonic collection equipment are also widely employed in the chemical industry.

SELECTED REFERENCES

Anon., "Water Conditioning Handbook," The Permutit Company, New York, 1954. Many diagrams and illustrations of equipment.

Nordell, Eskel, "Water Treatment for Industrial and Other Uses," Reinhold Publishing Corporation, New York, 1951. This very thorough and plainly written book has become a standard reference work.

Rudolfs, William, editor, "Industrial Wastes: Their Disposal and Treatment," A.C.S. Monograph 118, Reinhold Publishing Corporation, New York, 1953.

American Society for Testing Materials, "Manual on Industrial Water," A.S.T.M. Special Technical Publication 148, American Society for Testing Materials, 1953.

Besselievre, E. B., "Industrial Waste Treatment," McGraw-Hill Book Company, Inc., New York, 1952.

California Institute of Technology, "Water Quality Criteria," State Water Pollution Control Board, Sacramento, Calif., S.W.P.C.B. Publications No. 3, 1952.

Thomas, H. E., "The Conservation of Ground Water," McGraw-Hill Book Company, Inc., New York, 1951.

Kunin, R., and R. J. Myers, "Ion Exchange Resins," John Wiley & Sons, Inc., New York, 1950.

American Water Works Association, "Water Quality and Treatment," American Water Works Association, New York, 1950.

Nachod, F. C., et al., "Ion Exchange Theory and Application," Academic Press, Inc., New York, 1949.

Ryan, W. J., "Water Treatment and Purification," 2d ed., McGraw-Hill Book Company, Inc., New York, 1946.

CHAPTER 5

FUELS, POWER, AND AIR CONDITIONING

As a rule, a chemical engineer is not enough of a specialist to be capable of adequately designing plants for the production of power, for refrigeration, or for conditioning air. Since chemical process industries consume

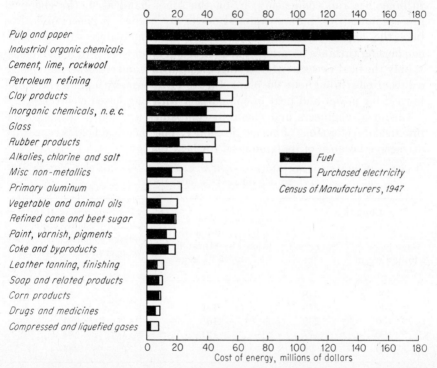

FIG. 1. Energy consumption in process industries as represented by fuel and purchased electricity.

more than a third of all energy[1] used by *all* the manufacturing industries, the chemical engineer should be familiar with the broad technical aspects of the production of power, cold, and air. He should also be prepared to work with power and refrigeration engineers in the proper coordination

[1] ANON., Process Energy, *Chem. Eng.*, **57** (5), 103 (1950); AYRES, Look Ahead at Our Energy Sources and Resources, *Chem. Eng.*, **57** (5) 110 (1950).

of the production of these essential tools and their use in chemical processes in order to attain the cheapest manufacturing costs. Frequently the cost of power, particularly if it is going to be used electrochemically,[1] is the deciding factor in the location of a given factory. Those process industries under the direction of chemical engineers are in most instances outstanding consumers of steam for evaporation, heating, and drying. Consequently these industries need large quantities of steam, usually in the form of low-pressure or exhaust steam from turbines or steam engines. Occasionally, however, certain exothermic reactions,[2] as in the contact sulfuric acid process, can be employed to generate steam for use.

If only electricity is desired from a steam power plant, naturally the turbines are run condensing; if, on the other hand as in the chemical process industries, both steam and power are needed, it is economical to take the high-pressure steam directly from the boilers through noncondensing turbines obtaining exhaust steam from these prime movers to supply the heat necessary for drying, evaporation, and endothermic chemical reactions throughout the plant. Figure 1 presents, by industry, the fuel burned for power and heat in comparison with purchased electricity.

Chemical engineers and chemical companies are contributing to the practical development of nucleonic energy. The chemical field is especially attractive because of its large need for heat energy.

TABLE 1. COMPARISON OF ENERGY FROM STEAM BY EXPANSION FOR POWER AND BY CONDENSATION FOR HEAT[a]

Condition 1		Work operation, B.t.u. per lb. by expansion from condition 1 to saturated steam at 15 lb. gage	Heat operation, B.t.u. per lb. by condensation of steam exhausted from work operation, to water at 212°F.
Gage pressure, lb. per sq. in.	Superheat, °F.		
300	348	240	984
200	279	192	984
150	235	161	984
100	177	121	984
50	95	65	984

NOTE: Superheat is necessary to prevent erosion of turbine blades by moisture in the steam. The amount is figured to furnish saturated steam after expansion to 15 lb. gage.

[a] Data calculated from Keenan and Keyes, "Thermodynamic Properties of Steam," John Wiley & Sons, Inc., New York, 1936.

[1] For an excellent chart giving unit consumption of electricity in the manufacture of over 100 chemical products, see *Chem. Eng.*, **58** (3), 115 (1951); *cf.* ANON., Estimating Requirements for Process Steam and Process Water, *Chem. Eng.*, **58** (4), 111 (1951).

[2] CUBBERLY, Waste Heat Recovery Has Almost Limitless Possibilities, *Chem. Eng.*, **57** (5), 140 (1950).

Heat Balance. The economics of the dual use of heat and power concerns the desirability of coordinating the generation of steam for power and for process heat so that the power needed is obtained as a by-product of the process steam demand. The first step in balancing these two energy demands should be a careful, accurate survey[1] of the heat and power requirements of the various processes.

Since superheat usually retards the rate of heat transfer for process operations, the condition of the steam at the turbine exhaust or at the bleeding point should be such that it will have sufficient superheat to overcome transmission losses but yet have little or no superheat when it reaches the point of use. This will result in the full utilization of the latent heat of steam for heating purposes.

TABLE 2. SOURCES OF INDUSTRIAL ENERGY[a]

Source	All manu-facturing industries	Process indus-tries	Indus-trial inor-ganic chem-icals	Indus-trial organic chem-icals	Mineral-based indus-tries	Ceramic indus-tries
Coal, M tons:						
Bituminous.........	103,778	56,344	6,187	7,749	11,155	5,296
Anthracite..........	7,081	3,372	94	395	135	225
Coke, M tons.........	66,171	2,592	1,562	428	352	13
Fuel oils, M bbl........	166,947	48,605	4,454	5,383	7,832	6,646
Gas, 10^6 cu. ft.........	4,004,953	1,228,506	68,126	82,155	101,381	154,484
Electricity, 10^6 kw.-hr.:						
Purchased..........	102,822	39,074	4,565	4,369	13,018	1,974
Generated..........	43,936	25,357	3,179	4,278	1,961	192
Total cost (thousands of dollars).............	$3,331,518	$926,911	$99,807	$105,813	$157,777	$113,187

[a] 1947 Census of Manufactures, later data not available. In the process industries about 4 per cent of the generated electricity is sold. For further breakdown and more complete data, see references.

The fundamental importance of this principle of coordination of the steam for power and the steam for process heating can be seen by inspection of Table 1 which gives the B.t.u. converted to power by expansion of steam at various pressures and superheat to saturated steam at 15 lb. gage as contrasted with the B.t.u. supplied by the condensation of this exhaust steam. As process steam must be furnished for the heat-transfer

[1] SWAIN, Byproduct Power in Process Industries, *Chem. & Met. Eng.*, **48** (3), 94 (1941), several different balances of steam and power are here described and diagrammed; STUDLEY, Heat and Power Balance in Chemical Plants, *Chem. & Met. Eng.*, **41**, 464 (1934); PERRY, *op. cit.*, p. 1635, for heat-balance calculations.

operations, it may be seen from Table 1 that the obtaining of what power is available by expansion is probably the most economical power a plant can get. Consequently the ideal plant would expand all of its steam through turbines for power and then lead the exhaust steam into the factory for the various heat-transfer operations. When there is no contamination of this process steam, the water from the condensation should be brought back for the boiler feed make-up water. All chemical industries should be studied for this dual use of steam. Those pertaining to manufacture of sugar (Chap. 30), caustic soda (Chap. 15), salt (Chap. 14), and fermentation (Chap. 31) have applied this dual energy balance very profitably.

To balance the power required as made by expansion of steam, with the process demands for steam exhausted from the steam engine or turbine so that there is no excess of either, should be the aim of the engineers in charge of any plant. This ideal can frequently be realized in the chemical process industries. Many studies[1] of different arrangements have been made but all point to the lowered cost of electrical energy and of steam by this dual use of the primary steam.

FUELS

Fuels can be divided into three classes: solid, liquid, and gaseous. To these as an energy source should be added water power. Figure 2 depicts the trends in the use of these four sources of energy. The actual and comparative costs of the different energy supplies vary with the different parts of the country. With coal at $5 per ton, 1,000,000 B.t.u. will cost in fuel 17 cents; with fuel oil at 5 cents per gal., these B.t.u. will cost 35 cents. With city gas at 50 cents per 1,000 cu. ft., these same B.t.u. will amount to 84 cents, or with electricity at 5 cents per kw.-hr., $1.47.[2] Coal is the most important fuel[3] used for power purposes but there is a trend to use a cleaner fuel such as fuel oil or gas and to develop better methods of coal combustion which result in less contamination of the atmosphere. This is especially true in large towns and cities.

Liquid fuels are derived mainly from petroleum and follow coal in importance as a source of heat for power generation. Petroleum products also furnish almost all of the energy for the numerous internal-combustion engines of this country.

The fuel gases are either natural or artificial and are presented in

[1] Various Authors, Modern Aspects of the Use of Steam in Chemical Engineering Industry, *Chem. & Met. Eng.*, **34**, 530 (1927); GORDON, Generate or Purchase Energy in Process Industries, *Chem. Eng.*, **57** (5), 119 (1950).

[2] PERRY, *op. cit.*, 1812, tabulates further fuel costs per 1,000,000 B.t.u.

[3] ANON., Outlook for Energy Sources; Shifting Pattern, *Chem. Eng. News*, **30**, 2891 (1952).

Chap. 7. These gases, although made primarily as a source for heat, are being consumed in increasing amounts as basic raw materials for chemical manufacture.

Solid Fuels.[1] *Coal* is the most important of the solid fuels, with an annual consumption around 600,000,000 tons. No entirely satisfactory scheme has been worked out for classifying coals but a generally accepted method divides coal into the following classes: anthracite, bituminous,

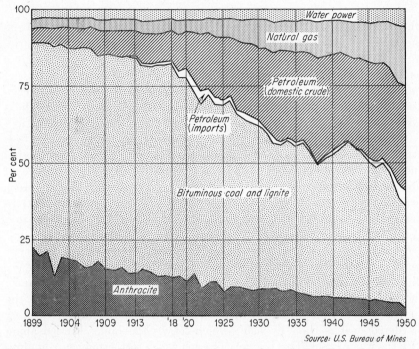

Source: U.S. Bureau of Mines

Fig. 2. Per cent of total United States energy supply, in equivalent B.t.u., from various sources.

subbituminous, and lignite, with further subclassification into groups. The bituminous coals are used most extensively for power purposes. Anthracite is a valuable domestic fuel because of its clean-burning characteristics.

Since coal compositions vary so widely, a fuel analysis is useful from both the purchasing and the combustion viewpoint. The *proximate analysis* determines the percentages of moisture, volatile matter, ash, and fixed carbon (by difference) in the coal. The sulfur content is determined also and *reported with the proximate analysis but it is not considered a part of it*. The procedures for determining the proximate analysis have been standardized by the A.S.T.M.

[1] PERRY, *op. cit.*, pp. 1561–1566, should be studied in this connection.

The *ultimate analysis* gives the percentages of carbon, hydrogen, sulfur, oxygen, nitrogen, and ash (by difference) in the coal. This analysis can be used for boiler test calculations and for determining the approximate heating value of the fuel. If this analysis is available, the formula of Dulong may be used with an accuracy of within 2 or 3 per cent.

$$\text{B.t.u. per lb.} = 14{,}544C + 62{,}028 \left(H - \frac{O}{8} \right) + 4{,}050S$$

where C, H, O, and S are expressed as fractional weights obtained from the analysis. The B.t.u. per lb. on ash- and moisture-free basis varies from 13,540 for Pennsylvania anthracite to 14,550 for West Virginia semibituminous. A more accurate method of determining the heat of combustion of the fuel consists of actually burning the coal in an oxygen atmosphere under pressure in a bomb calorimeter and measuring the heat evolved. See Table 2, Chap. 7, for various *gross* and *net* heats of combustion.

The storage of coal is an important problem in industrial practice. Storage by packing is frequently employed to avoid too rapid weathering and spontaneous combustion, by reducing air space. The presence of some moisture and pyrite, or any easily oxidizable material, in bituminous coal, may cause coal to ignite; the rise to 50°C. is slow, but from there to the ignition point the rise may be rapid if conditions for the dissipation of heat are poor.

Powdered coal has been used to an increasingly large extent in recent years in power-plant installations because of the high thermal efficiency with which it can be burned, the low cost of operation and maintenance, and its excellent flexibility. All these factors more than balance the increased cost of preparing the fuel.[1] One serious disadvantage in burning powdered coal is the "fly ash" which leaves the boiler carried along with the waste gases. This is a very fine ash which settles over surrounding territory as a nuisance. It can be removed from the flue gases by a Cottrell precipitator,[2] but the problem of disposal still remains. It has been made into bricks, building blocks, and even roofing tile, after compression, by reaction with slaked lime under steam pressure.[3] As only slaked lime and water are needed in addition to the fly ash, the development of this process may encourage the further employment of powdered coal as a fuel.

Coke is a fine fuel but it is too expensive at present for industrial use except in special cases as in blast-furnace operation, where it is a chemical raw material as well as a fuel. Coke is a valuable fuel for domestic heating plants. As the by-products of coal distillation increase in value

[1] PERRY, *op. cit.*, pp. 1567–1568.
[2] PERRY, *op. cit.*, pp. 1013–1050, but particularly Table 11 on p. 1044.
[3] Rostone Corp. of Lafayette, Ind.

with a decrease in other hydrocarbons such as from petroleum, the increased use of coke as a fuel is indicated. Other solid fuels[1] such as coke "breeze," wood, sawdust, bagasse and tanbark are used where they are available cheaply or where they are produced as by-products.

Liquid Fuels. *Fuel oil* is the only important commercial liquid fuel used for power purposes. It is the portion of the crude oil that cannot be economically converted by the refiner to the higher-priced products such as gasoline. It consists of a mixture of the liquid residues from the cracking processes with fractions of a suitable boiling point obtained from the distillation of crude oil. The fuel oil[2] is classified according to its properties such as the flash point, pour point, percentage of water and sediment, carbon residue, ash, distillation temperature, and viscosity. All of these are determined by tests that have been standardized by the A.S.T.M. The flash point is relatively unimportant for determining the behavior of the fuel in the burner, but it has some importance in the storage of the oil since storage tanks should be kept well below this temperature. Oil-burning equipment usually shows a higher thermal efficiency (75 per cent) than coal-burning boilers and labor costs are usually less. However, the latent heat loss of steam produced by the combustion of the hydrogen of the fuel oil is about two times greater than such losses from bituminous coal.

Other liquid fuels include coal tar, tar oil, kerosene, benzol, and alcohol, which are consumed to a relatively smaller extent than is fuel oil. Gasoline is consumed mainly in internal-combustion engines.

Gaseous Fuels. Gas is burned as a source of heat in domestic installations and occasionally in industry, especially where it is obtained as a by-product. Blast-furnace gas resulting from the smelting of iron is an outstanding example of where a by-product gas is employed for heating the blast stoves, with the remainder burned under boilers or for heating coke ovens. The other gases that may be used for power generation are natural gas and liquefied petroleum gas when available and the manufactured gases such as coke-oven gas, producer gas, and water gas. These are discussed more fully in Chap. 7, where a tabulation is given of B.t.u. values and other properties.

Combustion. Most modern industrial plants burn coal either on mechanically operated grates and stokers or in the powdered form. Table 3 gives a summary of the information on stokers. These present-day procedures enable the ratio of air to the fuel to be properly controlled, thus ensuring efficient combustion and reducing heat losses through stack and ash.

When fuel oil is burned, it is frequently necessary to provide heaters

[1] PERRY, *op. cit.*, p. 1568.

[2] PERRY, *op. cit.*, pp. 1568–1575, gives specifications, costs vs. coal, heats of combustion, chemical constituents, and oil-burning equipment.

TABLE 3. SUMMARY OF INFORMATION ON STOKERS[a]

	Traveling grates	Spreader stokers	Underfeed stokers
Description	Fuel is carried horizontally into furnace on a continuous web which is cooled coming out through the ashpit	Coal is projected onto grate by paddles or an air stream. Fine coal burns in suspension; larger pieces fall to grate and are burned	Raw coal is pushed up through the fuel bed and coked. Clinker falls off to side. Volatiles distilled off are burned in an oxidizing atmosphere
Fuel used	Coke breeze, steam sizes of anthracite or high-volatile Middle Western coals. In general any noncoking clinker coal may be used	Both coking and noncoking coals can be used	High-volatile coals, coking coals, and slack or fines may be burned. Ash must not be easily fusible
Draft	Natural: 0.25 to 0.60 in. water. Forced: 1 to 2 in. water pressure with coke or somewhat higher for Illinois and similar coals	Forced draft usually not over 2 in. water. Close air-fuel ratios required	All forced draft Normal: 2 to 4 in. water pressure in wind box, occasionally higher
Rate of combustion, lb. per sq. ft. per hr.	Average: 30 to 35 10 lb. per 0.1 in. H_2O, for natural drafts	Average: 35 to 45	Average: 30 to 40 10 lb. per 1 in. water pressure
Means of regulation	1. Height of coal grate 2. Speed of grate 3. Amount and distribution of air	1. Rate of coal feed 2. Amount and distribution of air	1. Rate of feed 2. Amount and distribution of blast
Miscellaneous	Watch for live coal going over end of grate	Close regulation of air is necessary. Critical factors are smoke and fly ash	Air is admitted to burn out cinder. Fuel bed from 12 to 24 in. deep

[a] Shortened from PERRY, *op. cit.*, p. 1566; see diagram, p. 1567.

to lower the viscosity of the oil sufficiently for the proper burner operation.[1] The burners consist of an atomizer which mixes the fuel with the primary air. The secondary air is usually supplied through the base of the furnace.

For gaseous fuels the burner consists of a gas orifice, an injecting tube in which the air is entrained and mixed with the gas, and ports from which the air-gas mixture is discharged into the combustion zone.

[1] PERRY, *op. cit.*, pp. 1572–1575.

The flue-gas analysis is valuable in controlling the combustion since the proportions of CO_2, CO, and O_2 in the flue gas will indicate incomplete combustion or excess air. Frequently powerhouse employees are paid a bonus for satisfactory combustion as indicated by flue-gas analyses. The chemical engineer has been particularly concerned with efficient combustion as one of his contributions to efficient plant operation.[1]

POWER GENERATION

Near the end of the seventeenth century the first successful attempt to generate steam under pressure in an enclosed vessel was made. Since

FIG. 3. Longitudinal section of a fire-tube boiler of the "economic" design arranged for stoker firing. This type of boiler is self-contained and can be used for coal, oil, or gas firing. (*Courtesy of Erie City Iron Works.*)

then the use of steam has increased to such an extent that today steam furnishes about 75 per cent of the total power developed in this country. The most recent developments have been toward improvements in boiler construction with the aim of producing higher-pressure steam, up to 1,400 lb. in central power stations. Such high pressures[2] increase the over-all efficiency in the production of electric power. The limiting factor is the failure of materials at the high temperatures and pressures involved. However, one plant (Twin Branch Station of Indiana Michigan Electric Co.) has boilers operating at 2,500 lb. per sq. in. gage and at 940°F.

[1] See particularly the combustion chapter, pp. 173*ff*., in WALKER, LEWIS, McADAMS, and GILLILAND, "Principles of Chemical Engineering," 3d ed., McGraw-Hill Book Company, Inc., New York, 1937.

[2] PERRY, *op. cit.*, p. 1634. The entire section on Power Generation, pp. 1628–1660, should be consulted; McCABE, Higher Costs Spark Advances in Process Steam and Power, *Chem. Eng.*, **57** (5), 121 (1950).

At an early date, 4½ to 5 lb. of the best coals was required per kilowatt-hour while currently some power plants produce a net kilowatt-hour from about 0.8 lb. of 1,300 B.t.u. coal. Table 4 presents a tabulation of steam-electric plant fuel consumption and costs.

TABLE 4. STEAM-ELECTRIC PLANT FUEL CONSUMPTION AND COSTS[a]
(Comparison of boiler plant costs for steam-electric utilities using coal, oil, and gas, respectively, 1950. Figures in parentheses cover range)
Weighted Average Cost per Million B.t.u., Cents

| | Boiler labor | Maintenance | | | | Fuel[b] |
		Coal storage, handling, and weighing	Furnace and boiler	Boiler apparatus	Total boiler, labor and maintenance	
Coal (44 plants)....	1.52 (1.01–3.08)	0.57 (0.06–1.37)	0.68 (0.11–1.27)	0.37 (0.04–1.39)	3.14 (2.04–7.11)	26.91 (19.75–35.03)
Oil (21 plants)......	1.57 (0.98–4.38)	0.01 (0.03–0.13)	0.96 (0.34–3.69)	0.77 (0.27–1.84)	3.31 (1.99–8.35)	30.65 (27.99–36.92)
Gas (36 plants).....	0.73 (0.50–2.25)	....	0.37 (0.10–0.86)	0.30 (0.14–0.48)	1.40 (1.09–2.53)	7.59 (5.71–18.99)

Simple Average Operating Costs, Mills per Net Kilowatt-hour

	Fuel	Wages and supervising	Maintenance boiler plant	Maintenance fuel handling	Total operating and maintenance including fuel
Coal (413 gross kw.-hr. million)	3.404 (1.88–5.26)	0.479 (0.24–1.12)	0.0673 (0.00026–0.1299)	0.0534 (0.004–0.14)	4.208 (2.44–7.01)
Oil (593 gross kw.-hr. million)	3.796 (3.171–4.6)	0.470 (0.224–0.76)	0.119 (0.0603–0.19)	0.006 (0.008–0.0252)	4.603 (3.61–5.4732)
Gas (265 gross kw.-hr. million)	1.106 (0.717–1.62)	0.372 (0.188–0.567)	0.069 (0.037–0.14)	....	1.780 (1.047–2.44)

[a] Courtesy of National Coal Association, Department of Coal Economics, Washington, D.C., 1950 and 1953. For data of individual companies see original publication under the title of heading of this table. Many data herein compiled from *Electrical World* of Aug. 27, 1951.
[b] The 1953 figures for fuel are: coal 27.3 (17.3–36.6), oil 32.3 (24.1–52.3), gas 16.7 (1.01–33.5).

There are two main types of boilers: the fire tube (Fig. 3) and the water tube (Fig. 4). The *fire-tube boiler* is usually of small and medium capacity and is designed for the generation of steam of moderate pressure. In this type the fire passes through the tubes. Fire-tube boilers have a low first cost and a relatively large reservoir of hot water. This is of particular advantage in small chemical plants where there may be a sudden demand on the steam plant. Locomotive boilers are also of this type.

Water-tube boilers are used almost exclusively in stationary installations where service demands a large amount of evaporation at pressures above 150 lb. per sq. in. The water is in the tubes and can be converted to steam more quickly than with the fire-tube type ("quicker steaming"). High efficiencies are obtained by this type. The positions of the drums

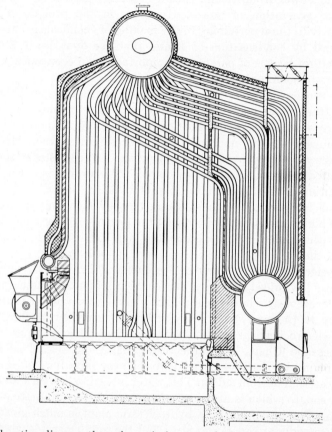

Fig. 4. Elevation diagram through vertical water-tube boiler of the bent-tube type. Capacity range of 10,000 to 50,000 lb. of steam per hour. Fired with spreader stoker, forced draft, and provided with water-cooled walls. (*Courtesy of Combustion Engineering-Superheater, Inc.*)

and tubes, the slope, and the shapes of the tubes are the distinguishing characteristics among different makes of these boilers.

Boiler feed water should be conditioned before introduction into the boilers (Chap. 4). Poor boiler water results in foaming, caustic embrittlement, corrosion, and scale formation with consequent loss in steam made and in efficiency. The higher the pressure, the more important is the use of properly conditioned water.

Figure 4 represents a small-size[1] modern water-tube boiler used for generating steam in two pressure ranges, 250 and 475 lb. per sq. in. This water enters in the lower part of the upper drum. The walls are relatively thin ceramic tiling backed up with block insulation and steel-paneled casing.

Electric Power from Steam. Steam is often regarded as being raised solely for generation of power. However, in the process industries, particularly in those pertaining to the making of chemicals, so much heat is obtained by condensation of steam, that the dual use of steam for power and for heat is of paramount importance. An economical engineer endeavors to coordinate and balance the two.

In these chemical processes, the object should be to expand the steam through the steam engine or turbine[2] and then employ the exhaust or lower-pressure steam for heating purposes. In this procedure the prime movers are run noncondensing. For turbines, where dry steam is necessary to prevent blade erosion, the entering steam should be superheated and condensation prevented. The turbine is a particularly flexible prime mover for chemical plants as it can be designed not only to furnish low-pressure exhaust steam but, by bleeding off, to supply steam of higher pressures. This enables the primary steam to be efficiently raised at the modern high pressures, too high to be suitable for ordinary plant heating.

Hydroelectric Power. Many of the chemical industries require large amounts of low-priced electric power for their operation. These companies usually locate near a hydroelectric plant where cheap power is available, especially to the large, steady day-and-night consumer. Such industries are the electrochemical ones covered by Chap. 16 on the Electrolytic Industries and Chap. 17 on Electrothermal Industries. These hydroelectric plants are situated where there is a head of water available either from a waterfall or from a dam. This water is used to drive a water wheel[3] of some sort to which is attached either a direct- or alternating-current generator. The initial cost of a hydroelectric plant is much greater than of a corresponding steam power plant, but the running cost is much lower.

Heat Transmission Other than by Steam. Where indirect heating is necessary, some method other than steam should be used for temperatures above about 400 or 450°F., where the pressure of steam becomes too high for economical design of the plant. As steam owes its importance as a heating medium to its convenience and cleanliness, but particularly

---

[1] For larger boilers, *cf.* KAISER, Frontiers in Heat Extraction from the Combustion Gases of Coal, *Mining Eng.*, **6** (3), 304 (1954).

[2] PERRY, *op. cit.*, pp. 1644–1646; for electric generators, see pp. 1763*ff.*; ROWLEY, I. C., Engines and Gas Turbines Raising Fuel Economy, *Chem. Eng.*, **57** (5), 126 (1950).

[3] PERRY, *op. cit.*, pp. 1655–1657.

to its large heat of condensation, the use of superheated steam is not indicated as a heating medium except in rare cases. Hence, where the conditions lie outside the range of steam, the engineer[1] turns progressively, as the temperature rises, to

Direct firing, above 300°F.: low cost and convenience but fire hazard.

Indirect firing, above 300°F.: low operating cost but elaborate setting and fire hazard.

Direct gas heating, above 300°F.: moderate cost and excellent control but fire hazard.

Hot oil, 300 *to* 600°F.: good control but high first cost and oil carbonization.

Dowtherm, 300 *to* 700°F.: good control and moderate operating cost but higher first cost.

Mercury vapor, 600 *to* 1200°F.: good control and moderate operating cost but highest first cost.

Mixed salts, 250 *to* 900°F.: good control and good heat transfer at high temperature.

Electricity, above 300°F.: most accurate control but operating cost usually high.

Direct or indirect heating with coal or gas is frequently surprisingly efficient when the furnace is well designed; however the open flame may be a bad fire hazard. Under conditions where oil is not carbonized, this heat-transfer medium has been so widely employed that furnaces for heating the oil and equipment for the heat transfer are both available on the market as standardized and tested designs. Dowtherm[2] (diphenyl or diphenyl oxide or a eutectic mixture of the two) is stable at higher temperatures than oil and has the added advantage that it can be employed as a vapor where its latent heat of condensation can be used as well as its sensible heat. Mercury is very successful in controlling the heat of reaction in the Downs[3] reactor for vapor-phase oxidation of naphthalene to phthalic anhydride. For years, mixtures of inorganic salts have been accepted as heat-transfer media, but it needed the modern large-scale demand for such salts to *remove* heat from petroleum cracking processes such as the Houdry catalytic one, to justify a careful study of the properties of the mixed salt[4] consisting of approximately

[1] A much more elaborate table accompanied by specific diagrams and descriptions is given by PERRY, *op. cit.,* pp. 1221–1224; *cf.* GEIRINGER, Why Use Vapors or Gases When It May Be Better to Heat with Liquids, *Chem. Eng.,* **57** (10), 136 (1950).

[2] HEINDEL, Developments in Heat Transfer with Organic Compounds, *Chem. & Met. Eng.,* **41,** 308 (1934).

[3] U.S. Pat., Downs 1604739 (1926); HULSART, Mercury Vapor as Applied to Process Industries, *Chem. & Met. Eng.,* **41,** 313 (1934); CRAIG and ANDERSON, "Steam Power and Internal Combustion Engines," p. 348, McGraw-Hill Book Company, Inc., New York, 1937.

[4] KIRST, NAGLE, and CASTNER, A New Heat Transfer Medium for High Temperatures, *Trans. Am. Inst. Chem. Engrs.,* **36,** 371 (1940).

40 per cent $NaNO_2$, 7 per cent $NaNO_3$, and 53 per cent KNO_3. Strange to say, tests in the reference cited indicate no danger even if a stream of hot petroleum were injected into the molten nitrate-nitrite bath. Electricity in contact, immersion, or radiant heaters is a most convenient, accurate, safe, and efficient though generally costly heating medium.

REFRIGERATION

Refrigeration[1] is the process of producing cold, particularly referring to cooling below atmospheric temperature. It is a vital factor in many chemical processes where cold or the removal of heat is necessary for optimum reaction control. Examples are the manufacture of azo dyes, separation of an easily freezing product from liquid isomers or impurities, and the food and beverage industries. Further examples are the catalytic manufacture of ethyl chloride from liquid ethylene and anhydrous hydrogen chloride under pressure and at $-5°C$., the polymerization at $41°F$. or lower, to furnish "cold" rubber, the freezing of mercury at $-100°F$. into complex molds which are coated by repeated dipping with a ceramic slurry, with the mercury then allowed to melt and run out.

Refrigeration operations involve a change of phase in a body so that it will be capable of abstracting heat, exemplified by the vaporization of liquid ammonia and the melting of ice.

Mechanical refrigeration can be divided into two general groups: the *compression system* and the *absorption system*.[2] Both systems cause the refrigerant to absorb heat at the low temperature by vaporization and to give up this heat at the higher temperature by condensation. The absorption system is used mainly in household units, but it finds economical industrial application where exhaust steam is available.

An ammonia refrigerating plant will give a typical illustration of the vapor-compression system and is depicted by Fig. 5. Here the vapor from the cold room is compressed and leaves with such enhanced pressure that the liquefaction temperature at this pressure is above that of the atmosphere or other coolant. From the compressor, the refrigerant goes to a liquefying condenser where the heat of condensation is removed by the atmosphere or cooling water. The now liquid refrigerant passes through an expansion valve which separates the high- from the low-pressure regions. The refrigerant in this low-pressure condition enters through the cold room where the heat of vaporization of the ammonia is abstracted from the surroundings. The cold room may not be a room

---

[1] PERRY, *op. cit.*, pp. 1676–1701. This section has extensive diagrams and tables of thermodynamic properties. FISKE, Lower Temperatures, New Cycles Benefit Refrigeration Uses, *Chem. Eng.*, **57** (5), 136 (1950).

[2] PERRY, *op. cit.*, pp. 1676, 1677, 1683.

at all but may consist of coils immersed in brine with the cold brine being then circulated to the points where refrigeration is necessary. The vapor then repeats this cycle with no loss of refrigerant except by leakage.

Besides the requirements dictated by the thermodynamics of refrigeration, a good refrigerant must also satisfy various economic and practical requirements. For example, a good refrigerant should be cheap, inert, and stable. It should have no corrosive tendencies, should be nontoxic and nonexplosive, and should have no properties injurious to goods and foods depending upon its application. Another important property should be ease of detection in case of leaks.

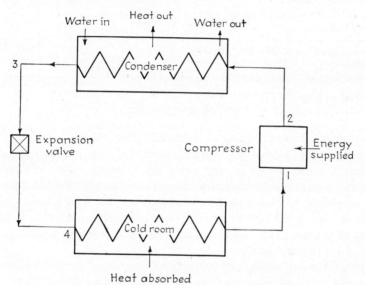

Fig. 5. Compression system for refrigeration.

Ammonia is by far the most commonly employed refrigerant, especially in large industrial installations. Carbon dioxide was used to a great extent on shipboard, where a nontoxic refrigerant is desired, but it has been replaced by Freon-12. Sulfur dioxide has been employed extensively in household refrigerators. All three of these refrigerants have certain disadvantages which have stimulated search for better agents without their bad qualities. Freon-12 (CCl_2F_2) is an outstanding development in this respect. It possesses the distinct advantage of being nonflammable, nontoxic, and noncorrosive to most metals. Two new refrigerants, Freon-14 (CF_4) and Freon-13 ($CClF_3$), are valuable additions to low-temperature requirements. Air has also returned because of the development of tonnage oxygen and expanded activity in air-separation cycles. Table 5 summarizes the properties of the usual refrigerants.

TABLE 5. PROPERTIES OF REFRIGERATING AGENTS[a]

Refrigerant	Boiling point at 760 mm., °F.	Critical temperature, °F.	Critical pressure, atmospheres	Latent heat at 760 mm., B.t.u. per lb.
Ammonia, NH_3..............	−28	270.5	111.5	589
Carbon dioxide, CO_2..........	−108.8[b]	88.3	73.0	126[c]
Sulfur dioxide, SO_2...........	+14	315.3	77.7	167
Methyl chloride, CH_3Cl.......	−11	298.9	65.8	184
Ethyl chloride, C_2H_5Cl.........	+55	369.3	52.0	168
Freon-12, CCl_2F_2..............	−21	.....	.....	71.9
Propane, C_3H_8..............	−44.4	206.6	42.0	159

[a] PERRY, op. cit., pp. 204–205, 210–214.

[b] Sublimes.

[c] Latent heat at −20°F. and 220.6 lb. per sq. in. abs.

AIR CONDITIONING

The use of air conditioning in industrial plants has become more and more common in the past few years. Control of the temperature, humidity and cleanliness of the air is very important in many chemical processes, particularly in artificial fiber and paper manufacture. Textile fibers are quite sensitive[1] to changing conditions of the air. The comfort of the worker is also important to efficient industrial organizations. This fact has led to the use of air conditioning in plants and offices where it is not essential for product quality.

Air-conditioning equipment consists of apparatus for the addition or removal of heat and moisture from the room being conditioned and automatic control for this apparatus so that the temperature and humidity can be conditioned within the desired limits. Humidification is usually done in an indirect humidifier in which water or steam is sprayed directly against the incoming air and the humidified air is then warmed by passage over tempering coils. For summer use the air is washed in a spray chamber and then cooled and dehumidified by passage over refrigerator coils.[2]

SELECTED REFERENCES

Various Authors, A Symposium on Smokeless Fuels, *Ind. Eng. Chem.*, **33**, 836–864 (1941).

Craig, D. P., and H. J. Anderson, "Steam Power and Internal Combustion Engines," 2d ed., McGraw-Hill Book Company, Inc., New York, 1937.

[1] PERRY, *op. cit.*, pp. 777–779, presents tables showing the effect of changing humidity upon various products of chemical factories.

[2] For equipment, see PERRY, *op. cit.*, pp. 778–797.

Perry, J. H., editor-in-chief, "Chemical Engineers' Handbook," bibliographies, 3d ed., McGraw-Hill Book Company, Inc., New York, 1950.

deLorenzi, Otto, editor, "Combustion Engineering," 3d ed., Combustion Engineering Company, Inc., New York, 1950.

Johnson, A. J., and G. H. Auth, "Fuels and Combustion Handbook," McGraw-Hill Book Company, Inc., New York, 1951.

Griswold, J., "Fuels, Combustion, and Furnaces," McGraw-Hill Book Company, Inc., New York, 1946

CHAPTER 6

COAL CHEMICALS

Chemicals from coal were initially and mostly obtained by destructive distillation of coal, furnishing chiefly aromatics. Indeed this chapter was originally titled "The Destructive Distillation of Coal." With the advancing application of chemical change to coal, many more chemicals are being made from coal. A chemical process of great promise is that of hydrogenation or hydrogenolysis of Carbide & Carbon Chemicals Company which is outlined later in this chapter by a provisional flow sheet

TABLE 1. CHEMICALS FROM COAL

Chemical process	Products and procedures (numbers refer to chapters)
Pyrolysis (destructive distillation, carbonization)	Coal gas, ammonia, benzene and homologs, phenol and homologs, heterocyclics, coal tar, coke (6), industrial carbon (9), precarbonization of power-plant fuel
Gasification (pyrolysis, partial oxidation)	Coal, water gas, producer gas (7), H_2 (8) for NH_3 and hydrogenations; H_2 and CO for CH_3OH, etc., motor fuels
Hydrogenation and hydrogenolysis	Carbide process for aromatics, etc. (6, flow sheet, Fig. 9), liquid fuels; creation of coking properties
Electrothermal	Graphite (9), artificial abrasives and calcium carbide (17), cyanamide (20)
Oxidation (controlled)	Organic acids, carbon monoxide
Combustion	Heat for manufacture of lime and cement (11), ceramics (10), CO_2 for Dry Ice (8), ashes for building blocks, fly ash as filler
Reduction	Metals, phosphorus (18)
Sulfur recovery	Gases (7), coal pyrites
Carbon recovery	Pigment for inks and surface coatings (9, 24), electrodes (9), structural material (9), activated carbon (9)
Sulfonation	Ion exchange, water softeners (4)
Solvent extraction	Ashless coal, montan wax, humic acids, resins

(Fig. 9 and accompanying text). Table 1 summarizes chemicals from coal as presented in this chapter and elsewhere in this book. It should also be noted that benzene, toluene, xylene, naphthalene, and other aromatic chemicals are being supplied also by the petroleum industry (see also Figs. 2 and 7 for many coal chemicals). Coal is not only the country's fundamental fuel but furnishes the basic raw materials for many essential industries from dyes, medicines, pesticides, and elastomers to modern plastics.[1] "Coal also forms the world's largest reserve of concentrated organic raw materials, and it serves not only as a chemical supplier but as a cheap source of heat and power needed for processing."[2]

THE DESTRUCTIVE DISTILLATION OF COAL

When coal is distilled by heating without contact with air, it is converted into a variety of solid, liquid, and gaseous products. The nature and amounts of each product depend upon the temperature used in the pyrolysis and the variety of coal. In ordinary practice, coke-oven temperatures are maintained above 1650°F. but may range anywhere from 950 to 1800°F. The principal product by weight is coke. If a plant uses temperatures from 950 to 1450°F., the process is termed *low-temperature* carbonization; with temperatures above this it is designated as *high-temperature* carbonization. In the low-temperature carbonization the quantity of gaseous products is small and that of the liquid products is relatively large, while in high-temperature carbonization the yield of gaseous products is larger than the yield of liquid products, with the production of tar being relatively low. In addition to coke, the solid products recovered after purification are naphthalene, anthracene, and "cyanogen" compounds; the liquid products are water, tar, and the various oils; the gaseous products are hydrogen, methane, ethylene, carbon monoxide, carbon dioxide, hydrogen sulfide, ammonia, and nitrogen. The products other than coke are collectively known as coal chemicals (*by-products* or *co-products*).

The destructive distillation of coal, or its carbonization, is really a striking example of the *unit process of pyrolysis*. This chapter will outline the equipment needed to carry out, on a commercial scale, the basic chemical changes that take place. The chemical theory of the pyrolysis of coal[3] indicates the following in a step-by-step decomposition:

1. As the temperature is raised the aliphatic "carbon to carbon bonds are the first to break."

2. "Carbon to hydrogen linkages are severed next as the temperature of 600°C. (1100°F.) is approached and exceeded."

[1] WAKEMAN and WEIL, Coal as a Source Material for the Plastics Industry, *Ind. Eng. Chem.*, **34**, 1387 (1942); GUY, Agricultural Uses of Coal and Its Products, *Ind. Eng. Chem.*, **35**, 139 (1943); SHEARON, *et al.*, Fine Chemicals from Coal, *Ind. Eng. Chem.*, **41**, 1812 (1949); WILSON and WELLS, Coal Chemical Industry, *Chem. Eng.*, **53** (12), 110 (1946); FRANKE and KIEBLER, Organic Acids by Direct Oxidation of Coal, *Chem. Ind.*, **58**, 580 (1945).

[2] ROSE, H. J., *private communication*.

[3] FUCHS and SANDHOFF, Theory of Coal Pyrolysis, *Ind. Eng. Chem.*, **34**, 567 (1942).

3. "The decompositions during carbonization are essentially reactions effecting the elimination of heterocycle complexes and progressive aromatization."

4. "The average molecular weights of the volatile intermediate products constantly decrease as the temperature of carbonization rises. This decrease is marked by the evolution of water, carbon monoxide, hydrogen, methane, and other hydrocarbons."

5. "Final decompositions are at a maximum between 600 and 800°C.," 1110 and 1470°F. Fuchs and Sandhoff give several examples of coal pyrolysis of which Fig. 1 is typical.

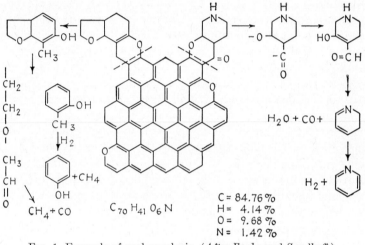

FIG. 1. Example of coal pyrolysis. (*After Fuchs and Sandhoff.*)

Historical. It is known that coke was an article of commerce among the Chinese over 2,000 years ago, and in the Middle Ages it was used in the arts and for domestic purposes. Nevertheless it was not until 1620 that there is any record of producing coke in an oven. In this year Sir William St. John was granted a patent in England for the beehive oven. Up until the middle of the nineteenth century, coal tar and coal-tar products were regarded as wastes, to be either thrown away or burned under coking retorts. About 1845 tar began to be used in Germany for making roofing felt; distillation products of tar were applied through impregnation as a wood preservative. A year or two earlier, in England, coal-tar naphtha had been successfully employed as a solvent for india rubber, a use still common today.

The synthesis of the first coal-tar color, by Sir William Perkin in 1856, caused a great demand for the crude coal tar and it became a commercial product of increasing value. Perkin, by his discovery of the brilliant violet dye mauve (see Chap. 38), while he was attempting a

TABLE 2. UNITED STATES PRODUCTION AND SALES OF TAR CRUDES, 1953[a]

Product	Produc-tion	Sales		
		Quan-tity	Value, $1,000	Unit value
Crude light oil, 1,000 gal.	304,091	23,898	5,610	$0.24
Intermediate light oil, 1,000 gal.	1,062	1,065	204	0.19
Light-oil distillates:				
Benzene, specification and industrial grades, total, 1,000 gal.	272,744	232,701	95,765	0.41
Tar distillers, 1,000 gal.	32,108	19,224	8,496	0.44
Coke-oven operators, 1,000 gal.	177,593	172,406	66,479	0.39
Petroleum operators, 1,000 gal.	63,043	41,071	20,790	0.51
Benzene, motor grade, coke-oven operators, 1,000 gal.	1,160	1,150	184	0.16
Toluene, all grades, total, 1,000 gal.	156,248	130,222	39,244	0.30
Tar distillers, 1,000 gal.	4,677	3,866	1,307	0.34
Coke-oven operators, 1,000 gal.	36,036	35,445	11,075	0.31
Petroleum operators, 1,000 gal.	115,535	90,911	26,862	0.30
Xylene, total, 1,000 gal.	113,474	65,588	16,968	0.26
Tar distillers, 1,000 gal.	660	580	213	0.37
Coke-oven operators, 1,000 gal.	9,928	9,759	3,118	0.32
Petroleum operators, 1,000 gal.	102,886	55,249	13,637	0.25
Solvent naphtha, total, 1,000 gal.	15,661	15,389	5,804	0.38
Tar distillers, 1,000 gal.	9,376	9,321	4,281	0.46
Coke-oven operators, 1,000 gal.	6,285	6,068	1,523	0.25
Other light-oil distillates:				
Total, 1,000 gal.	14,657	11,410	3,512	0.31
Tar distillers, 1,000 gal.	8,560	8,153	3,064	0.38
Coke-oven operators, 1,000 gal.	6,097	3,257	448	0.14
Pyridine crude bases (dry basis), 1,000 gal.	551	456	963	2.11
Naphthalene, crude, 1,000 lb.	275,799	200,086	11,100	0.05
Crude tar-acid oils, 1,000 gal.	27,757	24,379	6,445	0.27
Cresylic acid, crude, 1,000 lb.	4,537			
Creosote oil (dead oil), 1,000 gal.	145,300	125,285	25,020	0.20
Coal tar, 1,000 gal.	8,370	8,523	1,186	0.14
All other distillate products, 1,000 gal.	18,469	16,537	3,217	0.19
Tar, road, 1,000 gal.	109,832	95,677	14,278	0.15
Tar (miscellaneous uses), 1,000 gal.	36,415	36,095	7,585	0.21
Pitch of tar:				
Soft and medium, 1,000 tons.	1,174	602	21,061	34.99
Hard, 1,000 tons.	710	410	12,812	31.25
Pitch of tar coke and pitch emulsion, 1,000 tons.	38	36	1,242	34.50

[a] "Synthetic Organic Chemicals," 1953 Preliminary, U.S. Tariff Commission, 1954.

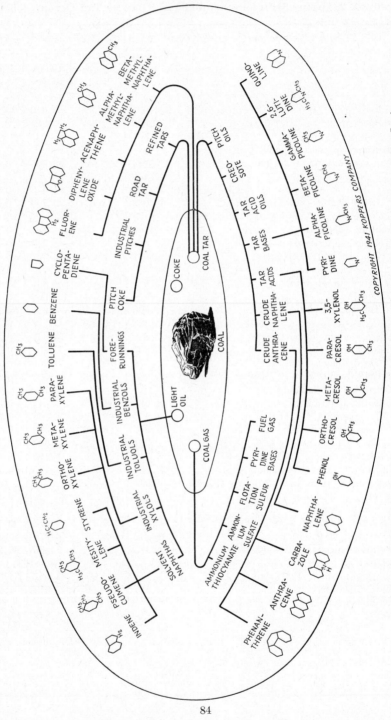

FIG. 2. How many grandchildren has a lump of coal? (*Courtesy of the Koppers Company, Inc.*)

synthesis of quinine through oxidation of crude aniline in England, laid the foundation of the world's coal-dye industry.

In 1792 the first successful experiment in the production of gas from coal was carried out by William Murdock, the father of the coal-gas industry. The results of this labor made it possible to light the streets of London with gas in 1812. The first rectangular or retort ovens were built in Germany in 1830. In 1835 the first retort coke, with its accompanying gas, was made by William Firnstone at the Mary Ann furnace in Pennsylvania. The first battery of Semet-Solvay ovens was erected in Syracuse, N.Y., in 1893 and was soon followed by ovens of the Otto-Hoffman, Koppers, and Collins types.

Uses and Economics. Coke is the product of largest tonnage from the distillation of coal. Over a hundred million tons of coal are coked each year, mostly in co-product[1] ovens. In 1953, United States production of coal tar was 924,000,000 gal., vs. 972,000,000 gal. as an average for the years of 1947–1951. See Table 2 for crudes from coal tar and petroleum; in this tabulation are the important quantities of benzene, toluene, and xylene from petroleum. In 1918 and before, beehive ovens produced a greater proportion of coke than came from the co-product ovens.

The liquid products, comprising coal tar and ammonia liquor, although not so large in volume, are at least as important industrially as the solid products of coal distillation. Hence the importance of the chemical-recovery ovens. The coal-tar products are made into dyes, intermediates, medicinals, flavors, perfumes, resins, rubber chemicals, and thousands of other useful products that are almost indispensable in our present-day civilization. The production and sales of intermediate and finished coal-tar products are summarized in Tables 2 and 4, Chap. 38.

Coking of Coal

The two main types of coking procedures are the beehive and the co-product. Beehive coking is the old and primitive method of securing coke for metallurgical purposes. In it the coal chemicals are wasted. The process is also slow. In the co-product ovens the blended-coal charge is heated on both sides so that the heat travels toward the center and thus produces shorter and more solid pieces of coke than are made in the beehive oven. No burning takes place within the oven, the heat being supplied completely from the flues on the sides. The oven gas, after being stripped of its co-products, is returned and burned to supply the heat for

---

[1] Formerly named *by-product* ovens, a term still deeply entrenched in commercial usage. *Chemical-recovery* ovens and *slot-type* ovens are terms favored by some to replace *by-product* ovens. Some authorities feel that the term *"slot-type"* oven is too limited as it does not account for horizontal ovens, such as the Curran, or for the second most widely used commercial oven in this country, namely, the Wilputte oven (also called the Otto-Wilputte oven).

coking. Substantial amounts of gas are piped to steel plants for fuel purposes, or the gas may be sold for domestic usage if the plant is located near a city.

Formerly much coal was distilled in small retorts primarily for the production of domestic coal gas. The coke formed was used to furnish heat for the retorts. However, this practice has been largely discontinued in favor of coke-oven gas.

Beehive Coking. This oven consists of a beehive-shaped brick chamber provided with a charging hole at the top of the dome and a discharging hole in the circumference of the lower part of the wall. The coal is introduced through the hole in the dome and spread over the floor. The heat retained in the oven is sufficient to start the distillation. The gases given off from the coal mix with the air entering at the top of the discharge door and burn; the heat of combustion is sufficient for the pyrolysis and distillation. The products of combustion pass out the top of the oven. These ovens, although they cost much less than the co-product ovens, are utilized today only to meet unusual demands for coke. They are uneconomic because they require comparatively excessive manual labor and do not recover coal chemicals. In normal times they account for about 1 per cent of the coke production in the United States.

Co-product Coking. The co-product coke oven is a narrow chamber usually about 38 to 40 ft. long, 13 ft. high, and tapering in width from 17 or 18 in. at one end to 15 or 16 in. at the other. The average oven holds about 16 tons of coal, although some of the larger ovens hold as much as 24 tons. These ovens are used for carbonizing coal only in large amounts and are built in batteries of 10 to 100 ovens. One of the longest batteries of co-product coking ovens in the world contains 106 Koppers-Becker underjet combination ovens. The cost of construction was more than 12 million dollars and 9 weeks was required to bring the ovens up to carbonizing temperature. The general arrangements for the operation of a co-product coke oven with its various accessories, followed by the initial treatment of its co-products, are depicted[1] in Fig. 3.

The co-product coke oven is one of the most elaborate and costly of masonry structures and is erected with the closest attention to engineering details so that it can withstand the severe strains incurred in its use. The oven block is built of refractory brick with heating flues between the coking ovens as shown in Fig. 4. There are various accessories for support, foundation, and heat insulation with regenerative chambers underneath for waste-heat utilization.

The *individual* co-product coke oven is intermittent in its operation but each oven is started and finished at different times so that the operation of the entire block produces continuously a gas of good average

---

[1] See also pictured flow sheet, Byproduct Coke Plants, *Chem. & Met. Eng.*, **48** (12), 104 (1941); GOLLMAR, Coke and Gas Industry, *Ind. Eng. Chem.*, **39**, 596 (1947).

composition. A charge of finely crushed coal is dropped from a larry car through charging holes (usually four, though the generalized flow sheet of Fig. 3 shows only two) in the top and into the oven where the walls are approximately at 2000°F. The surface of the coal is leveled in the oven and the charging holes are then covered. Heating is carried on and the charge left in the oven until it is completely coked and the evolution of the volatile matter has ceased. The average temperature at the center of the charge at the end of the heating period is usually about 1800°F., while the average flue temperature is about 2350°F. The temperatures vary with the conditions of operation, the coking time, the width of the oven, the kind of coal, its moisture content, and fineness of division.

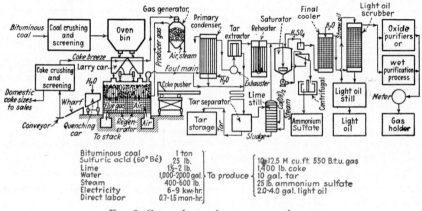

Bituminous coal	1 ton		
Sulfuric acid (60° Bé)	25 lb.		10–12.5 M cu.ft. 550 B.t.u. gas
Lime	1½–2 lb.		1,400 lb. coke
Water	1,000–2000 gal.	To produce	10 gal. tar
Steam	400–600 lb.		25 lb. ammonium sulfate
Electricity	6–9 kw.-hr.		2.0–4.0 gal. light oil
Direct labor	0.7–1.5 man-hr.		

Fig. 3. Co-product coke-oven procedures.

At the end of the coking time (approximately 17 hr.) the doors on the ends of the oven are opened and the entire red-hot mass is pushed out in less than a minute by a ram electrically driven through the oven from end to end. The coke falls into a quenching car which holds the charge from one oven. This car travels to a quenching station where an overhead nozzle sprays about 6,000 gal. of water into it. The car after draining for a minute is then moved to a coke wharf where the coke is dumped from the bottom of the car onto conveyers which take it to a crushing and screening plant.

Rarely, instead of water, an inert gas (as CO_2 or N_2) is used to cool the coke, called *dry quenching*, with the object of utilizing this heat.

The gas from the destructive distillation of the coal, together with entrained liquid particles, passes upward through a cast-iron gooseneck into a horizontal steel trough which is connected to all the ovens in a series. This trough is known as the *collecting main*, sometimes called hydraulic main. As the gas leaves the ovens, it is sprayed with weak ammonia water. This condenses some of the tar and ammonia from the gas into a liquid. These move through the main along with the gases until a settling tank is reached, where separation is effected according to density. Some of the ammonia liquor is pumped back into the pipes to help condensation; the rest goes to the ammonia still which releases the ammonia for subsequent chemical combination in the saturator. All the tar flows to storage tanks for tar distillers or for fuel.

TABLE 3. APPROXIMATE YIELDS[a] PER TON OF COAL CARBONIZED
(Depending on coal and conditions used)

	High temperature	Low temperature
Furnace coke..................................	1,400 lb.	
Coke breeze...................................	70–100 lb.	
Semicoke (12 per cent volatiles)................	....	1,500 lb.
Tar..	10 gal.	30 gal.
Ammonium sulfate............................	20 lb.	18 lb.
Light oil (removed from gas by oil scrubbing).....	2–4 gal.	2 gal.
Gas (550 B.t.u.).............................	11,000 cu. ft.	
Gas (950 B.t.u.).............................	....	3,000 cu. ft.

[a] PERRY, *op. cit.*, p. 1565. See Fig. 3, also. Note that 4 lb. of technical ammonium sulfate are equivalent to 1 lb. of ammonia.

The *types of oven* differ mainly in the arrangement of their heating flues, whether vertical or horizontal, the method of applying the regenerative principle to preheating the air for combustion, and also in the arrangement for introducing the heating gas and air to the flues. In yields, qualities of products, and methods of operation there is no material variation in the several co-product coke ovens. The important differences among the types of ovens will be taken up briefly.

The Semet-Solvay oven is the only horizontal-flued oven that has survived to the present time (see Fig. 4). It was a pioneer in the co-product coking industry and did much toward developing the art and overcoming the strong prejudices among the coke users in the early days of the industry. These ovens have two distinctive features: (1) They are heated by flames burning horizontally and serially instead of vertically and in parallel as in most ovens. (2) Though built in batteries, each oven is structurally independent of the others. Each oven has its heating flues separated from those of the adjoining oven by a solid wall of firebrick. Each oven has its individual regenerator if regenerative heating is used. In regeneration, reversal is made from end to end only between the air and waste gases while the fuel gas burns continuously at all burners.

The Koppers-Becker ovens are the most widely used vertical-flued ovens in America. The elevation is shown in Fig. 5. These ovens are all of the regenerative type and have individual regenerators from end to end, parallel with the longitudinal axis but underneath the oven. The reversal of the air and waste gas flow is made from end to end every half hour. Two characteristics of the ovens are individual control of the heating conditions in each flue through separate means of adjustment of the fuel gas, air supply, and draft, with the individual regenerators introducing heated air directly at the base of each individual heating flue.

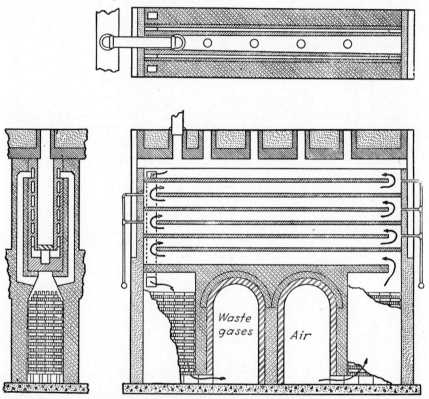

Fig. 4. Semet-Solvay by-product coke oven.

In 1922 there was introduced a newer Becker type of the Koppers regenerative oven in which the reversal of flow is not end to end but side to side; *i.e.*, from the flues on one side of an oven to those on the other through cross ducts in the brickwork above and below the oven. This eliminates the irregularities of temperature caused by the usual end-to-end system of reversal. The gas burns upward, crosses over the top of the oven, comes downward on the other side, and exits through the regenerative oven underneath. This travel is completely reversed periodically. Underjet firing and waste-gas recirculation are later improvements which contribute to uniform coking temperatures.

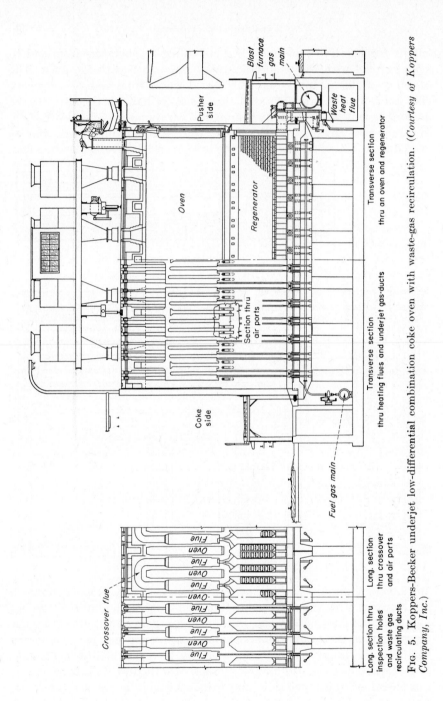

FIG. 5. Koppers-Becker underjet low-differential combination coke oven with waste-gas recirculation. (*Courtesy of Koppers Company, Inc.*)

Other ovens that are used in the United States are the Otto-Hoffmann, Otto-Schniewind, the Foundation, the Piette, the Roberts, the Piron, and the Kloenne. These ovens have not had the general acceptance that the Koppers and Semet-Solvay ovens have had. They are all of the vertical-flued regenerative type, with the exception of the Roberts which is a "flueless" type in which the gas and air are introduced vertically downward.

Recovery of Coal Chemicals. The gaseous mixture leaving the oven is made up of permanent gases which form the final purified coke-oven coal gas for the market, accompanied by condensable water vapor, tar, and light oils, with solid particles of coal dust, heavy hydrocarbons, and complex carbon compounds. The gas is passed from the foul main (Fig. 3) into the primary condenser and cooler at a temperature of about 165°F. Here the gases are cooled by means of water to 85°F. The gas is conducted to an exhauster which serves not only to compress the gas but also to remove about 75 per cent of the tar in it because of the high-speed swirling motion imparted to the gas. During the compression the temperature of the gas rises to as high as 120°F. The gas is passed to a final tar extractor where the tar is thrown out by impingement of gas jets against metal surfaces. In recent plants the tar extractor is replaced with electrostatic precipitators. On leaving the tar extractor the gas carries three-fourths of the ammonia and 95 per cent of the light oil originally present when leaving the oven.

The gas is led to a *saturator* (see Fig. 3) which contains a solution of 5 to 10 per cent[1] sulfuric acid, where the ammonia is absorbed with the formation of solid and crystalline ammonium sulfate. The saturator is a lead-lined closed vessel where the gas is fed in by a serrated distributor underneath the surface of the acid liquid. Newer plants use ammonia absorbers or scrubbers instead of saturators. These give a much lower pressure drop and decrease gas pumping costs. The acid concentration is maintained by the addition of 60° Bé. sulfuric acid and the temperature is kept at 140°F. by the reheater and the heat of neutralization. The crystallized ammonium sulfate is removed from the bottom of the saturator by a compressed air injector, or centrifugal pump, and is drained on a table from which the mother liquor is run back into the saturator. The salt is dried in a centrifuge and bagged, usually in 100-lb. sacks (see Chap. 20).

If it is not desired to get ammonium sulfate, aqua ammonia may be made by scrubbing the gas coming from the tar extractor with cold water in a bubble-cap tower or in a spray chamber through which the gas is passed countercurrent to the liquid, or by means of a rotary scrubber in which the gas is forced through a space in which large fresh surfaces of

[1] At the start of a charge, the acidity is often as high as 25 per cent, but ammonium bisulfate is liable to be formed when free sulfuric acid exceeds 10 to 11 per cent.

washing liquor are being constantly turned up by a vane or brushes on a rotating shaft. The solution obtained in this way contains about 1 per cent of ammonia and must be distilled and strengthened before it can be shipped or marketed. The ammonia still used is somewhat like that employed for the recovery of the ammonia in the Solvay process for making soda ash (see Chap. 15). Details of such an ammonia lime still are given in Fig. 6. Here the "lime leg" must be used to liberate that

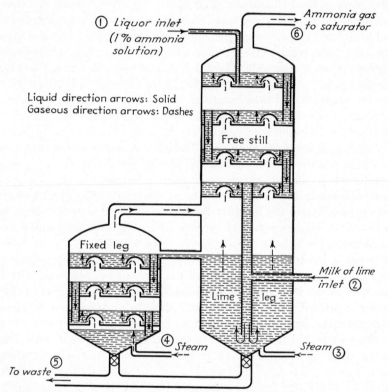

Fig. 6. Diagram of an ammonia still. This operates with drain from fixed leg open sufficiently to prevent accumulation of liquor in this section. Drain from lime leg is closed except for cleanout.

large part of ammonia which is fixed in the form of chloride and other salts. In the usual case, as depicted in Fig. 3, some weak ammonia liquor is separated from the tar. This is distilled with lime and steam as shown in Figs. 3 and 6, the ammonia gas in this case going into the saturator.

The gas leaving the saturator at about 140°F. is taken to final coolers or condensers where it is scrubbed with water until its temperature is 75°F. During this cooling some naphthalene separates and is carried along with the waste water and recovered. The gas is passed into a *light oil or benzol scrubber* (Fig. 3) over which is circulated, at about 75°F. as the absorbent medium, a heavy fraction of petroleum called *straw oil*, or sometimes a coal-tar oil. The straw oil is sprayed in the top of the absorption tower while the gas flows up through the tower. Most scrubbers use spiral metal packing, although wooden grids were formerly used. The straw oil is allowed to absorb about 2 to 3 per cent of its weight of light oil with a removal efficiency of about 95 per cent of the light oil vapor in the gas.

The rich straw oil, after being warmed in heat exchangers by vapors from the light oil still and then by hot debenzolized oil flowing out of the still, is passed to the stripping column, where the straw oil, flowing downward, is brought into direct contact with live steam. The vapors of light oil and steam pass off and upward from the still through the heat exchanger previously mentioned and to a condenser and water separator. The lean or stripped straw oil is returned through the heat exchanger to the scrubbers.

The crude *light oil* is distilled in the crude fractionating tank stills of 6,000 to 15,000 gal. capacity provided with short towers (see Fig. 8). These are batch stills and are heated first with indirect steam coils and later by direct steam to drive over the heavier fractions. If pure benzene, toluene, and solvent naphtha are desired, several fractions from the crude fractionating still are made and each of these fractions is redistilled in the fractionating still of Fig. 8. For motor fuel only one cut is made from the crude still. The crude products are washed with strong sulfuric acid to remove unsaturated impurities, next with caustic soda and water. The washed products are finally redistilled to remove any complex polymers formed by the action of any acid that might remain dissolved in the benzene. Note from Fig. 3, that coal furnishes both light oil and coal tar and, from Figs. 7 and 8, that the distillation of coal tar furnishes further amounts of light oil. These two fractions are usually united and rectified.

TABLE 4. TYPICAL COMPOSITION OF LIGHT OIL FROM GAS[a]

	Gallons per ton of coal
Benzene	1.85
Toluene	0.45
Xylene and light solvent naphtha	0.30
Acid washing loss (mostly unsaturateds)	0.16
Heavy hydrocarbons and naphthalene	0.24
Wash oil	0.20
Total crude light oil	3.20
Pure motor fraction	2.50

[a] PORTER, "Coal Carbonization," Reinhold Publishing Corporation, New York, 1924.

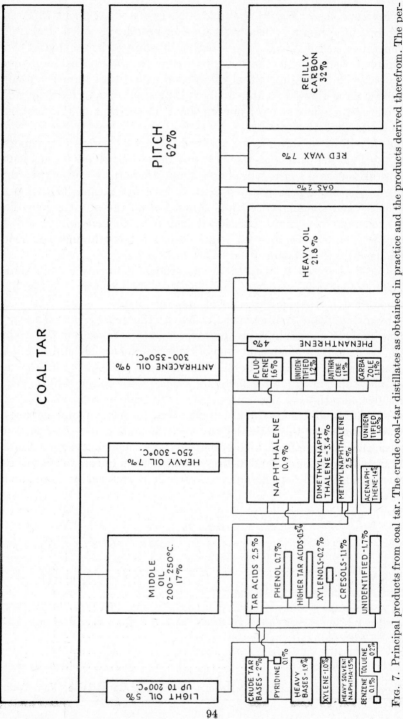

Fig. 7. Principal products from coal tar. The crude coal-tar distillates as obtained in practice and the products derived therefrom. The percentage yields as shown and represented by the areas of the rectangles are *average values* based on the original tar. Yields vary with different conditions and different coals. *(Courtesy of Reilly Tar & Chemical Corporation.)*

The gas after being stripped of its ammonia and light oil has the sulfur removed in purifying boxes which contain iron oxide on wood shavings or in wet scrubbing towers as is the best present-day practice. These procedures are fully described in Chap. 7 on Fuel Gases.

Low-temperature Carbonization.[1] During the present century there has been a large amount of experimental work carried out on the carbonization of coal at temperatures ranging from 750 to 1100°F., with the main object to obtain maximum yields of liquid products and to produce semi-cokes containing from 8 to 20 per cent volatile matter. Here again the characteristics and yields of the various products depend upon the coal, the temperature, and the treatment. Tables 3 and 5 show the difference

TABLE 5. VARIATION OF GAS FROM LOW- AND HIGH-TEMPERATURE
COAL CARBONIZATION[a]

Gases	Coking temperature, 500°C., per cent	Coking temperature, 1000°C., per cent
CO_2.................	9.0	2.5
C_nH_m...............	8.0	3.5
CO..................	5.5	8.0
H_2.................	10.0	50.0
CH_4 and homologs.....	65.0	34.0
N_2.................	2.5	2.0

[a] ROBERTS and JENKNER, "International Coal Carbonization," p. 198, Sir Isaac Pitman & Sons, Ltd., London, 1934.

in gas content and in yield products for high- and low-temperature systems. At present the Disco Company at McDonald, Pa., the first in this country to utilize a low-temperature carbonization process,[2] has a daily capacity to convert 1,000 tons of high-volatile coal into 800 tons of lightly carbonized balls plus tar and gas. The tar is refined to produce tar acid oil, tar acids, creosote, fuel pitch, and pitch oil. The gas, after liquid-product removal, is used for firing. The maximum temperature used in this process is 1050°F. Perhaps the most interesting aspect of the Disco process is its continuous flow of solids through the system as against the batch operation of a conventional coke oven. Low-temperature carbonization has been important in several European countries, especially England, for many decades.

The low-temperature production of fuel and coal chemicals may in the long run produce important quantities of both coal chemicals and fuel because of its superior thermal yield and cost.

[1] KIRK and OTHMER, op. cit., Vol. 3, pp. 171–174; BROWNLIE, Low-temperature Carbonization, Ind. Eng. Chem., **19**, 39 (1927), and eight preceding articles.

[2] McBRIDE, Low-temperature Coking Plant, Chem. Eng., **56** (6), 112 (1949).

Unit Operations and Unit Processes. As Chap. 2 points out, chemical engineering can be "resolved into a coordinated series of unit physical operations and unit chemical processes." The various flow sheets as presented in this book will frequently be broken down into such a sequence of unit operations (Op.) and unit processes (Pr.). These cause continuous attention to be directed to the unitary aspects of the various operations or processes, with the consequent transfer of the experience gained with given unit operation in one field to the same operation in another. Several of the flow sheets presented in this chapter are rather complicated, more so than in similar presentations in other sections of the book. However, Fig. 3 can be divided into different steps representing the flow of material through the various pieces of equipment wherein the proper unit operation or unit process takes place. The listing of these unitary aspects is in a sense the synopsis of the particular process. Figure 3 may be thus broken down into the following *unit operations* (Op.) and *unit processes* (Pr.):

Coal is transferred, crushed, and screened (Op.).
Coal is charged to a hot empty oven (Op.).
Coal is chemically transformed to coke and volatiles by pyrolysis (Pr.).
Hot coke is pushed out of oven, quenched, and transported (Op.).
Condensable products of distillation are liquefied and collected in hydraulic main (Op.).
Foul gas is cooled and tar extracted (Op.).
Ammonia is removed from gas as ammonium sulfate (Pr.).
Gas is cooled and subjected to benzol and toluol removal by absorption in straw oil (Op.).
Hydrogen sulfide is removed (Pr.).
Purified gas is metered and transferred to consumers (Op.).

The tar separated from the collecting main and the tar extractor or electrostatic precipitators is settled from ammonia liquor and subjected to the sequences represented by flow sheet (Fig. 8).

DISTILLATION OF COAL TAR

Coal tar is a mixture of many chemical compounds, mostly aromatic, which vary widely in composition (see Figs. 2 and 7). It is a co-product of the destructive distillation or pyrolysis of coal. Depending upon whether the primary objective is coal gas or coke and also on the nature of the coal, the amount of crude tar (with a specific gravity from 1.0 to 1.2) obtained varies from 8 to 12 gal. of tar per ton of coal. A typical tar composition is listed on the bottom of Fig. 8, where the steps to separate coal tar into these constituents are depicted. The objects of distillation are to produce the maximum yields of the valuable products with a minimum of free carbon in the pitch. These products must usually be sharply fractionated with a minimum of overlapping. The process also should be thermally economical.

Methods of Distillation. There have been many improvements in coal-tar distillation in the past few years; in general it may be stated that the trend is away from the simple batch still and toward modifications that will give the highest yields of the various "oils." There are at present in use a number of major types of stills such as batch stills, vacuum stills, steam-operated stills, gas recirculated stills, coke stills, and pipe stills.

TABLE 6. A COMPARISON OF COAL-TAR STILLS[a]

System	Temperature, degrees C.	Pitch, per cent	Oil, per cent	Free carbon, per cent
Atmospheric still................	413	57.8	40.1	40.7
Vacuum still....................	330	42.5	56.6	28.8
Steam distillation...............	340	47.5	50.6	28.8
Recirculating inert gas (CO_2) through still.................	358	46.9	52.6	29.0
Recirculating inert gas (N_2) through still.........................	331	46.4	52.0	27.2

[a] WEISS, The Distillation of Coal Tar, *J. Soc. Chem. Ind.*, **51**, 219 (1932).

1. *Batch Stills.* As might be imagined from their simplicity of operation, fire-heated batch stills were the first type of equipment used in tar distillation. Varying in size from 3,000 to 7,000 gal., they consist essentially of a large iron container with connection to a condenser, into which the tar is dumped and heat applied until the distillation is complete, as shown in Fig. 8. In the United States, a horizontal type of still is preferred, although on the continent vertical stills are in general use. The essential disadvantage of the batch still is discontinuous operation, with the pitch residue remaining in the still and being subject to heat during the entire period of distillation. This disadvantage may be somewhat overcome by some form of air or steam agitation to increase tar velocity and improve heat transfer. Steam is preferred. In the ordinary batch still, the procedure is of relatively long duration and the fractionation is not very sharp. When the temperature rises to between 500 and 700°F., during the anthracene condensation, the residue in the still remains for a long time in contact with highly heated surfaces, causing local overheating and decreased oil production, and furnishing a pitch containing considerable portions of free carbon.

2. *Vacuum Stills.* The object of vacuum distillation is to lower the final tar temperatures and thereby increase the yield of oils. Of necessity, special precautions, which include heavier retort shells and internal reinforcement, should be observed. Vacuum distillation has been adopted

with the idea of protecting the tar by reduction of the distillation temperature. Under vacuum distillation some difficulty is met in condensing the low-boiling oil fractions.

3. *Steam-operated Stills.* The use of sufficient steam to agitate the tar does not involve an amount of steam sufficient to affect the thermal distillation in any way; the use of larger volumes of steam, however, will materially lower the still temperature and give higher oil yields. In practice the operation means higher cost for steam and cooling water. In steam distillation, the great danger is that the pitch temperature might

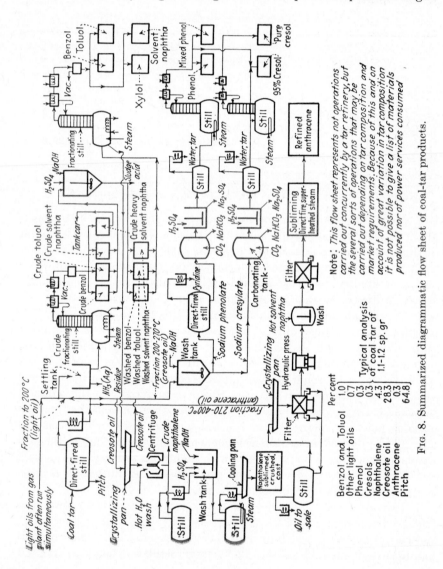

Fig. 8. Summarized diagrammatic flow sheet of coal-tar products.

drop to such an extent that the use of direct steam would prove very costly.

4. *Gas Recirculated Stills.* Since air exerts a deleterious oxidizing effect if used for stirring tar mixtures, Weiss in 1922 proposed the use of inert gas recirculated in a closed system.

5. *Coke Stills.* The general principle here employed involves contacting the tar with raw, hot coke-oven gas, thereby utilizing the sensible heat of these gases to volatilize the tar oils. High yields are obtained at little or no fuel expense.

6. *Pipe Stills.* The most recent developments in coal-tar distillation have been made in pipe still operation. The pipe still has been used for some time in America for the distillation of petroleum, and it is now being successfully adapted for the distillation of tar.[1] It consists essentially of a battery to tubes, arranged within a furnace, through which the tar to be distilled is passed at a relatively high rate in a continuous stream. Thus its construction is similar to that of a water-tube boiler, minus the steam drums. Since the tar remains in the heating coils only sufficiently long (a few minutes) for it to be raised to the requisite temperature for distillation, there is no overheating and the minimum proportion of free carbon is produced. Further, the presence of the lower-boiling tar constituents in the continuous heating process causes a *lowering* of the boiling points of the high-boiling fractions, so that the time element is not only reduced, but the heating temperature also, making the use of the vacuum unnecessary.

Modern practice, as exemplified by the pipe still, is producing such clean-cut fractions that often little further purification is necessary. However, below are given the fractions obtained in an ordinary batch still, and a brief outline of purification as illustrated in Fig. 8 (see also Fig. 7). The yields vary from different coal tars and under different conditions. This explains the differences between the quantities listed in Figs. 7 and 8.

a. Light oils usually embrace the cut up to 390°F. They are first crudely fractionated and agitated at a low temperature with concentrated sulfuric acid, neutralized with caustic soda, and redistilled, furnishing benzene, toluene, and homologs.

b. Middle oils, or *creosote oils,* generally are the fraction from 390 to 480 or 520°F., which contains naphthalene, phenol, and cresols. The naphthalene settles out upon cooling, is separated by centrifuging, and is purified by sublimation. After the naphthalene is removed, phenol and other tar acids[2] are obtained by

---

[1] GROUNDS, Tar Distillation, *Gas World*, **109** (2813), 77 (1938).

[2] "Tar acids," in the language of the tar distiller, represent phenol and its homologs which are soluble in caustic soda. A pictured flow sheet for separation of phenol, cresols, and xylenols is in *Chem. Eng.*, **59** (11), 212 (1952).

extraction with a 10 per cent caustic soda solution and neutralization or "springing" by carbon dioxide. These are fractionally distilled, as shown in Fig. 8.

c. *Heavy oil* may represent the fraction from 480 to 570°F., or it may be split between the middle oil and the anthracene oil.

d. *Anthracene oil* usually is the fraction from 520 or 570°F. up to 660 or 750°F. It is washed with various solvents to remove phenanthrene and carbazole; the remaining solid is anthracene.

Miscellaneous Uses of Coal Tar

Much coal tar is burned for fuel after heating[1] to reduce its viscosity and facilitate its spraying into the furnace. In countries other than the United States where motor fuels are not so abundant, coal tars are hydrogenated,[2] producing lighter-boiling hydrocarbons.

Coal tars have been studied regarding their pyrolysis[3] products and offer a future source for motor fuel. In the United States much coal tar is consumed on roads and roofs.[4] For this purpose the tar is distilled up to the point where thermal decomposition starts. This "base tar" is oiled back with creosote oil of the proper specification to ensure satisfactory rapid drying but to avoid brittleness in service. Somewhat similar tars are employed to impregnate felt and paper for waterproofing.

Liquid Fuels

A great deal of time and money is being spent in the United States for evaluating various processes,[5] principally from coal, for synthetic motor fuels in view of the large demands of our internal-combustion motors. When petroleum products become more costly, these processes will become economically feasible. Furthermore some of the fractions from hydrogenolysis of coal would be suitable for internal-combustion motors but at present are also more expensive than gasoline. The situation in Germany during the Second World War, when liquid fuels (aviation) were made from coal, was not comparable to the United States either then or now.

---

[1] PERRY, *op. cit.*, p. 1575. Fuel value = 15,000 to 16,500 B.t.u. per lb.

[2] HALL and CAWLEY, The Composition of the Products Obtained by the Hydrogenation-cracking of Low-temperature Tar, *J. Soc. Chem. Ind.*, **56**, 303 (1937).

[3] MORRELL, *et al.*, Cracking Tars and Distillates from Coal, *Ind. Eng. Chem.*, **32**, 39 (1940).

[4] HADFIELD, Modern Road Tars, *Gas World*, **108**, 71 (1938); KIRBY, Preparation of Road Tars, *Chemistry & Industry*, **1938**, 486.

[5] STORCH, Review of Development of Processes for Synthesis of Liquid Fuels by Hydrogenation of CO, *Chem. Eng. Progr.*, **44**, 469 (1948); SCHROEDER, Comparison of Major Processes for Synthetic Liquid Fuels, *Chem. Inds.*, **62**, 575 (1948); KASTENS, Liquid Fuel from Coal, *Ind. Eng. Chem.*, **41**, 870 (1949); ANON., Synthetic Fuels, *Chem. Eng.*, **55** (6), 131 (1948); Symposium, Developments in Synthetic Liquid Fuels, *Chem. Eng. News*, **30**, 3248 (1952); STORCH, GOLUMBIC, and ANDERSON, "The Fischer-Tropsch and Related Syntheses," John Wiley & Sons, Inc., New York, 1951.

Hydrogenolysis (Hydrogenation-Pyrolysis)

The present interest in coal hydrogenation or rather hydrogenolysis, is to obtain coal chemicals. Carbide and Carbon Chemicals Company[1] has built a pilot plant at Institute, W. Va., which treats 300 tons of Pittsburgh No. 8 coal daily. This unit cost 11 million dollars and culminated some 17 years of research. The Carbide process involves three distinct divisions as shown in the flow sheet of Fig. 9: (1) coal preparation and solution in oil, (2) reaction with hydrogen, and (3) chemicals separation. It may be further subdivided into the following *unit operations* (Op.) and *unit processes* (Pr.).

Coal is crushed to only 20 mesh, ground, dried, and mostly dissolved in a highly aromatic oil to make a paste. Catalyst (0.5 per cent) added here, if used (Op.).

The coal solution paste (25 to 40 per cent coal) is pumped under high pressure to the hydrogenators (Op.).

After preheating, the paste is mixed with 300 to 400 per cent excess hydrogen and fed to the converter. Operating data of the forged steel converters: temperature, 840 to 1000°F.; pressure, 4,000 to 6,000 lb. per sq. in.; and residence time, 3 to 4.5 min. Exothermic reaction (Pr.).

The hydrogenated-pyrolyzed or hydrogenolyzed mixture undergoes a hot separation to distill (Op.) gases, liquids, and vapors off the recycle oil (Op.). The recycle oil in turn is filtered to remove (Op.) unreacted solids (ash and the mineral charcoal or fusain portion of coal). The hot separation distillate is partially condensed (Op.) and followed by a cold separation to remove gases from the liquid stream (Op.). The unused hydrogen is recycled (Op.).

This liquid stream is the "golden fleece" of the process and is separated by chemical extraction (Pr.), solvent extraction (Op.), and distillation (Op.) into various chemical fractions or products which may be purified into a large number of end products, some of which are tabulated under the flow sheet of Fig. 9.

This coal hydrogenation process is very important to the chemical industry as it means the aromatics field will now have its own source of supply and will no longer be a secondary operation. Furthermore this hydrogenolysis *upgrades* the various products to a greater extent than is true of direct pyrolysis or destructive distillation which degrades more of the organic compounds to carbon or coke. The upgrading as well as the chemical reaction is facilitated by the excess of hydrogen employed and the short residence time. These factors also eliminate the troublesome coking in the reactor.

This novel coal process aims at higher-valued aromatics and minimizes the production of cheaper aliphatics that have been sought as gasoline substitutes. This is accomplished by adding a relatively small percentage of hydrogen to the aromatic coal. In comparison with yields from ordinary destructive distillation

[1] CALLAHAM, Coal Hydrogenation Process Unlocks Vast Aromatics Field, *Chem. Eng.*, **59** (6), 152 (1952); Staff Report, Carbide Takes the Hex Out of Coal, *Chem. Eng. News*, **30**, 1954 (1952).

of coal, this process yields 100 to 200 times the amount of cresols, 60 to 80 times as much phenol, 300 to 500 times the yield of quinolines, and naphthalene 3 to 8 times.

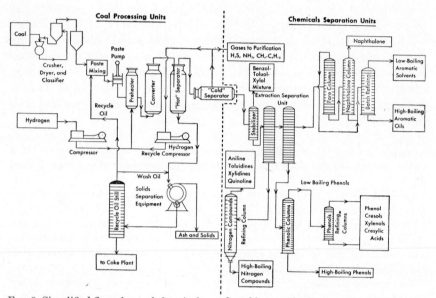

FIG. 9. Simplified flow sheet of chemicals produced by coal hydrogenation. (*Courtesy of Carbide and Carbon Chemicals Co.*)

Materials per 24 hours		*Products*
Coal dried 100 tons	Ash 8–15 tons	Gases:
Hydrogen 3 + tons	Fusain 8–15 tons	NH_3, H_2S, CH_4-C_4H_{10}
Labor 50 men up to 500 tons	High boiling oils for elec-	H_2 excess to recycle
coal	trode coke 30 $\pm$ tons	
Aromatic coal-tar dissolv-		
ing oil recycled		

Additional products from "cold" separation (widely variable with hydrogen consumption)

Hydrocarbons	*Phenols*	*Arylamines* & N-*hetereocyclics*
Benzene	Phenol	Aniline
Toluene	Cresols	Toluidines
Xylene	Xylenols	Xylidines
Naphthalene	Higher phenols	Alkyl-pyridines
Methyl-naphthalene		Quinolines
		Methyl-quinoline
		Indole etc.

Many engineering problems have been solved or are now being investigated in close connection with the chemical changes. The converters are 35 ft. long by 30 in. inside diameter with 7.5-in. walls constructed of a special alloy (6130 Cr, Mo, steel with enhanced Cr) to resist hydrogen embrittlement. There is a refractory lining. The solids separation may be filtration, centrifugation, or flash distillation or a combination.

SELECTED REFERENCES

Porter, H. C., "Coal Carbonization," Reinhold Publishing Corporation, New York, 1924.

Roberts, J., "Coal Carbonization," Sir Isaac Pitman & Sons, Ltd., London, 1927.

Gluud, W., American edition by D. L. Jacobson, "International Handbook of the By-product Coke Industry," Reinhold Publishing Corporation, New York, 1932.

Parrish, P., "Design and Working of Ammonia Stills," D. Van Nostrand Company, Inc., New York, 1924.

Morgan, J. J., "American Gas Practice," 2d ed., privately printed by J. J. Morgan, Maplewood, N.J., 1931.

Bangham, H. D., "Progress in Coal Science," Interscience Publishers, Inc., New York, 1950.

Wilson, P. J., and J. H. Wells, "Coal, Coke, and Coal Chemicals," McGraw-Hill Book Company, Inc., New York, 1950.

Lowry, H. H., editor, "The Chemistry of Coal Utilization," 2 vols., John Wiley & Sons, Inc., New York, 1945.

U.S. Bureau of Mines, various publications on coal and coal hydrogenation. Current lists upon request.

Kreulen, D. J. W., "Elements of Coal Chemistry," Nÿgh & Ditmar N. V., Rotterdam, 1948.

Storch, H. H., Norma Golumbic, and R. B. Anderson, "The Fischer-Tropsch and Related Syntheses," John Wiley & Sons, Inc., New York, 1951.

Abbott, W. W., et al., "The Future for Aromatic Chemicals," Harvard Business School, Boston, 1954.

Coal Tar Research Association, "Review of Coal Tar Technology," Gomersal, near Leeds, England, Semi-annual Review.

CHAPTER 7

FUEL GASES

The black smoke appearing from countless chimneys in many communities represents a loss of energy in our natural resources and a contamination of the air to the detriment of both animals and plants. The ideal situation would be one in which no coal was burned as such, but where each of its ingredients would be separated and utilized for the purpose *best* suited from a technical viewpoint. In such a case, coke, oil, or gas would be the universal fuels, because of their convenience, cleanliness, and efficiency. However, in most cases at the present time, this would make the fuel cost more than for coal. This chapter will consider the various types of fuel gases.

Historical. The first recorded use of combustible gas was by the Chinese about A.D. 900 when natural gas was piped through bamboo tubes and used for lighting. The first production of coal gas was about 1665 in England and its first utilization was for lighting purposes in 1792. Similar endeavors in this country began in Philadelphia around 1796. It was not long after this that gas companies began to be organized and the manufacture of gas put on a businesslike basis. The discovery of water gas or *blue gas*, as it is also called, in 1780 and that of producer gas were essential steps in the development of this industry. The exploitation of our natural gas fields gave the final impetus to the gas industry as we know it today.

The fuel gas industry is undergoing a radical and basic transformation. Coal gas, natural gas, water gas, and even producer gas are not only sources of heat and power, they are already very important raw materials for chemical synthesis. Examples of this will be considered under the specific gas in this chapter, as well as elsewhere in this book, but this statement may here be illustrated by citing the use of water gas as the first step in the manufacture of hydrogen for both inorganic and organic hydrogenations and also the use of methane or natural gas as a source of cheap hydrogen as well as the initial material for syntheses or for cracking to various types of carbon.

Table 1 summarizes the composition and heating values of the principal fuel gases. The choice in any case is between the composition, heating value, and the cost of producing and distributing the gas. If the

TABLE 1. PER CENT COMPOSITION AND HEATING VALUES OF VARIOUS
FUEL GASES[a]

	Natural gas, (Mid-continent)	Natural gas, (Penn-sylvania)	Coal gas (coke oven)	Water gas	Car-bureted water gas	Producer gas
Carbon monoxide.........	.....	....	6.3	43.5	34.0	30.0
Carbon dioxide..........	0.8	....	1.8	3.5	3.0	3.5
Hydrogen...............	.....	....	53.0	47.3	40.5	10.0
Nitrogen...............	3.2	1.1	3.4	4.4	2.9	54.5
Oxygen................	.....	....	0.2	0.6	0.5	0.5
Methane...............	96.0	67.6	31.6	0.7	10.2	1.5
Ethane................		31.3				
Illuminants.............	.....	....	3.7	.....	8.9	
Gross B.t.u. per cu. ft.....	967	1,232	586	302	550	135

[a] MORGAN, "American Gas Practice," p. 30, J. J. Morgan, Maplewood, N.J., 1931. Extensive tables are given on pp. 1577ff. of Perry, *op. cit.*, where more properties are tabulated, such as air required and products of combustion.

TABLE 2. HEATS OF COMBUSTION

Substance	B.t.u. per cu. ft. at 60°F. and 1 atm.		B.t.u. per lb.	
	Gross	Net	Gross	Net
Hydrogen.....................	325	275	61,100	51,623
Carbon monoxide..............	321.8	321.8	4,347	4,347
Methane.....................	1,013.2	913.1	23,879	21,520
Ethane......................	1,792	1,641	22,320	20,432
Carbon......................	....	....	14,093	14,093

NOTE: The net heating value is the practical value since it designates the heat of combustion with the water vapor uncondensed. If the products are cooled to the initial temperature and the water is condensed, its latent heat of condensation is liberated and the larger or gross heating value is obtained. The difference amounts to 18,919 B.t.u. per lb.-mole of water in the products of combustion. *Cf.* PERRY, *op. cit.*, pp. 1579, 1583.

gas has to be distributed over more than a short distance, the cheaply made producer gas has too low a B.t.u. content to be competitive with other manufactured gas. The B.t.u. of a gas is a summation of the heats of combustion of its constituents and can be very closely calculated from these. Table 2 summarizes the individual heats of combustion and explains the variation in the heats of combustion of the gases given in Table 1. Flame temperatures obtainable are very important in the utilization of fuel gases. In Perry,[1] the procedure for calculating these is exemplified.

NATURAL GAS

The seepage from the earth of gases that could be used for lighting was reported in the Ohio Valley as far back as 1775; but the earliest commercial utilization was in Fredonia, N.Y., in 1821. Although natural-gas wells may be found widely scattered over the country, the chief fields may be defined as follows: the Appalachian field covering eastern Kentucky, West Virginia, southern Ohio, eastern Pennsylvania, and part of New York; the Lima field in western Ohio and Indiana; the large field that covers southern Oklahoma and northern Texas; the field in the Texas Panhandle; the various Louisiana fields including the newly developed Gulf Coast fields; and finally, those in California. The explanation of the geological occurrence of natural gas and the description of well drilling and development are all beyond the scope of this text. The United States reserves alone are nearly 200 trillion cu. ft. In 1953 the total consumption of 5.2 trillion cu. ft. was employed as follows: 15 per cent for fuel for refinery and field consumption, 23 per cent for domestic fuel, 3 per cent for carbon black manufacture, and 59 per cent for all other industrial uses, including *chemical raw material* for various syntheses (see Chaps. 8, 20, and 37).

There are various by-products from raw natural gas that are of industrial significance, such as propane, butane, and natural gasoline. These are separated from the crude gas as liquids by fractionation or absorption under pressure and are marketed in steel cylinders and tank cars as a gas supply for rural homes and villages and as chemical raw materials for such derivatives as nitro-paraffins, chloro-paraffins, and acetone. The separation and utilization of natural gasoline, or *casing-head* gasoline as it is often called, will be taken up under petroleum products in Chap. 37.

Natural gas provides one-seventh of all the energy produced in this country. After necessary purification, as will be described, the natural gas is compressed and sent through the distribution mains which network the country, being recompressed at periodic distances by gas engines.[2] This natural gas is employed as fuel in many cities 2,000 miles or more from the producing wells. For peak demands natural gas may be stored in various ways. The best and a widely practiced procedure is to store in a depleted gas field near the consumer. Another important storage is where the gas is forced under pressure into a series of buried "coils" of heavy pipe. Liquefaction of gas ($-250°F.$) and storage in insulated

---

[1] *Op. cit.,* p. 347.

[2] Lee, Natural Gas—Its Heart and Arteries, *Chem. Eng.,* **57** (5), 113 (1950).

holders above ground has been purely experimental since the disastrous Cleveland fire in 1944. A new development is a low-temperature adsorption process where 200 volumes of natural gas are adsorbed at $-250°F$. on one volume of fuller's earth at a cost claimed to be competitive with other methods.

Besides being used alone as a fuel, natural gas is much employed as an enriching agent for gases of lower heating value. For example, coke-oven gas is diluted to a 380 B.t.u. mixture with producer gas and then this mixture is enriched to 540 B.t.u. by the addition of natural gas.

Fuel Gas Purification. In addition to the industrially valuable propane and butane, the raw natural gas contains undesirable water and hydrogen sulfide which must be removed before it can be placed in the transmission lines. *Such purification is also practiced on other fuel gases.* There are four important methods employed for the dehydration of gas: compression, treatment with drying substances, adsorption, and refrigeration. The plant for water removal by *compression* consists of a gas compressor followed by a cooling system to remove the water vapor by condensation. The treatment of gas with *drying* substance has found widespread usage in this country. The agents employed for this purpose are activated alumina and bauxite, silica gel, sulfuric acid, glycerine, diethylene glycol, and concentrated solutions of calcium chloride or sodium thiocyanate. Plants of this type usually require a packed tower for the countercurrent treatment of the gas with the reagent, together with a regenerator for the dehydrating agent. Gas may also be dehydrated by passing it over *refrigerated* coils. In general, this method is more costly than the others but, where exhaust steam is available to operate the refrigeration cycle, costs of refrigeration can be reduced. If the water occurring in most fuel gas is not removed, an unduly high corrosion will occur in the transmission lines, and trouble may also be had from the freezing of valves in cold weather.

The necessity of *removing* hydrogen sulfide[1] and other sulfides from gas is rather obvious, not only because of the corrosion problem but because the oxides of sulfur formed during combustion would be a nuisance to gas consumers. Also the sulfur compounds, particularly H_2S and S, have commercial value and are employed as a source of SO_2 for sulfuric acid plants (see Chap. 19 for sulfur and its uses).

In raw fuel gases, except for some natural gases, the amount of hydrogen sulfide present may range from about 100 grains per 100 cu. ft. in blue gas to several hundred grains per 100 cu. ft. in coke-oven and coal gas, up to several thousand grains per 100 cu. ft. for refinery gas from sulfur crudes and natural gas from the sulfur-bearing regions. Other

---

[1] MARSHALL, Gas Purification, Wet and Dry, *Gas World*, **129** (3338), Coking Section, 105 (1948); REED and UPDEGRAFF, Removal of Hydrogen Sulfide from Industrial Gases, *Ind. Eng. Chem.*, **42**, 2269 (1950).

sulfur compounds may be present also. The various methods for sulfur removal may be best divided into the *dry* and *wet methods*.

The principal *dry methods*[1] are the iron oxide process and the activated carbon catalytic process. The latter is not used commercially in this country. The iron oxide method is employed in most small plants that manufacture gas for public utilities and as a final cleanup in large plants following such wet methods as the Seaboard, Thylox, or vacuum carbonate processes. The sulfides are removed by passing the gas through a series of boxes filled with highly reactive iron oxide and wood shavings. Here reactions, such as this, take place:

$$Fe_2O_3 \cdot xH_2O + 3H_2S \rightarrow Fe_2S_3 + (x + 3)H_2O$$

Air is generally introduced to the gas before the dry boxes to provide a concentration of 0.6 to 1.0 per cent oxygen. The oxygen serves simultaneously to revivify the ferric sulfide, yielding iron oxide and elemental sulfur. Despite this it is generally necessary to finish revivification in open air:

$$2Fe_2S_3 + 3O_2 + xH_2O \rightarrow 2Fe_2O_3 \cdot xH_2O + 6S$$

When the total sulfur content reaches 50 to 60 per cent, this reactant may be discarded or the sulfur solvent extracted (Germany). This process displays the greatest selectivity of adsorption of hydrogen sulfide in the presence of carbon dioxide; however, its disadvantages are the amount of space and labor required and, ordinarily, the cost of sulfur recovery.

In the *wet methods* a solution is utilized which contains a reagent that chemically combines with H_2S to remove it from the gas stream. The processes all employ some type of continuous contactor, such as a packed tower or bubble-cap tower (Fig. 3), where the gas passes upward countercurrent to the flow of the solution. Reed and Updegraff (*op. cit.*) have grouped these wet processes according to the similarity of the disposition of the H_2S-laden solution into the following classifications:

(1) nonregenerative processes in which the hydrogen sulfide reacts with some chemical reagent and the product is discarded;

(2) regenerative processes in which the absorbing solution is recycled, but the hydrogen sulfide is necessarily discarded;

(3) regenerative processes in which the hydrogen sulfide is recovered as a gas;

(4) regenerative processes in which the hydrogen sulfide is recovered as elemental sulfur.

Nonregenerative Processes. These processes are mostly used when the quantity of H_2S is small or for cleaning up residual H_2S after the bulk

---

[1] SANDS and SCHMIDT, Recovery of Sulfur from Synthesis Gas, *Ind. Eng. Chem.*, **42**, 2277 (1950).

has been removed by some other process. It may not be economical for large quantities of H_2S as the cost of reagent replacement is high. A commonly used reagent is caustic soda for the following reaction:

$$H_2S + 2NaOH \rightarrow Na_2S + 2H_2O$$

The spent solution is discarded. In some installations the removal is performed in two stages with the first-stage product, sodium hydrosulfide, concentrated and sold. Some plants use a lime slurry process, but plugging of the equipment takes place. Both lime and caustic soda absorb carbon dioxide also. A widely used nonregenerative process for purifying CO_2 for production of Dry Ice utilizes potassium permanganate to remove a small amount of H_2S present. A buffered solution of sodium bichromate and zinc sulfate is also employed, but it is not so effective as permanganate for removing some of the other impurities found in commercial CO_2.

Regenerative Processes. The two major disadvantages of the non-regenerative processes are the cost of the reagent and the disposal of the product. In 1920 the Koppers Company developed the Seaboard process (Table 3) which was the first liquid regenerative process. It is

TABLE 3. OPERATING COST OF THE SEABOARD PROCESS[a]

Type of gas...	Refinery
Plant capacity, standard cu. ft. gas per day..............	5,000,000
Sulfur content, grains H_2S per 100 cu. ft.................	1,000
Sulfur removal, per cent...............................	98
Gas pressure, lb. per sq. in. gage.......................	60
	Per day
Labor: 6 hr. at $2 per hr...............................	$12.00
Power: 1,000 kw.-hr. at $0.01 per kw.-hr.................	10.00
Steam: 7,800 lb. at $0.50 per 1,000 lb....................	3.90
Soda ash: 400 lb. at $0.02 per lb........................	8.00
Maintenance...	2.00
Total operating cost per day............................	$35.90
Operating cost per 1,000 cu. ft. gas.....................	$0.72

[a] Courtesy of Koppers Company, Inc.

still in use. This is a *nonrecovery, regenerative process.* The purification is effected by scrubbing the gas with a dilute (3 to 3.5 per cent) solution of sodium carbonate. This treatment removes all the H_2S present, as well as any hydrogen cyanide and some of the CO_2.

Purifying:

$$H_2S + Na_2CO_3 \rightarrow NaHS + NaHCO_3 \qquad (1)$$
$$CO_2 + Na_2CO_3 + H_2O \rightarrow 2NaHCO_3 \qquad (2)$$
$$HCN + Na_2CO_3 \rightarrow NaCN + NaHCO_3 \qquad (3)$$

Actifying:

$$NaHS + NaHCO_3 \rightarrow Na_2CO_3 + H_2S \qquad (4)$$

The reaction proceeds as in equation (4) when the solution is contacted with a large flow of air or other gas or vapor to aid in removal of the H_2S. The standard equipment for this process is a packed or bubble-cap tower (Fig. 4) built in two separate sections or two separate towers, the fresh solution being sprayed down to meet the incoming gas in the upper section and air being blown upward countercurrently to the fouled solution in the lower section. Here the H_2S is not recovered, being largely diluted with the air used in the activator, though sometimes the discharged air is piped to a boiler to furnish air for combustion. H_2S removal is not complete, and the accompanying atmospheric pollution has caused several plants to change to other processes.

All the other processes discussed before have the common disadvantage that the H_2S is lost, which caused the development of the following *regenerative processes which recover the hydrogen sulfide.* These methods all depend upon absorption of the H_2S in a weakly alkaline solution, followed by regeneration of the absorbing solution, usually by heating.

A recent modification of the Seaboard process is the *vacuum carbonate* process,[1] which is in use to remove H_2S from coal gas and oil refinery gases. The recovered hydrogen sulfide gas is in concentrated form and can be utilized for the production of sulfuric acid or elemental sulfur. The vacuum carbonate process employs either a soda ash or a potassium carbonate solution to absorb the H_2S from the gas and is somewhat similar in principle to the original *Seaboard* process. It differs from that process in that water vapor under vacuum is passed through the actifier instead of air to regenerate the solution. Sufficient heat is added to the bottom of the actifier to produce the required volume of water vapor and the water vapor is condensed from the vapors leaving the top of the actifier to separate it from the hydrogen sulfide. A two-stage steam-jet ejector maintains the necessary vacuum on the system and propels the recovered H_2S gas to the point of utilization. Additional condensers after each of the steam jets are provided to condense the amount of steam that enters through the jets. These steps are illustrated by Fig. 1. It will be noted that the equipment includes a heat exchanger[2] to obtain the heat required by the actifier from the waste heat present in the flushing liquor that is normally recirculated through the gas-collecting mains of coke ovens. By this means, a major reduction of steam costs is obtained, and, incidentally, the primary gas coolers of the coke plant are relieved of part of their load and their water consumption is reduced. For costs, see Table 4. Soda ash solution is cheaper, but potassium carbonate solutions can also be used. When the H_2S content of the gas is higher, stronger solutions are needed and the use of the more soluble potash is advantageous.

[1] Leech, W. A., Jr., and F. D. Schreiber, Sulfuric Acid from Coke Oven Gas, *Iron Steel Engr.,* **23** (12), 93–101 (1946).

[2] Gollmar, U.S. Pat. 2464805 (1949).

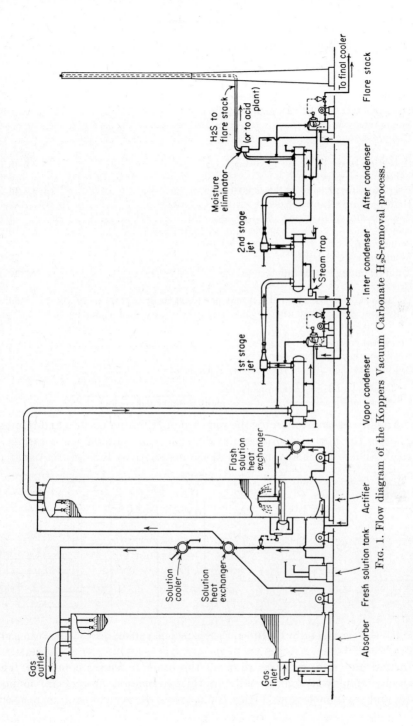

Gas outlet

Gas inlet

Solution cooler

Solution heat exchanger

Flash solution heat exchanger

1st stage jet

2nd stage jet

Steam trap

Moisture eliminator

H_2S to flare stack

(or to acid plant)

To final cooler

Absorber   Fresh solution tank   Actifier   Vapor condenser   Inter condenser   After condenser   Flare stack

Fig. 1. Flow diagram of the Koppers Vacuum Carbonate H_2S-removal process.

Plant capacity, standard cu. ft. per day	55,000,000
Type of gas	Coke oven
Sulfur content of inlet gas, grains H_2S per 100 cu. ft	500
Sulfur removal, per cent	90
Gas pressure, in. of water column	20
	Per day
Operating labor: 24 hr. at $2 per hr	$ 48.00
Laboratory supervision	6.00
Electric power: 3,645 kw.-hr. at $0.01 per kw.-hr	36.45
High-pressure steam: 186,000 lb. at $0.70 per M lb	130.00
Low-pressure steam: 9,600 lb. at $0.50 per M lb	4.80
Average cooling water:[b] 1,300,000 gal. at $0.015 per M gal	19.50
Sodium carbonate: 400 lb. at $0.02 per lb	8.00
Maintenance	75.00
Total operating cost before credits	$327.75
Credits:	
Purifying coke-oven gas at 1.0 cent per 1,000 cu. ft	550.00
Recovered H_2S when used to make sulfur or sulfuric acid 35,400 lb. at 1.0 cent	354.00
Total credits	$904.00
Net operating credit per day	$576.25
Net operating credit per 1,000 cu. ft. of gas, cents	1.05

[a] Courtesy of Koppers Company, Inc.

[b] Adjusted for water saved at coke-plant primary gas cooler.

The process most used for the removal of H_2S from natural and refinery gases is the Girbotol process developed by the Girdler Corporation in 1930.[1] There are many more of these installations for the treatment of

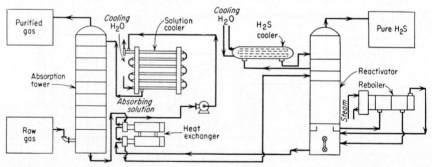

FIG. 2. Gas purification by the Girbotol aliphatic amine absorption process. For quantities, see Table 5.

natural and refinery gases than all the other processes combined. The amines employed commercially in this absorption process are mono-, di-, and triethanolamine. Figure 2 illustrates the type of equipment used.

[1] REED, Improved Design, Operating Techniques, for Girbotol Absorption Processes, *Petroleum Processing*, **2** (12), 907 (1947).

TABLE 5. GIRBOTOL ABSORPTION PROCESS[a]

	Plant A, high-sulfur refinery gas	Plant B, low-sulfur refinery gas near its dew point	Plant C, natural gas purification	Plant D, natural gas purification and dehydration
Gas rate, million standard cu. ft. per day.....	4.59	5.28	8.00	10.55
Gas temperature, °F......................	90	155	74	61
Absorber pressure, lb. per sq. in.............	100	290	400	400
Apparent inlet H₂S content, grains per 100 standard cu. ft[b]........................	2188	304	163	135
Apparent outlet H₂S content, grains per 100 standard cu. ft[b]........................	80	9		
Actual outlet H₂S content, grains per 100 standard cu. ft.........................	11	......	0	0
Solution rate, gal. per min..................	75	21.4	22.5	13.4
Amine content of solution, per cent..........	9.5[c]	13.5[c]	5.6[d]	11.1[d]
H₂S content of lean solution, grains per gal...	35	16	34	8
H₂S content of rich solution, grains per gal...	910	586	492	847
Steam for reactivation, lb. per hr............	2860	606	......	785
Pounds of steam per lb. of H₂S removed......	4.8	6.6	......	9.2
Reboiler steam pressure, lb. per sq. in........	7	10	7	37
Reactivator pressure, lb. per sq. in..........	2	6	1	1
Temperature of solution entering absorber, °F.	88	140	93	78
Temperature of solution leaving absorber, °F..	89	149	82	60
Temperature of solution entering reactivator, °F...................................	195	206	176	194
Temperature of solution leaving reactivator, °F...................................	223	232	215	265
Amine make-up, lb. per day[e]...............	7	15	......	1
Dew point lowering, °F....................	......	......	......	35

[a] STORRS, Cost of Hydrogen Sulfide Removal from Refinery and Sour Natural Gases, *Ind. Eng. Chem.*, *News Ed.*, **17**, 627 (1939).

[b] Including mercaptans.

[c] Per cent diethanolamine by weight.

[d] Per cent monoethanolamine by weight.

[e] Total losses including vaporization, chemical and mechanical, over a measurable period.

While the early available triethanolamine was the first to be used, it has been largely replaced by the others. Monoethanolamine has a greater capacity per unit volume of solution than diethanolamine for absorption of acid gas and the initial plant investment and operating cost is lower. However, it is rather difficult to make general statements on the selection of amines for gas purification. Diethanolamine as a 10 to 20 per cent aqueous solution is commonly employed for H_2S removal from refinery gases. For desulfurization of natural gas a 10 to 30 per cent aqueous solution of monoethanolamine is normally used. The ethanolamines differ in their selectivity for absorption of H_2S and CO_2 and this property, as well as oxygen and sulfur compounds present in a gas stream frequently determine the choice between monoethanolamine and diethanolamine. For example, in treating refinery gas diethanolamine is selected when carbon oxysulfide is known to be present as this amine does not react so readily as monoethanolamine with this impurity to form nonregenerable compounds. If simultaneous *dehydration* and desulfurization is desired, natural gas may be scrubbed with a combination solution consisting of amine, water, and diethylene glycol. Solution compositions for this purpose are from 10 to 36 per cent monoethanolamine, 45 to 85 per cent diethylene glycol, with the remainder water. The general reaction of amines with H_2S which is reversible on heating may be expressed as

$$2RNH_2 + H_2S \rightleftarrows (RNH_3)_2S$$

The apparatus consists of a bubble-cap absorption tower, a bubble-cap stripping tower, and various pumps, condensers, and heat exchangers. The principles of a bubble-cap tower are shown by Fig. 4 and explained by Perry.[1] The fouled liquid from the absorber passes through the heat exchangers to the stripper where it meets rising steam and is heated to about 250°F., and has its content of H_2S and other gases removed. The engineering aspects are presented in Table 5. Storrs[2] points out that the total cost of such purification "ranges from less than 0.5 cent per 1,000 standard cubic feet for natural gas with low hydrogen sulfide content to 2 cents per 1,000 standard cubic feet for refinery gas with unusually high hydrogen sulfide concentrations."

The Shell *tripotassium phosphate process* uses the same general flow scheme, and employs a 30 per cent solution of the salt. It depends for regeneration upon a pH shift in the solution at elevated temperatures. The system is more or less selective to H_2S in the presence of CO_2. For maximum efficiency a split flow cycle is employed. This requires a greater capital outlay and increased cost of utilities. Offsetting this somewhat is the lower volatility of the absorbent, which results in a lower solution make-up and permits the use of live steam for stripping in place of the reboiler, if so desired.

The regenerative processes described above recover hydrogen sulfide. In cases where the H_2S cannot be used, it is burned and the SO_2 dissipated to the atmosphere. In certain locations the H_2S content of a natural gas or refinery gas is sufficiently high that it is economically

[1] PERRY, *op. cit.*, pp. 597, 602, 550*ff.*, 752.

[2] STORRS, Cost of Hydrogen Sulfide Removal from Refinery and Sour Natural Gases, *Ind. Eng. Chem.*, *News Ed.*, Table 2, **17**, 627 (1939).

feasible to recover and market the sulfur in connection with the gas-purification plant operation. The modified Claus process is sometimes used for converting H_2S into elemental sulfur. This involves removing water from the gas which then enters the combustion furnace. The reactions which take place in the furnace are very complex, but an over-all reaction may be postulated as

$$H_2S + \tfrac{1}{2}O_2 \rightarrow S + H_2O$$

The volume of air is manually controlled to provide the correct amount for complete combustion of the hydrocarbons present and oxidation of the H_2S to sulfur. A sulfur of 99.97 purity may be obtained.

Another sulfur-recovery process[1] from high percentage H_2S involves the separate oxidation of one-third of the H_2S to SO_2 and the following reaction:

$$2H_2S + SO_2 \rightarrow 3S + 2H_2O$$

With modern control instrumentation, such a process is made to proceed with only one inspection every few hours.

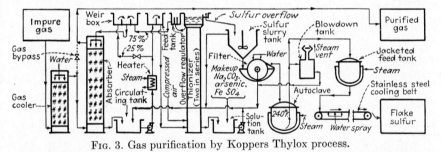

Fig. 3. Gas purification by Koppers Thylox process.

The *Thylox process*,[2] unlike the other regenerative processes described, recovers sulfur directly instead of H_2S. It is also unique since the scrubbing solution is regenerated by air oxidation rather than heating. This results in the formation in the solution of an elemental sulfur suspension. The sulfur is removed by flotation and is filtered and dried (Fig. 3). The reagent starts with an aqueous solution of arsenious oxide (about 7 grams per liter) in soda ash. The main reactions are

Absorption:

$$Na_4As_2S_5O_2 + H_2S \rightarrow Na_4As_2S_6O + H_2O$$

Regeneration:

$$Na_4As_2S_6O + \tfrac{1}{2}O_2 \rightarrow Na_4As_2S_5O_2 + S$$

[1] ANON., Sulfur from H_2S, *Chem. Eng.*, **59** (10), 210 (1952), pictured flow sheet; *cf.* SAWYER, *et al.*, Sulfur from Sour Gases, *Ind. Eng. Chem.*, **42**, 1938 (1950), modified Claus-Chance.

[2] FARQUHAR, Sulfur Removal from Coke Oven Gas, *Chem. & Met. Eng.*, **51** (7), 94, 130 (1944), pictured flow sheet.

The original processes used in this country to produce precipitated sulfur are known as the *Ferrox* and the *nickel* processes. It is believed that all these installations have been converted to the newer Thylox process which is more economical and produces a larger yield (see Table 6).

TABLE 6. OPERATING COST OF THE THYLOX PROCESS[a]

Type of gas...	Refinery
Capacity, standard cu. ft. gas per day...................	5,000,000
Sulfur content, grains H_2S per 100 cu. ft.................	1,000
Sulfur removal, per cent...............................	98
Gas pressure, lb. per sq. in. gage.......................	60
	Per day
Labor: 12 hr. at $2 per hr............................	$24.00
Power: 1,200 kw.-hr. at $0.01 per kw.-hr.................	12.00
Steam: 15,000 lb. at $0.50 per M lb.....................	7.50
Soda ash: 1,600 lb. at $0.02 per lb......................	32.00
Arsenic trioxide: 150 lb. at $0.075 per lb..........	11.25
Maintenance...	3.00
Total..	$89.75
Operating cost per 1,000 cu. ft. gas, cents................	1.8
Credit for sulfur, 2.5 tons at $25.......................	$62.50
Net operating cost....................................	$27.25
Net cost per 1,000 cu. ft. gas, cents.....................	0.55

[a] Courtesy of Koppers Company, Inc.

COAL GAS

The processes for the distillation of coal are discussed in Chap. 6. Here will be given merely an outline of the treatment of the gas obtained

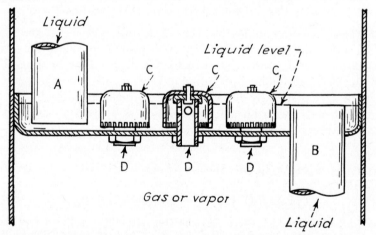

FIG. 4. Bubble-cap column, cross section. *A* is the downcomer bringing liquid from plate above. *B* is the downcomer for plate below. *C* represents the bubble caps for intimately mixing the vapor entering at *D* with the liquid flowing across plate. Frequently a baffle is placed between a downcomer and an adjacent bubble cap.

from the distillation. Such gases come either from retorts or more usually from chemical-recovery coke ovens. The co-products in the hydraulic main first go via the foul main through a primary condenser and a baffled tar extractor as shown in Fig. 3 of Chap. 6, where the coal gas[1] is separated from the ammonia liquor and the coal tar. The gas has its ammonia removed as ammonium sulfate by bubbling through sulfuric acid in a lead-lined saturator. The coal-tar products such as benzene, toluene, and some naphthalene are scrubbed by straw oil in a packed light-oil tower or scrubber. The final steps of sulfur purification are similar to those described above under Natural Gas. The uses of coal gas are also parallel to those of natural gas. Present experimentation on a pilot-plant scale is undertaking controlled underground gasification of coal in Alabama. Many people believe this may open a way to the profitable use of impure coal and seams too thin to mine, besides allowing a more complete recovery of coal than mining now affords.

WATER GAS (BLUE GAS)

Water gas,[2] often called *blue gas* because of the color of the flame when it is burned, finds important usage as a heating gas for coke ovens and as a low B.t.u. gas for diluting natural, oil, or coal gas. After mixing with oil gas, carbureted water gas results, which is widely sold for domestic consumption. Blue gas also serves as a step in making hydrogen (see Chap. 8). The production of water gas is carried out by the reaction[3] of steam on incandescent coke or coal at a temperature around 1000°C. (1830°F.) and higher where the rate and equilibrium are favorable, according to the principal equation:

$$C(amorph.) + H_2O(g) \rightarrow CO(g) + H_2(g); \qquad \Delta H_{1832°F.} = +53,850 \text{ B.t.u.}$$

This reaction also occurs apparently at several hundred degrees lower temperature:

$$C(amorph.) + 2H_2O(g) \rightarrow CO_2(g) + 2H_2(g); \quad \Delta H_{1832°F.} = +39,350 \text{ B.t.u.}$$

These reactions are endothermic and, therefore, tend to cool off the coke bed rather rapidly, thus necessitating alternate "run" and "blow" periods. During the run period, the foregoing blue-gas reactions take

---

[1] Operating results on coal gas are given in Table 17, p. 1582, of Perry, *op. cit.*

[2] PERRY, *op. cit.*, pp. 1576, 1579–1582. See p. 1580 particularly for discussion of efficiencies, heat losses, heat and material balances.

[3] PARKER, A Thermal Study of the Process of Manufacture of Water Gas, *J. Soc. Chem. Ind.*, **46**, 72T (1927); SCOTT, Mechanism of the Steam-carbon Reaction, *Ind. Eng. Chem.*, **33**, 1279 (1941). For rate and equilibrium results, see FULWEILER, pp. 617–619, in "Rogers' Manual of Industrial Chemistry," D. Van Nostrand Company, Inc., New York, 1942; LOWRY, "Chemistry of Coal Utilization," Vol. II, pp. 1673–1749, John Wiley & Sons, Inc., New York, 1945.

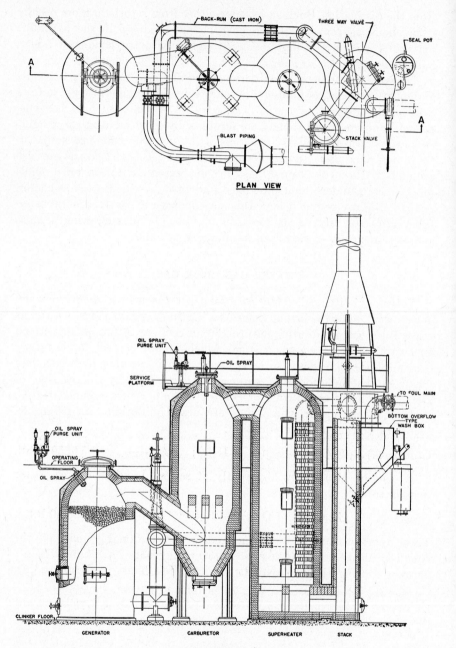

PLAN VIEW

ELEVATION - SECTION A-A

FIG. 5. Reverse-flow water-gas machine for light- or heavy-oil operation. (*Courtesy of Semet-Solvay Engineering Corp.*)

TABLE 7. BREAKDOWN OF FOUR-MINUTE CYCLE ON REVERSE-FLOW CARBURETED
WATER-GAS MACHINE OF FIG. 5[a]

(Fuel is bituminous coal)

Operation	Per cent	Seconds	Detail
Blow............	30	72	Primary air is admitted at base of generator and passes up through fuel bed for the purpose of bringing the carbon up to gas-making temperature. Secondary air is admitted into the large connection between the generator and carburetor to complete combustion of blast gases. This heats, to the highest temperature, the arches in lower part of carburetor. The blast gases pass up the carburetor, down the superheater, and up and out the stack, losing much of their heat to the brickwork as they pass.
Blowrun.........	5	12	The function of the blowrun, which is used generally when bituminous coal is the generator fuel, is to recover as much of the volatiles from the coal as possible and to prevent overheating of the carburetor and superheater. This blowrun is usually carried on immediately after the blow when the fire is at its highest temperature and the blast gases contain the highest per cent of CO, and volatiles from the coal are passing off at a high rate. The blowrun is accomplished by closing the secondary air valve and the stack valve and allowing this mixture of coal gas and producer gas to pass through the machine and into the washbox and out to the holder as make gas. Usually the blowrun is longer after a fresh fuel charge has been put in the generator, the length of the blowrun being decreased each run until a new charge is made.
Uprun...........	30	72	Steam is admitted at the base of the generator and passes up through the red-hot coke or coal, forming blue gas. Oil spraying into the carburetor begins 5 sec. after start of uprun, thus causing all oil cracking to take place in an atmosphere of blue gas. Oil gas is formed by the pyrolysis of the oil entering countercurrent into the uprising hot blue gas and from heat of radiation. The blue and oil gases mix and pass on to the superheater where the pyrolysis of the gasified oil is continued and the gases fixed (or made permanent).
Backrun.........	33	79	This replaces the old downrun as steam is now admitted in the bottom of superheater, passing up the superheater where it is heated, down the carburetor, reacting with the red-hot carbon on the carburetor arches deposited from oil cracking, further reacting with coal or carbon in generator, finally passing out of the bottom of generator directly through the cast-iron backrun pipe through the three-way valve into the washbox. Sometimes additional oil is sprayed into top of generator during this backrun to supply carbon for main blue gas reaction if oil is cheaper than coal, and also to furnish more low-gravity oil gas (rich in hydrogen) particularly when employing a high percentage of blowrun in the make gas.
Final uprun......	2	5	This short uprun makes a purge unnecessary. It puts a blanket of steam between the blue gas in base of generator and the air that follows. This leaves carburetor and superheater filled with backrun steam to be exhausted to atmosphere.

[a] DORMER, Experience with Nine-foot Reverse Flow Water Gas Machine, Mid-West Gas Association School, Iowa State College, Ames, Iowa, September, 1941; *private communication* from Semet Solvay Engineering Corp.

place and salable or *make* gas results; during the blow period, air is introduced and ordinary combustion ensues, thus reheating the coke to incandescence and supplying the B.t.u.'s required by the endothermic useful gas-making reactions plus the various heat losses of the system. The reactions are

$$C(amorph.) + O_2(g) \rightarrow CO_2(g); \qquad \Delta H_{1832°F.} = -173,930 \text{ B.t.u.}$$
$$CO_2(g) + C(amorph.) \rightarrow 2CO(g); \qquad \Delta H_{1832°F.} = +68,400 \text{ B.t.u.}$$

The generator itself consists of a steel shell lined with a refractory as depicted in Fig. 5. It has doors at the top and bottom for the addition of fuel and the removal of ash. Air for blow or blasting enters at the grate level, and there is provision for the entrance of steam and the removal of gas at both the top and the bottom. The usual cycle is of 4 to 6 min. in length, of which 25 per cent should be blow for usual operation. The run period is generally split into "uprun" and "downrun" periods. In such, the first part is usually an uprun with the steam being admitted at the bottom and the gas being removed at the top; this is then reversed to a downrun and finally reversed again to give sufficient uprun to clear the ashpit of gas just before the blow. The ratio of uprun to downrun varies considerably with type of fuel. Materials[1] used in making 1,000 cu. ft. of water gas from coke are: coke, dry, 34.7 lb.; air for blast, 2,230 cu. ft.; steam, 51.9 lb.

New developments for the continuous manufacture of water gas from solid carbonaceous fuels treated simultaneously with water and oxygen are now in progress because of recent reductions in cost of tonnage oxygen.[2] Blue water gas or *synthesis gas*, as it is called, is usually identified with synthetic fuels, or the synthesis of other chemicals such as alcohols and oxygenated compounds. This mixture of CO and H_2 is also a step in low-cost hydrogen for ammonia (see Chaps. 8 and 20) and other hydrogenations. Because of its low B.t.u. value, synthesis gas is usually an expensive fuel gas. Another approach to synthesis gas[3] involves oxidizing pulverized coal in mixture of steam and oxygen.

For city gas, where it is desired to enhance[4] the heating value of water gas, oil[5] is atomized into the hot blue gas. A plant producing this *carbureted blue gas* has, in addition to the ordinary generator, a carburetor and

[1] MORRIS, Carbonization of Coal with Blue Gas and Producer Gas, *Am. Gas Assoc. 4th Ann. Convention, Tech. Sec.*, **4**, 21 (1922).

[2] POWELL, Symposium on Production of Synthesis Gas, *Ind. Eng. Chem.*, **40**, 558 (1948); MARTIN, Synthesis Gas from Coal, *Chem. Ind.*, **66**, 365 (1950).

[3] ANON., Du Pont Tries New Route to Synthesis Gas, *Chem. Eng.*, **61** (3), 114 (1954).

[4] VITTINGHOFF, The Manufacture of High B.t.u. Carbureted Water Gas, *Gas Age*, **81** (12), 23 (1938); HULL and KOHLHOFF, Oil Gas Manufacture, *Ind. Eng. Chem.*, **44**, 936 (1952), flow sheet.

[5] This is not to be confused with the manufacture of fuel gases from oils. *Cf.* HULL and KOHLHOFF, Oil Gas Manufacture, *Ind. Eng. Chem.*, **44**, 936 (1952).

a superheater as shown in Fig. 5. These are also large refractory-lined steel shells with brick checkerwork, at least in the superheater to provide intensive heat-transfer surfaces. The combustion gases formed during the blow period serve to heat the arches, side walls, and the checkerwork. Then, during the run, oil is sprayed into the carburetor, is cracked or pyrolyzed, and is passed on mixed with the water gas. In most cases it is necessary to have tar traps to remove the heavy water-gas tar formed during the vaporization of the oil.

One of the newer installations producing 520 to 540 B.t.u. per cu. ft. of gas, using 23 to 25 lb. of coal and 2.7 to 3.1 gal. of heavy oil per M cu. ft. (1,000 cu. ft.), is detailed in Fig. 5 and Table 7. This is one answer to the demand for economically manufactured gas for city consumption wherein the use of low-priced bituminous coal and heavy oils is efficient. The carburetor is *not* filled with checkerwork but is provided with arches only; thus, a source of trouble is avoided when heavy petroleum oils are used which fill up and block checkerwork with the coke formed and reduce the heat transfer. The plant of Fig. 5 is called a *reverse-flow* water-gas machine because the usual flow of gas through the carburetor and super-heater is reversed by elevating the carburetor somewhat and changing the flues. This causes better pyrolysis of the carburetor oil as it is sprayed in countercurrent to the hot blue gas and permits the use of cheaper, heavier oils; this also results in better heat balance and lessened repairs from carbon blocks or stoppages.

PRODUCER GAS[1]

Producer gas is made by passing air and steam through a thick bed of hot fuel. The primary purpose of the steam (25 to 30 per cent of the weight of the coke) is to use up as much as possible of the exothermic energy from the reaction between carbon and oxygen to supply the endothermic reaction between the carbon and steam. The reactions[2] may be written as follows:

$$C(amorph.) + O_2(g) \rightarrow CO_2(g); \quad \Delta H_{60°F.} = -174,600 \text{ B.t.u.} \quad (1)$$

$$CO_2(g) + C(amorph.) \rightarrow 2CO(g); \quad \Delta H_{60°F.} = +70,200 \text{ B.t.u.} \quad (2)$$

$$C(amorph.) + H_2O(l) \rightarrow CO(g) + H_2(g); \quad \Delta H_{60°F.} = +70,900 \text{ B.t.u.} \quad (3)$$

$$C(amorph.) + 2H_2O(l) \rightarrow CO_2(g) + 2H_2(g); \quad \Delta H_{60°F.} = +71,600 \text{ B.t.u.} \quad (4)$$

$$CO(g) + H_2O(l) \rightarrow CO_2(g) + H_2(g); \quad \Delta H_{60°F.} = +700 \text{ B.t.u.} \quad (5)$$

[1] PERRY, *op. cit.*, pp. 1576, 1579; LOWRY, *op. cit.*, pp. 1586–1672.

[2] Equilibrium and rate conditions for these reactions are given by Fulweiler, *op. cit.*, p. 737.

The initial reaction in the producer is the formation of the CO_2 and $N_2(1)$. As the gases progress up the bed, the initial CO_2 is reduced to $CO(2)$ and the water vapor (made from liquid water in jacket) is partly decomposed to give H_2, CO, and CO_2. The allowable temperature of the fuel bed, which depends on the fusion point of the fuel ash, usually ranges from

Fig. 6. Typical arrangement of the Semet-Solvay Koller-type gas producer when gasifying coke or anthracite coal.

1800 to 2800°F., while the minimum bed height ranges from 2 to 6 ft. for most of the commonly used fuels.

The three main points observed in designing and operating a producer are: (1) the exposed fuel surface should be large and kept uniform, (2) the time of contact between gas and fuel should be as long as possible, (3) the temperature should be as high as economical. Producers are usually large, refractory-lined or water-jacketed steel shells with a gas outlet and fuel distributor at the top and a steam-air tuyère inlet and ash-removal system at the bottom. A modern gas producer is shown in Fig. 6. Here the firebrick lining has been superseded by a heavy steel inner wall with a water jacket. This prevents side-wall clinker and also furnishes hot water or steam at 5 lb. pressure for mixing with the air. Figure 6 depicts a rotating grate for continuous ash removal and for helping to maintain the even distribution of the coke. In operating a producer, either a regenerator or a recuperator should be used to transfer the heat from the outgoing gases to the incoming air. A regenerator recovers heat by alternate passing of the hot and cold gases through a checkerwork, while a recuperator operates by the continuous passage of the two gases through adjacent flues. For both producer-gas and water-gas plants, a waste-heat boiler is a valuable adjunct.

Producer gas is a cheap, low B.t.u. fuel gas used for all types of industrial heating purposes near where the gas is generated, a prime example being its application to heat coke ovens and other furnaces. The producer-gas reaction also serves as one of the basic reactions in making ammonia (see Chap. 20). Producer-gas manufacture with low-cost tonnage oxygen is also showing important new possibilities along with water gas.

LIQUEFIED PETROLEUM GASES

Liquid propane and butane gas are extensively employed as stand-by gases and peak-load supplements to municipal and industrial[1] systems using natural and manufactured gas. The petrochemical industry is the second largest consumer (Chap. 37). When added as a supplementary gas, the propane or butane is mixed with air in order to give satisfactory performance in customer appliances adjusted to the base gas. Detroit has 96 holders containing 30,000 gal. each to ease its peak loads and to enrich the heat content of its own product as do Chicago and New York. Over 400 small-town utilities have found it more profitable to convert from manufactured gas to liquefied petroleum gas exclusively. Since butane (3,270 B.t.u. per cu. ft.) will not vaporize below 31°F., it is preferred in the South, while propane (2,520 B.t.u. per cu. ft.) will vaporize down to −44°F. and is used in the North. Sometimes a mixture of these two is employed.

Liquid petroleum gas comes from the ground as a constituent of wet natural gas or crude oil or as a by-product from refining. For example, a gasoline plant treats raw "wet" natural gas by absorption, separating the usable fractions as depicted by Fig. 2 of Chap. 37.

[1] JAMISON, Liquefied Petroleum Gas—Industry's Standby, *Chem. Eng.*, **57** (5), 117 (1950).

SELECTED REFERENCES

Meade, A., "Modern Gas Works Practice," Ernest Benn, Ltd., London, 1921.

Morgan, J. J., "A Textbook of American Gas Practice," Vol. 1, Production of Manufactured Gas, J. J. Morgan, Maplewood, N.J., 1931.

Perry, editor-in-chief, "Chemical Engineers' Handbook," 3d ed., pp. 1575–1596, McGraw-Hill Book Company, Inc., New York, 1950.

Haslam, Robert T., and Robert P. Russell, "Fuels and Their Combustion," McGraw-Hill Book Company, Inc., New York, 1926.

American Gas Association, 420 Lexington Ave., New York. See various yearly *Proceedings*.

"Gas Chemists' Handbook," 3d ed., American Gas Association, 420 Lexington Ave., New York, 1929.

"Combustion," American Gas Association, 420 Lexington Ave., New York, 1932.

"Gaseous Fuels," American Gas Association, 420 Lexington Ave., New York, 1948.

Furnas, C. C., editor, "Rogers' Manual of Industrial Chemistry," 6th ed., Chaps. 15 and 18, pp. 578 and 736, by W. H. Fulweiler, D. Van Nostrand Company, Inc., New York, 1942.

Gumz, Wilhelm, "Gas Producers and Blast Furnaces," John Wiley & Sons, Inc., New York, 1950.

Lowry, H. H., editor, "The Chemistry of Coal Utilization," 2 vols., John Wiley & Sons, Inc., New York, 1945.

Huntington, R. L., "Natural Gas and Natural Gasoline," McGraw-Hill Book Company, Inc., New York, 1950.

Kirk, R. E., and D. F. Othmer, "Encyclopedia of Chemical Technology," Interscience Encyclopedia, Inc., New York, 1947.

Battelle Memorial Institute, J. F. Foster and R. J. Lund, editors, "Economics of Fuel Gas from Coal," McGraw-Hill Book Company, Inc., New York, 1950.

CHAPTER 8

INDUSTRIAL GASES

The industrial gases are important for many specific uses. As a class they have already become among the most vital raw materials for the chemical industry. Every day, new uses are being developed by aggressive researchers and trained sales personnel of the manufacturing companies.

CARBON DIOXIDE

Carbon dioxide in liquid and solid forms has been known for over a century. Although Thilorier produced solid carbon dioxide in 1835 from the liquid material, it was not until 1924 that the solid product gained industrial importance by its first and still most important use for refrigeration. This industry has grown rapidly, and in 1953 there were 179,230 tons of liquid and gaseous carbon dioxide and 554,109 tons of solid manufactured.

Uses. By far the largest use[1] of the solid form is for refrigerating ice cream, meat, and other foods. It has an added advantage in that a carbon dioxide atmosphere reduces meat and food bacteria spoilage. The solid form is also important as a source of carbon dioxide for inert atmospheres and occasionally for carbonated beverages. There are many other specialty uses such as chilling aluminum rivets and shrink-fitting of machine parts. The largest outlet of liquid carbon dioxide is for carbonated beverages. It is also important as a fire-extinguishing material. Gaseous carbon dioxide has many applications in the chemical industry such as in the making of salicylic acid (Chap. 39) and as a raw material for soda ash (Chap. 15).

Carbon dioxide has advantages over ordinary acids for neutralizing alkalies because it is easily shipped in solid form, is noncorrosive in nature, and is light in weight. Chemically it is equivalent to more than twice its shipping weight in sulfuric acid or about five times its weight in hydrochloric acid. In respect to food refrigeration, solid carbon dioxide is primarily a transport refrigerant. Its advantages cannot be attributed to any one single factor but result from its dryness, its relatively high specific gravity, its excellent refrigerating effect, its low

---

[1] KIRK and OTHMER, *op. cit.*, Vol. 3, p. 139.

temperature, and the insulating and desiccating action of the gas evolved. Generally around 1,000 lb. of solid carbon dioxide will refrigerate an average car for a transcontinental rail trip without recharging. A similar load of water ice would require 3,700 lb. initially plus several supplemental chargings along the way.

Manufacture of Pure CO_2. Although there are many sources of carbon dioxide, the following three are the most important for commercial production:

1. Flue gases which result from burning carbonaceous material and contain about 10 to 18 per cent carbon dioxide.

2. By-product from the fermentation industries through dextrose breakdown into alcohol and carbon dioxide, the gas containing about 99 per cent carbon dioxide.

3. By-product of limekiln[1] operation where carbonates are calcined to the oxides; the gases analyze from 10 to 40 per cent CO_2.

TABLE 1. COMPARISON OF PHYSICAL PROPERTIES OF SOLID CO_2 AND WATER ICE

	Solid CO_2	Water ice
Specific gravity	1.56	0.90
Sublimation point or melting point	−109.6°F.	32°F.
Critical temperature	88.43°F.	689°F.
Critical pressure	1,071 lb. abs.	2,860.6 lb. abs. at 32°F.
Latent heat of fusion, lb	82.0 B.t.u.	144 B.t.u.
Latent heat of vaporization, lb	158.6 B.t.u.	1,074.29 B.t.u. at 2°F.
Weight of gas, cu. ft	0.117 lb.	0.000304 lb.
Weight solid, cu. ft	90 lb.	57 lb.
Latent heat of sublimation, lb	248 B.t.u.	
Refrigerating effect, lb	275 B.t.u.	144 B.t.u.

An absorption system is used for concentrating the CO_2 gas obtained in (1) and (3) to over 99 per cent. In all cases the almost pure carbon dioxide must be given various chemical treatments for the removal of the minor impurities which contaminate the gas. One of the reactions[2] for the concentration of the carbon dioxide is

$$Na_2CO_3 + CO_2 + H_2O \rightleftarrows 2NaHCO_3$$

[1] ORR, Byproduct CO_2 Builds a New Refrigerant Business, *Chem. & Met. Eng.*, **40**, 250 (1933); ANON., Carbon Dioxide from Limekiln Gases, *Chem. & Met. Eng.*, **46**, 97 (1939), flow sheets.

[2] PERRY, *op. cit.*, pp. 677–679. Here are given equations for the partial pressure of CO_2 together with references to original work. *Cf.* Gas Absorption in PERRY, *op. cit.*, particularly pp. 703–705. SHERWOOD and PIGFORD, "Absorption and Extraction," pp. 354–368, 2d ed., McGraw-Hill Book Company, Inc., New York, 1952; QUINN and JONES, "Carbon Dioxide," Reinhold Publishing Corporation, New York, 1936.

This reaction is forced to the right by increasing the partial pressure of the CO_2 and by reducing the temperature. It is forced to the left by heating up the sodium bicarbonate solution. The absorption efficiency of 18 per cent CO_2 is not very good as the quantities of Fig. 1 indicate. This absorption could be increased by use of another absorbing tower. However the CO_2 available in this case comes from the combustion of carbon in a boiler plant generating the required steam; it happens that the steam is the critical, expensive, and controlling item. To carry out

CARBON DIOXIDE (SOLID OR LIQUID)

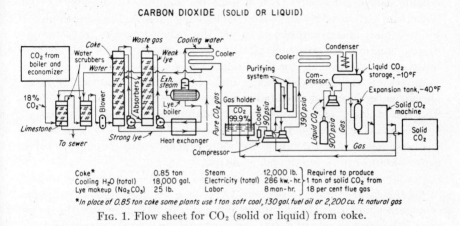

Coke*	0.85 ton	Steam	12,000 lb.	Required to produce
Cooling H₂O (total)	18,000 gal.	Electricity (total)	286 kw.-hr.	1 ton of solid CO₂ from
Lye makeup (Na₂CO₃)	25 lb.	Labor	8 man-hr.	18 per cent flue gas

*In place of 0.85 ton coke some plants use 1 ton soft coal, 130 gal. fuel oil or 2,200 cu. ft. natural gas

FIG. 1. Flow sheet for CO_2 (solid or liquid) from coke.

this manufacture, the principal *unit operations* (Op.) and *unit processes* (Pr.) that are necessary are detailed in the following tabulation:

Coke or other carbonaceous fuel burned, giving heat for steam and economizer, and furnishing 18 per cent CO_2 (Pr. and Op.).

Gas purified, cooled, and washed (Op.).

Gas reacted countercurrent forming $NaHCO_3$ solution from CO_2 and Na_2CO_3 solution (Pr.).

Concentrated (99.9 per cent) CO_2 boiled out of $NaHCO_3$ solution (Pr. and Op.).

CO_2 purified and dried (Pr.).

CO_2 compressed, cooled, and liquefied (Op.).

For "Dry Ice":

Liquid CO_2 subjected to reduction in pressure with consequent partial solidification (Op.).

Recirculation, with recompression and recooling of evaporated CO_2 (Op.).

CO_2 "snow" compressed to solid cake (Op.).

Dry Ice cakes sawed to shape (Op.).

A typical flow sheet, continuously producing either liquid or solid and embracing the sequences of these unit operations and unit processes, is shown in Fig. 1. In the merchandising of liquid carbon dioxide, the energy (and hence expense) involved in handling the cylinders, full and empty, is so great that this one fact has required the installation of many relatively small plants economically located in consuming centers. However, bulk shipment of relatively low-pressure liquid *cold*[1] carbon dioxide is now being practiced to save container cost and weight. Where pure carbon dioxide from fermentation, for example, is not available, the practice, largely conditioned by the energy balance, is to burn coke to furnish the necessary energy and the carbon dioxide at the same time. If heat exchangers are properly designed, it is necessary to buy but little outside energy for solid CO_2 and none for liquid CO_2 (see Fig. 1), the live steam generated by the coke boilers being sufficient to furnish power for pumping and compression, while the exhaust steam from steam-driven compressors will boil off the carbon dioxide from the sodium bicarbonate solution in the lye boiler. These coke plants are splendid examples of well-balanced energy and chemical requirements. It takes an efficiently designed coke boiler to generate 12,000 lb. of steam from 0.85 ton of coke. The temperature of combustion is so high in these special coke boilers when operated to furnish an 18 per cent CO_2 gas, that it has been economical to employ the more expensive but more serviceable carborundum bricks for the boiler setting.

In following Fig. 1, it should be observed that after the coke is burned in the boiler, producing 18 per cent CO_2, these hot gases pass through an economizer and then to the limestone water scrubbers where the gases are further cooled and the SO_2 and dust removed. In the meanwhile the "strong lye" (solution of $NaHCO_3$) after being warmed in the heat exchanger, is further warmed in the economizer (not shown in Fig. 1) before passing to the lye boiler where the $NaHCO_3$ is decomposed back to Na_2CO_3 by being boiled (about 245°F.) with the exhaust steam from the CO_2 compressors.

The concentrated (99.9 per cent) gas escapes through a rectifying section connected to the lye boiler body where it comes in contact with the entering hot strong lye from the economizer and the heat exchanger. The temperature of the entering lye is raised while the temperature of the gas is reduced. The gas is passed to a water cooler where the temperature is lowered further and the water-vapor content is greatly reduced. The condensate from the cooler returns to the weak lye circuit. The gas is collected in a gas holder.

From the first stage of compression the CO_2 passes to a purifying system, consisting of an oil separator and a scrubber containing $KMnO_4$ or $K_2Cr_2O_7$ solution which oxidizes organic impurities that would affect the taste. In the second purifying scrubber sulfuric acid, calcium chloride, silica gel, activated alumina, or activated bauxite dries the gas to prevent corrosion and freezing up of subsequent equipment.

[1] GETZ and GEERTZ, Transportation and Storage of Bulk Low-pressure Liquid Carbon Dioxide, *Ind. Eng. Chem.*, **33**, 1124 (1941).

The completely deodorized gas is further compressed[1] in a compressor driven by live steam from the coke boiler and delivering exhaust steam to the lye boiler. The first stage raises the pressure to 80 lb.; the second to 390 lb. A third compressor raises pressure to 900 lb., if liquid is desired. During compression, care should be taken to have very good cooling because the gas leaving the compressor may be above its critical temperature of 88.43°F. Therefore, it is passed first through a chiller and next to the third compression which is connected with the liquid filling stand. The gas charged into the cylinders as a liquid has a purity of at least 99.9 per cent, will not contain 0.1 per cent moisture, and is free of organic impurities.

The equipment used is almost all of steel, though the water limestone scrubbers are sometimes lined with concrete to lessen attack by aqueous sulfite. The absorbers are tall steel towers, 100 ft. high, with frequently placed steel platforms on which porous coke is supported to ensure good contact with the rising gases.

A very large source of carbon dioxide is the fermentation industry as described in Chap. 31. If yeast is used, alcohol and CO_2 are produced, while certain other microorganisms generate solvents and a gaseous mixture of H_2 and CO_2. The yield of CO_2 varies with the mode of fermentation. From starchy material, such as corn, there is obtained from 1 bushel, for example, $2\frac{1}{2}$ gal. of 190-proof ethyl alcohol and 17 lb. CO_2. The recovery and purification of CO_2 from fermentation differ from the absorption system, in that the temperature seldom exceeds 105°F., so that no special cooling is necessary and the CO_2 content of the gas starts usually above 99.5 per cent. When the fermentors are sealed for the recovery of the gases, a purer and higher yield of carbon dioxide per gallon of mash is obtained and the yield of alcohol is increased by at least 1 per cent by alcohol recovery from the CO_2 scrubbers.

A typical CO_2 recovery from fermentation follows the procedure of Reich[2] as illustrated in the flow sheet of Fig. 2. Here the purification consists of an oxidation of the organic impurities and a dehydration by means of chemicals in liquid form. The gas from the fermentors is passed through three scrubbers containing stoneware spiral packing and on to the gasometer. The first scrubber contains a weak alcoholic solution which acts as a preliminary purifier and removes most of the alcohol carried in the gas. The next two scrubbers, in which the scrubbing medium is deaerated water, remove almost all the water-soluble impuri-

[1] For flow diagrams with accompanying data, see KIRK and OTHMER, *op. cit.*, Vol. 3, pp. 134–135.

[2] REICH, Liquid CO_2—How Technology Has Harnessed Available Sources, *Chem. & Met. Eng.*, **38**, 136 (1931); REICH, Solid CO_2, Technology Defers to Distribution Problems, *Chem. & Met. Eng.*, **38**, 270 (1931). These articles include fundamental data, flow sheets, and temperatures of several processes.

ties. The scrubbing liquid is pumped either to the stills or to the fermentors for alcohol recovery.

From the gasometer the gas is conducted to a scrubber containing $K_2Cr_2O_7$ solution which oxidizes the aldehydes and alcohols in the gas, which is then cooled. In the second scrubber which contains sulfuric acid the oxidation is completed and the gas is dehydrated. The carbon dioxide leaving the acid scrubber contains some entrained acid which is removed in a tower filled with coke and over which a Na_2CO_3 solution is circulated. When the acid is neutralized, carbon dioxide is released. Before going to the compressor, the gas passes through a scrubber containing a small amount of glycerine which absorbs the oxidized products

FERMENTATION CO₂ PURIFICATION
(REICH PROCESS)

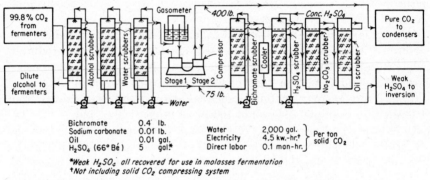

FIG. 2. Flow sheet on fermentation CO_2 purification—Reich process.

and delivers an odorless gas to the compressor. The sulfuric acid, after being used for deodorization and drying, is pumped to the distillery where it serves for the pH control in molasses fermentation.

There are a number of other methods for purifying carbon dioxide. Among them mention should be made of the *silica gel* process[1] wherein water and odors are removed from the partly compressed gas (80 lb.) by adsorption and the silica gel is revivified by heated air. The Backus process employs activated carbon for similar purposes but works on the uncompressed gas. The carbon is regenerated by heating with direct and indirect steam and finally is dried by hot air. Generally two sets of active carbon purifiers are employed so that while one is being "revivified" the other is in use to effect continuous operation.

Other *absorbing liquids* in addition to a soda ash solution are employed. Potassium carbonate offers slight advantages but it costs more than soda

---

[1] REICH, Liquid CO_2—How Technology Has Harnessed the Available Sources, *Chem. & Met. Eng.*, **38**, 140 (1931).

ash. However, still more expensive absorbents, namely, amino alcohols, are being used competitively because of their greater power to absorb CO$_2$ and the easier reversibility of this absorption. In particular is *mono-ethanolamine*[1] of industrial importance, because of its high rate of absorption for CO$_2$. It is being employed as a 10 to 20 per cent aqueous solution. Aqueous solutions of monoethanolamine are also used for the absorption of CO$_2$ from combustion gases as a step in making liquid CO$_2$. In some instances, solutions of monoethanolamine and diethylene glycol function to remove CO$_2$ and dehydrate the gases simultaneously.

Several factors determine the concentration of solutions of mono-ethanolamine. The more dilute the solution, the lower the evaporation and the mechanical losses. In most cases, the gases at atmospheric pressure are scrubbed in absorber towers packed with steel turnings, coke, or Raschig rings. Under these conditions a 10 to 15 per cent mono-ethanolamine solution will be concentrated enough to strip the CO$_2$ completely out of a combustion gas containing 12 to 15 per cent CO$_2$ when the minimum circulation rate necessary for good scrubbing is maintained. With this solution the quantity of CO$_2$ liberated per gallon of solution circulated, when scrubbing a gas at atmospheric pressure and temperature with about 15 per cent of CO$_2$, will be about 0.20 to 0.25 lb. The CO$_2$ is not completely removed from monoethanolamine solutions in commercial installations on boiling at atmospheric pressure, and the residual CO$_2$ content after reactivation amounts to about 0.012 lb. of CO$_2$ per gallon for each per cent of monoethanolamine present in the solution. By raising the operating pressure to about 40 lb. per sq. in. gage in order to increase the reactivator temperature to 140 or 145°C., this residual CO$_2$ can be almost completely removed from the mono-ethanolamine solutions by the effect of the higher temperature in dissociating the monoethanolamine carbonate. Under such conditions, net CO$_2$ removal rates as high as 0.88 lb. per gal. of solution have been obtained.[2]

With soda ash solutions under ordinary conditions the recovery will be from one-half to two-thirds of the 0.20 to 0.25 lb. mentioned above with the added necessity of using four or five times as much scrubbing contact between the flue gas and the soda ash solution and with more steam required for stripping the CO$_2$ from the solution. Less absorbing capacity is required for the amine than for sodium carbonate, but the recovery is the same in either case in a properly designed plant. It is

[1] MASON and DODGE, Equilibrium Absorption of Carbon Dioxide by Solutions of the Ethanolamines, *Trans. Am. Inst. Chem. Engrs.*, **32,** 27 (1936); *cf.* PERRY, *op. cit.*, pp. 677–678. This is the Girbotol process of the Girdler Corporation. See Chap. 7 under Fuel Gas Purification.

[2] *Private communication* from the Girdler Corporation. For plant, see pictured flow sheet in *Chem. & Met. Eng.*, **47,** 37 (1940).

possible to reduce the carbon dioxide in the exit gases to 1 per cent, but it is not always economical to do this.

The monoethanolamine solutions used for removing CO_2 from hydrogen are usually more concentrated than those used for recovering CO_2 from flue gases. The hydrogen is generally scrubbed at elevated pressures (up to about 250 lb. per sq in. gage), which proportionately reduces amine vaporization losses. Since bubble-plate absorbers are mostly employed, a wide range of solution circulation rates may be used. The CO_2 content of the hydrogen is usually fairly high (18 to 33 per cent), giving conditions that are favorable for high absorption capacities. In these plants the solution strength usually is kept between 20 and 30 per cent amine and the CO_2 liberated amounts to 0.35 to 0.40 lb. per gal. of solution circulated. This rate of CO_2 removal is obtained when the absorption is carried out so that the purified hydrogen will contain less than 0.1 per cent of CO_2.

One objection to the use of ethanolamine solutions is their corrosiveness due to their oxidation to glycine and oxalic acid, both compounds being corrosive to iron. The monoethanolamine is much less susceptible to oxidation than the di- and tri-compounds. Although usually all that is necessary is the continuous redistillation of a portion of the solution (discarding the residue), at times the entire solution has to be replaced by a new one. If a redistillation unit is used, it may be connected in series with the main regeneration unit; then the steam used for redistillation of the solution may be utilized in stripping CO_2 from the solution in the regeneration equipment.

Solid carbon dioxide[1] is manufactured from the chilled liquid, as outlined in Figs. 1 and 2. The return, or backblow gases, from the presses and the expansion bottles are recompressed. As required for the presses, chilled liquid is drawn through an expansion tank where the pressure is partly released in order to accomplish further cooling of the liquid (to −40°F.). The yield is increased from 25 to 50 per cent by precooling the liquid. The released gas passes to the second stage of the compressor. Liquid CO_2 from the expansion tank is then expanded through a nozzle into the press, provided with top and bottom rams.

The cycle of operation of the press is very simple. With the upper ram at the top and the lower ram closing the bottom of the expansion chamber, liquid CO_2 is admitted for a predetermined time until sufficient snow has formed. During this period, gas formed from expansion is conducted from the expansion chamber to the second stage of the compressor. The liquid feed is then cut off, and the residual pressure in the

---

[1] See KIRK and OTHMER, *op. cit.*, Vol. 3, pp. 136–139; REICH, Solid CO_2 Industry Thrives on Improved Production Methods, *Chem. Eng.*, **53** (1), 120 (1946), for flow charts and description.

expansion chamber is released to the gasometer. When this is done, the upper ram is lowered to compact the snow to a dense cake which has a specific gravity of about 1.5. The upper ram is raised and then the lower ram, on which rests the finished block, is lowered. The block is discharged, packed, and stored. Occasionally for solid CO_2, special purification is practiced on the partly compressed CO_2 by washing with $KMnO_4$ solution followed by a drying tower with either calcium chloride or sulfuric acid.

HYDROGEN

Uses and Economics. Hydrogen is an important and diverse raw material for the chemical industry. In the 4-year period ending with 1950,

TABLE 2. HYDROGEN REQUIRED FOR TYPICAL PRODUCTS[a]

Raw material except hydrogen	Product	Hydrogen required, cu. ft., 60°F.[b]	Raw material except hydrogen	Product	Hydrogen required, cu. ft., 60°F.[b]
Phenol......	Cyclohexanol	25,000	Olein............	Stearin	2,600
Nitrogen....	Ammonia	84,000	Diisobutylene....	Isooctane	6,700
Naphthalene.	Tetralin	12,000	Carbon monoxide.	Methanol	230

[a] STENGEL and SHREVE, Economic Aspects of Hydrogenation, *Ind. Eng. Chem.*, **32**, 1212 (1940).

[b] All hydrogen requirements are per ton of product except synthetic methanol (per gallon) and isooctane (per barrel).

hydrogen production rose from 20,000,000 to 45,163,000,000 cu. ft.; however, much of the hydrogen made is consumed in the producing plant itself and is not included in these census figures. The largest quantity is employed in the synthesis of ammonia, but the hydrogenation processes especially in the chemical, petroleum, and food industries consume important quantities. Table 2 compares amounts of hydrogen required for various hydrogenation[1] reactions. In addition to these chemical applications, hydrogen is very widely employed for welding and other heating processes. For such purposes the hydrogen is supplied in the form of a compressed gas in cylinders.

[1] An excellent presentation of the unit process of hydrogenation together with cost for producing hydrogen by different procedures is given by Fenske in his chapter on Hydrogenation, in GROGGINS, "Unit Processes in Organic Synthesis," 4th ed., McGraw-Hill Book Company, Inc., New York, 1952; *cf.* STENGEL and SHREVE, Economic Aspects of Hydrogenation, *Ind. Eng. Chem.*, **32**, 1212 (1940); TAYLOR, "Industrial Hydrogen," Reinhold Publishing Corporation, New York, 1921.

HYDROGEN MANUFACTURE

Prior to 1900, the uses of hydrogen were few, and the supply was filled almost entirely by electrolytic processes. Since then, the demand for large-scale hydrogen production for chemical reactions has increased so greatly that there are now available the following important methods for manufacture:[1]

TABLE 3. PROCESS REQUIREMENTS PER THOUSAND STANDARD CUBIC FEET OF HYDROGEN

Material or utility	Quantity		
	Steam-iron process[a]	Water-gas catalytic process[a]	Steam-hydro-carbon process[b]
Coke, lb..............................	65–85	42	
Steam, lb.............................	500–600	445	360
Cooling water, gal......................	1,000	1,980	1,800
Power, kw.-hr.........................	2.0	3.0	2.0
Ore, catalyst, and chemicals, cents..........	8.0	2.0	1.0
Fuel, B.t.u. (gas or oil)...................	30,000	.....	350,000
Propane, gal...........................	....	.....	2.75

[a] REED, Present-day Hydrogen Manufacturing Processes, *Trans. Am. Inst. Chem. Engrs.*, **42**, 379 (1946).

[b] The Commercial Production of Pure Hydrogen from Hydrocarbons and Steam, *Trans. Am. Inst. Chem. Engrs.*, **41**, 453 (1945).

1. Steam-hydrocarbon process.
2. Water-gas catalytic process.
3. Steam-iron process.
4. Electrolysis of water.
5. Thermal dissociation of hydrocarbons such as natural gas.

In addition hydrogen is obtained as a by-product in the operation of a number of processes, *e.g.*, from the electrolysis of aqueous sodium chloride (Chap. 15) and from butanol fermentation (Chap. 31). Hydrogen is also prepared from the cracking of ammonia. During the Second World War portable units for the manufacture of hydrogen and carbon dioxide reacting methanol and steam were built for the armed forces.[2]

Since 1952 more hydrogen has been produced by reacting hydrocarbons, particularly natural gas, with steam than by all the other methods combined. This is a fairly recent economical development mainly be-

[1] REED, Present-day Hydrogen Manufacturing Processes, *Trans. Am. Inst. Chem. Engrs.*, **42**, 379 (1946), quantitative data and flow sheets.

[2] For description and flow sheet, see REED, *op. cit.*, p. 388.

cause of improvements in heat-transfer knowledge and equipment, and gas-purification procedures. Although plants were installed in the 1930's for this process, it was not until 1940 that it was used as a source of hydrogen for ammonia synthesis. In 1952 over 80 per cent of the United States capacity for synthetic ammonia employed this process for their hydrogen. This hydrogen is also important in methanol synthesis, hydrogenation of vegetable oils and petroleum, and other hydrogenations and syntheses. Table 3 compares the process requirements for the steam-iron, water-gas catalytic, and steam-hydrocarbon methods. For a small unit, hydrogen can be produced most easily electrolytically, particularly where electricity is cheap. The steam-iron method for producing hydrogen is still used in a number of small plants especially those hydrogenating vegetable oils where *pure* hydrogen is required to prevent any objectionable taste. The water-gas catalytic method is the second largest process for producing hydrogen and is widely employed in ammonia and methanol syntheses. Excluding the much larger amounts of hydrogen for production of NH_3 and CH_3OH, there were produced in 1952, 27,732,-000,000 cu. ft. of this gas.

Steam-hydrocarbon Process. The reaction between hydrocarbons, especially methane and propane,[1] and steam to produce carbon oxides and hydrogen is highly endothermic. With propane as the raw material the reactions are

$$C_3H_8(g) + 3H_2O(g) \rightleftarrows 3CO(g) + 7H_2(g);$$
$$\Delta H_{1500°F} = +230{,}800 \text{ B.t.u.} \quad (1)$$
$$C_3H_8(g) + 6H_2O(g) \rightleftarrows 3CO_2(g) + 10H_2(g);$$
$$\Delta H_{1500°F.} = +187{,}100 \text{ B.t.u.} \quad (2)$$

Desulfurized propane is mixed with steam and passes through the hydrogen furnace where reaction takes place at about 1500°F. over a nickel catalyst. At the furnace outlet, more steam is added to cool the gas to about 750°F. and to increase the partial pressure of the H_2O. The mixture is passed into an iron oxide shift converter where most of the CO is oxidized to CO_2. The gas is conducted through a heat exchanger and into the first CO_2 absorber where a stream of monoethanolamine solution removes the CO_2. At the absorber outlet, steam is mixed with the gas, and the mixture is passed through the heat exchanger, where it is heated and the oxidation and absorption cycle is repeated two more times. The final product (hydrogen) is more than 99.9 per cent pure, with less than 0.01 per cent of CO or CO_2, and less than 0.1 per cent residual hydrocarbons. Pure CO_2 is obtained as a by-product through continuous regeneration of the monoethanolamine solution by boiling and

---

[1] ANON., Hydrogen, *Chem. Eng.*, **53** (5), 122, 162 (1946), pictured flow sheet with quantities.

steam stripping. This amounts to 35 lb. of CO_2 per M cu. ft. of H_2 and may be recovered for sale or use.

The synthesis gas ammonia production is made by reforming natural gas as follows: Natural gas is passed over zinc oxide at 675 to 750°F. to remove all traces of sulfur compounds. The desulfurized gas is mixed with approximately 3.5 volumes of steam and passed to the reforming furnace which contains a supported nickel catalyst. The catalyst is kept at 1300 to 1500°F. by external heat. The natural gas is reformed by the steam endothermically to form CO and H_2, with lesser amounts of CO_2, unconverted methane (about 7 per cent), oxygen, and nitrogen.

$$CH_4(g) + H_2O(g) \rightarrow CO(g) + 3H_2(g); \qquad \Delta H_{1500°F.} = -194,000 \text{ B.t.u.}$$

This product gas is mixed with enough air to complete the conversion and to add the nitrogen required for ammonia synthesis before entering a second reforming unit. The product gas is passed into a shift converter (see Water-gas Catalytic Process) and these gases are compressed in three stages usually, to approximately 250 lb. per sq. in. for scrubbing with water or an ethanolamine solution to remove CO_2. It is further compressed in two stages to 1,800 lb. per sq. in. and scrubbed with a solution of copper ammonium formate to take out essentially all of the remaining CO and CO_2. The gas is then washed with a 5 per cent caustic solution, leaving a product with the theoretical $3H_2/N_2$ ratio required for ammonia synthesis.

The synthesis gas for methanol production contains essentially hydrogen and carbon monoxide in a 2 to 1 ratio. When natural gas is reformed, the primary reformer is adjusted to lower the usual 3 to 1 = H_2/CO ratio in the effluent by adding heavier hydrocarbons or CO_2 to the reformer feed. Since nitrogen, obviously, is not required, a secondary reformer is not used. The CO_2 in the primary effluent is removed conventionally and recycled to the reformer feed. The $2H_2/CO$ gas mixture is compressed to around 300 atm. for methanol synthesis.

Water-gas Catalytic Process. Water gas and steam will react catalytically at high temperatures to produce hydrogen:

$$CO(g) + H_2O(g) \rightleftarrows CO_2(g) + H_2(g); \qquad \Delta H_{700°F.} = -16,500 \text{ B.t.u.}$$

The equilibrium constant for the reaction may be expressed as

$$K_1 = \frac{pCO_2 \times pH_2}{pCO \times pH_2O} \qquad \text{or} \qquad K_2 = \frac{pCO \times pH_2O}{pCO_2 \times pH_2}$$

K_2 is the so-called "shift reaction," or water-gas conversion reaction. Since the reaction is exothermic, the equilibrium conversion decreases with increasing temperature. At the low pressures involved, K_2 is substantially equal to the thermodynamic equilibrium constant, and the change in K_2 with temperature may be found from the equation

$$\frac{d \ln K_p}{dT} = \frac{\Delta H}{RT^2}$$

In addition, it has been found[1] that, over the temperature range of 80 to 1800°F., K_2 values are correlated by the empirical equation

$$K_2 = \frac{49.5}{e^{\left(\frac{7,350}{°F. + 400}\right)}}$$

Substituting in this equation, the following values are obtained: for 752°F., $K_2 = 0.084$; for 800°F., $K_2 = 0.11$; for 842°F., $K_2 = 0.134$; and for 932°F., $K_2 = 0.201$. This adverse effect of enhanced temperature on the equilibrium constant reduces the advantages of increased rates obtained at higher temperatures. As a result, the reaction is generally carried out in two stages: operating temperatures in the first are 800 to 900°F. in order to secure high initial rates; in the second, temperatures of 700 to 750°F. are utilized to secure the maximum yield. Heat exchangers are employed to transfer the sensible heat of the gases leaving the catalyst chambers to the incoming gases. Improvements in catalysts for the reaction have decreased the necessary ratio of water gas to steam, until, at present, ratios as low as 2 to 1 are used. The catalyst[2] generally employed is iron oxide activated by chromium compounds. If the hydrogen is to be used at high pressures, such as in the synthesis of ammonia or methanol, it is subjected to the established purification methods (see Chap. 20, Fig. 3.)

Steam-iron Method. Pure hydrogen is produced by the steam-iron method by passing excess steam over spongy iron (a large exposed surface being a vital factor) at temperatures of 1400 to 1900°F. On passing a reducing gas such as water gas or producer gas through the retort, the following reversible reactions occur:

$Fe_3O_4(c) + H_2(g) \rightleftarrows 3FeO(c) + H_2O(g)$;
$$\Delta H_{1650°F.} = +27,300 \text{ B.t.u.} \quad (1)$$
$Fe_3O_4(c) + CO(g) \rightleftarrows 3FeO(c) + CO_2(g)$;
$$\Delta H_{1650°F.} = +13,200 \text{ B.t.u.} \quad (2)$$
$FeO(c) + H_2(g) \rightleftarrows Fe(c) + H_2O(g)$; $\quad \Delta H_{1650°F.} = +6,500 \text{ B.t.u.} \quad (3)$
$FeO(c) + CO(g) \rightleftarrows Fe(c) + CO_2(g)$; $\quad \Delta H_{1650°F.} = -7,700 \text{ B.t.u.} \quad (4)$

---

[1] REED, The Commercial Production of Pure Hydrogen from Hydrocarbons and Steam, *Trans. Am. Inst. Chem. Engrs.*, **41**, 453 (1945).

[2] BRIDGER, *et al.*, Development, Production, and Performance of Water-gas Conversion Catalyst, *Chem. Eng. Progr.*, **44**, 363 (1948).

After the reducing period of 5 to 7 min., steam is passed through the reduced oxides for an equal amount of time, reversing reactions (1) and (3) producing hydrogen and the original oxides. The cycle is then repeated. When CO is present in the reducing gas the net heat change is

$$CO(g) + H_2O(g) \rightleftarrows CO_2(g) + H_2(g); \qquad \Delta H_{1650°F.} = -14,000 \text{ B.t.u.} \quad (5)$$

Usually the heat resulting from the oxidation of CO is not enough to overcome heat losses and the spent reducing gas is burned in a refractory superheater section above the ore bed to provide the additional heat needed. Since most of these plants have capacities in the range of 50,000 to 250,000 cu. ft. of hydrogen per day, the production is small compared with the water-gas catalytic process and the steam-hydrocarbon process although the number of plants using this process is large.

Electrolytic Method. The electrolytic process consists in passing direct current through a dilute aqueous solution of alkali, decomposing the water according to the following equation:

$$2H_2O(l) \rightarrow 2H_2 + O_2; \qquad \Delta H = +136,700 \text{ cal.}$$

The theoretical decomposition voltage for this electrolysis is 1.23 volts at room temperature; however, owing to overvoltage of hydrogen on the electrodes and also to cell resistance itself, voltages of 2.0 to 2.25 volts are usually required. A typical commercial[1] cell electrolyzes a 15 per cent NaOH solution, uses an iron cathode and a nickel-plated iron anode, has an asbestos diaphragm separating the electrode compartments, and operates at temperatures from 60 to 70°C. The nickel plating of the anode reduces the oxygen overvoltage. Most types of cells produce about 7.0 cu. ft. (9.408 cu. ft. theoretically) of hydrogen and half as much oxygen per kilowatt-hour. The gas is around 99.7 per cent pure and is suitable even for hydrogenation for edible oils. The cells are of two types: the bipolar or filter-press type, where each plate is an individual cell; and the unipolar or tank cell, usually containing two anode compartments with a cathode compartment between them. The unipolar cells may be open or closed tanks. In most installations the oxygen produced is wasted unless it can be used locally.

Thermal Dissociation of Hydrocarbons. Hydrogen is produced from natural gas by thermal decomposition (see Carbon Black). The gas is passed over a heated brick checkerwork at a temperature of 2200°F. until the temperature of the brickwork drops to about 1700 to 2000°F., thus decomposing the gas endothermally into carbon black and hydrogen. Since 1931 only one plant has utilized hydrogen after purification from this process in making ammonia. Another company has also operated a similar process for a number of years but uses the impure hydrogen obtained for fuel.

[1] PERRY, *op. cit.*, p. 1796,

Cracked Ammonia.[1] A mixture of nitrogen, 1 volume, and hydrogen, 3 volumes, may be prepared from the cracking of ammonia. The process consists in vaporizing the liquid NH_3 from cylinders, heating it to 1600°F., passing it over an active catalyst, and then cooling it in heat exchangers where the incoming gas is vaporized. Brandt states, "a single 150-lb. cylinder of anhydrous ammonia will produce 6,750 cu. ft. of cracked ammonia. This is equivalent to the contents of some 33 hydrogen cylinders." Since hydrogen for ammonia is produced in large plants at a very low cost, intermediate-sized hydrogenators of oil and fatty acids, even after paying freight and unwanted nitrogen costs, have found it practical and economical to install ammonia dissociators for operations using 5,000 to 6,000 cu. ft. H_2 per hr. It is not economically feasible to separate the nitrogen and hydrogen from this process; however, almost pure nitrogen can be easily made by burning out the hydrogen. This nitrogen will cost much less than pure nitrogen in cylinders. Cracked NH_3 gives too cold a flame to replace H_2 in oxyhydrogen torches. It has found widespread usage in the heat-treating of metals, however.

OXYGEN AND NITROGEN

Uses and Economics. The production in 1953 of 25.3 billion cu. ft. of "high-purity" *oxygen* (99.5 per cent and upward) is approximately five times the quantity turned out in 1939. Of this total about 24.5 billion was obtained by the liquefaction of air, the rest by electrolysis of water. During 1952, shipments of oxygen, valued at 63 million dollars, were about 80 per cent of the total for all elemental gases. The biggest use is in steel operations such as welding, cutting, and scarfing. "Low-purity" or tonnage[2] oxygen (90 to 95 per cent) is employed in chemical manufacture and in some open-hearth and blast furnaces as it raises temperatures and accelerates steel production. There is a large production of tonnage oxygen (in 1952, 622,432 tons) and a great deal of work is being done to lower the cost. Recent refinements in the Linde-Frankl and other designs have reduced minimum economical production from 500 tons per day to amounts smaller.

In addition to the nearly 3,000,000 tons of *nitrogen* which enter ammonia synthesis, its 1952 production as a gas was 2,699,000,000 cu. ft. This gas is employed as a protective atmosphere in the bright annealing of metals, as a shield to prevent oxidation in food products, similarly in welding areas, as a reagent, and as a unique grinding aid for very hard or heat-sensitive materials.[3]

[1] BRANDT, Cracked Ammonia, *Chem. Inds.*, **48**, 186 (1941); *Chem. Eng.*, **57** (2), 119 (1950).

[2] DOWNS and RUSHTON, Tonnage Oxygen, *Chem. Eng. Progr.*, **43** (1), 12 (1947), tables.

[3] ANON., Grinding with Liquid N_2, *Chem. Eng.*, **58** (6), 107 (1951).

Manufacture. Oxygen is produced by two markedly different methods.[1] The electrolysis of water process is comparatively expensive and of little interest except under special conditions. The liquefaction and subsequent rectification of liquid air is the one of most importance. The first modification which will be considered here is the manufacture of "high-purity" oxygen. To make it easier to understand these processes, Table 4 lists the properties of air and its constituents.

TABLE 4. PROPERTIES OF AIR AND CONSTANT CONSTITUENTS[a]

Gas	Volume, per cent	Boiling point, °C.	Boiling point, °K.	Critical temperature, °K.	By weight
Air................	100	−194	79	132.3	
Nitrogen..........	78.03	−195.81	77.19	126.0	
Oxygen...........	20.99	−182.96	90.04	154.2	
Argon............	0.94	−185.84	87.16	156	
Hydrogen.........	0.01[b]	−252.44	20.56	33.1	
Neon.............	0.0015	−246.3	26.7	53	1 lb. in 44 tons
Helium...........	0.0005	−268.98	4.02	5.2	1 lb. in 173 tons
Krypton..........	0.00011	−152.9	120.1	210	1 lb. in 725 tons
Xenon............	0.000009	−107.1	165.9	258	1 lb. in 1,208 tons
Carbon dioxide[c]....	0.03–0.07	− 79.0	194.0[d]	304.1	
Water[c]...........	0.01–0.02	+100.0	373.0	647	

[a] Data tabulated from *Chem. Eng.*, **54** (3), 127 (1947).

[b] Variable; sometimes reported much less.

[c] Variable constituents.

[d] Solid carbon dioxide sublimes.

High-purity oxygen (99.54 per cent) and nitrogen are produced commercially from air[2] by a typical flow sheet as presented in Fig. 3. The composition of the atmosphere is given in Table 4. The air is first compressed, and the CO_2 and any dust present are removed by scrubbing with KOH solution. The air is further compressed to 200 atm. in four stages, with water cooling between each stage. Any moisture that condenses out during this operation is drawn off or is removed by passage through a tower packed with solid KOH or activated alumina. The gas coming from the fourth compression stage is at 170°C.; it is water-cooled to 10 to 30°C. and usually then further cooled to −30°C. by ammonia

[1] See ANON., Oxygen, Past, Present and Prospects, *Chem. Eng.*, **54** (1), 123 (1947); ANON., Air Separation Principles and Technology, *Chem. Eng.*, **54** (3), 125 (1947); BLISS and DODGE, Oxygen Manufacture—Thermodynamic Analyses of Processes Depending on Low Temperature Distillation of Air, *Chem. Eng. Progr.*, **45** (51), 129 (1949), many diagrams, detailed application of first law.

[2] PERRY, *op. cit.*, pp. 1701–1717, outline is included of minimum work required to separate two gases by liquefaction (Dodge).

refrigeration. The air, at 200 atm. and −30°C., goes to a combined liquefier and separator, as shown roughly in Fig. 3 and in detail in Fig. 4.

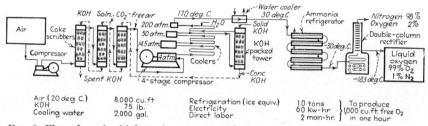

FIG. 3. Flow sheet for high-purity oxygen and nitrogen through liquefaction of air.

Here the purified, compressed, and cooled air is liquefied and separated
into its constituents according to the following fundamental principles:

1. The interchange of heat in heat exchangers such as double pipe coils.

2. The adiabatic expansion of the compressed air to cool by the Joule-Thompson[1] effect, owing to energy being consumed in overcoming the attraction between
the molecules.

3. The cooling of the compressed gases by allowing them to perform work
(Claude modification). One kilo of air at 200 atm. and 10°C. when simply expanding to 5 atm. produces a cooling effect of 10 kg.-cal. (Joule-Thompson effect),
while if the same quantity of air expands to 5 atm. in a cylinder *doing work*, the
cooling effect is 23 kg.-cal., assuming that the working engine has an efficiency
of 70 per cent.[2] This latter effects a cooling of 135°C.

4. The cooling of the liquids by evaporation.

5. The separation of liquid oxygen from the more volatile nitrogen in a bubble-
cap column. Nitrogen boils at −195.8°C. and oxygen at −183°C. The difference
of 12.8° in boiling point permits a fractional separation of the two liquids, owing
to the fundamental fact of any fractionation in a column that the more volatile
will have a higher percentage in the vapor in equilibrium with a lower percentage
of this constituent in the liquid.[3] Thus the repetition of these equilibriums, more
or less perfect, constitutes the "plates" of the fractionating column and causes
the more volatile or substantially pure nitrogen to come off at the top, while
substantially pure oxygen is obtained at the bottom.

These principles are applied[4] in practice according to two systems: the
Linde and the Claude. Both cool the compressed gas and depend upon a
gradual or "self" lowering of the temperature by countercurrent cooling

[1] PERRY, *op. cit.*, pp. 203, 333, 1709.

[2] ANON., The Briey Liquid Oxygen Plant, *Engineering*, **140**, 135 (1935).

[3] PERRY, *op. cit.*, p. 575, where vapor and liquid equilibriums are plotted.

[4] The principles involved here are presented by RUHEMAN, "The Separation of
Gases," Oxford University Press, New York, 1945. Typical plants are described in
the following articles: ANON., The Briey Liquid Oxygen Plant, *Engineering*, **140**,
135 (1935); ANON., Liquid Oxygen, *Chem. Eng.*, **54** (3), 136 (1947), a pictured flow
sheet; also PERRY, *op. cit.*, pp. 1701–1716.

of the incoming gas against outgoing gas, to the air liquefaction temperature. The Linde system employs the Joule-Thompson effect for its critical cooling while the Claude system uses the Joule-Thompson cooling for only 30 per cent of the incoming air, the other 70 per cent being cooled by performing external work. In this latter case it is better not to cool the compressed air below −30°C., or the work to be performed, and hence the cooling, is lessened by the energy heatwise removed. After a liquefier is working, the operating pressure can usually be reduced to about 50 atm.

Much of the oxygen manufactured is obtained by the system developed by Carl von Linde in Germany around 1900. The heart of this system is the double-column liquefier and rectifier as shown in Fig. 4. The Claude system is slightly more complicated as it diverts 70 per cent of the high-pressure air to perform useful low compression of the incoming air and to cool itself simultaneously. [This system is apparently more efficient and is meeting some modern acceptance, as is the Heylandt cycle, which incorporates features from both of the others.]

The double-column equipment shown in Fig. 4 is actually constructed with its special heat exchangers, columns, and expansion valves all a part of one setup and encased in the same insulating covering. The cooled and compressed air enters countercurrent to the outgoing nitrogen through a heat exchanger. Although only one such exchanger is shown in the figure, it is common practice to install two. These are used alternately, so that, when one is plugged by ice from water that escaped previous removal, the air may be passed through the second. This permits removal of the ice without interrupting the procedure. The cold compressed air issuing from the heat exchanger (p) is still warmer than the liquid in the column; hence it is passed through the coil in the bottom of the column (d) and thus supplies the heat necessary for the vaporization in this lower section. This colder compressed air is finally expanded through valve (c) into the lower column (d) from initially 200 atm. and later on from 50 atm. down to 4 to 6 atm., being sufficiently cooled here through the Joule-Thompson effect to be liquefied. As a liquid, the air enters the lower section of the column and flows downward against the rising vapors of its more volatile constituent, nitrogen. As is true of any such fractionation, the less volatile constituent, oxygen, collects in the bottom at (b). Part is vaporized to carry on the rectification, but any accumulation of this liquid containing about 40 per cent oxygen is forced by the pressure drop between (d) at 4 to 6 atm. and (g) at 1.3 atm. (absolute), to pass through the valve (e) to the upper rectifying section, entering at (f). The 40 per cent liquid oxygen passes down the upper column losing its more volatile nitrogen until it accumulates at (h) as liquid oxygen of 99 and more per cent purity. Although some of this liquid oxygen boils off and thus renders latent the heat given off by the condensation of the nitrogen vapor at the higher pressure on the lower side of the dome at (j), much of it is drawn off through valve (i) into double-wall vacuum containers for storage or sale.

The nitrogen in the liquid air entering at (c), as the more volatile constituent gradually volatilizes, passes upward and is cooled and condensed by the tubes and dome of (j). The curved dome here deflects the

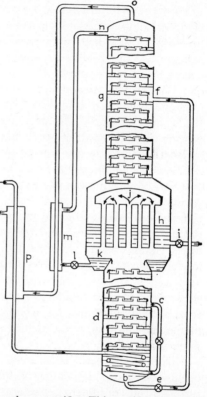

a. Entrance for compressed air at 200 atm.
b. Accumulated liquid rich in oxygen
c. Cooled and liquefied air entering lower column
d. Lower rectifying column
e. Exit valve for liquid, 40 ± per cent oxygen
f. Liquid entering upper column
g. Upper rectifying column
h. Accumulated oxygen liquid
i. Exit valve for oxygen, 99 + per cent pure
j. Condensing tubes and dome for lower column
k. Condensed overhead from lower column, rich in nitrogen
l. Release valve for flow to upper column
m. Heat exchanger, nitrogen-rich liquid to nitrogen gas
n. Nitrogen-rich liquid entering upper column
o. Cold gaseous nitrogen
p. Heat exchanger, entering air to leaving gaseous nitrogen

Fig. 4. Diagram of Linde liquefier and double-column rectifier. This rectifier separates liquid air into the more volatile nitrogen (b.p. −195.8°C. or 77.3°K.) and the less volatile oxygen (b.p. −183°C. or 90.1°K.).

drippings to the collector trough at (k) where a liquid quite rich in nitrogen collects. This nitrogen-rich liquid is moved to the top of the upper column by the prevailing pressure differential through the control valve (l), though some of this nitrogen-rich liquid spills off the trough to supply reflux liquid to the upper plates of column (d). The reason why the lower-boiling nitrogen (−195.8°C. at 1 atm.) is liquefied by the higher-boiling (−183°C. at 1 atm.) oxygen is because of the *higher* pressure on the liquid rich in nitrogen in the lower column. As the liquid rich in nitrogen goes to the upper column, it is cooled further by the gaseous nitrogen leaving the column at (o), in order that it will not evaporate too quickly when it enters this region of lower pressure. As the liquid rich in nitrogen passes down the plates of column (g), the more volatile nitrogen vapors are fractionated off, are washed fairly free of oxygen, and pass out of the top of the column as cold nitrogen vapor of around −195°C. This cold nitrogen as it leaves the apparatus is warmed in the heat exchangers (m) and (p).

Most commercial *tonnage-oxygen* plants are based on the German developed Linde-Frankl process or its modifications. In the Linde-Frankl process, the air is first compressed to $4\frac{1}{2}$ atm. by centrifugal compressors and purified in "cold accumulators" which transfer heat and simultaneously remove water vapor and carbon dioxide. These accumulators (four in number) are pressure vessels packed with corrugated sheet-aluminum spirals and are cooled by either the separated waste nitrogen or by the oxygen product. The entering air has its temperature lowered by passing through a pair of previously cooled accumulators where the water and carbon dioxide are frozen out. At the same time the oxygen and nitrogen are conducted through the other pair, cooling them, and evaporating and purging the previously collected ice and solid carbon dioxide. At about 3-min. intervals the accumulators are reversed. After purification the cold air enters into the bottom of the double, conventional rectifying column (Fig. 4) and the partially liquefied air expands into the upper column where it is rectified. Refrigeration is supplied by expanding gaseous nitrogen in a centrifugal expander after slight warming against a small incoming supplementary air stream. To make up for the slight deficiency in available refrigeration, about 4 to 5 per cent of the total air supply is introduced at 200 atm., purified, precooled by ammonia refrigeration, and further cooled against waste nitrogen and unexpanded nitrogen.

Modifications of the basic Linde-Frankl process include systems to utilize low-pressure, high-capacity, high-speed, economical compression and refrigeration equipment; efficient system for removal of impurities; and prevention of dangerous acetylene accumulation. The Elliott process is characterized by three modifications[1] of the Linde-Frankl method for improved continuity of operation and for reducing the acetylene hazard. This is done by an improved air-purification system and a nitrogen circuit which supplies high-pressure nitrogen in two streams, one for refrigeration, the other for reflux. The M. W. Kellogg Company process[2] is also typical of the reversing exchanger cycles. These exchangers do not contaminate the oxygen product as do the accumulators used in the

[1] CRAWFORD, Elliott Oxygen Process and Impurity Removal System, *Chem. Eng. Progr.*, **46**, 74 (1950).

[2] LOBO, Production of Oxygen for Industrial Purposes, *Chem. Eng. Progr.*, **1**, 21 (1947).

Linde-Frankl process; so a higher-purity product results. Bliss and Dodge (*op. cit.*) have outlined the various other processes and modifications.

RARE GASES OF THE ATMOSPHERE

The rare gases argon, neon, xenon, and krypton are obtained from the atmosphere[1] (see Table 4). These gases are separated by side rectification columns from take-offs at various points in a double rectifying column such as is employed for obtaining oxygen and nitrogen from air, as depicted in Fig. 4. The most abundant such gas, *argon*, has a boiling point near to that of oxygen. It is rectified in a side column with its feed at maximum concentration taking off from toward the top of the upper column, the separated liquid oxygen being returned to this upper column. The *krypton* and *xenon*, having higher boiling points, are removed near the bottom of the upper column below the oxygen take-off. The *neon* and *helium*, because of their very low boiling points which make them noncondensable even in liquid air, accumulate on the lower or nitrogen side of the condenser, separating the upper from the lower column.

One of the surprising developments of the past few years is the industrial consumption of these rare and chemically inert materials. They are utilized in the light industry because they are *chemically* inert and possess very desirable *electrical* properties. Such usage is divided between the gas-conductor-tube lamps, the so-called "neon" lights, and fluorescent lights. Argon, however, is now used in small amounts in every light

TABLE 5. COMMERCIAL COLOR CHART FOR "NEON" LIGHTS[a]
(Clear or colored glass, uncoated)

Color	Gas	Pressure, mm.	Glass	Mercury
Deep red	Neon	10–18	Soft red	No
Red	Neon	10–18	Clear	No
Gold (yellow)	Helium	3– 4	Noviol (amber)	No
Light green	Argon-neon mixture[b]	10–20	Uranium (green)	Yes
Dark green	Argon-neon mixture[b]	10–20	Noviol (amber)	Yes
Light blue	Argon-neon mixture[b]	10–20	Clear	Yes
Dark blue	Argon-neon mixture[b]	10–20	Purple	Yes
White	Helium	3– 4	Clear	No

[a] GROSS, Rare Gases in Everyday Use, *J. Chem. Educ.*, **18**, 533 (1941).
[b] To meet extreme winter conditions, an argon-neon-helium mixture is substituted.

[1] METZGER, Traces from Tons, *Ind. Eng. Chem.*, **27**, 112 (1935); GROSS, Rare Gases in Everyday Use, *J. Chem. Educ.*, **18**, 533 (1941); KIRK and OTHMER, *op. cit.*, Vol. 7, p. 415, diagrams.

bulb made. *Neon lights* are of glass tubing with the electrodes sealed in each end and filled with the rare gases including helium or mixtures thereof, with or without mercury. The light is caused by the flow of the current which may be 25 milliamperes at 15,000 volts, with the light emission determined by the gas in the tube. Table 5 summarizes the commercial colors. The power consumption is low in comparison with that of incandescent lamps.

TABLE 6. LUMINESCENT OR FLUORESCENT CHEMICALS[a]

Phosphor	General color	Phosphor	General color
Calcium tungstate.........	Blue	Zinc beryllium silicate.....	Yellow-white
Magnesium tungstate......	Blue-white	Cadmium silicate..........	Yellow-pink
Zinc silicate..............	Green	Cadmium borate..........	Pink

[a] GROSS, Rare Gases in Everyday Use, *J. Chem. Educ.*, **18**, 537 (1941); KIRK and OTHMER, *op. cit.*, Vol. 8, p. 540.

Fluorescent tubes produce a soft, nonglaring light under very economical conditions. They are filled with one of these rare gases and are provided with a fluorescent coating of a "phosphor" on the inside of the glass. The function of the latter is to supplement the visible light given out by the rare gas, by the transformation of the invisible or ultraviolet rays of the gas into those wavelengths visible to the human eye. This supplementary or "extra" light imparts a very pleasing effect. Table 6 presents some of these phosphor, chemicals or fluorescent materials, which to give the proper clarity of transformed light must be of a purity that has never before been obtained in any chemicals of commerce. Phosphors are also extremely important in coating of television tubes. New phosphors have been developed for infrared ("snooperscopes" and night driving) and for electroluminescence.[1]

Argon is produced in by far the largest quantities of the rare gases (450,000,000 cu. ft. in 1955). One of the most interesting applications of argon and one which is constantly growing is its use as an inert gas shield in arc welding. Helium is also utilized. As employed for aluminum, aluminum bronze, silicon bronze, copper nickels, and stainless steels, the shielding gas forms a protective envelope around the welding area.[2] This protects the weld metal, electrode wire, and the work. Slag formation and the use of flux are avoided, thus contributing to the speed and efficiency.

[1] WARD, Lighting New Horizons, *Chem. Eng. News*, **31**, 4418, 4772 (1953).

[2] Examples are Heliarc marketed by Linde Air Products, and the Aircomatic process for welding by Air Reduction Company.

HELIUM

This industry began with the discovery of helium in certain Kansas[1] natural gases about 1900. The first plants were constructed to supply helium for the lighter-than-air airships of the Allies in the First World War. During the Second World War helium extraction was greatly expanded to four plants which were all owned and operated by the government; but under normal conditions several suffice.

The composition of the untreated gas varies as follows: helium, 1 to 8 per cent; nitrogen, 12 to 80 per cent; and the balance chiefly methane and small amounts of higher hydrocarbons.[2] The gas from the wells is compressed to 600 lb. per sq. in. and after NaOH treatment to remove the carbon dioxide, hydrogen sulfide, and water vapor, enters the first heat exchanger where it is almost completely liquefied. The product is throttled at 200 to 300 lb. per sq. in., where a crude separation takes place yielding 60 per cent helium. A second partial liquefaction is then effected yielding 98.5 per cent helium. Further purification by adsorption on activated carbon at $-275°F.$ yields a purity of 99.7 per cent or higher. The helium is shipped in long, seamless steel cylinders at pressures of 2,000 to 2,400 lb. per sq. in. in special railroad cars. Refrigeration is the key to helium extraction and is supplied from two sources: (1) Joule-Thompson expansion of the gas from 600 lb. per sq. in. gage and (2) an auxiliary nitrogen refrigeration cycle involving engine expansion from 600 to 15 lb. per sq. in. abs.

The most important use for helium is in lighter-than-air aircraft and weather-observation balloons where it has replaced the very flammable hydrogen. It has 92.5 per cent of the lifting power of hydrogen. Another less widely known use has been in a mixture with oxygen to give a synthetic atmosphere for the use of deep-sea divers and tunnel workers. The advantage is that helium is much less soluble in the body fluids than is nitrogen which is present in air; this substitution prevents "bends," to a large extent. Other uses include mixing with argon and neon in display signs, cooling of electrical equipment, inert gas shield for welding, and as a tracer gas to determine underground migration of petroleum.

ACETYLENE

Uses and Economics. Acetylene is employed in the manufacture of an ever increasing number of industrial chemicals, such as vinyl chloride, acrylonitrile, and acetic acid. While some of these are also derived from other sources, chemicals made exclusively from acetylene include vinyl

[1] CADY, Beginnings of the Helium Industry, *Ind. Eng. Chem.*, **30**, 845 (1938).
[2] MULLINS, Helium Production Process, *Chem. Eng. Progr.*, **44**, 567 (1948), with flow sheet and tables; PERRY, *op. cit.*, p. 1716.

acetate, trichloroethylene, and chloroprene and its polymer neoprene. Studies of acetylene reactions at high pressures (Reppe high-pressure technique) are very significant in that vinylation, ethynylation, and polymerization reactions have opened up a new field of chemistry by introducing many new compounds.[1] In 1954, 7,030,000,000 cu. ft. were produced with an approximate value of 90 million dollars.

Manufacture. Until very recently all acetylene was made by the reaction of calcium carbide with water:

$$CaC_2(c) + 2H_2O(l) \rightarrow Ca(OH)_2(c) + C_2H_2(g); \qquad \Delta H = -30,000 \text{ cal.}$$

There are two methods for generating acetylene from calcium carbide. The batch carbide-to-water or wet method takes place in a cylindrical water shell surmounted by a housing with hopper and feed facilities. The carbide is fed to the water at a measured rate until exhausted. The calcium hydroxide is discharged in the form of a lime slurry containing about 90 per cent water. For large-scale industrial applications "dry generation," a continuous process featuring automatic feed, is popular. Here 1 lb. of water is used per pound of carbide and the heat of the reaction (166 B.t.u. per cu. ft. acetylene) is largely dissipated by water vaporization leaving the by-product lime in a dry, fairly easily handled state. Part of this can be recycled to the carbide furnaces. Continuous agitation is necessary to prevent overheating.

The newest method of manufacturing acetylene is through the conversion of natural gas or liquid hydrocarbon feeds. The processes of the most interest include partial oxidation, thermal cracking, and electrical techniques. An electric-arc procedure was used commercially at Hüls, Germany. A silent electric discharge is featured in a laboratory process developed by *Dr. E. P. Schoch* at the University of Texas. The *Sachse* process and its modifications involve the partial combustion of natural gas with 95 per cent oxygen followed by a rapid water quench. Monsanto Chemical Company at Texas City uses a modified version of this process as does Carbide and Carbon Chemicals Company. The cracking takes place at 2700°F. at atmospheric pressure, and the reaction time is less than 0.05 sec. The product gas contains 8 to 9 per cent acetylene and valuable high quantities of Fischer-Tropsch synthesis gas. Significant amounts of high acetylenes which are explosive contaminants help make this difficult process more complex. Water scrubbing, solvent extraction, and absorption are all mentioned as being used for commercial-scale separations. In the *Wulff* process a specially designed double regenerative furnace is used to carry out the thermal-cracking reaction. The natural gas is fed alternately in about 1-min. cycles to each of two refractory-

---

[1] For an example, see ANON., Acetylene Chemicals, *Chem. Eng.*, **58** (6), 180 (1951), a pictured flow sheet of polyvinyl-pyrrolidone, or PVP, a blood-plasma substitute, is presented.

lined furnaces. The reaction takes place at approximately 2600°F., and the product gas contains a high proportion of ethylene. Here, too, the purification is difficult and complex.

SULFUR DIOXIDE

The output of liquid sulfur dioxide in 1952 was 43,856 tons. It may be produced by the burning of sulfur or by the roasting of metal sulfides[1] in special equipment as described in Chap. 19. It may be obtained also by the recovery from the waste gases of other reactions. Its production and the subsequent compression and cooling to form liquid SO_2, which boils at $-10°C$., are shown in Fig. 5. With very careful control of the amount

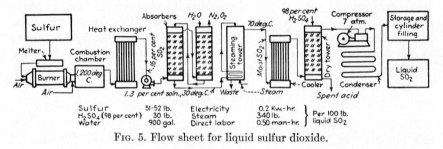

Sulfur	51-52 lb.	Electricity	0.2 Kw.-hr.	
H_2SO_4 (98 per cent)	30 lb.	Steam	340 lb.	Per 100 lb.
Water	900 gal.	Direct labor	0.50 man-hr.	liquid SO_2

FIG. 5. Flow sheet for liquid sulfur dioxide.

of air entering the combustion chamber, sulfur dioxide can be produced up to 18 per cent at a temperature of 1200°C. As the gases from the combustion chamber pass through the heat exchanger, they heat the water for the boilers. The cooled gases, containing from 16 to 18 per cent SO_2, are pumped into the absorbers through acidproof pumps. The strength of the solution from the absorbers is dependent upon the temperature and the strength of the gases entered, but the concentration usually runs about 1.3 per cent with the temperature close to 30°C. A very small amount of the SO_2 is lost in the exhaust from the second absorber—about 0.02 per cent. The temperature of the vapors coming from the steaming tower depends upon its design but usually runs about 70°C. The vapors are cooled and passed through a drying tower in which 98 per cent sulfuric acid is used. Other drying agents may be employed and some plants by special procedure eliminate the use of this sulfuric acid drier altogether. The SO_2 is liquefied by compressing to about 7 atm. and cooling. It is stored or put into cylinders.

Sulfur dioxide is shipped as a liquid under 2 or 3 atm. pressure. It is obtainable in steel cylinders[2] of from 50 to 100 lb. capacity, in 1-ton

[1] ANON., SO₂ by Fluidization, *Chem. Eng.*, **60** (1), 238 (1953), pictured flow sheet from sulfide ores. Dimethyl-aniline is absorption medium in *Chem. Eng.*, **60** (4), 274 (1953), with flow sheet.

[2] WILLSON, *et al.*, Liquid Sulfur Dioxide, *Chem. Ind.*, **52**, 178 (1943).

tanks, or in 15-ton tank cars. Its uses are numerous. A quite pure commercial grade containing not more than 0.05 per cent of moisture is suitable for most of its applications. However, a very pure grade, containing less than 50 p.p.m. of moisture, is supplied for refrigeration. Sulfur dioxide also serves as the raw material for the production of sulfuric acid. It finds application as a bleaching agent in the textile and food industries. Following the use of chlorine in waterworks or in textile mills, sulfur dioxide is an effective antichlor for removing excess chlorine. It is an effective disinfectant and is employed as such for wooden kegs and barrels and brewery apparatus, and for the prevention of mold in the drying of fruits. Sulfur dioxide effectively controls fermentation in the making of wine. It is used in the sulfite process for paper pulp, as a liquid solvent in petroleum refining, and as a raw material in many plants, *e.g.*, in place of purchased sulfites, bisulfites, or hydrosulfites. The convenience of the application of liquid SO_2 has persuaded many small or intermittent users to purchase this rather than to make their own.

CARBON MONOXIDE

Carbon monoxide is one of the chief constituents of water gas as described in Chap. 7. It is obtained in fairly pure form when hydrogen is prepared from water gas by liquefaction of other components, but it is generally used for a fuel in connection with the process. It is an important raw material for methanol and other alcohols and for hydrocarbons. It is a powerful poison.

NITROUS OXIDE

Nitrous oxide is generally prepared by heating very pure ammonium nitrate to 200°C. in retorts.

$$NH_4NO_3(c) \rightarrow N_2O(g) + 2H_2O(g); \qquad \Delta H = -8,800 \text{ cal.}$$

The purification consists in treatment with caustic to remove nitric acid and with dichromate to remove nitric oxide. It is shipped in steel cylinders as a liquid at a pressure of 100 atm. It is used as an anesthetic. In 1952, 289,145,000 gal. were produced.

SELECTED REFERENCES

Martin, Geoffrey, "Industrial Gases," Crosby Lockwood & Son Ltd., London, 1918.
Greenwood, H. C., "Industrial Gases," Baillière, Tindall & Cox, London, 1920.
Ruheman, M., "The Separation of Gases," 2d ed., Oxford University Press, New York, 1949.

Kirk, R. E., and D. F. Othmer, editors, "Encyclopedia of Chemical Technology," The Interscience Encyclopedia, Inc., New York, 1947–1956.

Quinn, E. L., and C. L. Jones, "Carbon Dioxide," Reinhold Publishing Corporation, New York, 1936.

Taylor, H. S., "Industrial Hydrogen," Reinhold Publishing Corporation, New York, 1921.

CHAPTER 9

INDUSTRIAL CARBON

The element carbon exists in three allotropic modifications; these three varieties, namely, amorphous carbon, graphite, and diamond, are also employed industrially.[1] In general, carbon is chemically inert and is infusible at atmospheric pressure. Graphite and diamond resist oxidation even at fairly high temperatures. Some of the industrial applications depend upon the chemical inertness of carbon. On the other hand, the amorphous carbon can be activated, in which case it has a great capacity for selective adsorption from either the gaseous or the liquid state. For nonmetallic substances, carbon and graphite possess a very satisfactory electrical and heat conductivity. The heat conductivity of graphitized, coke-base carbon is superior to that of most metals. Both fabricated amorphous and graphitic carbon products have very low coefficients of thermal expansion and good thermal conductivity, thus giving them high resistance to thermal shock.

Carbon is an extremely versatile element in the way it is of service to man. Its applications are growing each year. In 1928, Mantell[2] wrote, "The possibility of the expansion of carbon industries is very great, for they are intimately bound up with our highly complex life of the present day." The expansion is now being realized, to such an extent that there is a growing shortage of raw materials, particularly petroleum coke and wood charcoal.[3] The helpfulness of carbon is apparent only when we single out the many phases of our everyday living where this adaptable element is essential—in the black pigment of the ink of our books, magazines, and newspapers, in carbon paper, in pencils, as the black color in many paints, automobile finishes, and shoe blacking, as a strengthening and toughening constituent of rubber tires, tubes, and other rubber goods, and as an essential element in the construction of a very large amount of electrical equipment from the household vacuum cleaner to the largest dynamos. The carbon arc is used in the production of visible and ultraviolet radiations for use in an increasingly large number of in-

[1] The fuel value of carbon as coal is considered in Chap. 5.

[2] MANTELL, "Industrial Carbon," 2d ed., D. Van Nostrand Company, Inc., New York, 1946.

[3] LADOO and STOKES, Industrial Carbon, *Chem. Inds.*, **63**, 609 (1945).

dustrial processes dependent on photochemical reactions. The irradiation of milk to produce a higher vitamin D potency is one example of this use. Carbon and graphite products as structural materials have found new and increasingly extensive applications to chemical and metallurgical industries. Electrodes made of carbon and graphite are very important industrial equipment.

TABLE 1. SOME PROPERTIES OF DIFFERENT MODIFICATIONS OF CARBON[a]

	Amorphous forms			Graphite (artificial)	Dia-mond
	Coke base	Lampblack base	Anthracite base		
Vaporization temperature .		All forms 3925–3970°K.			
Specific gravity.	1.98–2.10[b]	1.80–1.85[b]	1.79[b]	2.20–2.24	3.51
Electrical resistivity at 20°C., ohms per cm. cube.	0.0035–0.0046	0.0058–0.0081	0.0033–0.0066	0.0008–0.0013	
Specific heat,					
26–76°C.....	0.168	....	....	0.165	0.160
26–282°C....	0.200	....	....	0.195	0.315
26–538°C....	0.199	....	....	0.234	0.415
36–902°C....	0.315	....	....	0.324	
47–1193°C...	0.352	....	....	0.350	
56–1450°C...	0.367	....	....	0.390	
Thermal conductivity gm.-cal./ (sec.)(cm.²) (°C./cm.)..	0.0125–0.0165	....	0.021–0.025	0.29–0.30	
B.t.u./(hr.) (sq.ft.)(°F. /ft.)(or k)..	3–4	....	5–6	70–94	
Coefficient of thermal expansion per °C. × 10⁶ (0–100°C.)......	2.41–3.85	....	2.23–2.41	0.97–2.23	

[a] Courtesy of W. C. Kalb, National Carbon Company.

[b] Dependent on source, character of bond, and degree of calcination. The above figures are the real densities of the solids; however, when formed into electrodes where some voids occur, the apparent specific gravity lies in the range of 1.50 to 1.60 for amorphous carbon from coke and in the range of 1.50 to 1.65 for graphite.

Nonfabricated industrial carbon is represented by lampblack, carbon black, activated carbon, graphite, and industrial diamonds. The first three are examples of *amorphous carbon*. *Lampblack* is soot formed by the incomplete burning of carbonaceous solids or liquids. It is gradually being replaced in some uses by *carbon black*, the most important of these amorphous forms and also the product of an incomplete combustion. *Activated carbon* is amorphous carbon that has been treated with steam and heat until it has a very great affinity for adsorbing many materials. *Graphite* is a soft crystalline modification of carbon that differs greatly in properties from amorphous carbon and from the diamond. *Industrial diamonds* are often spoken of as off-grade gems, borts, or carbonadoes and are used for drill points, special tools, glass cutters, wire-drawing dies, diamond saws, and many other applications where this hardest of all substances is essential.

LAMPBLACK

Lampblack[1] or soot is an old product, made for many years by the restricted combustion of resins, oils, or other hydrocarbons. It has been replaced gradually in the pigment trade, particularly in America, by carbon black, which has superior tinting strength and coloring qualities, but in the manufacture of carbon brushes for electrical equipment and lighting carbons, lampblack is still a very important constituent. Its color is a bluish-gray black, rather than the deep black of carbon black; this steely black is desired for some metal polishes and pencils. Over 15,000,000 lb. are still being produced yearly.

In America either tar oils or petroleum oils are burned with restricted air to form soot or lampblack, a suitable furnace being represented in Fig. 1. The soot is collected in large chambers from which the *raw* lampblack is removed, mixed with tar, molded into bricks or *pugs* and calcined up to about 1000°C. to destroy bulkiness. The calcined pugs are ground to a fine powder. Some furnaces remove the empyreumatic impurities by calcination in the gas stream of the furnaces where formed.

Carbon brushes for use in electrical machinery are made by mixing lampblack with pitch to form a plastic mass. Petroleum coke or graphite may be added to this mix to impart special properties. Plates or blocks from which the brushes are later machined are formed by extrusion or high-pressure molding and these *green* plates are then baked at a high temperature for several days to drive off volatile matter. Some grades are heated in electrical furnaces at temperatures as high as 3000°C. (5432°F.) to convert the amorphous carbon into the soft, crystalline graphite which reduces the friction, increases the life, and generally improves the quality of the product (*cf.* Graphite).

When carbons for the production of special arc lights are desired, a mixture of petroleum coke and thermally decomposed carbon is extruded in the form of a tube. This tube is baked at 1450°C. and a *core* of selected

[1] See KIRK and OTHMER, *op. cit.*, Vol. 3, pp. 1–34, 80–84.

material is forced into its center and calcined again. The type of radiation emitted by the arc is largely dependent on the core material employed, which is frequently a mixture of some lampblack flour, rare-earth oxides, and fluorides with coal tar as a binder. Many millions of

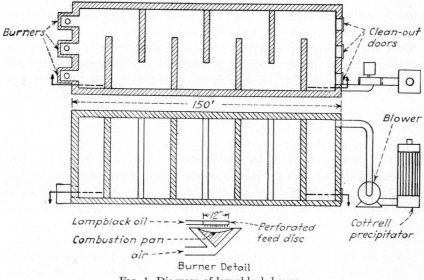

Fig. 1. Diagram of lampblack house.

such lighting carbons are sold per month in peacetime for movie projectors. In war years, a great quantity of such lighting carbons was consumed by searchlights.

CARBON BLACK

The first factory for the making of carbon black[1] in this country was built at New Cumberland, W. Va., in 1872. The black was produced by cooling a burning gas flame against soapstone slabs and scraping off the carbon produced. A short time later, 1883, the roller process was patented and, in 1892, McNutt perfected the present-day channel process. Early production was moderate, 25,000,000 lb. per year, West Virginia and Pennsylvania being the only two producing states.

In the summer of 1912, however, the B. F. Goodrich Company, having been convinced of the value of carbon black in the rubber industry, ordered a carload of the material and later in the same year placed an order for 1,000,000 lb. per year. The advent of this new market stimu-

[1] In a sense, carbon black is a variety of lampblack, both being produced by the incomplete burning of hydrocarbons. Both lampback and carbon black are the same chemically, being over 99 per cent C, but they differ greatly in their physical form such as shape of the particles and also in adsorbed gases.

lated the industry. Expansion has been rapid but, since natural gas was the raw material, the industry was forced to follow the excess gas supply as it changed from Pennsylvania to Indiana, West Virginia, Louisiana, and more recently to Texas, where about 75 per cent of the carbon black is presently produced. The selling price has been constantly reduced in keeping with the expansion of the industry, dropping from $2.50 per pound in 1872 to an average of about 6 cents at present.

Uses and Economics. About 95 per cent of the domestic carbon black consumption is in rubber products, especially tires, heels, and mechanical goods, where it is used to improve wearing qualities by imparting toughness. Carbon black is significantly responsible for the adoption of synthetic rubber for tires during peacetime. High-abrasion furnace blacks when combined with "cold rubber" produce tire treads that consistently give 30 to 50 per cent greater wear than controls compounded with natural rubber and channel blacks. The rubber compound in the modern tire contains around 40 per cent carbon black, which accounts for the rubber industry's role as the leading consumer of carbon black. Carbon black is also the basis for most printing inks. The blacks here must be uncompressed, grind easily, and absorb oil readily. The pigments in black plastics, paints, lacquers, and enamels usually consist of carbon black. Color-grade blacks used for inks and paints are produced almost exclusively by the channel process. Even typewriter ribbons and carbon papers employ this pigment.

TABLE 2. PRODUCTION OF CARBON BLACKS IN THE UNITED STATES[a]
(Millions of pounds)

Year	Total carbon black	Total furnace black	Contact process, chiefly channel
1949	1,223	596	628
1950	1,382	765	617
1951	1,677	1,031	645
1952	1,604	1,040	564
1953	1,610	1,157	453

[a] "Minerals Yearbook," 1953.

Channel black up until 1940 accounted for over 80 per cent of the United States black production. The channel process is producing proportionally less each year (Table 2) because of low (around 4 per cent) yields, high steel requirements and capital investment,[1] and increasing difficulty

[1] The world's largest plant for the manufacture of channel-type carbon black is at Odessa, Tex. Here approximately 1.6 million flames in 536 burner houses play on the moving channels. Each flame consumes 40 to 80 cu. ft. of natural gas per day. See Cox, High Quality–High Yield Carbon Black, *Chem. Eng.*, **57** (6), 116 (1950).

in securing long-term sources of cheap natural gas. Much of the gas available for carbon-black manufacture is being diverted to furnace plants which give higher (up to 35 per cent) yields of black and require smaller capital investments. Probably of still more importance is the competition that channel blacks are facing from the newer furnace blacks made from oil instead of natural gas. *Oil blacks*,[1] superior for many uses, are preferred to the channel blacks even at slightly higher prices. In general, oil-black processes recover from 30 to 60 per cent of the available carbon in the oil.

Manufacture. The two major processes for making carbon black are the channel and the furnace processes. By far the greatest percentage of the world's supply of carbon black is produced from natural gas, although liquefied petroleum gases, natural gasoline, gas oils, fuel oils, or residuum are used alone or to enrich the natural gas for some of the finer grades of furnace blacks.

Channel Process. The older channel process will be considered first. Channel black is nearer true black in color, and, in some of its forms is more finely divided than furnace black. The *unit changes*[2] involved are:

Natural gas is "dried" of its gasoline, usually by adsorption (Op.).

Natural gas is cracked or pyrolyzed by contact with moving and cooled channel iron (Pr.); here the temperature of the products of combustion of 1000°C. is reduced to 500°C.

Carbon black is scraped off the channel, conveyed to packing house, sifted, and packaged (Op.).

Reactions:

$$CH_4(g) + 2O_2(g) \rightarrow CO_2(g) + 2H_2O(g); \quad \Delta H = -191{,}800 \text{ cal.}$$
$$CH_4(g) \rightarrow C(amorph.) + 2H_2(g); \quad \Delta H = +20{,}300 \text{ cal.}$$

In manufacturing carbon black the very low chemical efficiency of changing CH_4 to C, whereby the unconverted CH_4 and the H_2 burn completely to $CO_2(CO)$ and H_2O, supplies the endothermic heat and energy necessary to crack or pyrolyze CH_4 to C. Thus, no outside energy input is needed here. However, as 1,000 cu. ft. of CH_4 contains about 35 lb. of C, while the yield is only 1.50 to 2.25 lb. of carbon black, great wastage is evident.

The natural gas, as it comes from the ground, is first treated to remove the natural gasoline and then sent to the burner houses. These are long, low sheet-iron buildings containing from 3,000 to 4,000 burner tips where the gas is burned with an insufficient supply of air, controlled by the sides of the sheds, to produce a luminous flame that impinges or contacts the underside of the channels. The channels, made of mild steel and

---

[1] SHEARON, *et al.*, Oil Black, *Ind. Eng. Chem.*, **44**, 685 (1952). This is one of the excellent staff-industry reports with operating data, diagrams, and flow sheets.

[2] For flow diagram, see *Chem. Inds.*, **64**, 40 (1949).

8 to 10 in. wide, move continuously backward and forward suspended from overhead rails. The carbon black thus produced is removed from the channels as they pass over stationary scrapers and falls into hoppers which feed screw conveyers carrying the carbon to the central packing house. The spent gases in the newer plants are conducted through modern dust-recovery systems, using Orlon filter bags. These not only completely recover all the black but avoid the dark pall that used to overhang such plants. In the packing house the black is *bolted* to remove coarse particles and grit. The material is extremely light and fluffy and must be agitated to reduce the bulk. The resulting black is a commercial grade known as *uncompressed;* its density is 12 to 13 lb. per cu. ft.; and it is used in the paper, ink, and paint industries.

All but a small fraction of shipments of all carbon blacks are pelletized for convenient bulk handling and to reduce the tendency to dust. There are several examples of the two principal pelletizing[1] processes, wet and dry. In the commonly used wet process, the fluffy black is agitated and mixed with water in a trough by a shaft with radially projecting pins which forms the pellets. They are dried in a horizontal, gas-fired rotating drier drum. A commonly used dry pelleting process utilizes one or more horizontal drums, 5 to 10 ft. in diameter and 20 to 40 ft. long, supported by steel rollers. The pellets are formed by the gentle agitation and rolling (5 to 10 r.p.m.) of the black. Operation is continuous and residence time in the drum is from 12 to 36 hr.

Channel blacks are classified principally on the basis of their ease of processing into rubber or their electrical conductivity. The principal types are EPC, easy-processing channel; MPC, medium-processing channel; and HPC, hard-processing channel blacks. It can be said that channel blacks find their greatest utility when compounded with natural rubber.

Furnace Process.[2] In the furnace process (Fig. 2) all of the combustion takes place in a confined, insulated refractory chamber containing turbulent blast gases already burning at a temperature around 2500°F. The volume of air forced in is about 50 per cent of that required for complete combustion. The feed for high-quality furnace black is preheated either by the complete combustion of a portion of the gas through direct mixing, or by heat transfer from surface-type heat exchangers. Since preheated gas complicates burning conditions in a 2500°F. furnace somewhat, preheated oil or combinations of oil and gas can be controlled more easily for the high-quality blacks. The furnace process permits yields as high as 12 lb. per M cu. ft. of natural gas and still leaves enough fuel value to furnish the necessary heat to keep the process going.

[1] ANON., Agglomeration, *Chem. Eng.*, **58** (10), 161 (1951).

[2] KIDOO, Carbon Black, *Chem. Eng.*, **58** (3), 104 (1951). For a pictured flow sheet, see ANON., Carbon Black, *Chem. Eng.*, **58** (7), 176 (1951). STOKES and DOBBIN, Carbon Black Shifts to Furnace Process, *Chem. Inds.*, **64**, 40 (1949).

The rapid intermingling of the hot and relatively cold streams in the furnace results in almost instant heat transfer and the pyrolysis to carbon particles. The carbon-laden gases are led through flues to a spray cooling tower. Actual collection of the carbon particles is effected by clustering with an electrostatic precipitator followed by final separation through centrifugal "cyclones." The carbon is pelleted as described under the channel process. Furnace blacks are classified according to reinforcement of rubber electrical conductance, or particle fineness. In the order of decreasing particle size and increasing rubber-reinforcing properties, the principal furnace blacks are (F designates furnace black): SRF (semi-reinforcing), HMF (high modulus), MAF (medium abrasion), FF (fine

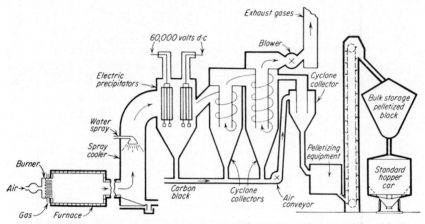

FIG. 2. Flow diagram, carbon black, furnace process. See text for quantities. (*Courtesy of Chemical Industries.*)

furnace), and HAF (high abrasion). HAF is the principal "oil black." It imparts to both natural and synthetic, especially "cold rubber," a high degree of reinforcement and abrasion resistance, making it exceptionally useful in tire-tread manufacture.

Other Processes. In the thermal-decomposition furnace process the CH_4 is pyrolyzed into hydrogen and carbon over heated brick checkerwork. The operation is cyclic, with a heating and "make" periods. In the first the combustion of natural gas or other combustibles with air heats the furnace to 3000°F., whereupon natural gas alone is fed into the furnace. The reaction is

$$CH_4 \rightarrow C(amorph.) + 2H_2(g); \qquad \Delta H = +20,300 \text{ cal.}$$

The cracked products pass from the furnace and are cooled by a water spray before separation and packaging.

Carbon black is also manufactured by the disk-contact process, where the flame impinges on a moving disk instead of a channel. The roller process produces a special type of black which is used in the ink industry. Often classified as thermal blacks are acetylene blacks made by the exothermic decomposition of acetylene. These blacks are employed in dry cells and for imparting high electrical and thermal conductivities to rubber.

CARBON AND GRAPHITE STRUCTURAL MATERIALS[1]

Since they combine chemical resistance with a variety of physical properties desirable in chemical plant structural materials, carbon and

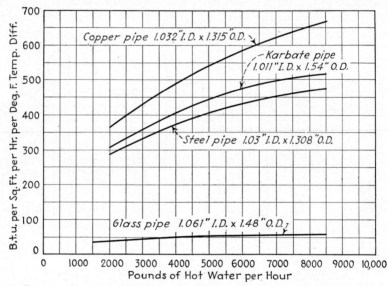

FIG. 3. Comparative over-all heat transfer. The curves show comparative rates of heat transfer through 1-in. standard copper, steel, glass, and Karbate pipes. The test was hot water to cold water with the cold water held at 12,000 lb. per hr. throughout the test. (*Courtesy of National Carbon Company.*)

graphite are among the most widely used nonmetallics in this field. Carbon and graphite are both highly resistant to thermal shock and graphite has an unusually high thermal conductivity (Table 1). This, combined with excellent machinability, makes graphite and impervious graphite the preferred choice for very many items of chemical equipment. Impervious graphite (or impervious carbon) is made by impregnating the somewhat porous base graphite (or carbon, if impervious carbon is to be produced) with a synthetic resin. The impregnation employs a vacuum-

[1] For a most excellent review, see the Carbon and Graphite section of the Materials of Construction reviews, October issue of *Ind. Eng. Chem.*, annual since 1947.

pressure cycle for complete resin penetration. The resin generally used is a phenolic type, which is polymerized by curing at elevated temperatures in steam-heated autoclaves.

The chemical resistance of Karbate impervious graphite and impervious carbon materials produced in this manner is practically identical with that of the original stocks. The impervious materials are recommended for use at material body temperatures up to 338°F. Specifically, Karbate impervious graphite is recommended for practically all mineral acids, salt solutions, alkalies, and organic compounds at temperatures to boiling. The only exceptions are when strong oxidizing conditions exist, such as with sulfuric acid above 96 per cent concentration, nitric acid above 20 per cent concentration, strong chromic acid and bromine, fluorine, and iodine. Cements for assembling impervious graphite use resins

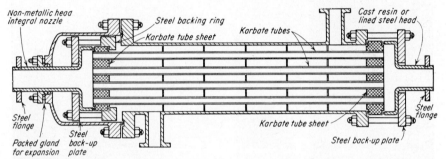

Fig. 4. Sectional view—graphite tube exchanger—single-tube pass: used for heating dilute sulfuric acid in rayon processing. (*Courtesy of Struthers-Wells.*)

similar to those which produce the impervious material. Permanent weld-like joints are formed with corrosion resistance and strength equivalent to that of the basic material.

Carbon and graphite are most commonly used in the form of brick and large blocks or plates for chemical-process applications. Single-piece shapes are made in diameters up to 3 ft. 4 in. and in lengths up to 19 ft. 2 in. Figure 5 shows typical large-block construction with carbon and graphite. The "quonset-hut" type structure is a graphite chamber for the combustion of phosphorus with oxygen to form P_2O_5, which is then hydrated in the silolike carbon structure alongside to form phosphoric acid. Similar construction is used for linings of sulfuric acid concentrators and for electrostatic precipitators, where dimensional stability is important. Tank linings of carbon brick are encountered in metal pickling, cleaning, and finishing work, particularly where exposure to hydrofluoric acid is involved.

Impervious graphite is the most important of the carbon and graphite structural materials to the chemical industry. Graphite's easy machining qualities, together with its availability in many sizes and shapes, permits construction of a complete range of process equipment, including heat exchangers, pumps, valves, pipe and fittings, towers, and absorbers. Karbate impervious graphite's high thermal conductivity (see Fig. 3) is particularly important in heat-exchange applications. Most common of the standard constructions are the conventional shell-and-tube heat exchangers, shown in Fig. 4, which range in size to units containing as much

Fig. 5. The right-hand structure is built completely of electric furnace graphite, while the tower at the left is assembled of amorphous carbon blocks. Unit for production of phosphoric acid. (*Courtesy of National Carbon Company.*)

as 2,300 sq. ft. of transfer surface. Operating pressures range up to 75 lb. per sq. in., with steam pressures of 50 lb. per sq. in. gage. Other uses of Karbate carbon include plate-type heat exchangers, double-pipe concentric-unit cascade coolers, and centrifugal pumps (see Fig. 1, Chap. 21).

Structural shapes of extremely high purity have recently become of great importance in work connected with the atomic bomb and nucleonic reactions and power development in piles. Graphite blocks are used to hold the slugs of uranium or enriched nuclear fuel in position in the space lattice which forms the nuclear reactor. These have the required structural strength at high temperatures and a high thermal conductivity to facilitate the removal of the enormous amounts of heat generated in the nuclear reaction. In addition to these advantages carbon is apparently the unique choice for use in the fixed lattice pile because it is inert with respect to reaction with neutrons. The atoms of carbon "moderate," or slow down, the fast-moving neutrons to speeds at which they can be captured by uranium and so enable the chain reaction to continue. The reason for the extremely high level of purity required for the carbon moderator is that almost any likely impurity would compete with the uranium in capturing neutrons to such an extent that the chain reaction would stop because of an insufficient supply of neutrons.

ACTIVATED CARBON

Activated carbon first came into prominence through its use as an adsorbent in gas masks in the First World War. However, the knowledge that carbon produced by the decomposition of wood can remove coloring matter from solutions dates back to the fifteenth century. The first commercial application of this property was not made, however, until 1794, when charcoal filters were used in a British sugar refinery. About 1812, bone char was discovered by Figuer. Activated carbons can be divided into two main classes—those used for adsorption of gases and vapors for which a granular material is generally employed, and those in purification of liquids for which a powdered material is desired.

Uses. There is no particular activated carbon that is effective for all purposes (see Table 3). As a decolorant, activated carbon, with its very great surface area, is hundreds of times more efficient than charcoal and at least forty times more than bone black. It is estimated that 5 lb. of activated carbon has an active area of 1 sq. mile or more. The amount of materials adsorbed by activated carbon is surprisingly large, amounting frequently to from a quarter to an equal weight of such vapors as gasoline, benzene, or carbon tetrachloride. These substances can be *recovered and reused.* Adsorption is a physical phenomenon depending largely upon the surface area.[1]

The major use[2] of activated carbon is in solution purification, such as the cleanup of cane, beet, and corn sugar solutions and for the removal of tastes and odors from water supplies, vegetable and animal fats and oils, alcoholic beverages, chemicals, and pharmaceuticals. The recovery of streptomycin probably represents the furthest advance in the continuous treatment of liquids.

The vapor-adsorbent type of activated carbon was first used in military gas masks because of its ability to adsorb certain poisonous gases, and it

[1] For an excellent discussion of the theories of adsorption see LEWIS, SQUIRES and BROUGHTON, "Industrial Chemistry of Colloidal and Amorphous Materials," Chap. 5, The Macmillan Company, New York, 1942.

[2] STAFF, Separation by Adsorption, *Chem. Inds.*, **61**, 625 (1947).

is now widely employed in both military and industrial gas masks. An important field of application is in the industrial recovery of vapors (see Fig. 6). Recovery of such vapors amounts to billions of pounds per year, with a recovered value of several hundred million dollars. Activated carbon is able to adsorb practically any organic solvent at about 100°F. and release it when heated[1] to 250°F. Activated carbon can now be made in extruded form which in vapor adsorbing presents only about half the air

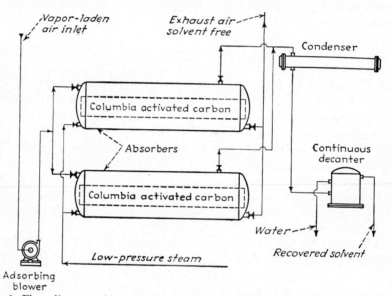

FIG. 6. Flow diagram of one type of solvent-recovery plant employing Columbia activated carbon. A typical plant of this type in recovering a hydrocarbon vapor at a rate of 1,100 lb. per hr. from 13,000 cu. ft. per min. of vapor-laden air will have the following approximate average utility requirements per pound of recovered solvent: steam—3.5 lb.; water—7.5 gal.; electric power—0.05 kw.-hr. (*Courtesy of Carbide and Carbon Chemicals Co.*)

resistance of the older granulated heterogeneous powder. A very important continuous process[2] for close fractionation for light-hydrocarbon recovery from gas streams has been developed. This *Hypersorption* process employs a moving bed of activated coconut shells which have high adsorptive capacity and are more resistant to abrasion than the other carbons.

Manufacture. Many carbonaceous materials, such as sawdust, lignite, coal, peat, wood, charcoal, nutshells, and fruit pits, may be used for the

[1] ANON., Solvent Recovery with Activated Carbon, *Chem. Eng.*, **54** (1), 136 (1947), with a pictured flow sheet.

[2] BERG, Hypersorption Process for Separation of Light Gases, *Trans. Am. Inst. Chem. Engrs.*, **42**, 665 (1946).

manufacture of activated carbon, but the properties of the finished material are governed by the source.[1]

Decolorizing activated carbons are usually employed as powders. Thus the raw materials for this type are either structureless or have a weak

FIG. 7. View of solvent-recovery plant using Columbia activated carbon. Adsorbers are in the open while other equipment is housed. Equipment arranged for addition of other adsorbers when increased capacity is required. (*Courtesy of Carbide and Carbon Chemicals Co.*)

structure. Sawdust and lignite yield carbons of this kind. Vapor-adsorbent carbons are used in the form of hard granules and are generally produced from coconut shells, fruit pits, and briquetted coal and charcoal.

Activation is a physical change wherein the surface of the carbon is tremendously increased by the removal of hydrocarbons from the carbon surface. Several methods are available for this activation. The most widely employed are the treatment of the carbonaceous material with oxidizing

[1] Mantell's section on Adsorption in PERRY, *op. cit.*, should be consulted for formulas pertaining to adsorption, flow sheets of plants using adsorbents, engineering data and generalized theory of adsorption, particularly pp. 886, 888, 897–909; on p. 905 is given a tabular comparison of activated carbon, activated alumina, and silica gel. *Cf.* MORGAN and FINK, Binders and Base Materials for Active Carbon, *Ind. Eng. Chem.*, **38**, 219 (1946).

gases such as air, steam, or carbon dioxide and the carbonization of the raw material in the presence of chemical agents such as zinc chloride or phosphoric acid.

The gaseous oxidation activation employs material that has been carbonized at a temperature high enough to remove most of the volatile constituents but not high enough to crack the evolved gases. The carbonized material is subjected to the action of the oxidizing gas, usually steam or carbon dioxide, in a furnace or retort at 1475 to 1800°F. Conditions are controlled to permit removal of substantially all the adsorbed hydrocarbons and some of the carbon so as to increase the surface area.

The use of chemical impregnating agents causes the carbonization to proceed under conditions that prevent the deposition of hydrocarbons on the carbon surface. The raw material, sawdust or peat, is mixed with the chemical agent, dried, and calcined at temperatures up to 1560°F. When

TABLE 3. APPLICATIONS OF ACTIVATED CARBON[a]

A. *Adsorbing Gases or Vapors (Gas-adsorbent Carbon):*
  1. Adsorbent in military and industrial gas masks and other devices.
  2. Recovery of gasoline from natural gas.
  3. Recovery of benzol from manufactured gas.
  4. Recovery of solvents vaporized in industrial processes such as manufacture of rayon, rubber products, artificial leather, transparent wrappings, film, smokeless powder, and plastics, and in rotogravure printing, dry cleaning of fabrics, degreasing of metals, solvent extraction, fermentation, etc.
  5. Removing impurities from gases such as hydrogen, nitrogen, helium, acetylene, ammonia, carbon dioxide, or carbon monoxide.
  6. Removing organic sulfur compounds and other impurities from manufactured gas.
  7. Removing odors from air in air conditioning, stench abatement, etc.
B. *Decolorizing and Purifying Liquids (Decolorizing Carbon):*
  1. Refining of cane sugar, beet sugar, glucose, and other sirups.
  2. Refining oils, fats, and waxes such as cottonseed oil, coconut oil, lard, and mineral oil.
  3. Removing impurities from food products such as gelatine, vinegar, cocoa butter, pectin, fruit juices, and alcoholic beverages.
  4. Removing impurities from pharmaceutical and other chemical products, including acids.
  5. Water purification—removal of taste, odor, and color.
  6. Removing impurities from used oils, dry-cleaning solvents, electroplating solutions, sirups, etc.
  7. Removal of metals from solution—silver, gold, etc.
C. *Catalyst and Catalyst Carrier (Gas-adsorbent Carbon):*
  1. Manufacture of phosgene.
  2. Carrier for hydrogenation catalysts, etc.
D. *Medicine:*
  1. Internal medicine for adsorption of gases, toxins, and poisons.
  2. Administering adsorbed medicinals.
  3. External adsorbent for odors from ulcers and wounds.

[a] RAY, Carbide and Carbon Chemicals Co.

the carbonization has been completed, the residual impregnating agent is removed by leaching with water.

Revivification. After an activated carbon has become saturated with a vapor or an adsorbed color, either the vapor can be steamed out, condensed, and recovered as shown in Fig. 6, or the coloration can be destroyed and the carbon made ready for reuse. The oldest example of this process is exemplified by that decolorizing carbon long known as *bone char* or *bone black*.[1] This consists of carbon deposited on a skeleton of tricalcium phosphate and is made by the carbonization in closed retorts at 1380 to 1740°F. of fat-freed bones. Over 50,000,000 lb. of bone char with a value of around $2,500,000 to $3,000,000 are produced annually in the United States, and much of this is employed in the manufacture of sugar.[2] After saturation with impurities, the bone char is washed free of sugar and recalcined at around 750°F. under restricted oxidizing conditions that destroy the impurities and restore the adsorbing properties of the carbon.

GRAPHITE

Graphite, as it occurs naturally, has been known to man for many centuries. Probably its first use was for decorative purposes in prehistoric times. By the Middle Ages it was being employed for writing and drawing purposes. The name *graphite* was given to this substance by the mineralogist Werner, in 1879. Natural graphite was the only kind available except in laboratory quantities until 1896, when Edward G. Acheson invented the first successful process for the commercial production of artificial graphite, as an outgrowth of his work on silicon carbide. He discovered that, when most forms of amorphous carbon are placed together with certain catalysts such as silica or alumina in an electric furnace and subjected to a temperature of approximately 3000°C., they are converted into the allotrope, graphite. It is now known that the industrial process converts amorphous carbon directly to graphite in an electric furnace.

Uses and Economics. Foundry facings constitute the largest single use of *natural graphite* followed by lubricants, batteries, and crucibles. About 11 per cent of the United States consumption of natural graphite goes into the manufacture of crucibles. For this purpose it is mixed with clay, sand, and water and then set away to age. The crucible is formed on "jiggers" and then air-dried and baked in a kiln. The graphite of the crucible wall begins to oxidize at about 450°C., and the life of the crucible

[1] PERRY, *op. cit.*, pp. 897–898, including flow charts; DIETZ, V. R., "Preliminary Survey of Bone Char Revivification and Filtration," National Bureau of Standards, Special Report (1947).

[2] See Chap. 30.

depends on keeping the *rate* of oxidation down. This rate depends on temperature but also on composition of furnace gases and of binder or glaze. Another large consumer of natural graphite is the pencil industry, which requires a fairly pure raw material containing around 90 per cent graphite. The lower grades of the natural material, containing 35 to 50 per cent carbon, are used[1] in paints, stove polishes, lubricants, etc.

The United States production of *natural graphite* or *plumbago* has been practically nonexistent or small in recent years. Imports, however, have continued at around 52,000 tons, four-fifths of which came from Mexico. Total world production of all graphite in 1948 was 147,000 metric tons, excluding Russia.

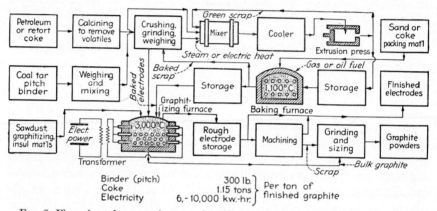

Binder (pitch) 300 lb.
Coke 1.15 tons } Per ton of
Electricity 6,-10,000 kw.-hr. } finished graphite

FIG. 8. Flow sheet for manufacture of artificial graphite electrodes and powders.

Artificial graphite can be substituted for any of the uses of the natural product except in the making of clay-graphite crucibles, although many crucibles and trays of artificial graphite are manufactured. On the other hand, the very pure artificial graphite has many fields of exclusive use, such as a high-temperature lubricant or for electrodes in various chemical manufactures and for nucleonic reactors. For lubricating purposes it is suspended in water or oil and placed in contact with the moving parts. The liquid media evaporate, leaving the graphite well distributed over the entire surface. The electrical industry uses graphite for electrodes, brushes, contacts, and electronic-tube rectifier elements. A considerable amount is employed for a parting compound to prevent molds of such articles as glass bottles and rubber tires from sticking together. Various friction elements, such as brake linings, are treated with graphite to prevent grabbing, and it is incorporated as an ingredient in lubricating oils and greases.

[1] SZYMANOWITZ, Preparation, Properties and Uses of Colloidal Graphite, *J. Chem. Educ.*, **16**, 413 (1939).

Manufacture. *Artificial graphite* is made electrically from retort or petroleum coke, in line with the flow sheet depicted in Fig. 8. The reaction for this allotropic change is essentially

$$C(amorph.) \rightarrow C(graphite); \qquad \Delta H = -2,500 \text{ cal.}$$

The *unit changes* involved in commercializing these reactions, as charted in Fig. 8, may be summarized for electrodes or other graphite articles:

Coke (petroleum or retort) is selected and shipped to graphite plant (Op.).
Carbon material is calcined (1400°C.) to volatilize impurities (Op. and Pr.).
Raw materials are carefully analyzed.
Raw materials are ground, mixed with binder giving green electrodes, and arranged in furnace (Op.).
Green electrodes are baked at 1100°C. to carbonize binder and furnish amorphous electrodes (Pr.).
Amorphous electrodes are graphitized in electric furnace at high temperature (3000°C.) (Pr.).
Graphite is shaped to industrial demands and the scrap powdered (Op.).

In manufacturing graphite the furnace used consists essentially of a core of the coke being graphitized, surrounded by a heavy layer of sand, coke, and sawdust as insulation. The floor and ends of the furnace are built mainly of concrete, with cooling coils in the ends to reduce the temperature of the electrodes in contact with air to prevent them from burning. The side walls, built of loose blocks and plates, are torn down after each run. The average charge is approximately 30,000 lb. of material. The resistance of the charge produces a temperature of around 3000°C. As the coke graphitizes,[1] the voltage, owing to lowered resistance, drops from 200 to 40 volts. The high temperature employed decomposes, for instance, any silicon carbide that may be present and volatilizes products other than graphite. A complete cycle of the furnace consists in: loading, 1 day; power on, 5 to 6 days; cooling, about 25 days; unloading, 2 days. Thus about 1 month is required from charge to charge. After cooling, the furnace is torn down and the graphitized carbon taken out, crushed, and ground. The insulating sand is used over again. There is also used a graphitizing countercurrent electric furnace for uniform blocks.

In the manufacture of *amorphous carbon electrodes*[2] the petroleum coke or anthracite used is crushed and hot mixed with a pitch binder thinned with oil (see Fig. 9). The resulting soft mass is either extruded or molded to the finished electrode shape. These green electrodes are then baked at

[1] SPRAGUE, The Graphitizing Furnace, *Trans. Electrochem. Soc.*, **70**, 57 (1936).

[2] Detailed flow sheets for both graphite and carbon electrodes are given by MANTELL on p. 726 of "Rogers' Manual of Industrial Chemistry," 6th ed., D. Van Nostrand Company, Inc., New York, 1942.

around 1100°C. in either a gas-fired furnace or an electric furnace. After cooling and removal from the furnace these electrodes are turned down and threaded on a lathe. A similar process is involved in making brushes for motors, the carbon being made into small plates which are then cut to the necessary shape for making the brushes. Graphite electrodes have less electrical resistance and consequently can conduct more current per

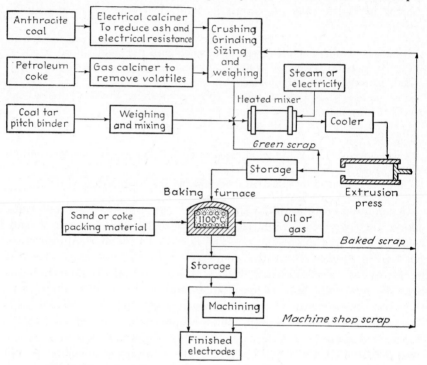

FIG. 9. Flow chart for manufacture of amorphous carbon electrodes.

cross section, but they cost more than the usual amorphous[1] carbon electrode.

INDUSTRIAL DIAMONDS

Because the diamond is the *hardest* and most permanent of all known substances, it has great industrial importance in cutting, shaping, and polishing hard substances. For a thousand years diamonds have been employed for this purpose in the East. Their use is increasing, particularly in countries like the United States where much high-speed machining of hard materials is required. All electric-light filaments and millions of

[1] For a tabular comparison of the properties of graphite and amorphous carbon electrodes, see PERRY, *op. cit.*, pp. 1822, 1820–1824.

miles of other wires are drawn through diamond dies. Consequently this country is the largest consumer of industrial diamonds in the world. The world production of industrial diamonds in 1952 was 15,800,000 carats[1] (6,960 lb.), of which the United States imported 13,677,248 carats in 1952, valued at 51.8 million dollars.

Three types are employed: (1) crystalline and cleavable *diamonds* more or less off grade and off color; (2) *bort*, translucent to opaque, gray or dark brown, with a radiated or confused crystalline structure (inferior grades of crystalline diamonds are also called *bort*); (3) *carbonado*, frequently known as a *black diamond* or carbon. It occurs in an opaque, tough, crystalline aggregate without cleavage. Bort is the most widely used of the industrial diamonds.

Over 90 per cent of industrial diamonds comes from Africa, the remainder from Brazil, British Guiana, and Venezuela. Diamond powder manufactured from bort costs about $3 a carat, although bort commands a price of $2.25 per carat (July, 1954, as set by the world selling organization). In addition to the usual industrial varieties, there are available chips and small fragments of gem diamonds which, however, are utilized in the making of diamond powder for polishing gem diamonds and other hard materials and for other purposes, without crushing. These chips also serve as the "point" in glass cutters.

TABLE 4. CHIEF CONSUMPTION OF INDUSTRIAL DIAMONDS, BY WEIGHT

	Per cent
Crushing bort for bonded wheels and powder	66
Diamond drilling	20
Diamond tools	10
Diamond dies and miscellaneous	4

An extensive use of industrial diamonds is in manufacturing shaped tools for turning and boring. The *extreme hardness* of the diamond during the operation of a lathe enables the operator greatly to increase machining speed. Tools set with natural industrial diamonds are a practical necessity in truing and dressing worn artificial abrasive wheels in all industry where precision grinding is performed. Bonded diamond wheels for grinding hard materials such as cemented carbide tools are made from crushed bort. Since the continual drawing of wire through dies causes much wear, dies for accurate wire drawings are made out of diamonds. Such dies are preferably made from fine quality of clear stones with an appropriate hole drilled therein. Such holes are started by using sharp diamond points and finished by lapping with diamond dust. Such dies should be carefully mounted so that they will not be fractured while in use. When worn, dies must be reopened to the next larger size of wire. In *drilling* through rock for oil or water or for the placing of dynamite in quarries the steel drill

[1] The international carat is 0.200 gm.

bits are set with whole small industrial diamonds in metallic heads; here the diamonds do the actual work, the steel heads simply serving to hold them in the cutting position. These diamond drills enable actual cores of the rock to be taken out and examined with consequent greatly increased knowledge of what minerals or deposits lie underground. The use of industrial diamonds is so important that automobile manufacturers have stated that, while only a few cents worth are consumed per car, the automobiles would cost more than double were it not for diamond tools.

SELECTED REFERENCES

Grodzinski, P., "Diamond and Gem Stone Industrial Production," N.A.G. Press, London, 1942.

Hassler, J. W., "Active Carbon," Chemical Publishing Company, Inc., New York, 1951.

Mantell, C. L., "Industrial Carbon," 2d ed., D. Van Nostrand Company, Inc., New York, 1946.

————, "Industrial Electrochemistry," 3d ed., McGraw-Hill Book Company, Inc., New York, 1950.

————, "Adsorption," 2d ed., McGraw-Hill Book Company, Inc., New York, 1951.

Creighton, H. J., "Principles and Applications of Electrochemistry," 4th ed., John Wiley & Sons, Inc., New York, 1943.

Koehler, W. A., "Applications of Electrochemistry," 2d ed., John Wiley & Sons, Inc., New York, 1944.

Kortüm, G., and J. O'M. Bockris, "Textbook of Electrochemistry," 2 vols., Elsevier Press, Inc., New York, 1951.

CHAPTER 10

THE CERAMIC INDUSTRIES

The ceramic industries, also sometimes called the *clay products* or *silicate industries*, have as their finished materials a variety of articles that are essentially silicates. These products may be classified as follows:

1. Whitewares—chinaware, earthenware, pottery, porcelain, stoneware, and vitreous ware.
2. Heavy clay products—common brick, face brick, terra cotta, sewer pipe, and drain tile.
3. Refractories—fire-clay brick, chromite, silica brick, basic bricks (magnesite and forsterite), alumina products, silicon carbide refractories, pure oxide refractories (alumina, magnesia, beryllia, stabilized zirconia, and thoria), and metal-bonded ceramics (oxides, nitrides, borides, and carbides).
4. Enamels and enameled metal.
5. Glass.

The first four of these will be presented later in this chapter; the glass industry will be dealt with separately in Chap. 12.

The making of pottery is one of the most interesting and ancient of man's industries; the Chinese and the Egyptians engaged in the art over 6,000 years ago. Ceramics are an important hobby for American men and women. Museums contain, as a record of man's culture, the clay products produced throughout the ages, many of which have an artistic as well as a utilitarian aspect. Although the essential manufacturing processes used in most of the ceramic industries have remained largely unchanged for a long time, since 1920 many significant new developments[1] have taken place, such as pure oxide refractories, metal-bonded oxides, carbides, nitrides, and borides.

Uses and Economics. The value of the pottery produced in the United States from 1930 to 1940 fluctuated between $40,000,000 and $112,-000,000 annually. The present position is around $150,000,000. Table 1 shows certain statistics for the ceramic industry. Brick production varies greatly with the general building program for the country. In 1925 the production of common brick reached 7.6 billions and in 1924 face brick

[1] See Ceramics, in Materials of Construction reviews, published annually in *Ind. Eng. Chem.*, for October, since 1944.

173

TABLE 1. PRODUCTION AND SHIPMENTS OF CERAMICS, FOR THE
UNITED STATES: 1952[a]
(Money figures in thousands of dollars)

Product	Production quantity	Shipments and interplant transfers	
		Quantity	Value
Clay brick and hollow tile:			
Unglazed clay brick (common and face), M brick	5,881,748	5,635,249	154,566
Unglazed clay structural tile, ton	962,837	919,761	11,243
Hollow facing clay tile, M brick equivalents	413,479	389,376	22,104
Glazed and unglazed clay floor and wall tile and accessories, M sq. ft.	125,966	117,544	60,962
Drain tile, tons	819,919	815,490	14,073
Clay sewer pipe, tons	1,646,110	1,544,809	58,943
Clay refractories			161,934
Fire-clay brick, standard and special shapes, except super-duty, M 9-in. equivalents	628,262	610,254	70,849
Super-duty fire-clay brick, standard and special shapes, M 9-in. equivalents	96,495	93,428	16,951
High-alumina brick, standard and special shapes, M 9-in. equivalents	22,251	21,655	6,655
Insulating firebrick, M 9-in. equivalents	60,343	60,127	11,510
Ladle brick, M 9-in. equivalents	209,511	199,913	13,490
Hot-top refractories, M 9-in. equivalents	49,148	48,892	5,042
Sleeves, nozzles, runner brick, and tuyères, M 9-in. equivalents	55,085	54,231	7,789
Glass-house pots, tank blocks, upper structure, and floaters, tons	20,513	19,404	3,373
Vitreous and semivitreous plumbing fixtures:			
Vitreous china	n.a.	n.a.	82,295
Glazed earthenware, concrete, and composition	n.a.	n.a.	2,935
Nonclay refractories			138,643
Silica brick, standard and special shapes, M 9-in. equivalents	336,579	327,997	46,797
Magnesite and magnesite-chrome (magnesite predominating) brick, standard and special shapes, M 9-in. equivalents	38,420	38,150	21,949
Chrome and chrome-magnesite (chrome predominating), M 9-in. equivalents	48,708	48,187	23,658
Graphite and other carbon crucibles and retorts, tons	9,810	9,844	5,573
Other graphite and carbon refractories, tons	1,358	1,329	593
Other nonclay refractories, standard and special shapes			18,973
Silicon carbide			7,761
Mullite and kyanite			3,766
Fused alumina and bauxite			2,560
Zirconia, forsterite, fused magnesia, pyrophyllite, sillimanite, and other nonclay shapes			4,886

[a] Annual Survey of Manufactures, 1952.

attained 2.5 billions. Both have declined since those maxima. Ohio and Pennsylvania are the chief manufacturing states for the ceramic industries with New Jersey, West Virginia, California, and Missouri following in sequence.

BASIC RAW MATERIALS

The three main raw materials used in making the common ceramic products are (1) clay, (2) feldspar, called *spar* in the industry, (3) sand, called *flint* in the industry. Clays are more or less impure hydrated aluminum silicates that have resulted from the weathering of igneous rocks in which feldspar was a noteworthy original mineral. The reaction may be expressed,

$$K_2O \cdot Al_2O_3 \cdot 6SiO_2 + CO_2 + 2H_2O$$
Potash feldspar

$$\rightarrow K_2CO_3 + Al_2O_3 \cdot 2SiO_2 \cdot 2H_2O + 4SiO_2$$
Kaolinite   Silica

There are a number of mineral species called *clay minerals* but the most important are kaolinite, $Al_2O_3 \cdot 2SiO_2 \cdot 2H_2O$; beidellite, $Al_2O_3 \cdot 3SiO_2 \cdot H_2O$; montmorillonite, $Al_2O_3 \cdot 4SiO_2 \cdot H_2O$; and halloysite, $Al_2O_3 \cdot 2SiO_2 \cdot 3H_2O$. From a ceramic viewpoint clays are plastic and moldable when sufficiently finely pulverized and wet, rigid when dry, and vitreous when fired at a suitably high temperature. Upon these properties depend the manufacturing procedures.

TABLE 2. BASIC RAW MATERIALS FOR CERAMICS

	Kaolinite	Feldspar	Quartz or flint
Formula...............	$Al_2O_3 \cdot 2SiO_2 \cdot 2H_2O$	$K_2O \cdot Al_2O_3 \cdot 6SiO_2$	SiO_2
Plasticity..............	Plastic	Nonplastic	Nonplastic
Fusibility..............	Refractory[a]	Easily fusible binder	Refractory[a]
Melting point..........	3245°F.; 1785°C.	2100°F.; 1150°C.	3110°F.; 1710°C.
Shrinkage on burning....	Much shrinkage	Fuses	No shrinkage

[a] Infusible at highest temperature of coal fire (1400°C.).

Accompanying the clay minerals in the clays of commerce are varying amounts of feldspar, quartz, and other impurities such as oxides of iron. In nearly all the clays used in the ceramic industry, the basic clay mineral is kaolinite, although bentonite[1] clays based on montmorillonite are used to some extent where very high plasticity is desired. This property of the plasticity[2] or workability of clays is influenced most by the physical

---

[1] See PERRY, *op. cit.*, pp. 1085–1091 for flotation.

[2] LEWIS, SQUIRES, and BROUGHTON, "Industrial Chemistry of Colloidal and Amorphous Materials," bentonite, pp. 241–248; plasticity, pp. 453–456, The Macmillan Company, New York, 1942.

condition of the clay and varies greatly among the different types of clay. Clays are chosen for the particular properties desired and are frequently blended to give the most favorable result. Clays vary so much in their physical properties and in the impurities present, that it is frequently necessary to upgrade them by the *beneficiation* procedure. Figure 1 shows the steps[1] necessary for such a procedure wherein sand and mica are removed. The steps in this flow sheet apply almost altogether to the physical changes or *unit operations* such as size separation by screening or selective settling, filtration, and drying. However, the colloidal properties are controlled by appropriate addition agents, such as sodium silicate and alum.

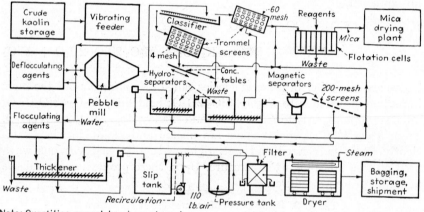

Note: Quantities cannot be given since clay recovery varies from 8 to 18 percent, depending on crude clay used. Plant shown here designed for 30 tons per day output regardless of crude clay variations

FIG. 1. China clay beneficiation. (*Courtesy of Harris Clay Company.*)

There are three common types of feldspar: potash feldspar, $K_2O \cdot Al_2O_3 \cdot 6SiO_2$; soda feldspar, $Na_2O \cdot Al_2O_3 \cdot 6SiO_2$; and lime feldspar $CaO \cdot Al_2O_3 \cdot 6SiO_2$, all of which are used in ceramic products to some extent. The first is the most common. Feldspar is of great importance as a fluxing constituent in ceramic formulas. It may exist in the clay as mined, or it may be added as needed.

The third main ceramic constituent is sand or *flint*. Its essential properties for the ceramic industries are summarized along with the similar characteristics of clay and feldspar in Table 2. For the light-colored ceramic products, sand with a low iron content should be chosen.

In addition to the three principal raw materials there is a wide variety of other minerals, salts, and oxides that are used as fluxing agents and special refractory ingredients. Some of the more *common fluxing agents* are

[1] SMITH, Deflocculation and Controlled Separation Improve Domestic China Clay, *Chem. & Met. Eng.*, **44**, 594 (1937).

Borax, $Na_2B_4O_7 \cdot 10H_2O$

Boric acid, H_3BO_3

Soda ash, Na_2CO_3

Sodium nitrate, $NaNO_3$

Pearl ash, K_2CO_3

Fluorspar, CaF_2

Cryolite, Na_3AlF_6

Iron oxides

Antimony oxides

Lead oxides

Some of the more common *special refractory ingredients* are

Alumina, Al_2O_3

Olivine, $(FeO, MgO)_2SiO_2$

Chromite, $FeO \cdot Cr_2O_3$

Aluminum silicates, $Al_2O_3 \cdot SiO_2$
 (cyanite, sillimanite, andalusite)

Dumortierite,
 $8Al_2O_3 \cdot B_2O_3 \cdot 6SiO_2 \cdot H_2O$

Magnesite, $MgCO_3$

Lime, CaO, and limestone, $CaCO_3$

Zirconia, ZrO_2

Titania, TiO_2

Hydrous magnesium silicates,
 e.g., talc, $3MgO \cdot 4SiO_2 \cdot H_2O$

Carborundum, SiC

Mullite, $3Al_2O_3 \cdot 2SiO_2$

UNIT PROCESSES INCLUDING FUNDAMENTAL CERAMIC CHEMISTRY

All ceramic products are made by combining various amounts of the foregoing raw materials, shaping, and heating to firing temperatures. These temperatures may be as low as 700°C. for some overglazes or as high as 1300 to 1400°C. for many vitrifications. Such temperatures cause a number of reactions which are the chemical bases for the *unit processes* of

1. Dehydration or "chemical water smoking" at 150 to 650°C.
2. Calcination, *e.g.*, of $CaCO_3$ at 600 to 900°C.
3. Oxidation of ferrous iron and organic matter at 350 to 900°C.
4. Silicate formation at 900°C and higher.

Some of the initial chemical changes are relatively simple, like the calcination of $CaCO_3$ and the dehydrations and decompositions of kaolinite. Other reactions, such as silicate formations, are quite complex and change with the temperature and constituent ratios as depicted by Figs. 2 and 4.

The phase-rule[1] studies as exemplified by Fig. 2 and also by Fig. 4 have been of *revolutionary importance* in interpreting the empirical observations in the ceramic industries and in making predictions for improvements. For instance, the data of Fig. 2 on the Al_2O_3-SiO_2 system have led to the important development of processes for mullite refractories (see page 192). This diagram shows that any percentage of liquefaction

---

[1] BIRCH, Phase-equilibrium Data in the Manufacture of Refractories, *J. Am. Ceram. Soc.*, **24**, 271 (1941); HALL and INSLEY, A Compilation of Phase Rule Diagrams of Interest to the Ceramist and Silicate Technologist, *J. Am. Ceram. Soc.*, **16**, 455 (1933).

can be obtained, dependent on a definite temperature, except at the mono-variant points. Thus, if the progressive melting be kept from going too far by controlling the rise in temperature, sufficient solid skeletal material will remain to hold the hot mass together. This Al_2O_3-SiO_2 diagram shows that mullite is the only stable compound of alumina and silica at high temperature.

Being primarily silicates, ceramic products are all more or less refrac-tory, *i.e.*, resistant to heat, and the degree of refractoriness of a given product is determined by the relative quantities of refractory oxides and fluxing oxides. The principal refractory oxides are SiO_2, Al_2O_3, CaO, and

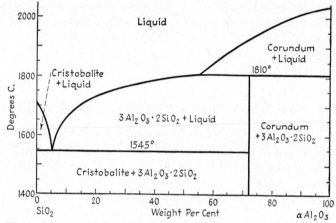

Fig. 2. Phase diagram of the system alpha Al_2O_3-SiO_2. Mullite has the formula $3Al_2O_3\cdot2SiO_2$.

MgO, with ZrO_2, TiO_2, Cr_2O_3, and BeO used less commonly. The prin-cipal fluxing oxides are Na_2O, K_2O, B_2O_3, and SnO_2, with fluorides also used as fluxes in certain compositions.

The essential ingredient of all ceramic products is clay (kaolinite, usu-ally) and therefore the chemical reactions which occur on heating clay are quite important. The first effect of the heat is to drive off the water of hydration which occurs at around 600 to 650°C. and which absorbs much heat, leaving an amorphous mixture of alumina and silica, as shown by X-ray studies.

$$Al_2O_3\cdot2SiO_2\cdot2H_2O \rightarrow Al_2O_3 + 2SiO_2 + 2H_2O$$

In fact a large proportion of the alumina can be extracted with hydro-chloric acid at this stage. As heating is continued, the amorphous alu-mina changes quite sharply at 940°C. to a crystalline form of alumina, gamma alumina, with the evolution of considerable heat. At a slightly higher temperature, beginning at about 1000°C., the alumina and silica combine to form mullite, $3Al_2O_3\cdot2SiO_2$. At a still higher temperature, the remaining silica is converted into crystalline cristobalite. Therefore the fundamental over-all reaction in the heating of clay is as follows:

$$3(Al_2O_3 \cdot 2SiO_2 \cdot 2H_2O) \rightarrow 3Al_2O_3 \cdot 2SiO_2 + 4SiO_2 + 6H_2O$$

Kaolinite   Mullite   Cristobalite

The equilibrium state of Al_2O_3-SiO_2 mixtures as a function of temperature is summarized in the phase equilibrium diagram of this system shown in Fig. 2. The presence of fluxes tends to lower the temperature of formation of mullite and of attainment of the equilibrium conditions reported in the equilibrium diagram.

An actual ceramic body contains many more ingredients than clay itself. Hence the chemical reactions are more involved, and there will be other chemical species besides mullite and cristobalite present in the final product. For example, various silicates and aluminates of calcium, magnesium, and possibly the alkali metals might be present. However, the alkali portion of feldspar and most of the fluxing agents become a part of the glassy or vitreous phase of the ceramic body. All ceramic bodies undergo a certain amount of vitrification or glass formation during heating and the degree of vitrification depends upon (1) the relative amounts of refractory and fluxing oxides in the composition, (2) the temperature, and (3) the time of heating. The vitreous phase imparts desirable properties to some ceramic bodies, e.g., acting as a bond and imparting translucency in chinaware. Even in refractories some vitrification is desirable to act as a bond but extensive vitrification would destroy the refractory property. Thus it is seen that any ceramic body is composed of a vitreous matrix plus crystals, of which mullite and cristobalite are two of the most important.

The *degree of vitrification* provides the basis for a useful classification of ceramic products as follows:

1. Whitewares. Varying amounts of fluxes, heat at moderately high temperatures, varying vitrification.

2. Heavy clay products. Abundant fluxes, heat at low temperatures, little vitrification.

3. Refractories. Little fluxes, heat at high temperatures, little vitrification.

4. Enamels. Very abundant fluxes, heat at moderate temperatures, complete vitrification.

5. Glass. Moderate fluxes, heat at high temperatures, complete vitrification (see Chap. 12).

WHITEWARES

The whitewares include chinaware, earthenware, pottery, porcelain, stoneware, and vitreous ware. These are based on selected grades of clay bonded together with varying amounts of fluxes and heated to a moderately high temperature in a kiln (1200 to 1500°C.). Because of the different amounts and kinds of fluxes there is a corresponding variation in the degree of vitrification among the whitewares from earthenware to vitrified china. These may be broadly defined as follows:

Earthenware[1] is "a porous nontranslucent ware with a soft glaze."
Earthenware is sometimes called *semivitreous* dinnerware.
Chinaware[1] is "a commercially vitrified translucent ware with a medium glaze which resists scratching to a greater or less degree."
Porcelain[1] is "a thoroughly vitrified, translucent ware with a hard glaze which resists scratching to the maximum degree." This includes dinnerware but also the exceedingly important insulation porcelain so essential in the electrical field.
Stoneware especially chemical stoneware[2] is closely related to porcelain. The stoneware may be regarded as a crude porcelain, the raw materials being of poorer grade and the manufacturing not so carefully carried out.
Pottery is usually a broad classification including earthenware, china, and porcelain.

Detailed presentations of the different kinds of whiteware should be sought in the specialized books to which reference is given at end of this chapter. To represent the typical manufacturing procedures in this group, porcelain is chosen.

Manufacture of Porcelain. There are three lines of production: (1) the *wet process porcelain* used for production of fine-grained highly glazed insulators for high-voltage service, (2) the *dry process porcelain* employed for rapid production of more open-textured low-voltage pieces, and (3) the *cast porcelain* necessary for the making of pieces too large or too intricate for the other two methods. These three processes are based on the same raw materials, the differences in manufacturing being largely in the drying and forming (shaping) steps. The wet process is illustrated[3] by Fig. 3. This flow sheet may be broken down into the following sequences of *unit operations* (Op.) and *unit processes* (Pr.):

The raw materials of proper proportions and properties to furnish porcelain of desired quality are weighed from overhead hoppers into the weighing car (Op.).
The feldspar, clays, and flint are mixed with water in the blunger (clay-water mixer) and then passed over a magnetic separator, screened, and stored (Op.).
Most of the water is removed (and wasted) in the filter press (Op.). All the air is taken out in the pug mill assisted by vacuum and slicing knives. This results in a denser and stronger porcelain (Op.).
The prepared clay is formed into blanks in a hydraulic press or by hot pressing in suitable molds (Op.).

---

[1] Watts, The Selection of Dinnerware for the Home, *Ohio State Univ. Eng. Expt. Sta. Circ.* 21, 3d ed., 1940; Classification of Ceramic Dinnerware, *Bull. Am. Ceram. Soc.*, **16**, 246–247 (1937).
[2] Pictured flow sheet, *Chem. & Met. Eng.*, **47**, 637 (1940).
[3] Pictured flow sheet, *Chem. & Met. Eng.*, **46**, 421 (1939).

The blanks are preliminarily dried, trimmed, and finally completely dried—all under carefully controlled conditions (Op.).

A high surface luster is secured by glazing with selected materials (Op.).

The vitrification of the body and the glaze is carried out in tunnel kilns with exact controls of temperature and movement (Pr.).

The porcelain articles are protected by being placed in saggers[1] fitted one on top of the other in the cars. This represents a one-fire process wherein body and glaze are fired simultaneously. The porcelain pieces are rigidly tested electrically and inspected before storage for sale (Op.).

Much *tableware* is manufactured by more complicated procedures than illustrated by the somewhat related porcelain product. Some objects are shaped by "throwing" on the potter's wheel by skilled hands working

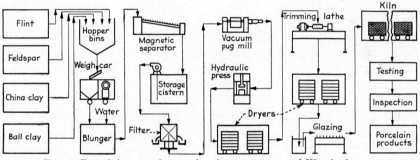

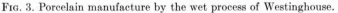

FIG. 3. Porcelain manufacture by the wet process of Westinghouse.

the revolving plastic clay into the desired form; some objects are "cast" from the clay slip in molds of absorbent plaster of Paris. After drying, the latter are removed and further processed. Mass production of simple round objects like cups, saucers, or plates, is carried out economically by "jigging" where the plastic clay is pressed into or on a single revolving mold, the potter often being aided in shaping the other surface and in removing excess clay by a lever which he lowers over the mold, shaped in the profile of the object desired. The mold is placed in the drying room.

The vitrification as shown in Fig. 3 is by the one-fire process. Frequently the two-fire method is used wherein the body is fired, cooled, glazed, and fired again.

Glazing is always important in whitewares; it is particularly so for tableware. A glaze is a thin coating of glass that is melted onto the surface of the more or less porous ceramic ware. It contains ingredients of

[1] Saggers are made by mixing coarse granules obtained from grinding old saggers with new clay and water in a pug mill and discharging the doughlike mass from an extrusion machine in loaf form. These loaves are placed in a molding machine, where box shape is imparted, and then fired. They may be used several times.

two distinct types in different proportions: (1) refractory materials such as feldspar, silica, and china clay and (2) fluxes such as soda, potash, fluorspar, and borax. Different combinations of these materials and different temperatures at which they are fired give a wide range of texture and quality. The glaze must bond with the ware, and its coefficient of expansion must be sufficiently close to that of the ware to avoid defects such as "crazing" and "shivering." The glaze may be put on by dipping, spraying, pouring, or brushing. All of these methods need a great deal of care. Decorations may be applied by carving, painting with a thick paint, marbling (dabbing on paint), tracing with a glass tube, or combing. For high-grade tableware, the decorations are by decalcomania paper which is simply a mechanical means for manifold duplication of the same design. However, such designs are "touched up" by an artist. For the highest type of tableware much hand decorating is practiced. Decoration of such ware may be "underglaze" or "overglaze."

Glost firing is the technical term for the firing of the glaze. Care should be taken in packing the kiln or the saggers so that the ware does not touch except for the three necessary underneath supports. As much space as practical is allowed between the different pieces of the wares since the glazes often bubble and rise before flattening. The temperature of the glost kiln may be increased more rapidly than during the first firing, but heating should not be hurried as strains would be set up. Large shapes should be packed in the center of the kiln to avoid uneven heating and should be fired more slowly than small ones. Earthenware should be glazed between 1050 and 1100°C.; stoneware between 1250 and 1300°C.

HEAVY CLAY PRODUCTS

Low-cost but very durable products, such as common brick, face brick, terra cotta, sewer pipe, and drain tile, are frequently manufactured from the cheapest of common clays with or without any glazing. The clays used generally carry sufficient impurities to provide the needed fluxes for binding. When glazed, as in sewer pipe or drain tile, this may be done by throwing salt ("salt glaze") upon the kiln fire. The volatilized salt reacts to form the fusible coating or glaze.

Manufacture of Building Brick. One of the most important of clay products is building brick, which comprises common and face brick. The raw materials are clays from three groups: (1) red burning clay, (2) white burning clay, (3) buff burning clay, usually a refractory. The requirements for a face-brick clay are freedom from warping, absence of soluble salts, sufficient hardness when burned at a moderate temperature, and general uniformity in color upon burning. Requirements for common brick are much less stringent. Red burning clay is most used for both common and face brick; however, the semirefractory buff-colored clay is in great demand because coloring matter may be added to vary the color effects. Manganese, with white or buff burning clay, gives a very attractive color.

Bricks are manufactured by one of three processes:[1] the soft-mud, the stiff-mud, or the dry-press. The *soft-mud* procedure consists in molding the clay mixture containing 20 to 30 per cent water in molds coated with a thin layer of either sand or water to prevent sticking. The molded brick is burned. Such bricks are of a uniform and excellent quality with good edges. This soft-mud process is much employed for firebrick and is the ancient method for making building bricks. In the now predominant *stiff-mud* procedure, the clay is just wet enough (12 to 15 per cent) to stick together when worked. This clay is forced out through a die in a screw or auger machine. An important new development, called deairing, is the operation of the auger in a vacuum chamber (14 to 29 in. Hg). *Deairing* increases the workability, plasticity, and strength of the undried brick by reducing voids, for all but a few clays. The extruded clay bar passes along a short belt conveyer onto a cutting table on which a frame with a number of wires automatically cuts the bar into appropriate lengths. These bricks (as well as those from the soft-mud process) may be repressed to make face brick. This repressing not only ensures a more uniform shape but overcomes the internal stresses set up by the extrusion in the screw. These molded bricks may be stacked 6 to 10 ft. high without damage before being dried. In the *dry-press* procedure the water content is from 4 to 7 per cent (usually the "as-is" condition) which makes the clay relatively nonplastic. The brick unit here is molded at pressures around 5 tons per sq. in. A typical dry press for brick manufacture costs about $30,000, uses 30 to 40 hp., and delivers a maximum of 750 tons pressure.

The stiff-mud process is employed for the manufacture of practically every clay product, including all types of brick, sewer pipe, drain tile, hollow tile, fireproofing, and terra cotta. The clay in some cases can be worked directly from a bank into the stiff-mud machine, but a more desirable product will result if the clay is ground and tempered before being used. The greater percentage of clay ware is made by the stiff-mud process.

Bricks are *dried* in various ways: outdoors, in sheds, or in tunnel driers. After drying, the bricks are *fired* in kilns of such type as described later in the chapter, to a temperature from 875 to somewhat above 1000°C.

---

[1] KIRK and OTHMER, *op. cit.*, Vol. 3, pp. 521–545. Competitive with these ceramic bricks in certain areas are sand-lime bricks (see Chap. 11).

REFRACTORIES

Refractories[1] embrace those materials which are used to withstand the effect of thermal, chemical, and physical effects that are met with in furnace procedures. Refractories are sold in the form of firebrick, silica brick, magnesite brick, chromite brick, magnesite-chromite brick, silicon carbide refractories, zirconia refractories, aluminum silicate products, olivine products, and others. The variety of refractories available is increasing, thus making possible a better selection of a refractory for a particular use. In making refractories the main material is chosen to adapt itself best to the thermal, chemical, and mechanical conditions to be met with. The fluxes required to bind together the particles of the refractories are kept at a minimum. Largely because of this there is but little vitrification. The possibility of shaping articles made from bodies without clay and even with no natural plasticity led to the manufacture of single-component ceramics with superior qualities, e.g., pure oxide refractories. These are monocrystalline and self-bonded as compared with the conventional vitreous-bonded refractories.

Properties of Refractories. In determining the refractory best suited for a definite operation it is necessary to consider the working temperature of the furnace where the refractory is needed, the rate of temperature change, the load applied during heats, and the chemical reactions that are encountered. Generally, several types of refractories are required for the construction of any one furnace because usually no single refractory can withstand all the different conditions that prevail in the various parts of the furnaces. In order to guard against reaction between the different kinds of bricks a separating cement or brick that has little tendency to react with either of the adjacent refractories should be used.

Chemical Properties. The usual classification of commercial refractories divides them into acid, basic, and neutral groups, although in many cases a sharp distinction cannot be made. Silica bricks are decidedly acid, and magnesite bricks are strongly basic; however, fire-clay bricks are generally placed in the neutral group though they may belong to either of these classes depending upon the relative silica-alumina content. Also, in the alumina-silica series of refractories many types can be made with wide differences in their chemical reactions. It is usually inadvisable to employ an acid brick in contact with an alkaline product, or vice versa. Neither chemical reactions nor physical properties are sole criteria of acceptable behavior; both should be considered. Chemical action may be due to contact with slags, fuel ashes, and furnace gases as well as with products such as glass or steel. Among the gases that have a deleterious

[1] NORTON, "Refractories," 3d ed., McGraw-Hill Book Company, Inc., New York, 1949. This volume is most essential for everyone working in this field particularly, because of the hundreds of classified references to further details in the literature.

effect are carbon monoxide, sulfur dioxide, natural gas, hydrogen, and steam.

TABLE 3. FUSION TEMPERATURES OF REFRACTORIES[a]

Material	Temperature, °C.	Temperature, °F.
Fire-clay brick......................	1600–1750	2912–3182
Kaolinite, $Al_2O_3 \cdot 2SiO_2 \cdot 2H_2O$..........	1785	3245
Silica brick........................	1700	3090
Silica, SiO_2.......................	1710	3110
Bauxite brick.......................	1732–1850	3150–3362
High-alumina clay brick..............	1802–1880	3276–3416
Mullite, $3Al_2O_3 \cdot 2SiO_2$...............	1810	3290
Sillimanite, Al_2SiO_5.................	1816	3300
Forsterite, $2MgO \cdot SiO_2$..............	1890	3434
Chromite, $FeO \cdot Cr_2O_3$...............	1770	3218
Chrome brick.......................	1950–2200	3542–3992
Alumina, Al_2O_3....................	2050	3720
Spinel, $MgO \cdot Al_2O_3$..................	2135	3875
Silicon carbide, SiC.................	2700	4890
Magnesite brick.....................	2200	3992
Zirconia brick......................	2200–2700	3992–4892

[a] NORTON, "Refractories," pp. 356–361, 3d ed., McGraw-Hill Book Company, Inc., New York, 1949. For other data on refractory materials, see PERRY, *op. cit.*, pp. 1538, 1549.

Porosity. The porosity is directly related to many other physical properties of brick including resistance to chemical attack. The higher the porosity of the brick the more easily it is penetrated by molten fluxes and gases. For a given class of brick the one with lowest porosity has the greatest strength, thermal conductivity, and heat capacity.

Fusion Point. Before use, the softening point of a refractory should be determined. It is found by use of pyrometric cones of predetermined softening points. Most commercial refractories soften gradually over a wide range and do not have sharp melting points because they are composed of several different minerals both amorphous and crystalline in type. The pyrometric cones (once known as *Seger* cones) are small pyramids made of mixtures of oxides and are useful for the approximate measurement of temperatures by steps averaging about 36° from 1100 to 3700°F. These are considered indispensable, not because of high-temperature accuracy but because their temperature–time performance is similar to that of the materials being fired. The fusing points of these pyrometric cones are available in the literature.[1] Typical fusion points

[1] A.S.T.M. Designation: C24-42. Many other specifications for refractories and refractory materials are given in the A.S.T.M. standards. See PERRY, *op.cit.*, p. 1272.

of refractories, both for pure substances and for technical products, are given in Table 3.

Spalling. A fracturing or a flaking off of a refractory brick or block due to uneven heat stresses or compression caused by heat is known as *spalling.*[1] Refractories usually expand when heated. Bricks with the highest expansion and least uniform rate are most susceptible to spalling when subjected to rapid heating and cooling. When refractories are heated for a great length of time at high temperatures, they may have a permanent volume change, either expansion or contraction, which may be caused by mineral inversion, softening, or overfiring.

Strength. Cold strength usually has only slight bearing on strengths at high temperatures. Although most of the applications place refractories under compressive loads, in rare cases they may be subjected to tension or shear alone. Resistance to abrasion or erosion is also very important for many furnace constructions such as co-product coke-oven walls, and linings of the discharge end of rotary cement kilns.

Resistance to Rapid Temperature Changes. Generally speaking, bricks with the lowest thermal expansions and coarsest textures are most resistant to rapid thermal change; less strain develops also. Bricks that have been used for a long time are usually altered in their properties, often being melted to glassy slags on the outside surface or even being more or less corroded away.

Thermal Conductivity. The densest and least porous bricks have the highest thermal conductivity, owing to absence of air in voids. Though heat conductivity is wanted in some furnace constructions, as in muffle walls, it is not so desirable as some other properties of the refractories such as resistance to firing conditions and is given minor consideration. Insulation is desired in special refractories.

Heat Capacity. Furnace heat capacity depends upon the thermal conductivity, the specific heat, and the specific gravity of the refractory. The low quantity of heat absorbed by lightweight brick works as an advantage when furnaces are operated intermittently because the working temperature of the furnace can be obtained in less time with less fuel. Conversely, the dense and heavy fire-clay brick would be best for regenerator checkerwork, as in coke ovens, glass furnaces, and stoves for blast furnaces.

Manufacture of Refractories. The usual methods for manufacturing refractories include these *unit physical operations* and *unit chemical processes:* (1) grinding and screening, (2) mixing, (3) pressing or molding and repressing, (4) drying, and (5) burning or vitrification. Usually the most important single property to produce in manufacture is high bulk density, which affects many of the other important properties such as

---

[1] NORTON, *op. cit.* Chapter 15 is devoted entirely to spalling with many literature references.

strength, volume stability, slag, and spalling resistance, as well as heat capacity. On the other hand, for insulating refractories a porous structure is required, which means a low density.

Grinding. Obviously, one of the most important factors is the size of the particles in the batch. It is known that a mixture in which the proportion of coarse and fine particles is about 55 to 45, with only few intermediate particles, gives the densest mixtures. Careful screening, separation, and recycling are necessary for close control. This works very well on highly crystalline materials but is difficult to obtain in mixes of high plasticity.

Mixing. The real function of mixing is the distribution of the plastic material so as to *coat* thoroughly the nonplastic constituents. This serves the purpose of providing a lubricant during the molding operation and permits the bonding of the mass with minimum voids.

Molding. The great demand for refractory bricks of greater density, strength, volume, and uniformity has eventually resulted in the adoption of the dry-press method of molding with mechanically operated presses and the discarding of hand molding and extruding processes. The dry-press method is particularly suited for batches that consist primarily of nonplastic materials. In order to use high-pressure forming it is necessary to deair the bricks during pressing to avoid laminations and cracking when the pressure is released. There are four ways of deairing dry-press bricks: (1) Decreasing the rate of pressure application and release so that the air in the voids has opportunity to seep through the sides of the brick and mold box. (2) Double pressing of the materials. In this method the bricks are pressed and allowed to crack. Repressing then closes the cracks. (3) Deairing by use of a gas, such as butane, which is piped to the mold box to displace the air. When pressure is applied, the gas is absorbed by the clay or condensed. If a flammable gas is used, it should be more carefully handled to reduce the fire hazard. (4) The use of a vacuum applied through vents in the mold box (*cf.* vacuum pug mill in Fig. 3). Large special shapes are not adapted to machine molding; however, their manufacture has been improved by the use of tamping with pneumatic tools to attain very high densities.

Drying. Drying is used to remove the moisture that was added before molding to develop plasticity. It should be noted that the elimination of water leaves voids and causes high shrinkages and internal strains. For this reason the dry-press process (requiring only 4 to 7 per cent of moisture, instead of 10 to 15 per cent in the stiff-mud method) has been favored in the manufacture of practically all types of refractory materials. In some cases drying is omitted entirely and the small amount necessary is accomplished during the heating stage of the firing cycle.

Burning. Burning may be carried out in the typical round down-draft kilns or continuous tunnel kilns. Two important things take place during burning: (1) the development of a permanent bond by a *partial vitrification* of the mix and (2) the development of the stable mineral forms for future service as shown in the phase diagrams of Figs. 2 and 4. The changes that take place are the removal of the water of hydration and, then, the calcination of carbonates and the oxidation of ferrous iron. During these changes, the volume may shrink as much as 30 per cent, and severe strains are set up in the refractory. This shrinkage may be eliminated by the *prestabilization* of the materials used. There are commercial refractories (see Fig. 4) in which the burning operation is entirely eliminated because the raw materials are prestabilized, appropriately sized, and pressed.

Varieties of Refractories. About 95 per cent of the refractories manufactured are nonbasic—with silica (acid) and fire-clay (neutral) brick predominant. Although a refractory is usually thought of in terms of its ability to withstand temperature, it is really only in exceptional cases that heat is the sole agent that effects the final destruction which is usually caused by chemical action at that temperature; hence the need for refractories of different chemical composition.

Fire-clay Brick. Fire clays are the most widely used of all the various refractory materials since they are well suited for a variety of applications and may be obtained in quantity. Fire clays range in chemical composition from those with a large excess of free silica to those with a high-alumina content. With material of such variation in quality, there is a price spread from $50 to $75 per M for bricks made therefrom. The steel industries are the largest consumers of refractories for the linings of blast furnaces, stoves, open hearths, and other furnaces. Other industries having use for these are foundries, limekilns, pottery kilns, cupolas, brass and copper furnaces, continuous ceramic and metallurgical kilns, boilers, gas-generating sets, and glass furnaces.

Silica Brick. Silica bricks contain about 95 to 96 per cent SiO_2 and about 2 per cent of lime added during grinding to furnish the bond. Silica bricks have a permanent expansion which occurs during firing and which is caused by an *allotropic transformation* that takes place in the crystalline silica. When reheated, silica bricks again expand about 1.5 per cent, but the effect is reversible, the bricks returning to size when cooled. This fact should be considered in their installation. Silica bricks are manufactured in many standard sizes by power pressing. They have a very homogeneous texture free from air pockets and molding defects and possess a low porosity. These are highly desirable properties for the resistance to slag penetration. The price is around $78 per M.

The physical strength of silica bricks when heated is much higher than for those made from clay. Consequently they are suitable for arches in large furnaces. Furnaces using these must, however, be heated and cooled gradually to lessen spalling and cracking. Open-hearth furnaces have silica bricks in their main arch, side walls, port arches, and bulkheads, but the newest installations here are the super-duty silica bricks and basic bricks. Because of their high thermal conductivity silica bricks have been utilized in co-product coke ovens and gas retorts. Other uses are in glass furnaces, electric furnaces, and copper-smelting reverbatory furnaces. Superduty silica brick results from the greater chemical purity of the silica. The sum of the alumina, titania, and alkali impurities in the super-duty brick does not exceed 0.5 per cent. Super-duty silica bricks have higher refractoriness and lower permeability to gases than conventional silica bricks.

High-alumina Refractories. The present demand for these high-alumina refractories is largely caused by the improvements in the quality and by the growing demand for refractories that can withstand severe conditions for which the older fire-clay and silica bricks were not suitable. High-alumina bricks are really high-alumina clay bricks made from clays rich in bauxite and diaspore. The refractoriness and the temperature of incipient vitrification increase with the alumina content (see phase diagram, Fig. 2). Another valuable property of high-alumina bricks is that they are practically inert to carbon monoxide and are not disintegrated by natural gas atmospheres up to 1000°C. Alumina content ranges from 48 per cent upward. High percentages are classed among the superrefractories, and almost pure alumina (97 per cent) is considered among the recently developed special refractories termed "pure oxides." High-alumina brick prices vary directly with the alumina content, with an average value of $176 per M.

High-alumina bricks are employed in the cement industry and papermill refractories. They have proved successful in boiler settings because of the resistance to the chemical action of fuel ash which contains basic oxides. They have proved economical for the linings of glass furnaces, oil-fired furnaces, high-pressure oil stills, in the roofs of lead-softening furnaces, crowns of silicate of soda furnaces, and in regenerator checkers of blast furnaces.

Basic Refractories.[1] The important basic bricks are made from magnesia, chromite, and forsterite. To achieve the required strength and other physical properties, the basic bricks are usually power pressed and are either chemically bonded or hard burned. The disadvantages of lack of bond and volume stability in *unburned* basic or other bricks have been overcome by three improvements in manufacturing: (1) Interfitting of grains has been developed to a maximum by using only *selected particle*

[1] ROCHOW and BRASHARES, Recent Developments in Refractories and Their Applications, *Chem. Eng. Progr.*, **44**, 869 (1948); Demmerle, *et al.*, Manufacture of Basic Refractory Brick, *Ind. Eng. Chem.*, **40**, 1762 (1948); Byrns, Integrated Basic Refractories Operation in California, *Chem. Eng.*, **57**, (5), 153 (1950); **57** (5), 200, pictured flow sheet.

sizes combined in the proper proportions to fill all the voids. (2) The forming pressure has been increased to 10,000 lb. per sq. in. and deairing equipment used to reduce the air voids between the grains. (3) The use of a refractory chemical bond. The flow sheet for the manufacture of unburned refractories, as compared with the burned-brick process, is shown in Fig. 4. The unburned bricks have a higher density and, therefore, better slag-resisting properties than burned brick and an outstanding resistance to spalling.

The *magnesia* refractories are made from domestic magnesites, or magnesia extracted from brines (Chap. 11). Magnesia bricks do not stand much load at elevated temperatures, but this difficulty has been overcome by blending with chrome ores. Many blends are possible, ranging

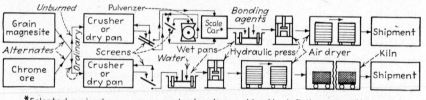

*Selected grain sizes are screened out and recombined in definite proportions for maximum density. It has been found that a suitable proportion for many purposes is 55 parts of coarse to 45 parts of fine particles, with elimination of intermediate sizes. Unburned refractories made by several manufacturers; process shown is that of General Refractories Co.

FIG. 4. Flow chart for unburned refractories by Ritex process, compared with burned-brick process. (*Courtesy of General Refractories Company.*)

from predominantly magnesia to predominantly chrome. In the nomenclature the *predominant* blend constituent is given first. There is a large price variation because of the composition variation, but the average value is about $350 per M which makes these bricks among the most expensive.

Chemically bonded magnesite-chrome bricks are frequently supported with mild steel to hold the brickwork and minimize spalling loss. These refractories are used in open-hearth and electric-furnace walls, in the burning zones of cement kilns, and in the roofs of various nonferrous reverberatory furnaces. Hard-burned chrome-magnesite bricks have many important physical properties because of their special composition, particle sizes, high forming pressure, and high firing temperature. They are of particular interest in the basic open-hearth furnaces.

Forsterite ($2MgO \cdot SiO_2$) is employed both as a bond and as a base for high-temperature refractories. Where forsterite forms the base, the refractories are generally made from olivine. This naturally occurring silicate contains $2(Mg,Fe)O \cdot SiO_2$ and is characterized by its refractoriness. In the manufacture of forsterite refractories, dead-burned magnesite is usually added to convert some accessory minerals also to forsterite, which is the most stable magnesium silicate at high temperatures, as shown by

Fig. 5. For example, enstatite (or clinoenstatite of Fig. 5) occurring in the rock olivine as mined, is converted to forsterite,

$$\underset{\text{Enstatite}}{MgO \cdot SiO_2} + \underset{\text{Magnesia}}{MgO} \rightarrow \underset{\text{Forsterite}}{2MgO \cdot SiO_2}$$

Such refractories have the advantages of a high melting point, no transformations during heating, and unsurpassed volume stability at high temperatures. No calcining is necessary in their preparation. The most important use of forsterite is in glass tank superstructures and checkers as

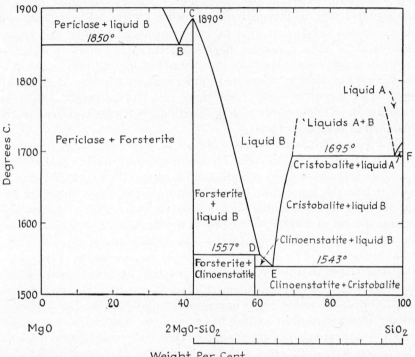

Fig. 5. Phase diagram of the system MgO-SiO₂. [*From Hall and Insley, J. Am. Ceram. Soc.,* **16,** 493 (1933).]

its high chemical resistance to the fluxes employed and good strength at high temperatures allow enhanced tank output. These refractories also find many other industrial applications such as in open-hearth end walls and copper-refining furnaces.

Silicon Carbide Refractories. These super-refractories are noted for their chemical resistance and ability to withstand sudden temperature changes. In their manufacture the crude material from the silicon carbide furnace is ground and the ceramic bond is added. The latter may be finely divided silicon carbide itself, or clay. The mixture is molded to shape and the less than 10 per cent of bond vitrified. These bricks are extremely refractory and possess a high thermal conductivity, low expansion, and high resistance to abrasion and spalling. They are strong mechanically and withstand loads in furnaces to temperatures as high as 1650°C. At higher temperatures this strength is less. Such refractories are used chiefly in muffles because of their thermal conductivity. Their ability to absorb and release heat rapidly and their resistance to spalling under repeated temperature changes make them desirable for recuperators. Refractories of this type can be made thinner than those from fire clay.

Refractories from Crystalline Alumina or Aluminum Silicates.[1] Research has revealed that mullite and corundum have high slag resistance and remain in the crystalline state at temperatures of 1600°C. and higher (see Fig. 2 for phase diagram). High-temperature kilns now furnish alumina bricks that closely approach pure corundum in properties and mullite bricks that are made from calcined Indian cyanite with the old clay bond replaced by a mullite bond consisting of interlocking crystals. Such refractories are finding many new applications, particularly where severe slagging has been a problem.

Electrocast Refractories. Many kinds of bonded refractories are made from electrically fused mullite. These are manufactured by introducing a mixture of diaspore clays of high-alumina (to furnish $3Al_2O_3 \cdot 2SiO_2$ ratio) content into the top of an electric furnace. If necessary, these are adjusted to furnish the stable mullite ratio of $3Al_2O_3 \cdot 2SiO_2$. Molten aluminum silicate at 3400°F. is tapped from the furnace at intervals and run into molds built from sand slabs. The molds containing these blocks are annealed from 6 to 10 days before the blocks are usable. The refractory obtained from this process has a vitreous, nonporous body which shows a linear coefficient of expansion of about one-half that of good firebrick. The blocks cannot be cut or shaped but may be ground on Alundum wheels; however, skill in casting has progressed rapidly and now many sizes and intricate shapes are available. This electrocast mullite has *only* 0.5 *per cent voids* in contrast with the usual 17 to 29 per cent in fire-clay blocks. Cast refractories are employed in glass furnaces, as linings of hot zones of rotary kilns, in modern boiler furnaces exposed to severe duty, and in metallurgical equipment such as forging furnaces. The refractories have the advantages of long life and minimum wear, against which must be balanced their greater initial cost. A newer and superior variety of fused cast refractories with from 83 to 95 per cent alumina is available. Here the interstitial glass content is greatly reduced, along with voids induced during the usual casting process.[2]

[1] REMMEY, New Alumina-silica Refractories, *Chem. Eng. Progr.*, **44**, 943 (1948).

[2] GEIGER, *et al.*, Applications of Super Refractories Made from Electric Furnace Products, *Chem. Engr. Progr.*, **44**, 933 (1948).

Pure Oxide Refractories.[1] The refractories industry is constantly faced with increased demands for products which will withstand higher temperatures and more severe operating conditions. To meet these requirements, a group of special or pure oxide refractories has been developed. The superior qualities are based mostly on freedom from fluxes. Refractory oxides of interest in order of increasing cost per unit volume include alumina, magnesia, zirconia, beryllia, and thoria. All these have been developed commercially for light refractory wear, but only alumina, magnesia, and zirconia have been used in heavy refractory products. These last three have certain properties in common: (1) they have high purity (a minimum of 97 per cent alumina, magnesia, or stabilized zirconia) and (2) they are principally composed of electrically fused grain. Beryllia is not used commercially in heavy wear because of its high cost and volatilization above 3000°F. in the presence of water vapor. Thoria has a number of disadvantages, particularly since its radioactivity places it under the control of the Atomic Energy Commission.

The material that has the widest application of these pure oxide refractories is sinter alumina. It is used successfully at temperatures up to about 3400°F. Magnesia is a basic refractory and is easily reduced at high temperatures. Its applications are limited to oxidizing atmospheres at temperatures not much over 4000°F. Since pure zirconia undergoes a *crystalline change from monoclinic to tetragonal* form at about 1800°F. accompanied by a drastic volume change on inversion, stabilization of the crystal structure to the cubic which undergoes no inversion was necessary. This is accomplished by adding certain metallic oxides (particularly CaO and MgO). Processing temperatures in the range of 4600 to 4700°F. are now commercial with available fused stabilized zirconia. Only present large-scale use is as kiln furniture for the firing of barium titanate resistors, but future large usage seems probable.

Insulating Brick. Insulating bricks are of two types: (1) for backing of refractory bricks and (2) in place of regular refractory bricks. Most bricks used for backing are made from naturally porous diatomaceous earth, while the second type, usually called lightweight refractories, are similar in composition to heavy bricks and owe their insulating value to the method of manufacturing. For instance, waste cork is ground and sized; this is mixed with the fire clay, molded, and burned. In the kiln the cork burns out leaving a highly porous and light brick. These lightweight refractories may be used safely for temperatures of 2500 to 2900°F., while diatomaceous-earth brick are not suitable above 2000°F. under ordinary conditions.

[1] WHITTEMORE, Pure Oxide Heavy Refractories, *Chem. Eng. Progr.*, **44,** 872 (1948); BALDWIN, Zircon and Zirconia Refractories, *Chem. Eng. Progr.*, **44,** 875 (1948); ANON., Fused Stabilized Zirconia, *Chem. Eng.*, **58** (2), 199 (1951).

ENAMELS AND ENAMELED METAL

Porcelain or vitreous enamel is a ceramic mixture containing a large proportion of fluxes, applied cold and fused to the metal at a moderate red heat. *Complete vitrification* takes place. The application of enamels to metals is one that dates back to the ancients. Various pieces of gold, silver, and copper enamelware, as well as of enameled earthenware, are in existence from the ancient Egyptian, Greek, and Byzantine nations. Commercial enameling on iron was started in Czechoslovakia in 1830 and in the United States about 1867 and has since spread widely. Enameling on other metal bases, especially aluminum, is increasing. The well-established uses of porcelain enamel, however, are in home appliances, plumbing fixtures, cooking utensils, industrial equipment, and many miscellaneous applications. Porcelain enamel, long valued as a material of great beauty in the field of decorative art, is coming more and more into general commercial use because it provides a product of great durability and wide applications. It is easy to clean and resists corrosion. Glass-enameled steel for chemical use has become one of the indispensable tools of the chemical engineer.

Raw Materials. Raw materials for enamels must have not only high purity but also fineness, suitable mineral composition, proper grain shape, and other physical conditions depending on the specific enamel. The raw materials used in enamels may be divided into six different groups: refractories, fluxes, opacifiers, colors, floating agents, and electrolytes. The *refractories* include such materials as quartz, feldspar, and clay which contribute to the acidic part of the melt and give body to the glass. The *fluxes* include such products as borax, soda ash, cryolite, and fluorspar, which are basic in character and *react* with the acidic refractories to form the glass. They tend to lower the fusion temperatures of the enamels.

The *opacifiers* are compounds added to the glass to give it the white opaque appearance so characteristic of vitreous enamels. They are of two principal types: insoluble opacifiers (titanium dioxide, tin oxide, and zirconium oxide) and devitrification opacifiers (cryolite and fluorspar). In 1945 titanium dioxide opacified enamels were commercially developed[1] and they have gained general acceptance in the industry because of high opacity and good acid resistance. The chief advantage is that they may be applied as thinner coatings than the best previous opacifiers and therefore are more resistant to chipping as well as being smoother and of greater reflectance. The devitrification opacifiers also act as fluxes rendering the enamel more fusible. The *color* materials may be oxides, elements, salts, or frits and may act either as refractories or as fluxes. The

---

[1] SPENCER-STRONG and PATRICK, Titanium in Porcelain Enamels, *Ind. Eng. Chem.,* **42,** 253 (1950).

color contributed to an enamel may be influenced by the enamel composition and the processing.

The *floating agents* such as clay and gums are chosen to suspend the enamel in water or in some other liquid. A plastic clay quite free from impurities is required. To peptize the clay and properly suspend the enamel, *electrolytes* are added. These are such compounds as borax, soda ash, magnesium sulfate, and magnesium carbonate, which, when added in very small amounts, aid the clay in keeping the enamel in suspension.

Manufacture of the Frit. The preparation of the enamel glass, or frit, is similar to the first stages of the manufacture of ordinary glass. The raw materials are mixed in the proper proportions and charged into a melting furnace maintained near 2500°F., from 1 to 3 hr., depending upon the composition of the enamel and the size of the mixture. After the batch has been uniformly melted, it is allowed to pour from the furnace into a quenching tank of cold water, shattering the melt into millions of friable pieces. This is called *frit*.

This frit is now ground in a ball mill containing balls of dense white porcelain; then the opacifying material is charged and the coloring oxides, the clay and more frit, and lastly the water. The product from the mill is discharged and passed through a 200-mesh screen to eliminate any oversized particles. The enamel slip is aged at temperatures close to those at which it is to be applied. In the aging of the enamel slips, an equilibrium is set up between the clay, the frit, and the solution.

Preparation of Metal Parts. The success of enameling depends on the nature and uniformity of the metal base to which the enamel is fused and the obtaining of a parallelism between the coefficients of expansion of the enamel and the metal. The compositions of irons that can be enameled cover a wide range from commercially pure iron to high-carbon steels and cast irons, but no great variation can be tolerated for a given enameling process. In the cast-iron enameling industry the castings are frequently made in the same factory in which they are enameled. The sheet-metal enameler usually purchases sheets to meet a definite specification. Before the liquid enamel (suspension in water) is applied to the metal, the surface must be thoroughly cleaned of all foreign matter, so that the enamel coating will adhere well to the metal and also not be affected itself. Cast iron is cleaned by pressure sandblasting. Occasionally the castings may also be annealed. Sheet metal is cleaned by pickling in 8 per cent sulfuric acid at 140°F. after the iron has been annealed.

The recent development of a special enameling steel has made possible the complete elimination of the ground coat, and consequently a further reduction in enamel thickness. This steel is a completely deoxidized ("killed") steel containing from 0.20 to 0.50 per cent titanium. Although a nickel flash[1] on the base metal is still necessary to promote optimum adherence, the complete deoxidation of the metal prior to enameling has eliminated surface defects such as reboiling which can often be traced to the evolution of gas by the metal at temperatures necessary for maturing the enamel coating.

Application of the Enamel. Enamel may be applied to the metal in a number of different ways. Sheet-iron coats are generally applied by dipping or slushing, since the ware is usually coated on all sides. Slushing differs from draining in that the enamel slip is thicker and must be shaken from the ware. It is convenient for small odd-shaped pieces. A third method of application is spraying. Any of these three processes may be employed wet or dry. Cast-iron treatment is very similar to that for sheet iron, but slushing here consists of pouring the enamel slip over the casting and allowing the excess to run off. The enamel is now air-dried, and colors are brushed and stenciled on if wanted. The enamel is usually applied in two coats for premium products.

Firing. All enamels should be fired on the ware to melt them into a smooth, continuous, glassy layer. The requirements for successful firing of a good enamel are (1) proper firing temperature 1400 to 1500°F., (2) time 1 to 15 min., (3) proper support of the ware, (4) uniform heating and cooling of the ware, and (5) an atmosphere free from dust. Heat is provided in either intermittent-fired muffle furnaces or continuous-tunnel furnaces. The product is taken from the furnace and given many tests for its thermal, optical, physical, and chemical properties. Enamel coats average about 0.0065 in. as compared with 0.026 in. a few years ago. The ware is now ready for use. The special enamel- or glass-lined equipment so extensively used in chemical plants is tested even by high-frequency waves to exclude any defects which only this method will detect but which in course of use would offer an avenue for acid penetration.

KILNS

The vitrification of ceramic products and the prior *unit processes* of *dehydration, oxidation,* and *calcination* are carried out in kilns that may be operated in a periodic or continuous manner. Muffle kilns are also employed. Usually all the newer installations are continuous-tunnel kilns which have many advantages over the batch kilns, such as lower labor costs, greater thermal efficiency, shorter processing time cycle, and better operating control. Coal and oil are the most important fuels for firing, but gas and electricity are used in some cases. The choice of the kiln and fuel[2] is largely a question of economics and product quality.

[1] HARMAN and KING, Applications of Nickel Compounds in Ceramics, *Ind. Eng. Chem.*, **44**, 1015 (1952).

[2] NORTON, *op. cit.*, pp. 242, 244, and 252, tabulates fuel consumption for periodic, tunnel, and chamber kilns.

Continuous Kilns. The most important kilns are the continuous-car *tunnel kilns* used for the firing of brick, tile, porcelain, tableware, and refractories. There are two general types of such kilns: the direct-fired type where the combustion gases burn directly into the wares and the indirect (muffle) type where the products of combustion are not allowed to contact the wares. The wares are loaded directly onto open cars or enclosed in saggers which keep the wares clean. The cars pass through the tunnel counterflow to the combustion gases from the high-fire zone.

The continuous *chamber kiln* consists of a series of connected chambers. The heat from one chamber is passed to another countercurrent to the ware. Because the chambers are burned in succession, the operation is continuous. There is always one chamber cooling, another being fired, and another being heated by the waste heat of the two other chambers. This type of kiln is used to burn brick and tile.

Periodic Kilns. *Downdraft kilns*, which are round or rectangular shaped, are used in burning face brick, sewer pipe, stoneware, tile, and common brick. In them the heat is raised from room temperature to the finishing temperature for each burning operation. The kiln is "set" (filled with wares to be burned); the heating is started and the temperature raised at a definite rate until the firing temperature is reached. The downdraft kiln is so named because the products of combustion go down in passing over the ware set in the kiln. The gases leaving the furnace go up inside the walls to the crown of the kiln and are pulled through the ware by means of a system of flues connected to an outside stack.

The *updraft kiln* has been most commonly used in burning pottery ware but is rapidly being replaced by tunnel kilns. It is similar to the downdraft type except for the movement of the gases. It gives better heat control than does the downdraft type. Common bricks are burned in *scove kilns*, which are really variations on the updraft type. The kiln itself is built from the green brick with the outside walls daubed or "scoved" with clay. The *clamp kiln* is a variation on the preceding in which the side walls are permanent. After burning, the kiln is completely dismantled.

SELECTED REFERENCES

Norton, F. H., "Refractories," 3d ed., McGraw-Hill Book Company, Inc., New York, 1949. Standard book.

Norton, F. H., "Elements of Ceramics," Addison-Wesley Publishing Company, Cambridge, Mass., 1952. Introductory book.

Ries, H., "Clays, Their Occurrence, Properties and Uses," John Wiley & Sons, Inc., New York, 1908.

Searle, A. B., "An Encyclopedia of the Ceramic Industries," 3 vols., Ernest Benn, Ltd., London, 1930.

———, "Chemistry and Physics of Clays and Other Ceramic Materials," 2d ed., Ernest Benn, Ltd., London, 1933.

McNamara, E. P., "Ceramics," 3 vols., Pennsylvania State College, State College, 1945.

Newcomb, R., Jr., "Ceramic Whitewares," Pitman Publishing Corporation, New York, 1947.

Anon., "Refractories," General Refractories Company, Philadelphia, 1949.

Andrews, A. I., "Enamels," The Twin City Ptg. Co., Champaign, Ill., 1935.

Ladoo, R. B., and W. M. Myers, "Nonmetallic Minerals," 2d ed., McGraw-Hill Book Company, Inc., New York, 1951.

Kirk, R. E., and D. F. Othmer, "Encyclopedia of Chemical Technology," Interscience Encyclopedia, Inc., New York, 1947–1956.

Bulletins and Journals of the American Ceramic Society, Columbus, Ohio.

CHAPTER 11

CEMENTS, CALCIUM AND MAGNESIUM COMPOUNDS

The industrial uses of limestone and cements have provided important undertakings for chemists and engineers since the early years when lime mortars and natural cements were introduced. In modern times one need only mention reinforced-concrete walls and girders, tunnels, dams, and roads to realize the dependence of present-day civilization upon these products. The convenience, cheapness, adaptability, strength, and durability of both lime mortar and cement products have been the foundation of these tremendous applications. The once crude and intermittent type of production has been perfected to a point where over 8,000,000 tons of lime and over 275,000,000 bbl. of cement are produced in the United States (Table 1).

CEMENT

In spite of the modern concrete roads and buildings everywhere around us, it is difficult to realize the tremendous growth of the cement industry during the past century. Man had early discovered certain natural rocks which through simple calcination gave a product that hardened on the addition of water. Yet the real advance did not take place until physicochemical studies and chemical engineering laid the basis for the modern efficient plants working under closely controlled conditions on a variety of raw materials.

Historical. Cement dates back to antiquity and one can only speculate as to the discovery.[1] A cement was used by the Egyptians in constructing the pyramids. The Greeks and Romans used volcanic tuff for cement and a number of these structures are still standing. In 1824 an Englishman, Joseph Aspdin, patented an artificial cement made by the calcination of an argillaceous limestone. He called this *portland* because concrete made from it resembled a famous building stone obtained from the Isle of Portland near England. This was the start of the *portland cement* industry as we know it today. The hard clinkers resulting from the burning of argillaceous limestone is known by the term *portland cement* to distinguish it from natural or pozzuolana and other cements.

[1] BOGUE, "The Chemistry of Portland Cement," Reinhold Publishing Corporation, New York, 1947. Chapter 1 is an excellent presentation of the history of this industry.

Uses and Economics. A generation ago concrete was little used in this country because the manufacture of portland cement was a complicated expensive process. Thanks to the invention of laborsaving machinery, cement is now low in cost and is applied everywhere in the construction of homes, public buildings, roads, industrial plants, dams, bridges, and in many other places. Table 1 indicates the large volume of this industry.

TABLE 1. CEMENT SHIPMENTS IN 1953[a]

Type	Active plants	Barrels	Value per barrel	Total value
Portland (Types I and II).........	156	215,103,044	$2.65	$569,217,300
H.E.S. portland (Type III)........	99	7,794,006	3.05	23,743,313
Low-heat portland (Type IV)......	2	171,717	2.95	507,290
Sulfate-resisting portland (Type V).	4	89,631	3.55	317,792
Oil-well portland.................	17	1,822,887	3.00	5,463,901
White portland..................	4	1,091,016	5.58	6,087,641
Portland-puzzolan................	6	2,448,861	2.63	6,440,686
Air-entrained portland...........	95	31,474,609	2.62	82,593,723
Miscellaneous portland...........	21	882,764	3.28	2,891,162
Total........................	156	260,878,535	$2.67	$697,262,808

[a] "Mineral Industry Surveys." For 1949, 150 active plants shipped 174,000,000 bbl., valued at $2.27 per barrel and with a total value of 396 million dollars. A barrel of cement weighs 376 lb. and is equivalent to four sacks. For 1954, there was a 3 per cent increase over 1953.

CEMENT MANUFACTURE

There are various types of cements:

1. *Portland cement* has been defined as:[1] "the product obtained by pulverizing clinker consisting essentially of hydraulic calcium silicates, to which no additions have been made subsequent to calcination other than water and/or untreated calcium sulfate, except that additions not to exceed 1.0 per cent of other materials may be interground with the clinker at the option of the manufacturer. . . . " Five types of portland cement are recognized in the United States:

Type I. *Regular* portland cements are the usual products for general concrete construction. Masonry cements are mixtures of cement with hydrated lime, crushed limestone, diatomaceous earth, with or without small additions of calcium stearate, petroleum, or highly colloidal clays. These are easily workable because of the high plasticity. There are other types of this cement such as white, which contains less ferric oxide, oil-well cement, quick-setting cement, and others for special uses.

Type II. *Moderate-heat-of-hardening* portland cements are for use where

[1] A.S.T.M. Specifications: C150-49 (1949).

moderate heat of hydration is required, or for general concrete construction exposed to moderate sulfate action. The heat evolved from these cements should not exceed 70 and 80 cal. per gm. after 7 and 28 days, respectively.

Type III. *High-early-strength* (H.E.S.) cements are made from a raw material with a high lime-to-silica ratio, frequently burned twice and very finely ground. They contain a higher proportion of tricalcium sili-

TABLE 2. CHEMICAL SPECIFICATIONS FOR PORTLAND CEMENTS[a]

	Regular Type I	Moderate heat of hardening Type II	High-early-strength Type III	Low heat of hydration Type IV	High-sulfate resistance Type V
Silicon dioxide (SiO_2), min. per cent......	....	21.0			
Aluminum oxide (Al_2O_3), max. per cent..	....	6.0	......	.....	[b]
Ferric oxide (Fe_2O_3), max. per cent......	....	6.0	......	6.5	[b]
Magnesium oxide (MgO), max. per cent..	5.0	5.0	5.0	5.0	4.0
Sulfur trioxide (SO_3), max. per cent:					
When $3CaO \cdot Al_2O_3$ is 8 per cent or less	2.0	2.0	2.5	2.0	2.0
When $3CaO \cdot Al_2O_3$ is more than 8 per cent................	2.5	2.0	3.0	2.0	2.0
Loss on ignition, max. per cent.........	3.0	3.0	3.0	2.3	3.0
Insoluble residue, max. per cent........	0.75	0.75	0.75	0.75	0 75
Tricalcium silicate ($3CaO \cdot SiO_2$), max. per cent................	....	50	......	35	50
Dicalcium silicate ($2CaO \cdot SiO_2$), min. per cent................	....	......	......	40	
Tricalcium aluminate ($3CaO \cdot Al_2O_3$), max. per cent................	....	8	15	7	5

[a] A.S.T.M. Designation: C150-49.

[b] The tricalcium aluminate shall not exceed 5 per cent, and the tetracalcium aluminoferrite ($4CaO \cdot Al_2O_3 \cdot Fe_2O_3$) plus twice the amount of tricalcium aluminate shall not exceed 20 per cent.

cate, C_3S, than regular portland cements and hence harden much more quickly and with greater evolution of heat. Roads constructed from H.E.S. cement can be put into service more quickly than if regular cement had been employed.

Type IV. *Low-heat* portland cements contain a higher percentage of tetracalcium aluminoferrite, C_4AF, and dicalcium silicate, C_2S, and hence set with the evolution of much less heat, as can be seen from the data given in Table 6. Also the tricalcium silicate, C_3S, and the tricalcium aluminate, C_3A, are lower. Actually the heat evolved should not exceed

60 and 70 cal. per gm. after 7 and 28 days, respectively, and is 15 to 35 per cent less than the heat of hydration of regular or H.E.S. cements.

Type V. *Sulfate-resisting* portland cements are those which by their composition or processing resist chemicals better than the other four types. These cements are higher in tetracalcium aluminoferrite, C_4AF, and lower in tricalcium aluminate, C_3A, than the regular cements. Additions during grinding of small percentages of calcium stearate or sodium silicate increase this resistance somewhat. There is, however, no such thing as an acidproof portland cement.

Since about 1940 the use of air-entraining agents (minute quantities of resinous materials, tallows, and greases) has assumed great importance. These agents increase the resistance of the hardened concrete to scaling and also protect against damage incurred by alternate freezing and thawing. The Federal specifications[1] of 1946 permit the addition of an air-entraining material in amounts less than 1 per cent to each of the five types which are then designated as IA, IIA, IIIA, etc.

2. *Pozzuolana Cement.* Since the beginning of the Christian era the Italians have successfully employed pozzuolana cement, made by grinding two to 4 parts of a pozzuolana with 1 part of hydrated lime. A pozzuolana is a material which is not cementitious in itself but which becomes so upon admixture with lime. The natural pozzuolanas are volcanic tuffs; the artificial ones are burnt clays and shales.

3. *Calcium aluminate cement,* sometimes called *high-alumina cement,* is manufactured by fusing a mixture of limestone and bauxite, the latter usually containing iron oxide, silica, magnesia, and other impurities. It is characterized by a very rapid rate of development of strength and superior resistance to sea water and sulfate-bearing water.

4. *Special* or *corrosion-resisting cements*[2] are used in large quantities for the fabrication of corrosionproof linings for chemical equipment such as brick-lined reactors, storage tanks, absorption towers, fume ducts and stacks, pickling tanks, floors, sumps, trenches, and acid digesters to name but a few. Many kinds of special cements are described in the literature, but the furane, phenolic, sulfur, and silicate cements are the most important.

Raw Materials. Portland cement is made by mixing and calcining calcareous and argillaceous materials in the proper ratios. Table 3 summarizes the raw materials consumed. Formerly a large proportion of cement was burned from an argillaceous limestone known as *cement rock* which is found in the Lehigh district of Pennsylvania and New Jersey. This

---

[1] Specifications are given for these various types of portland cement in Federal Standard Stock Catalog, Sec. IV (Part 5); Federal Specification SS-C-192, Cements; Portland. Also see Bogue, *op. cit.*, Chap. 2; A.S.T.M. C175-48T.

[2] See the Cements section of the Materials of Construction annual review in the October issue of *Ind. Eng. Chem.* since 1947.

material was first used as a natural cement but, when found deficient in lime, was corrected by adding a small proportion of limestone. In addition to the natural materials some plants use artificial products such as blast-furnace slag and precipitated calcium carbonate obtained as a by-product in the alkali and synthetic ammonium sulfate industry. Sand, waste bauxite, and iron ore are sometimes consumed in small amounts to adjust the composition of the mix. Gypsum (2 to 3 per cent) is added to prevent too rapid setting of the tricalcium aluminate.[1]

Cement Rock Beneficiation. Froth flotation, or beneficiation,[2] is now the principal step in a process for obtaining cement kiln charges of correct chemical and physical composition, for all types of cement manufacture, from available raw materials which may be either inferior or actually unusable as quarried. The trend in cement composition has been toward higher silica, lower alumina, less alkali, and more iron.

TABLE 3. RAW MATERIALS FOR CEMENT IN 1949 AND 1952[a]
(Short tons)

	1949	1952
Limestone (including oystershells)....	44,968,739	53,828,942
Cement rock......................	12,628,494	13,404,234
Clay and shale....................	6,698,408	7,939,326
Gypsum........................	1,543,198	1,855,274
Blast-furnace slag.................	847,375	1,017,976
Sand and sandstone...............	724,624	893,682
Marl............................	722,606	1,065,164
Iron materials....................	346,542	375,852
Miscellaneous....................	140,999	170,104
Total........................	68,620,985	80,550,554

[a] "Minerals Yearbook," 1949 and 1952. Average total raw material weight required per barrel (376 lb.) of finished cement was 654 lb. in 1949 and 646 lb. in 1952.

Chemically these specification changes result in a cement with slower setting time, less heat of hydration, and more resistance to alkaline earths and waters. In a physical way these new specifications have demanded a more thorough control of the actual mechanical operation of the cement plant itself. Clinker has to be burned at constant temperatures using pyrometers to indicate the condition in the kilns; finer grinding is necessary to give better strengths at earlier dates to offset the retarding of the setting time due to the change in specifications. All these

[1] LERCH, The Influence of Gypsum on the Hydration and Properties of Portland Cement Pastes, *ASTM, Bull.* 12, Chicago, March, 1946, preprints.

[2] ENGELHART, Flotation as Applied to Modern Cement Manufacture, *Ind. Eng. Chem.*, **32**, 645 (1940); BOGUE, *op. cit.*, pp. 35–38; for an excellent short summary of flotation, including agents, equipment, and many references, see PERRY, *op. cit.*, pp. 1085–1091.

changes have been in the direction of improving the endurance of the concrete.[1]

The complete beneficiation process involves a combination of grinding, classification, flotation, and thickening operations, each adapted to satisfy the specific requirements of the cement desired and the peculiar characteristics of the individual raw materials. The purpose is to "beneficiate" available materials; *i.e.*, to correct the proportions of the mineral sources of the four oxides of calcium, silicon, aluminum, and iron, essential for cement manufacturing, and discard useless constituents. This may involve the raising of the lime content of the raw material or it may call

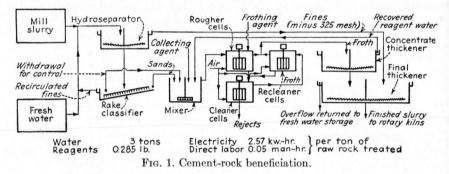

| Water | 3 tons | Electricity | 2.57 kw.-hr. | per ton of |
| Reagents | 0.285 lb. | Direct labor | 0.05 man-hr. | raw rock treated |

FIG. 1. Cement-rock beneficiation.

for the elimination of the greater part of the silica as compared to the alumina. To do this requires flexibility in the processing and the choice of varying reagents, which in one plant will float off one mineral and which at a different plant will remove another constituent.

The raw materials are usually ground very finely to free the mineral constituents and then put through a hydroseparator, as shown in Fig. 1. Here the hydrooverflow is not processed, going directly to the final thickener. With some other minerals the hydrooverflow would need to have some constituent removed by flotation. But in Fig. 1 the hydrounderflow, after further size classification, has the sands or coarser particles subjected to flotation to remove calcite and reject mica and talc.

The success of the process in making these differential separations is attributed principally to the use of very small quantities of collecting reagents added in small increments to the pulp in each cell in a stage-oiling circuit. The collecting agent must selectively wet or "film" the mineral to be removed and act with the air to cause the particles to be lifted to the surface, there to be caught in the froth and removed. In Fig. 1, oleic acid may be employed as the collector in the concentration of 0.5 lb. per ton of feed. The typical frothers are satisfactory (monohydric long-chain alcohols, dilute resinates, and cresylic acid). A concentration of 0.04 lb. per ton of rock suspended in 4 tons of water has given

[1] DOUGLASS, Separation Process Company, Catasauqua, Pa., *private communication.*

good results. Frothing aids in the separation. As is shown in Fig. 1, the concentrate thickener returns to the circuit, as well as the *recovered* reagent and water.

Unit Operations, Unit Processes, Energy Requirements. Essentially the unit operations prepare the raw materials in the necessary proportions and in the proper physical state of fineness and intimate contact so that the chemical reactions (unit processes) can take place at the calcining temperature in the kiln to form, by double decomposition or neutralization, the following compounds:

Formula	Name	Abbreviation
$2CaO \cdot SiO_2$	Dicalcium silicate	C_2S
$3CaO \cdot SiO_2$	Tricalcium silicate	C_3S
$3CaO \cdot Al_2O_3$	Tricalcium aluminate	C_3A
$4CaO \cdot Al_2O_3 \cdot Fe_2O_3$	Tetracalcium aluminoferrite	C_4AF
MgO	In free state	

K_2O and Na_2O form small amounts of various compounds with CaO, Al_2O_3, SiO_2, and SO_3.

Other reactions take place, such as dehydration of clay and decarbonization or calcination of limestone, these both being endothermic, with values of about 380 and 665 B.t.u. per lb., respectively. The clinker formation is exothermic with a probable value of 200 B.t.u. per lb. of clinker.[1] Probably the net heat requirements are in the neighborhood of 900 B.t.u. per lb. of clinker. However, the coal consumption indicates an expenditure of 3,000 or 4,000 B.t.u. per lb. of clinker.[2] This heat is evolved in the kiln in carrying out the following reactions, as tabulated by Lea and Desch:

Temperature	Reaction	Heat change
100°C	Evaporation of free water	Endothermic
500°C. and above	Evolution of combined water from clay	Endothermic
900°C. and above	Evolution of carbon dioxide from calcium carbonate	Endothermic
900–1200°C	Main reaction between lime and clay	Exothermic
1250–1280°C	Commencement of liquid formation	Endothermic
1280°C. and up	Further formation of liquid and compounds	Probably endothermic

[1] LEA and DESCH, "Chemistry of Concrete," p. 105, Longmans, Green & Co., Inc., New York, 1935.

[2] *Cf.* LACEY and WOODS, Heat and Material Balances for a Rotary Cement Kiln, *Ind. Eng. Chem.*, **27**, 379 (1935).

It should be noted that most of the reactions in the kiln proceed in the solid phase and that only toward the end does incipient fusion occur. All these reactions are embraced in the "burning of cement."[1]

Manufacturing Procedures. Two methods of manufacture are used: the wet and the dry processes. In both processes *closed-circuit grinding* is pre-

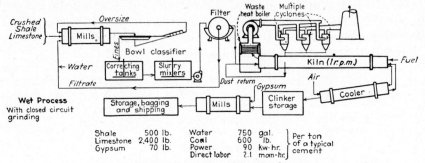

Shale   500 lb.   Water   750 gal.
Limestone 2,400 lb.   Coal   600 lb.   } Per ton
Gypsum   70 lb.   Power   90 kw-hr. } of a typical
                        Direct labor 2.1 man-hr. } cement

FIG. 2. The manufacture of portland cement.

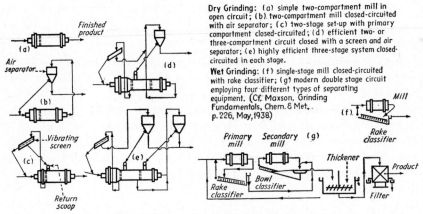

Dry Grinding: (a) simple two-compartment mill in open circuit; (b) two-compartment mill closed-circuited with air separator; (c) two-stage set-up with primary compartment closed-circuited; (d) efficient two- or three-compartment circuit closed with a screen and air separator; (e) highly efficient three-stage system closed-circuited in each stage.

Wet Grinding: (f) single-stage mill closed-circuited with rake classifier; (g) modern double stage circuit employing four different types of separating equipment. (Cf. Maxson, Grinding Fundamentals, Chem. & Met., p. 226, May, 1938)

FIG. 3. Dry- and wet-grinding hookups.

ferred in preparing the raw materials over *open-circuit grinding* because in the former the fines are passed on and the coarse material returned, while in the latter the raw material is ground continuously until its mean fineness has reached the desired value (see Fig. 3 for some grinding hookups). However, Perry[2] presents more details of actual grinding circuits with power requirements. The *wet process*, though the original one, was

---

[1] MARTIN, "Chemical Engineering and Thermodynamics Applied to the Cement Rotary Kiln," The Technical Press, Ltd., London, 1932. This book is filled with data and calculations pertaining to cement. Chapter 9 considers the heat absorbed in making clinker. Chapter 15 presents the concept of entropy in burning cement as "high-grade heat" or heat at the right thermal pressure or temperature.

[2] PERRY, *op. cit.*, tube and ball mills, pp. 1152–1154; roller mills, pp. 1137–1140. The entire Sec. 16 of Perry should be carefully studied in this connection.

displaced for a time by the dry process but is now being adopted largely for new plants because of the more accurate control and mixing of the raw mixture which it affords. This is illustrated in the generalized flow sheet[1] of Fig. 2. The solid material after dry crushing is reduced to a fine state of division[2] in wet tube or ball mills and passes as a slurry through bowl classifiers or screens. The slurry is pumped to correcting tanks where rotating arms make the mixture homogeneous and allow the final adjustment in composition to be made. This slurry is filtered in a continuous rotary filter and fed into the kiln. The *dry process* is especially applicable to natural cement rock and to the mixtures of limestone and shale or slate. In this process the materials are roughly crushed in jaw crushers followed by gyratory mills, then dried, sized, and more finely ground in tube mills (see Fig. 3). This dry powdered material is fed directly to the rotary kilns where the previously mentioned chemical reactions take place. Heat is provided by burning oil, gas, or pulverized coal, using preheated air from cooling the clinker.

The tendency in recent years has been to lengthen the rotary kiln in order to increase its thermal efficiency. Dry-process kilns may be as short as 150 ft., but in the wet process, 300- to 500-ft. kilns are not uncommon. The internal diameter is usually from 8 to 15 ft. The kilns are rotated at from $\frac{1}{2}$ to 2 r.p.m., depending on size. The kilns are slightly inclined so that materials fed in at the upper end travel slowly to the lower and firing end, taking from 2 to 3 hr.

In order to obtain greater heat economy, unit operations are used for removing part of the water from the slurry. Some of the methods used are slurry filters (as Fig. 2 shows) and Dorr thickeners. Some other common adjuncts to rotary kilns are cyclone dust separators and Cottrell precipitators. Waste-heat boilers are sometimes used to conserve heat and are particularly saving on dry-process cement where the waste gases from the kiln are hotter than from the wet process and may reach 800°C.

Because the lining of the kiln has to withstand severe abrasions and chemical attack at the high temperatures in the clinkering zone, the choice of a refractory lining is difficult. For this reason high-alumina bricks and high-magnesia bricks are widely used, although portland cement clinker itself is satisfactory.

The final product formed consists of hard granular masses from $\frac{1}{8}$ to $\frac{3}{4}$ in. in size called *clinker*. The clinker falls through openings in the stationary firing ring of the kiln into rotating coolers which simultaneously preheat the combustion air. Pulverizing followed by fine grinding in tube ball mills and automatic packaging complete the steps to the finished

---

[1] A pictured flow sheet with details of grinding and other equipment is given in *Chem. & Met. Eng.*, **46,** 629 (1939). This is a description of the wet process of the Lone Star Cement Co., Hudson, N.Y.

[2] PERRY, *op. cit.*, pp. 930–936, 1152–1154, presents some details on this matter.

cement. During the fine grinding the retarders, such as gypsum, plaster, or calcium lignosulfate; air-entraining agents; dispersing agents and waterproofing agents are added. The clinker is ground dry by various hookups, as illustrated by Fig. 3 and by Perry.[1]

Compounds in Cements. In portland cements we have a mixture of compounds (previously listed) present in amounts partly dependent on

TABLE 4. ANALYSES OF PORTLAND CEMENTS
(In percentage)

	CaO	SiO$_2$	Al$_2$O$_3$	Fe$_2$O$_3$	MgO	Alkali	SO$_3$
Regular cement (average of 102)							
Minimum.....	61.17	18.58	3.86	1.53	0.60	0.66	0.82
Maximum....	66.92	23.26	7.44	6.18	5.24	2.9	2.26
Average......	63.85	21.08	5.79	2.86	2.47	1.4	1.73
High-early-strength (average of 8): high C$_3$S							
Minimum.....	62.7	18.0	4.1	1.7	....	....	2.2
Maximum....	67.5	22.9	7.5	4.2	....	....	2.7
Average......	64.6	19.9	6.0	2.6	....	....	2.3
Low-heat-of-setting (average of 5): high C$_4$AF and C$_2$S, low C$_3$S and C$_3$A							
Minimum.....	59.3	21.9	3.3	1.9	....	....	1.6
Maximum....	61.5	26.4	5.4	5.7	....	....	1.9
Average......	60.2	23.8	4.9	4.9	....	....	1.7

TABLE 5. PERCENTAGE COMPOSITION OF 102 REGULAR PORTLAND CEMENTS IN TERMS OF COMPOUNDS. CALCULATED FROM TABLE 4

	C$_3$S	C$_2$S	C$_3$A	C$_4$AF	CaSO$_4$	MgO
Minimum................	35.3	0	0	4.7	1.4	0.60
Maximum................	70.6	33.2	15.5	18.4	3.8	5.24
Average.................	51.7	21.4	10.5	8.7	2.9	2.47

NOTE: These compound compositions are computed from the oxide analysis as follows: (1) Put all SO$_3$ in CaSO$_4$, (2) put all Fe$_2$O$_3$ in C$_4$AF, (3) put remaining Al$_2$O$_3$ in C$_3$A, (4) divide remaining CaO and SiO$_2$ stoichiometrically between C$_2$S and C$_3$S, (5) assume MgO is in free state and neglect Na$_2$O and K$_2$O.

the degree of attainment of equilibrium conditions during burning. Tables 4 and 5 give analyses of various types of portland cement and an average composition of some 102 regular cements. From these analyses it is seen that portland cement composition lies in a rough approximation in the system CaO-SiO$_2$, in a closer approximation in the system

[1] Perry, *op. cit.*, pp. 1130–1139, 1153, 1154.

$CaO\text{-}SiO_2\text{-}Al_2O_3$, and to a still closer approximation in the five-component system $CaO\text{-}SiO_2\text{-}Al_2O_3\text{-}Fe_2O_3\text{-}MgO$. A complete understanding of portland cement would require a knowledge of the phase equilibrium relations of the high-lime portions of all the two-, three-, four-, and five-component systems involved. Of these, all 12 of the principal two- and three-component systems are known and those parts of the four-component systems, $CaO\text{-}SiO_2\text{-}Al_2O_3\text{-}Fe_2O_3$ and $CaO\text{-}SiO_2\text{-}Al_2O_3\text{-}MgO$, in which portland cement compositions are located.[1] In 1946 part of the five-component system $CaO\text{-}MgO\text{-}Al_2O_3\text{-}Fe_2O_3\text{-}SiO_2$ was studied by Swayze;[2] such studies are being continued. Modern cement technology is largely based on the system $CaO\text{-}Al_2O_3\text{-}SiO_2$ which was worked out by Rankin and Wright[3] at the Geophysical Laboratory.

It can be observed for the regular cement compositions presented in Tables 4 and 5 that a change of CaO percentage from 61.17 to 66.92 alters the C_3S percentage from 35.3 to 70.6 and the C_2S from 0 to 33.2.

Setting or Hardening of Cement. Although many theories have been proposed to explain the setting or hardening of cement, it is generally agreed that this takes place by *hydration* and *hydrolysis*.[4] The following equations represent these reactions:

$$C_2S + xH_2O \rightarrow C_2S \cdot xH_2O \ (amorph.) \tag{1}$$
$$C_3S + xH_2O \rightarrow C_2S \cdot (x - 1)H_2O \ (amorph.) + Ca(OH)_2(c) \tag{2}$$
$$C_3A + 6H_2O \rightarrow C_3A \cdot 6H_2O(c) \tag{3}$$
$$C_3A + 3(CaSO_4 \cdot 2H_2O) + 25H_2O \rightarrow C_3A \cdot 3CaSO_4 \cdot 31H_2O \tag{4}$$
$$C_4AF + xH_2O \rightarrow C_3A \cdot 6H_2O(c) + CaO \cdot Fe_2O_3 \cdot (x - 6)H_2O \tag{5}$$
$$MgO + H_2O \rightarrow Mg(OH)_2 \tag{6}$$

The hydration products have very low solubility in water. If this were not true, concrete would be rapidly attacked in contact with water.

In recent years much attention has been given to the heat evolved during the hydration of cement. The various compounds contribute to the heat of setting as follows:

$$C_3A > C_3S > C_4AF > C_2S*$$

[1] BOGUE, *op. cit.*, Part II, Chaps. 11 through 20, deals with the phase equilibria of clinker components.

[2] SWAYZE, *Am. J. Sci.*, **244** (1), 63 (1946).

[3] RANKIN and WRIGHT, The Ternary System: $CaO\text{-}Al_2O_3\text{-}SiO_2$, *Am. J. Sci.*, **39**, 1–79 (1915).

[4] SLIEPCEVICH, GILDART, and KATZ, Crystals from Portland Cement Hydration, *Ind. Eng. Chem.*, **35**, 1178 (1943); BOGUE, *op. cit.*, Part III, Chaps. 21 to 30, studies in detail the chemistry of cement utilization.

* WOODS, STEINOUR, and STRAKE, Effect of Composition of Portland Cement on Heat Evolved during Hardening, *Ind. Eng. Chem.*, **24**, 1207 (1932); *cf.* BOGUE and LERCH, Hydration of Portland Cement Compounds, *Paper* 27, Portland Cement Association Fellowship at National Bureau of Standards, Washington, 1934.

Table 6 shows why low-heat-of-setting cements are made low in C_3A and C_3S but high in C_2S. This is accomplished (1) by adding more Fe_2O_3 which takes the Al_2O_3 out of circulation as C_4AF, thereby diminishing the amount of C_3A and (2) by decreasing the CaO/SiO_2 ratio. Notice these facts in the analyses in Table 4. This low-heat-of-setting cement

TABLE 6. HEAT OF HYDRATION[a]
(Calories per gram)

Compound	Days				
	3	7	28	90	180
C_4AF....................	29	43	48	47	73
C_3A.....................	170	188	202	188	218
C_2S.....................	19.5	18.1	43.6	55.2	52.6
C_3S.....................	98.3	110	114.2	122.4	120.6

[a] ROBERTSON, Boulder Dam, *Ind. Eng. Chem.*, **27**, 242 (1935).

was used in the construction of Hoover Dam to avoid cracking the structure from heat stresses during setting and cooling. As an additional safeguard the structure was cooled during setting by circulating cold water through 300 miles of lightweight 1-in. pipe placed in the concrete mass.[1]

TABLE 7. STRENGTH CONTRIBUTION OF VARIOUS COMPOUNDS[a]
(Strength of briquettes of pure compounds)

1 day..............................	$C_3A > C_3S > C_4AF > C_2S$
3 days..............................	$C_3A > C_3S > C_4AF > C_2S$
7 days..............................	$C_3A > C_3S > C_4AF > C_2S$
28 days..............................	$C_3A > C_3S > C_4AF = C_2S$
3 months..............................	$C_2S > C_3S = C_3A = C_4AF$
1 year..............................	$C_2S > C_3S > C_3A = C_4AF$
2 years..............................	$C_2S > C_3S > C_4AF > C_3A$

NOTE: $C_2S \cdot xH_2O$ (amorph.), whose structure and nature are unknown, is the principal source of strength of the set cement.

[a] *Cf.* GONNERMAN, Study of Cement Compositions, *Am. Soc. Testing Materials, Proc.*, **34**, 244 (1934).

Tables 7 and 8 present further facts regarding the functions of the different compounds in the setting of cement. To hold up the "flash set" caused by C_3A, some investigators assert that the gypsum added as a retarder[2] causes the temporary formation of $C_3A \cdot 3CaSO_4 \cdot 31H_2O$, while others believe that the gypsum gives free $Ca(OH)_2$ by reaction with alkali, and this in turn forms the more stable tetracalcium aluminate, $4CaO \cdot Al_2O_3$.

[1] ROBERTSON, Boulder Dam, *Ind. Eng. Chem.*, **27**, 242 (1935).
[2] LEA and DESCH, *op. cit.*, pp. 191–194.

TABLE 8. FUNCTION OF COMPOUNDS

TABLE 8. FUNCTION OF COMPOUNDS

Compound	Function
C_3A	Responsible for initial set (flash set)
C_3S	Responsible for first strength (at 7 or 8 days)
C_2S and C_3S	Responsible for final strength (at 1 year)
Fe_2O_3, Al_2O_3, Mg, and alkalies	Lower clinkering temperature

SPECIAL CEMENTS

For many corrosive conditions portland cement is unsuitable or not economical. Hence many special cements have been developed, of which four types are industrially important. Furan resin cements, commonly called *furane cements*, are used to the extent of several million pounds per year. They are usually prepared on the job by mixing approximately 2 parts by weight of a powder with 1 part of a liquid resin. Resins used for such cements may be based on condensation products of furfural and phenol, phenol and furfuryl alcohol, furfuryl alcohol and furfural, furfural and acetone, and polymers of furfuryl alcohol. Blends of phenolic resins and polymers of furfuryl alcohol are also sold as furane resins. The powders are composed of pure carbon, mixtures of carbon and silica, and mixtures of carbon and emery dust and asbestos. With such a wide range of compositions corrosion resistance varies but the rapid acceptance of these cements by industry is based on their resistance to many chemicals and solvents at temperatures up to 370°F., as well as on their excellent physical properties.

Phenol-formaldehyde resin cements, called *phenolic cements*, are also prepared on the job by mixing appropriate ratios of a powder with liquid resins. Powders used commercially are based on barium sulfate, silica, asbestos, and carbon. The latter is more economical, more resistant to chemical attack, and usually stronger. Several phenolic resins are available, but the product obtained from an alkaline condensation of phenol with a molecular excess of formaldehyde has superior chemical and physical properties. When mixed with carbon filler, this cement is most resistant to chemical attack. Typical uses are the joining of bricks in a pickling mill and in sulfuric acid saturators.

Since 1900 *sulfur cements* have been available commercially as simple mixtures of fillers and since 1930 as homogeneous plasticized-filled sulfur ingots possessing low coefficients of expansion. Sulfur cements are resistant to nonoxidizing acids and salts but should not be used in the presence of alkalies, oils, greases, or solvents. The crystalline change in sulfur structure at 200°F. limits their use. Thiokol-plasticized silica-filled sulfur cements have been accepted as a standard material for joining bricks, tile, and cast-iron pipe.

Silica-filled chemically setting *silicate cements* will withstand higher temperature (1000°F.) than the above cements. Usually 2 parts by weight of finely divided silica powder are used to 1 part of sodium silicate (35 to 40°Bé.). Silicate cements are resistant to all inorganic acids in all concentrations except hydrofluoric. Silicate cements are not suitable at pH's above 7 or in the presence of crystal-forming systems. Two typical applications are joining of bricks in chromic acid reaction tanks and in alum tanks.

LIME

Historical. The manufacture of lime and its application can be traced back throughout Roman, Greek, and Egyptian civilizations, but the first definite written information concerning lime was handed down from the Romans. In his book, "De Architectura," Marcus Pollio, a celebrated engineer and architect who lived during the reign of Augustus (27 B.C. to A.D. 14), deals quite thoroughly with the use of lime for mortar involved in the construction of harbor works, pavements, and buildings.

In the early days of the young American colony, the crude burning of limestone was one of the initial manufacturing processes engaged in by the settlers, using "dug-out" kilns built of ordinary brick or masonry in the side of a hill, with a coal or wood fire at the bottom and a firing time of 72 hr. These can still be seen in many of the older sections of the country. It was not until recent years that, under the influence of scientific cooperative research, the manufacture of lime has developed into a large industry under exact technical control, with the resulting uniformity of products.

Uses and Economics. Lime itself may be used for medicinal purposes, insecticides, plant and animal food, gas absorption, precipitation, dehydration, and causticizing. It is employed as a reagent in the sulfite process for papermaking, dehairing hides, recovering by-product ammonia, manufacturing of high-grade steel and cement, water softening, manufacturing of soap, rubber, varnish, refractories, and sand-lime brick. Lime is indispensable for mortar and plaster use and serves as a basic raw material for calcium salts and for improving the quality of certain soils. Figure 4 summarizes the main statistics.[1] As in most industries, there has been a trend in this industry toward elimination of the smaller inefficient plants. During 1948, 20 of the 89 plants produced more than half of the total output.

Lime is sold as a high-calcium quicklime containing not less than 90 per cent of calcium oxide and from 0 to 5 per cent of magnesia with small percentages of calcium carbonate, silica, alumina, and ferric oxide present as impurities. The suitability of lime for any particular use depends on its composition and physical properties, all of which can be con-

---

[1] *Cf.* BOYNTON, Lime—An Industrial Chemical, *Chem. Eng.*, **57** (7), 104 (1950).

trolled by the selection of the limestone and the detail of the manufacturing process. Much lime must be finely ground before use.[1]

Depending on composition, there are several distinct types of limes. Hydraulic limes are obtained from the burning of limestone containing clay, and the nature of the product obtained after contact with water

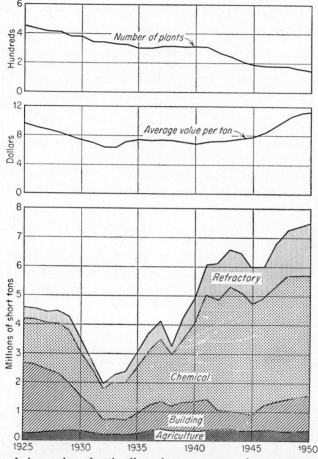

Fig. 4. Trends in number of active lime plants, average value per ton and principal uses, 1925–1950. (*From U.S. Bureau of Mines* "Minerals Yearbooks.")

varies from a putty to a set cement. The high-calcium-content limes harden only by absorption of carbon dioxide from the air, which is a slow process; hydraulic limes also harden slowly but they can be used under water. For chemical purposes high-calcium lime is required except for the sulfite paper process where a magnesian lime works better.

Although in many sections of the country the high-calcium lime is

[1] PERRY, *op. cit.*, pp. 1150–1151, 1154.

preferred by the building industry for the manufacture of its mortar or its lime plaster, there are places where limestone containing some magnesium is burned or where even a dolomitic stone is calcined. Typical compositions of such stones are given in Table 9. These products, called *magnesian* limes or *dolomitic* limes,[1] find favor in the hands of some plasterers who claim they work better under the trowel. In the metallurgical field, "refractory lime" as dead-burned dolomite or as raw dolomite is employed as a refractory patching material in open-hearth fur-

TABLE 9. APPROXIMATE COMPOSITION OF DOLOMITIC LIMESTONES[a]

Constituent	Per cent	Constituent	Per cent
CO_2	30–45	CaO	35–45
SiO_2	1–5	MgO	10–25
Fe_2O_3	0–2	$Na_2 + K_2O$	0–3
Al_2O_3	0–5		

NOTE: All components are expressed as the oxides.

[a] PIERCE and HAENISCH, "Quantitative Analysis," p. 300, John Wiley & Sons, Inc., New York, 1937.

naces, being applied between heats to repair scored and washed spots in the bottom of the furnace.

Hydrated lime is finding increased favor in the chemical and building trades over the less stable quicklime, despite its increased weight. The quicklime is almost invariably slaked or hydrated before use. Because of the better slaking and the opportunity to remove impurities, factory hydrate[2] is purer and more uniform than the slaked lime prepared on the job.

LIME MANUFACTURE

Lime has always been a cheap commodity because limestone deposits are readily available in so many sections of the United States and hence permit its burning near centers of consumption.

Raw Materials. The carbonates of calcium or magnesium are obtained from naturally occurring deposits of limestone, marble, chalk, or dolomite. For chemical usage, a rather pure limestone is preferred as a starting material because of the high-calcium lime that results. The quarries furnish a rock that contains as impurities low percentages of silica, clay, or iron. Such impurities are important because the lime may react with the silica and alumina to give calcium silicates or calcium alumino-sili-

[1] To prevent "popping out," the MgO must be completely hydrated such as by steam hydration at 160°C. and under such pressure as 60 lb. per sq. in.

[2] PERRY, *op. cit.*, p. 1120, tabulates the results from grinding and air-separating hydrated lime from much of the impurities originally present in the quicklime wherein the purity is raised from 89 to 98 per cent, the tailing going to agricultural applications.

cates which possess not undesirable hydraulic properties. The lumps sometimes found in "overburned" or "dead-burned" lime result from changes
in the calcium oxide itself as well as from certain impurities acted upon
by excess heat, recognized as masses of relatively inert, semivitrified
material. On the other hand, it often happens that rather pure limestone
is calcined insufficiently, and lumps of calcium carbonate are left in the
lime. This lime is spoken of as "underburned" lime.

Energy Changes, Unit Operations, Unit Processes. Energy is required
for blasting out the limestone, for transporting and sizing it, and for the
burning or calcining process.[1] The reactions involved are for

Calcining:

$$CaCO_3(c) \rightleftarrows CaO(c) + CO_2(g); \quad \Delta H_{1200-1300°C.}$$
$$= +4,250,000 \text{ B.t.u. per ton of lime produced}$$

Hydrating:

$$CaO(c) + H_2O(l) \rightarrow Ca(OH)_2(c); \quad \Delta H = -15,900 \text{ cal.}$$

During the calcining the volume contracts and during the hydrating it
swells. For calcination the average fuel ratios are, using bituminous coal:
3.23 lb. of lime from 1 lb. of coal in shaft kilns and 3.37 lb. in rotary
kilns.[2] As is shown above, the calcination reaction is reversible. Below
650°C. the equilibrium decomposition pressure of CO_2 is quite small. Between 650 and 900°C. the decomposition pressure increases rapidly and
reaches 1 atm. at about 900°C. In most operating kilns the partial pressure of CO_2 in the gases in direct contact with the outside of the lumps is
less than 1 atm.; therefore initial decomposition may take place at temperatures somewhat less than 900°C. The decomposition temperature at
the center of the lump probably is well above 900°C., since there the
partial pressure of the CO_2 not only is equal or near to the total pressure but also must be high enough to cause the gas to move out of the
lump where it can pass into the gas stream.

The total heat required for calcining may be divided into two parts:
sensible heat to raise the rock to decomposition temperature and latent
heat of dissociation. Theoretical heat requirements per ton of lime produced, if the rock is heated only to a calcining temperature of 900°C.,
are approximately 1,300,000 B.t.u. for sensible heat and 2,600,000 B.t.u.
for latent heat. Actual calcining operations because of practical considerations, *e.g.*, lump size, time, require that the rock be heated to between
1200 and 1300°C., thereby increasing sensible heat requirements by some

[1] PERRY, *op. cit.*, pp. 347–348, presents the calculations for heat balance and gas
analysis of a vertical limekiln. For a most excellent article, see CUNNINGHAM,
Fundamentals of Lime Burning, *Ind. Eng. Chem.*, **43**, 635 (1951).

[2] MYERS, Lime: Fuel Ratios of Commercial Lime Plants in 1939, *U.S. Bur. Mines,
Inform. Circ.* 7174, 1941.

350,000 B.t.u. per ton of lime produced. Then theoretical heat requirements will be approximately 4,250,000 B.t.u. per ton of lime produced. About 40 per cent is sensible heat; the rest is latent heat of decomposition.

The sequence of *unit operations* (Op.) and *unit processes* (Pr.) connected with manufacturing in such a kiln as shown in Fig. 5 is

Blasting down of limestone from quarry face, or occasionally from underground veins (Op.).

Transportation from quarry to mills, generally by industrial railroad (Op.).

Crushing and sizing of stone in jaw and gyratory crushers[1] (Op.).

Screening to remove various sizes (for example, a 4- to 8-in. stone implies that all pieces passing a 4-in. screen or retained on an 8-in. screen have been separated out) (Op.).

Carting of this large stone to top of vertical kilns (Op.).

Conveying of small rock to rotary kiln (Op.).

Conveying of fines to pulverizer to make powdered limestone for agricultural and other demands (Op.).

Burning of limestone according to size, in vertical kilns to give lump lime (Pr.), or horizontal rotary kilns to furnish fine lime (Pr.).

Packaging of finished lime in barrels (180 or 280 lb.) or sheet-iron drums (Op.), or conveying of lime to hydrator (Op.).

Hydration of lime (Pr.).

Packaging of slaked lime in 50-lb. paper bags.

Manufacturing Procedures. For the burning of lump limestones, vertical kilns are almost universally employed (see Fig. 5). Their outside construction is sheet steel for strength and prevention of gas leakage, with a firebrick inner lining. In many cases the gases escape from the top, but in the ammonia soda industry the upright kilns are closed and under slight suction with pipes conducting the gases to compressors and thence to the carbonating towers. If the limestone is properly chosen and sized[2] (-6 to $+4$ in. or -4 to $+2$ in.), it passes through the kiln with the formation of a minimum amount of fines or overburned or underburned lime. Different-sized stones burn at different rates. These kilns are heated either by mixing the fuel in with the stone (in which case the ash contaminates the product) or by the use of coal grates or gas burners arranged along the outside of the kiln, as shown in Fig. 5. Such upright kilns operate continuously and produce up to 80 tons in 24 hr.

In quarried limestone there is always a certain amount of stone that is so fine it would clog the upright kilns and prevent the passing of hot gases, causing uneven burning of the stone. This smaller limestone can be sold for metallurgical purposes or pulverized for agricultural use, or, after fines are screened out, it can be burned in rotary kilns. This latter

---

[1] PERRY, *op. cit.*, pp. 1120–1126.

[2] AZBE, "Theory and Practice of Lime Manufacture," p. 388, Azbe Corporation, St. Louis, Mo., 1946; Economical Manufacture of Quality Lime, *Trans. Am. Inst. Mining Met. Engrs.*, **49**, 267 (1946).

procedure is becoming more common as the business of furnishing lime has been centralized in larger operations. These rotaries will calcine up to 200 tons of product in 24 hr., producing a fast slaking lime caused partly by the relatively short time of 3 hr. in the kiln. Marble, being crystalline and cleavable, breaks into smaller pieces and can be burned

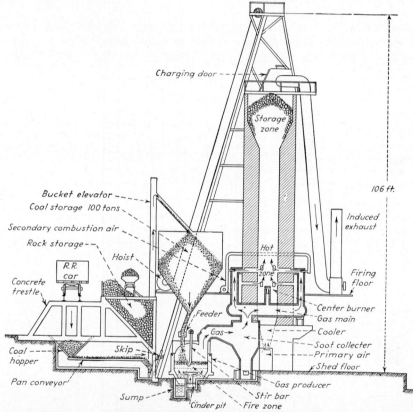

FIG. 5. Gas-fired vertical limekiln, producing 80 tons of high-calcium lime per kiln per day. (*Victor J. Azbe, St. Louis, Missouri patent granted.*)

only in horizontal rotary kilns after being suitably sized. Precipitated calcium carbonate, as from causticizing plants, can be burned only in rotary kilns.

The lime in the vertical kiln is partly cooled by the incoming air. It may be taken from the kiln and further cooled. It is packed for shipment as lumps in barrels and drums or shipped in bulk. It may be pulverized before sale. In many plants, instead of disposing of the product as quicklime, it is converted to the hydroxide and sold in the form of slaked or hydrated lime.

GYPSUM

Gypsum is a mineral that occurs in large deposits throughout the world. It is hydrated calcium sulfate, with the formula $CaSO_4 \cdot 2H_2O$. When heated slightly, the following reaction occurs:

$$CaSO_4 \cdot 2H_2O(c) \rightarrow CaSO_4 \cdot \tfrac{1}{2}H_2O(c) + 1\tfrac{1}{2}H_2O(g); \quad \Delta H = +19,700 \text{ cal.}$$

If the heating is at a higher temperature, gypsum loses all of its water and becomes anhydrous calcium sulfate or "anhydrite." Calcined gypsum can be made into wall plaster by the addition of filler materials such

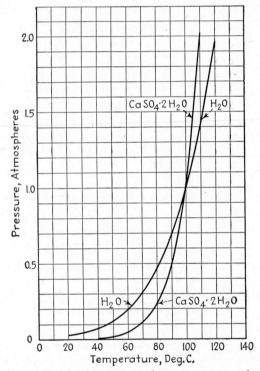

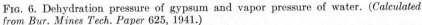

Fig. 6. Dehydration pressure of gypsum and vapor pressure of water. (*Calculated from Bur. Mines Tech. Paper 625, 1941.*)

as asbestos, wood pulp, or sand. Without additions, it is plaster of Paris and is used for making casts and for plaster.

Calcination of Gypsum. The usual method of calcination of gypsum consists of grinding the mineral and placing it in large calciners which hold from 10 to 25 tons. The temperature is raised to about 120 to 150°C. with constant agitation to maintain a uniform temperature. The materials in the kettle, known to the public as *plaster of Paris* and to the manufacturer as *first-settle* plaster, may be withdrawn and sold at this point, or it may be heated further to 190°C. to give a material known as *second-settle* plaster. First-settle plaster is approximately the half hydrate, $CaSO_4 \cdot \frac{1}{2}H_2O$, and the second form is anhydrous. Practically all the gypsum plaster sold is in the form of first-settle plaster mixed with sand or wood pulp. The second form is used in the manufacture of plasterboard and other gypsum products. Gypsum may be calcined also in rotary kilns similar to those used for limestone.

Hardening of Plaster. The hardening of plaster is essentially a hydration reaction, as represented by the equation

$$CaSO_4 \cdot \tfrac{1}{2}H_2O(c) + 1\tfrac{1}{2}H_2O(l) \rightarrow CaSO_4 \cdot 2H_2O(c); \qquad \Delta H = -3{,}800 \text{ cal.}$$

This equation is the reverse of that for the dehydration of gypsum. The plaster sets and hardens because the liquid water reacts to form a solid crystalline hydrate. Referring to Fig. 6, it is apparent that hydration with liquid water will take place at temperatures below about 99°C., and that the gypsum must be heated above 99°C. for practical dehydration. Commercial plaster usually contains some glue in the water used or a material such as hair or tankage from the stockyards to retard the setting time in order to give the plasterer opportunity to apply the material.

MISCELLANEOUS CALCIUM COMPOUNDS

Calcium Carbonate. Calcium carbonate is a very widely used industrial chemical, in both its pure and its impure state. As marble chips, it is sold in many sizes as a filler in artificial stone, for the neutralization of acids, or for chicken grit. The marble dust is employed in abrasives and in soaps. Some pulverized and levigated limestone, to replace the imported chalk and whiting, is manufactured quite carefully from very pure raw material and is finding acceptance.[1] *Whiting* is pure finely divided calcium carbonate prepared by wet grinding and levigating natural chalk. Whiting mixed with 18 per cent boiled linseed oil furnishes *putty* which sets by oxidation and by formation of the calcium salt. Much whiting also is consumed in the ceramic industry. Precipitated or artificial whiting arises through precipitation as by reacting a boiling solution of calcium chloride with a boiling solution of sodium carbonate, or by passing carbon dioxide into a milk of lime suspension. This latter form has its largest uses in the paint, rubber, pharmaceutical, and paper industries.

Calcium Sulfide. Calcium sulfide is made by reducing calcium sulfate with coke. Its main use is as a depilatory in the tanning industry and in cosmetics. In the finely divided form it is employed in luminous paints.

[1] Turner, "Condensed Chemical Dictionary," 4th ed., Reinhold Publishing Corporation, New York, 1950. This book is invaluable for presenting outline specifications for industrial chemicals.

Polysulfides, such as CaS_2 and CaS_5 made by heating sulfur and calcium hydroxide, are consumed as fungicides.

Halide Salts. Calcium chloride is obtained commercially as a by-product of chemical manufacture, principally the Solvay process and from natural brines. For this reason and since large tonnages are available, it is a very cheap chemical. Its main applications are in solutions that are used to lay dust on highways (because it is deliquescent and remains moist) and in low-temperature refrigeration. Calcium bromide and iodide have properties similar to those of the chloride. They are prepared by the action of the halogen acids on calcium oxide or calcium carbonate. They are sold as the hexahydrates for use in medicine and photography. Calcium fluoride occurs naturally as a fluorspar.

Calcium Arsenate. This chemical is produced by the reaction of calcium chloride, calcium hydroxide, and sodium arsenate or lime and arsenic acid.

$$2CaCl_2(aq) + Ca(OH)_2(c) + 2Na_2HAsO_4(aq) \rightarrow$$
$$Ca_3(AsO_4)_2 + 4NaCl(aq) + 2H_2O(l); \qquad \Delta H = -6,640 \text{ cal.}$$

There is usually some free lime present (see Chap. 26). Calcium arsenate has a large application as an insecticide and as a fungicide. It is especially useful on cotton plants to poison the boll weevil.

Calcium Organic Compounds. Calcium acetate and lactate are prepared by the reaction of calcium carbonate or hydroxide with acetic or lactic acid. The acetate was formerly pyrolyzed in large amounts to produce acetone but now it is employed largely in the dyeing of textiles. The lactate is sold for use in medicines and in food as a source of calcium; it is an intermediate in the purification of fermentation lactic acid. Calcium soaps such as stearate, palmitate, and the abietate are made by the action of the sodium salts of the acids on a soluble calcium salt such as the chloride. These soaps are insoluble in water but are soluble in hydrocarbons. Many of these form jellylike masses which are a constituent of greases. These soaps are used mainly as waterproofing agents.

Sand-lime Brick. Where a cheap white face brick is desired as for courts in apartment houses and buildings or where sand is more available than clay, the sand-lime brick industry has flourished. These bricks are largely competitive with common bricks and are sold at around the same price. They are manufactured by mixing about 8 per cent of thoroughly hydrated lime with a good grade of sand, pressing this mixture to the shape desired, and hardening it in a steam autoclave under about 125 lb. steam pressure for around 8 hr. If the hydrated lime used contains any quicklime, this will eventually hydrate or carbonate with expansion. This has caused cracking in the past. However, the operators of modern sand-lime brick factories have been trained to hydrate the lime completely. Consequently no trouble along this line may be expected from sand-lime brick. The bond holding together the sand particles is a monocalcium silicate.[1]

MAGNESIUM OXYCHLORIDE CEMENT

This cement, discovered by the French chemist Sorel and sometimes called *Sorel's cement* is produced by the exothermic action of a 20 per cent solution magnesium chloride on a blend of magnesia obtained by calcining magnesite and magnesia obtained from brines:

$$3MgO + MgCl_2 + 11H_2O \rightarrow 3MgO \cdot MgCl_2 \cdot 11H_2O$$

The resulting crystalline oxychloride, $3MgO \cdot MgCl_2 \cdot 11H_2O$, contributes the cementing action to the commercial cements. The product is hard and strong but is attacked by water which leaches out the magnesium chloride. Its main applications are as a flooring cement with an inert filler and a coloring pigment, or as a base for such interior floorings as tile and terazzo. It is strongly corrosive on iron pipes in contact with it. Sand and wood pulp may be added as fillers. The expense of these cements restricts their use to special purposes. They do not reflect sound. They can be made sparkproof[2] and as such have been widely employed in ordnance plants.

The magnesia used may contain small amounts of calcium oxide, calcium hydroxide, or some calcium silicates, which during the setting process increase the volume changes thus decreasing strength and durability. To eliminate this lime effect hydrated magnesium sulfate, $MgSO_4 \cdot 7H_2O$, or 10 per cent of finely divided metallic copper is added to the mixture. The use of copper powder not only corrects the excessive expansion but greatly increases the water resistance, the adhesion, and the dry and wet strength over the ordinary magnesium oxychloride cement.[3]

MAGNESIUM COMPOUNDS

Magnesium is one of the most widely distributed elements, occupying 1.9 per cent of the earth's crust. It occurs usually as the chloride, silicate, hydrated oxide, sulfate, or carbonate, in either complex or simple salts. Magnesium metal first became available commercially shortly before 1914 when the Germans initiated production, using magnesium chloride[4] from the Stassfurt deposits as the raw material. In 1915, consump-

[1] EMLEY, Manufacture and Properties of Sand-lime Brick, *Natl. Bur. Standards (U.S.) Technol. Paper* 85, Washington, 1917.

[2] SEATON, Magnesium Oxychloride Spark-proof Floors, *Chem. Inds.*, **51** (1), 74 (1942).

[3] KIRK and OTHMER, *op. cit.*, Vol. 3, pp. 435–438; *cf.* HUBBELL, A New Inorganic Cement and Adhesive, *Ind. Eng. Chem.*, **29**, 123–131 (1937), references.

[4] Available as a by-product of the production of potassium salts.

tion of the metal[1] in the United States was 87,500 lb., at an average price of $5 per pound. Table 10 gives recent production figures for magnesium and its compounds.

Raw Materials and Uses. Important domestic sources of magnesium salts are sea water, bitterns from salt brines and from sea brine, salines, dolomite, and magnesite, $MgCO_3$.

The largest and growing consumption of magnesium compounds is for the production of metallic magnesium (*cf.* Chap. 16). Magnesium compounds are used extensively for refractories and insulating compounds

TABLE 10. MAGNESIUM AND RELATED COMPOUNDS[a]

Products	Quantity produced 1952, tons	Quantity produced 1951, tons	Average value, 1952
Magnesium, primary..............	105,521	40,881	$ 24.54 lb.
Magnesite, crude.................	510,750	670,167	5.62 ton
Magnesia, caustic-calcined.........	38,055	49,981	99.00 ton
Magnesia, refractory..............	386,873	432,197	44.00 ton
Magnesia, special (U.S.P., etc.)......	1,986	2,251	550.00 ton
Dolomite, dead-burned.............	1,928,025	1,966,460	13.00 ton
Magnesium carbonate, ppd.........	43,267	60,530	161.00 ton

[a] "Minerals Yearbook," 1952.

as well as in the manufacture of rubber, printing inks, pharmaceuticals, and toilet goods.

Manufacture. The manufacture of magnesium compounds from salines has long been successful in Germany. As the result of thorough physical and chemical study, the International Minerals and Chemical Corp. is making magnesium chloride from langbeinite[2] crystallizing out carnallite, $KCl \cdot MgCl_2 \cdot 6H_2O$. This double salt is decomposed to furnish residual magnesium chloride of the requisite high purity needed for electrolysis to metallic magnesium.

The production of magnesium compounds by separation from aqueous solutions may be divided into four processes:

1. Manufacture from sea water without evaporation, using sea water and lime as the principal raw materials. This is done by Dow Chemical Company at Freeport, Tex. (Fig. 3, Chap. 16), and by Marine Magnesium Products Corporation (Merck & Co.) at South San Francisco (Fig. 7).

2. Manufacture from bitterns or mother liquors from the solar evaporation of sea water for salt. Westvaco Division of Food Machinery and

---

[1] *Cf.* Chap. 16 for manufacture of the metal.

[2] MANNING and KIRKPATRICK, Better Utilization of Mineral Resources through New Chemical Technology, *Chem. & Met. Eng.*, **51** (5), 92, 142 (1944), pictured flow sheet.

Chemical Corp. employs this source, with its plant on San Francisco Bay (Fig. 8).

3. Manufacture from dolomite and sea water with factories operating at Cape May, N.J., and in England (Fig. 9).

4. Manufacture from deep-well brines. This has been done by Dow Chemical Company at Midland, Mich.

TABLE 11. COMPOSITION OF SEA WATER[a]

(In grams per liter of sp. gr. = 1.024)

NaCl...................	27.319	Ca(HCO$_3$)$_2$................	0.178
MgCl$_2$...................	4.176	K$_2$SO$_4$...................	0.869
MgSO$_4$...................	1.668	B$_2$O$_3$...................	0.029
MgBr$_2$...................	0.076	SiO$_2$...................	0.008
CaSO$_4$...................	1.268	Iron and alumina, R$_2$O$_3$......	0.022

[a] CHESNY, Magnesium Compounds from Ocean Water, *Ind. Eng. Chem.*, **28**, 383 (1936).

A typical analysis of sea water is given in Table 11. The production of magnesium compounds from sea water is made possible by the almost total insolubility of magnesium hydroxide in water. The successful obtaining of magnesium compounds by such a process depends upon

a. The means to soften the sea water cheaply, generally with lime.

b. The preparation of a purified lime slurry of proper characteristics.

c. The economical removal of the precipitated hydroxide from the large volume of water.

d. The inexpensive purification of the hydrous precipitates.

e. The development of means to filter the viscous slimes.[1]

The reactions are

$$MgCl_2(aq) + Ca(OH)_2(c) \rightarrow Mg(OH)_2(c) + CaCl_2(aq);$$
$$\Delta H = 2,260 \text{ cal.}$$

$$MgSO_4(aq) + Ca(OH)_2(c) + 2H_2O(l) \rightarrow$$
$$Mg(OH)_2(c) + CaSO_4 \cdot 2H_2O(c); \quad \Delta H = -3,170 \text{ cal.}$$

Figure 7 shows[2] a flow sheet of magnesium products from sea water. This process specializes in producing such fine chemicals and pharmaceuticals as milk of magnesia and several basic magnesium carbonates such as $3MgCO_3 \cdot Mg(OH)_2 \cdot 4H_2O$ for tooth powders and antacid remedies, for coating of table salt to render it noncaking, and for paint fillers. Certain of these basic magnesium compounds are also employed with rubber accelerators.

[1] CHESNY, Magnesium Compounds from Ocean Water, *Ind. Eng. Chem.*, **28**, 383 (1936).

[2] MANNING, Magnesium Metal and Compounds, *Chem. & Met. Eng.*, **45**, 478 (1938); CHESNY, *op. cit.*, pictured flow sheet; ANON., *Chem. & Met. Eng.*, **54** (8), 132 (1947).

The Dow Chemical Company of Freeport, Tex., also manufactures magnesium compounds[1] directly from sea water using lime produced by roasting oystershells. This is employed to make magnesium hydrate which is dissolved in 10 per cent hydrochloric acid to furnish a solution of magnesium chloride. This is concentrated in direct-fired evaporators followed by shelf driers, producing 76 per cent magnesium chloride ready

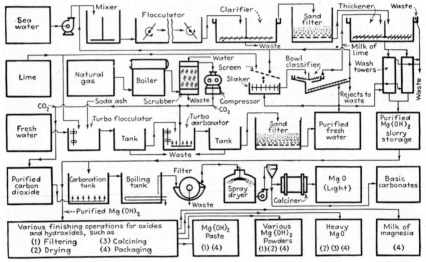

Fig. 7. Purified magnesium products from sea water. (*Courtesy of Marine Magnesium Products Corporation, now owned by Merck & Co.*)

to be shoveled into the electrolytic cells to make metallic magnesium (see Fig. 3 of Chap. 16).

Figure 8 presents a flow sheet for the manufacture of magnesium products (and gypsum) from the bitterns or mother liquors from the evaporation of sea water to obtain salt, as practiced on the south part of the San Francisco Bay. The bittern is first chlorinated to recover the bromide (not shown). The flow sheet depicts first the removal of gypsum by the reaction:

$$MgSO_4(aq) + CaCl_2(aq) + 2H_2O(l) \rightarrow MgCl_2(aq) + CaSO_4 \cdot 2H_2O(c);$$
$$\Delta H = -910 \text{ cal.}$$

Such a step is not necessary in those processes based on sea water when the dilution is sufficient to hold the $CaSO_4$ in solution. While calcined oystershells were formerly used, now dolomite is calcined to furnish "dolime." This is ground, air-separated, and hydrated in the presence of the purified bittern to produce a granular, easy-settling $Mg(OH)_2$, which

[1] ANON., Magnesium from Sea Water, *Chem. & Met. Eng.*, **48** (11), 130 (1941), pictured flow sheet and description; MURPHY, Magnesium from the Sea, *Chem. Inds.*, **49**, 618 (1942), flow sheet and description; SCHRAMBA, The Dow Magnesium Process at Freeport, Texas, *Trans. Am. Inst. Chem. Engrs.*, **41**, 35 (1945).

is thickened, washed, filtered, and calcined to active, chemical, insulation, or periclase MgO, the grade being largely dependent upon calcining temperature. This $Mg(OH)_2$ is quite different from the slow-settling $Mg(OH)_2$ precipitated by a soluble alkali or by milk of lime.

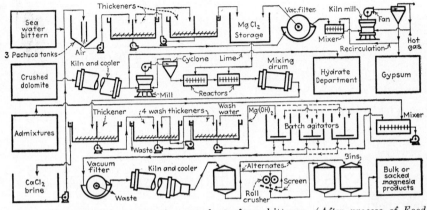

FIG. 8. Flow sheet for magnesium products from bitterns. (*After process of Food Machinery and Chemical Corp.*)

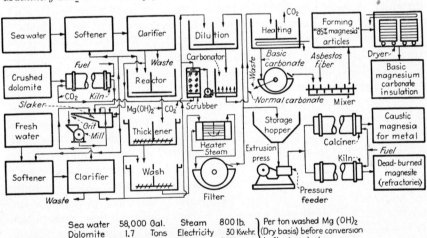

Sea water	58,000 Gal.	Steam	800 lb.	Per ton washed Mg (OH)$_2$
Dolomite	1.7 Tons	Electricity	30 Kw-hr.	(Dry basis) before conversion
Fresh water	500 Gal.	Direct labor	0.66 Man-hr.	to final products

FIG. 9. Flow sheet for magnesium products from sea water and dolomite.

Where dolomite is used instead of calcium carbonate only about one-half of the magnesia must come from the magnesium salts in the sea water.[1] Consequently the size of the plant is much smaller, and the cost of production is probably lower.

[1] Sea water has normally 2.2 grams per liter of equivalent MgO, actually present as $MgCl_2$ and $MgSO_4$. Hence for 1 ton of MgO there is required theoretically 111,000 gal. of sea water. Based on a 70 per cent yield, there would be pumped about 158,000 gal. if all the magnesia comes from the sea water, or about half this gallonage if dolomite is used.

The reactions, as illustrated in the flow sheet of Fig. 9, are principally the following:

Calcination:

$$2CaMg(CO_3)_2(c) \rightarrow 2CaO(c) + 2MgO(c) + 4CO_2(g);$$
$$\Delta H = +145,880 \text{ cal.}$$

Slaking:

$$2CaO(c) + 2MgO(c) + 4H_2O(l) \rightarrow 2Ca(OH)_2(c) + 2Mg(OH)_2(c);$$
$$\Delta H = -40,320 \text{ cal.}$$

Precipitation:

$$2Ca(OH)_2(c) + 2Mg(OH)_2(c) + MgCl_2(aq) + MgSO_4(aq) + 2H_2O(l) \rightarrow$$
$$4Mg(OH)_2(c) + CaCl_2(aq) + CaSO_4 \cdot 2H_2O(s); \quad \Delta H = -5,430 \text{ cal.}$$

Calcination:

$$4Mg(OH)_2(c) \rightarrow 4MgO(c) + 4H_2O(g); \quad \Delta H = +59,280 \text{ cal.}$$

Only about 7 per cent of the slaked calcined dolomite is needed for softening the sea water, the rest precipitating a crystalline magnesium hydroxide which is easily filtered and washed. This hydroxide is frequently sold to the makers of 85 per cent magnesia, or converted to other products.

Magnesium Carbonates. These vary from dense $MgCO_3$ used in magnesite bricks to the very low density $4MgCO_3 \cdot Mg(OH)_2 \cdot 5H_2O$ or $3MgCO_3 \cdot Mg(OH)_2 \cdot 3H_2O$ employed so extensively for insulation. The basic magnesium carbonate, usually $3MgCO_3 \cdot Mg(OH)_2 4H_2O$, is made by diluting the washed $Mg(OH)_2$, reacting it with CO_2 from the dolomite calcination, and heating it to release some of the CO_2 and form the basic salt. This is then mixed with 15 per cent asbestos, cast into the desired shapes and dried for the market as "85 per cent magnesia" insulation (Fig. 9). There are also other basic carbonates on the market, as described by Chesny,[1] with variations in adsorptive index and apparent density. Many of these are employed as fillers in inks, paints, and varnishes (see Fig. 9 for manufacture). The newest process for magnesia insulation, now in use by the majority of producers, prepares needlelike crystals of magnesium carbonate with self-setting properties.[2] Dolomite (see Fig. 10) or magnesium oxide[3] is used as the starting material. The dolomite is burned, slaked, and carbonated to separate out the soluble magnesium bicarbonate from the insoluble calcium carbonate, after which the magnesium

[1] CHESNY, *op. cit.*, pp. 388–389.

[2] ABRAHAMS, Better Magnesia Insulation by New Process, *Chem. Eng.*, **58** (9), 140 (1951).

[3] OLIVE, Control Methods for a Batch Process, *Chem. Eng.*, **59** (1), 140 (1952); ANON., Precision Magnesia Insulation, *Chem. Eng.*, **58** (12), 208 (1951), a pictured flow sheet.

bicarbonate is heated under controlled conditions to precipitate the normal carbonate or basic carbonate.

Oxides and Hydroxide of Magnesium.[1] On heating magnesium carbonate or hydroxide, magnesium oxide, MgO, is formed. This oxide has many uses, such as in the vulcanization of rubber, as a material for making other magnesium compounds, as an insulating material, as a refractory material, and as an abrasive. The magnesium hydroxide, $Mg(OH)_2$, is now made directly from sea water as Fig. 7 shows. After purification this

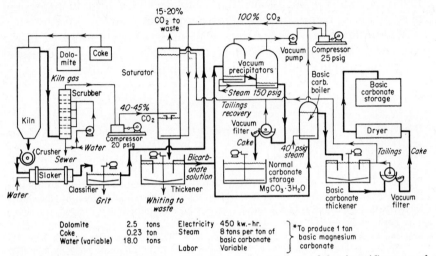

Dolomite	2.5	tons	Electricity	450 kw.-hr.	⎫
Coke	0.23	ton	Steam	8 tons per ton of	*To produce 1 ton
Water (variable)	18.0	tons		basic carbonate	⎬ basic magnesium
			Labor	Variable	⎭ carbonate

FIG. 10. Magnesium carbonates (normal and basic) from dolomite. (*Courtesy of Philip Carey Manufacturing Co.*)

is the well-known milk of magnesia used in medicine. See also the flow charts depicted in Figs. 8 and 9. *Magnesium peroxide* is available from the reaction of magnesium sulfate and barium peroxide. It is employed as an antiseptic and as a bleaching agent.

Magnesium Sulfate. Commercially, this is prepared by the action of sulfuric acid on magnesium carbonate or hydroxide. It is sold in many forms, one of which is the hydrate, $MgSO_4 \cdot 7H_2O$, long known as *epsom salt*. The less pure material is used extensively as sizing and as a fireproofing agent.

Magnesium Chloride. As would be expected, this salt is made from hydrochloric acid and magnesium carbonate, hydroxide or oxide, although it occurs in brines and salines in nature from which commercial amounts are obtained directly. The compound itself much resembles calcium chloride and has many of the same uses. In addition, it finds application in ceramics, in the sizing of paper, and in the manufacture of oxychloride

[1] Smith, Complex Processing Used for Light Magnesium Oxide, *Chem. Eng.*, **53** (10), 119 (1946).

cement. For making metallic magnesium its manufacture is described earlier in this chapter and in Chap. 16 (Fig. 3).

Magnesium Silicates. A consideration of magnesium silicates[1] includes two widely used naturally occurring compounds: asbestos and talc. Asbestos is a magnesium silicate mixed with varying quantities of silicates of calcium and iron. It is a fibrous, noncombustible mineral and is used in the manufacture of many fireproof and insulating materials. Talc is a rather pure magnesium silicate in the form of $3MgO\cdot4SiO_2\cdot H_2O$ which is found naturally in soapstone. It is employed as a filler in paper and plastics and in many cosmetic and toilet preparations.

Magnesium Soaps. Magnesium soaps in general are prepared in the same way and have the same properties as calcium soaps. An additional use of magnesium stearate is as a drier in protective coatings.

SELECTED REFERENCES

Bogue, R. H., "The Chemistry of Portland Cement," Reinhold Publishing Corporation, New York, 1947. A most excellent book.

Witt, J. C., "Portland Cement Technology," Chemical Publishing Company, Inc., New York, 1947.

Portland Cement Association, 33 West Grand Ave., Chicago, Ill. Various bulletins, many reporting on research in cooperation with National Bureau of Standards.

Eckel, E. C., "Cements, Limes and Plasters," 3d ed., John Wiley & Sons, Inc., New York, 1928.

Martin, Geoffrey, "Chemical Engineering and Thermodynamics Applied to the Cement Rotary Kiln," The Technical Press, Ltd., London, 1932. Filled with pertinent data, calculations, and designs.

Lea, F. M., and C. H. Desch, "The Chemistry of Cement and Concrete," Longmans, Green & Co., Inc., New York, 1935.

Lime: Its Properties and Uses, *Natl. Bur. Standards Circ.* 30, Washington, 1920.

Bowles, Oliver, and D. M. Banks, Lime, *U.S. Bur. Mines Inform. Circ.* 6884R, 1941. Extensive bibliography.

Azbe, V. J., "Theory and Practice of Lime Manufacture," Azbe Corporation, St. Louis, Missouri, 1946.

National Lime Association, various bulletins.

Armstrong, E. F., and L. M. Miall, "Raw Materials from the Sea," Constructive Publications, Ltd., Leicester, 1946.

Gross, W. H., "The Story of Magnesium," American Society for Metals, Cleveland, 1949.

[1] *Cf.* phase diagram of the system $MgO-SiO_2$ in Chap. 10.

CHAPTER 12

GLASS INDUSTRIES

Glass has three important properties that have made it indispensable as a building material in modern civilization: its hardness, its transparency, and its chemical resistance. To these should be added refractive and dispersive powers, compressive and tensile strengths, as well as coefficient of expansion. Whatever has been done in recent years to extend the usefulness of glass has depended largely upon the ability of the glass technologist to vary and control these essential properties, particularly the three first named.

History.[1] Like many other commonplace materials of our modern civilization, the discovery of glass is very uncertain. One of the earliest references to this material was by Pliny, who related the familiar story of how some ancient Phoenician merchants discovered it while cooking a meal in a vessel placed accidentally upon a mass of trona at the seashore. The union of the sand and alkali caught the men's attention and led to subsequent efforts at imitation.

As early as 6,000 or 5,000 B.C. the Egyptians were making sham jewels of glass which were often of fine workmanship and marked beauty. During medieval times Venice enjoyed a monopoly as the center of the glass industry; and, it was not until the sixteenth century that any glass was made in either Germany or England. Window glass is mentioned as early as A.D. 290. The hand-blown window-glass cylinder was invented by a twelfth-century monk. However, it was not until the fifteenth century that the use of window glass became general. Plate glass appeared as a rolled product in France in 1688.

The first glassworks in America were founded at the beginning of the seventeenth century at Jamestown in 1608 and at Salem, Mass., in 1639. For more than three centuries after it had been established in America, the glass industry remained essentially stagnant as far as technological advance was concerned. The processes were practically all manual and rule of thumb. From the chemical point of view, the only major improvements during this period were confined to purifying the batch materials and increasing the economy in fuel. To be sure, some relations were established between the chemical composition of glasses and their optical

---

[1] SILVERMAN, Glass, What Is Old, What Is New? *Ind. Eng. Chem.*, **32**, 1415 (1940).

and other physical properties but, all in all, the industry prior to 1900 was an art, with closely guarded secret formulas and empirical processes of manufacture based primarily upon experience.

Toward the end of the nineteenth century Lubbers invented a mechanical adaptation of the hand-blown window-glass cylinder process, and in 1914 the Fourcault process for drawing a sheet of glass continuously was developed in Belgium. These were followed by other direct continuous-sheet processes, including the Colburn, Pittsburgh Plate Glass, and Libbey-Owens processes. The advent of the closed automobile created an enormous demand for small sizes of plate glass, which was partly met by the entrance of the automobile manufacturers themselves into this manufacture. Meanwhile, nearly all branches of the industry were in process of rapid evolution. Scientists and engineers entered the field in increasing numbers. Automatic machines were invented to speed up production of bottles, light bulbs, etc., and new products appeared as the result of intensive research. As a result, today the glass industry is a highly specialized field employing all the tools of modern science in the production, control, and development of its many products.

Uses and Economics. The glass and glassware production by types is shown in Table 1. The uses and applications of glass are very numerous but some conception of the versatility of this material can be gained from the discussion of the various types, as described in the rest of this chapter.

TABLE 1. VALUE OF GLASS AND GLASSWARE SHIPPED[a]
(Thousands of dollars)

	1952	1947
Flat glass, total............................	$231,508	$196,703
Sheet window glass............................	88,375	72,525
Plate glass...................................	....	84,164
Other flat glass..............................	....	40,014
Glass containers...............................	559,952	422,963
Pressed and blown glassware (except containers)..	324,579	234,795
Other glass products:		
Laminated glass...............................	179,812	101,033
Mirrors.......................................	....	55,428
Other glass products..........................	....	86,959

[a] Annual Survey of Manufactures, 1952.

MANUFACTURE

Glass may be defined: *physically* as a rigid, undercooled liquid having no definite melting point and a sufficiently high viscosity (greater than 10^{13} poises) to prevent crystallization; *chemically* as the union of the non-volatile inorganic oxides resulting from the decomposition and fusing of the alkali and alkaline earth compounds, sand, and other glass constituents. Glass is a *completely vitrified* product or at least such a product with a relatively small amount of nonvitreous material in suspension.

TABLE 2. CHEMICAL COMPOSITION OF TYPICAL GLASSES[a]
(In per cent)

No.	SiO_2	B_2O_3	Al_2O_3	Fe_2O_3	As_2O_3	CaO	MgO	Na_2O	K_2O	PbO	SO_3
1	67.8	.....	4.4	....	....	4.0	2.3	13.7	2.3	....	1.0
2	69.4	.....	3.5	1.1	....	7.2	....	17.3			
3	70.5	.....	1.9	0.4	....	13.0	....	12.0	1.9		
4	71.5	.....	1.5	....	....	13.0	....	14.0			
5	72.88	.....	0.78		....	12.68	0.22	12.69			
6	72.9	.....	0.7		....	7.9	2.8	15.0			
7	72.68	.....	0.50	0.07	....	12.95	....	13.17	.....	....	0.44
8	74.50	.....	0.81	0.09	....	5.5	4.1	15.0			
9	72.4	.....	0.8	0.4	....	5.3	3.7	17.4			
10	73.88	16.48	2.24		0.73	.....	....	6.67	Trace		
11	74.2	0.4	....	....	0.2	4.3	3.2	17.7			
12	67.2	.....	....	....	0.5	0.9	....	9.5	7.1	14.8	
13	69.04	0.25	....	....	....	12.07	....	5.95	11.75		
14	64.7	10.6	4.2	....	....	0.6	....	7.8	0.3		
15	80.75	12.00	2.20		0.40	0.30	....	4.10	0.10		
16	80.9	12.6	1.8	....	....	....	....	4.4			
17	96.0	3.6									

[a] Data from either SHARP, Chemical Composition of Commercial Glasses, *Ind. Eng. Chem.*, **25**, 755 (1933) or BLAU, Chemical Trends, *Ind. Eng. Chem.*, **32**, 1429 (1940).
   1. Egyptian from Thebes (1500 B.C.) (Blau).
   2. Pompeian window (Blau).
   3. German window (1849) hand-blown (Blau).
   4. Representative window and bottle glass of nineteenth century (Sharp).
   5. Machine cylinder glass (Sharp).
   6. Fourcault process sheet with 0.7 per cent BaO (Sharp).
   7. Polished plate with 0.18 per cent Sb_2O_3 (Sharp).
   8. Owens machine bottle (Sharp).
   9. Electric light bulb (Sharp).
   10. Jena, incandescent gas chimney (Sharp).
   11. Tableware, lime crystal (Sharp).
   12. Tableware, lead crystal (Sharp).
   13. Spectacle with 0.9 per cent Sb_2O_3 (Sharp).
   14. Jena with 10.9 per cent ZnO, 1911 laboratory (Sharp).
   15. Corning Pyrex laboratory (Sharp).
   16. Laboratory Pyrex 774 (Blau).
   17. 96 per cent silica No. 790 (1940) (Blau).

Composition. In spite of hundreds of new developments in glass during the past thirty years, it is worthy of note that lime, silica, and soda still form over 90 per cent of all the glass of the world, just as they did 2,000 years ago. It should not be inferred that there have been no important changes in composition during this period. Rather, there have been minor changes in major ingredients or major changes in minor ingredients. The major ingredients are sand, lime, and soda ash, and any other raw materials may be considered to be minor ingredients, even though the effects produced may be of major importance. Table 2 shows the chemical composition of various glasses.

In general, commercial glasses fall into six different classes:

1. Vitreous silica—a glass made by fusing pure silica without a flux, and very resistant thermally and chemically.

2. Alkali silicates—soluble glasses used only as solutions.

3. Lime glass—the soda-lime-silica glass of such wide applications, for windows, transparent fixtures, and all manner of containers.

4. Lead glass—the product obtained from lead oxide, silica, and alkali for decorative and optical effects.

5. Borosilicate glass—boric oxide and silica glasses for optical and scientific work.

6. Special glass—such as colored glass, translucent glass, safety and laminated glass, fiber glass, photosensitive glass, phosphate glass, and specialties for chemical uses.

Vitreous silica, sometimes referred to erroneously as *quartz glass*, is the end member of the silicate glasses. It is characterized by low expansion and high softening point, which impart high thermal resistance and permit this to be used beyond the temperature ranges of other glasses. This glass is also extraordinarily transparent to ultraviolet radiation.

The *alkali silicates* are the only two-component glasses of commercial importance. These are water-soluble. The sand and soda ash are simply melted together and the products designated as sodium silicates,[1] having a range of composition from $Na_2O \cdot SiO_2$ to $Na_2O \cdot 4SiO_2$. A knowledge of the equilibrium relations[2] in these two component systems has aided the glass technologist in understanding the behavior of the more complicated systems. Silicate of soda solution, also known as *water glass*, is widely consumed as an adhesive for paper in the manufacture of corrugated paper boxes. Other uses include fireproofing and egg preservation. The higher alkaline varieties enter into laundering as detergents and as soap builders.

Lime glass represents by far the largest tonnage of glass made today and serves for the manufacture of containers of all kinds, flat glass (window, plate, wire and figured), tumblers and tableware. There has been a general betterment in the physical quality of all flat glass such as increased flatness and freedom from waves and strains, but the chemical

---

[1] See Chap. 14 for fuller descriptions.

[2] See MOREY, "The Properties of Glass," Reinhold Publishing Corporation, New York, 1938.

composition has not varied greatly. This composition as a rule lies between the following limits:[1] (1) SiO_2, 69 to 72 per cent, (2) CaO, 12.5 to 13.5 per cent, (3) Na_2O, 13 to 15 per cent, because products of these ratios do not melt too high and are sufficiently viscous so that they do not devitrify and yet are not too viscous to be workable at reasonable temperatures. The great improvement has been in the substitution of instrument-controlled mechanical devices for the individualism of the hand operator. Similarly in container glass, the progress has been largely of a mechanical nature. However, the influence of the liquor trade has caused a tendency among manufacturers to make glassware particularly high in alumina and lime and low in alkali. This type of glass melts with more difficulty but is more chemically resistant. It might be mentioned in passing that the color of container glass is much better than formerly because of a better selection and purification of raw materials, and the use of selenium as a decolorizer.

The applications of phase-rule[2] studies have explained many of the earlier empirical observations of the glassmaker, have led to some improvements such as more exactness in the manufacture of lime glass, and have laid the basis for new glass formulations. The phase diagrams for many systems are known and published, but the system Na_2O-CaO-SiO_2 has been particularly detailed.[3]

Lead glasses are of very great importance in optical work because of their high index of refraction and high dispersion. Lead contents as high as 92 per cent (density 8.0, refractive index 2.2) have been made. The brilliancy of good "cut glass" is due to its lead-bearing composition. Large quantities are used also for the construction of electric light bulbs, neon-sign tubing, and radiotrons, because of the high electrical resistance of the glass.

The borosilicates[4] usually contain about 10 to 13 per cent of B_2O_3 and 80 to 83 per cent of silica and have low expansion coefficients, superior resistance to shock, excellent chemical stability, and high electrical resistance. Wide and ever-increasing uses for these glasses have revolutionized the ideas of the laymen toward the properties of glass. Among the diversified applications of these glasses are baking dishes, laboratory glassware, pipe lines, high-tension insulators, and washers. Probably the most

---

[1] MOREY, in "Rogers' Manual of Industrial Chemistry," 6th ed., p. 781, D. Van Nostrand Company, Inc., New York, 1942.

[2] LEWIS, SQUIRES, and BROUGHTON, "Industrial Chemistry of Colloidal and Amorphous Materials," pp. 285–304, The Macmillan Company, New York, 1942; MOREY, Phase Equilibrium Relationships Determining Glass Compositions, *Ind. Eng. Chem.*, **25**, 742 (1933); SHARP, Chemical Composition of Commercial Glasses, *Ind. Eng. Chem.*, **25**, 755 (1933).

[3] MOREY, in "Rogers' Manual of Industrial Chemistry," 6th ed., pp. 776–781, D. Van Nostrand Company, Inc., New York, 1942.

[4] Frequently sold under the name of Pyrex.

famous casting of the borosilicate glasses is the 200-in. disk for the giant telescope at Mt. Palomar.

The *special glasses* include (1) colored glass, (2) translucent glass, (3) safety or laminated glass, (4) fiber glass, (5) high-silica glass, (6) photosensitive glass, and (7) phosphate and borate glasses.

1. Though for many centuries colored glass was used merely for decoration, today colored transparent glasses are essential for both technical and scientific purposes and are produced in many hundreds of colors. *Colored* glass may be one of three types: (*a*) Color is produced by the *absorption* of certain light frequencies by agents in solution in the glass. The coloring agents of this group are the oxides of the transition elements, especially the first group, Ti, V, Cr, Mn, Fe, Co, Ni, and Cu. This class can be subdivided as to those in which the color is due to chemical structural environment or those in which the color is caused by differences in state of oxidation. As an example of the former, NiO dissolved in sodium-lead glass yields a brown color, but in a potash glass it produces a heliotrope. In the latter, chromium oxides will produce colors ranging from green to orange depending on the proportions of the basic oxide, Cr_2O_3, to the acidic oxide and the composition of glass as to whether it is basic or acidic. (*b*) Color is produced by *colloidal particles* precipitated within an originally colorless glass by heat-treatment. The classical example is the precipitation of colloidal gold producing gold ruby glass. (*c*) Color is produced by *microscopic or larger particles* which may be colored themselves such as selenium reds (SeO_2) used in traffic lights, lantern globes, etc., or the particles may be colorless, producing opals.

2. *Opal* or *translucent* glasses are clear when molten but become opalescent as the glass is worked into form, owing to the separation and suspension of minute particles in the medium which disperse the light passing through them. They are important commercially as diffusing media in illumination, as containers, and as construction material. Fluorides are among the ingredients required as well as special manufacturing procedures.

3. *Safety* or *laminated* glasses may be defined as of a composite structure consisting of two layers of glass with an interleaf of plastic, plasticized polyvinyl butyral resin. When the glass is broken, the fragments are held in place by the interlayer. Another type is casehardened safety glass, which, with a blow sufficiently hard to break it, disintegrates into many small pieces without the usual sharp cutting edges. The manufacture of safety glass is presented later in this chapter.

4. Modern *fiber glass*[1] (*cf.* Chap. 34, Synthetic Fibers), although not a new product, owes its enhanced usefulness to its extreme fineness (of the order of 0.00005 in. and as small as 0.00002 in.). It can be spun into yarn,

---

[1] ANON., Fiber Glass, *Chem. Eng.*, **54** (6), 130 (1947), pictured flow sheet of both glass wool and textile fibers.

gathered into a mat, made into insulation, tape, air filters, and a great variety of other products such as pipe with plastic bond.

5. The making of *high-silica* glass is considered on page 249.

6. In 1947 Corning Glass Works announced the development of *photo-sensitive*[1] glass which makes it possible to print three-dimensional colored photographic images within glass articles. Photosensitive metals, such as gold, silver, and copper, and sensitizers, either thermo-reducing or optical, are added to conventional silicate glasses containing at least 5 per cent alkali metal oxide. The optical sensitizer cerium is preferred because it is the most versatile in color. Conventional glass-melting and forming methods are used with the batch. A black-and-white negative is placed on the sensitized glass and exposed to ultraviolet light. Color variations depend directly on exposure time. Orange and red colors, characteristic of strong exposures, develop faster than the purples and blues. The picture is developed by heating the glass to the annealing temperature or above. The result is a fadeproof photograph resistant to abrasion, heat, moisture, or dirt.

7. *Phosphate* glass contains phosphorous pentoxide as a major ingredient wholly or partially displacing silica. An important property of phosphate glass is its ability to resist hydrofluoric acid, for example, in fluorinations. Sight glasses for the handling of uranium hexafluoride in the separation of uranium isotopes for making atomic bombs are made from phosphate glass. Phosphate glass is also used in special optical, ultraviolet, heat-absorbing, and fluorescent glasses.[2]

Raw Materials. In order to produce all these various glasses, over 5,000,000 tons of glass sand are used in the United States each year. To flux this silica requires over 1,500,000 tons of soda ash, 113,000 tons of salt cake, and 875,000 tons of limestone or equivalent lime. In addition to these, there is a heavy consumption of lead oxide, pearl ash (potassium carbonate), saltpeter, borax, boric acid, arsenic trioxide, feldspar, and fluorspar, together with a great variety of metallic oxides, carbonates, and the other salts required for colored glass. In finishing operations, such diverse products as abrasives and hydrofluoric acid are consumed.

Sand for glass manufacture should be almost pure quartz. A glass-sand deposit has, in many cases, determined the location of glass factories. Its iron content should not exceed 0.045 per cent for tableware or 0.015 per cent for optical glass, as iron affects adversely the color of most glass.

Soda, Na_2O, is principally supplied by dense soda ash, Na_2CO_3. Other sources are sodium bicarbonate, salt cake, and sodium nitrate. The latter is useful in oxidizing iron and in accelerating the melting. The important

[1] STOOKEY, Photosensitive Glass, *Ind. Eng. Chem.*, **41**, 856 (1949).

[2] WEYL, Phosphate Glasses, *Chem. Eng. News*, **27**, 1048 (1949).

sources for *lime*, CaO, are limestone and burnt lime from dolomite, $CaCO_3 \cdot MgCO_3$ the latter introducing MgO into the batch.

Feldspars have the general formula $R_2O \cdot Al_2O_3 \cdot 6SiO_2$, where R_2O represents Na_2O or K_2O or a mixture of these two. They have many advantages over most other materials as a source of aluminum oxide, because they are cheap, pure, and fusible and are composed entirely of glass-forming oxides. Al_2O_3 itself is used only when cost is a secondary item. Feldspars also supply Na_2O or K_2O and SiO_2. The alumina content serves to lower the melting point of the glass and to retard devitrification.

Borax, as a minor ingredient, supplies the glass with both sodium oxide and boric oxide. Though seldom employed in window or plate glass, borax is now in common use in certain types of container glass. There is also a high-index borate glass which has a lower dispersion value and higher refractive index than any glass previously known. This is valuable as an optical glass. Besides its high fluxing power, borax not only lowers the expansion coefficient but increases chemical durability. Boric acid is used in batches where only a small amount of alkali is wanted. Its price is about twice that of borax.

Salt cake, long accepted as a minor ingredient of glass, and also other sulfates, such as ammonium and barium sulfates, are encountered frequently in all types of glass. Salt cake is said to remove the troublesome scum from tank furnaces. Carbon should be used with sulfates to reduce them to sulfites. *Arsenic trioxide* may be added to facilitate the removal of bubbles. *Nitrates* of either sodium or potassium serve to oxidize iron and make it less noticeable in the finished glass. Potassium[1] *nitrate* or carbonate is employed in many of the better grades of table, decorative, and optical glass.

Cullet is the crushed glass from imperfect articles, trim or otherwise waste glass. It facilitates the melting and utilizes a waste. It may be as low as 10 per cent of the charge or as high as 80 per cent.

Refractory blocks for the glass industry have been developed especially because of the severe conditions encountered here. Electrocast alumina, zirconia-alumina, mullite, mullite-alumina, magnesia-alumina, and chrome-alumina combinations are typical of these for glass tanks. Latest practice in regenerators and recuperators utilizes basic refractories (see Chap. 10) because of the alkali dust.

Chemical Reactions. The chemical reactions involved may be summarized:

$$Na_2CO_3 + aSiO_2 \rightarrow Na_2O \cdot aSiO_2 + CO_2 \tag{1}$$

$$CaCO_3 + bSiO_2 \rightarrow CaO \cdot bSiO_2 + CO_2 \tag{2}$$

$$Na_2SO_4 + cSiO_2 + C \rightarrow Na_2O \cdot cSiO_2 + SO_2 + CO \tag{3}$$

---

[1] FINN, Potash in the Glass Industry, *Ind. Eng. Chem.*, **30**, 891 (1938).

The last reaction may take place as in equations (4) or (5), and (6):

$$Na_2SO_4 + C \rightarrow Na_2SO_3 + CO \tag{4}$$
$$2Na_2SO_4 + C \rightarrow 2Na_2SO_3 + CO_2 \tag{5}$$
$$Na_2SO_3 + cSiO_2 \rightarrow Na_2O \cdot cSiO_2 + SO_2 \tag{6}$$

It should be noted that the ratios Na_2O/SiO_2 and CaO/SiO_2 need not be 1 to 1 molecular ratios. The compounds may be of the type formula $Na_2O \cdot 1.8SiO_2$, for example. In an ordinary window glass the molecular ratios are approximately: 2 moles Na_2O, 1 mole CaO, 5 moles SiO_2. Other glasses vary widely (see Table 2).

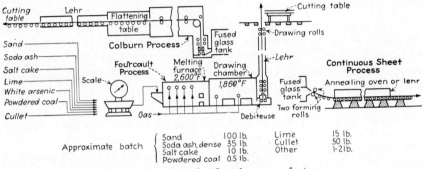

FIG. 1. Flow sheet for flat-glass manufacture.

Unit Operations and Unit Processes. Typical manufacturing sequences can be broken down into the following *unit operations* (Op.) and *unit processes* (Pr.) (*cf.* Fig. 1):

Transportation of raw materials to plant (Op.).
Sizing of some raw materials (Op.).
Storage of raw materials (Op.).
Conveying to, weighing and feeding raw materials into glass furnace (Op.).
Reacting in furnace to form the glass (Pr.).
Burning of fuel to secure temperature needed for glass formation (Pr.).
Heat saving by regeneration or recuperation (Op.).
Shaping of glass products (Op.).
Annealing of glass products (Op.).
Finishing of glass products (Op.).

To carry out these unit operations and unit processes, the modern glass factories are characterized by the use of materials-handling machinery supplying automatic and continuous manufacturing equipment, in contrast to the "shovel and wheelbarrow" methods of the older factories. In spite of the modernization of many plants, however, manual charging of furnaces is still carried on, though a dusty atmosphere is created. The trend, however, is toward mechanical batch transporting and mixing systems so completely enclosed that practically no dust is emitted at any stage of the handling of glass or raw materials. This is important, because in most states the restrictions against silica dust are becoming more rigorous.

METHODS OF MANUFACTURE

The manufacturing procedures may be divided (*cf.* Fig. 1) into four major phases: (1) melting, (2) shaping, (3) annealing, and (4) finishing.

1. Melting. Glass furnaces may be classified as either pot or tank furnaces and subclassified as either regenerative or recuperative (*cf.* Fig. 2 of tank furnace).

Pot furnaces, approximate capacity of 2 tons or less, are used advantageously for small production of special glasses or where it is essential to protect the melting batch from the products of combustion. They are employed principally in the manufacture of optical glass, art glass, and plate glass by the casting process. The pots are really crucibles made of selected clay or platinum. It is very difficult to melt glass in these vessels without contaminating the product or partly melting the container itself except when platinum is used.

In a *tank furnace* (Fig. 2) batch materials are charged into one end of a large "tank" built of refractory blocks. Some measure 125 by 30 by 5 ft. with a capacity of 1,400 tons of molten glass. The glass forms a pool in the hearth of the furnace, across which the flames play alternately from one side or the other. The "fined" glass is worked out of the opposite end of the tank, the operation being continuous. In this type of furnace, as in the pot, the walls gradually wear away under the action of the hot glass. The quality of the glass and the life of the tank are dependent upon the quality of the blocks of construction. For this reason, much study has been given to glass furnace refractories.[1]

Each of the foregoing types of furnaces may be of either regenerative or recuperative design. The *regenerative* furnace operates in two cycles with two sets of checkerwork chambers. The flame gases, after giving up their heat in passing across the furnace containing the molten glass, go downward through one set of chambers stacked with open brickwork or checkerwork, as shown in Fig. 2. A great deal of the sensible heat content of the gases is removed thereby—the checkerwork reaching temperatures ranging from 2800°F., near the furnace, to 1200°F. on the exit side. Simultaneously, air is being preheated by passing up the other previously heated regenerative chamber and is mixed with the fuel gas[2] and

---

[1] See Refractories, Chap. 10; Symposium, High Temperature Refractories, *Chem. Eng. Progr.*, **44**, 869–878, 933–942 (1948).

[2] If the fuel is producer gas, it is preheated also, but not if a higher B.t.u. type is employed, such as natural gas or oil.

burned, the resulting flame being of greater temperature than would have
been possible if the air had not been preheated. At regular intervals, the
flow of air-fuel mixture or the cycle is reversed, entering the furnace from
the opposite side, through the previously heated checkerwork, and passing through the original checkerwork, now considerably cooled. The time
required for each cycle is 20 to 30 min. Much heat is saved by this regenerative principle and a higher temperature is reached.

Recuperation accomplishes the same effect as regeneration, namely, the
preheating of entering air, but the incoming gases flow continuously in

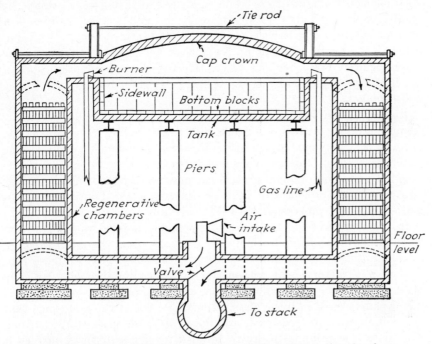

Fig. 2. Cross section of glass tank furnace showing regenerative chambers.

one direction only. In a recuperative furnace the hot gases pass through
one set of tile passages on their way to the stack, and the air passes
through adjacent parallel passages and is preheated as it moves to the
furnace. No reversing mechanism is necessary, but disadvantages due to
leaking and clogging make it difficult for these furnaces to compete with
regenerative furnaces, especially in larger designs.

The temperature of a furnace just entering production can be raised
only certain increments each day depending upon the ability of the refractory used to stand the expansion. Once the regenerative furnace has
been heated, a temperature at least of 2200°F. is maintained at all times.
Melting cost is about $2 per ton of glass. The larger part of the heat is
lost by radiation from the furnace and the much smaller part is actually

expended in the melting. However, unless the walls were allowed to cool somewhat by radiation, their temperature would get so high that the molten glass would dissolve or corrode them much faster. To reduce the action of the molten glass on the furnace wall, water cooling pipes are frequently placed in the furnace wall.

2. Shaping or Forming. Glass may be shaped by either machine or hand molding. The outstanding factor to be considered in *machine molding* is that the design of the glass machine should be such that the article is completed in a very few seconds. During this relatively short time the glass changes from a viscous liquid to a clear solid. It can, therefore, be readily appreciated that the design problems to be solved, such as flow of heat, stability of metals, and clearance of bearings, are very complicated. The success of such machines is an outstanding tribute to the glass engineer. Following is a description of the most common types of machine-shaped glass, *i.e.*, window glass, plate glass, bottles, light bulbs, and tubing.

Window Glass. For many years window glass was made by an extremely arduous hand process that involved gathering a gob of glass on the end of a blowpipe and blowing it into a cylinder. The ends of the latter were cut off, the hollow cylinder split, heated in an oven, and flattened. This tedious manual process has now been entirely supplanted by two continuous processes or their modifications, the Fourcault process and the Colburn process, as outlined in the flow sheets of Fig. 1.

In the Fourcault process a drawing chamber is filled with glass from the melting tank. The glass is drawn vertically from the kiln through a so-called *débiteuse* by means of a drawing machine. The débiteuse consists of a refractory boat with a slot in the center through which the glass flows continuously upward when the boat is partly submerged. A metal bait lowered into the glass through the slot at the same time that the débiteuse is lowered starts the drawing as the glass starts flowing. The glass is continuously drawn upward in ribbon form as fast as it flows up through the slot, and its surface is chilled by adjacent water coils. The ribbon, still traveling vertically and supported by means of asbestos-covered steel rollers, passes through a 25-ft.-long annealing chimney or lehr. On emerging from the lehr, it is cut into sheets of the desired size and sent on for grading and cutting. This is shown diagrammatically in Fig. 1.

The Pittsburgh Plate Glass Company operates a modified Fourcault process which produces their Pennvernon glass. These sheets are drawn 90 in. wide and of all thicknesses up to $\frac{7}{32}$ in. by varying the drawing rate from 38 in. a minute for single strength[1] to 12 in. for $\frac{7}{32}$ in. This process substitutes for the floating débiteuse a submerged drawbar for

[1] Single-strength window glass has a thickness of 0.087 to 0.100 in.; double-strength glass measures 0.118 to 0.132 in.

controlling and directing the sheet. After being drawn vertically through a distance of 26 ft., most of which is an annealing lehr, the glass is cut. For thicknesses above single and double strength, a second annealing is given in a 120-ft. standard form horizontal lehr.

During 1917 the Libbey-Owens Sheet Glass Company (now Libbey-Owens-Ford Glass Company) began drawing sheet glass by the Colburn process. In this process drawing is started vertically from the furnace, as in the Fourcault process, but after traveling for about 3 ft., the glass is heated and bent over a horizontal roller and is carried forward by grip bars attached to traveling belts. The sheet moves over the flattening table through the horizontal annealing lehr, with its 200 power-driven rolls, onto the cutting table.

Plate Glass. Previous to the First World War, plate glass was manufactured by pouring the molten charge on a flat, cast-iron table, just ahead of a heavy cast-iron, water-cooled roller which rolled the glass into a plate of uniform thickness. These tables were usually about 16 by 30 ft. and were covered with fine sand to prevent sticking and chilling. The glass was then pushed into a series of five annealing ovens. Great skill and careful timing were required to coordinate the roll speed and rate of pouring so that the glass produced might be rolled smoothly without seams or folds. This process has now been entirely abandoned in favor of several continuous processes.

Between 1922 and 1924 the Ford[1] Motor Company and the Pittsburgh Plate Glass Company each developed a continuous automatic process for removing rough-rolled glass in a continuous ribbon (*cf.* Continuous Sheet Process of Fig. 1). The glass is melted in large continuous furnaces holding about 1,000 tons at a time. The raw materials are fed into one end of the furnace, and the melted glass passes through the refining zone and out of the opposite end in an unbroken flow. From the wide refractory outlet, it passes between two water-cooled forming rolls and travels down an incline onto a table of moving metal plates, where rollers squeeze the glass into a ribbon of uniform thickness. While still red hot, the sheet passes over conveyer rolls to a continuous annealing lehr several hundred feet in length. The glass is removed from the lehr, cut into sheets, and then sent on for grinding and finishing, as illustrated in Fig. 3.

The continuous processes have very large capacities and are particularly adapted to the production of a glass with a uniform thickness and a composition suited to the requirements of the automobile industry. Short runs of plate or special glass cannot be produced economically by these machines but are handled in pots and mechanically cast by machines made especially for this type of operation.

Bottle Glass. Glass blowing, one of the most ancient arts, has until the last century depended solely upon human lungs for power to form

[1] McBRIDE, Again Ford Shows the Way, *Chem. & Met. Eng.*, **46** (3), 150 (1939).

and shape the molten glass. Modern demands for blown glass, however, have required the development of more rapid and cheaper methods of production.[1]

The machine making of bottles is really only a casting operation using air pressure to create a hollow. There are several types of machines producing "parisons," the partly formed bottle or bottle blank. One is the suction-feed type used, with certain variations, in bulb and tumbler production. Another is the gob-feed type, which has been applied to the

FIG. 3. After the rough plate glass comes from the rolls and the annealing lehr, it is ground and polished under many rapidly revolving wheels as it moves along beneath them on a table. The glass is embedded in plaster to hold it firmly. This view shows the final polishing operation, after the glass has been ground by wheels using successively finer sand mixed with water. When one side is finished, the large sheets are turned over and the same operations repeated on the other side. The completed glass has both surfaces absolutely parallel, hence the lack of distortion characteristic of plate glass. (*Courtesy of Pittsburgh Plate Glass Company.*)

manufacture of all types of ware made by pressing, blowing, or a combination of "press and blow."

In the suction-feed type, glass contained in a shallow circular revolving tank is drawn up into molds by suction. The mold then swings away from the surface of the glass, opens, and drops away, leaving the parison sustained by the neck. The bottle mold next rises into position around the parison, and a blast of compressed air flows the glass into the mold. The latter remains around the bottle until another gathering operation

[1] HODKIN and COUSEN, "A Textbook of Glass Technology," D. Van Nostrand Company, Inc., New York, 1929.

has been performed; it then drops the bottle and rises to close around a fresh parison. The operations are completely automatic, and speeds of 60 units per minute are not uncommon.

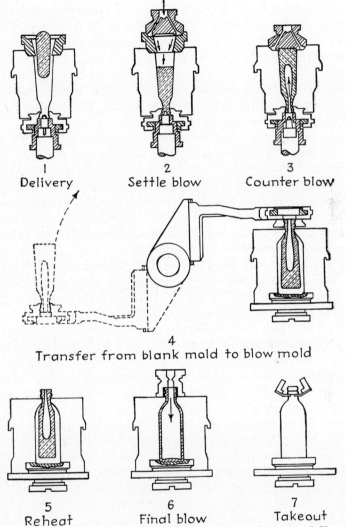

FIG. 4. Automatic bottle manufacture by I-S machine. (*Courtesy of Glass Packer.*)

The gob feeder represents one of the most important developments in automatic glassworking. In this operation the molten glass flows from the furnace through a trough, at the lower end of which is an orifice. The glass drops through the orifice and is cut into a gob of the exactly desired size by mechanical shears. It is delivered through a funnel into

the parison mold which starts the formation of the bottle in an inverted
position, as shown in Fig. 4. A neck pin rises into place and another
plunger drops from the top, whereupon compressed air in the "settle
blow" forces the glass to the finished form of the neck. The mold is
closed on top (bottom of the bottle), the neck pin is retracted, and air is
injected in the "counterblow" through the newly formed neck to form
the inner cavity. The parison mold opens and the parison is inverted as
it passes to the next station, so that the partly formed bottle is now upright. The blow mold closes around the parison which is reheated for a
brief interval. Air is now injected for the final blow, simultaneously shaping the inner and outer surfaces of the bottle. The blow mold swings
away and the bottle moves on to the lehr.

Automatic bottle-blowing machines usually consist of two circular
tables, known as the *parison mold* table, and the *blow* table. As the glass
moves around the periphery of the table, the various operations described above take place. Table movement is controlled by compressed
air which operates reciprocating pistons, while the various operations
occurring on the table are coordinated with the table movement by a
motor-timing mechanism. This latter device constitutes one of the most
vital and expensive parts of the equipment.

Light Bulbs. The blowing of a thin bulb[1] differs from bottle manufacture in that the shape and size of the bulb are determined initially by
the air blast itself and not by the mold. The molten glass flows through
an annular opening in the furnace and down between two watercooled
rollers, one of which has circular depressions that cause swellings on a
glass ribbon coinciding with circular holes on a horizontal chain conveyer
onto which the ribbon moves next. Through these holes the glass sags of
its own weight. Below each hole is a rotating mold. Air nozzles drop on
the surface of the ribbon, one above each of the glass swellings or conveyer holes. As the ribbon moves along, these nozzles eject a puff of air
which forms a preliminary blob in the ribbon. The spinning mold now
rises and a second puff of air, under considerably less pressure than the
first, shapes the blob to the mold and forms the bulb. The mold opens
and a small hammer knocks the bulb loose from the ribbon. The bulbs
drop onto an asbestos belt which carries them to the lehr rack, where
they slip neck down between two parallel vertical strips which support
them as they are annealed. The total time for the entire series of operations, including annealing, is about 8 min. Machine speeds of 400 to
600 bulbs per minute are common and speeds as high as 700 bulbs per
minute have been attained. Because of the numerous sizes and styles of
bulbs, the machines are assembled as light cars and pushed on rails to the

---

[1] KILLEFFER, Automatic Glass Blowing, *Ind. Eng. Chem.*, **28**, 789 (1936). This
reference includes illustrations and details.

melting tank. The cooled bulbs are frosted by spraying the interior with hydrofluoric acid, in a semiautomatic frosting machine.

Glass Tubing. For many years glass tubing has been drawn by hand and, for certain special tubings, it is still being made in that way. However, most tubing sold today is produced by machines, using either of two processes: the Danner process[1] or the Vello process. In the Danner process, glass that has been melted in either a tank or a pot furnace is transferred to a special pot which feeds into a constant-level trough or forehearth. This trough is divided into three compartments by bridges which hold back surface impurities from the molten glass passing through. The flow is controlled by a gate as shown in Fig. 5. The glass escapes over

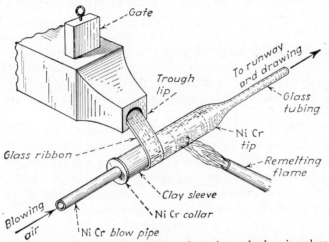

FIG. 5. Machine (Danner) for automatically and continuously drawing glass tubing or rods.

a lip onto the revolving mandrel in the form of a ribbon. The mandrel is a tube of nickel-chrome alloy on which is mounted a sleeve of clay or other refractory material. The mandrel is provided with a nichrome tip (see Fig. 5) and is housed in a muffle heated by a gas burner to a controlled temperature. The inclination of the mandrel (12 to 18 deg.) causes the glass to flow toward the tip from which it is drawn off as a tube or a rod, depending on whether or not air pressure is supplied to the mandrel. The glass passes over pulleys and through an annealing oven for several hundred feet on its way to the drawing machine and the cutter.

In the Vello process[1] molten glass flows into a drawing compartment from which it drops vertically through an annular space surrounding a

[1] PHILLIPS, "Glass the Miracle Maker," 2d ed., pp. 215–218, Pitman Publishing Corporation, New York, 1948; THORPE, "Dictionary of Applied Chemistry," 4th ed., Vol. 5, p. 589, Longmans, Green & Co., Inc., New York, 1941.

rotating rod or blowpipe in which air pressure is maintained to produce tubing of the desired diameter and wall thickness.

The drawing of thermometer tubing is one of the most difficult of glass-forming operations. A certain quantity of hot glass is selected, backed on one side with opaque white glass and covered with clear glass, and a small depression is blown in by hand. The end of the composite glass mass is attached to an elevating mechanism and the tube drawn by machinery 125 ft. up a tower.

Glass tower plates and bubble caps, prisms, and most other optical glass, most kitchenware, insulators, certain colored glasses, architectural glass, and many similar items are *hand-molded*. The process consists essentially in drawing a quantity of glass, known as the *gather*, from the pot or tank and carrying it to the mold. Here the exact quantity of glass required is cut off with a pair of shears, and the ram of the mold driven home by hand or by hydraulic pressure. Certain glass forming is carried out by semiautomatic methods which involve a combination of the machine- and hand-molding processes previously described. Volumetric flasks and cylindrical Pyrex sections for towers are fabricated in this manner.

3. Annealing. To reduce strains, it is necessary to anneal all glass objects, whether formed by machine- or hand-molding methods. Briefly, annealing involves two operations: (1) holding a mass of glass above a certain critical temperature long enough to reduce internal strain by plastic flow to less than a predetermined maximum and (2) cooling the mass to room temperature slowly enough to hold the strains below this same maximum. The lehr or annealing oven is nothing more than a carefully designed heated chamber in which the rate of cooling can be controlled so as to meet the foregoing requirements.

The establishment of a quantitative relationship[1] between stress and birefringence caused by the stress has enabled glass technologists to design glass to meet certain conditions of mechanical and thermal stress. With the foregoing data as a basis, engineers have produced continuous annealing equipment with automatic temperature regulation and controlled circulation, which permits better annealing at lower fuel cost and with less loss in product.

4. Finishing. All types of annealed glass must undergo certain finishing operations, which, though relatively simple, are very important. These include cleaning, grinding, polishing, cutting, sandblasting, enameling, grading, and gaging. Although all of these are not required for every glass object, one or more is almost always necessary.

[1] PHILLIPS, *op. cit.*, pp. 229, 117; MOREY and WARREN, Annealing of Pyrex Chemical Resistant Glass, *Ind. Eng. Chem.*, **27,** 966 (1935); MOREY, Physical Tendencies, *Ind. Eng. Chem.*, **32,** 1423 (1940).

MANUFACTURE OF SPECIAL GLASSES

Optical Glass. It should be noted at the very beginning that optical glass[1] includes only those glasses with high homogeneity and special composition which have definite predetermined optical characteristics of such accuracy as to permit their use in scientific instruments. Spectacle glass and ordinary mirror glass are not included.

Optical glass should fill certain rigid requirements: (1) Its composition should be such as to ensure the required optical properties. (2) The batch should produce glass of sufficiently low viscosity. (3) The glass should not devitrify, even upon long annealing. (4) It should produce as nearly a colorless product as possible without the use of decolorizing agents. (5) It should be free from bubbles and striae. (6) Its properties with respect to grinding and polishing should be advantageous. (7) It should be capable of withstanding the action of the atmosphere and of maintaining its surface after long usage under all climatic conditions.

The melting pots for optical glass are made from selected high-purity clays and are of different compositions for different types of glass. Platinum is also used. The raw materials of the batch are chosen for purity and composition and compounded very carefully. The empty pots are heated slowly for 4 or 5 days, till a temperature of 1900°F. is reached, after which they are transferred to the melting furnace, where they are heated to 2600°F. for several hours before the batch and cullet are charged into them. After the batch has melted, stirring is carried out with a hollow clay tube. The stirring, rapid at first, is gradually reduced after the cooling begins and the glass becomes more viscous. The tube is removed just before the glass is taken from the furnace.

After removal from the furnace the pot is covered with a thermally insulated jacket so the glass will cool slowly enough to break into large chunks.[2] The pot is broken open and, after removal of visible imperfections, the rough chunks are broken or sawed to a convenient size for hot molding in a steel or ceramic mold. On cooling the molded blanks are inspected by immersion in a liquid having a refractive index similar to the glass to reveal subsurface imperfections. Annealing, followed by another inspection, are the final steps before the blank is ready for grinding and polishing.

An important new development in melting of optical glass involves reusable platinum pots resulting in little or no corrosion or contamination and sometimes yielding up to 90 per cent first-class quality optical glass

[1] MOULTON, Optical Characteristics, *Ind. Eng. Chem.*, **32**, 1428 (1940), spectral transmission curves.

[2] For picture sequence and description, see HAHNER, Optical Glass Production, *Chem. Eng.*, **54** (4), 122 (1947).

as compared with 20 per cent or less in conventional refractory pots. Small platinum-lined tank furnaces are also being employed by Corning Glass Works for continuous melting of optical glass. Essentially the process consists of melting the batch in a T-shaped furnace heated by graphite electrodes immersed in the liquid glass which is stirred, fined, and extruded in the shape of a bar.

Safety Glass. Safety glasses[1] may be grouped into two general classes: laminated safety glass and heat-strengthened or tempered safety glass. Structural wire glass may also be considered a safety glass.

Laminated safety glass, which is by far the most widely used in this country, consists of two sheets of thin plate glass, each of which is about 0.125 in. thick, with a sheet of nonbrittle plastic material between. The manufacturing procedure is somewhat as follows: The plastic and glass are washed and an adhesive is applied to the glass (if the plastic used requires it, such not always being the case). The glass and plastic sheet are pressed together under moderate heat to seal the edges. The glass is subjected to high temperatures and hydraulic pressures in an autoclave, in order to bring the entire interlayer into intimate contact, after which the edges of the sandwich may be sealed with a water-resistant compound.

The glass used in the manufacture of laminated safety glass has the same physical properties as ordinary glass; so that the safety features depend solely upon the ability of the plastic interlayer to hold the fragments caused by accidental breaking of the glass itself. The first plastic used commercially was cellulose nitrate which was replaced by cellulose acetate. Now practically all laminated safety glass uses polyvinyl butyral resin. This vinyl plastic is more elastic than the cellulose acetate, since it stretches under relatively low stresses up to its elastic limit, after which considerable additional stress is necessary to make it fail. It remains clear and colorless under all conditions of use, is not affected by sunlight, and does not need adhesives or water-resistant compounds in manufacturing.

The second type of safety glass, tempered safety glass, is considerably more resistant to forces that produce bending and to objects that do not crack or penetrate the compressional layer, but it is weaker to the impact of missiles traveling at sufficiently high velocities to break the compression layer. It is merely a single sheet of glass, heat-treated so that the outer surface is in a state of compression caused by cooling. When the outer layer is punctured, it shatters into many small pieces.

Structural wire glass has great value as a fire retardant. In the manufacture of this material, steel wire netting is laid onto ordinary soft lime glass immediately after its discharge from the furnace and passed be-

[1] RANDOLPH, Evolution of Safety Glass, *Modern Plastics*, **18** (10), 31 (1941); *cf.* WEIDLEIN, History and Development of Laminated Safety Glass, *Ind. Eng. Chem.*, **31**, 563 (1939).

tween two rolls. The operation is continuous and the glass is cut into the desired shape by bending the wire, which breaks easily.

High-silica Glass. This product[1] constitutes an even greater advance toward the production of a glass approaching fused silica in composition and properties. This has been accomplished with the avoidance of former limitations of melting and forming. The finished articles contain approximately 96 per cent silica, 3 per cent boric oxide, and the rest alumina and alkali. Borosilicate glass compositions of about 75 per cent silica content are used in the earlier stages of the process, in which the glasses are melted and molded.[2] After cooling, the articles are subjected to heat-treatment which induces the glass to separate into two distinct physical phases. One of these phases is so high in boric and alkaline oxides that it is readily soluble in hot acid solutions, while the other is rich in silica and therefore insoluble in these same solutions. After heat-treatment and annealing, the glass article is immersed in a 10 per cent hydrochloric acid (98°C.) bath for sufficient time to permit the soluble phase to be virtually all leached out. It is washed thoroughly to remove traces of the soluble phase as well as impurities and subjected to another heat-treatment which serves to dehydrate the body and to convert the cellular structure to a nonporous vitreous glass. In the course of these processes the glassware undergoes a shrinkage in linear dimensions amounting to 14 per cent of its original size. Table 3 compares its properties with those of other glasses. This method of glass manufacture furnishes a product that can be heated to a cherry red and then plunged into ice water without any ill effects. Also this glass has high chemical durability and is extremely stable to all acids except hydrofluoric which attacks this glass considerably more slowly than others.

Chemical Engineering Applications.[3] Glass, because of its reasonable price, its surface hardness and smoothness, its low coefficient of expansion, and its chemical inertness and transparency has taken an important place in industry as an essential chemical engineering material. According to Smith, glass is used in three forms that are of interest to the process engineer:

(1) in bulk, in fairly large pieces of equipment, such as pipe, towers and pumps;
(2) as a coating, over steel and cast iron, as in tanks, reactors and pipe;
(3) as fibers, in insulation, fabrics, tower packings, and plastic laminates.

Only borosilicate glass, high-silica glass, and pure fused silica are of much interest as materials of construction in process industries. By reasons of

[1] This is known as Vycor and is made by the Corning Glass Works, U.S. Pat. 2106744 (1938); 2221709 (1940).

[2] PHILLIPS, *op. cit.*, pp. 49–50, 388.

[3] SMITH, Glass—Its Place in Chemical Processing, *Chem. Eng.*, **58** (4), 117 (1951); *cf.* the Ceramics section of the Materials of Construction reviews, *Ind. Eng. Chem.*, October issue, annual since 1947.

improvements in the formulas for glass, these materials have had their chemical resistance as well as their mechanical properties greatly improved (see Table 3).

TABLE 3. COMPARATIVE PROPERTIES OF GLASSES[a]

	Common lime	Pyrex No. 774	96 per cent silica No. 790	Fused quartz
Softening point, °C.....	696	819	1442	1667
Annealing point, °C....	510	553	931	1140
Strain point, °C.......	475	510	857	1070
Maximum temperature for use (for limited periods), °C.........	....	500–550	1000–1090	1400
Specific gravity......	2.47	2.23	2.18	2.01
Coefficient of linear expansion (per °C.)...	92×10^{-7}	$32\text{–}33 \times 10^{-7}$	$7.8\text{–}8 \times 10^{-7}$	$5.5\text{–}5.95 \times 10^{-7}$

[a] BLAU, Chemical Trends, *Ind. Eng. Chem.*, **32**, 1419 (1940); *cf.* PERRY, *op. cit.*, p. 1548. The coefficient of linear expansion in the change in length (centimeters) per unit of length (centimeters) per centigrade degree change in temperature.

ROCK OR MINERAL WOOL

Allied to the making of glass are the fusing and spinning of a suitable rock to form rock wool. Slag wool is a similar product from the melting of by-product furnace slag. These mineral wools are of great value for both heat and sound insulation, particularly as they have a low coefficient of heat transfer, do not attract moisture, are permanent, and are absolutely fireproof and verminproof. They are also relatively inexpensive and can be fabricated wherever there is the suitable rock available. The mineral wools are employed in the loose form or shaped into blankets for insulating homes or railroad cars. Specially molded sheets or blocks enter into the making of refrigerators. In the loose form, much rock wool is blown into the open spaces in walls and ceilings of already constructed houses. For these purposes 100,000 tons of rock wool are manufactured annually with additional tonnages of slag and glass wool. Each year sees mineral wool become more important in chemical construction, especially with the current trend to outdoor plants.[1]

The wool rock[2] should contain silica, alumina, lime, and magnesia

[1] For further information, see VON LUDWIG, Insulating Unhoused Plants, *Chem. Eng.*, **54** (3), 114 (1947); OTTO, Estimating Mineral Wool Insulation, *Chem. Eng.*, **54** (7), 102 (1947).

[2] FRYLING and WHITE, Considerations in Developing a Mineral Wool Industry, *Chem. & Met. Eng.*, **42**, 550 (1935); THOENEN, Mineral Wool, *U.S. Bur. Mines Inform. Circ.* 6984 (1938); AZBE, Solution of Problems in Manufacturing Rock Wool, *Rock Products*, **51** (11), 97 (1948).

approximating the ratio shown in the formula on the flow sheet of Fig. 6, so as to give a product molten over a sufficiently long interval to enable the fibers to be made. To meet these specifications for wool rock there is usually chosen a self-fluxing siliceous and argillaceous dolomite which may have a composition as shown in Table 4. This composition balances

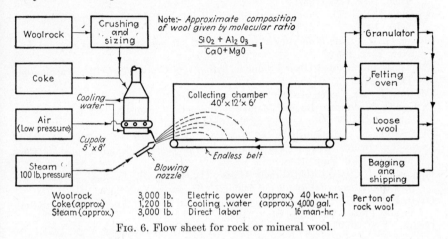

Woolrock	3,000 lb.	Electric power (approx) 40 kw-hr.	
Coke (approx)	1,200 lb.	Cooling water (approx) 4,000 gal.	Per ton of
Steam (approx.)	3,000 lb.	Direct labor 16 man-hr.	rock wool

FIG. 6. Flow sheet for rock or mineral wool.

the fluxing properties of the constituents. Such natural wool rock is mined in the states of Indiana, Ohio, and elsewhere.

The process for making rock wool involves the simple melting, in a cupola, of the wool rock at around 3000°F. and the blowing of this into the fibers by means of steam at 100 lb. pressure. The steam first atomizes the molten rock to small globules which stream through the air leaving a fibrous tail behind. The centrifugal action of a rapidly revolving disk

TABLE 4. LIMITS OF COMPOSITION OF WOOL ROCK[a]

	Minimum, per cent	Maximum, per cent
Silica................................	24	32
Ferric oxide...........................	2	3
Alumina.............................	8	12
Calcium oxide........................	16	21
Magnesium oxide.....................	10	13
Volatile matter.......................	26	29

[a] DAKE, Rock as an Insulator, *Mineralogist*, **10**, 177 (1942).

is also employed to furnish fine fibers (1 to 3 in. long and 3 microns in diameter). The fibers are collected on a belt and subjected to the operations needed to furnish the desired finished wool. Somewhat allied to mineral wool is fiber glass, which is presented in Chap. 34.

SELECTED REFERENCES

Hodkin, F. W., and A. Cousen, "A Textbook of Glass Technology," Constable & Co., Ltd., London, 1929; D. Van Nostrand Company, Inc., New York, 1929.

Sharp, Donald E., "Feldspar as a Constituent of Glass," National Feldspar Association, New York, 1937.

Sosman, R. B., "The Properties of Silica," Reinhold Publishing Corporation, New York, 1927.

Morey, G. W., "The Properties of Glass," 2d ed., Reinhold Publishing Corporation, New York, 1954.

Flat Glass and Related Glass Products, *U.S. Tariff Comm. Rept.* 123, Washington, D.C., 1937.

The Glass Packer, Ogden Watney, Inc., New York.

Furnas, C. C., editor, "Rogers' Manual of Industrial Chemistry," 6th ed., Chap. 20, Glass, by G. W. Morey, D. Van Nostrand Company, Inc., New York, 1942.

Glass Symposia, various authors, *Ind. Eng. Chem.*, **25**, 742–764 (1933); **32**, 1415 (1940).

Angus-Butterworth, L. M., "The Manufacture of Glass," Pitman Publishing Corporation, New York, 1948.

Phillips, C. J., "Glass, the Miracle Maker, Its History, Technology, Manufacture and Applications," Pitman Publishing Corporation, New York, 1948.

Davis, Pearce, "The Development of the American Glass Industry," Harvard University Press, Cambridge, Mass., 1949.

Dickson, J. H., "Glass," Chemical Publishing Company, Inc., New York, 1951.

CHAPTER 13

POTASSIUM SALTS AND MIXED FERTILIZERS

Potassium salts must be present in the soil solution in order to have normal plant growth. Hence potassium salts have a high and an essential value in fertilizers needed for the food of the nations. The yardstick by which potassium compounds are measured is the content of potash as K_2O. Indeed, this term has become by usage descriptive of the industry. The various potassium salts are also basically important as raw materials for many commodities such as soaps, detergents, glass, dyes, gunpowder, and pyrotechnics.

The establishment of this industry in America has been difficult. Prior to the middle of the nineteenth century the United States was even an important exporter of a crude potassium carbonate from the leaching of hardwood ashes. Potash was first imported from Germany in 1869 and for over 45 years that country furnished America and the rest of the world with potash. After the German salts became available, there was little interest in domestic production of potash until the First World War prevented its importation. At this time the scarcity of potash became a matter of national concern and prices rose to $500 a ton of 50 per cent muriate. Efforts by the Federal, state, and commercial companies developed several sources of potash supply. Among these were brines from the saline lakes in the West, kelp harvested from the Pacific coast, calcined fermentation slop, cement kiln dust, wood and cotton hull ashes, and many minerals of great variety such as alunite, leucite, greensand, feldspar, and shale. Production rose from 1,000 tons in 1915 to 45,700 tons of potash, K_2O, in 1919. When the end of the war came, imports were resumed and domestic production fell.

Since that time the discovery of new deposits, followed by new developments in methods of processing, has caused a constant increase in the amount and quality of potash salts produced and in competition with low-priced European imports.

In 1941 and 1942 the United States produced its entire need of potash for the first time. Table 1 illustrates the growth of this industry.

Raw Materials. The largest domestic production of potassium salts comes from deep Permian sedimentary deposits of sylvinite (a natural mixture of sylvite, KCl, and halite, NaCl) and langbeinite, K_2SO_4·-

253

$2MgSO_4$, of the Carlsbad, N. Mex., region. The sylvinite is mined and treated to yield high-grade potassium chloride. Langbeinite is processed to make potassium sulfate. The second important domestic source of potassium salts is Searles Lake at Trona, Calif., which is a deposit of solid sodium salts permeated by a saturated complex brine. This brine is processed to separate high-grade potassium chloride and borax together with numerous minor saline products (Fig. 1). Other sources contribute in a minor way to the annual potash production: alcohol fermentation using molasses as a raw material, by-product from natural salt

TABLE 1. STATISTICS OF POTASH INDUSTRY SINCE 1919[a]
(In thousands of tons of K_2O)

Year	Production	Exports	Imports	Consumption
1919	46	0.5	40	85
1925	26	1	258	283
1931	64	16	215	262
1937	267	62	352	556
1943	732	70	17	679
1948	1,140	70	27	1,100
1949	1,118	70	19	1,070
1950	1,286	65	199	1,409
1951	1,420	68	313	1,653
1952	1,665	56	190	1,733
1953	1,912	49	130	1,813

[a] Chem. Eng., **55** (6), 313 (1948); "Minerals Yearbook," 1952, 1953.

brines, and potassium sulfate recovered by one portland cement company from its kiln dust. Bonneville, Ltd., evaporates by solar heat, the Salduro Marsh brines, at the western edge of the Salt Lake Basin[1] in Utah, crystallizing out the sodium and potassium chloride. The two salts are repulped and separated by froth flotation to yield potassium chloride. Subterranean deposits of potash salts occur in Europe notably in Russia, Poland, Germany, France (Alsace), and Spain. The brine of the Dead Sea in Palestine also is being successfully exploited as a source of potassium chloride and other saline products.

POTASSIUM CHLORIDE

In this country potassium chloride is being produced principally as a high-grade salt of around 98 per cent purity. As such it is suitable for use in both the chemical and the fertilizer industries, some 90 per cent of the total being used in the latter. In the fertilizer trade it is referred

[1] SMITH, Utah Desert Yields Potassium Chloride for Western Agriculture, Chem. & Met. Eng., **51** (8), 94 (1944).

to as *muriate of potash* and in smaller amounts is marketed in the less refined state as "60 per cent muriate," "manure salts," and the crude material as mined, "run-of-mine salts." The refined potassium chloride is the basis of the manufacture of most of the other potassium salts. The more important commercial processes in the United States will be described.

Manufacture by the Trona Process. From Searles Lake, California, the shipment of potash was begun in 1916 and, including numerous other products, has continued since that time on an ever-expanding scale. The "lake" is composed of four layers. The upper layer of crystalline salt is from 70 to 90 ft. deep; the second layer about 12 to 15 ft. of mud; the third layer about 25 ft. of salt; and finally mud interspersed with minor salt seams. In processing, the brine is pumped from the interstices in the salt body from the first and third layers. The handling of the third layer is a recent development. The brines have the following approximate constant composition:

Expressed as	Upper deposit, per cent	Lower deposit, per cent
KCl	4.85	3.00
NaCl	16.25	16.25
Na_2SO_4	7.20	6.75
Na_2CO_3	4.65	6.35
$Na_2B_4O_7$	1.50	1.77
Na_3PO_4	0.155	
NaBr	0.109	
Miscellaneous	0.116	0.35
Total salts (approx.)	34.83	34.60
H_2O	65.17	65.40
Specific gravity	1.303	1.305
pH (approx.)	9.45	9.60

As the unraveling of the composition of the various salts of the German potash deposits at Stassfurt by van't Hoff from 1895 to 1910 helped greatly in the development of the German potash industry, likewise the phase-rule study[1] of the much more complex systems existing at Searles Lake by Morse, Teeple, Burke, Mumford, Gale, and many others was

---

[1] TEEPLE, "Industrial Development of Searles Lake Brines," Reinhold Publishing Corporation, New York, 1929; ROBERTSON, The Trona Enterprise, *Ind. Eng. Chem.*, **21**, 520 (1929); ROBERTSON, Expansion of the Trona Enterprise, *Ind. Eng. Chem.*, **34**, 133 (1942); GALE, Chemistry of the Trona Process, from the Standpoint of the Phase Rule, *Ind. Eng. Chem.*, **30**, 867 (1938). The triangular phase diagrams of the more common constituents of Searles Lake brine at 20 and 100°C. are presented and described on pp. 71–74*ff.* in KOBE, "Inorganic Chemical Processes," The Macmillan Company, New York, 1948. These are for the brines saturated with NaCl and for burkeite, Na_2SO_4, glaserite and KCl and Na_2CO_3.

Raw lake brine + soda products and borax mother liquors
↓
Warmed by condensing vapors in vacuum crystallizers
↓
Evaporated in triple-effect evaporators
Salts separated hot
$(Na_2CO_3 \cdot 2Na_2SO_4)$ + NaCl + Li_2NaPO_4 | KCl + $Na_2B_4O_7$ both in hot solution
↓

Halite: NaCl, coarse crystals
Burkeite $(Na_2CO_3 \cdot 2Na_2SO_4)$ and Li_2NaPO_4:
fine crystals
Separated by countercurrent washing

Mother liquor: Quick vacuum
cooling to 38°C.

KCl centri-
fuged, dried,
and *shipped*

→Underflow NaCl,
 washed away
Overflow filtered and washed with lake brine

Mother liquor ←
cooled to 24°C., seeded, and
crystallized
↓
Filtered—

→Brine

Crude borax
Recrystallized
↓
Refined borax

Burkeite, dissolved in H_2O, cooled, and
Li_2NaPO_4 froth floated

→Impure Li_2NaPO_4 hot leached
↓→Burkeite liquor
Li_2NaPO_4 (20 per cent LiO_2)
Dried

Burkeite liquor cooled to
22°C., filtered

$Na_2SO_4 \cdot 10H_2O$
↓
NaCl added to lower
transition to 17°C. to Na_2SO_4.
Filter

Liquor heated
to 70°C. and
treated with NaCl

→Burkeite (to start ↑)
Cooled to 30°C. and filtered

→Some NaCl
Cooled to 5°C. and filtered

→NaCl mother liquor

Na_2SO_4 *Refined salt cake*
Dried

→Brine
$Na_2CO_3 \cdot 10H_2O$
Recrystallized hot
↓
$Na_2CO_3 \cdot H_2O$
Calcined
↓
Soda Ash 58 *per cent* Na_2O

FIG. 1. Outline of Trona procedures.

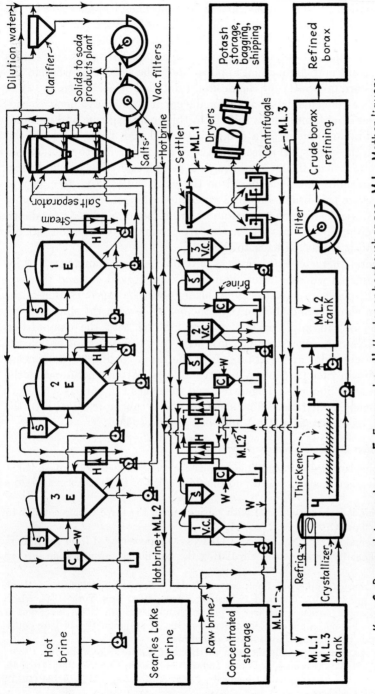

Key: **C**, Barometric condenser; **E**, Evaporator; **H**, Heater or heat exchanger, **M.L.**, Mother liquor; **S**, Separator; **V.C.**, Vacuum crystallizer; **W**, Cooling or dilution water

Fig. 2. Potassium chloride and borax by Trona procedure. See Fig. 1 and Hightower, The Trona Process, *Chem. Eng.*, **58** (8), 104 (1951) for breakdown into 6 flow sheets.

another striking investigation carried to a successful application in the Trona process. In the first-layer brine of Searles Lake the main system is composed of Na-K-H-SO$_4$-CO$_3$-B$_2$O$_4$-Cl-F-H$_2$O. The references cited, particularly the one by Gale, demonstrate with appropriate solubility charts this important and commercial application of the *phase rule* wherein the conditions are presented for the desired fractional crystallization.

The phase-rule chemists and the engineers at Trona have been exceedingly clever in obtaining *pure* salts from this complex brine and in building a profitable industry in a competitive field and under the handicap of being in the desert 200 miles from the nearest city. The town of Trona, Calif., houses over 2,000 inhabitants dependent on this one industry. Figure 1 outlines the steps, based on the phase-rule study, necessary to commercialize this brine. Figure 2 gives more details of the divisions of the procedures leading to potassium chloride, borax, and soda products. There is no profitable market for the large tonnages of common salt obtained, and it is washed back to the lake.

In general this successful process is founded upon many years of intensive research wherein exact conditions were worked out and then applied in the plant. In barest outline this involves the concentration of the potassium chloride and the borax in the *hot* brine with the simultaneous separation of salt and burkeite, a new mineral with the composition Na$_2$CO$_3$·2Na$_2$SO$_4$. By virtue of the "lazy" crystallization of borax, the potassium chloride can be obtained by the rapid cooling of the concentrated brine in vacuum coolers and crystallizers.[1] After centrifugation the potash mother liquor is refrigerated and furnishes the borax.

The somewhat detailed[2] flow sheet of Fig. 2 can be resolved into the following *unit operations* (Op.) and *unit processes* (Pr.):

Concentration and Soda Products Separation:

Raw brine is mixed with end liquors from the soda products and potash borax crystallizing house, and pumped into the third effect of triple-effect evaporators (Op.).

The brine is hot concentrated with salting out in the three effects counter to the steam flow (Op. and Pr.). (see Fig. 3).

The suspended salts, NaCl + Na$_2$CO$_3$·2Na$_2$SO$_4$, are removed from the liquors of each effect by continuously circulating the hot liquor through cone settlers

---

[1] PERRY, *op. cit.*, pp. 1065–1069; see particularly Turrentine, "Potash in North America," pp. 105–107, Reinhold Publishing Corporation, New York, 1943, where the first vacuum cooler-crystallizer is pictured and described. This invention of Turrentine's has had a profound influence upon the cheap production of pure potassium chloride both in the United States and abroad.

[2] MUMFORD, Potassium Chloride from the Brine of Searles Lake, *Ind. Eng. Chem.*, **30**, 872 (1938); KIRKPATRICK, A Potash Industry—At Last, *Chem. & Met. Eng.*, **45**, 488 (1938); ANON., Searles Lake Chemicals, *Chem. & Met. Eng.*, **52** (10), 134 (1945), for pictured flow sheet.

called *salt separators* or *salt traps*. The underflow from the first-effect cone containing the salts passes through an orifice into the second-effect cone, receiving a countercurrent wash with clarified liquor from the second-effect cone. The combined salts from the first and second cones are given a countercurrent wash with liquor from the third cone as they pass through an orifice into this third cone. The combined salts of the first, second, and third cones are given a countercurrent wash with raw brine as they leave the third-effect cone (Op.). All these are hot washes. The combined underflow is filtered and the filtrate returned to the evaporators (Op.).

The cake (salt: $NaCl$ + burkeite: $Na_2CO_3 \cdot 2Na_2SO_4$) is sent to the soda products plant (Op.) (left part of Fig. 1).

The final hot concentrated liquor is withdrawn from the overflow of the first-effect cone to an auxiliary settler called a *clarifier* (Op.). The overflow from the clarifier is pumped to storage at the potash plant (Op.).

The underflow from the clarifier is filtered and treated in the same manner as the previous underflow[1] (Op.).

Separation of Potassium Chloride:

The hot concentrated liquor leaving the clarifiers is saturated with potassium chloride and borax. The potassium chloride is obtained by cooling quickly to 100°F. and crystallizing in three-stage vacuum cooler-crystallizers (Op. and Pr.).

Enough water is added to replace that evaporated so that the sodium chloride remains in solution (Op.).

The suspension of solid potassium chloride in the mother liquor is passed to a cone settler where the thickened sludge obtained in the underflow goes to a battery of Weston-type sugar centrifuges (Op.).

The potassium chloride is dried in rotary driers, yielding 97 per cent KCl (Op.). This salt is conveyed to storage, to the bagging plant, or to a recrystallizing procedure (Op.).

Separation of Borax:

The overflow, combined with the filtrate from the centrifuges, is pumped to the borax plant for the removal of borax (Op.).

The potash mother liquor is cooled by evaporation to 75°F. in vacuum crystallizers by expansion of liquid ammonia in reflux condensers, as shown in Fig. 3 (Op.). The water lost by evaporation is returned to the boiling (but cooling) solution to prevent the concentration of this solution with consequent crystallization of potassium chloride with the crude borax.

The borax crystallizes out (Pr.) and is settled in a thickener (Op.).

The crude borax is filtered off and washed (Op.).

The overflow from the thickener and from the filter is returned to the start of the evaporator cycle (Op.).

When necessary, the crude borax is refined by recrystallization (Op.).

This salt is centrifuged, dried, and packaged for market (Op.).

---

[1] MUMFORD, *op. cit.*, pp. 876, 877; HIGHTOWER, The Trona Process, *Chem. Eng.*, **58** (8), 104 (1951), excellent flow sheets.

The preceding description deals with the processing of the upper brine layer. In 1948 a new plant was finished at Trona for the lower brine layer. This involves carbonation of this brine with flue gas from the boiler plant.[1] The sodium bicarbonate separated by this reaction is calcined and converted to dense soda ash. Crude borax is crystallized from the carbonated end liquor by cooling under vacuum and the filtrate is returned to the lake. The daily production of American Potash and Chemical Company in 1954 was approximately 700 tons of muriate of potash, 350 tons of borax and boric acid, 650 tons of salt cake, and 400 tons of soda ash. This large production was not achieved without solving many more problems than those of the phase-rule diagrams. The evaporation is at the rate of several million gallons of water per day. To effect the requisite heat transfer when salts crystallize out at the same time was a major chemical engineering problem. This was brought about by removing the miles of piping from the inside of the evaporators and doing the heating in outside heaters arranged with spares around and beneath each evaporator,[2] as shown in Fig. 3. Heat transfer is also facilitated (footnote, page 258) by vacuum cooling through vaporization instead of using cooling liquids in coils which would become fouled with encrusting solids.

The *soda and lithium products*[3] are a development of recent years by an extension of the phase studies and sound engineering. Figure 1 outlines the production of soda ash, anhydrous sodium sulfate, and lithium sodium phosphate.

Manufacture from Sylvinite. In 1925, potash was discovered at Carlsbad, N. Mexico.[4] After much prospecting and drilling, a shaft to mine the mineral was sunk to about 1,000 ft. In 1932 a refinery was constructed and now the largest proportion of the supply of potassium chloride for the United States is being produced here. The ore is sylvinite, which is the accepted term for the natural mixture of sylvite, KCl, with halite, NaCl.

The process employed by the United States Potash Company[5] depends primarily upon the fact that sodium chloride is less soluble in a hot than in a cold saturated solution of potassium chloride. Thus, when

---

[1] Hightower, New Carbonation Technique—More Natural Soda Ash, *Chem. Eng.*, **58** (5), 162 (1951); Anon., *Chem. Eng.*, **56** (4), 102 (1949).

[2] Manning, Capital + Vision + Research = An American Potash Industry, *Chem. & Met. Eng.*, **36**, 268 (1929).

[3] Robertson, Expansion of the Trona Enterprise, *Ind. Eng. Chem.*, **34**, 133 (1942); Gale, Lithium from Searles Lake, *Chem. Inds.*, **57**, 442 (1945).

[4] Smith, Potash in the Permian Salt Basin, *Ind. Eng. Chem.*, **30**, 854 (1938). For the separation of two salts with a common ion like NaCl-KCl, see the phase diagrams Figs. 3-1 and 3-2 of Kobe "Inorganic Process Industries," The Macmillan Company, New York, 1948. The text on pp. 60–63 elucidates these diagrams.

[5] *Private communication* from Henry H. Bruhn; cf White and Arend, Potash Production at Carlsbad, *Chem. Eng. Progr.*, **46**, 523 (1950).

a saturated solution of the mixed salts in water is cooled from its boiling point, KCl separates out contaminated with only what NaCl is entrained. The cold mother liquor is heated to 110°C. by use of heat exchangers employing exhaust steam, as shown in Fig. 4. The hot mother liquor is passed through a series of steam-heated turbo-mixer dissolvers countercurrent to a flow of ore crushed to −4-mesh size, which is moved

Fig. 3. Vacuum evaporator unit at Trona, Calif. Outside heaters are underneath pan. (*Courtesy of American Potash & Chemical Corp.*)

from dissolver to dissolver by mechanical elevating equipment. Potassium chloride goes into solution together with a small amount of sodium chloride. In this step colloidal and semicolloidal clay present in the ore is suspended in the potash-bearing solution. The enriched mother liquor passes through thickener equipment where this insoluble mud is settled out. The underflow mud is washed by countercurrent decantation in a tray thickener, while the hot clear saturated overflow solution is pumped to vacuum coolers and crystallizers. Tailings from this process, largely NaCl, after passing through Bird centrifuges where adhering potash-bearing brine is removed, are carried out of the plant to waste storage. Vacuum in the coolers and crystallizers is maintained by means of steam ejectors. In these vessels the solution is cooled to 27°C. and the potassium chloride falls out of solution and, in suspension, is pumped to settling tanks where a large part of the liquor is decanted through launders to be used again. The thickened crystal mass is filtered, washed, and

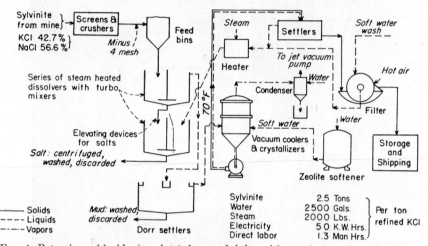

Fig. 4. Potassium chloride (muriate) from sylvinite with continuous flow dissolving for hot-solution refining. (*Courtesy of U.S. Potash Co.*)

dried on Oliver filters. The dried cake is crushed, screened, and conveyed either to warehouse or to cars.

The United States Potash Company's granular plant for producing 50 per cent KCl used almost entirely by the fertilizer industry operates as follows: Crushed and sized ore suspended in a brine saturated with both sodium and potassium chloride is carried to a bank of Wilfley tables, where sodium chloride and potassium chloride are separated by difference in gravity. A product carrying 50 to 51 per cent K_2O is debrined in drag classifiers and passed through gas-fired rotary driers from which it goes to storage and shipping. A middling product is further tabled after debrining, while the tailing is debrined and carried to a salt storage pile.

The process of the Potash Company of America separates the KCl from the NaCl chiefly by a metallurgical concentration method using a soap-flotation process and represents the first adaptation to water-soluble ores of the flotation principle so long familiar in the concentration of insoluble ores. "The sylvinite ore, having been coarsely crushed underground, is fed to a Symons cone intermediate crusher, which in turn discharges to a series of fine crushers close-circuited with the screens." The ore is then wet-ground by ball mills to 100 mesh. "The mill product, having been ground sufficiently to release the KCl and NaCl, is treated in two series of flotation cells to float off a NaCl concentrate and depress a KCl concentrate. The NaCl crystals are washed and separated from the solution by means of a Dorr thickener and a Moore filter and sent to waste while the KCl concentrate, together with KCl crystals recovered from various circulating solutions, is separated by a classifier into fine and coarse fractions. Recovery of fines is accomplished by a thickener and centrifuges."[1]

The flotation process is used also by the International Minerals and Chemical Corporation in the refining of sylvinite to produce potassium chloride.[2] This company also processes potassium sulfate[3] from the mineral langbeinite, $K_2SO_4 \cdot 2MgSO_4$, by reacting with KCl to yield the sulfate and the by-product $MgCl_2$. This latter is of particular interest as a raw material for the production of metallic magnesium, potassium chloride, and sulfate of potash-magnesia.

VARIOUS POTASSIUM SALTS

Potassium Sulfate. Prior to 1939, the German potash industry was the chief source of potassium sulfate for American chemical and fertilizer industries, although considerable tonnages were being produced in this country by the interaction of potassium chloride and sulfuric acid as a side product of salt-cake manufacture. With the termination of European imports the production of the salt was undertaken on the larger scale by the American Potash and Chemical Corporation through the interaction of burkeite, $Na_2CO_3 \cdot 2Na_2SO_4$, with potassium chloride,[4] followed in turn by the successful recovery of this salt from langbeinite by the International Minerals and Chemical Corporation as mentioned above. Recently the Potash Company of America inaugurated a modified Hargreaves process where potash will be reacted with sulfur dioxide, air, and steam to yield potassium sulfate. In its agricultural use potassium sulfate is preferred for the tobacco crop of the Southeast and for the citrus crop of southern California.

Potassium Hydroxide and Carbonate. These two chemicals are very closely related. Some years ago most of the potassium hydroxide was made from potassium carbonate by reaction with calcium hydroxide.

---

[1] KIRKPATRICK, *op. cit.*, p. 491; MAGRAW, New Mexico Sylvinite, *Ind. Eng. Chem.*, **30,** 861 (1938).

[2] WREGE and DANEY, Quality by the Ton, *Chem. Inds.*, **65,** 46 (1949); see ANON., Potassium Chloride and Sulfate, *Chem. Eng.*, **57** (1), 168 (1950), for pictures and flow sheet.

[3] HARLEY and ATWOOD, Langbeinite . . . Mining and Processing, *Ind. Eng. Chem.*, **39,** 43 (1947).

[4] ROBERTSON, Expansion of Trona Enterprise, *Ind. Eng. Chem.*, **34,** 136 (1942).

$$K_2CO_3(aq) + Ca(OH)_2(s) \rightarrow 2KOH(aq) + CaCO_3(s);$$
$$\Delta H = -2,080 \text{ cal.}$$

But the production of potassium hydroxide by electrolysis of potassium chloride solutions has led to the production of potassium carbonate from potassium hydroxide. The abundant supplies of refined potassium chloride now cheaply available, combined with low-cost electrical energy, indicate that this will continue to be the principal method of production for the future. About 34,000,000 lb. of caustic potash are consumed per year in the soap, detergent, and dye fields. The carbonate, like the caustic, is used mainly for soaps and chemicals (about 36,000,000 lb. per year) and is the preferred source of potash in the glass industry (about 30,000,000 lb. per year).

Potassium Nitrate. This salt is made by the double decomposition reaction of sodium nitrate and potassium chloride.

$$NaNO_3(aq) + \underline{KCl(s)} \rightarrow \underline{NaCl(s)} + KNO_3(aq); \qquad \Delta H = +3,160 \text{ cal.}$$

A strong hot solution of the sodium nitrate is made and the solid potassium chloride dumped into the kettle. Upon heating, the KCl changes to NaCl, whereupon the hot KNO_3 solution is run through the NaCl crystals in the bottom of the kettle. A little water is added to prevent any further deposition of NaCl, and the solution is cooled. A good yield of potassium nitrate results.

Potassium nitrate is frequently referred to as essential in the manufacture of slow-burning black powder which is used in fuses and in the ignition of smokeless powder. Other uses are in the manufacture of pyrotechnics and glass.[1]

Potassium Acid Tartrate. At the present time a domestic tartrate industry is being developed by processing pomace,[2] which is the discarded mass from wine fermentors and contains from 1 to 4 per cent potassium bitartrate. Still the greater part of the supply is imported crude argols from wine vats. The pure salt is obtained from the argols by leaching and crystallizing. The main uses are as the acid ingredient of baking powder, for the preparation of tartaric acid, and in medicine.

Potassium and Potassium Peroxide. The metal potassium is usually made by fusing potassium chloride with an excess of metallic sodium in a stainless-steel fusion pot. The following reaction takes place:

$$Na + KCl \rightarrow NaCl + K$$

and is carried out concurrently with distillation separation of the potassium and sodium with a bottoms temperature on the still reactor of about

---

[1] FINN, Potash in the Glass Industry, *Ind. Eng. Chem.*, **30**, 891 (1938).

[2] METZNER, Tartrates from Winery Pomace, *Chem. Eng. Progr.*, **43**, 160 (1947); HALPERIN, Tartrates Recovered from Winery Wastes, *Chem. & Met. Eng.*, **52** (9), 116 (1945).

1650°F. Potassium is distilled overhead through a stainless-steel packed column giving a product of 99 per cent purity.

During the Second World War a somewhat similar reaction using sodium and caustic potash was employed but this has been superseded by the above-mentioned reaction. The larger proportion of the potassium made is used to produce KO_2 for use in protective breathing equipment. Here the KO_2 reacts with the expelled breath to liberate oxygen and remove CO_2 and H_2O in the so-called "re-breather" gas mask. Some potassium is used to make a eutectic or other alloy of sodium and potassium which is liquid at room temperature and is a good heat-transfer medium because of its unusually high thermal conductivity, stability, and low volatility at high temperature. Indeed it is employed at temperatures above 1200°F.

For safe transportation, potassium should be stored in an inert nitrogen atmosphere in sealed cans. In the past, potassium has been stored under oil but oxygen has been carried through the oil, forming KO_2. The latter is such a strong oxidant that explosions with hydrocarbons have resulted.

MIXED FERTILIZERS

When a balance is struck showing the removal of plant food from our soils by the crops we eat or wear or employ as a raw material in our factories, the paramount importance of fertilizers becomes strikingly clear. In fertilizers, we add back to the soil either the materials removed by plants or those chemicals needed in native soils to make them either productive at all or more productive. The food and clothing of the nations at our present rate of production are dependent largely on the use of fertilizers. Tables 2 and 3, pertaining to potash, illustrate balance and withdrawals from our soils. Table 3, Chap. 20, presents the nitrogen balance for the United States and shows the heavy annual loss.

Man early discovered that the excreta of animal life are the food for plant life. Indeed, the Chinese have maintained the fertility of their soil for 5,000 years by the application of this principle. Even in the superaesthetic civilization of the United States we recognize the need and apply animal manure on a large scale to maintain a better plant yield from our soils.

In fertilizers[1] there are three main chemicals and many minor ones that are needed by our crops. The three principal ones are nitrogen, N, phosphoric acid, P_2O_5, and potash, K_2O. We generally speak of fertilizers as having formulas, such as 3-12-12, 2-12-6, or 5-10-5, which mean that these fertilizers have 3,12,12, or 2,12,6, or 5,10,5 per cent, respectively, of total nitrogen, N, of available phosphate, P_2O_5, and of soluble potash,

[1] ANON., Mixed Fertilizer, *Chem. Eng.*, **54** (7), 132 (1947), pictured flow sheet.

K_2O. Note, for a memory jog, that these constituents are in alphabetical order. Another way of evaluating these fertilizer formulas is as "units." Here one unit is 1 per cent of a ton or 20 lb. Hence the first of the formulas given above would contain 3 units of nitrogen, 12 units of P_2O_5,

TABLE 2. BALANCE SHEET OF POTASH FROM THE SOILS OF THE UNITED STATES, 1930[a]

Losses:	Acreage	Tons K_2O
By harvested crops...........................	367,554,485	3,824,149
By grazing...................................	464,154,524	11,355,534
By erosion...................................	367,554,486	34,990,589
By leaching..................................	352,380,258	9,960,000
		60,130,272
Additions:		
Fertilizers....................................		359,464
Manures......................................		3,331,523
Rainfall (dust)................................		1,835,280
Irrigation.....................................		592,531
Seeds...		62,492
		6,181,290

[a] FREAR, D. E. H., editor, "Agricultural Chemistry," Vol. II, pp. 215, 218, D. Van Nostrand Company, Inc., New York, 1951. On p. 218 it is noted that the additions for 1948 would probably be about the same except that the figure for potash in fertilizers would be around 900,000 tons of K_2O. Table 1 shows that in 1952 the fertilizer industry would consume over 1.5 million tons of K_2O.

TABLE 3. POTASH REMOVED PER ACRE BY VARIOUS CROPS[a]

Crop	Yield per acre	Potash removed, lb. K_2O
Alfalfa...............	4 tons	178.4
Clover hay...........	2 tons	65.2
Corn................	75 bu. (plus stalks)	82.8
Cotton..............	600 lb. lint (entire plant)	59.6
Oats................	50 bu. (plus straw)	40.8
Potatoes............	300 bu.	95.0
Rye.................	35 bu. (grain)	40.0
Soybeans............	25 bu. (beans)	86.0
Sugar beets..........	10 tons	64.0
Tobacco.............	1,000 lb. leaves (plus stalks)	78.0
Wheat..............	30 bu. grain (plus straw)	25.2

[a] LODGE, Potash in the Fertilizer Industry, *Ind. Eng. Chem.*, **30**, 878 (1938).

and 12 units of K_2O. These formulas are listed in the order of magnitude of their sales in 1951, the 3-12-12 being the largest sold. In addition, many of the commercial fertilizers contain the minor chemicals needed by plants. Table 4 gives a summary of the important chemicals that are commercially used to supply these three fertilizing radicals.

Not all chemicals or other constituents of fertilizers are available to all plants with equal facility because so much depends upon the nature of the chemical used, upon the other materials in the soil, and in particular on the soil pH or its chemical reaction as well as upon the crop itself. From this it can be seen that not only must the mixing but also the application of the fertilizers be carried out properly. Fortunately the farmers of the nation have at their call the various county agents of the Department of Agriculture who act in cooperation with various experimental stations and can select and supply that fertilizer which will give the best results for the dollar expended.

TABLE 4. THE MORE IMPORTANT COMMERCIAL FERTILIZERS CONSUMED IN THE
UNITED STATES, 1950[a]
(In thousands of short tons)

Commodity	Quantity	Commodity	Quantity
Mixtures:			
N-P-K (Complete)	11,198	Phosphates:	
N-P	178	Ammonium phosphate	143
P-K	831	Basic slag	287
N-K	74	Bone meal	12
K	28	Calcium metaphosphate	10
Chemical nitrogen materials:		Ca-Mg-phosphate, fused	5
Ammonia, anhydrous	86	Fused tri-Ca phosphate	16
Ammonia, aqua	11	Phosphoric acid	7
Ammonium nitrate	578	Phosphate rock, ground	729
Ammonium sulfate	235	Colloidal phosphate	21
Calcium cyanamide	82	Superphosphate, normal	1,857
Calcium nitrate	22	Superphosphate, conc	265
Sodium nitrate	627	Potash:	
Urea	18	Manure salts, 22–30 per cent	19
Organics:		Muriates, 50–60 per cent	109
Manures, dried	165	Potassium sulfate	14
Sewage sludge	90		
Castor pomace	10		
Cottonseed meal	13		

[a] SCHOLL and WALLACE, Commercial Fertilizers, *Agr. Chemicals*, **VI** (6), 31 (1951). The total consumption of fertilizers for this period, including minor and secondary elements, was 18,354,636 tons.

As many of the constituents necessary for fertilizers must be shipped a considerable distance, the trend in recent years has been to use the more concentrated fertilizers. In a 3-12-12 mixture there is a total of only 27 per cent of active fertilizer constituents. The other 73 per cent consists of filler, carrier, or soil-conditioning materials. The day will come everywhere, as the day has come in many places, when much more concentrated fertilizers are economically available to the farmers. If necessary, the diluting materials can be added from the farmers' own back yards to prevent a too strong or a burning action on the delicate young plants. Examples of concentrated fertilizer chemicals are ammonia, ammonium nitrate, potassium metaphosphate, ammonium phosphate, and potassium nitrate.

Minor constituents that research has shown to be necessary for plant life are sodium, calcium, and magnesium compounds in small amounts accompanied by much smaller quantities of boron, iron, sulfur, manganese, zinc, and copper compounds. Some of these derivatives, such as boron, are disadvantageous if their presence is larger than a certain minimum. Everyone knows that water and carbon dioxide are consumed by the plants in enormous amount and that humus is helpful to better the general soil condition.

The modern fertilizer chemist in cooperation with the soil scientist actually feeds the plants and overcomes much of the necessity of letting the fields regenerate their fertility by lying fallow every third season as was the custom from ancient times. To be sure, the modern soil scientist also utilizes certain crops to replenish some elements of soil fertility, as is done so extensively to supply nitrogen by the use of legumes such as clover and alfalfa.

Nitrogen Fertilizing Constituents. Chapter 20 presents the source and methods of manufacture of various nitrogen compounds which are used both in industry and fertilizers. Table 4 indicates that nitrogen is employed in the form of ammonia, ammonium salts, nitrates, and organic nitrogenous materials. Nitrogen compounds stimulate the vegetative growth in plants through nitrogen-containing proteins and chlorophyll. Plants lacking nitrogen have yellow leaves. Too much nitrogen causes rank growth and delays maturity.

Phosphate Fertilizing Constituents. Throughout the world there exist very large deposits of apatite or phosphate rock. This has the formula, $3Ca_3(PO_4)_2 \cdot CaF_2$, from which it can be seen that this compound is really calcium fluorphosphate. If simply placed on the soil after being very finely ground, it becomes gradually available. As Table 4 shows, over 729,000 tons are consumed yearly. If, however, this phosphate rock is decomposed by the action of sulfuric acid, superphosphate results in which 18 to 20 per cent of P_2O_5 is immediately available. Superphosphate manufacture is described in Chap. 18. To save some cost in transporting and to secure a more concentrated fertilizer, the phosphate rock is decomposed with phosphoric acid, yielding a stronger fertilizer known as *triple superphosphate*, which contains 48 per cent P_2O_5. Bone meal, made by grinding old or fresh bones, is also an important source of this fertilizing constituent. Indeed, it is known that many years after the herds of buffaloes were slaughtered for their hides, their whitened bones were collected from the plains of the West for their fertilizer value. The function of phosphorus in plants is really complex, the phosphates stimulating plant growth, causing resistance to disease, producing more vigorous seedlings, and hastening crop maturing. Phosphorus like nitrogen is a part of protoplasm that is essential to life.

Potash Fertilizing Constituents. For three quarters of a century, the rich deposits of Germany satisfied the potash demands of the world. However, the uncertain supplies in wartime forced the United States and other nations to develop their own potash resources to ensure the productivity of their soils. Potassium chloride or muriate of potash, either as an almost pure salt or in the form of impure manure salt, is widely used in fertilizer mixes. On certain crops, as, for instance, tobacco, the chloride ion in high concentration is disadvantageous; consequently potassium sulfate or potassium nitrate, when available, is preferred. When fields lie fallow, and even in the process of ordinary weathering, potassium minerals such as feldspar gradually decompose, liberating from year to year considerable amounts of potash to the plants. Some of the potash absorbed by the plant remains in the vegetative parts which are not normally sold off the farm. Potassium is an essential element in all growing plants and in particular in all crops; it is necessary in all cell metabolic processes. Lodge[1] summarizes the effect of potash on plants by writing,

(a) It facilitates either the production or the translocation of sugars and starches from the leaf, hence its value for sugar- and starch-making crops; (b) it stiffens the straw of cereal crops and the grass tribe generally; and (c) it enables the plant to withstand adverse conditions of soil, climate, and disease, making it more resistant to drought, rust, and other diseases. By balancing the plant food ration, potash tends to counteract rankness of growth developed by abundant nitrogen.

While this chapter has considered the different types of fertilizers, the use of chemicals in agriculture has broadened in recent years. Indeed, insecticides, herbicides, and fungicides are considered together under the broad title of pesticides in Chap. 26. Antibiotics for the agricultural field are presented in Chap. 31. The last division of agricultural chemicals may be classified under soil conditioning, of which Krilium of Monsanto Chemical Company has received the most publicity. It is a polyacrylonitrile product that makes a more desirable soil structure for improving the growing of plants.

[1] LODGE, Potash in the Fertilizer Industry, *Ind. Eng. Chem.*, **30**, 878 (1938); TROUG and JONES, Fate of Soluble Potash Applied to Soils, *Ind. Eng. Chem.*, **30**, 882 (1938); HOFFER, Potash in Plant Metabolism, *Ind. Eng. Chem.*, **30**, 885 (1938); also Symposium—Potash in Agriculture, *Soil Sci.*, **55**, 87*ff*. (1943).

SELECTED REFERENCES

Teeple, J. E., "Industrial Development of Searles Lake Brine," Reinhold Publishing Corporation, New York, 1929.

Turrentine, J. W., chairman, Symposium on Potash, *Ind. Eng. Chem.*, **30**, 853–896 (1938). This symposium embraced 12 papers on the actual accomplishments in the United States in this field.

——, "Potash; A Review, Estimate and Forecast," John Wiley & Sons, Inc., New York, 1926.

——, "Potash in North America," Reinhold Publishing Corporation, New York, 1943.

Cowie, G. A., "Potash," Edward Arnold & Co., London, 1951.

Waggaman, W. H., "Phosphoric Acid, Phosphate, and Phosphatic Fertilizers," 2d ed., Reinhold Publishing Corporation, New York, 1952.

U.S. Department of Agriculture, Washington, D.C., publishers of various farmers' bulletins and circulars pertaining to fertilizers. Lists are available on request.

Collings, G. H., "Commercial Fertilizers," 4th ed., Blakiston Division, McGraw-Hill Book Company, Inc., New York, 1947.

Sanchilli, V., "Manual on Fertilizer Manufacture," Davison Chemical Company, Baltimore, 1947.

Kirk, R. E., and D. F. Othmer, "Encyclopedia of Chemical Technology," Vol. 6, pp. 376–452, The Interscience Encyclopedia, Inc., New York, 1951.

CHAPTER 14

SALT AND MISCELLANEOUS SODIUM COMPOUNDS

There are a considerable number of sodium salts that are of definite industrial necessity. Most of these are derived directly or indirectly from ordinary salt so far as their sodium content is concerned. In one sense, the sodium may be viewed simply as a carrier for the more active anion to which the compound owes its industrial importance. For instance, in sodium sulfide it is the sulfide part that is the more active. Similarly this is the case with sodium thiosulfate and sodium silicate. We could use in most cases the corresponding potassium salts which in past years were consumed more extensively. The present situation is that sodium salts can be manufactured more cheaply and in sufficient purity to meet the industrial demands. Therefore, industry has turned, in the last few decades, to a greater utilization of the various sodium salts. Sodium salts are described elsewhere as follows: Sodium chlorate and perchlorate in Chap. 16; sodium hypochlorite in Chap. 15, which includes the various sodium alkali compounds; the sodium phosphates are in Chap. 18; sodium nitrate in Chap. 20; and sodium bichromate and sodium borate in Chap. 21.

SODIUM CHLORIDE OR COMMON SALT

Historical. Salt has long been an essential part of the human diet. It has served as an object of worship and as a medium of exchange, lumps of salt being used in Tibet and Mongolia for money. Its distribution has been employed as a political weapon by ancient governments and even today in Oriental countries high taxes are placed on salt.

Uses and Economics. Sodium chloride is the basic raw material of a great many chemical compounds such as sodium hydroxide, sodium carbonate, sodium sulfate, hydrochloric acid, sodium phosphates, and sodium chlorate and chlorite.[1] It should be remembered also that it is the source of many other compounds through its derivatives. Practically all chlorine comes from the electrolysis of sodium chloride. It is important in the zeolite process of water softening, and it has many uses in the field of organic chemistry such as the salting out of soap and the precipitation

[1] LOOKER, Salt as a Chemical Raw Material, *Chem. Inds.*, **49**, 594, 790 (1941).

of dyes. It is employed to preserve fish, meat, and hides both directly and indirectly through the medium of refrigeration. The dairying and pickling industries also consume large quantities of sodium chloride. Probably the most important use of sodium chloride is as an essential part of everyone's diet. Large quantities of the purest of sodium chloride are sold as table salt. The latter may have a small amount of iodide added in certain sections of the country.

The total salt output in the United States in 1952, including evaporated salt brine and rock salt, amounted to 19,544,492 tons valued at $70,992,925.

TABLE 1. THE UNITED STATES PRODUCTION (TONS) OF SODIUM SALTS
IN 1947 AND 1952[a]

	1947	1952
Sodium chloride	16,138,374	19,544,952
Sodium sulfate (anhydrous)		202,813
Sodium sulfate (crude Na_2SO_4)	693,373	662,373
Glauber's salt ($Na_2SO_4 \cdot 10H_2O$)	202,285	177,929
Sodium bisulfate (niter cake)	41,663	38,275
Sodium sulfite	36,364	43,483
Sodium hydrosulfide (NaSH)		19,680
Sodium hydrosulfite ($Na_2S_2O_4$)	20,910	24,574
Sodium sulfide (60–62 per cent)	39,245	24,016
Sodium thiosulfate	34,809	36,081
Sodium silicates, water glass	492,837	519,039
Sodium silicates, meta ($Na_2SiO_3 \cdot 5H_2O$)	76,035	117,635
Sodium silicates, ortho (Na_4SiO_4)	35,566	27,753

[a] "Minerals Yearbook," 1952. Statistics that have been published for 1953, show somewhat more than 10 per cent increase for these items.

Manufacture. Salt occurs throughout the United States and is obtained in three different ways. One of these methods is by solar evaporation of sea water or salt lake water, or by evaporation and crystallization from brines pumped from wells. The second method is the mining of rock salt while the third involves the direct consumption of the salt brine. Over 1,000,000 tons are produced annually by solar evaporation, a large portion of which comes from the San Francisco Bay region and the Great Salt Lake of Utah.[1] The purity of salt first obtained from the evaporation of salt water is usually about 95 per cent; salt that is mined varies very widely in composition depending on the locality in which it is found. Some rock salt, however, runs as high as 99.5 per cent pure sodium chloride. The solution obtained from wells is usually only about 98 per cent pure.

For many purposes the salt obtained from the mines and by direct

[1] SCHRIER, Passing the Salt, *Chem. Eng.*, **58** (10), 138 (1952).

evaporation of salt solutions is pure enough for use; however, a large portion must be purified. If the evaporated salt from brines is to be treated, the solid may be dried in a kiln at 300°F. and the principal impurity, Glauber's salt, dehydrated and blown up by the air blast in the drier.[1] The only other treatment given this salt is crushing and screening. A purity of 99.8 per cent is easily obtained. Artificial brine, though used directly in many processes, is frequently evaporated mostly by the

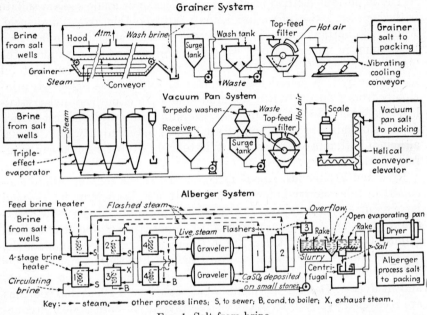

FIG. 1. Salt from brine.

vacuum pan procedure, under controlled conditions to furnish a very pure product (see Fig. 1).[2] The treatment of the rock salt that is mined depends upon the purity of the salt, but in many cases it is sufficiently high grade for direct use.

The *caking* of salt crystals is very troublesome and can be minimized as pointed out by Perry[3] if the following conditions are maintained:

1. Highest possible critical humidity is increased in case of salt by the removal of such impurities as calcium chloride, magnesium chloride, or free acid, all of which have a lower critical humidity than pure sodium chloride.

[1] BRIGHTON and DICE, Increasing the Purity of Common Salt, *Ind. Eng. Chem.*, **23**, 336 (1931); SIMMONS, Something New in Saltmaking, *Chem. Eng.*, **57** (11), 156 (1950).

[2] For a detailed description of the purification and manufacture of salt, see BADGER and BAKER, "Inorganic Chemical Technology," 2d ed., Chap. 2, McGraw-Hill Book Company, Inc., New York, 1941; PERRY, *op. cit.*, pp. 922–923; LEE, How Morton Salt Refines Salt, *Chem. Eng.*, **58** (1), 102 (1951).

[3] *Op. cit.*, pp. 1070–1071, critical humidity defined.

2. Most uniform graining which brings about the greatest percentage of voids for the size of crystals desired and the least points of contact.

3. Coating with a powder capable of absorbing some moisture. For salt, magnesia or tricalcium phosphate is employed.

SODIUM SULFATE (Salt Cake and Glauber's Salt)

The important method of obtaining salt cake or crude sodium sulfate is through the action of sulfuric acid on salt to obtain hydrochloric acid. Another important source is the recovery of natural sodium sulfate as a by-product in mining natural mineral deposits. A prime example is the Trona operations (Chap. 13) which accounts for over half of the total natural output. A considerable tonnage of salt cake is imported, principally from Canada. When the crude salt cake is purified and crystallized, Glauber's salt ($Na_2SO_4 \cdot 10H_2O$) results. The world's largest known deposits of natural sodium sulfate are located in Saskatchewan,[1] Canada, although both anhydrous sodium sulfate and Glauber's salt occur naturally in this country.

Uses and Economics. About three-fourths of the sodium sulfate consumed in this country is for the manufacture of kraft pulp. The second largest current consumption is as a diluent in powdered synthetic detergents which usually contain from 50 to 75 per cent by weight of sodium sulfate. Other important uses are in the manufacture of sodium sulfide, glass, Glauber's salt, sodium silicate, sodium hyposulfite, nickel smelting, barium sulfate, sodium aluminum sulfate, hog and cattle powders, and in dyeing. Besides the manufactured salt cake about 100,000 tons are recovered yearly from spent viscose rayon spin-bath liquor. Production statistics are given in Table 1.

Manufacture of Salt Cake. The equations for the production of salt cake from sulfuric acid and salt are[2]

$$NaCl + H_2SO_4 \rightarrow NaHSO_4 + HCl$$
$$NaHSO_4 + NaCl \rightarrow Na_2SO_4 + HCl$$

The equipment and the procedure for commercializing these reactions are described under Hydrochloric Acid in Chap. 21. When the temperature has reached the proper level in the furnace, the finely ground salt and other raw material are charged. The furnace runs continuously, batch after batch, until shut down for the necessary periodical cleaning and repair. Most products from the Mannheim furnace go into the manufacture of other materials in the same plant where this type of furnace is operated.

[1] HOLLAND, More Saskatchewan Salt Cake, *Chem. Eng.*, **55** (12), 121 (1948).

[2] LAURY, "Hydrochloric Acid and Sodium Sulfate," Reinhold Publishing Corporation, New York, 1927.

Another method of making sodium sulfate, which originated in Europe, is the Hargreaves process. The equation for the reaction is as follows:

$$4NaCl + 2SO_2 + 2H_2O + O_2 \rightarrow 2Na_2SO_4 + 4HCl$$

This is carried out by passing sulfur dioxide and air from a furnace over prepared salt lumps in vertical steel chambers with false bottoms. Several of these chambers are run in series, and the gas is moved countercurrently. The complete cycle for the reaction, cleaning, and repacking is three days for each individual chamber. Very good cake and hydrochloric acid are made in this process, but the fact that it requires a large amount of hand labor has prohibited its wide use in this country. The Bay Chemical Co. of Weeks Island, La., is the only American Hargreaves plant.

Because of the increased demand for sodium sulfate in the kraft-paper manufacture, "synthetic salt cake" has resulted. "Synthetic salt cake" is a sintered mixture of soda ash and sulfur in the proportions of 3 parts

$$Na_2CO_3 + S + 1\frac{1}{2}O_2 \rightarrow Na_2SO_4 + CO_2;$$
$$\Delta H = -1950 \text{ B.t.u. per lb.}[1]$$

of sulfur to 10 of soda ash. This product[1] is not satisfactory as a substitute for sodium sulfate in applications other than the kraft-paper industry.

Manufacture of Glauber's Salt. Glauber's salt is made by dissolving salt cake in mother liquor, removing the impurities, clarifying, and crystallizing. The salt cake is dissolved in large, circular, lead-lined wooden tanks. The solution is then treated with a paste of chloride of lime followed by milk of lime in sufficient quantities to neutralize the solution. Stirring is carried out by a paddle and heating by a lead pipe running to the bottom. The precipitated impurities of iron, magnesium, and calcium are allowed to settle, and the clear solution is run to crystallizers by side outlets. The precipitated mud is washed with water and the water is used as make-up for the process. Crystallization is carried out in pans lined with lead. When the solution cools to room temperature, the pan is drained and the crystals are collected and centrifuged.

Pure *anhydrous sodium sulfate* is also sold in the market. It is made by dehydrating Glauber's salt in a brick-lined rotary furnace, by crystallizing out from a hot concentrated solution, or by chilling and dehydrating.[2] Figure 2 shows the steps in the production of anhydrous sodium

---

[1] SAVELL, The Application of Synthetic Salt Cake, *Paper Trade J.*, **111** (8), 31 (1940); New Ideas on the Use of Salt Cake in Kraft Pulp Process, *Paper Trade J.*, **109** (24), 18 (1939).

[2] DOUGLASS and ANDERSON, Submerged Combustion as Applied to Sodium Sulfate Productions, *Chem. & Met. Eng.*, **48** (5), 135 (1941); HOLLAND, New Type Evaporator, *Chem. Eng.*, **58** (1), 106 (1951).

sulfate from naturally occurring Glauber's salt. Because of the expanding kraft-paper industry, the development of sodium sulfate from these natural sources has been greatly stimulated.

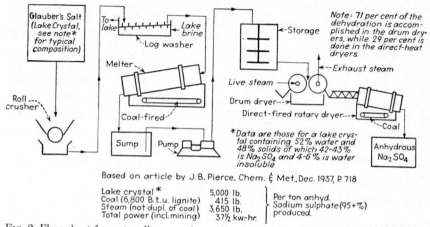

Based on article by J. B. Pierce. Chem. & Met., Dec. 1937, P. 718

Lake crystal *	5,000 lb.	
Coal (6,800 B.t.u. lignite)	415 lb.	Per ton anhyd.
Steam (not dupl. of coal)	3,650 lb.	Sodium sulphate (95+%)
Total power (incl. mining)	37½ kw-hr.	produced.

FIG. 2. Flow sheet for naturally occurring sodium sulfate by the three-stage procedure.

SODIUM BISULFATE OR NITER CAKE

Sodium bisulfate, $NaHSO_4$, is commonly called *niter cake* because it was obtained by the now almost obsolete reaction of sodium nitrate or "niter" with sulfuric acid.

$$NaNO_3 + H_2SO_4 \rightarrow NaHSO_4 + HNO_3$$

The acid sodium sulfate may be manufactured from salt and sulfuric acid. This compound is used as a mild acid ingredient in dye baths, in the cleaning of sanitary porcelain objects, and as a cleaner in automobile radiators. It is also employed as a flux in metallurgical industries.

SODIUM BISULFITE

Uses and Economics. Sodium bisulfite finds industrial employment either in solution or as a solid. The solid is of the anhydrous form and has the formula $NaHSO_3$ for the pure reagent. The commercial product usually consists almost entirely of $Na_2S_2O_5$ known as *sodium pyrosulfite* or *sodium metabisulfite*, which is the dehydrated derivative of two molecules of sodium bisulfite. The solutions may be easily shipped, stored, and handled in lead-lined equipment. In the tanning industry this acid salt is used as a reducing agent for chrome solutions; in the textile field it is a bleaching agent, an antichlor, and a raw material for the manufacture of hydrosulfite solutions. It is also consumed in the paper, photographic, and organic chemical industries.

Manufacture. Sodium bisulfite is produced by passing sulfur dioxide through mother liquors from previous processes containing in solution small amounts of sodium bisulfite and in suspension a considerable amount of soda ash. The reaction taking place is

$$2NaHSO_3 + 2Na_2CO_3 + 2H_2O + 4SO_2 \rightarrow 6NaHSO_3 + 2CO_2$$

The product is obtained as a *suspension* which is removed from the solution by centrifuging. The dried product is really the sodium metabisulfite, $Na_2S_2O_5$.

SODIUM SULFITE

Uses and Economics. Sodium sulfite is a compound that is very easily oxidized. For this reason it is employed in many cases where a gentle reducing agent is desired. It is employed to bleach wool and silk, as an antichlor after the bleaching of yarns, textiles, and paper, as a preservative for foodstuffs, and to prevent raw sugar solutions from coloring upon evaporation. It is very widely used in the preparation of photographic developers as a preventive of the oxidation of hydroquinone and other agents. It has a small application in the field of medicine as an antiseptic and as an antizymotic for internal use. The reason for the increase in the use of sodium sulfite is the recent discovery that its addition to boiler feed water will remove oxygen from the water and thus help prevent corrosion and scale formation. Any excess of this salt is sold to the sulfate pulp mills.

Manufacture. The most important commercial procedure for this compound is by passing sulfur dioxide into a solution of soda ash until the product has an acid reaction. At this point the solution consists chiefly of sodium bisulfite. This may be converted into sodium sulfite by adding more soda ash to the solution and boiling until all the carbon dioxide is evolved. The reaction is carried out in large lead-lined wooden vessels. After the solution has settled, it is concentrated, whereupon crystals of $Na_2SO_3 \cdot 7H_2O$ settle out upon cooling.

Another commercial source of this compound in the crude anhydrous form is from the preparation of phenol by the fusion of sodium benzene sulfonate with sodium hydroxide.[1]

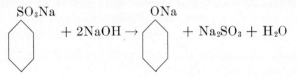

$$SO_3Na \qquad ONa$$

<hr>

[1] GROGGINS, "Unit Processes in Organic Synthesis," 4th ed., p. 691, McGraw-Hill Book Company, Inc., New York, 1952.

SODIUM HYDROSULFITE[1]

One of the most important chemicals in the dyeing and printing industries is sodium hydrosulfite. It is a very powerful reducing agent with a specific action on many dyes, particularly the "vat dyes," reducing them to the soluble form. This reducing agent is employed for stripping certain dyes from fabrics and for bleaching straws and soaps. Formerly one of the main difficulties with this compound was the lack of stability; however, this has been corrected and it may be shipped and stored. Another name for this substance is *sodium hyposulfite*, though the dye-house workers call it simply *hydro*.

Manufacture. There are two methods of manufacture both of which require zinc dust. In the first process the zinc dust is allowed to reduce sodium bisulfite at room temperature:[2]

$$2NaHSO_3 + H_2SO_3 + Zn \rightarrow ZnSO_3 + Na_2S_2O_4 + 2H_2O$$

The products of the reaction are treated with milk of lime to neutralize any free acid and hence to reduce the solubility of the $ZnSO_3$ which is filtered off. Sodium chloride is added to salt out the $Na_2S_2O_4 \cdot 2H_2O$. This is dehydrated with alcohol and dried. The crystals are stable only in the dry state.

The second process consists of treating an aqueous suspension of zinc dust in formaldehyde with sulfur dioxide at 80°C. A double decomposition reaction is carried out with soda ash forming the sodium salt. A pure product is obtained by evaporation in vacuum.

SODIUM SULFIDE

Uses and Economics. Sodium sulfide, Na_2S, is an inorganic chemical that has attained a very important position in the organic chemical industry. It is consumed as a reducing agent in the manufacture of amino compounds, and it enters into the preparation of many dyes. It is also employed extensively in the leather industry as a depilatory, *i.e.*, for the removal of hair from hides. Sodium polysulfide is one of the necessary reactants for making Thiokol synthetic rubber. Other industries where its use is important are the rayon, metallurgical, photographic, and engraving fields. The production of sodium sulfide is given in Table 1.

Manufacture. This chemical may be obtained as 30 per cent crystals or as 62 per cent flakes. Here the percentage refers to Na_2S. Solutions of it may be shipped in steel very conveniently. One disadvantageous

---

[1] This compound is named *sodium hyposulfite* by *Chemical Abstracts*. In commerce it is also called *sodium sulfoxylate*.

[2] RANSHAW, Hydrosulfites and Their Derivatives, *Chem. Age*, **41**, 359 (1939); PRATT, Sodium Hydrosulfite as a Dry Powder, *Chem. & Met. Eng.*, **31**, 11 (1924).

property of sodium sulfide is its deliquescence. It crystallizes with nine molecules of water, $Na_2S \cdot 9H_2O$.

There are three methods of producing this chemical. The oldest and the most used is the reduction of sodium sulfate with powdered coal in a reverberatory furnace. Another similar process is the reduction of barite in the same manner, leaching, and double decomposition with soda ash. The third and newest method of production involves the saturation of a caustic soda solution with hydrogen sulfide and the addition of another equal portion of sodium hydroxide. For the reactions involving the reduction of salt cake

$$Na_2SO_4 + 4C \rightarrow Na_2S + 4CO$$
$$Na_2SO_4 + 4CO \rightarrow Na_2S + 4CO_2$$

very drastic conditions are needed. Since the reaction must be carried out above 850°C., there has been a great deal of work undertaken to improve not only the medium in which the reaction is carried out but also the conditions for the reaction so that lower temperatures may be used.[1] Specially designed small reverberatory furnaces seem to give the least difficulty because they avoid overheating the charge. The reaction takes place in a liquid phase and is very rapid. Rotary kilns of the type used for calcining limestone have been applied with some success to this reaction. The reduction of barium sulfate takes place very similarly. Newer plants are using nickel or nickel-clad equipment to reduce iron contamination.

The substance issuing from the furnace is known as *black ash*. This product is run into iron tanks and allowed to cool. It may be used in this crude form but it contains many impurities. This crude sulfide may be dissolved hot; after settling, it may be run into shallow crystallizing tanks where colorless crystals of $Na_2S \cdot 9H_2O$ separate out. A more concentrated sulfide may be obtained by evaporating the liquor at 160°C. for 4 to 6 hr. in a cast-iron pot. The molten hot sulfide is then pumped into ordinary caustic soda steel drums for shipping.

SODIUM THIOSULFATE

Sodium thiosulfate crystallizes in large, transparent, extremely soluble prisms with five molecules of water. It is used as a mild reducing agent like sodium sulfite. It is employed as an antichlor following the bleaching of cellulose products and as a source of sulfur dioxide in the bleaching of wool, oil, and ivory. In photography it is used to dissolve unaltered silver halogen compounds from negatives or prints where it is commonly called

[1] WHITE and WHITE, Manufacture of Sodium Sulfide, *Ind. Eng. Chem.*, **28**, 244 (1936); *cf.* NYMAN and O'BRIEN, Catalytic Reduction of Sodium Sulfate, *Ind. Eng. Chem.*, **39**, 1019 (1947).

hypo. It is a preservative against fermentation in dyeing industries and serves in the preparation of mordants. Other minor uses of sodium thiosulfate are in the reduction of indigo, in the preparation of cinnabar, in the preparation of silvering solutions, and in medicine.

Manufacture. There are several methods for the production of sodium thiosulfate, the most important of which is from sodium sulfite and free sulfur.

$$Na_2SO_3 + S \rightarrow Na_2S_2O_3$$

The reaction of the sulfur with a concentrated solution of sodium sulfite is carried out in a ceramic-lined iron pot provided with agitation. The resulting liquor is concentrated and crystallized. The crystals formed, $Na_2S_2O_3 \cdot 5H_2O$, should be packed immediately in airtight containers to prevent efflorescence.

A second method of preparation is from sodium sulfide. Sulfur dioxide is passed into a solution of sodium sulfide and sodium carbonate of low concentration (not more than 10 per cent of each).

$$Na_2CO_3 + 2Na_2S + 4SO_2 \rightarrow 3Na_2S_2O_3 + CO_2$$

The sodium thiosulfate is obtained by evaporation and crystallization.

SODIUM NITRITE

From the standpoint of the dye industry, sodium nitrite is a very important chemical. Here it is employed for the diazotization of amines for making azo dyes. It does not have a great many other uses. Formerly, it was prepared by the reaction,

$$NaNO_3 + Pb \rightarrow NaNO_2 + PbO$$

Sodium nitrite is now manufactured by passing the oxidation product of ammonia into soda ash solution.

$$Na_2CO_3 + 2NO + \tfrac{1}{2}O_2 \rightarrow 2NaNO_2 + CO_2$$

Any sodium nitrate also formed may be separated by crystallization. Lead-lined equipment is satisfactory.

SODIUM SILICATES

Uses and Economics. Sodium silicates are unique in that the ratio of their constituent parts, Na_2O and SiO_2, may be varied to obtain the desired properties. At the present time there are over forty varieties of commercial sodium silicates, each with a specific use. Silicates that have a ratio from $1Na_2O/1.6SiO_2$ up to $1Na_2O/4SiO_2$ are called *colloidal* silicates. Sodium metasilicate has a ratio of 1 mole of sodium oxide to 1 mole of silica, Na_2SiO_3. A compound with a higher content of sodium oxide with $1\frac{1}{2}$ moles of Na_2O to 1 mole of SiO_2 is called *sesquisilicate*. Another compound still higher in sodium oxide content is sodium orthosilicate, Na_4SiO_4, which contains 2 moles of Na_2O to 1 mole of SiO_2.

About 400,000 tons yearly of the lower colloidal silicates (*water glass*) are sold as 32 to 47 per cent solutions for use as adhesives for many kinds of materials, especially paperboard for corrugated containers. These solutions are also consumed alone or in mixture with many other materials as adhesives for plywoods, wallboard, flooring, and metal foils.[1] Besides a large number of other uses, silicates are important for detergency, metal cleaning, fireproofing, and sizing. The sodium metasilicate exists in the hydrated form and is sold as a solid. It is more alkaline than soda ash and is used in metal cleaning and as a strongly alkaline detergent. Sodium sesquisilicate, $Na_4SiO_4 \cdot Na_2SiO_3 \cdot 11H_2O$, and sodium orthosilicate, Na_4SiO_4, are employed in the same fields as the metasilicates but where a more strongly alkaline product is needed.

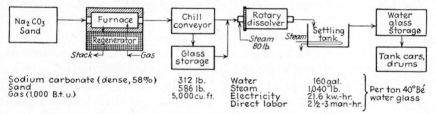

FIG. 3. Flow sheet for manufacture of sodium silicate.

Manufacture. These silicates are made by fusing sodium carbonate and silica (sand) in a furnace resembling that for the manufacture of glass as shown in Fig. 3. The reaction takes place around 1300°C. as follows:[2]

$$Na_2CO_3 + nSiO_2 \rightarrow Na_2O \cdot nSiO_2 + CO_2$$

The most common commercial silicates occur when n equals 2.0 and 3.2. The intermediate compositions are obtained by mixing, and the more alkaline ratios by adding caustic soda or by initially fusing the sand with caustic soda.

The product upon cooling forms a clear light bluish-green glass. This color is due to impurities of less than 1 per cent, usually iron. If the material is sold as a solution, the product is ground and dissolved in water or by steam under pressure when the ratio of silica to alkali is above 2. This procedure is shown in Fig. 3, but where the liquids are

[1] MERRILL, Industrial Applications of the Sodium Silicates, *Ind. Eng. Chem.*, **41**, 337 (1949); WILLS and SAMS, Industrial Adhesives, *Ind. Eng. Chem.*, **41**, 81 (1949); VAIL, "Soluble Silicates," 2d ed., 2 vols., Reinhold Publishing Corporation, New York, 1952.

[2] MERRILL, Chemistry of the Soluble Silicates, *J. Chem. Educ.*, **24**, 262 (1947).

made directly, the melt flows from the furnace and without chilling passes into an open rotary dissolver where it is hydrated in steam and water not under pressure. The resulting solution from either method is usually sold as concentrated as possible. In the case of $1Na_2O/3.2SiO_2$, 43°Bé. or 40 per cent solids is the upper limit, while $1Na_2O/2SiO_2$ has an upper limit of 54 per cent solids or 60°Bé.

SODIUM PEROXIDE

Sodium peroxide is a pale-yellow hygroscopic powder. It absorbs moisture from the air and forms a snow-white hydrate, $Na_2O_2 \cdot 8H_2O$. When added to water, this compound forms sodium hydroxide and oxygen. It is a powerful oxidizing agent, and its principal uses depend upon this property. It is employed for the bleaching of wool, silk, and fine cotton articles and in chemical synthesis.

Manufacture. It is prepared by burning sodium in an excess of air. The reaction is carried out in heated revolving drums or continuously by placing sodium in wagons and moving them through a furnace maintained at 300°C. A current of dry air is passed through the furnace countercurrent to the wagons containing the sodium. The product has a purity of about 95 per cent. Sodium peroxide must be packed in clean dry iron or nickel. Care should be taken in handling since, when it is placed on paper or wood, the heat of hydration of the material is sufficient to cause ignition. Fused sodium peroxide reacts with platinum, iron, copper, tin, and brass but not with nickel.

SODIUM PERBORATE

Sodium perborate,[1] $NaBO_3 \cdot 4H_2O$, is a mild oxidizing agent that has recently gained widespread use in the medical and dental fields. It is recommended as a mouthwash because of its oxidizing and cleansing effects. Other uses are as oxidizing and bleaching agents in cosmetics, soaps, and textiles. It is made by mixing solutions of borax, sodium peroxide, and hydrogen peroxide, heating slightly, and allowing to crystallize.

$$Na_2B_4O_7 + Na_2O_2 + 3H_2O_2 \rightarrow 4NaBO_3 + 3H_2O$$

SODIUM AMIDE

Sodium amide[2] is another chemical that has found many special uses in organic chemistry. It is a vigorous dehydrating agent and, for this reason, is used in the synthesis of indigo and in the preparation of pure

[1] See Boron Compounds in Chap. 21.
[2] LEVINE and FERNELIUS, Alkali Amides, *Chem. Revs.*, **34**, 449 (1954).

hydrazine. It is also an intermediate in the preparation of sodium cyanide and finds application as an aminating agent.

It is prepared by passing ammonia into metallic sodium at 200 to 300°C.

$$NH_3 + Na \rightarrow NaNH_2 + \tfrac{1}{2}H_2$$

This reaction may be carried out in iron equipment; in many cases a ball-mill type reactor[1] is satisfactory. This compound should be handled with care as it decomposes with water explosively. Also it should not be kept, as disastrous explosions have resulted from handling material that had been stored. It should be consumed as made.

SODIUM CYANIDE AND FERROCYANIDE

Sodium cyanide is not only important in the inorganic and organic chemical fields but also has many metallurgical applications. It is used in treating gold ore, in the casehardening of steel, in electroplating, in organic reactions, in the preparation of hydrocyanic acid, and in making adiponitrile. Sodium cyanide can be made from sodium amide heated with carbon at 800°C., the carbon as charcoal being thrown into the molten sodium amide.

$$2NaNH_2 + C \xrightarrow{600°C.} Na_2NCN + 2H_2$$
$$Na_2NCN + C \xrightarrow{800°C.} 2NaCN$$

Another method of manufacture is to melt together sodium chloride and calcium cyanamide in an electric furnace. The most recent commercial method consists of the dehydration of formamide by heat and a catalyst into hydrocyanic acid. The hydrocyanic acid is then converted to sodium cyanide by treatment with caustic soda.

$$HCONH_2 \rightarrow HCN + H_2O$$
$$HCN + NaOH \rightarrow NaCN + H_2O$$

Sodium ferrocyanide[2] is manufactured from a crude sodium cyanide made from calcium cyanamide by fusion with sodium chloride in an electric furnace. The ferrocyanide reaction is carried on in a hot aqueous solution with ferrous sulfate. Soluble sodium and calcium ferrocyanides are formed and calcium sulfate precipitated. The calcium ferrocyanide is changed to the sodium salt by addition of soda ash precipitating cal-

[1] Shreve, Riechers, Rubenkoenig, and Goodman, Aminations by Sodium Amide, *Ind. Eng. Chem.*, **32**, 173 (1940).

[2] American Cyanamid Company, "The Chemistry of Ferrocyanides," American Cyanamid Co., 105 pp., 1953, 742 references, New York; Anon., Sodium Ferrocyanide, *Chem. Eng.*, **60** (2), 240 (1953), pictured flow sheet.

cium carbonate. The slurry is filtered and washed and the decahydrate $Na_4Fe(CN)_6 \cdot 10H_2O$ crystallizes out on cooling.

SELECTED REFERENCES

Snell, F. D., and C. T. Snell, "Chemicals of Commerce," D. Van Nostrand Company, Inc., New York, 1939.

Thorpe, "Dictionary of Applied Chemistry," 4th ed., Longmans, Green & Co., Inc., New York, 1937.

Ullmann, Fritz, "Enzyklopaedie der technischen Chemie," 3d ed., Urban & Schwarzenberg, Berlin and Vienna, 1951–.

Kirk, R. E., and D. F. Othmer, "Encyclopedia of Chemical Technology," 15 vols., The Interscience Encyclopedia, Inc., New York, 1947–1956.

Eskew, G. L., Salt—The Fifth Element, J. G. Ferguson & Associates, Chicago, 1948.

CHAPTER 15

SODA ASH, CAUSTIC SODA, AND CHLORINE

The manufacture of soda ash, caustic soda, and chlorine is one of the most important heavy chemical industries.[1] These chemicals rank next to sulfuric acid in quantity produced and in wide diversity of use. Soda ash finds application in glass, detergents, soaps, pulp and paper, textiles, and water softeners as well as in the manufacture of caustic soda, sodium phosphates, and sodium bicarbonate. Caustic soda from soda ash and from the electrolysis of salt brine is consumed in large quantities in the manufacture of rayon, explosives, soap, paper, and in many other processes. The demand for chlorine has developed phenomenally in the past few years.

Historical. The present process for the manufacture of soda ash is the Solvay process. Before this method was developed, the LeBlanc process was in universal use. Nicholas LeBlanc devised his famous process for soda ash manufacture around 1773.[2] It was based on roasting salt cake with carbon and limestone in a rotary furnace, with subsequent leaching of the product with water. The reactions were

$$2NaCl + H_2SO_4 \rightarrow Na_2SO_4 + 2HCl$$
$$Na_2SO_4 + 2C \rightarrow Na_2S + 2CO_2$$
$$Na_2S + CaCO_3 \rightarrow Na_2CO_3 + CaS$$

The crude product of the reaction was called *black ash*. It was leached cold, whereupon some hydrolysis of sulfides took place. These were changed to carbonate by treatment with the carbon dioxide containing gases from the black ash furnace. The resulting sodium carbonate solution was concentrated to obtain crystalline sodium carbonate,[3] which was

---

[1] KIRK and OTHMER, *op. cit.*, Vol. 1, pp. 358–430; KOBE, "Inorganic Process Industries," Chap. 4, pp. 48–49, 81–120, The Macmillan Company, New York, 1948.

[2] HOU, "Manufacture of Soda," 2d ed., Reinhold Publishing Corporation, New York, 1942. For further details on alkali and chlorine production, see also Chap. 10 by the same authority in "Rogers' Manual of Industrial Chemistry," 6th ed., D. Van Nostrand Company, Inc., New York, 1942.

[3] A flow sheet of this obsolete process is given in Badger and Baker, "Inorganic Chemical Technology," 2d ed., p. 137, McGraw-Hill Book Company, Inc., New York, 1941.

then dried or calcined. No LeBlanc plant was ever built in the United States, and none is now being operated anywhere in the world.

In 1869 Ernest Solvay began developing the ammonia-soda process. At first this method had great difficulty in competing with the older and well-established LeBlanc process. But in a few years the Solvay process

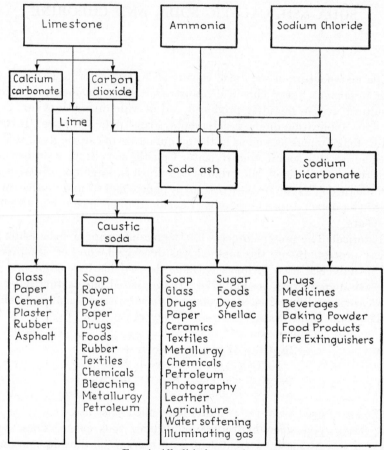

FIG. 1. Alkali industry chart.

reduced the price of soda ash to almost one-third the original price. After a struggle during which the producers of LeBlanc soda sold at a loss for many years, the ammonia-soda process completely had displaced the LeBlanc by 1915.

The electrolytic production of caustic soda was known in the eighteenth century, but it was not until 1890 that caustic was actually produced in this way for industrial consumption. Electrolytic chlorine developed with electrolytic caustic is the more valuable of the two products. The use of commercially fixed chlorine, in the form of bleaching powder, had been developed earlier with chlorine made from the oxidation of HCl with air, catalyzed by MnO_2 or by Cu_2Cl_2.[1]

The first American production of electrolytic chlorine was at Rumford Falls, Maine, in 1892.[2] Electrolytic caustic and chlorine require cheap electricity, a ready source of salt, and proximity to markets. For this reason a large number of plants are located near Niagara Falls, Freeport, Texas, and in West Virginia.

TABLE 1. UNITED STATES PRODUCTION OF SODA ASH[a]
(In thousands of short tons)

Year	Ammonia-soda process	Natural sodium carbonate	
		Production	Value
1943–1947 (over)	4,426	211	$3,547,342
1948	4,575	289	6,623,280
1949	3,916	201	4,163,714
1950	3,991	351	7,543,769
1951	5,094	351	8,368,037
1952	4,442	323	7,828,033
1953	4,879	424	n.a.

[a] "Minerals Yearbook," 1952, Preprint, 1953.

Uses and Economics. *Soda ash* is a lightweight solid, readily soluble in water, and usually contains 99.2 per cent Na_2CO_3. It is sold on the basis of the sodium oxide content which is generally 58 per cent. It is used in the manufacture of many chemicals, the most important of which are caustic soda and sodium bicarbonate. It also crystallizes with water to form $Na_2CO_3 \cdot 10H_2O$ which is known as *sal soda* or *washing soda*. Besides the applications listed in Table 2 and Fig. 1, another use for soda ash is as a desulfurizing agent in ferrous metallurgy. In 1954 the selling price was $27 per ton.

Pure *caustic soda* is a brittle white solid which readily absorbs moisture and carbon dioxide from the air. It is sold on the basis of its sodium oxide content and usually contains about 76 per cent Na_2O or 98 per cent NaOH. Special uses, such as in rayon manufacture, require very pure caustic. It is shipped either as a solid or as 50 or 73 per cent solutions in tank cars. At present there is a tendency toward shipping more caustic as concentrated solutions. The price of solid caustic soda in 1954 was $77, and liquid $54 both per ton and on the basis of 76 per cent Na_2O.

[1] Reaction: $4HCl + O_2 \rightarrow 2H_2O + 2Cl_2$. U.S. Pat. 85370 (1868); *cf.* BADGER and BAKER, *op. cit.*, p. 186.

[2] MURRAY, The Chlor Alkali Industry in the United States, *Ind. Eng. Chem.*, **41**, 2155 (1948).

TABLE 2. ESTIMATED DISTRIBUTION OF SODA ASH IN THE UNITED STATES IN
1949, 1950, AND 1951[a]

(In thousands of short tons)

Consuming industries	1943–1947 average	1950	1951	1952
Glass...............................	1,330	1,225	1,640	1,610
Soap................................	143	105	120	110
Caustic and bicarbonate...............	1,083	700	940	701
Other chemicals......................	975	1,050	1,253	1,178
Cleansers and modified sodas.........	110	110	142	135
Pulp and paper......................	190	200	470	305
Water softeners.....................	99	100	128	95
Petroleum refining...................	22	24	29	31
Textiles.............................	67	65	56	37
Nonferrous metals...................	260	245	333	363
Exports.............................	76	50	152	75
Miscellaneous.......................	342[b]	151	287	100
Total.............................	4,621	4,025	5,550	4,740

[a] "Minerals Yearbook," 1952.
[b] Exports in Miscellaneous.

TABLE 3. UNITED STATES PRODUCTION OF CAUSTIC SODA[a]

(Short tons of 100 per cent NaOH)

Year	Lime soda	Electrolytic	Total
1921	163,044	75,547	238,591
1925	355,783	141,478	497,261
1929	524,985	236,807	761,792
1933	439,363	247,620	686,983
1937	488,807	479,919	968,726
1942	634,291	939,878	1,514,169
1946	742,932	1,129,956	1,872,888
1948	767,000	1,573,000	2,340,000
1949	566,230	1,656,788	2,223,018
1950	505,300	2,005,420	2,510,720
1951	668,310	2,437,997	3,106,307
1952	507,537	2,523,893	3,031,430
1953	504,052	2,758,432	3,262,484

[a] U.S. Bureau of the Census. Electrolytic caustic soda figures up to 1941 do not
include that made and consumed at wood-pulp mills, estimated at about 30,000 tons
in 1929, 21,000 tons in 1933, and 19,000 tons in 1937.

Chlorine is a chemical of wide industrial importance. About 20 per cent of the chlorine is used for the direct treatment of a given product, *i.e.*, pulp, paper, and textile bleaching; water treatment; and sewage purification. About 30 per cent is employed in processes whose end products contain no chlorine, *e.g.*, lead tetraethyl, ethylene glycol, phenol, and magnesium. Chlorine in the finished product, such as vinyl and vinylidene polymers, chlorinated rubber and other plastics, and solvents account for at least 40 per cent, while the remainder is used in insecticides, fungicides,

TABLE 4. ESTIMATED DISTRIBUTION OF CAUSTIC SODA IN THE UNITED STATES
IN 1948, 1949, AND 1950[a]
(In thousands of short tons)

Consuming industries	1948	1949	1950
Soap....................	154	145	145
Chemicals................	720	650	750
Petroleum refining..........	170	130	200
Rayon and film.............	500	450	475
Lye, cleansers.............	130	110	125
Textiles...................	100	90	100
Rubber reclaiming..........	26	15	22
Vegetable oils.............	21	22	24
Pulp and paper.............	176	170	185
Exports...................	193	185	130
Miscellaneous.............	167	147	94
Totals.................	2,357	2,200	2,250

[a] *Chem. Eng.*, **58** (2), 133 (1951).

bactericides, and herbicides. The electrolysis of sodium or potassium chloride solutions accounts for about 93 per cent of the United States chlorine production (78.6 per cent of the total stemming from diaphragm cells and 14.5 per cent from mercury cells in 1953). The electrolysis of fused sodium chloride accounts for about 6 per cent, and Solvay's nitrosyl process for 1 per cent. Total production in 1952 was 2,600,000 tons. About 70 per cent of the chlorine made is consumed directly by the producers.

MANUFACTURE OF SODA ASH

Soda ash is manufactured chiefly by the Solvay or ammonia-soda process. Natural soda ash is obtained from the brines of saline lakes in the West, particularly Searles Lake and Owens Lake in California. Wyoming is also producing from salines (Table 1).

Raw Materials. The raw materials for the Solvay process are salt, lime, and ammonia. The salt is used in the form of a brine which is made from rock salt, natural or artificial brine, or sea salt. Limestone is burned in kilns to furnish both the carbon dioxide for the soda ash and lime for the recovery of the ammonia. No strict specifications are required for the limestone except that a minimum of the usual impurities of SiO_2, Al_2O_3, and Fe_2O_3 is desirable.

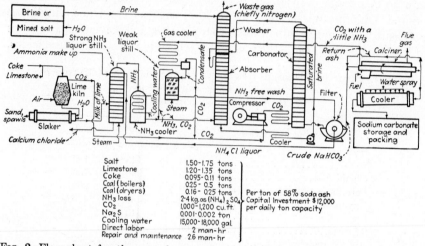

Salt	1.50–1.75 tons
Limestone	1.20–1.35 tons
Coke	0.095–0.11 tons
Coal (boilers)	0.25– 0.5 tons
Coal (dryers)	0.16– 0.25 tons
NH_3 loss	2–4 kg. as $(NH_4)_2SO_4$
CO_2	1,000–1,200 cu. ft.
Na_2S	0.001–0.002 ton
Cooling water	15,000–18,000 gal.
Direct labor	2 man-hr
Repair and maintenance	2.6 man-hr

Per ton of 58% soda ash
Capital investment $12,000
per daily ton capacity

FIG. 2. Flow sheet for the manufacture of soda ash by the ammonia-soda process.

Reactions and Energy Changes. The Solvay process is carried out by the following principal reactions:

$$CaCO_3(c) \rightarrow CaO(c) + CO_2(g); \qquad \Delta H = +43,400 \text{ cal.} \qquad (1)$$
$$C(amorph.) + O_2(g) \rightarrow CO_2(g); \qquad \Delta H = -96,500 \text{ cal.} \qquad (2)$$
$$CaO(s) + H_2O(l) \rightarrow Ca(OH)_2(c); \qquad \Delta H = -15,900 \text{ cal.} \qquad (3)$$
$$NH_3(g) + H_2O(l) \rightarrow NH_4OH(aq); \qquad \Delta H = -8,400 \text{ cal.} \qquad (4)$$
$$2NH_4OH(aq) + CO_2(g) \rightarrow (NH_4)_2CO_3(aq) + H_2O(l);$$
$$\Delta H = -22,100 \text{ cal.} \qquad (5)$$
$$(NH_4)_2CO_3 + CO_2 + H_2O \rightarrow 2NH_4HCO_3 \qquad (6)$$
$$NH_4HCO_3 + NaCl \rightarrow NH_4Cl + NaHCO_3 \qquad (7)$$
$$2NaHCO_3(c) \rightarrow Na_2CO_3(c) + CO_2(g) + H_2O(g);$$
$$\Delta H = +30,700 \text{ cal.} \qquad (8)$$
$$2NH_4Cl(aq) + Ca(OH)_2(c) \rightarrow 2NH_3(g) + CaCl_2(aq) + 2H_2O(l);$$
$$\Delta H = +10,700 \text{ cal.} \qquad (9)$$

Unit Operations and Unit Processes. The reactions are industrialized by the following sequence of *unit operations* (Op.) and *unit processes* (Pr.) as exemplified in the flow sheet[1] of Fig. 2.

Preparation and Purification of the Salt Brine:

Mining and solution of salt, or pumping of water to salt beds and of brine from these deposits (Op.).

Purification of brine (Pr. and Op.).

[1] See also the pictured flow sheet, *Chem. & Met. Eng.*, **49** (2), 134 (1942).

Ammoniation of Brine:

Solution of NH_3 in the purified brine (Op. and Pr.).
Solution of weak CO_2 in the purified brine (Op. and Pr.).

Carbonation of Ammoniated Brine:

Formation of ammonium carbonate (Pr.).
Formation of ammonium bicarbonate (Pr.).
Formation and controlled precipitation of sodium bicarbonate (Pr.).
Filtration and washing of the sodium bicarbonate (Op.).
Burning of limestone with coke to form CO_2 and CaO (Pr.).
Compressing and cooling of limekiln or lean CO_2 and piping to carbonator (Op.).

Calcination of Sodium Bicarbonate:

Conveying and charging of moist sodium bicarbonate to calciner (Op.).
Calcination of sodium bicarbonate (Pr. and Op.).
Cooling, screening, and bagging of soda ash (for sale) (Op.).
Cooling, purifying, compressing, and piping of rich CO_2 gas to carbonator (Op.).

Recovery of Ammonia:

Slaking of quicklime (Pr.).
Treatment of sodium bicarbonate mother liquors with steam and $Ca(OH)_2$ in strong NH_3 liquor still to recover NH_3 (Pr.).

Manufacturing Procedures. *Preparation of the Brine.* The salt used in the process is in the form of an almost saturated NaCl solution as a natural or artificial brine pumped from wells. Such brines come usually from underground salt deposits. Sea water contains much more impurity than does the rock salt brine and is seldom employed. The chief impurities in rock salt brine are calcium sulfate, magnesium, and iron salts. These may be removed by special pretreatments of the brine with lime and soda ash as well as by the ordinary precipitation with weak ammonia and weak carbon dioxide in the washer tower where residual gases are scrubbed or washed before discharge. Although Fig. 2 does not so indicate, the brine is clarified by settling in vats before it flows to the strong ammonia absorber, to remove the precipitated impurities of calcium carbonate, magnesium carbonate and hydroxide, and iron hydroxide. The clarified brine is also cooled.

Ammoniation of Brine. The clarified brine flows to the strong ammonia or first absorber where it takes up the necessary amount of ammonia. The ammoniation liberates much heat from the dissolving of the NH_3 gas as shown by reaction (4). This brine contains about 83 grams of NH_3 and 260 grams of NaCl per liter. Some carbon dioxide is also absorbed with the ammonia. The brine is settled, cooled to 25°C, and pumped to the carbonating towers.

Carbonation of Ammoniated Brine. Carbon dioxide is obtained along with calcium oxide by calcining limestone *mixed* with coke. Thus some additional carbon dioxide is yielded from the burning of the coke necessary to supply the heat required to decompose the limestone. At least a part of this carbon dioxide gas, 41 to 43 per cent strong, is compressed and conducted to the bottom of a fouled carbonating tower, operating in series with four working or precipitating towers, while the ammoniated brine is fed into the top. In this way, the towers, clogged and fouled by 4 days' service as "making" or precipitating towers, are cleaned by solution in fresh ammoniated brine of the crusts of sodium bicarbonate previously deposited on the baffles and cooling pipes. *Thus the heat transfer rate is increased by removal of the fouling on the interfaces; likewise the absorption of the carbon dioxide is improved by solution of the crusts that interfered with the contact of gas and liquid.* In practice, the fresh ammoniated brine flows down one such fouled tower with its cooling coils shut off, and this partly carbonated and warm brine is fed to four making towers by carbon dioxide lifts. In the first carbonating tower reaction (5) takes place forming ammonium carbonate in solution. Each carbonating tower is about 75 ft. high, 6 or 7 ft. inside diameter, and is constructed largely of cast-iron sections bolted together. Typical absorbing and cooling sections of such a tower are illustrated in Fig. 3. The absorption is not very efficient. Hence a comparatively great height is needed. In the second or making tower[1] ammonium bicarbonate is formed and, reacting with salt, forms sodium bicarbonate which is gradually precipitated out.[2] The rich carbon dioxide (90 to 95 per cent) from the calcination of the sodium

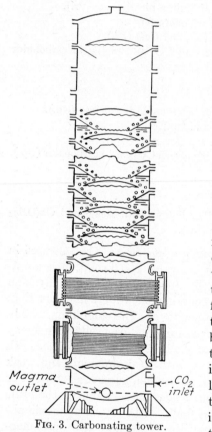

Magma outlet

CO_2 *inlet*

Fig. 3. Carbonating tower.

[1] Figure 2 for simplicity makes no separation of the lean from the rich CO_2 gas— as is the actual practice in a few plants—nor does this figure differentiate between the cleaning and "making" carbonations.

[2] SHERWOOD and PIGFORD, "Absorption and Extraction," 2d ed., McGraw-Hill Book Company, Inc., New York, 1952.

bicarbonate is compressed and used here. Each making tower produces the equivalent of about 50 tons of soda ash per 24 hr.

The procedure in these towers is the heart of the ammonia-soda process. It is a liquid-gas absorption but is complicated by the precipitation of the solid sodium bicarbonate. The absorption units should be constructed to permit the downward travel of the growing sodium bicarbonate crystals. This is done as shown in Fig. 3 by having each unit simulate a very large *single* bubble cap with down sloping floors.

Also, the absorption is conducted with the towers *filled* with liquid; hence the gas must be compressed. Because of this compression the partial pressure, hence the solubility, of the CO_2 is increased at the end of the carbonating cycle where it favors reactions (5) to (7).

The crude sodium bicarbonate formed in the making tower is drawn off from the bottom as a suspension. Careful control of all the conditions in the column is necessary to ensure that the precipitated sodium bicarbonate is easily filterable and efficiently washed. This is largely effected by regulating the temperature and concentration in the making tower so that the initially formed fine crystals of $NaHCO_3$ are allowed to grow. For example, at the top of the making tower the temperature is 25°C., which is allowed to rise by heat of reaction to 55°C. about halfway down. This temperature is gradually reduced by use of cooling sections (see Fig. 3) to 20°C. at bottom, resulting in the growing of the $NaHCO_3$ crystals particularly in size. The suspension is filtered on a rotary open-drum filter. The vacuum on the drum filter helps to dry the bicarbonate and also to recover the ammonia. The filter cake is washed on the drum to remove salt and ammonium chloride. About 10 per cent of the bicarbonate is dissolved during the washing. From here the sodium bicarbonate may be sent to a centrifugal filter which reduces the moisture content to about 7 per cent, or it may be calcined directly.

Calcination or "Drying" of the Sodium Bicarbonate. This operation is one of the most troublesome steps in the manufacture of soda ash. The washed, moist sodium bicarbonate from the filter is charged into the furnace by feed tables which have an efficient gas seal. The difficulties are due to the fact that moist sodium bicarbonate has a tendency to cake into lumps and form a nonconducting scale on the steel shell of the calciner. Engineers have developed for this operation a steel rotary furnace closed at both ends so as to be able to collect the gases evolved. The kiln is of the horizontal type heated through the shell and with the firing furnace at the feed end so that the heating is not countercurrent. This prevents some of the caking. The inside of the drier has a heavy scraper chain dragging on the shell to keep it free from soda lumps. To reduce the caking of the wet bicarbonate some of the hot soda ash taken from the calciner is fed back and mixed with the fresh bicarbonate as "dry feed" (see Fig. 2). The usual capacity for the rotary driers, about

8 ft. in diameter and 75 ft. long, is from 50 to 60 tons of soda ash per 24 hr.

The exit gases contain some ammonia, carbon dioxide, much steam, and a little soda ash dust. These are cooled, precipitating a small quantity of an aqueous ammoniacal solution but permitting the large amount of rich CO_2 to be freed. This is compressed and used in the making carbonator tower to form the sodium bicarbonate. The hot soda ash from the calciner is passed through a rotary cooler and is screened through a vibrating screen of 8 to 12 mesh. It is then packed in bags for sale. This is the light ash of commerce. The coarser or dense soda ash occupies only about half the bulk of the light ash, the dense ash weighing 64 to 67 lb. per cu. ft. when loosely packed. It costs slightly more but this dense ash is advantageous for the glass industry where less dusting results. The dense ash is manufactured by adding sufficient water to the light soda ash to form $Na_2CO_3 \cdot H_2O$, an agglomerated product, whose recalcination furnishes the dense ash.

Recovery of the Ammonia. Much of the economical operation of the Solvay process depends upon the efficiency of the ammonia recovery. For any given time the value of the ammonia in the system is several times the value of the soda ash produced. The ammonia is recovered in a distillation column called the *strong ammonia liquor still* and consisting of two parts. The top part above the lime inlet is called the *heater;* the bottom part below the lime inlet is called the *lime still.* The liquor from the bicarbonate filter is fed into the heater or upper part of the ammonia still, where the free ammonia is driven out by the following reactions:

$$NH_3(\text{soln.}) + \text{heat} \rightarrow NH_3(g)$$
$$NH_4HCO_3 + \text{heat} \rightarrow NH_3 + H_2O + CO_2$$
$$NaHCO_3 + NH_4Cl \rightarrow NaCl + NH_3 + H_2O + CO_2$$
$$Na_2CO_3 + 2NH_4Cl \rightarrow 2NaCl + 2NH_3 + H_2O + CO_2$$
$$Na_2S + 2NH_4Cl \rightarrow 2NaCl + 2NH_3 + H_2S$$

Milk of lime suspension is fed through the lime inlet and mixes with the liquor from the upper or heater part. As this flows down the column, the following reactions take place in the lime part of the still:

$$Na_2CO_3 + Ca(OH)_2 \rightarrow 2NaOH + CaCO_3$$
$$2NH_4Cl + Ca(OH)_2 \rightarrow CaCl_2 + 2NH_3 + 2H_2O$$
$$(NH_4)_2SO_4 + Ca(OH)_2 \rightarrow CaSO_4 + 2NH_3 + 2H_2O$$

The liquor from the bottom of the lime still is free from ammonia and contains about 50 grams per liter of residual and unreacted sodium chloride as well as the calcium chloride formed. Calcium carbonate is in suspension. A small part of this residual liquor is settled, evaporated for separation of salt, and marketed for its calcium chloride content either as a concentrated liquor or as a solid upon further evaporation. However, most of this calcium chloride is wasted into the streams of the country.

Soda ash is manufactured from natural alkaline *brines* at Searles Lake and Owens Lake in California.[1] The natural brine is carbonated with carbon dioxide from limekilns and from sodium bicarbonate calciners. The precipitated $NaHCO_3$ is filtered off, washed, and calcined.

MANUFACTURE OF SODIUM BICARBONATE

Sodium bicarbonate, or baking soda, is not made by refining the crude sodium bicarbonate obtained from the filters in the Solvay process. There are several reasons for this: (1) There is great difficulty in completely drying this bicarbonate. (2) The value of the ammonia in this crude bicarbonate would be lost. (3) Even a small amount of ammonia gives the bicarbonate an odor that renders it unfit for many uses. (4) The bicarbonate made in this way contains a great many other impurities.

To make sodium bicarbonate, there is first prepared a saturated solution of soda ash which is run into the top of a column similar to the carbonating tower in soda ash manufacture. Carbon dioxide is sent in from compressors at the bottom of the tower, which is maintained at about 40°C. The suspension of bicarbonate formed is removed from the bottom of the tower, filtered, and washed on a rotary drum filter. After centrifugation, the material is dried on a continuous-belt conveyer at 70°C. Bicarbonate from this process is about 99.9 per cent pure.

Sodium bicarbonate finds large usage for the manufacture of baking powder, carbonated waters, leather goods, and in fire extinguishers. Annually around 160,000 tons are manufactured in the United States.

MISCELLANEOUS ALKALIES

There are consumed commercially a number of various alkalies of different strengths according to the contained amounts of $NaOH$, Na_2CO_3, or $NaHCO_3$. Some of these are mechanical mixtures as *causticized ash* (soda ash with 10 to 50 per cent of caustic) for bottle washing or metal cleaning, and *modified sodas* (soda ash with 25 to 75 per cent of sodium bicarbonate) for mild alkali demands as in the tanning industry. *Sodium sesquicarbonate*, or the natural mineral trona, has the composition $Na_2CO_3 \cdot NaHCO_3 \cdot 2H_2O$ and is very stable. It finds use in wool scouring and in laundering. *Sal soda*, $Na_2CO_3 \cdot 10H_2O$, is also known as *washing*

[1] HIGHTOWER, New Carbonation Technique—More Natural Soda Ash, *Chem. Eng.*, **58** (5), 162 (1951); see Chap. 13.

soda or *soda crystals*. It has always been a pure product, but its consumption is declining because of the cost of transporting its water of crystallization in competition with the now quite pure soda ash manufactured by the ammonia-soda process.

MANUFACTURE OF CAUSTIC SODA BY THE LIME-SODA PROCESS

Caustic soda is one of the main products from soda ash and is frequently made in the soda ash plant. The production of additional carbon dioxide frequently needed for the Solvay process furnishes calcium oxide used in the causticization of the soda ash. The heat of this reaction is small.

$$Na_2CO_3 + Ca(OH)_2 \rightleftarrows 2NaOH + CaCO_3$$

This reaction depends on the low solubility product of Ca^{++} and CO_3^{--} ions, forming calcium carbonate. The equilibrium varies with the concentration of the Na_2CO_3 solution, a 10 per cent soda solution giving a 97 per cent conversion while a 16 per cent Na_2CO_3 solution furnishes only a 91 per cent conversion.[1] The equation for this is as follows:

$$K = \frac{K_1}{K_2} = \frac{(Ca^{++})(OH^-)^2}{(Ca^{++})(CO_3^{--})} = \frac{(OH^-)^2}{(CO_3^{--})}$$

As the heat change of this reaction is so low, the K and hence the equilibrium are but little affected by temperature. However both the *speed* of the reaction and the rate of settling of the $CaCO_3$ increase with the temperature. Hence, in practice, the reaction is carried out near the boiling point of the solution. The higher percentage of conversion at the more dilute solution also follows from this equation since the concentration of the hydroxyl ions varies as the square in relation to the first power of the concentration of the carbonate ions. The chemical engineer in charge of causticizing soda ash must balance the additional fuel and plant charges for concentrating the more dilute caustic against the advantages of the greater conversion of the more dilute carbonate solution. At soda ash plants, usually the crude bicarbonate directly from the rotary filters is dissolved in water and changed to the carbonate by boiling with steam. The carbon dioxide evolved is returned to the soda ash process.

The Dorr continuous, countercurrent decantation procedure is illustrated in Fig. 4, where a solution of sodium carbonate is made in an agitated tank using weak liquor from a former reaction. Reburned lime

---

[1] Hou, *op. cit.*, Chap. 19. The mathematical treatment of this equilibrium is here presented.

and make-up lime, or all fresh lime, is fed along with some of the soda ash solution to a combination classifier-slaker. Milk of lime is formed while grit is removed from the slurry by the classifier.

The soda solution is causticized with a slight excess of lime in three agitators in series. The solution is settled in thickeners,[1] usually of multi-tray design as shown in Fig. 4. The overflow solution taken from the first thickener is sent to the evaporators or is used directly as in the soda process for paper pulp manufacture. This solution contains about 11 per cent NaOH. The sludge in the bottom of the first thickener is pumped with a

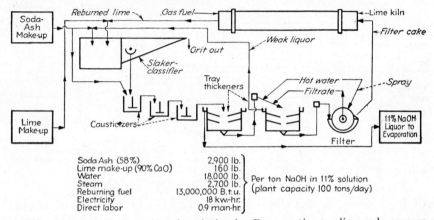

Soda Ash (58%)	2,900 lb.	
Lime make-up (90% CaO)	160 lb.	
Water	18,000 lb.	Per ton NaOH in 11% solution
Steam	2,700 lb.	(plant capacity 100 tons/day)
Reburning fuel	13,000,000 B.t.u.	
Electricity	18 kw-hr.	
Direct labor	0.9 man-hr.	

FIG. 4. Flow sheet for caustic soda solution by Dorr continuous lime-soda process.

diaphragm pump to the second thickener. Here filtrate from the next operation and water are added. The overflow from this thickener is used as a weak liquor to make up the original soda solution. The sludge from the second thickener is filtered on an Oliver filter and washed. The filtrate is returned to the second thickener as mentioned and the cake is calcined in the limekiln.[2]

The evaporation of caustic from soda ash causticization resembles that from electrolysis of brine (see Fig. 5, and text) except that here only one-twentieth to one-tenth of the sodium salts is present to crystallize out upon concentration of the NaOH solution. In this case the sodium salts recovered consist mostly of unreacted Na_2CO_3 with whatever NaCl was in the original soda ash.

[1] For details of Dorr thickener and Dorr multitray thickener, see PERRY, *op. cit.*, pp. 941, 942.

[2] Frequently another Dorr thickener is required to remove more of the caustic from the precipitated $CaCO_3$. Calculations of countercurrent decantation (c.c.d.) as applied to this reaction are exemplified on pp. 154*ff.* of BADGER and BAKER, *op. cit.* See also OLSEN and DIRENGA, Settling Rate of Calcium Carbonate in Causticizing of Soda Ash, *Ind. Eng. Chem.*, **33**, 204 (1941). The methods, equipment, and examples given in Perry, *op. cit.*, pp. 941–943, 950–954, 976, 988 are particularly pertinent.

MANUFACTURE OF ELECTROLYTIC CAUSTIC SODA AND CHLORINE[1]

Raw Materials. The primary raw material for the manufacture of chlorine and electrolytic caustic is common salt which is available in large quantities and high purity in many parts of the United States. Some plants, like those in the Kanawha Valley of West Virginia or in the salt belt of Michigan, obtain their salt from the natural brines of underground deposits, while other plants, such as around St. Louis, ship in

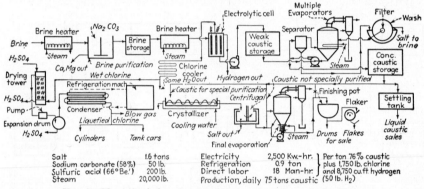

Salt	1.6 tons	Electricity	2,500 Kw.-hr.	Per ton 76% caustic
Sodium carbonate (58%)	50 lb.	Refrigeration	0.9 ton	plus 1,750 lb. chlorine
Sulfuric acid (66°Bé.')	200 lb.	Direct labor	18 Man-hr.	and 8,750 cu.ft hydrogen
Steam	20,000 lb.	Production, daily	75 tons caustic	(50 lb. H₂)

FIG. 5. Flow sheet for electrolytic caustic soda and chlorine.

salt from mines located elsewhere and make the brine at the plant. In California, salt is obtained from the evaporation of sea water. Other raw materials are listed on the lower part of the flow sheet in Fig. 5.

Reactions and Energy Changes. *Decomposition Voltage and Voltage Efficiency.* The energy consumed in the electrolysis of the brine is the product of the current flowing and the potential of the cell. The *theoretical* or minimum *voltage* required for the process may be derived from the Gibbs-Helmholtz equation which expresses the relation between the electrical energy and the heat of reaction of a system:

$$E = \frac{-J\Delta H}{nF} + \frac{TdE}{dT}$$

where E = theoretical decomposition voltage.

ΔH = enthalpy change of reaction, cal.

J = electrical equivalent of heat, or joules per calorie (4.182).

T = absolute temperature.

F = Faraday constant, coulombs per gram-equivalent (96,500).

n = number of equivalents involved.

The heat of reaction for the electrolysis of salt may be found from heats of formation of the components of the over-all reaction or from the

[1] KOBE, "Inorganic Process Industries," Chap. 5, The Macmillan Company, New York, 1948.

negative of these values—the change in the heat contents of the systems. The over-all reaction is

$$NaCl(aq) + H_2O(l) \rightarrow NaOH(aq) + \tfrac{1}{2}H_2(g) + \tfrac{1}{2}Cl_2(g)$$

This may be broken down to the following reactions of formation:

$$Na(s) + \tfrac{1}{2}Cl_2(g) \rightarrow NaCl(aq); \qquad \Delta H = -97,105 \text{ cal.}$$
$$H_2(g) + \tfrac{1}{2}O_2(g) \rightarrow H_2O(l); \qquad \Delta H = -68,372 \text{ cal.}$$
$$Na(s) + \tfrac{1}{2}O_2(g) + \tfrac{1}{2}H_2(g) \rightarrow NaOH(aq); \qquad \Delta H = -112,053 \text{ cal.}$$

The net ΔH for the over-all reaction results from

$$+97,105 + 68,372 - 112,053 = +53,424 \text{ cal.}$$

If this value of ΔH is substituted in the Gibbs-Helmholtz equation and the change in voltage with temperature is neglected, the value of E calculates to 2.31 volts. The omission of $T \cdot dE/dT$ involves an error of less than 10 per cent for most cells.[1]

The ratio of this theoretical voltage to that actually used is the *voltage efficiency* of the cell. Voltage efficiencies range from 45 to 65 per cent. According to Faraday's law 96,500 coulombs of electricity passing through a cell will produce 1 gram-equivalent of chemical reaction at each electrode. Because of unavoidable side reactions, cells usually require more than this amount. The ratio of the theoretical to the actual current consumed is defined as the *current efficiency*. Current efficiencies run 95 to 97 per cent and, unless otherwise specified, are understood to be *cathode* current efficiencies. The current divided by the area in square inches, upon which the current in amperes acts, is known as the *current density*. A high value is desirable in cases where the product formed is subject to decomposition. The product of voltage efficiency and current efficiency gives the *energy efficiency* of the cell. Another consideration is the *decomposition efficiency*, which is the ratio of equivalents produced in the cell to equivalents charged.[2] In the usual commercial cells this decomposition efficiency is about 50 per cent. If the cell is operated to attain a higher decomposition efficiency, the natural flow of brine through the cell is decreased with migration of OH^- ions back to anode with formation of hypochlorite which means loss of caustic and chlorine. Also when OH^- ions reach the anode the following reaction occurs:

$$2OH^- \rightarrow H_2O + \tfrac{1}{2}O_2 + 2e$$

The oxygen formed reacts with the graphite of the anodes causing decreased anode life.

[1] BADGER and BAKER, *op. cit.*, p. 165; *cf.* PERRY, *op. cit.*, pp. 298, 344, 1784 and tables pp. 236–243.

[2] A tabulation of such data for typical commercial cells is given by Perry, *op. cit.*, p. 1810.

Unit Operations and Unit Processes. The main procedures for a typical electrolytic flow sheet,[1] as depicted in Fig. 5, may be represented in the following *unit operations* (Op.) and *unit processes* (Pr.):

Brine Purification:

To make a purer caustic soda and to lessen clogging of the cell diaphragm with consequent voltage increase, purification of the NaCl solution from Ca, Fe, and Mg compounds is practiced, using soda ash with some caustic soda. Sometimes sulfates are removed with $BaCl_2$ or the hot brine is treated with hydroxyl and carbonate ions.[2] The clear brine is neutralized with hydrochloric acid (Pr.). This brine is stored, heated, and fed to the cells through a float feed system, designed to maintain constant level in the anode compartments (Op.).

Brine Electrolysis:

Typical cells employed are depicted and described in the following section. Each cell usually requires 3.0 to 4.5 volts; consequently, 30 or more are put in series to increase the voltage of a given group (Pr.).

Evaporation[3] and Salt Separation:

The decomposition efficiency of the cells being in the range of only 50 per cent, about half of the NaCl charged is in the weak caustic and is recovered by reason of its low solubility in caustic soda solutions after concentration. Hence the weak or about 10 or 15 per cent NaOH solution is evaporated to around 50 per cent NaOH in a double- or triple-effect evaporator with salt separators, followed by a washing filter. The salt so recovered is made again into charging brine. In the evaporators, nickel tubes are usually used to lessen iron contamination. Sometimes even the evaporators are nickel lined to avoid this contamination and also caustic embrittlement of the steel. With the caustic soda liquor from the evaporator containing 50 per cent NaOH, it will dissolve only about 1 per cent of NaCl and other sodium salts after cooling. This liquor may be sold, after thorough settling, as liquid caustic soda in tank cars or drums.

---

[1] Further details as to the varied procedures used may be found on pp. 159*ff.* of BADGER and BAKER, *op. cit.* In this book there is a particularly fine and detailed presentation of the evaporation of caustic soda and of the equipment required. See also the pictured flow sheets, *Chem. & Met. Eng.,* **49** (12), 114 (1942); *Chem. Eng.,* **57** (6), 178 (1950).

[2] SHEARON, *et al.,* Modern Production of Chlorine and Caustic Soda, *Ind. Eng. Chem.,* **40,** 2002 (1948); HIGHTOWER, Chlorine-caustic Soda, *Chem. Eng.,* **55** (12), 112 (1948), plus pictured flow sheet; ANON., Integrated Alkali Industry, *Chem. Eng.,* **53** (2), 172 (1946), with pictured flow sheet.

[3] See PERRY, *op. cit.,* pp. 1041–1078, for general principles of heat transfer, salt separation, single- and multiple-effect evaporation, and necessary equipment involved in the concentration of caustic soda solutions. See p. 1600 for calculations of c.c.d. washing of the salt separated, and pp. 2102–2103 for materials of construction. A detailed study of the evaporation of cell liquor is presented on pp. 172–185 of BADGER and BAKER, *op. cit.* SHERWIN, the Concentration of Caustic Soda Solution, *Trans. Inst. Chem. Engrs.,* **24,** 109 (1946).

Final Evaporation:

Either the cooled and settled 50 per cent caustic or a specially purified caustic may be concentrated in a single-effect final or high evaporator to 70 or 75 per cent NaOH, using steam of 75 to 100 lb. gage. This very strong caustic must be handled in steam-jacketed pipes to prevent solidification. It is run to the finishing pots. Another method of dehydrating 50 per cent caustic utilizes the precipitation of sodium hydroxide monohydrate. This monohydrate contains less water than the original solution. The precipitation is accomplished by the addition of ammonia to the 50 per cent solution.[1] This also purifies the caustic. If the 50 per cent caustic is treated with anhydrous ammonia[2] particularly in countercurrent manner, there separate from the resulting aqua ammonia, free-flowing anhydrous crystals. Naturally this procedure should be carried out in pressure vessels (Pr.).

Finishing of Caustic in Pots:

Although 50 per cent caustic was at one time finished in special close-grained cast-iron direct-fired pots, the heat efficiency is so low that good practice now handles only 70 or 75 per cent NaOH in this fashion. The final temperature is 500 to 600°C. and boils off all the water but about 1 per cent or less. These pots are now being replaced by Dowtherm heated evaporators for caustic evaporation above 50 per cent. The hot anhydrous caustic is treated with sulfur to precipitate iron and settled. The product is pumped out by lowering, into the molten caustic, a centrifugal pump that discharges the caustic into thin steel drums holding about 700 lb. or to the flaking machine (Op.).

Special Purification of Caustic:

Some of the troublesome impurities in 50 per cent caustic are colloidal iron, sodium chloride, and sodium chlorate. The iron is often removed by treating the caustic with 1 per cent by weight of 300-mesh calcium carbonate and filtering the resulting mixture through a Vallez filter on a calcium carbonate precoat. The chloride and chlorate may be removed by allowing the 50 per cent caustic to drop through a column of 50 per cent aqueous ammonia solution. This treatment produces caustic almost as free of chlorides and chlorates as that made by the mercury process. To reduce the salt content of the caustic necessary for certain uses, it is cooled to 20°C. in equipment such as outlined in Fig. 5. However, another crystallization method used industrially involves the actual separation of the compounds $NaOH \cdot 3\frac{1}{2}H_2O$ or $NaOH \cdot 2H_2O$ leaving the NaCl in the mother liquor. A different procedure reduces the salt content of the caustic soda solution by formation of the slightly soluble complex salt $NaCl \cdot Na_2SO_4 \cdot NaOH$.[3]

A new development in the continuous extraction of NaCl and $NaClO_3$ in

[1] MacMullin, Concentration of Sodium Hydroxide, U.S. Pat. 1961590 (1934); Muskat, Concentration of Caustic, U.S. Pat. 2285300 (1942); Muskat and Ayres, Purification of Caustic, U.S. Pat. 2285299 (1942).

[2] Muskat, Method for Producing Anhydrous Caustic, U.S. Pat. 2196593 (1940).

[3] Hubel and Sweetland, Removal of Salt from Caustic Soda Produced by Diaphragm Cells, *Can. Chem. Met.*, **17**, 52 (1933).

50 per cent caustic solution is countercurrent extraction in vertical columns with 70 to 95 per cent ammonia.[1] It should be noted that mercury cells furnish a caustic soda free from salt. These purification or manufacturing methods give a *high-grade* caustic with less than 1 per cent impurities (anhydrous basis). The *standard grade* contains $2\frac{1}{2}$ to 3 per cent impurities (anhydrous basis) (Pr.).

Chlorine Drying:

The hot chlorine evolved from the anode carries much water vapor. It is first cooled to condense most of this vapor and then dried in a sulfuric acid scrubber

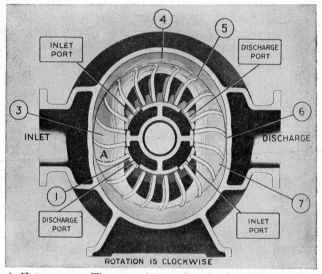

FIG. 6. Nash Hytor pump. The rotor (5) revolves freely within the elliptical casing (6) containing a liquid which is usually water or sulfuric acid. The latter is used when the pump is on chlorine service. The liquid turning with the rotor is forced up against the casing (6) by centrifugal action and alternately recedes from (4) and is forced back into the rotor at (3) twice in a revolution. As the liquid recedes from the rotor, it draws the gas to be compressed through the inlet ports into the rotor by means of openings in the bottom of the rotor chambers. When the liquid is forced back into the rotor by the converging casing, the compressed gas is discharged through appropriate discharge ports at the bottom of the rotor chambers and out the pump discharge.

or tower as shown in Fig. 5. Up to the sulfuric acid tower, the wet chlorine should be handled in stoneware, Duriron, or similar resistant material; after drying, iron or steel can be employed (Op. and Pr.).

Chlorine Compression and Liquefaction:[2]

The dried chlorine is compressed to 35 lb. gage or sometimes as high as 80 lb. The usual type of compressor employed is the Nash Hytor (Fig. 6) constructed

[1] TWICHAUS and EHLERS, Caustic Purification by Liquid-liquid Extraction, *Chem. Inds.*, **63**, 230 (1948).

[2] PERRY, *op. cit.*, p. 990; EICHENHOFER and FEDOROFF, Chlorine Liquefaction Modernized, *Chem. Eng.*, **58** (12), 142 (1951).

of iron and with concentrated sulfuric acid as the sealing liquid. The heat[1] of compression is removed progressively by water and finally by refrigeration to about $-20°F.$; when all the chlorine must be liquefied, it is cooled to as low as $-50°F.$ The liquid chlorine is stored and filled into either small cylinders, ton cylinders, pipe line, or the 55-ton tank cars that are shipped to large consumers.[2] There is always some residual or "blow gas," this being the equilibrium mixture of chlorine and air. The blow gas is used to make chlorine derivatives, either organic or inorganic, especially bleaching powder (Op.).

Hydrogen Disposal:

The hydrogen is very frequently made into other compounds such as hydrochloric acid or ammonia (see page 399) or is employed for hydrogenations of organic compounds (Pr.).

Electrolytic Cells.[3] The cells used are of two general types: diaphragm and mercury cathode as means for keeping apart the anode and cathode products. This separation is essential to prevent interaction of the primary products forming hypochlorites, which would greatly cut down the current efficiency of the cell, contaminate the caustic soda, and oxidize the anode graphite electrodes.

Diaphragm Cells. These cells contain a porous asbestos diaphragm to separate the anode from the cathode. This allows ions to pass through by electrical migration but reduces diffusion of products. Diaphragms permit the construction of compact cells of lowered resistance because the electrodes can be placed close together. The diaphragms become clogged with use, as indicated by higher voltage and higher hydrostatic pressure on brine feed. They must be replaced from every 100 to 200 days. The diaphragm permits a *flow of brine* from the anode to cathode, and thus greatly lessens or prevents by-reactions (sodium hypochlorite). In some of the cells the cathode compartment is "dry" and in others there is cathode liquor and kerosene, but in any case at a *lower head* than in the anode compartment, in order to ensure liquor movement from anode to cathode.

As shown in Table 5, the installed capacity of the *Hooker diaphragm cells* represents about 45 per cent of the United States total. The Hooker Type S cell was originally designed in 1929 and is still preferred for small plants. It is roughly cubical, being so built to conserve floor space and outside surface. The anodes are graphite plates which project upward from a lead slab and between finger-type cathodes made from crimped

---

[1] SHEARON, *et al., op. cit.*, p. 2007, for diagrams.

[2] In 1951 there were 10 chlorine barges in operation, 2 with a capacity of 380 tons each and 8 with a capacity of 600 tons each.

[3] *Cf.* PERRY, *op. cit.*, pp. 1806–1810, for cuts of various caustic cells and for a tabular comparison of operating results; MANTELL, "Industrial Electrochemistry," 3d ed., McGraw-Hill Book Company, Inc., New York, 1950.

steel wire. This cathode is directly covered with asbestos and forms the diaphragm which is completely submerged. The diaphragm is remarkably easy to apply. The steel screen cathode is dipped into a bath of asbestos slurry and the asbestos is drawn onto the screen by applying a vacuum to the hydrogen outlet. The outside is constructed of concrete on a steel frame, heavily insulated to conserve heat since the cell operates at a higher temperature than most cells.[1]

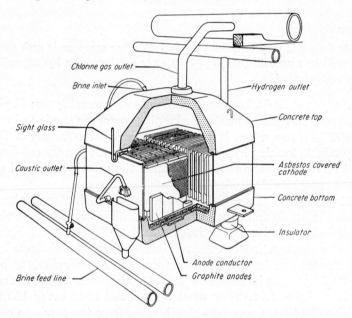

Chlorine gas outlet

Brine inlet

Hydrogen outlet

Concrete top

Sight glass

Caustic outlet

Asbestos covered cathode

Concrete bottom

Insulator

Anode conductor

Graphite anodes

Brine feed line

HOOKER TYPE "S-3A" CELL

FIG. 7. (*Courtesy of Hooker Electrochemical Co.*)

The Hooker Type S-3 was designed to provide a two- to threefold capacity advantage over the older Type S. Actually the fundamental design of the S-3 varies little from the S. The S-3 is larger and the various leads and connections are relocated. The S-3A cell depicted in Figs. 7 and 8 is essentially the S-3 rotated 90 deg. It has heavier copper connections than the S-3 to provide for operation at overloads up to 30,000 amp. The S-3 and S-3A are cheaper to install and operate and take up less building space per ton of capacity than Type S. Table 6 gives comparative performance figures on these Hooker cells.[2]

There are two modifications of the cylindrical diaphragm *Vorce cell*, the single-cathode cell (Fig. 9) and the newly developed double-cathode

---

[1] For an elevation and typical installation of this cell, see 1st ed. of this book, pp. 292–293; PERRY, *op. cit.*, pp. 1807, 1810.

[2] *Cf.* HUBBARD, Optimum Operating Currents for Hooker Type S Cells, *Chem. Eng. Progr.*, **46**, 435 (1950).

cell. The latter is 26 in. in diameter and 42 in. in height. Twenty-four graphite anodes (2 sq. in. in cross section and 36 in. long) extend down from the dome of the cell into the brine and are fastened to copper anode rings outside the cell. The cathodes taper to secure uniform current density over the anode surface. The asbestos paper diaphragm rests on a thin screen separator which lies against the cathode. The double-cathode cell operates under a current of 2,000 to 2,500 amp. and 3.0 volts per

FIG. 8. Typical Hooker S-3A cell installation. (*Courtesy of Hooker Electrochemical Co.*)

cell with about 80 cells in series. The single-cathode cell is usually operated with about 70 cells in series under a current of 1,000 amp. and 3.5 volts per cell.

There are several other cells in operation at various plants, mostly of the rectangular type. The *Dow filter-press* cell is important. The *Nelson* cell has an asbestos diaphragm and a U-shaped steel cathode throughout its length. The *Allen-Moore*, the *Buck-McRae*, and the *Hargreaves-Bird* cells are described in outline in Perry, *op. cit.*

Mercury Cells. As in the diaphragm cells, the graphite anodes evolve the chlorine from the brine solution. The cathode is a moving pool of mercury and the sodium from the brine solution is deposited in it to form an amalgam. This amalgam is transferred either intermittently or continuously to a separate decomposing chamber where, under contact with water, graphite grids, and the accelerating action of an electric couple, the dissolved sodium reacts with water to form sodium hydroxide. Simultaneously, hydrogen is evolved at the grids. Contamination from the brine feed of the sodium hydroxide is almost entirely eliminated because the

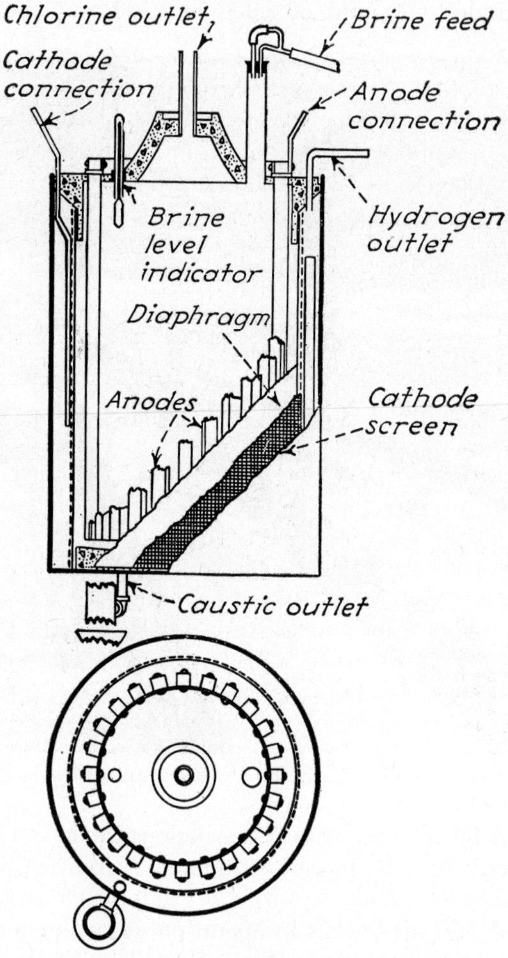

FIG. 9. Vorce cell, elevation and cross section.

caustic is formed in an operation completely removed. This makes it possible for rayon manufacturers to employ this caustic directly while that obtained from diaphragm cells must be further purified. Another advantage is that the caustic is up to five times as concentrated as the 10 to 15 per cent produced from the diaphragm cells, thus cheapening the evaporation operation.

The *Castner cell*, as operated by Mathieson Chemical Corporation, was one of the first successful mercury cells. It consists of a concrete box 4 ft. long, 4 ft. wide, and 6 in. deep, which is divided into three compartments by partitions that extend to within $\frac{1}{16}$ in. of the bottom. A layer of mercury as an intermediary cathode is on the bottom and separates yet connects the three compartments. In the outer compartments several T-shaped graphite anodes extend within an inch of the mercury. The inner compartment contains an iron grid which is the cathode. To start the cell, the two outer sections are filled with brine and the center division with water. The cell is pivoted at one end and rests on an eccentric at the other end, which rocks the mercury back and forth between the compartments about once every minute. When the amalgam flows into the water compartment, the sodium reacts to give caustic soda and hydrogen. Salt is added continuously to the brine, and the caustic is drawn off when it reaches a desired concentration. Ten per cent of the current is shunted around the cathode compartment to prevent oxidation of the mercury to HgO. The current at the anode is 630 amp. with a voltage of 4.3. A newer cell operated by this same company is the *Mathieson cell*. This is an American version of the horizontal mercury cell, largely developed in Germany during the Second World War, but requires less floor space and has a lower energy consumption.[1]

The *De Nora* mercury cell is a long, narrow steel trough lined with syenite, a chemically resistant stone. Suspended in the trough are blocks of dense graphite which serve as anodes. The cathode is a thin film of mercury flowing along the bottom of the trough. Brine flows on top of the mercury and is decomposed by the electric current passing between the mercury and graphite electrodes releasing 97 to 98 per cent chlorine gas. Operating data for this cell are: current, 30,000 amp.; voltage across cell, 4.3 volts; current efficiency, 94 to 96 per cent; and temperature, 60 to 75°C. The first major installation in the United States of this cell was at Muscle Shoals, Ala., in 1952.[2] The *Dow, Solvay, I.C.I.*, and *Wyandotte* mercury cells are also operating successfully.

Many *chemical* or nonelectrolytic processes for chlorine manufacture have been proposed,[3] although only one, the Solvay nitrosyl chloride process at Hopewell, Va., is in commercial operation. Common salt is treated with nitric acid to form sodium nitrate and chlorine with nitrosyl chloride (containing 4 to 10 per cent nitrogen tetroxide) as a by-product. The nitrosyl chloride vapor is contacted with oxygen to produce nitrogen tetroxide and chlorine: $2NOCl + O_2 \rightarrow N_2O_4 + Cl_2$. After liquefying and

---

[1] GARDINER, New Mercury Cell Makes Its Bow, *Chem. Eng.*, **54** (11), 108 (1947).

[2] ANON., Acres of De Nora Chlorine Cells, *Chem. Eng.*, **59** (8), 146 (1952).

[3] JOHNSONTE, Chlorine Production Nonelectrolytic Processes, *Chem. Eng. Progr.*, **44**, 657 (1948); *cf.* ANON., Indirect Electrolytic Process Makes Chlorine Cheaply from By-product HCl, *Chem. Inds.*, **66**, 501 (1950).

TABLE 5. How the United States Makes Chlorine[a]

	Tons per day	Per cent of total
Diaphragm cells, total..........................	8,400	78.6
Hooker Type S and Hooker-Columbia.......	3,500	32.8
Hooker Type S-3 and S-3A...............	1,300	12.2
Dow filter-press cell......................	2,700	25.3
Other diaphragm cells, including Diamond, Gibbs, Vorce, etc........................	900	8.3
Mercury cathode cells, including Castner, Mathieson, de Nora, Dow, Solvay, I.C.I., Wyandotte.............................	1,550	14.5
Fused-salt cells..............................	600	5.7
Chemical processes.........................	135	1.2
Total..................................	10.685	100.0

[a] ANON., Trend to Bigger Cells, *Chem. Eng.*, **59** (11), 234 (1952).

TABLE 6. How Hooker Cells Perform[a]

	Type S	Types S-3 and S-3A		
Current, amp...........................	10,000	15,000	20,000	24,000
Volts.................................	3.75	3.4	3.65	3.85
Temperature of effluent, °C................	94	91	95	97
NaOH in effluent, per cent................	11.30	11.1	11.65	11.8
NaClO$_2$ per 1,000 parts NaOH............	1.0	1.0	1.0	1.0
Current efficiency, per cent................	96.0	95.5	96.0	96.0
Power consumption, kw-hr. per ton Cl$_2$......	2,690	2,440	2,610	2,760
Average anode life, days...................	360	425	360	300
Lb. graphite per ton Cl$_2$...................	6.7	7.8	6.9	6.9
Average diaphragm life, days..............	120	140	120	100
Cl$_2$ per cell per day, tons.................	0.333	0.500	0.667	0.800
NaOH per cell per day, tons..............	0.367	0.564	0.750	0.900
Cl$_2$ per sq. ft. of floor space..............	9.0	11.8	15.7	18.9

[a] ANON., Trend to Bigger Cells, *Chem. Eng.*, **59** (11), 236 (1952).

distilling the chlorine out, the nitrogen tetroxide is absorbed in water to make nitric and nitrous acids which are recycled: $N_2O_4 + H_2O \rightarrow HNO_3 + HNO_2$. The advantage of this process is that it produces chlorine but no caustic soda. The limited demand for sodium nitrate regulates the amount of chlorine that can be made in this way. The over-all reactions may be simplified as follows:

$$3NaCl + 4HNO_3 \rightarrow 3NaNO_3 + Cl_2 + NOCl + 2H_2O$$
$$2NOCl + 3HNO_2 + 3O_2 + H_2O \rightarrow 5HNO_3 + Cl_2$$

BLEACHING POWDER

A decreasing tonnage of chlorine goes into the production of bleaching powder largely because of its instability and the large proportion of inert material. The reaction by which bleaching powder is made is

$$Ca(OH)_2 + Cl_2 \rightarrow Ca \underset{Cl}{\overset{O-Cl}{<}} \cdot H_2O$$

This reaction is carried out below 50°C. in a countercurrent fashion by passing chlorine through a rotating steel cylinder with inner lifting blades which shower the solid in the path of the gas. When allowed to stand in the air, the bleaching powder absorbs carbon dioxide. (Other inorganic acids will also liberate the HOCl.)

$$2CaCl(OCl) + CO_2 + H_2O \rightarrow CaCl_2 + CaCO_3 + 2HClO$$
$$2HClO \rightarrow 2HCl + O_2$$

However, simply on standing, the following decomposition takes place:

$$2CaOCl_2 \rightarrow 2CaCl_2 + O_2$$

When dissolved in water, the reaction gives ionized calcium chloride and hypochlorite.

$$2CaCl(OCl) \rightarrow Ca^{++} + 2Cl^- + Ca^{++} + 2OCl^-$$

The OCl$^-$ ion decomposes, liberating oxygen. We say that, in general, bleaching powder is an oxidizing agent. However, its activity is measured in what is termed *available chlorine*, which is, by definition, the same weight as that of gaseous or liquid chlorine that would exert the same action as the chlorine compound in question. In case of bleaching powder, CaOCl$_2$, the available chlorine is the same as the percentage of chlorine, but in case of calcium hypochlorite, Ca(OCl)$_2$, the available chlorine is twice the percentage (49.6) of chlorine in Ca(OCl)$_2$ or 99.2 per cent. This is another way of saying that 1 mole of Cl$_2$ is equivalent in oxidizing power to 1 mole of HOCl, or to the ion OCl$^-$. Bleaching powder by this convention contains about 35 or less per cent of available chlorine when freshly manufactured. The available chlorine concept may be further explained by the reactions:

For calcium hypochlorite:

$$Ca(OCl)_2 + 2HCl \rightarrow CaCl_2 + 2HOCl$$

or

$$Ca(OCl)_2 \rightarrow Ca^{++} + 2OCl^-$$

One mole of bleaching powder will furnish only half this amount of OCl⁻ ions.

For chlorine:

$$Cl_2 + H_2O \rightarrow HOCl + HCl$$

Calcium hypochlorite,[1] $Ca(OCl)_2$, itself may be made in several ways. One method that has been used is the chlorination of calcium hydroxide as in the manufacture of bleaching powder, followed by the separation of the calcium hypochlorite through salting out from solution with sodium chloride. It is also manufactured by the formation under refrigeration of the salt, $Ca(OCl)_2 \cdot NaOCl \cdot NaCl \cdot 12H_2O$,[1] which is prepared by the chlorination of a mixture of sodium and calcium hydroxides. This is reacted with a chlorinated lime slurry, filtered to remove salt, and dried, resulting finally in a stable product containing 65 to 70 per cent $Ca(OCl)_2$. The final reaction is

$$2[Ca(OCl)_2 \cdot NaOCl \cdot NaCl \cdot 12H_2O] + CaCl_2 + Ca(OCl)_2 \rightarrow$$
$$4Ca(OCl)_2 \cdot 2H_2O + 4NaCl + 16H_2O$$

The great advantage in calcium hypochlorite is that it does not decompose on standing as does bleaching powder. It is also twice as strong as ordinary bleaching powder, and it is not hygroscopic.

SODIUM HYPOCHLORITE

Sodium hypochlorite is employed as a disinfectant and deodorant in dairies, creameries, water supplies, sewage disposal, and for household purposes. It is also used as a bleach in laundries. During the First World War, it was employed for treatment of wounds as a stabilized isotonic solution. As a bleaching agent, it is very useful on cotton, linen, jute, artificial silk, paper pulp, and oranges. Indeed much of the chlorine bought for bleaching cellulose products is converted into sodium hypochlorite before use. The most common method for making it is the treatment of sodium hydroxide solution with gaseous chlorine.

$$Cl_2 + 2NaOH \rightarrow NaCl + H_2O + NaOCl$$

The other once widely used method was the electrolysis of a concentrated salt solution wherein the same product was made. These electrolytic cells do not have any diaphragm and are operated at high current density in nearly neutral solution. The cells are designed to function at a low temperature and to bring the cathode caustic soda solution in contact with the chlorine given off at the anode.

[1] MacMullin and Taylor, U.S. Pat. 1787048 (1930); Avery and Evans, Modified MgO Process Yields $MgCl_2$ and Calcium Hypochlorite, *Chem. & Met. Eng.*, **52** (4), 94 (1945), with pictured flow sheet p. 130.

SODIUM CHLORITE

Sodium chlorite, $NaClO_2$, was introduced in 1940 by the Mathieson Chemical Corporation. The 80 per cent commercial material has about 125 per cent "available chlorine." It is manufactured[1] from chlorine through calcium chlorate to chlorine dioxide, ending with the reaction

$$4NaOH + Ca(OH)_2 + C + 4ClO_2 \rightarrow 4NaClO_2 + CaCO_3 + 3H_2O$$

After filtering off the calcium carbonate, the solution of $NaClO_2$ is evaporated and drum-dried. Sodium chlorite is a powerful but stable oxidizing agent. It is capable of bleaching much of the coloration in cellulosic materials without tendering the cellulose. Hence it finds use in the pulp and textile industries, particularly in the final whitening of kraft paper. Besides being employed as an oxidizer, sodium chlorite is also the source of another chlorine compound, chlorine dioxide, through the reaction

$$NaClO_2 + \tfrac{1}{2}Cl_2 \rightarrow NaCl + ClO_2$$

Chlorine dioxide has $2\tfrac{1}{2}$ times the oxidizing power of chlorine and is important in water purification[2] and for odor control.

SELECTED REFERENCES

Hou, T. P., "Manufacture of Soda," 2d ed., Reinhold Publishing Corporation, New York, 1942.

Badger, W. L., and E. M. Baker, "Inorganic Chemical Technology," 2d ed., McGraw-Hill Book Company, Inc., New York, 1941.

Mantell, C. L., "Industrial Electrochemistry," 3d ed., McGraw-Hill Book Company, Inc., New York, 1950.

Perry, J. H., editor-in-chief, "Chemical Engineers' Handbook," 3d ed., McGraw-Hill Book Company, Inc., New York, especially Alkaline Chloride Electrolysis, pp. 1806–1810; Evaporation, pp. 500–522.

Kirk, R. E., and D. F. Othmer, "Encyclopedia of Chemical Technology," 15 vols., The Interscience Encyclopedia, Inc., New York, 1947–1956.

Kortüm, G., and J. O. M. Bockris, "Textbook of Electrochemistry," 2 vols., Elsevier Press, Inc., New York, 1951.

[1] Taylor, et al., Sodium Chlorite, Properties and Reactions, Ind. Eng. Chem., 32, 899 (1940); Holst, Production of Sodium Chlorite, Ind. Eng. Chem., 42, 2359 (1950).

[2] Vincent, et al., Two New Chlorine Compounds, J. Chem. Educ., 22, 283 (1945).

CHAPTER 16

ELECTROLYTIC INDUSTRIES

Electrical energy is extensively consumed by the chemical process industries not only to furnish power through electrical motors but to give rise to elevated temperatures and directly to cause chemical change. Energy in the form of electricity causes chemical reactions to take place in the electrolytic industries presented in this chapter. The heat produced thereby is the basis for the high temperature required in the electrothermal industries, which will be discussed in Chap. 17. Most of the electrolytic processes have been developed since the First World War and few of them are older. The materials manufactured by the aid of electricity vary from chemicals that are also produced by other methods, such as caustic soda, hydrogen, and magnesium, to chemicals that at present cannot be made economically in any other way, such as aluminum and calcium carbide. See Table 2 for chemicals and metals made electrochemically.

TABLE 1. TYPICAL POWER COSTS FROM WATER POWER EXCEPT WHERE OTHERWISE NOTED[a]

	Cents per kw.-hr.
New York Harbor (steam)	0.67–1.3
Norway	0.1 –1.5
Sweden	0.1 –1.5
England	0.4 –0.5
Germany (brown coal)	0.38
Niagara Falls	0.3 up
Tennessee (steam)	0.38–0.6
Ontario, Canada	0.15–0.4

[a] PERRY, *op. cit.*, p. 1825, abridged.

The cost of electrical power is usually the deciding factor in the electrochemical industries. Thus, these industries have tended to become established in regions of cheap electrical power based on falling water, as at Niagara Falls and in Norway. The recent establishment of new areas of abundant and inexpensive electricity in the West and Northwest points the way to the growth of electrochemical industries in those regions. Typical power costs in various parts of the United States and

TABLE 2. CHEMICALS AND METALS MADE ELECTROCHEMICALLY[a]

Material	Process	Kw.-hr. per lb.	Voltage per cell or furnace	Yearly kw.-hr. consumed
Alumina, fused..........	Electrothermal fusion	1–1.5	100–110	Large
Aluminum..............	Electrolytic reduction of alumina to aluminum	10–12	5.5–7	Very large
Ammonia, synthetic......	Electrolytic hydrogen; pressure hydrogenation	6.5	....	Large
Cadmium..............	Electrolytic precipitation of zinc-lead residues	0.8	2.6	Small
Calcium................	Electrothermal reduction	22–24	....	Small
Calcium carbide..........	Electrothermal reduction	1.3–1.4	....	Very large
Calcium cyanamid........	Electrothermal reduction	1.4	....	Large
Carbon disulfide.........	Electrothermal reaction	0.4–0.5	60	Large
Caustic soda chlorine.....	Electrolysis of brine	1.1–1.5	3.4–4.3	Very large
Copper.................	Copper electrowinning	1–1.5	1.9–2.4	Large
Copper.................	Electrolytic refining	0.09–0.16	0.18–0.4	Very large
Ferrochromium, 70%.....	Electrothermal smelting	2–3	90–120	Large
Ferromanganese, 80%....	Electrothermal reduction	1.5–3	90–115	Very small
Ferromolybdenum, 50%..	Electrothermal smelting	3–4	50–150	Small
Ferrosilicon, 50%........	Electrothermal smelting	2–3.5	75–150	Very large
Ferrotungsten, 70%......	Electrothermal smelting and refining	1.5–2	90–120	Small
Ferrouranium...........	Electrothermal smelting	3–5	....	Very small
Ferrovanadium..........	Electrothermal smelting	2–3.5	150–250	Small
Gold...................	Electrolytic refining	0.15	1.3–1.6	Very small
Graphite...............	Electrothermal change	1.5–2.0	80–200	Large
Hydrogen and oxygen.....	Electrolysis of alkalized water	140[b]	....	Small
Hypochlorite............	Electrolysis of salt solution with mixing	....	....	Medium
Iron...................	Reduction in arc furnace	1–1.25	....	None
Iron castings............	Electric melting duplex system continuous..........	0.07 0.225	....	Very small
Iron, sponge............	Electrothermal low-temperature reduction	0.2	....	Very small
Lead...................	Electrolytic refining	0.04–0.05	0.35–0.6	Small
Magnesium, metallic......	Electrolysis of magnesium chloride	8–13	6–7	Very large
Phosphoric acid..........	Electrothermal reduction to phosphorus; oxidation	2.7	....	Large

TABLE 2. CHEMICALS AND METALS MADE ELECTROCHEMICALLY[a] (Continued)

Material	Process	Kw.-hr. per lb.	Voltage per cell or furnace	Yearly kw.-hr. consumed
Phosphorus..............	Electrothermal reduction	4–5.5	....	Large
Potassium chlorate.......	Electrolysis of potassium chloride solution (mixing)	3	....	Small
Potassium hydroxide.....	Electrolysis of potassium chloride solution	1–1.2	....	Small
Quartz, fused...........	Electrothermal fusion	5–8	....	Small
Silicon.................	Electrothermal reduction	6	....	Small
Silicon carbide..........	Electrothermal reduction	3.2–3.85	75–230	Large
Silver..................	Electrolytic refining	0.15–0.37	2.7–3.5	Very small
Sodium, metallic.........	Electrolysis of fused sodium chloride	7.1–7.3	....	Large
Sodium chlorate.........	Electrolysis of sodium chloride solution (mixing)	2.55–13.0	2.8–3.5	Small
Steel castings...........	Electric melting cold charge	0.25–0.38	....	Large
Steel ingot..............	Electric melting or refining or superrefining of molten charge	0.1	....	Large
Zinc...................	Electrolytic precipitation	1.4–1.56	3.5–3.7	Very large

[a] Based on House Document 103, 73d Congress, as reported in *Chem. & Met. Eng.*, **44**, 539 (1937), and supplemented by Mantell's tabulation in PERRY, *op. cit.*, p. 1825. Other chemicals made electrolytically: lithium, fluorine, fluorocarbons, tin (pure), manganese, titanium, nickel (pure), hydrogen peroxide, organic chemicals.

[b] Kw.-hr. per M cu. ft.

other countries are given in Table 1, while Table 2 lists the kilowatt-hours needed to produce 1 lb. of the various materials.

Landis writes,[1] "The electrochemical process has completely *revolutionized* the production of certain primary products and at such *lowered cost* as to permit the development of new secondary industries utilizing these cheaper raw materials." Examples of such lowered costs are for chlorine, sodium, and hydrogen peroxide, as well as for aluminum.

Direct current is used in the electrochemical industries. Since 1938 the single-anode mercury-arc rectifier is used in 90 per cent of the electro-

[1] FURNAS, editor, "Rogers' Manual of Industrial Chemistry," 6th ed., p. 479, D. Van Nostrand Company, Inc., New York, 1942. Italics in quotation are by Shreve.

chemical industries to convert alternating current into direct current.[1] The balance is divided between motor-generator sets, synchronous converters, and multianode rectifiers. A recent development in the aluminum industry is the use of direct-current generators actuated by gas engines.[2]

ALUMINUM

Aluminum is potentially the most abundant metal in the world. It makes up 8.05 per cent of the solid portion of the earth's crust. Every country possesses large supplies of aluminum-containing materials, but as yet processes for obtaining metallic aluminum from most of these compounds are not economical.

History. Although Wöhler is usually credited with the first production of metallic aluminum in 1827, this metal was actually first obtained in 1825 by Oersted, a Dane. He heated aluminum chloride with a potassium-mercury amalgam. In 1845, Henri Sainte-Claire Deville produced aluminum from sodium-aluminum chloride by heating with metallic sodium. This process was operated for about 35 years and the metal sold for $100 a pound. By 1886 the price had been reduced to $8 a pound, chiefly by reason of the use of cryolite as a flux in the bath, the lowered cost of the metallic sodium needed for the reduction, and the improvements in the equipment.

Large-scale manufacture of aluminum was not achieved until the advent of the Hall process. In 1886, Charles Hall produced the first aluminum by the present-day process: electrolysis of alumina dissolved in a fused bath of cryolite. The same year Paul Héroult was granted a French patent for a process similar to that of Hall. He was not able to obtain a United States patent, however, as Hall's patents were granted the priority.[3] By 1893, the production of aluminum had increased so rapidly by Hall's procedure that the price had fallen to $2 per pound. The industry grew steadily, based soundly on new and expanding markets, created largely by its own study of the properties of aluminum and of the avenues for economic consumption of this new metal. With this growth in manufacture came a decrease in cost which the Aluminum Company of America largely passed on to its customers, even reducing the price first to 17 cents per pound and then to 15 cents per pound (1943–1947 average). The price in 1954 was 20 cents per pound.

Economics and Uses. Consumption of aluminum is increasing very rapidly (Table 3) and has not reached the demands of domestic and governmental needs. Table 4 exhibits the main avenues of distribution.

[1] COEN and OLSON, How Today's Conversion Devices Fit into Process Needs, *Chem. Eng.*, **57** (5), 133 (1950).

[2] ANON., Gas Makes Power for Aluminum, *Chem. Eng.*, **57** (7), 102 (1950).

[3] VAN DOREN, Studies in Chemical Patent Procedure, *Ind. Eng. Chem.*, **21**, 120 (1929).

TABLE 3. APPARENT CONSUMPTION OF PRIMARY ALUMINUM, TONS[a]

Year	Sold or used by producers	Imports net	Apparent consumption
1943–1947 (average)	633,876	47,651	678,529
1948	625,834	40,041	684,575
1949	587,532	48,424	625,956
1950	731,087	167,249	893,386
1951	845,392	129,870	975,262
1952	938,181	134,505	1,072,686
1953	1,252,000	344,300	1,542,200

[a] "Minerals Yearbook," 1952, 1953.

TABLE 4. DISTRIBUTION OF ALUMINUM FOR 1952[a]

	Per cent		Per cent
Transportation: land, sea, air...	32	Destructive uses.............	6
Construction, building.........	15	Machinery, equipment........	6
Electric, electronic............	13	Packaging, containers.........	4
Consumer durables...........	10	Miscellaneous...............	14

[a] "Minerals Yearbook," 1952.

The unusual combination of lightness and strength makes aluminum applicable for many uses that other metals cannot fill. Weight for weight, aluminum has twice the conductivity of copper and it also has a high ductility at elevated temperatures. Aluminum is commonly alloyed with other metals, such as copper, magnesium, zinc, silicon, chromium, and manganese and thus has its usefulness increased.[1] Metallic aluminum or aluminum alloys are employed for structural shapes for aircraft, automobiles, trucks, and railway cars, for electrical conductors, and for cast and forged structural parts.

Manufacture. Metallic aluminum is produced by the electrolytic reduction of pure alumina in a bath of fused cryolite. The production of the pure alumina will be discussed in Chap. 21.[2] It is not possible to reduce alumina with carbon because at the temperature required for this reduction the aluminum comes off as a vapor and is carried away with the carbon monoxide. This metallic vapor cannot be condensed by cooling because the reaction reverses at lower temperatures and thus converts the

[1] FRARY, The Aluminum Industry, *Chem. Eng. News*, **20**, 1646 (1942); FRARY, Economics of Aluminum Industry, *Ind. Eng. Chem.*, **28**, 146 (1936).

[2] ANON., Making Alumina, *Chem. & Met. Eng.*, **47**, 707 (1940), pictured flow sheet.

aluminum back to alumina. The *energy change* involved in the reaction[1]

$$Al_2O_3 + 1\tfrac{1}{2}C \rightarrow 2Al + 1\tfrac{1}{2}CO_2; \qquad \Delta H = +235,000 \text{ cal.}$$

amounts *practically* to around 10 kw.-hr. per lb. Consequently this metal cannot be made economically unless low-priced electrical energy is available. The carbon for the reaction comes from the anode, for which is required from 0.6 to 0.7 lb. of carbon per pound of metal. The carbon dioxide evolved contains from 10 to 50 per cent carbon monoxide.

The *unit operations* (Op.) and *unit processes* (Pr.) involved in the production of metallic aluminum are as follows:

The cryolite bath is prepared (Pr.).
Alumina is dissolved in the molten cryolite bath (Op.).
The molten solution of alumina in cryolite is electrolyzed to form metallic aluminum (Pr.).
The carbon electrode is oxidized by the oxygen liberated (Pr.).
The molten aluminum is tapped off and cooled (Op.).

The cells used for the reduction are made of steel, lined with firebrick, and covered with carbon to conduct the current,[2] as depicted in Fig. 1.

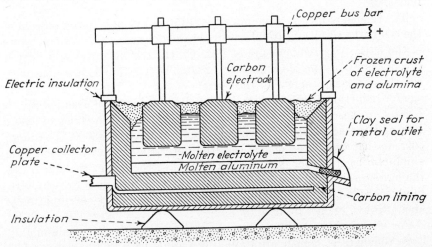

FIG. 1. Electrolytic aluminum cell.

The anodes are made from a mixture of coke, pitch, and tar and extend to within about 2 in. of the molten aluminum in the bottom of the cell. As they are gradually consumed by the oxygen liberated, they are hung from an overhead bar so that they may be lowered as needed. For new

[1] Some CO is formed. This reaction requires more energy.
[2] MANTELL, "Industrial Electrochemistry," 3d ed., p. 480, McGraw-Hill Book Company, Inc., New York, 1950; KIRK and OTHMER, *op. cit.*, Vol. 1, p. 602; FRARY, The Electrolytic Production of Aluminum, *Trans. Electrochem. Soc.*, **94** (1), 31 (1948).

facilities, the trend is toward continuous self-baking electrodes (Söderburg type). Any impurities in the anodes would be liable to contaminate the metal. The molten aluminum metal that gathers on the bottom serves as the cathode for the cell. The bottom of the cell is slanted to permit the metal to be tapped off daily or it is removed by siphoning.

The "solvent" for the alumina is fused cryolite, $AlF_3·3NaF$, obtained from Greenland or manufactured synthetically by the action of hydrofluoric acid on aluminum hydroxide in the presence of soda. Fluorspar is introduced into the bath to lower the melting point. The average bath has the following approximate composition: $2AlF_3·6NaF·CaF_2$. The alumina to be reduced is added to the molten cryolite at such intervals as to maintain a 3 to 6 per cent dissolved alumina content in the bath at all times.

If the bath fails to wet the carbon anode the resistance of the cell increases, causing a signal lamp shunted across the cell to increase in brightness. Additional alumina is then stirred in. The melted cryolite is covered with a blanket of alumina which rests on a crust of frozen electrolyte. This alumina is thus preheated before being dissolved in the bath. The carbon dioxide and monoxide by-products are vented off through hoods.

The tendency for the aluminum metal formed to sink to the bottom of the cell is the result of careful control of the density of the various layers of the bath. At a temperature of 1000°C., the specific gravity of molten cryolite is 2.095; molten aluminum, 2.29. The aluminum, being heavier, can thus be easily tapped off the bottom of the cell. The theoretical voltage for reduction of the alumina is 2.0 volts, but in actual practice, 5.5 to 7 volts are necessary per cell. The cells are connected in series of about 100, and the amperage of each cell is approximately 50,000. The more current that can be used in a cell, the lower the cost of producing the aluminum as the labor is about the same, but the higher the amperage, the more mechanical and handling difficulties. A furnace 8 by 4 by 4 ft. produces about 120 lb. of aluminum per day. The energy consumption is about 10 kw.-hr. per lb. of aluminum.

For electrical establishments such as those manufacturing aluminum, large tonnages of copper are ordinarily required for bus bars, electrical wiring, motors, and other such demands. During the national emergency of the Second World War, the silver ordinarily stored in the vaults at West Point was lent to the extent of thousands of tons to lessen demands for copper.[1]

Aluminum is refined electrolytically. A copper-aluminum alloy in contact with carbon forms the anode of the cell, the cathode is purified molten aluminum, and the electrolyte is a layer of fused cryolite, aluminum

[1] JOLLY, The Recent Expansion of the Aluminum Industry, *Science*, **96** (2480), 29 (1942).

fluoride, and barium fluoride. The anode alloy, electrolyte, and cathode aluminum are arranged vertically in a three-layer system. The differences in specific gravity of each layer maintain their separate identity. The pure aluminum is dissolved from the anode and deposited on the cathode.[1] The purity of this aluminum is 99.90 to 99.99 per cent. The highly refined aluminum is appreciably softer than ordinary aluminum. Many alloys[2] of aluminum are employed to give greater strength or hardness. These are important because of their pleasing appearance, corrosion resistance, and strength per unit of weight. The latter property makes aluminum and its alloys of the utmost necessity for the manufacture of airplanes.

MAGNESIUM

Magnesium is a very light silvery white metal which has achieved widespread industrial use. Magnesium is the eighth element in order of occurrence in the world. The raw materials are widely distributed throughout the globe, particularly as sea water is a practical and very important source for magnesium compounds. Hence there need never be any shortage of the economical raw materials for magnesium metal and most of its salts. Magnesium salts are presented in Chap. 11.

History. Although metallic magnesium was first isolated by Bussy in 1829, its existence was discovered by Davy in 1808. Uses for this metal were slow in being developed. As late as 1918 almost all of the magnesium produced was used for flashlight powder, although during the First World War part of the production was consumed in pyrotechnics. The United States output in 1918 was only 284,118 lb. and this quantity dropped sharply as soon as the war was over.[3] During the next 15 years intensive research brought forth many new uses for magnesium. By 1930 it was being fabricated into complicated castings, sheets, and forgings, and a method of welding it was also perfected. Extremely lightweight, strong magnesium alloys of great importance to the aircraft industry were developed during the period 1930–1940.[4] The demands of the Second World War for better and lighter airplanes were met by these light magnesium alloys. Consequently magnesium production was expanded tremendously to meet this new demand and also to supply the material for incendiary bombs. Some representative magnesium alloys are Dowmetal H: Al, 6.5

[1] FRARY, Electrolytic Refining of Aluminum, *Trans. Am. Electrochem. Soc.*, **47**, 275 (1925); EDWARDS, Contributions of Aluminum to Metallurgical Progress, *Metal Progr.*, **29**, 234 (1936); KIRK and OTHMER, *op. cit.*, Vol. 1, p. 604.

[2] PERRY, *op. cit.*, pp. 1527, 1542, tabulates such alloys.

[3] KILLEFFER, Magnesium from the Sea, *Ind. Eng. Chem.*, News Ed., **19**, 1189 (1941).

[4] For an extensive review of the corrosion-resistant properties of magnesium-aluminum alloys, see BENSON and MEARS, Aluminum-magnesium Alloys Resist Attack, *Chem. & Met. Eng.*, **49** (1), 88 (1942).

per cent; Mn, 0.2 per cent; Zn, 3.0 per cent; Mg, the rest; and Dowmetal
M: Mn, 1.5 per cent, with Mg the rest.

Uses and Economics. The primary use for magnesium is in the production of lightweight structural alloys. Magnesium is especially important
in wartime for this reason and for incendiary bombs, flashlight powder,
and flares. An important postwar demand for this metal has been anodes
for protection against corrosion of other metals. In 1951, 2,000 tons of
magnesium went into the ground and into sea-water installations to protect pipe lines, flumes, and steel piling and 1,200 tons went into home
water-heater anodes.

During the Second World War, magnesium production averaged over
100,000 tons yearly; it then dropped to around 10,000 tons annually but
with the rearmament demand rose to 93,075 tons for 1953. About one-
third is produced by Dow Chemical Co. at Freeport, Tex., with the rest
coming from the government-owned plants. As usual in the development
of a material from a relative rarity to a tonnage article, the price of
magnesium dropped from $1.81 per pound in 1918 to approximately 27
cents per pound in 1954.

Manufacture. The cheapest method of making magnesium is by the
electrolytic process which is the only one used except in cases of national
emergency. During the Second World War magnesium was made by two
other processes: the silicothermic or ferrosilicon process and the carbon
reduction process. Figure 2 depicts simplified flow sequences for all three
processes. Demands for magnesium have again caused the silicothermic-
process plants to be reactivated. The carbon reduction process never
operated satisfactorily and the plant has been completely closed for a
number of years.[1]

Electrolysis of Magnesium Chloride. The magnesium chloride needed
is obtained (1) from salines,[2] (2) from brine wells, (3) from the reaction of
magnesium hydroxide (from sea water or dolomite) with hydrochloric
acid, and (4) from the reaction of magnesium oxide with carbon and
chlorine.

The pioneer producer, Dow Chemical Co., at Freeport, Tex., makes
magnesium by electrolyzing magnesium chloride from sea water, using
oystershells for the lime needed. The oystershells, which are almost pure
calcium carbonate, are burned to lime, slaked, and mixed with the sea
water, thus precipitating magnesium hydroxide (Fig. 3 and also Chap. 11).
This magnesium hydroxide is filtered off and treated with hydrochloric
acid, prepared from natural gas and the chlorine evolved from the cells.
This forms a magnesium chloride solution which is evaporated to solid
magnesium chloride in direct-fired evaporators followed by shelf drying.

---

[1] For further description and references, see 1st ed. of this book, pp. 310–311.

[2] MANNING and KIRKPATRICK, Better Utilization of Mineral Resources through New
Chemical Technology, *Chem. Met. Eng.*, **51**(5), 92 (1944), with pictured flow sheet.

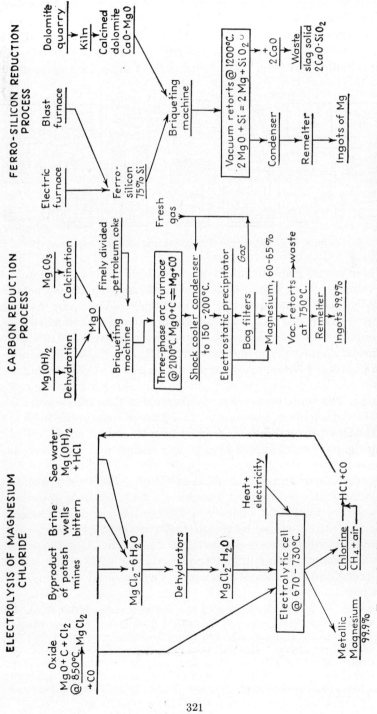

FIG. 2. Outline of processes for production of metallic magnesium used during the Second World War.

ELECTROLYSIS OF MAGNESIUM CHLORIDE

Oxide MgO+C+Cl₂ @ 850°C. MgCl₂ +CO

$MgO + C + Cl_2 \xrightarrow{@850°C.} MgCl_2 + CO$

Byproduct of potash mines

Brine wells bittern

Sea water $Mg(OH)_2 + HCl$

$MgCl_2 \cdot 6H_2O$

Dehydrators

$MgCl_2 \cdot H_2O$

Electrolytic cell @ 670 – 750°C.

Heat + electricity

Metallic Magnesium 99.9%

Chlorine $\rightarrow$ HCl + CO $CH_4 + air$

CARBON REDUCTION PROCESS

$Mg(OH)_2$ Dehydration

$MgCO_3$ Calcination

MgO

Finely divided petroleum coke

Briqueting machine

Three-phase arc furnace @ 2100°C. $MgO + C \rightleftharpoons Mg + CO$

Fresh gas

Shock cooler condenser to 150 - 200°C.

Electrostatic precipitator

Gas

Bag filters

Magnesium, 60-65%

Vac. retorts at 750°C. $\rightarrow$ waste

Remelter

Ingots 99.9%

FERRO-SILICON REDUCTION PROCESS

Dolomite quarry

Kiln

Calcined dolomite CaO-MgO

Blast furnace

Electric furnace

Ferro-silicon 75% Si

Briqueting machine

Vacuum retorts @ 1200°C. $2MgO + Si = 2Mg + SiO_2$

$+ 2CaO$ $\rightarrow$ Waste slag solid $2CaO \cdot SiO_2$

Condenser

Remelter

Ingots of Mg

321

After thorough drying the magnesium chloride[1] is fed to the Dow electrolytic cell where it is decomposed into the metal and chlorine gas.

These cells are large, rectangular ceramic-lined steel pots, 5 ft. wide, 11 ft. long, and 6 ft. deep with a capacity of about 10 tons molten magnesium chloride and salts. The internal parts of the cell act as the cathode

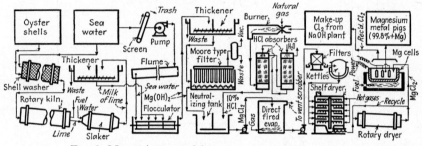

FIG. 3. Magnesium metal from sea water—Dow process.

and there are 22 graphite anodes suspended vertically in the top of the cell. Sodium chloride is added to the bath to lower the melting point and also to increase the conductivity. The salts are kept molten by the electric current used to extract the magnesium plus external heat supplied by gas-fired outside furnaces. The usual operating temperature is 710°C. which is sufficient to melt the magnesium (m.p. 651°C.). Each cell operates at about 6 volts and 30,000 to 70,000 amp. with a current efficiency of about 80 per cent. The power requirements are 8 kw.-hr. per lb. of magnesium produced. The molten magnesium is liberated at the cathode and rises to the bath surface where troughs lead to the metal wells in the front of the cell. The 99.9 per cent pure magnesium metal is dipped out several times during the day, each dipperful containing enough metal to fill an 18-lb. ingot mold.[2]

Silicothermic or Ferrosilicon Process.[3] During the Second World War the United States government financed construction of six silicothermic plants with a total *rated* capacity of 70,000 tons per year. The cost of magnesium then produced by this process averaged 27.4 cents per pound as compared with 18.2 cents per pound for electrolytic. After the war when normal peacetime competition returned, these plants were mothballed until the Korean situation developed. The essential reaction of this

[1] MANTELL, *op. cit.*, pp. 505*ff.*; ANON., Magnesium from Sea Water, *Chem. & Met. Eng.*, **48** (11), 130 (1941), pictured flow sheet; SCHAMBRA, The Dow Magnesium Process at Freeport, Texas, *Trans. Am. Inst. Chem. Engrs.*, **41**, 35 (1945); GROSS, "The Story of Magnesium," American Society for Metals, Cleveland, 1949.

[2] MANTELL, *op. cit.*; PERRY, *op. cit.*, p. 1811, gives data and cross section of cell.

[3] SCHRIER, Silicothermic Magnesium Comes Back, *Chem. Eng.*, **59** (4), 148 (1952), with a pictured flow sheet, p. 212.

process is as follows:

$$2(MgO \cdot CaO) + \tfrac{1}{6}FeSi_6 \rightarrow 2Mg + (CaO)_2SiO_2 + \tfrac{1}{6}Fe$$

The process consists of mixing ground dead-burned dolomite with ground ferrosilicon and pelleting. The pellets are charged into the furnace. High vacuum and heat (2140°F.) are applied. The calcium oxide present in the burnt dolomite forms infusible dicalcium silicate that is easily removed from the retort at the end of the run. The chrome-alloy retort is equipped with a condenser tube with a removable lining. The reaction is run at very high vacuum (100 to 150 microns Hg), and the magnesium that is liberated is collected on the lining of the condenser. At the end of the run the furnace is partly cooled and the magnesium is removed from the condenser by the differential contraction of the magnesium and the steel. At present much study is being devoted to this batch operation to make it continuous and possibly more competitive.

SODIUM[1]

Sodium is a silvery white, very active metal. It reacts violently with water and is usually preserved by storage under kerosene or preferably in containers under a nitrogen blanket. About 137,000,000 lb. of sodium enters annually into the manufacture of tetraethyl lead, 50,000,000 lb. into sodium cyanide, and 45,000,000 lb. for sodium alkyl sulfate, and 20,000,000 lb. for miscellaneous uses, e.g., Na_2O_2, hydride descaling and for making other metals as potassium (see Chap. 13). The total production is 250,000,000 lb. for 1953.

Manufacture. The most important method of preparation of sodium is by the electrolysis of fused sodium chloride. Originally, most of the metallic sodium was produced by the electrolysis of fused caustic soda, but the salt process has supplanted this older process. This has the advantages that it uses a natural raw material, NaCl, instead of a manufactured product, NaOH, and also that it produces a valuable by-product, chlorine.

The reaction involved in this process is as follows:

$$2NaCl \rightarrow 2Na + Cl_2$$

The cell for this electrolysis consists of a closed, rectangular refractory-lined steel box (see Fig. 4). The anode is made of carbon and the cathode of iron.[2] The anode and cathode are arranged in separate compartments to facilitate the recovery of the sodium and the chlorine. Sodium chloride

---

[1] SITTIG, "Sodium . . . Its Manufacture, Properties and Uses," A.C.S. Monograph, Reinhold Publishing Corporation, New York, 1955.

[2] DOWNS, Electrolytic Process and Cell, U.S. Pat. 1501756 (1924). Downs received the Schoellkopf medal in 1934 for the development of this cell. ZABEL, Metallic Sodium, *Chem. Inds.*, **65**, 714 (1949).

has a high melting point (804°C.), but calcium chloride is added to lower this so that the cell is operated at 600°C. The electrolyte is a eutectic of 33.2 per cent sodium chloride and 66.8 per cent calcium chloride. The lower temperature increases the life of the refractory lining of the cell, makes it easier to collect the chlorine, and prevents the sodium from forming a difficultly recoverable fog. A sodium-calcium mixture deposits at

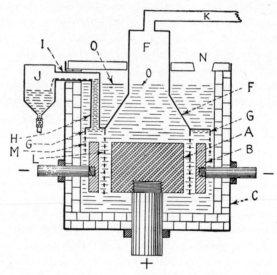

FIG. 4. Down's sodium cell. A is the graphite anode, B is the iron cathode, F is the dome for collecting the chlorine, and K the pipe for conducting this chlorine away. G is the annular sodium collector with H and I as pipes to conduct this sodium to the vessel J. L and M are metal screens supported by F and serving to separate the cell products. C is the shell of the cell made of steel but lined with refractory bricks. N is the charge port for salt and O is the bath level.

the cathode, but the solubility of calcium in sodium decreases with decreasing temperatures so that the heavier calcium crystals, which form as the mixture is cooled, settle back to the bath. The crude sodium is filtered at 105 to 110°C. giving a sodium 99.9 per cent pure. This is frequently run molten into a nitrogen-filled tank car, allowed to solidify, and shipped.

HYDROGEN PEROXIDE

Hydrogen peroxide,[1] H_2O_2, may be prepared by both electrolytic and chemical methods. It is sold in water solution in concentrations of 3, 35, and 90 per cent. Many new uses for this chemical are being currently developed. At present it is widely employed as a bleach, for wood pulp,

[1] REICHERT, Hydrogen Peroxide, Chem. Eng. News, **21**, 480 (1943); ZOTOS, Hydrogen Peroxide, Chem. Eng., **58** (4), 114 (1951); SHANLEY and GREENSPAN, Highly Concentrated Hydrogen Peroxide, Ind. Eng. Chem., **39**, 1536 (1947).

but particularly for *animal* products: silk, wool, feathers, fur, and hair; as a mild antiseptic, in the manufacture of metallic peroxides and in the making of "per" salts. The new 90 per cent solutions represent a self-contained energy source which leaves no residues or corrosive toxic gases, ideal for explosives, rocket propellants, and synthetic chemicals. Its unique property is that water is the only by-product of its oxidizing action. The rate of oxidation is much influenced by temperature, concentration, and the pH of the medium; buffers are added to control the pH as the reaction proceeds (silicates, phosphates, or carbonates). Its sale has so increased that tank-car shipments of the strong solutions are common.

Manufacture. In the electrolytic methods of manufacture of hydrogen peroxide, the active oxygen is produced by the anodic oxidation of sulfate radicals. These are supplied in the electrolyte from sulfuric acid or alkali sulfate. Pure sulfuric acid has the lowest current efficiency (70 to 75 per cent) and a low concentration of persulfuric acid is formed; however, there is no trouble with crystallization as when ammonium sulfate is used. Usually 80 per cent and more current efficiency is obtained with mixtures of ammonium sulfate and sulfuric acid. The lower solubility of the resulting ammonium persulfate limits the allowable saturation in active oxygen because of crystal formation which would block the cell. The *straight liquid process* is a closed system comprising both electrolytic and hydrolyzing plants. The electrolyte is fed into a typical electrolytic cell which is held at 35°C. or below with platinum metal for the anode:

$$2H_2SO_4 \rightleftarrows H_2S_2O_8 + H_2$$

The cell products, *i.e.*, the persalt or peracid, sulfuric acid, and water, are then hydrolyzed at temperatures from 60 to 100°C. to yield hydrogen peroxide as shown by the following simplified over-all reactions:

$$H_2S_2O_8 + H_2O \rightleftarrows H_2SO_4 + H_2SO_5$$
$$H_2SO_5 + H_2O \rightleftarrows H_2SO_4 + H_2O_2$$

In the *potassium conversion process* following the electrolysis, the ammonium persulfate is converted by potassium bisulfate to potassium persulfate and ammonium bisulfate.

Barium peroxide is not prepared electrolytically but by the passing of dry air or oxygen over barium oxide at 600°C. This process may be symbolized as follows:

$$BaCO_3 + C \rightarrow BaO + 2CO$$
$$BaO + \tfrac{1}{2}O_2 \rightarrow BaO_2$$
$$\underline{BaO_2 + H_2SO_4 \rightarrow BaSO_4 + H_2O_2}$$
$$BaCO_3 + C + \tfrac{1}{2}O_2 + H_2SO_4 \rightarrow BaSO_4 + 2CO + H_2O_2$$

Another chemical method, developed in Germany during the Second World War, utilizes an easily oxidizable material such as 2-ethyl-anthraquinone. The main reactions can be summarized as follows:

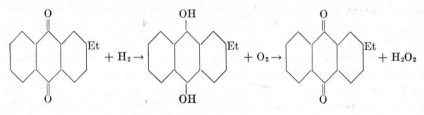

CHLORATES AND PERCHLORATES

Sodium chlorate is manufactured in large quantities (about 22,000 tons annually) as a weed killer. It is also used in textile printing and dyeing. It cannot be employed in explosives because of its hygroscopicity, although potassium chlorate (about 9,000 tons annually) is satisfactory in explosives, matches, and fireworks. Sodium perchlorate does not have many commercial applications because of its extreme solubility in water but is used to prepare potassium and ammonium perchlorates which are consumed in explosives.

Manufacture. Sodium chlorate is produced by the electrolysis of saturated acidulated brine mixed with sodium dichromate (about 2 grams per liter) to reduce the corrosive action of the hypochlorous acid liberated by the hydrochloric acid present. Figure 5 shows the essential steps in the

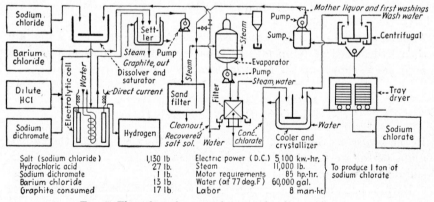

Salt (sodium chloride)	1,130 lb	Electric power (D.C.) 5,100 kw.-hr.
Hydrochloric acid	27 lb.	Steam 11,000 lb.
Sodium dichromate	1 lb.	Motor requirements 85 hp.-hr.
Barium chloride	13 lb	Water (at 77 deg.F) 60,000 gal.
Graphite consumed	17 lb	Labor 8 man-hr.

To produce 1 ton of sodium chlorate

FIG. 5. Flow sheet for manufacture of sodium chlorate.

production of this chemical. The brine solution is made from soft water or condensate from the evaporator and rock salt, and purified from any Ca and Mg. The rectangular steel cell is filled with either the brine solution or recovered salt solution made from recovered salt containing chlorate, dissolved in condensate from the evaporator. The temperature of the cell is maintained at 40°C.[1] by cooling water. The products of the electrolysis are actually sodium hydroxide at the cathode and chlorine at the anode but, as there is *no diaphragm* in the cell, mixing occurs and sodium hypochlorite is formed which is then oxidized to chlorate. The over-all reaction is

$$NaCl(aq) + 3H_2O(l) \rightarrow NaClO_3(aq) + 3H_2(g); \quad \Delta H = +223,900 \text{ cal.}$$

The finished cell liquor is pumped to tanks where it is heated with live steam to 90°C. to destroy any hypochlorite present. The liquor is analyzed to determine the chromate content, and the required amount of barium chloride is introduced to precipitate almost all of the chromate present. The graphite mud from the electrodes and the barium chromate settle to the bottom of the tank, and the clear liquor is pumped through a sand filter to evaporator storage tanks. The liquor in the storage tank is neutralized with soda ash and is evaporated in a double-effect evaporator until it contains approximately 700 grams per liter of sodium chlorate. After evaporation, the liquor is allowed to settle to remove the sodium chloride which constitutes the *recovered* salt and chlorate, to be used over again. The settled liquid is filtered and cooled. This cooling requires 3 to 5 days, and the crystals of sodium chlorate are spun in a centrifugal and dried.

Potassium perchlorate[2] is made by converting sodium chlorate into sodium perchlorate in steel electrolytic cells which have platinum anodes and operate at 5.5 to 6.0 volts, 2,500 amp., and a temperature of 65°C. Filtered potassium chloride is added to the sodium perchlorate, precipitating potassium perchlorate crystals which are centrifuged, washed, and dried. The mother liquor now contains sodium chloride which can be used as cell feed for sodium chlorate manufacture.

OTHER PRODUCTS

Elsewhere in this book a few electrolytic processes are presented as in the special chapter (15) pertaining to caustic soda and chlorine. Electrolytic hydrogen and oxygen are included with the other procedures for hydrogen in Chap. 8 on Industrial Gases. Mention is made of electrolytic fluorine in Chap. 21.

[1] ANON., Electrolytic Sodium Chlorate, *Chem. Met. & Eng.*, **51** (11), 130 (1944), with pictured flow sheet of plant of Pennsylvania Salt Mfg. Co., operating at 80 to 90°C.

[2] SCHUMACHER, Continuous Electrolytic Process for Perchlorate, *Chem. & Met. Eng.*, **51** (12), 108 (1944), with a pictured flow sheet; Chlorates and Perchlorates, *Chem. Eng. Progr.*, **43**, 177 (1947).

ORGANIC COMPOUNDS

Electroorganic chemical preparations are not of great commercial importance at the present time, although the literature contains much information on organic reactions that can be carried out by the aid of electricity.[1] One of the few industrially important organic electrolytic reactions was the production of mannitol and sorbitol from glucose; this electrolytic reduction has been superseded by a cheaper catalytic hydrogenation (Chap. 30).

PRIMARY AND SECONDARY CELLS

Chemical reactions can be utilized to convert chemical energy into electrical energy, the converse of the procedures presented in the earlier parts of this chapter. The chemical reaction can be caused to take place in a unit specially designed for the purpose of obtaining the electrical energy. These units are commonly called *cells* or *batteries*.[2] Primary cells produce electricity by means of a chemical reaction that is not easily reversible, and thus the chemicals must be replaced after the reaction has taken place. Secondary cells depend upon chemical reactions that are reversible by electrical energy and thus do not require replacement of the chemical components. Obviously then the cost of electrical energy from primary batteries is very high, especially if they are used for the production of large quantities of energy.

The commonest primary cell today is the *dry cell*. This consists of a zinc container which serves as one electrode and a carbon rod which is the other electrode. The electrolyte is a water solution of ammonium chloride and zinc chloride adsorbed in flour or starch and manganese dioxide. The manganese dioxide is added as a depolarizer. Graphite is usually introduced into this mixture to increase the conductivity. The whole cell is insulated by a cardboard container.

The most important secondary cell is the *lead storage battery*. The reactions that take place on discharge are

At positive plate:

$$PbO_2(s) + 4H^+(aq) + 2e \rightarrow Pb^{++}(aq) + 2H_2O(l)$$
$$\underline{Pb^{++}(aq) + SO_4^{--}(aq) \rightarrow PbSO_4(s)}$$
$$PbO_2(s) + 4H^+(aq) + SO_4^{--}(aq) + 2e \rightarrow PbSO_4(s) + 2H_2O(l)$$

[1] For an extensive list of electrochemical preparations, see SWANN, Electro-organic Chemical Preparations, I and II, *Trans. Electrochem. Soc.*, **69**, 287 (1936); **77**, 459 (1940); SITTIG, Put Electro Organic Chemistry to Work, *Chem. Eng.*, **59** (1), 150 (1952).

[2] PERRY, *op. cit.*, pp. 1788–1793, gives diagrams and descriptions of various cells.

At negative plate:

$$Pb(s) \rightarrow Pb^{++}(aq) + 2e$$
$$\underline{Pb^{++}(aq) + SO_4^{--}(aq) \rightarrow PbSO_4(s)}$$
$$Pb(s) + SO_4^{--}(aq) \rightarrow PbSO_4(s) + 2e$$

The over-all reaction would then be:

$$Pb(s) + PbO_2(s) + 4H^+(aq) + 2SO_4^{--}(aq) \rightarrow 2PbSO_4 + 2H_2O$$

Electrical energy is generated when these reactions take place. To restore the activity or recharge the battery, electrical energy is applied to it and the reactions are reversed. On discharge, the *negative* plate acts as an anode and on charge as a cathode. On discharge, the *positive* plate acts as a cathode and on charge as an anode. The battery consists of lead plates in the form of a grid filled, when charged, with lead peroxide on the positive plate and sponge lead on the negative plate. The plates are insulated from each other by means of separators which formerly were made of cedar but at present are made of glass. The battery is filled with dilute sulfuric acid. The ordinary battery consists of 13 or 15 plates per cell and has 3 cells in series. It will deliver 2 volts per cell or 6 volts for the complete battery.

The only other widely used secondary cell is the *Edison battery*.[1] The positive plate consists of nickel peroxide and flaked metallic nickel; the negative plate is finely divided iron. The electrolyte consists of a mixture of potassium hydroxide and lithium hydroxide. A newer type employs nickel and cadmium electrodes.

SELECTED REFERENCES

Mantell, C. L., "Industrial Electrochemistry," 3d ed., McGraw-Hill Book Company, Inc., New York, 1950.

Koehler, W. A., "Applications of Electrochemistry," 2d ed., John Wiley & Sons, Inc., New York, 1944.

Creighton, H. J., "Principles and Applications of Electrochemistry," 4th ed., John Wiley & Sons, Inc., New York, 1943.

Glasstone, S., "An Introduction to Electrochemistry," D. Van Nostrand Company, Inc., New York, 1942.

Kortum, C., and J. O'M. Bockris, "Textbook of Electrochemistry," Vol. 1, Elsevier Press, Inc., Houston, Tex., 1951. Thermodynamic viewpoint.

Brockman, C. J., "Electrochemistry, Principles and Practice," D. Van Nostrand Company, Inc., New York, 1931.

MacInnes, D. A., "The Principles of Electrochemistry," Reinhold Publishing Corporation, New York, 1939.

[1] PERRY, *op. cit.*, p. 1793.

CHAPTER 17

ELECTROTHERMAL INDUSTRIES

Many chemical products, made at high temperatures, demand the use of an electric furnace. Electric furnaces are capable of producing temperatures as high as 4100°C. This may be contrasted with the highest commercial combustion-furnace temperatures of about 1700°C. The effects of high temperature are twofold: the *speed* of the reaction is *increased* and *new conditions* of *equilibrium* are established. These new equilibrium conditions have resulted in the production of compounds unknown before the electric furnace. Silicon and calcium carbides are examples of new products thus formed. The electric furnace affords more exact control and more concentration of heat with less thermal loss than is possible with other types of furnace. This favorable situation is caused by lack of flue gases and by the high temperature gradient between the source of heat and the heated mass. The electric furnace is much cleaner and more convenient to operate than the combustion furnace. It is operated by alternating current of large amperage usually with moderate voltage, while the electrolytic industries require direct current.

The three chief types of electric furnaces are arc, induction, and resistance. The heat in the arc furnace is produced by an electric arc between two or more electrodes, which are usually graphite or carbon between the electrodes and the furnace charge or between two or more electrodes, which are usually graphite or carbon and may or may not be consumed in the operation. The furnace itself is generally a cylindrical shell lined with a refractory material. Its use is not limited to those industries for which it is a necessity; there are some companies with rolling-mill operations on common-quality steels where electric-arc furnaces are the sole source of their ingots.

The induction furnace may be applied only for conducting substances such as metals where the electrical energy is converted into heat by the induced currents set up in the charge. The furnace can be considered as a transformer with the secondary consisting of the metallic charge while the primary consists of heavy copper coils connected to the power source. Induction furnaces operate at frequencies from 60 to 500,000 cycles per second, but those used in commercial-scale electrothermal processes do not usually use frequencies above 6,000 cycles per sec. The heating effect is obtained with lower field strengths as the frequency is increased. The

330

charge should be placed around an iron core in the low-frequency furnace, but this core is unnecessary for high-frequency furnaces.

When the charged material furnishes the electrical resistance required for the necessary heat, the furnace is a *direct-heated* resistance one; when high-resistance material is added to the charge for the purpose of creating heat, the furnace is *indirect-heated*.[1] In the electrochemical industry, the arc and the resistance furnaces are used mostly.

ARTIFICIAL ABRASIVES

History. Previous to 1891 all the abrasives used were natural products such as diamonds, corundum, emery, garnet, quartz, kieselguhr, and rouge. In that year E. G. Acheson produced the first man-made abrasive in a homemade electric-arc furnace while attempting to harden clay. Acheson found these new hard purple crystals to be silicon carbide. Discovering that these crystals were hard enough to cut glass, he sold them, under the trade-mark Carborundum, to gem polishers for $880 per pound.[2] Another make of silicon carbide is sold under the trade-mark Crystolon. Fused aluminum oxide, the most extensively used abrasive, is manufactured in the electric thermal furnace. Boron carbide, the hardest substance yet made synthetically, is also an electrothermal product.

Uses and Economics. The discovery and production of artificial abrasives were the springboards for the evolution of modern grinding tools which are of paramount importance in the modern precise fabrication of multitudinous metal parts for automobiles, airplanes, rifles, cannon, and other manufactured items of present-day industrial endeavor. To reduce wear, harder and harder alloys are being developed by the metallurgist, many of which can be finally shaped economically only by these hard artificial abrasives. Silicon carbide and alumina are also used as a refractory material, both in the form of brick and as loose material for ramming in place. In 1952 the United States and Canada produced 91,531 short tons of silicon carbide and 180,375 short tons of fused aluminum oxide. Of these quantities 47 per cent of silicon carbide and 4 per cent of aluminum oxide were used for nonabrasive purposes,[3] principally as refractories.

Silicon Carbide. The raw materials for the production of silicon carbide[4] are sand and carbon. The carbon is obtained from anthracite, coke, pitch,

---

[1] STANSEL, "Industrial Electric Heating," pp. 85–89, John Wiley & Sons, Inc., New York, 1933.

[2] COOPER, Modern Abrasives, *J. Chem. Educ.*, **19,** 122 (1942); UPPER, The Manufacture of Abrasives, *J. Chem. Educ.*, **26,** 676 (1949).

[3] "Minerals Yearbook," 1952.

[4] RUFF, Formation and Dissociation of Silicon Carbide, *Trans. Electrochem. Soc.*, **68,** 87 (1935); TONE, High Temperature Products of Silicon, *Ind. Eng. Chem.*, **23,** 1312 (1931).

or petroleum cokes. The sand contains 98 to 99.5 per cent silica. The equations usually given for the reactions involved are

$$\mathrm{SiO_2}(c) + 2\mathrm{C}(amorph.) \rightarrow \mathrm{Si}(c) + 2\mathrm{CO}(g); \qquad \Delta H = +144{,}800 \text{ cal.}$$
$$\mathrm{Si}(c) + \mathrm{C}(amorph.) \rightarrow \mathrm{SiC}(c); \qquad \Delta H = -30{,}500 \text{ cal.}$$

The total reaction, obtained by combining these equations, is

$$\mathrm{SiO_2}(c) + 3\mathrm{C}(amorph.) \rightarrow \mathrm{SiC}(c) + 2\mathrm{CO}(g); \qquad \Delta H = +114{,}300 \text{ cal.}$$

Figure 1 is a flow sheet for the production of silicon carbide. Sand and carbon are mixed in the approximate mole ratio of 1 to 3 and charged into

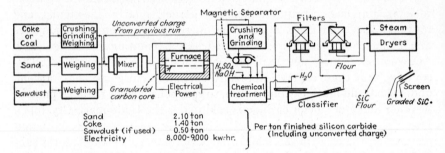

Sand	2.10 ton	
Coke	1.40 ton	Per ton finished silicon carbide
Sawdust (if used)	0.50 ton	(Including unconverted charge)
Electricity	8.000–9,000 kw.-hr.	

FIG. 1. Flow sheet for silicon carbide.

the furnace. Sawdust, if added, increases the porosity of the charge to permit the circulation of vapors and the escape of the carbon monoxide produced. The charge is built up in the furnace around a heating core of granular carbon. This core is in the center of the 30- to 50-ft.-long furnace and connects the electrodes. The walls of the furnace are loose firebrick supported by iron castings and are taken away at the end of a charge to facilitate product removal. Excessive heat loss does not occur because the outside unreacted charge serves as an insulator. A typical initial current between the electrodes is 6,000 amp. at 230 volts and the final is 20,000 amp. at 75 volts.[1] This change in voltage is due to the decrease in the resistance of the charge as the reaction progresses. The temperature at the core is 2200°C. The temperature should not get too high or the silicon carbide will decompose with volatilization of the silicon and formation of graphite. Indeed artificial graphite was so discovered. The energy efficiency is about 50 per cent with a chemical conversion of from 70 to 80 per cent.

The time of the reaction is about 60 hr.—36 hr. of heating and 24 hr. of cooling. After cooling, the silicon carbide crystals are removed with a yield of about 6 to 8 tons per furnace. The larger pieces of crystals are broken, washed, and cleaned by chemical treatment with sulfuric acid and caustic soda. The crystals are classified and screened, the finished

[1] PERRY, op. cit., p. 1819.

product ranging from 6 mesh to fine powder. The outer unreacted part of the charge is combined with the next charge for the furnace.

A part of the core used in the furnace can be made of coke suitable for graphite manufacture. After the run is completed, the graphite can be separated from the silicon carbide and converted to desired shapes.[1]

Fused Aluminum Oxide. The raw material for fused aluminum oxide abrasives such as those sold under the trade-marks Alundum and Aloxite may be an impure bauxite, often called *red bauxite*. The impurities,

FIG. 2. Electric-resistance furnace in which Carborundum brand silicon carbide is produced. (*Courtesy of The Carborundum Company.*)

mainly iron and silicon oxides, have a great effect on the structure and properties and must be carefully controlled. Pure alumina is also fused for particular demands as where the grinding-wheel temperature must be kept low. In any case the aluminous material should be calcined before charging into the furnace.

The vertical arc-resistance furnace consists of a circular steel shell about 7 ft. high resting on a crucible carbon base about 5 ft. in diameter. The shell has a slight taper at the top for easy removal from the pig. The outside surface of the furnace is water-cooled so that the unfused alumina around the walls furnishes a refractory lining for the furnace. The round carbon electrodes are lowered into the furnace and arcs are drawn between them and the fused furnace charge. The fusion is usually started by forming a trench in the top of the "starting batch" and packing it with coarse

[1] VARZANOV and NEGOVSKII, Production of Graphite in Silicon Carbide Furnace, Russian Pat. 52908 (1938).

coke. The electrodes are lowered to make contact with opposite ends of the trench. As soon as the alumina begins to fuse, it carries the current and the starting coke is rapidly consumed. A typical charge to the furnace is calcined bauxite (89 per cent), coke (2 per cent), and scrap iron (9 per cent). The charge is added as fast as it fuses between the arcs, and this molten alumina carries the current while much of the iron and silica is reduced to form a heavy alloy and sinks to the bottom. As the level of fused alumina rises,[1] the electrodes are raised and more charge is added until finally the furnace is full. Then the current is shut off and the entire mass cooled under controlled conditions to obtain the texture desired. Although this product has the hardness 9 in the Moh scale for corundum, it is blebbular in structure and not uniform, and therefore bearings cannot be made from it. The cooled ingots are broken up by roll crushers, washed with chemical solutions, and sieved. The product is fabricated into abrasive wheels, papers, and powders, or into refractory shapes. For the hard bearings necessary for watches and modern instruments, *artificial corundum* or white sapphire is made by crystallizing through fusion *pure* alumina in a hydrogen-oxygen upside-down flame by the Verneuil process. The crystal boules are cut and polished as desired. Many gems are also made by this same process.

Boron Carbide.[2] This is the hardest abrasive ever made artificially, though far from the hardness of the diamond. It first made its appearance in 1934 under the name *Norbide*. The reaction for its production is as follows:

$$2B_2O_3 + 7C \rightarrow B_4C + 6CO$$

The boric oxide is caused to react with coke in a carbon resistance furnace at 2600°C. The product is about 99 per cent B_4C. It finds specialized use as a powdered abrasive and in molded shapes such as nozzles for sandblasting. Other such products as tungsten and tantalum carbide are also manufactured.

CALCIUM CARBIDE

History. The first production of calcium carbide was an accident. In 1892, Thomas L. Willson was attempting to prepare metallic calcium from lime and tar in an electric furnace at Spray, N.C. The product obtained, obviously not calcium, was thrown into a near-by stream and Willson was amazed to note that it liberated great quantities of combustible gas.

---

[1] PERRY, *op. cit.*, p. 1819, energy consumption and other technical data are given; COOPER, *op. cit.*

[2] RIDGWAY, Boron Carbide, *Trans. Electrochem. Soc.*, **66**, 117 (1934); U.S. Pat. 1897214; KIRK and OTHMER, *op. cit.*, Vol. 2, pp. 830–834.

The first factory for the production of calcium carbide was built at Niagara Falls in 1896.[1]

Uses and Economics. Calcium carbide is consumed by two principal procedures: to manufacture cyanamide by combining it with nitrogen and to prepare acetylene by reacting it with water. The cyanamide is made by heating calcium carbide in an atmosphere of nitrogen (see Chap. 20). A substantial proportion of the total calcium carbide produced is converted to cyanamide, but about 70 per cent of the carbide made is used in making acetylene. Acetylene is a very important raw material for a great variety of chemical syntheses and as a fuel for welding torches. A small amount of calcium carbide is employed as a reducing agent in some metallurgical processes and as a drying agent. In 1953, 793,335 tons of calcium carbide were produced.

Manufacture. Calcium carbide[2] is prepared from quicklime and carbon at 2000 to 2200°C. The source of carbon is usually coke, anthracite, or petroleum coke. Coke is most widely used. It should be

$$CaO(c) + 3C(amorph.) \rightarrow CaC_2(l) + CO(g); \qquad \Delta H = +111,000 \text{ cal.}$$

compact and have a low ash content, a low ignition point, and high electrical resistivity so that the bulk of the furnace charge is highly resistant to the flow of energy. Thus the energy is concentrated, resulting in more rapid and complete reaction. Phosphorus should be absent as it forms a phosphide which is converted to poisonous phosphine, PH_3, when the carbide is made into acetylene. The quicklime is produced by burning limestone containing at least 97 per cent calcium carbonate. Impurities such as magnesia, silica, and iron hamper production and give a less pure carbide.

The carbide furnace is not a true arc-resistance furnace, but has been developed from the familiar arc furnace. Ingot furnaces, similar to those producing fused aluminum oxide, have been replaced in the carbide industry by continuous or intermittent tapping furnaces producing molten carbide. The furnace consists of a steel shell with the side walls lined with ordinary firebrick and the bottom covered with carbon blocks or anthracite to withstand the extremely hot, alkaline conditions. Most of the larger furnaces use three-phase electrical current and have suspended in the shell three vertical electrodes.

Improvements include the "closed" furnace where almost all the carbon monoxide from the reaction is collected and utilized, and Söderberg continuous self-baking electrodes which permit larger-capacity furnaces

---

[1] ANON., Carbide and Acetylene, *Chem. Eng.*, **57** (6), 129 (1950).

[2] KIRK and OTHMER, *op. cit.*, Vol. 2, p. 337; NIEBANCK, The Carbide Industry, *Chem. Eng.*, **57** (6), 131 (1950); see pictured flow sheet, *Chem. & Met. Eng.*, **47**, 253 (1940).

than did the old prebaked electrodes. The capacity range of the furnaces is generally between 5,000 to 18,000 kw.-hr. or higher, and a three-phase tapping furnace of 25,000 kw-hr. produces about 200 tons of commercial product (usually 85 per cent carbide) per day. The approximate consumption of materials per ton of carbide is 1,900 lb. lime, 1,300 lb. coke, 35 lb. electrode paste, and 3,000 kw.-hr. energy (see Fig. 1, Chap. 20). The lime and coke are charged continuously with intermittent or continuous tapping of the liquid product directly into cast-iron chill pots of about 5 tons capacity each. The carbide is cooled, crushed, and sized, then packed in 10- to 220-lb. steel drums or up to 5 ton containers for shipping.

MISCELLANEOUS ELECTROTHERMAL PRODUCTS

Carbon Disulfide. About 500,000,000 lb. of carbon disulfide are produced in the United States annually with a value of around $25,000,000. Although it is employed mostly for the manufacture of viscose rayon and cellophane, it does have many smaller uses such as a solvent and as an insecticide.

Carbon disulfide is made by the reaction:

$$C + 2S \xrightarrow{\text{750--1000°C.}} CS_2$$

This reaction is carried out by either the retort or the electrothermal process. A newer process uses hydrocarbons and sulfur as the raw materials,[1] but at present there is only one small commercial installation. The retort process utilizes direct-fired steel or cast-iron retorts. These retorts are generally cylinders, 8 to 10 ft. long and 2 to 3 ft. in diameter with a daily carbon disulfide production of 1,000 to 3,000 lb. each. The retorts are set in gas-heated furnaces in a bank or series where liquid sulfur and charcoal are charged batchwise to the individual retort. The products are distilled through overhead condensers where the carbon disulfide is separated. Generally, the carbon disulfide is purified by lime, but more efficient practice utilizes refrigeration. The electrothermal process is carried out[2] in a shaft electric-arc furnace where the sulfur melted by the arc comes into contact with the charcoal, forming the carbon disulfide which is then volatilized. This is an illustration of the applicability of the electric furnace to specialized conditions with excellent efficiency. The furnace is constructed with an inner tube containing the charcoal and up which the carbon disulfide passes. Around this is a concentric ring with the

---

[1] KIRK and OTHMER, *op. cit.*, Vol. 3, pp. 142–148; FOLKINS, *et al.*, Carbon Disulfide from Natural Gas and Sulfur, *Ind. Eng. Chem.*, **42**, 2202 (1950).

[2] TAYLOR, Carbon Disulfide, *Trans. Am. Electrochem. Soc.*, **1,** 115 (1902); **2,** 185 (1902); PERRY, *op. cit.*, p. 1820 (data given); for a pictured flow sheet, see *Chem. Eng.*, **58** (1), 174 (1951).

sulfur. The multiple electrodes are at the bottom where the reaction occurs.

Fused Silica. This very useful material of construction for the chemical industries is heated to fabrication temperature in an electric furnace.

Artificial Graphite and Electrodes. These are described in Chap. 9 devoted to carbon, while *phosphorus* is presented in Chap. 18 on Phosphorus Industries. See also Table 2 in Chap. 16 for a summary of the various products made by electrochemical processes.

SELECTED REFERENCES

Mantell, C. L., "Industrial Electrochemistry," 3d ed., McGraw-Hill Book Company, Inc., New York, 1950.

Pond, G. G., "Calcium Carbide and Acetylene," Pennsylvania State College, State College, Pa., 1908.

Stansel, N. R., "Industrial Electric Heating," John Wiley & Sons, Inc., New York, 1933.

Taussig, R., "Die Industrie des Calciumcarbides," W. Knapp Verlag, Halle, Germany, 1930.

Landis, W. S., Chap. 12 in "Rogers' Manual of Industrial Chemistry," 6th ed., C. C. Furnas, editor, D. Van Nostrand Company, Inc., New York, 1942.

Mantell, C. L., Electrochemistry, Sec. 28 in Perry, *op. cit.* This section, embracing pp. 1771–1826, is a very practical summary with many excellent tabulations (*e.g.*, Materials of Construction) and diagrams of furnaces.

CHAPTER 18

PHOSPHORUS INDUSTRIES

Owing chiefly to an aggressive and intelligent consumption promotion on the part of the various manufacturers as well as the Federal agencies, the use of artificial fertilizers, phosphoric acid, and phosphate salts and derivatives has increased greatly. However, before these products could be as widely consumed in their fast developing fields, newer, more efficient, and less expensive methods of production had to be developed. During the recent decades, the various phosphate industries have made rapid strides in cutting the costs of production and have thus enabled phosphorus, phosphoric acid, and its salts to be employed in wider fields, and newer derivatives to be introduced. The phosphorus[1] industry is the fastest-growing branch of the inorganic field and one of the few that has not been overshadowed by the fast-moving organic chemical developments of recent years. Indeed, phosphorus-organic compounds are of increasing industrial importance each year.

CALCIUM PHOSPHATES

Historical. The use of phosphatic materials as fertilizers was practiced unknowingly long before the isolation and discovery of phosphorus by the German alchemist, Brand, in 1669. As early as 200 B.C., the Carthaginians recommended and employed bird dung for increasing the yields from their fields. The Incas of Peru prized guano and bird dung on their islands so highly that it was made a capital offense to kill any of the birds. Then too, we are all familiar with the use of fish and bones by the American Indian in his crude agricultural methods. Bones and guano continued to be the chief sources of phosphorus and phosphoric acid until after the middle of the nineteenth century, but these supplies were and still are limited.

In 1842 a British patent was issued to John B. Lawes for the treatment of bone ash with sulfuric acid. This patent marked the beginning of the

[1] WAGGAMAN, "Phosphoric Acids, Phosphates, and Phosphatic Fertilizers," 2d ed., Reinhold Publishing Corporation, New York, 1952. This is an excellent book and should be freely consulted.

large acid phosphate industry which became the basis of our domestic fertilizer industry.

Soon afterward various grades of phosphate ores were discovered in England. These were first finely ground and applied directly to the soil. It was soon recognized, however, that treatment of these phosphate minerals with sulfuric acid increased the availability and efficiency of the phosphate for agricultural purposes. This process was so timely that by 1862 the annual production of superphosphates in England had reached 200,000 tons. Table 1 shows the United States distribution of phosphate rock by uses.

Raw Material. Phosphate rock, when very finely pulverized, has an important but limited use as a fertilizer itself, owing chiefly to the relatively slow availability of the P_2O_5. However, its main consumption is as a raw material for the manufacture of phosphoric acid and superphosphate. Florida has been the principal producing area for phosphate rock with Tennessee ranking second until recently. Now Idaho ranks above Tennessee. The United States has slightly over half of the world's estimated reserves of nearly 29 billion tons of phosphate rock.[1] Table 2 shows phosphate rock mined over a period of years.

In Florida both hard and pebble rock phosphate are mined. Hard rock phosphate occurs as nodules and boulders in irregular pockets but only one company is now actively exploiting these deposits. The more extensive and cheaply mined pebble deposits occur with an average of 20 ft. of overburden whose phosphatic value is too low to process and from 10 to 30 ft. of ore called *matrix* in the industry. This matrix is composed of clay slimes, silica sand, and phosphate pebble. The sizes range from pebbles at $1\frac{1}{2}$ to 2 in. (small amount) down to 400 mesh. The overburden is removed generally by a drag line which dumps into a previously mined-out cut. Drag-line operations remove the matrix and drop it into an excavated area. Hydraulic guns break down the mud in the matrix and wash it to the pump suction where it is transported through hoses by large sand pumps to the beneficiation plant (Fig. 1).

In Tennessee four types of phosphate rock are found—nodular, blue, white, and brown. Only the latter is mined at present, following somewhat the Florida procedures. The overburden here is at extreme varying depths with an average of from 6 to 8 ft.

Although originally deposited in horizontal layers,[2] the large Western

[1] WILKERSON, Processing Phosphate Rock for Use in Agriculture, *Ind. Eng. Chem.*, **41**, 1316 (1949); *cf.* Chap. 33, Phosphate Rock, by FULTON in "Industrial Minerals and Rocks," 2d ed., American Institute of Mining and Metallurgical Engineers, 1949; MANSFIELD, Phosphate Deposits of the World, *Ind. Eng. Chem.*, **34**, 9 (1942).

[2] See WAGGAMAN and BELL, Western Phosphates . . . Factors Affecting Development, *Ind. Eng. Chem.*, **42**, 269 (1950); Western Phosphates . . . Potential Markets, *Ind. Eng. Chem.*, **42**, 286 (1950).

TABLE 1. USE DISTRIBUTION OF PHOSPHATE ROCK IN THE UNITED STATES[a]
(In long tons)

•	1949	1952
Superphosphate..............................	5,598,423	6,494,921
Phosphates, phosphoric acid, phosphorus, ferro-phosphorus................................	1,254,615	2,024,206
Direct application to soil......................	732,695	1,205,993
Fertilizer filler..............................	18,815	15,737
Stock and poultry feed........................	62,236	179,186
Undistributed................................	3,330	2,166
Exports......................................	1,316,819	1,401,949
Total....................................	8,986,933	11,324,158
Total value at mines........................	$51,415,027	$68,120,918

[a] "Minerals Yearbook," 1950 and 1952.

TABLE 2. PHOSPHATE ROCK SOLD OR USED IN THE UNITED STATES[a]
(In thousands of long tons)

Average value at mine per long ton	Year	Florida	Tennessee	Western states	United States
$3.54	1934	2,465	394	39	2,898
3.46	1938	2,723	1,000	138	3,860
3.57	1942	2,985	1,568	266	4,819
4.52	1946	5,280	1,316	572	7,169
5.17	1947	6,381	1,490	1,240	9,111
5.83	1948	7,184	1,500	704	9,388
5.72	1949	6,695	1,403	779	8,877
5.76	1950	8,597	1,472	1,045	11,114
5.97	1951	8,497	1,419	1,178	11,095
5.94	1952	8,781	1,452	1,091	11,324
6.13	1953	9,167	1,622	1,729	12,518

[a] Various "Minerals Yearbooks" up to 1952. "Chemical Statistics Handbook," Manufacturing Chemists' Association, Washington, 1955. The statistics for phosphate rock in Tables 1 and 2 refer to the beneficiated rock. As mined during 1953, for example, the long tons for the impure rock were 40,139,000, which furnished the U.S. consumption indicated in Table 2 plus 1,950,158 long tons net exports.

fields of phosphate rock have been severely folded, faulted, and elevated by crustal deformations and resemble fissure veins. The rock may contain approximately 75 per cent bone phosphate of lime[1] but, owing to admixture with wall material, it usually averages nearer 70 per cent b.p.l. Because of its rather soft structure, the rock has a moisture content of 4 to 6 per cent. It is generally mined by underground methods.

[1] This is usually abbreviated b.p.l. and actually means tricalcium phosphate, that being the chief inorganic constituent of bones.

Florida and Western phosphate rock contain anywhere from 0.2 to 0.8 lb. uranium per ton of rock. The complicated and costly recovery process now in use extracts uranium from phosphate rock via wet-process phosphoric acid, where the uranium goes into solution upon treatment with sulfuric acid. After filtration, the bulk of the uranium is found in the acid filtrate. All details of this process are restricted by the Atomic Energy Act. Much research is focused on uranium recovery from normal superphosphate manufacture where larger tonnages are involved. Fluorine and vanadium are also valuable by-products from phosphate rock.

In the Florida pebble district, the recovery was initially only of the coarse phosphate rock which had a high b.p.l. while the fines, with a much lower b.p.l., representing about an equal tonnage, were wasted. In the 1920's experimental work was started to develop a froth-flotation process which would increase the b.p.l. of the fines or raw matrix to at least 66 or 68 per cent from about 40 per cent or under. This procedure is frequently spoken of as *beneficiation*, and one of the successful processes currently employed is illustrated by Fig. 1. Such upgrading operations are of far-reaching and increasing importance as the easily mined or better-grade deposits of phosphate rock, or any other mineral, become exhausted. These operations not only produce a higher grade of product but enable larger amounts to be recovered, beneficiated, and used, even in the case of such a low-priced product as phosphate rock which sells for about $6 per long ton. Beneficiation was largely abandoned in Tennessee when it was found that the deslimed phosphatic sand on which it worked best could be used directly in electric furnaces to produce elemental phosphorus. The bulk of the high-grade lump rock and sands in Tennessee has been exhausted and operations would mostly be abandoned were it not for cheap electricity for the phosphorus furnaces and economical mechanical mining operations.

The matrix from the Florida phosphate pebble deposits is beneficiated through three general sequences as shown in Fig. 1: (1) washing, milling, classifying, and screening to give *coarse rock* and *fine rock;* (2) hydroseparation, classification, and table concentration of the -14- to $+150$-mesh raw feed, to give *classifier product* and *table concentrate product;* and (3) hydroseparation and flotation of the -35 to $+150$ mesh to give a *flotation concentrate product*. In the flotation (third sequence), the ore is separated as a froth in the first flotation cells, from the sand which is sent to tailings waste. Following this, the phosphate ore is acidulated, deoiled, and subjected to another flotation machine where the remaining silica is floated off using an amine for the flotation agent. The coarse and fine rock, and the other products are taken to the phosphate plant for acidulation or other chemical treatment.

Uses and Economics. As can be seen in Table 1 the most important use of phosphate rock is in fertilizers. Table 3 gives a compilation of phosphate-rock treatment processes. Tricalcium phosphate in raw and/or steamed and degreased bones and in basic slag is also used after grinding as a direct phosphate fertilizer. A small percentage of the former is sometimes treated with sulfuric acid for superphosphate or as a source material for phosphate chemicals. Some phosphate rock is applied directly on the

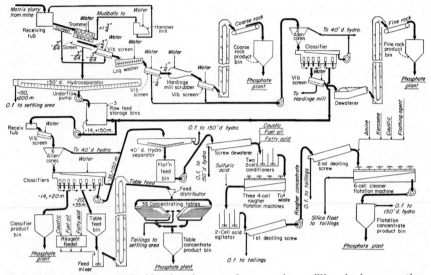

FIG. 1. Beneficiation of Florida phosphate ore by screening, milling, hydroseparation, classification, table concentration, and flotation in various sequences. O.f.: overflow. Numbers when marked '' are sizes in inches, but when given as −14, +150 mean fines through 14-mesh screen and over 150-mesh screen. In place of the Allen *cones*, some engineers prefer a rake or spiral classifier. See PERRY, *op. cit.*, pp. 924–926 classifiers, p. 940 Allen cones, pp. 941–947 hydroseparators (thickeners), pp. 955*ff.* screening, p. 1080 tabling, p. 1089 froth flotation. (*Courtesy of R. C. Specht.*)

soil after being dried and very finely ground, but most of it for fertilizer use is acidulated with sulfuric or nitric acid to form superphosphate. However, it has long been recognized that in the soil much of the citrate-soluble superphosphate is changed to water-insoluble tricalcium phosphate.[1] This is not a change from one form of $Ca_3(PO_4)_2$ to a finer divided one as "domestic phosphate rocks are essentially fluorapatite, admixed with various proportions of other compounds of calcium, fluorine, iron, aluminum and silicon."[2]

[1] Or to insoluble iron, aluminum, or magnesium phosphates; *cf.* BEAR and TOTH, Phosphate Fixation in Soil and Its Practical Control, *Ind. Eng. Chem.*, **34**, 49 (1942).

[2] ELMORE, *et al.*, Defluorination of Phosphate Rock in the Molten State, *Ind. Eng. Chem.*, **34**, 40 (1942); *cf.* EASTERWOOD, Recent Developments in the Phosphate Field, *Ind. Eng. Chem.*, **34**, 13 (1942); HENDRICKS, *et al.*, Structural Characteristics of Apatite-like Substances and Composition of Phosphate Rock and Bone as Determined from Microscopical and X-ray Diffraction Examinations, *Ind. Eng. Chem.*, **23**, 1413 (1931).

The formula of fluorapatite may be expressed,

$$(CaF)Ca_4(PO_4)_3 \text{ or } CaF_2 \cdot 3Ca_3P_2O_8$$

This compound is extremely insoluble. The various means for making the P_2O_5 content more soluble, not necessarily in water but in the plant juices,[1] are the manufacture of the various superphosphates, the defluorination of fluorapatite by the melting at about 1450°C. of phosphate rock, and the products of the processes where phosphate rock is fused with alkali metal salts or olivine.

The uses to which phosphate compounds are put in the fertilizer field are largely dependent upon the solubilities or the availability to the plants. These compounds may be classified:

1. *Water-insoluble products:* rock phosphate or fluorapatite, $CaF \cdot Ca_4(PO_4)_3$. This can be solubilized by the sulfuric or nitric acid of the superphosphate process or by the *slow* dissolving action of plant juices.

TABLE 3. PHOSPHATE-ROCK PROCESSING, PRODUCTS, AND BY-PRODUCTS[a]

Process	Raw materials and reagents	Main products and derivatives	By-products
Acidulation...	Phosphate rock, sulfuric acid, or nitric acid	Superphosphate, phosphoric acid, triple superphosphate, monoammonium phosphate, diammonium phosphate, monopotassium phosphate	Uranium, fluorine compounds, vanadium
Thermal reduction (electric or blast furnace)	Phosphate rock, siliceous flux, coke (for reduction), electric energy or fuel coke, condensing water	Phosphorus, phosphoric acid, triple superphosphate, monoammonium phosphate, diammonium phosphate, monopotassium phosphate, potassium metaphosphate	Fluorine compounds, carbon monoxide, slag (for RR ballast), ferrophosphorus, vanadium[b]
Calcium metaphosphate	Phosphate rock, phosphorus, air or oxygen	Calcium metaphosphate	Fluorine compounds
Calcination[c] or defluorination	Phosphate rock, silica, water or steam, fuel	Defluorinated phosphate	Fluorine compounds

[a] Data compiled from WAGGAMAN and BELL, Western Phosphates . . . Factors Affecting Development, *Ind. Eng. Chem.*, **42**, 269 (1950).

[b] Vanadium is present in appreciable quantities only in the Western phosphates.

[c] Includes processes wherein phosphate rock is fused with alkali metal salts or magnesium silicate (olivine).

[1] As measured by "citrate solubility."

2. *Citrate-soluble products:* dicalcium phosphate, $CaHPO_4$, commonly called *precipitated phosphate* or *precipitated bone;* basic slag, the calcium and potassium metaphosphates, the defluorinated phosphates (calcined phosphates and fused phosphate rock). Also part of the tricalcium phosphate of bone meal is citrate-soluble. These products are soluble in ammonium citrate solution and are considered to be available for plant food.

3. *Water-soluble products:* monocalcium phosphate, $CaH_4(PO_4)_2$, is the principal member of this class and is the chief ingredient of superphosphate. Here also are monoammonium and diammonium phosphates and monopotassium phosphate and some organic phosphates.

Manufacture of Superphosphate. The acidulation of phosphate rock to produce superphosphate[1] has been the most important method of making phosphate available for fertilizer purposes for nearly a century. The reactions have long been given as

$$Ca_3(PO_4)_2 + 2H_2SO_4 + 4H_2O \rightarrow CaH_4(PO_4)_2 + 2(CaSO_4 \cdot 2H_2O)$$

Monocalcium phosphate   Gypsum

$$CaF_2 + H_2SO_4 \rightarrow CaSO_4 + 2HF$$
$$4HF + SiO_2 \rightarrow SiF_4 + 2H_2O$$

In water, $\quad 3SiF_4 + 2H_2O \rightarrow SiO_2 + 2H_2SiF_6$

The following is a more probable expression of the main reaction:

$$2[(CaF)Ca_4(PO_4)_3] + 7H_2SO_4 + 3H_2O \rightarrow 3CaH_4(PO_4)_2 \cdot H_2O$$

Phosphate rock   Monocalcium phosphate

$$+ 2HF + 7CaSO_4 \cdot anhydrite$$

The hydrofluoric acid reacts as shown above, forming fluosilicic acid (see Chap. 21). An excess of sulfuric acid is consumed by such impurities in the phosphate rock as $CaCO_3$, Fe_2O_3, Al_2O_3, and CaF_2. The product increases in weight over the 70 to 75 per cent b.p.l. phosphate rock used as much as 70 per cent, resulting in a superphosphate with 16 to 20 per cent available P_2O_5. In 1950 about 60 per cent of the 54 to 56°Bé. sulfuric acid used in normal superphosphate was made in coexisting acid plants, 92 per cent from elemental sulfur.

The manufacture of superphosphate involves four steps: (1) preparation of phosphate rock, (2) mixing with acid, (3) curing and drying of the material, and (4) excavation, milling, and bagging of the finished product. Although a few plants use continuous processes, most plants still conduct these operations in the various separate steps described below. All plants first pulverize their rock. With modern pulverizing and air separation equipment, most rock is ground to an average fineness of 80 to 90 per cent through a 100-mesh screen, with the following benefits: (1) the reaction

[1] Symposium, Phosphates for Agriculture, *Ind. Eng. Chem.*, **41**, 1314 (1949). Phosphorics and Phosphates, *Ind. Eng. Chem.*, **44**, 1319 (1952).

rate is faster, (2) more efficient use is made of the sulfuric acid with consequent less acid, (3) a higher grade of product in better condition is
obtained. Figure 2 indicates the sequences of these steps, together with
ammoniation, when it is practiced.

1. *Den Process.* The reaction between the sulfuric acid and the mineral
rock in this method usually takes place in pan mixers (Fig. 4). The mixer
has a capacity of approximately 2 tons per charge, is of lead-covered cast

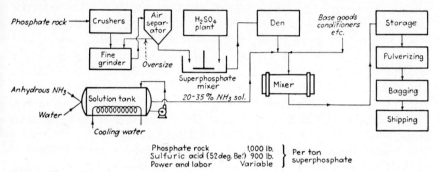

Phosphate rock   1,000 lb. } Per ton
Sulfuric acid (52deg. Bé') 900 lb.   } superphosphate
Power and labor   Variable

FIG. 2. Flow sheet for superphosphate. The product from the den is also sold after
aging, pulverizing, and bagging.

iron, and may be approximately 8 ft. in diameter and 2½ ft. in depth.
The pan itself is sometimes revolved on a vertical axis, while a set of
blades is rotated in the opposite direction. The phosphate rock and a
predetermined quantity of chamber or stronger sulfuric acid[1] (50 to
56°Bé.) are usually added simultaneously to the mixer and agitated 1 to
3 min. The sirupy mixture is usually dumped directly into a "den" below
the mixer. The den may be rectangular in shape, but it is frequently of a
cylindrical or silo type and is constructed of concrete or brick, holding
100 to 300 tons. To ensure complete reaction, the material is left in the
den for 6 to 24 hr. The temperature of the mass is usually above 100°C.,
and carbon dioxide, steam, and gaseous compounds of fluorine escape,
leaving a fairly dry and porous product. The superphosphate is removed
from the den by a clamshell shovel or other mechanical means and after
aeration is transferred to the storage pile where it is allowed to cure from
4 to 16 weeks. The superphosphate may be sold in this form directly, or
it may be artificially further dried and disintegrated to a uniform size.

2. *Continuous Processes.* The two continuous processes are: the Broadfield process and Sackett Super-Flow process. However, most superphosphate is made by the batch process described above. In the Broadfield
process the acid and dust rock are fed simultaneously, continuously, and
automatically into a cast-steel trough covered with a hood. In the trough
is a horizontal rotating shaft with mixing blades which advances the

[1] SHOELD, *et al.*, Rock-acid Ratio in Superphosphate Manufacture, *Ind. Eng. Chem.*,
41, 1334 (1949).

material and discharges it into a mechanical den. This is a slow-moving (4 ft. per min.) conveyer 30 ft. in length with moving sides also made of steel slats. Reaction time in the den is $1\frac{1}{4}$ hr., after which the material is stored.

The Sackett Super-Flow process[1] differs radically in the initial mixing of the rock and acid. Pulverized rock is delivered as a dust stream to the top of an acidulating tower along with an atomized spray of 56°Bé. sulfuric acid. During the movement through the tower the material undergoes rapid and final acidulation evolving hydrogen fluoride and other by-product gases which are flashed off, dissolved in water, and concentrated. The superphosphate drops from the bottom of the tower as a thin slurrylike material to a puddler which conveys it to the solidifier. The solidifier, a channel-like pallet conveyer, functions as the den in the older process and the material leaving it is ready for storage and curing. The final product has a hard, porous grain structure of good physical properties.

Granular Superphosphate.[2] The Oberphos process early utilized a method differing greatly from the den process to produce a granular product directly. This was expensive and other methods of granulation are used. Most feature self-aggregation of particles by moistening, tumbling, and rotary drying. The Davison process which will be described uses, as do all the other methods, the material as it comes from the den in the regular process.

The moist and warm crude superphosphate is brought by crane from the den to a feed hopper for the granulating and conditioning system. A variable-speed screw feeder transfers classifier dust to a conveyer system where it is mixed in with this moist superphosphate. The second step is extremely important since the granulating properties of the superphosphate depend upon the moisture content. The superphosphate goes from the feeding device to a "conditioner" which is a rotating cylinder and where the material is subjected to water sprays to form balls or granules and to accelerate the chemical acidulation. An operator is stationed at the discharge end, to watch constantly the material discharged and to adjust the sprays as necessary.

The conditioned material is fed into the oil-fired rotary drier, which is about 8 ft. in diameter and 50 ft. long, and discharged into a pit at its lower end. The combustion gases are drawn from the lower end and forced by a draft fan through a cyclone dust collector. The material is

---

[1] DEMMERLE and SACKETT, Continuous Superphosphate Production, *Ind. Eng. Chem.*, **41**, 1306 (1949); GARIBY, Instrumentation for Superphosphate Manufacture, *Ind. Eng. Chem.*, **41**, 1338 (1949).

[2] MACKALL and SHOELD, Granulating Phosphate Fertilizers, *Chem. & Met. Eng.*, **47**, 102 (1940); *cf. Chem. & Met. Eng.*, **50** (4), 132 (1943), for parallel picture flow sheets for the den and granulated superphosphates.

aged for at least 10 days as compared with the 4 to 12 weeks of storage required by the den process. The shorter period of cure is due to the accelerated acidulation of this process caused by improved mixing, proper moisture adjustment, and enhanced temperature. The granular product also is free flowing and handles and mixes better than the old powdery den product.

Nitric and Mixed Acid Acidulation of Phosphate Rock.[1] Europe probably first used nitric and mixed acid acidulation of phosphate rock. Nitric substitution for sulfuric acid is desirable since nitrogen has an essential value as plant food and can be resold at its purchase price. Also this saves sulfur. Simple acidulation with nitric acid produces a hygroscopic superphosphate since it contains calcium nitrate. T.V.A. has studied and recommended four processes for commercial purposes. In one the phosphate rock is *extracted* by mixed nitric and sulfuric acids, followed by ammoniation, drying, and addition of potassium chloride (optional). Another features mixed nitric and sulfuric *acidulation* followed by the previously described steps and the other two use nitric acid alone for the acidulation. These processes, as well as the conditioning against moisture absorption as practiced for ammonium nitrate, give promise to an extension of this use of nitric acid.

Triple Superphosphate. This material is a much more concentrated fertilizer than ordinary superphosphate, containing from 45 to 50 per cent of available P_2O_5 or nearly three times the amount in the regular superphosphate. Triple superphosphate is made by the action of phosphoric acid on the phosphate rock, and thus no diluent calcium sulfate is formed.

$$(CaF)Ca_4(PO_4)_3 + 7H_3PO_4 + 5H_2O \rightarrow 5CaH_4(PO_4)_2H_2O + HF$$

The cost per unit of P_2O_5 in this concentrate as compared with ordinary superphosphate is higher because of greater capital investment and additional labor and processing. However, this is offset to a great extent by the ability to use a lower-grade, cheaper phosphate rock than possible in the manufacture of ordinary superphosphate and the substantial savings on handling, bagging, shipping, and distributing. The production for 1953 of the *concentrated* superphosphate had grown to 457,235 short tons in terms of 100 per cent A.P.A. (available phosphoric acid). The *normal* superphosphate production had dropped slightly for 1953 to 1,678,459 tons A.P.A.

Most triple superphosphate is made from phosphoric acid produced by the sulfuric acid or wet method. T.V.A. has made many investigations

[1] TURRENTINE, Phosphate Production without Sulfuric Acid, *Chem. Eng. News*, **29**, 3454 (1951); HIGNETT, Nitric Acidulation of Rock Phosphate, *Chem. Eng.*, **58** (5), 166 (1951); CRITTENDEN, What's Ahead for Nitric Acid, *Chem. Eng.*, **59** (6), 177 (1952); YATES, *et al.*, Enriched and Concentrated Superphosphates, *Ind. Eng. Chem.*, **45**, 496 (1953).

into the use of electric-furnace acid and now recommends a continuous method. Bridger[1] and his associates recommend the following: Phosphoric acid "wet method" (2,800 lb. at 140°F.) and phosphate rock (1,500 lb. at 80 per cent -100 mesh) are added simultaneously to a 2-ton Steadman mixer (*cf.* den process). The mixture is thoroughly stirred for 3 min., and the slurry discharged into a bin or upon a conveyer belt which carries it to a reaction chamber where it sets up into a fairly stiff mass. After several hours it is removed to a pile for curing over a course of 3 weeks. The triple superphosphate is dried, cooled, crushed, screened, and stored. It may be granulated by moistening to form pellets and again dried.

Ammoniated Superphosphates. Ammoniation of superphosphate (Fig. 2), triple superphosphate, or mixtures produces a fertilizer with the desirable properties of chemical stability, uniformity in texture, and resistance to moisture. This has been proved an effective way of introducing nitrogen into finished fertilizers. Too much *uncombined* ammonia added to superphosphate causes excessive reversion of phosphate into insoluble forms. Because of this "nitrogen solutions" containing urea or ammonium nitrate are preferred in current ammoniation practice. Two typical solution compositions are, percentagewise: (1) Nitrogen solution 2A: NH_4NO_3, 65.0; NH_3, 21.7; H_2O, 13.3. (2) Urea ammonia liquor A: urea, 32.5; NH_3, 28.9; ammonium carbamate, 18.1; H_2O, 20.5. The ammoniation is done simply by spraying a measured weight or volume of ammoniation solution into a weighed quantity of solid material and mixing in a 1- or 2-ton rotary batch mixer. As discharged from the mixer, the material feels warm and moist. Upon cooling it becomes dry and friable. Ammoniated products cure rapidly and are easy to handle.

Calcium Metaphosphate.[2] In 1937, T.V.A. developed from phosphate rock a concentrated fertilizer, $Ca(PO_3)_2$, by the following reaction:

$$(CaF)Ca_4(PO_4)_3 + 3P_2O_5 + HPO_3 \rightarrow 5Ca(PO_3)_2 + HF$$

where the P_2O_5 contacts the lump rock in a vertical shaft.

Fused Tricalcium Phosphate and Other Calcined Phosphates. *Tricalcium phosphate*[3] containing about 28 per cent P_2O_5 is produced by defluorinating rock phosphate in an oil-fired shaft furnace as shown by the following presumed reaction:

$$2(CaF)Ca_4(PO_4)_3 + H_2O + SiO_2 \rightarrow 3Ca_3(PO_4)_2 + CaSiO_3 + 2HF$$

[1] BRIDGER, *et al.*, Continuous-mixing Process for Manufacture of Concentrated Superphosphate, *Ind. Eng. Chem.*, **39**, 1265 (1947); ANON., Continuous Triple-superphosphate, *Chem. Eng.*, **58** (5), 208 (1951), pictured flow sheet.

[2] YATES, *et al.*, Improved Fertilizer Plant Design, *Chem. Eng.*, **58** (6), 135 (1951).

[3] HIGNETT and HUBBUCH, Fused Tricalcium Phosphate, *Ind. Eng. Chem.*, **38**, 1208 (1946); HIGNETT and SIEGEL, Recovery of Fluorine from Stack Gases, *Ind. Eng. Chem.*, **41**, 2493 (1949).

If needed, silica is also charged to the furnace. The molten product, as it is tapped from the furnace, is granulated by high-velocity water jets and is prepared for shipment by drying, screening, and grinding the small percentage of oversize. More than 90 per cent of the fluorine in the stack can now be recovered through absorption in a limestone bed.

Calcium magnesium phosphate is a calcined phosphate fertilizer[1] resulting from the electric-furnace fusion of olivine (a natural magnesium silicate) and phosphate rock. Only Manganese Products, Inc., at Seattle produces this product commercially because of the limited operating requirements, *i.e.*, abundant supplies of olivine and electric power. This fertilizer is comparable with superphosphate in plant-food value, yet needs no curing, is noncorrosive, and is nonhygroscopic.

Dicalcium Phosphate. At the end of the Second World War production was less than 40,000 tons. In 1952 over 100,000 tons were manufactured and proposed expansion will bring this to 275,000 tons by 1955. Its growing use is as an animal-feed supplement. Dicalcium phosphate ordinarily is manufactured from phosphoric acid, or from water-soluble phosphates produced by the action of nitric or hydrochloric acid on bones or mineral phosphates, by neutralizing with lime. A new process[2] reacts phosphoric acid and phosphate rock removing the toxic fluorine and furnishing animal-feed-grade salt.

The following procedure has been used for the manufacture of *monocalcium phosphates*[3] for baking powders:

Monocalcium phosphate is made by placing a weighed amount of phosphoric acid of about 75 per cent strength in a stainless steel or ceramic-lined batch tub equipped with efficient agitators. Hot lime in slightly less than the calculated amount for the equation $CaO + 2H_3PO_4 \rightarrow CaH_4(PO_4)_2 \cdot H_2O$ is added at such rate that the temperature of the batch is maintained at about 75 to 110°C. Near the end of the reaction period the final traces of free phosphoric acid are neutralized with hydrated lime. The resulting product is a fairly dry lumpy material which is further dried under controlled temperature conditions and milled. The milled material is then screened or air separated into granular and powder products and bagged.

PHOSPHORUS

This element was first produced on a small commercial scale by treating calcined bone with sulfuric acid, filtering off the phosphoric acid, and evaporating it to specific gravity of 1.45. It was mixed with charcoal or

[1] MOULTON, Electric Furnace Fertilizer: Ca-Mg-Phosphate, *Chem. Eng.*, **56** (7), 102 (1949).

[2] ANON., A New Way to Make Dicalcium Phosphate, *Chem. Eng.*, **59** (12), 258 (1952).

[3] EASTERWOOD, in WAGGAMAN, *op. cit.*, p. 443.

coke, again heated, and the water evaporated off until the moisture content was less than 6 per cent. This mixture was placed in retorts and brought to white heat. The phosphorus was thus distilled off, collected under water, and purified by redistillation.

The production of phosphorus today still depends on the volatilization of the element from its compounds under reducing conditions. During the past decades, the method has changed chiefly in details and size of production. At the present time, elementary phosphorus is manufactured on a large scale as a heavy chemical and is shipped in tank cars from the point of initial manufacture, where the raw materials are cheap, to distant plants for its conversion to phosphoric acid, phosphates, and other compounds.

Uses and Economics. With the commercialization of cheaper methods for producing phosphorus on a large scale, widening fields have been developed for it and its compounds. Table 4 shows the production of the more important commercial compounds of phosphorus in recent years. Channels of consumption for phosphorus derivatives other than as fertilizers may be divided into four groups: (1) water treatment, (2) food and medicine, (3) phosphate esters, and (4) miscellaneous uses.

Excluding fertilizers, the main outlet for phosphorus derivatives is in *water treatment and detergents* as various sodium phosphates. These salts, because of their ability to precipitate or sequester lime and magnesia, to emulsify or disperse solids in the detergent solution, and to augment the inherent detergent properties of soap and synthetic surface-active agents, are much used as soap builders or detergent synergists. Trisodium phosphate (TSP) was the first and for many years the largest seller. It is still used in many household cleaning and washing powders, but the preference[1] for a sequestering agent which would tie up the Ca and Mg ions in water as soluble complexes without precipitation led to the development of tetrasodium pyrophosphate (TSPP) and sodium tripolyphosphate (STP). About three-fourths of all STP is made from electric-furnace acid and the rest by converting disodium phosphate into tripoly. Over 85 per cent of the tripoly production is employed as a builder in synthetic detergents. This salt was first brought onto the market in significant quantities only in 1945 but production in 1952 was around 360,000 tons, almost entirely as a builder in detergents. Mono- and disodium phosphates and metaphosphate also have water-softening properties and are extensively employed for boiler-water conditioning.

The *food* uses include the important medicinal compounds of the glycerophosphates and the hypophosphites as well as the sodium and calcium phosphates. Monocalcium phosphate is employed more extensively than all other chemical leavening agents. Sodium pyrophosphate is incorporated in the formulation of self-rising flours and baking powders as a bak-

[1] AALL, The American Phosphorus Industry, *Ind. Eng. Chem.*, **44**, 1520 (1952).

TABLE 4. PRODUCTION OF CERTAIN PHOSPHORUS COMPOUNDS[a]
(In short tons)

Compound	1949	1951	1953
Phosphoric acid, 50% H_3PO_4:			
Total	1,394,544	1,846,841	2,646,967
From phosphorus	716,944	911,361	1,277,139
From phosphate rock	677,600	935,480	1,369,828
Calcium phosphate:			
Monobasic, 100 per cent $CaH_4(PO_4)_2$	n.a.	n.a.	n.a.
Dibasic, 100 per cent $CaHPO_4$	n.a.	38,421	100,937[b]
Sodium phosphate:			
Monobasic, 100 per cent NaH_2PO_4	12,722	18,479	20,738
Dibasic, 100 per cent Na_2HPO_4	130,555	182,650	n.a.
Tribasic, 100 per cent Na_3PO_4	70,367	67,605	50,494
Meta, 100 per cent $NaPO_3$	27,823	51,020	52,437
Tetra, 100 per cent $Na_4P_2O_7$	78,376	84,867	95,287
Acid pyro, 100 per cent $Na_2H_2P_2O_7$	....	11,434	12,580
Tripoly, 100 per cent $Na_5P_3O_{10}$	n.a.	312,283	468,035

[a] "Inorganic Chemicals, United States Production, Facts for Industry," Series M19A, U.S. Department of Commerce, Washington, 1952; "Statistics Handbook," Manufacturing Chemists' Association, Washington, 1955.
[b] Preliminary.

ing acid reacting with sodium bicarbonate when heated. The soft-drink industry buys tonnage quantities of pure acid to add tartness. Mono- and diammonium phosphate are consumed in tonnage amounts in yeast culture and fermentation. These compounds supply the phosphorus and nitrogen required in the growth and propagation of yeast cells needed in the baking, brewing, and alcohol manufacturing industries. Calcium salts are employed in tooth powders, in foods as mineral supplements, and for pharmaceuticals.

Tricresyl (TCP) and triphenyl phosphates are *organic esters* of phosphoric acid and are widely employed as plasticizers. Sales of the former alone amounted to over 5 million dollars in 1952. A recent insistent demand for TCP has been created by skillful advertising, as a petroleum additive. The chief method of production of these is by the condensation of phosphorus oxychloride with sodium cresol or phenol. Tetraethyl pyrophosphate (sales of 386,000 lb. in 1954) is a valuable insecticide. Alkyl alkali phosphates are employed as nonflammable hydraulic fluids and humectants. With some research and development, many other organic derivatives of phosphorus may open up entirely new and profitable fields in the future.

A seemingly infinite number of *miscellaneous uses* may be mentioned for phosphorus and its derivatives, among which the following are important: Phosphorus enters the metallurgical fields as an alloying agent. Phosphorus and its compounds are constituents of match compositions. Phosphoric acid is employed as a petroleum refining agent and as a catalyst for polymerizing olefins and for alkylating reactions. The sodium salts also find application as emulsifiers in making process cheese, for conditioning oil-well-drilling muds, and in preparation of enamels, glazes for pottery, and many more uses. In fact it seems that in almost any industry that one might analyze one is certain to find phosphoric acid used or some other phosphorus derivative, in at least one step of the process.

MANUFACTURE OF PHOSPHORUS AND PHOSPHORIC ACID

Reactions. Phosphorus has been produced by both the blast-furnace and the electric-furnace[1] methods. Currently only the electric-furnace method is active. The following reaction is considered to take place, the raw materials being phosphate rock, silica, and coke:

$$2(CaF)Ca_4(PO_4)_3 + 9SiO_2 + 15C \rightarrow CaF_2 + 9CaOSiO_2 + 6P + 15CO$$

or more simply expressed,

$$Ca_3(PO_4)_2 + 3SiO_2 + 5C \rightarrow 3CaSiO_3 + 2P + 5CO$$

The phosphorus is employed frequently as an intermediate product, being burned or oxidized to P_2O_5, which is dissolved in water to form the acids[2] or other compounds.

Phosphorus pentoxide:	$4P + 5O_2 \rightarrow 2P_2O_5$
Metaphosphoric acid:	$P_2O_5 + H_2O \rightarrow 2HPO_3$
Pyrophosphoric acid:	$P_2O_5 + 2H_2O \rightarrow H_4P_2O_7$
Orthophosphoric acid:	$P_2O_5 + 3H_2O \rightarrow 2H_3PO_4$

In addition, the old sulfuric acid or wet method is employed to manufacture phosphoric acid directly, by the reaction

$$Ca_3(PO_4)_2 + 3H_2SO_4 + 6H_2O \rightarrow 2H_3PO_4 + 3(CaSO_4 \cdot 2H_2O)$$

The foregoing reactions are commercialized in the following sequences

[1] ZERGIEBEL and LUCAS, Phosphorus Furnace Reactions, *Trans. Electrochem. Soc.*, **31**, 97 (1942).

[2] DURGIN, LUM, and MALOWAN, The Chemical and Physical Properties of Strong Phosphoric Acids, *Trans. Am. Inst. Chem. Engrs.*, **33**, 643 (1937); *Chem. & Met. Eng.*, **44**, 721 (1937); BELL, Composition of Strong Phosphoric Acids, *Ind. Eng. Chem.*, **40**, 1464 (1948).

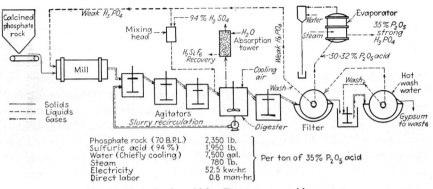

Phosphate rock (70 B.P.L.)	2,350 lb.	
Sulfuric acid (94%)	1,950 lb.	
Water (Chiefly cooling)	7,500 gal.	Per ton of 35% P_2O_5 acid
Steam	780 lb.	
Electricity	52.5 kw.-hr.	
Direct labor	0.8 man-hr.	

FIG. 3. Phosphoric acid by Dorr strong-acid process.

of *unit operations* (Op.) and *unit processes* (Pr.), as exemplified by Figs. 3 and 5:

Sulfuric Acid:

Phosphate rock ground and calcined (Op. and Pr.)

Ground rock reacted in mill with part of weak H_3PO_4 (Pr.)

Reaction continued in three agitators (Pr. and Op.)

Reaction continued with rest of weak H_3PO_4 and with H_2SO_4 (Pr.)

SiF$_4$ recovered (Op. and Pr.)

Calcium sulfate filtered off and washed (Op.)

This sludge pulped, refiltered, and re-washed (Op.)

Strong acid from first filter evaporated to stronger acid (Op.)

Electric Furnace:

Phosphate rock ground (Op.)

Rock and sand mixed with coke and sintered, introduced into electric furnace (Op.)

Mix heated to reaction temperature (Pr.)

Slag and ferrophosphorus run off (Op.)

Phosphorus and CO drawn off, P condensed or oxidized with air (Pr.)

P_2O_5 cooled and hydrated (Op. and Pr.)

Strong H_3PO_4 filtered and purified (Op. and Pr.)

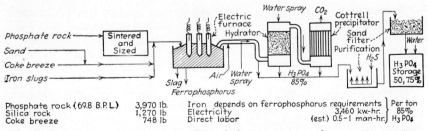

Phosphate rock (69.8 B.P.L)	3,970 lb.	Iron depends on ferrophosphorus requirements		Per ton
Silica rock	1,270 lb	Electricity	3,460 kw-hr.	85%
Coke breeze	748 lb	Direct labor	(est.) 0.5–1 man-hr.	H_3PO_4

FIG. 4. Phosphoric acid flow sheet. Electric-furnace process by one-step system. The two-step system separates the phosphorus after condensation, ships it to consuming centers to save freight, and there oxidizes the phosphorus.

Sulfuric Acid or the Wet Method. In the past, most of the phosphoric acid produced was prepared by the action of dilute sulfuric acid, 30°Bé., on ground phosphate rock or bones. This method has been supplanted by the Dorr strong-acid process[1] which produces a stronger, cheaper, and purer acid. This follows the flow sheet of Fig. 3. The equipment should be lead-lined, and sufficient time provided in the various agitators for the reaction to go to completion. The temperature in the digester should be kept low enough to ensure the precipitation of gypsum, $CaSO_4 \cdot 2H_2O$, and not anhydrite. If the latter is formed, it hydrates subsequently and causes plugging of pipes. Acid made by this process is almost entirely used in fertilizer production where impurities are unimportant, or after some purification for various sodium phosphates. Pure acid is obtained by the electric-furnace process.

Electric-furnace Method. The electric-furnace[2] process was first employed commercially in 1920. This process permits the use of lower-grade rock than does the wet process as the slag carries off impurities. Indeed the lower grades are frequently preferred because of the better CaO to SiO_2 balance for slag formation. The principal requirement is cheap electricity.

The phosphate rock must be charged in a lump form. Fine material tends to block the exit of the phosphorus vapors and to cause bridging and uneven descent of the furnace charge, resulting in puffs and the carrying over of excessive quantities of dust. Phosphate lumps may be prepared in the following ways: (1) pelletizing by tumbling or extrusion, (2) agglomeration by nodulizing at high temperatures, (3) sintering a mixture of phosphate fines and coke, and (4) briquetting with the addition of a suitable binder. After agglomeration, coke breeze and siliceous flux (sand) are added, and the materials are charged to the electric furnace. Iron slugs are added to the charge if more ferrophosphorus is desired. A flow sheet with quantities required is shown in Fig. 4. "A typical large commercial furnace (15,000 kw-hr.), having a daily (24 hr.) output of 28 tons of phosphorus consists of an oblong water-cooled steel shell 32 ft. in length, 15 ft. wide, and 12 ft. deep. The bottom of the furnace

---

[1] WEBER, SHAFOR, and ROBERTS, Dorr Strong Acid Process, U.S. Pat. 2049032 (1936); PERRY, op. cit., pp. 951–952, presents the c.c.d. practice still used in many plants; ibid., p. 988, for filter media; WAGGAMAN and BELL, Western Phosphates . . . Comparison of Sulfuric Acid and Thermal Reduction Processing, Ind. Eng. Chem., **42**, 276 (1950); ANON., Equipment and Construction Materials for Phosphoric Acid, Chem. Eng., **55** (11), 108 (1948).

[2] CURTIS, The Manufacture of Phosphoric Acid by the Electric Furnace Method, Trans. Am. Inst. Chem. Engrs., **31**, 278 (1935); CURTIS, et al., Process Developments at T.V.A. Phosphoric Acid Plant, Chem. & Met. Eng., **45**, 193 (1938); CALLAHAM, How Virginia-Carolina Makes Phosphorus, Chem. Eng., **58** (4), 102 (1951); KOBE, "Inorganic Process Industries," pp. 326ff., The Macmillan Company, New York, 1948, for details.

is composed of carbon blocks and this lining extends up the wall to a point well above the slag pool. From this point a high-grade fire-brick lining is used."[1] A domelike steel top with a cast refractory lining caps the furnace. Openings for the electrodes and for introducing the raw materials are included here. The electrodes are threaded so as to facilitate replacements as the carbon is consumed. The gases and phosphorus vapor are removed at one end of the furnace. The calcium-rich slag from the furnace is usually tapped periodically and is crushed for use in the manufacture of glass, for liming of soil, and as a roadbed ballast. The ferro-phosphorus runs out with the slag, is separated and sold as a phosphorus additive to steel. In this process most of the fluorine stays with the slag. The small portion that leaves with the gas is absorbed in the water used in condensing the phosphorus.

Blast-furnace Method. The first patent on the blast furnace[2] for making phosphorus was issued in France in 1867 and, at the time, was not considered practicable. Little was done about it for the next 30 or 40 years, and it was not until 1929 that commercial production by this process actually was successfully put into practice. The blast furnace used is similar in appearance to that employed in the steel industry. The last blast furnace operated was approximately 95 ft. high and had a maximum capacity of 250,000 lb. P_2O_5 per day. This has been shut down since 1939 but some engineers expect to see this process started again using air blast enriched as to its oxygen content.

SODIUM PHOSPHATES

Although trisodium phosphate has long been an important article of commerce (Table 4), since 1930 intensive development has resulted in the manufacture of a number of new and very useful phosphates which are replacing TSP for many demands.[3]

The industrially important sodium phosphates may be classified:

Alkali metal *metaphosphates*, such as $NaPO_3$, sodium metaphosphate, and sodium hexametaphosphate, $(NaPO_3)_6$, or Graham's salt.

Alkali metal *polyphosphates*, such as $Na_5P_3O_{10}$, sodium tripolyphosphate.

---

[1] WAGGAMAN, *op. cit.*, p. 141.

[2] EASTERWOOD, Making Phosphoric Acid in the Blast Furnace, *Chem. & Met. Eng.*, **40**, 283 (1933); *Trans. Am. Inst. Chem. Engrs.*, **29**, 1 (1933); pictured flow chart, *Chem. & Met. Eng.*, **46**, 269 (1939). For further details and flow sheet, *cf.* 1st ed. of this book, pp. 343–344; *cf.* HIGNETT, Development of Blast Furnace Process for Production of Phosphoric Acid, *Chem. Eng. Progr.*, **44**, 753, 820, 895 (1948).

[3] AALL, *op. cit.*; SCHWARTZ and MUNTER, Phosphates in Water Conditioning, *Ind. Eng. Chem.*, **34**, 32 (1942). This is a very excellent article with phase diagrams and a splendid bibliography; for various sodium phosphates with phase diagram, *cf.* KOBE, *op. cit.*, pp. 335ff.

Alkali metal *pyrophosphates*, such as $Na_4P_2O_7 \cdot 10H_2O$, sodium or tetrasodium pyrophosphate.

Alkali metal *orthophosphates*, such as $NaH_2PO_4 \cdot H_2O$, $Na_2HPO_4 \cdot 7H_2O$, and $Na_3PO_4 \cdot 12H_2O$.

The first three groups may be looked upon as molecularly dehydrated from the orthophosphates. The alkali metal polyphosphates[1] are of rather indefinite molecular composition and are frequently included among the phosphate glasses, which also may embrace sodium metaphosphates, Graham's salt.

The development of these various molecularly dehydrated phosphates, with a range of properties particularly directed toward conditioning water, was stimulated, if not started, by the work of R. E. Hall[2] and his associates of the Hall Laboratories. Water varies so much in its impurities and its pH that softening agents are needed of the varying properties of phosphates, from the strongly alkaline Na_3PO_4 through all ranges to the strongly acid NaH_2PO_4. However, in water softening, the behavior toward the deleterious constituents, calcium, magnesium, iron, and aluminum, is of the most importance. Although Na_3PO_4 precipitates insoluble phosphates or hydroxides usually of a loose form and hence easily removable, yet the newly discovered properties of metaphosphates, polyphosphates, and tetraphosphate in solubilizing or *repressing* the calcium and magnesium precipitates, even *in presence of soaps*, are of the utmost industrial significance. Such action takes place by binding, for example, the calcium and magnesium into such complexes as $Na_2(Ca_2P_6O_{18})$ and $Na_2MgP_2O_7$.

The molecularly dehydrated phosphates supplement the long-known orthophosphates in practical water treatment by being able:[3]

1. To provide acid, neutral, or alkaline solutions for control of pH value by both neutralization and buffer action.

2. To act as emulsifying agents.

3. To reduce metal-ion concentration by precipitation.

4. To reduce metal-ion concentration by complex formation.

5. To reduce alkalinity by hydrolysis to orthophosphate.

6. To stabilize solutions supersaturated with respect to ordinarily insoluble salts.

7. To form adsorbed films on metal surfaces.

8. To disperse insoluble compounds through adsorption on the solid particles.

Metaphosphates. Soluble, glassy sodium metaphosphate, $(NaPO_3)_n$, is made by fusing practically pure monosodium phosphate at 760°C. The

---

[1] PARTRIDGE, HICKS, and SMITH, A Thermal Microscopic and X-ray Study of the System $NaPO_3$-$Na_4P_2O_7$, *J. Am. Chem. Soc.*, **63**, 454 (1941); PARTRIDGE, The Peculiar Phosphates, *Chem. Eng. News*, **27**, 214 (1949).

[2] HALL, U.S. Pat. 1956515 (1934), Reissue 19719 (1935).

[3] Quoted from SCHWARTZ and MUNTER, *op. cit.*, p. 36.

molten product is discharged to a belt where it is chilled by water sprays on the underside. After flaking it is packaged and shipped. It finds wide usage in water treatment.[1] The reactions may be expressed:

$$2H_3PO_4 + Na_2CO_3 \rightarrow 2NaH_2PO_4 + CO_2 + H_2O$$
$$nNaH_2PO_4 \rightarrow (NaPO_3)_n + nH_2O$$

T.V.A. has studied and manufactured many thousands of tons of metaphosphates chiefly for fertilizers. Potassium metaphosphate is composed of 100 per cent of plant-food ingredients (approximately 40 per cent K_2O and 60 per cent P_2O_5), but a successfully economic process has not been developed.

Polyphosphates. According to the phase diagram of Partridge, Hicks, and Smith,[2] only three molecular compositions, namely, $NaPO_3$, $Na_4P_2O_7$, and $Na_5P_3O_{10}$, are definite in the system $NaPO_3$-$Na_4P_2O_7$. Although the chemistry is very complex, the polyphosphates possess highly desirable characteristics. Sodium tripolyphosphate is produced in the largest tonnages of all the phosphate salts (Table 4) with about 85 per cent employed as a builder in detergents.

To produce the sodium tripolyphosphate[3] a definite temperature control is necessary. When mono- and disodium phosphates in correct proportions or equivalent mixtures of other phosphates are heated for a substantial time between 300 and 500°C. and slowly cooled, the product will practically all be in the form of the tripolyphosphate. If, however, the mixture is fused and rapidly cooled, the product will be substantially a mixture of meta- and pyrophosphates. This mixture may be converted to the tripolyphosphate by reheating and tempering at a temperature above 300°C. but below the fusion point.

The chemical properties of the alkali metal tripolyphosphates would appear to place them somewhere between pyro- and metaphosphates, having less calcium and more magnesium repressing value than the metaphosphates, and more calcium and less magnesium repressing value than the pyrophosphates.

Pyrophosphates. Tetrasodium pyrophosphate is one of the best all-around builders for detergents of the dodecyl-benzene-sulfonate type. It is also an excellent builder for soap, which helps account for its high level of consumption. In its manufacture phosphoric acid and soda ash are reacted to yield disodium phosphate solution which may be drum dried to give anhydrous Na_2HPO_4 or crystallized to give $Na_2HPO_4 \cdot 2H_2O$ or $Na_2HPO_4 \cdot 7H_2O$. These are calcined at a high temperature in an oil or gas-fired rotary kiln to yield tetrasodium pyrophosphate. The reactions

---

[1] *Cf.* PARTRIDGE and TEXTER, Calgon, *Chem. Eng. News,* **27,** 840 (1949).

[2] A Thermal, Microscopic and X-ray Study of the System $NaPO_3$-$Na_4P_2O_7$, *J. Am. Chem. Soc.,* **63,** 454 (1941).

[3] EASTERWOOD, Recent Developments in the Phosphate Field, *Ind. Eng. Chem.,* **34,** 13 (1942); *cf.* SCHWARTZ and MUNTER, *op. cit.,* particularly for application.

may be written:

$$2Na_2HPO_4 \rightarrow Na_4P_2O_7 + H_2O$$
$$2Na_2HPO_4 \cdot 2H_2O \rightarrow Na_4P_2O_7 + 5H_2O$$

A nonhygroscopic sodium acid pyrophosphate is used extensively as a chemical leavening agent in making doughnuts, cakes, and packaged biscuit doughs. It is manufactured by partially dehydrating monosodium acid orthophosphate at a temperature between 25 and 250°C. over the course of 6 to 12 hr.

$$2NaH_2PO_4 \rightarrow Na_2H_2P_2O_7 + H_2O$$

Trisodium Phosphate. $Na_3PO_4 \cdot 12H_2O$ is employed in industry because of its two chief properties: (1) It is hydrolyzed in a water solution to give a high pH solution well buffered against neutralization. (2) It possesses the ability to form soft and granular precipitates with heavy-metal

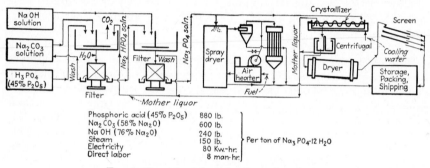

Phosphoric acid (45% P₂O₅) 880 lb.
Na₂CO₃ (58% Na₂O) 600 lb.
Na OH (76% Na₂O) 240 lb. } Per ton of Na₃PO₄·12 H₂O
Steam 150 lb.
Electricity 80 Kw.-hr.
Direct labor 8 man-hr.

FIG. 5. Flow sheet for trisodium phosphate.

ions such as magnesium, iron, aluminum, and calcium. For years TSP was the most important compound of phosphoric acid used as a water softener and detergent. The polyphosphates have now greatly replaced TSP because they are superior in detergency, water softening, lower alkalinity, and sequestering ability. However, TSP will probably maintain a certain position because of its low cost of manufacture.

Its manufacture must be carried out in two steps:

$$Na_2CO_3 + H_3PO_4 \rightarrow Na_2HPO_4 + CO_2 + H_2O$$
$$Na_2HPO_4 + NaOH \rightarrow Na_3PO_4 + H_2O$$

The procedure[1] as depicted in the flow sheet of Fig. 5, is as follows: 6,000 lb. of 58 per cent soda ash are introduced into a 4,000-gal. tank with 800 gal. of hot liquor from previous crystallization of $Na_3PO_4 \cdot 12H_2O$; 8,800 lb. of phosphoric acid solution, containing 45 per cent P_2O_5, are

[1] SNELL, Trisodium Phosphate—Its Manufacture and Use, *Ind. Eng. Chem.*, **23,** 470 (1931).

added at the surface of the tank so that CO_2 can be liberated easily. A slight excess of soda ash is added and the solution is boiled by steam until all of the CO_2 has been driven out as confirmed by the test sample. Since the pH level at which the third H of the acid is neutralized is higher than that at which the second H of carbonic acid is converted to form sodium carbonate, it is not to be expected that H_3PO_4 can be neutralized further than to the disodium stage with sodium carbonate. The disodium phosphate solution is filtered in a plate-and-frame filter press at 85 to 100°C., and the filtrate is pumped to storage tanks or to the trisodium process tank. This clear solution of disodium phosphate contains 14.5 per cent P_2O_5 and 13 per cent Na_2O. The small amount of white mud (Fe and Al phosphates plus SiO_2) in the press is wasted.

Fifteen hundred gallons of hot disodium phosphate solution is changed to trisodium phosphate, in a 4,000-gal. iron tank, by adding 2,800 lb. of caustic soda in 300 gal. of water at 90°C.; an additional 1,000 gal. of disodium phosphate solution is then added. Samples are titrated to control this operation. The hot solution of trisodium phosphate is filtered and passed to Swenson-Walker crystallizers. The crystals are dried in a centrifuge, further dried in a rotary drier, cooled, screened, and aged for 3 or 4 days by storage in piles. A spray congealed grade is also produced by pumping a clear filtered solution of Na_3PO_4 to the top of a spray tower 70 ft. high where an atomizer discharges it. During the fall of 70 ft. countercurrent to hot air, the particles assume a spherical form and congeal.

AMMONIUM PHOSPHATES

Both monoammonium phosphate, $NH_4H_2PO_4$, and diammonium phosphate, $(NH_4)_2HPO_4$, are used as fertilizers, as yeast nutrients, and as flameproofing agents for paper, wood, and textiles. High-grade monoammonium phosphate is manufactured simply by the absorption of ammonia gas in 75 per cent H_3PO_4 made from elemental P. Considerable heat is given off in the reaction, and the mass becomes pasty and crystallizes almost solid on cooling. The white crystals are centrifuged free from the mother liquor and dried for sale. Wet-process phosphoric acid and ammonia liquor from coking operations are reacted batchwise to form a fertilizer-grade salt. The Dorr continuous process for granulated concentrated fertilizers neutralizes phosphoric acid or a mixture of phosphoric and sulfuric acids with ammonia to monoammonium or diammonium (Fig. 6) phosphate. The product is mixed with a large quantity of previously produced granules and dried. After screening to a closely sized fraction, the remainder circulates in the process.

Purified diammonium phosphate is made from phosphoric acid and ammonia in two stages. The NH_3 introduced in the first stage removes the bulk of the Fe, Al, F, Ca, and Mg present in wet-process acid as filterable impurities. The filtrate, practically a pure solution of monoammonium phosphate, is evaporated. It is saturated with ammonia to a NH_3/P_2O_5 mole ratio of 2 to 1 in a continuous single-stage saturator. The product is crystallized, centrifuged, and dried for sale. T.V.A. has

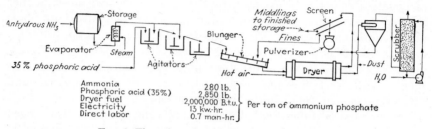

FIG. 6. Flow sheet for diammonium phosphate.

perfected on a pilot-plant scale a continuous process for the crystalline *di* salt.[1] This consists of passing anhydrous ammonia gas and pure 75 to 85 per cent H_3PO_4 into a saturated mother liquor. The heat of reaction vaporizes water from the liquor while the crystals are withdrawn, centrifuged, washed, and dried.

BAKING POWDERS

The baking powder industry is an important consumer of phosphate rock. The use of leavening agents to produce aeration and lightness in breads and cakes has been known since the time of the Egyptians and handed down through the Greeks and Romans. Leavened and unleavened bread are both mentioned in the Bible. Some form of yeast or ferment acting on the carbohydrates of the flour giving CO_2 and an alcohol was the first of the leavening agents used. Later, baking soda (sodium bicarbonate) was widely used but, because it often imparted an unpleasant taste or even a yellowish color due to the alkalinity of the Na_2CO_3 formed, the search for better reagents continued.

Baking powders consist of a dry mixture of sodium bicarbonate with one or more chemicals capable of completely decomposing it. The principal "baking acids" used are monocalcium phosphate monohydrate, anhydrous monocalcium phosphate, sodium acid pyrophosphate, sodium aluminum sulfate, tartaric acid, and the acid tartrates. The monocalcium phosphates are consumed more than all the others, the estimate being 78,000,000 lb. annually in the United States. A filler or drying agent, such as starch or flour, is usually added to the active ingredients

---

[1] Thompson, *et al.*, Diammonium Phosphate, *Ind. Eng. Chem.*, **42**, 2176 (1950); Thompson, *et al.*, Properties of Diammonium Phosphate Fertilizer, *Ind. Eng. Chem.*, **41**, 485 (1949).

to give a better distribution throughout the dough and to act as a diluent or preventative of the reaction until water and heat are applied. The following equations represent the actions of the different baking powders:

$$Na_2Al_2(SO_4)_4 + 6NaHCO_3 \rightarrow 6CO_2 + 4Na_2SO_4 + 2Al(OH)_3$$
$$3CaH_4(PO_4)_2H_2O + 8NaHCO_3 \rightarrow 8CO_2 + Ca_3(PO_4)_2$$
$$+ 4Na_2HPO_4 + 11H_2O$$
$$KH_2PO_4 + NaHCO_3 \rightarrow CO_2 + KNaHPO_4 + H_2O$$
$$NaH_2PO_4 + NaHCO_3 \rightarrow CO_2 + Na_2HPO_4 + H_2O$$
$$Na_2H_2P_2O_7 + 2NaHCO_3 \rightarrow 2CO_2 + 2Na_2HPO_4 + H_2O$$
$$KHC_4H_4O_6 + NaHCO_3 \rightarrow KNaC_4H_4O_6 + CO_2 + H_2O$$

In the United States, baking powders must yield not less than 12 per cent available CO_2, and most powders are so made up that they contain from 26 to 29 per cent $NaHCO_3$ and enough of the acid ingredients to decompose the bicarbonate and yield from 14 to 15 per cent CO_2. The rest of the powder, 20 to 40 per cent, consists of corn starch or flour.

SELECTED REFERENCES

Waggaman, W. H., "Phosphoric Acid, Phosphates and Phosphatic Fertilizers," 2d ed., Reinhold Publishing Corporation, New York, 1952.

Various Authors, A Symposium on Phosphorus and Phosphates, *Ind. Eng. Chem.*, **44**, 1519 (1952).

Striplin, M. M., "Development of Processes and Equipment for Production of Phosphoric Acid," Chemical Engineering Report, No. 2, T.V.A., Wilson Dam, Alabama, 1948.

Anon., "Process Flow Diagrams," T.V.A., Wilson Dam, Alabama, 1949.

Various Authors, A Symposium on Phosphates for Agriculture, *Ind. Eng. Chem.*, **41**, 1314 (1949).

Curtis, H. A., The Design of a Phosphate-smelting Furnace, T.V.A., *Chemical Engineering Bull.* 1, Knoxville, Tenn., 1953.

CHAPTER 19

SULFUR AND SULFURIC ACID

One of the most important and basic raw materials in the chemical process industries is sulfur. It exists in nature both in the free state and combined in ores such as pyrite, FeS_2. The mining of sulfur in Louisiana and Texas by the Frasch process, with the production of single blocks of pure sulfur 100 to 300 ft. wide, 600 to 1,200 ft. long, and over 50 ft. high, is a large and essential industry. Beside its most important application in the manufacture of sulfuric acid, sulfur is used extensively in explosives, refrigerants, rubber, pulp, and paper.

Historical. Sulfur has a history as old as any other recorded and has developed from a mystic yellow of the alchemist to one of the most useful substances in modern civilization. It was burned in early pagan rites to drive away evil spirits, but even then the fumes were used as a bleach for cloth and straw.

For many years a French company held a monopoly on elemental sulfur by controlling the world production from mines in Sicily. Partly for this reason and partly because of the abundance of pyrite, sulfur itself was little used prior to 1914. Though sulfur was discovered in the Gulf region of the United States by oil prospectors in 1869, it was difficult to mine because of overlying beds of quicksand. Before 1914 the United States made most of its sulfuric acid from imported and domestic pyrite and by-product sulfur dioxide from copper and zinc smelters. The mining of sulfur in Texas and Louisiana by the Frasch process was increased starting around 1914 to such an extent as to provide for all domestic needs and to enter world markets.

Uses and Economics.[1] Production of elemental sulfur in the United States in 1952 was 6,432,000 long tons. That year the United States sources of sulfur were 82 per cent from Frasch mines, 9 per cent from pyrites, 5 per cent from hydrogen sulfide, and 4 per cent from smelter gases. Sulfur usage has increased tremendously during the past few years. About three-fourths of all the sulfur consumed in this country is converted into sulfuric acid. There are countless other outlets for the ele-

[1] ANON., Sulfur, Acid, *Chem. Eng.*, **60** (3), 190 (1953); ANON., Sulfur, *Chem. Eng. News*, **29**, 2126 (1951); *Chem. Eng. News*, **30**, 3094 (1952), new producers.

ment. Large quantities of sulfur dioxide are needed in sulfite paper manufacture. A few of the many uses of elemental sulfur are in wood pulping and in the making of carbon disulfide, medicinals, rubber, sulfur dyes, insecticides, and fungicides.

Because of this increased sulfur usage, there was a serious shortage in 1951. Although many sources[1] of sulfur exist, none is currently available at the low price of Gulf Coast sulfur. Since Gulf Coast deposits may be depleted around 1985, other sulfur sources are being sought under the following: elemental, pyrites, hydrogen sulfide from both natural and refinery gases, smelter gases, calcium sulfate, coal, and low-grade sulfur deposits. Calcium sulfate[2] and coal are the most plentiful and widely distributed, but sulfur recovery from these is costly. The Chemical Construction Corporation is erecting a large plant in Colombia to obtain elemental acid-grade sulfur from surface deposits.[3] It is claimed that deposits containing over 20 per cent sulfur are competitive with the Frasch process. This new process consists of grinding native sulfur-bearing ore and suspending it in water. The mixture is heated above the melting point of sulfur when the fine sulfur particles coalesce. After cooling, the sulfur is froth flotated, and filtered.

MINING AND MANUFACTURE OF SULFUR

Sulfur is obtained as elemental sulfur from sulfur dioxide and from hydrogen sulfide. Pure sulfur is mined but the sulfur dioxide comes from the roasting of sulfide ores and the hydrogen sulfide is removed from industrial gases.

Frasch Process. Ninety per cent of all the elemental sulfur of the world is obtained from the sulfur-bearing porous limestones in the saltdome cap rocks of Texas and Louisiana by the Frasch process.[4] As early as the late 1890's, Herman Frasch devised the following ingenious method of melting the sulfur underground and of pumping it up to the surface: Ordinary oil-well equipment is used to bore holes to the bottom of the sulfur-bearing strata, a distance underground of from 500 to 2,500 ft. A nest of three concentric pipes, varying in size from 6 in. to 1 in., is slipped down the well casing. The outside pipe of this nest, 6 in. in diameter,

---

[1] LUNDY, Known and Potential Sulfur Resources of the World, *Ind. Eng. Chem.*, **42**, 2199 (1950); TODD, Offshore Sulfur Production, *Ind. Eng. Chem.*, **42**, 2210 (1950).

[2] HIGSON, CaSO₄ as a Raw Material for Chemical Manufacture, *Chem. Eng. News*, **43**, 4469 (1951).

[3] U.S. Pat. 2537842 (1951); O'CONNOR, New Sulfur Recovery Process, *Chem. Eng.*, **58** (3), 128 (1950).

[4] SHEARON and POLLARD, Modern Sulfur Mining, *Ind. Eng. Chem.*, **42**, 2188 (1950); a pictured flow sheet is given in *Chem. & Met. Eng.*, **48** (3), 104 (1941); *cf.* HAYNES, "The Stone That Burns," D. Van Nostrand Company, Inc., New York, 1942.

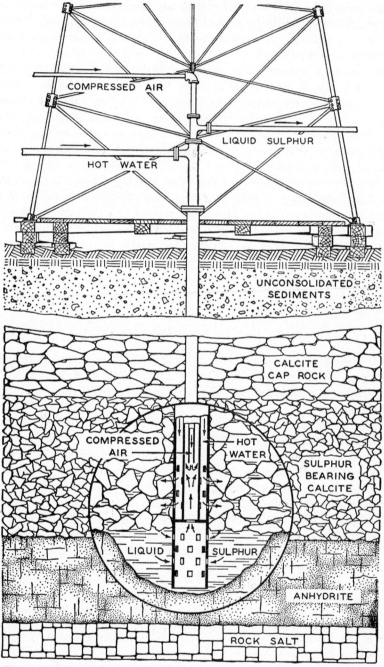

FIG. 1. Sulfur-well piping. (*Courtesy of Texas Gulf Sulphur Company, Inc.*)

passes through the sulfur-bearing stratum and rests on the upper portion of the barren anhydrite, as shown in Fig. 1. A 3-in. pipe passes through the 6-in. one so that an annular space exists between the two, extends nearly to the bottom of the sulfur-bearing rock, and rests on a collar that seals the annular space between the 6-in. and the 3-in. pipes. An air pipe, 1 in. in diameter, inside the others, reaches to a depth slightly above the collar mentioned above. The 6-in. pipe is perforated at two different levels, one above and the other below the annular collar. The upper set of perforations permits escape of the hot water while the molten sulfur enters the system through the lower perforations.

For operation of the well, hot water at about 330°F. is passed down the annular space between the 6-in. and the 3-in. pipes. It discharges through the perforations into the porous formation near the foot of the well. The sulfur-bearing rock about the well through which this water circulates is raised to a temperature above the melting point of sulfur, 235°F. Molten sulfur, being heavier than water, sinks to form a pool around the base of the well where it enters through the lower perforations and rises in the space between the 3-in. and the 1-in. pipes, as depicted in Fig. 1. The height to which the sulfur is forced by the pressure of the hot water is about halfway to the surface. Air, compressed to 400 lb. at the pump house and at the bottom of the central 1-in. pipe, rises and mixes in the sulfur column in the 3-in. pipe, thus producing an air lift that raises the sulfur to the surface. At the surface, the sulfur from the wells is collected in steam-heated sumps at pumping stations from which it is pumped through pipes heated by an inner steam pipe into large storage vats where the sulfur solidifies. The block of sulfur is drilled, broken down by blasting, and loaded into cars by a locomotive crane.

It is far-sighted business to maintain a large supply of sulfur aboveground sufficient for over a year, because the production of sulfur may be seriously curtailed or entirely stopped for months at a time because of underground movements following the sulfur removal.

Sulfur from Smelter Gases. Sulfur recovery from SO_2 and from H_2S are not only becoming more important as a sulfur source, but are mandatory in many localities because of stringent air-pollution regulations. Many processes[1] have been developed to recover SO_2 from waste gases resulting from roasting of sulfide ores, smelting of ores, coal combustion in power stations, and burning of acid sludge from petroleum refining. The possible products are elemental sulfur, sulfuric acid, and liquid sulfur dioxide. It is estimated that sulfur loss to the atmosphere from zinc plants and lead, copper, and nickel smelters alone is 5,000,000 tons an-

---

[1] KATZ and COLE, Recovery of Sulfur Compounds from Atmospheric Contaminants, *Ind. Eng. Chem.*, **42**, 2258 (1950); *cf.* FLEMING and FITT, High Purity Sulfur from Smelter Gases, *Ind. Eng. Chem.*, **42**, 2249 (1950); Liquid Sulfur Dioxide from Waste Smelter Gases, *Ind. Eng. Chem.*, **42**, 2253 (1950).

nually. The recovery of SO_2 from smelter gases[1] at Trail, B.C., is a famous and unique installation. Here the following units are in operation: absorption at the smelter operating on sintering plant gas, absorption at the zinc plant operating on zinc roaster gas, acidification unit treating solution from both absorption plants, five conventional sulfuric acid plants operating on enriched zinc roaster gas, and one cyclic-process sulfuric acid plant operating on pure sulfur dioxide. Besides these there are units treating the H_2SO_4 plant tail gases for recovery of SO_2; and for processing zinc plant stripped electrolyte, for recovery of sulfuric acid. In 1946, 375,595 tons of H_2SO_4 and 484,720 tons of elemental sulfur and fertilizer were recovered from sulfur dioxide at Trail.

Sulfur from Industrial Gases. Hydrogen sulfide is removed in the purification of natural and manufactured gas and in petroleum refining, furnishing either pure hydrogen sulfide or free sulfur depending on the recovery systems[2] (see Chap. 7). The hydrogen sulfide thus produced may be burned in specially constructed furnaces to form sulfur dioxide for sulfuric acid. From these gases, the equivalent of approximately 260,000 long tons of sulfur are recovered annually.

Sulfur from Pyrites. This method of producing sulfur is largely limited to those plants which, because of their location, are favored by low shipping and other costs. The majority of United States producers are around Tennessee, although suitable ores also occur in eight other states. The ore is usually flash roasted to recover the sulfur dioxide. A recent development by the Dorr Company is expected to give a considerable boost to pyrites utilization. Here the ore is crushed to 35 to 200 mesh and the partially suspended sulfide particles are removed in an upward-moving stream of air. This *fluidization* ensures complete combustion of the particles to sulfur dioxide, which may be converted to sulfuric acid.

Sulfur Dioxide from By-products. Sizable quantities of ferrous sulfate are wasted into streams each year, coming mostly from steel mills and titanium plants. The steel industry consumes over 500,000 tons of 60°Bé. acid yearly for pickling. These wastes are water solutions[3] containing from 2 to 15 per cent sulfuric acid and 10 to 15 per cent ferrous sulfate. Much work has been done upon the recovery of the values of these liq-

---

[1] KING, Economic Utilization of Sulfur Dioxide from Metallurgical Gases, *Ind. Eng. Chem.*, **42**, 2241 (1950); KIRKPATRICK, Trail Refuses to Trail in Chemical Engineering, *Chem. Eng.*, **55** (4), 96 (1948).

[2] REED and UPDEGRAFF, Removal of Hydrogen Sulfide from Industrial Gases, *Ind. Eng. Chem.*, **42**, 2269 (1950); SANDS and SCHMIDT, Recovery of Sulfur from Synthesis Gas, *Ind. Eng. Chem.*, **42**, 2277 (1950); SAWYER, *et al.*, Sulfur from Sour Gases, *Ind. Eng. Chem.*, **42**, 1938 (1950); ANON., Sulfur from H_2S, *Chem. Eng.*, **59** (10), 210 (1952), pictured flow sheet.

[3] BARTHOLOMEW, Chemico's New Pickle Liquor Process, *Chem. Eng.*, **57** (8), 118 (1950); KRAIKER, Dispose of Pickle Liquor at a Profit, *Chem. Eng.*, **56** (3), 112, 114 (1949); HOAK, Waste Pickle Liquor, *Ind. Eng. Chem.*, **39**, 416 (1947).

uors for nearly 75 years. Although ferrous sulfate recovery systems were installed at two titanium pigment plants,[1] they were uneconomical because of heavy water-evaporation costs.

About 2,000,000 tons of spent acids are reused each year: (1) spent sludge acids from petroleum refining; (2) spent alkylation catalyst as black but still relatively strong and uncontaminated acid; and (3) nitration spent acid, diluted but frequently uncontaminated. Sludge and alkylation acids are recovered by decomposing to sulfur dioxide with heat alone or by help of coke. In either case the resultant sulfur dioxide is remade to acid in a sulfuric acid contact plant. Figure 2 shows the

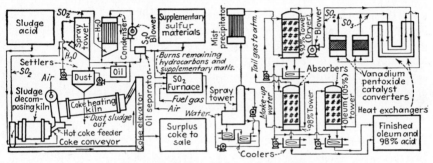

FIG. 2. Sulfuric acid from sludge acid.

Chemico[2] *sludge-conversion process* wherein the acid sludge plus red-hot coke is heated to about 550°F. resulting in more solid coke, water vapor, some hydrocarbons, and sulfur dioxide (15 to 25 per cent SO_2 by volume). After being cooled and purified, the sulfur dioxide is converted to sulfuric acid by the contact process.

SULFURIC ACID

It seems hard to believe that a very active chemical, such as sulfuric acid, is at the same time one of the most widely used and most important of technical products. It is of such paramount significance that the remark has frequently been made that the per capita use of sulfuric acid is an index of the technical development of a nation. Sulfuric acid is the agent for sulfate formation and for sulfonation but is used more frequently by virtue of being a rather strong and economically priced inorganic acid. It enters into countless industries, though infrequently ap-

[1] See 1st ed. of this book, pp. 357–358, for description and flow sheet.

[2] SPANGLER, Modified Acid Recovery Process Treats Troublesome Acid Sludges, *Chem. & Met. Eng.*, **44**, 368 (1937); ANON., Sulfuric Acid from Refinery Sludge, *Chem. & Met. Eng.*, **48**, No. 5, 144 (1941). The latter presents an excellent pictured flow sheet, depicting particularly the purification of the sulfur dioxide that is formed.

pearing in the finished material. It thus aids in the manufacture of leather and tin plate, in the purification of petroleum, and in the dyeing of fabrics.

Historical.[1] The origin of the first sulfuric acid is unknown, but it is mentioned as far back as the tenth century. The preparation is first described by Valentinus in the fifteenth century by burning saltpeter with sulfur. In 1746, Dr. Roebuck of Birmingham, England, introduced the lead chamber. His process consisted of placing a mixture of brimstone and saltpeter in iron carts and rolling them into the chamber. In 1774, steam was first used in the chambers. Early in the nineteenth century, the continuous method replaced batch operation. Another notable improvement in the process was the invention of the Gay-Lussac tower for the recovery of nitrogen oxides in 1827, which, however, was not applied until the invention of the Glover tower in 1859. The Glover tower furnished a means of denitrating the nitrous acid from the Gay-Lussac tower without diluting it with too much water; it complemented the use of the Gay-Lussac tower. Since that time both towers have been standard equipment on all lead-chamber processes.

The contact process was first discovered in 1831 by Phillips, an Englishman, whose patent included the essential features of the modern contact process, namely, the passing of a mixture of sulfur dioxide over a catalyst followed by absorption of the sulfur trioxide in water. Phillips's invention was not a commercial success for more than 40 years, probably owing to (1) the lack of demand for fuming acids, (2) inadequate knowledge of catalytic gas reactions, and (3) the slow progress of chemical technology. The early years of the dye industry afforded a rising demand for fuming acids for the manufacture of alizarin and other organic coloring matters.

At first, fuming sulfuric acid was made by decomposing chamber acid by means of heat.

$$H_2SO_4 \xrightarrow{\Delta} H_2O + SO_2 + \tfrac{1}{2}O_2$$

The sulfur dioxide and oxygen were dried and then passed over a catalyst and absorbed in the chamber acid. This method was used until 1881, when sulfur trioxide was made by passing sulfur dioxide and a *theoretical* amount of air over a mixture of platinized asbestos. In 1889 it was demonstrated that *excess* of oxygen in the gaseous mixture was advantageous. In recent years the contact process has been improved in all its details until it is now one of industry's low-cost, almost wholly automatic processes (see Fig. 8). In 1953, 79 per cent of the new sulfuric acid was made by the contact process.

[1] FAIRLIE, "Manufacture of Sulfuric Acid," Reinhold Publishing Corporation, New York, 1936. This is the standard reference book on sulfuric acid and should be freely consulted. Many references and sketches are included.

Properties of Sulfuric Acid. Sulfuric acid is a strong dibasic acid. In addition, it is also an oxidizing and a dehydrating agent particularly toward organic compounds. The dehydrating action is important in absorbing water formed in such unit processes as nitration, esterification, and sulfonation, thus ensuring high yields. Solutions of sulfuric acid may be concentrated economically to about 93 per cent by weight of H_2SO_4. Stronger sulfuric acids may be made by dissolving sulfur trioxide in this concentrated acid. Sulfur trioxide forms many hydrates that have fairly definite melting points, as shown in Table 1. The irregularities in the relation between strengths of the sulfuric acids and the corresponding specific gravities and freezing points are due to these hydrates.

TABLE 1. HYDRATES OF SULFURIC ACID[a] AND SULFUR TRIOXIDE

	Formula	Melting point, °C.	Specific gravity
Pyrosulfuric acid..................	$H_2S_2O_7$	35	$1.9^{20°}$
Monohydrate......................	H_2SO_4	10.49	$1.834^{13/4°}$
Double hydrate...................	$H_2SO_4 \cdot H_2O$	8.62	$1.842^{15/4°}$
Triple hydrate....................	$H_2SO_4 \cdot 2H_2O$	−38.9	$1.650^{9/4°}$
Quintuple hydrate...............	$H_2SO_4 \cdot 4H_2O$	−25	

[a] PERRY, *op. cit.*, p. 127; FAIRLIE, "Manufacture of Sulfuric Acid," p. 48, Reinhold Publishing Corporation, New York, 1936.

Sulfuric acid is widely sold in the form of various solutions of H_2SO_4 in water or of SO_3 in H_2SO_4. These latter are called *oleums* and are marketed on the basis of the percentage of SO_3 present; 20 per cent oleum means that in 100 lb. there are 20 lb. of SO_3 and 80 lb. of H_2SO_4. This 20 per cent oleum if diluted with water to make monohydrate, H_2SO_4, would furnish 104.5 lb. For convenience, now grown into an established custom, the ordinary solutions of sulfuric acid and water are sold according to their specific gravity, or their Baumé degree. Table 2 illustrates the sulfuric acids of commerce. The usual temperature to which specific gravity or Baumé (Bé.) is referred is 60°F. for sulfuric acids. The specific gravity of sulfuric acid increases gradually to 1.844 at 60°F. for 97 per cent sulfuric acid, after which it decreases to 1.835 at 60°F. for 100 per cent acid. Consequently in this upper range, *i.e.*, above 95 per cent, the strengths should be determined by other means, such as electrical conductivities, titrations, or heat rises. For some of the medium-range oleums, however, specific gravity is again helpful.

The normal strengths of commercial oleums are usually 20, 40, 60, and 65 per cent of free sulfur trioxide, the 20 and 60 being the most common. The 20 per cent oleum has a melting point of about −10°C., and the 65 per cent oleum has a melting point of 0°C. It is interesting to note that the melting point of 45 per cent oleum is about 35°C. This fact accounts for the relatively small shipments of the 45 per cent oleum; the 40 or 45 per cent oleum may be made and mixed with nitric acid with consequent reduction in the melting point.

TABLE 2. COMMERCIAL STRENGTHS OF SULFURIC ACID (60°F.)[a]

	Degree Bé., 60°F. or 15.6°C.	Specific gravity, 60°F. or 15.6°C.	Sulfuric acid, per cent
Battery acid................	29.0	1.250	33.4
Chamber acid, fertilizer acid, 50° acid................	50	1.526	62.18
Glover or tower acid, 60° acid	60	1.706	77.67
Oil of vitriol (O.V.), concentrated acid, 66° acid.......	66	1.835	93.19
98° acid................	66.2	1.841	98.0
Monohydrate, H_2SO_4........	65.98	1.835	100.0
20 per cent fuming, 20 per cent oleum, 104.5° acid....	.....	1.927	104.49, 20 per cent free SO_3
40 per cent oleum, 109° acid.	.....	1.965	109.0, 40 per cent free SO_3
65 per cent oleum..........	.....	1.990	114.6, 65 per cent free SO_3

[a] PERRY, op. cit., pp. 184, 38. There are minor differences between different sulfuric acid tables.

Uses of Sulfuric Acid. Fertilizer manufacture, as shown in Table 3, is the greatest single use for sulfuric acid. About a dozen different grades[1] are supplied, each with a particular use. Grades of 53 to 56°Bé. or stronger are employed in superphosphate manufacture, where much of this weaker acid is supplied by chamber process. The 60°Bé. grade is used for sulfates of ammonia, copper (bluestone), aluminum (alum), magnesium (epsom salts), zinc, iron (copperas), etc.; mineral acids; organic acids, such as citric, oxalic, acetic, and tartaric; pickling iron and steel before galvanizing and tinning; refining and producing of heavy metals; electroplating; and preparing of sugar, starch, and sirup. The 66 to 66.2°Bé. grades are utilized in purification of petroleum products; preparation of titanium dioxide; alkylation of isobutane; manufacture of many nitrogen chemicals; synthesis of phenol; recovery of fatty acids in soap manufacture. Oleums are needed for nitrocellulose, nitroglycerine, TNT, and dye manufacture and for fortifying weaker acids. Many other uses exist as can be attested to by the fact that few chemical products are made that sulfuric acid does not enter into the manufacture in some way or other.

[1] Cf. SKEEN, Sulfuric Acid, Chem. Eng., **57** (4), 337 (1950).

TABLE 3. ESTIMATED DISTRIBUTION OF SULFURIC ACID USED IN THE UNITED
STATES, INCLUDING RECYCLED ACID[a]
(In 1,000 short tons, 100 per cent acid)

	1950	1951	1953
Fertilizers:			
Superphosphate...........	3,800	3,900	4,050
Ammonium sulfate........	1,450	1,500	1,200
Chemicals.................	3,625	3,800	4,180
Petroleum................	1,500	1,550	1,720
Paints and pigments........	1,270	1,250	1,370
Rayon and film............	700	710	760
Iron and steel.............	1,050	1,080	1,160
Other metallurgical.........	190	200	220
Industrial explosives........	115	110	420
Textile finishing...........	40	40	40
Miscellaneous.............	380	380	410
Total...................	14,120	14,520	15,530

[a] *Chem. Eng.*, **60** (3), 191 (1953). Recycled acid including reused acid, concentrated, fortified, and reconstituted acid is estimated at 2,060,000 tons in 1950 and 2,130,000 tons each in 1951 and 1952.

Manufacture. There have long been two main procedures for the making of sulfuric acid: the chamber process and the contact process. Both are based on sulfur dioxide, both are catalytic, both use air as the source of oxygen for making the sulfur trioxide, and both have been operated on a large scale for many years.[1] The chamber process produces directly a weaker acid of from 50 to 55°Bé., and up to 66°Bé. acid by concentration. On the other hand, the contact process produces 98 and 100 per cent acids and the various oleums. Much 66°Bé. acid results by dilution. Unless the weak chamber acids can be consumed directly, the present economics point to a production of more and more oil of vitriol (93.19 per cent H_2SO_4) by the contact process rather than by concentration of chamber acid.

MANUFACTURE BY THE CHAMBER PROCESS

A typical flow sheet for the chamber process is presented in Fig. 3. The process starts when either the sulfur or pyrite is burned and the hot gases are conducted through a combustion chamber which also may collect some dust. Sufficient oxides of nitrogen, NO and NO_2, are introduced

[1] For a chart of the distribution of sulfuric acid plants in the United States, see FAITH, KEYES, and CLARKE, "Industrial Chemicals," John Wiley & Sons, Inc., New York, 1950.

into the hot mixture of air and sulfur dioxide from the burner. This may be done either by the use of niter pots or by an ammonia oxidation unit. The hot gaseous mixture passes up the Glover tower where it is met by the downward flow of the diluted Gay-Lussac acid or the nitrous vitriol. In the Glover tower about 10 per cent of the sulfuric acid is produced, the so-called *tower acid*. If an ammonia oxidation unit supplies the nitrogen oxide, this is preferably entered into the gas stream, as shown by Fig. 3 after the gas has been cooled by its passage up the Glover tower. The cooled gases are blown to the chambers where most of the acid is made and condensed. Finally, the unreacted gases pass to the Gay-Lussac tower for the absorption of the oxides of nitrogen in the strong Glover acid, producing the Gay-Lussac acid or the nitrous vitriol.

Reactions. The conversion of the sulfur dioxide to sulfuric acid involves many fairly complex chemical changes. The over-all reaction is[1]

$$SO_2(g) + \tfrac{1}{2}O_2(g) + H_2O(l) \rightarrow H_2SO_4(l); \quad \Delta H = -54,500 \text{ cal.}$$

The detailed reactions may be formulated (Lunge-Berl):

In the gaseous phase, homogeneous:

$$2NO + O_2 \rightarrow 2NO_2 \tag{1}$$

On the gas-liquid interface, heterogeneous on wetted walls:

$$SO_2 + H_2O \rightarrow H_2SO_3 \tag{2}$$

$$H_2SO_3 + NO_2 \rightarrow H_2SO_3 \cdot NO_2 \text{ (violet acid or nitrosulfuric acid)} \tag{3}$$

$2(H_2SO_3 \cdot NO_2) + \tfrac{1}{2}O_2 \text{ (from } NO_2 \rightarrow NO + \tfrac{1}{2}O_2) \rightarrow$

$H_2O + 2(HSO_3 \cdot NO_2)$ (nitrosyl sulfuric acid or nitro acid sulfite or

$$\text{chamber crystals)} \tag{4a}$$

$$2(HSO_3 \cdot NO_2) + SO_2 + 2H_2O \rightleftarrows 2(H_2SO_3 \cdot NO_2) + H_2SO_4 \tag{5a}$$

In the liquid phase, homogeneous:

$$H_2SO_3 \cdot NO_2 \rightleftarrows H_2SO_4 + NO \tag{4b}$$

$$2(HSO_3 \cdot NO_2) + H_2O \rightleftarrows 2H_2SO_4 + NO + NO_2 \tag{5b}$$

$$HSO_3 \cdot NO_2 + HNO_3 \rightleftarrows 2NO_2 + H_2SO_4 \tag{5c}$$

($HSO_3 \cdot NO_2$ is sometimes written SO_5NH, and $H_2SO_3 \cdot NO_2$ as $H_2SO_4 \cdot NO$)

The important characteristics of the chamber process are the circulation of the catalytic oxides of nitrogen and the equipment needed for this, but the heat of reaction must be dissipated to secure the desired favorable equilibriums.

[1] FAIRLIE, *op. cit.*, p. 37; BERL, Studies of the Lead Chamber Process, *Trans. Am. Inst. Chem. Engrs.*, **31**, 193 (1935).

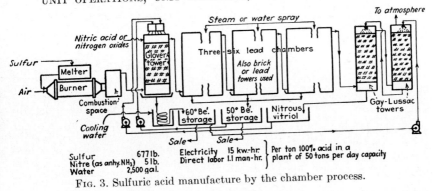

FIG. 3. Sulfuric acid manufacture by the chamber process.

Unit Operations, Unit Processes, and Energy Changes. The flow chart (Fig. 3) may be broken down into the following coordinated sequence of *unit operations* (Op.) and *unit processes* (Pr.):

Transportation of sulfur or sulfides to plant (Op.).

Melting of sulfur (Op.).

Burning of sulfur or sulfide (Pr.).

Recovery of heat from hot sulfur dioxide gas (Op.).

Purification of sulfur dioxide gas (Op.).

Mixing of sulfur dioxide gas with the nitrogen oxides catalyst in Glover tower (Pr. and Op.).

Oxidation of sulfur dioxide to sulfur trioxide (see Reactions) (Pr.).

Hydration of sulfur trioxide to sulfuric acid in Glover tower and chambers (Pr.).

Settling of sulfuric acid mist and dissipation of heat of reactions (Op.).

Absorption of nitrogen oxides from residual gas, forming nitrous-vitriol in Gay-Lussac tower (Pr.).

Pumping of acids over towers and through coolers (Op.).

Blowing of gases through system (Op.).

Oxidizing of ammonia to nitrogen oxide, NO, for catalyst make-up (Pr.).

The energy changes necessary to carry the chamber process into effect involve not only the dissipation of the energy set free by the over-all reaction but the supplying of the small amount of power shown on the flow sheet (Fig. 3) for the moving of the gases and liquids. In a few of the newer plants part of the over-all chemical energy is turned into useful work through by-product boilers following the sulfur dioxide furnace.

In some detail, these unit sequences may be elaborated in connection with the chamber-process flow sheet, classified largely by the typical equipment commercially employed. Corrosion in such equipment can be avoided by the proper choice of the materials for construction.[1]

[1] ANON., Sulfuric Acid, *Chem. Eng.*, **57** (11), 139 (1950). The materials of construction for Fig. 3 are also given here.

Burners and Furnaces.[1] The chief raw material is sulfur or brimstone, although pyrite, FeS_2, is used very extensively, as well as pyrrhotite, Fe_7S_8. Other processes for obtaining sulfur dioxide have been devised and are now in operation, producing it as a by-product in the refining of zinc and copper from sulfide ores, from the pyrite from coal waste and from hydrogen sulfide gases from natural and refinery gases and other sources.

Most chamber plants and earlier contact plants, when burning sulfur itself, use the *Glen Falls burner* shown in Fig. 3. This consists of a horizontal rotating steel drum in which the sulfur burns as a continuous film on the inside surface. The drum is surmounted by a pan for melting the sulfur before introduction into the cylinder. The new contact plants mostly use either the cascade type of burner or the spray type. The former is a steel vessel lined with insulation brick and the upper half a firebrick checker. The molten sulfur flows by gravity over the checker where it is completely burned to sulfur dioxide gas. The bottom section acts as a mixing chamber to ensure a homogeneous exit gas. In the spray type depicted in Fig. 8, molten sulfur is atomized through a gun and burns in suspension before it strikes the walls or bottom of the furnace.

Much fine sulfide of copper or zinc or iron is burned. Here a multiple hearth is employed with mechanical stirring and moving of the "fines" to secure efficient oxidation. The roasters generally consist of a central rotating shaft with arms extended from the center over each hearth. The fines are fed into the top of the roaster and dropped upon the top hearth where burning of the ore is started. The partly burned ore is caused to drop downward to the lower hearth by the rotating arm. This is continued to the bottom hearth where the cinder is removed. The gases pass out the top to be used.[2] Several of the newer plants are burning very fine pyrite or other sulfide ore by blowing it into the furnace usually in connection with by-product boilers.

In general, the production of sulfur dioxide for the contact process is the same for the chamber process. The types of furnace and raw materials do not change, nor the furnace that would be adapted to a given raw material. The percentages of sulfur dioxide and oxygen in the gas issuing from the burner are very carefully controlled and the desired concentrations varied with the process used. For platinum catalysts 10 per cent sulfur dioxide is desired while vanadium catalysts operate best with gas containing from 7 to 8 per cent sulfur dioxide. It should be noted that the percentage of oxygen decreases as that of the sulfur dioxide increases and that where gases of lower percentage of sulfur dioxide are processed larger volumes of gas must be handled.

[1] BUTCHER, Pyrites Roasting and Sulphur Burning, *Chem. Age*, **41**, 411 (1939); LIPPMAN, Improvements in Rotary Sulfur Burner, *Ind. Eng. Chem.*, **42**, 2215 (1950).
[2] FAIRLIE, *op. cit.*, pp. 98–107.

Dust Removal. When sulfide ores are the source of the sulfur dioxide, dust removal becomes important. Many methods have been tried for removing dust from the gases, but now Cottrell dust precipitators and centrifugal-type dust collectors are the most used.[1] In centrifugal cyclone dust catchers the particles are separated from the gas stream by impingement on the walls of the apparatus. In the Cottrell or electrical precipitator the gases are allowed to pass through a direct-current, high-voltage (30,000 to 80,000 volts) electrical field, where a silent discharge of negative polarity ionizes the gas, causing the dust particles to become electrically charged and, therefore, to be precipitated on the collecting electrode. The dust falls to hoppers from which it is removed. The gases, after going through the dust collectors and by-product boilers, pass to where the nitrous oxides are introduced.

Introduction of the Oxides of Nitrogen.[2] The introduction of the "oxides of nitrogen" may be done in one of the following ways: (1) by the heating of sodium nitrate and 60°Bé. sulfuric acid in cast-iron pots inside the sulfur dioxide gas flue, (2) by feeding mixed nitric and sulfuric acid into the top of a Glover tower or at times liquid nitric acid alone, (3) by the oxidation of ammonia and the conduction of the oxides either into the Glover tower or the first chamber.

The success of the ammonia oxidation and the cheap synthetic ammonia available have rendered the use of sodium nitrate obsolete. The ammonia is mixed with air and passed through a platinum-rhodium gauze catalyst maintained at 950 to 1000°C. by the heat of reaction. Hot nitrogen oxide is used to preheat the incoming air and to maintain the catalyst at red heat. This gives a relatively inexpensive method for producing nitrogen oxide. The advantages of this method are (1) no sulfuric acid needed, (2) low cost of raw materials, (3) high purity of the gases produced (no hydrochloric acid present to injure the lead chamber), (4) a constant and continuous supply of the oxide, (5) lower labor costs because of simplicity of operation, (6) equipment that is longer lasting and lower in maintenance, and (7) no by-product to dispose of. When nitrogen oxide from ammonia is used, it is introduced continuously into the SO_2 gas after the latter has passed up the Glover tower.

Glover Towers. The functions of the Glover tower are

1. The denitration of nitrous vitriol (Gay-Lussac acid). This is effected by reducing the solubility of nitrogen oxides by dilution and heat, aided by the passage of gases.

[1] JONES, Chamber Process Manufacture of Sulfuric Acid, *Ind. Eng. Chem.*, **42**, 2208 (1950); PERRY, *op. cit.*, chambers, p. 1035, cyclones, p. 1036, electrical precipitation, pp. 1039*ff.*, especially p. 1044; LAPPLE, Processes Use Many Collector Types, *Chem. Eng.*, **58** (5), 144 (1951).

[2] FAIRLIE, *op. cit.*, Chap. 7, p. 143,

2. The conversion of the make-up nitric acid to nitrous acid and to nitrogen oxides (omitted when NO from NH_3 is introduced).

3. The concentration of that part of the chamber acid which is added to dilute the 60°Bé. (77.7 per cent) Gay-Lussac acid to 57°Bé. (72.8 per cent) at the top of the tower.

4. The cooling of the furnace gases.

5. The production of acid from about 10 per cent of the sulfur dioxide. This takes place in the upper part of the tower.

6. The cleaning of the furnace gases.

7. The production of steam for the chambers.

8. The production of partly concentrated acid (60°Bé. or 77.7 per cent or slightly stronger) suitable for passing down the Gay-Lussac tower.

The Glover towers[1] are either all-masonry towers built from acidproof bricks with acidproof cement or of lead supported by an outside steel frame. At the bottom of the tower there is a brick flue inlet for the gases, and at the top there is a distributing device for the Gay-Lussac acid which is diluted to 57°Bé. or 72.8 per cent and caused to flow down the tower. The interior of the tower is packed[2] with hard-burned brick or tile made in a number of different designs. The cooled gases pass out near the top of the tower and are piped to the first chamber. The hot (140 to 160°C.) Glover or "tower" acid is collected at the bottom of the tower in a lead pan and passed through an acid cooler. Part is used over in the Gay-Lussac tower and the rest concentrated for consumption or sale. The amount of acid necessary to circulate over the Gay-Lussac tower and then to the Glover tower is from three to four times the daily production of acid, based on 60°Bé.

The sulfurous gases enter the tower between 425 and 600°C. About 10 per cent of the sulfur dioxide is oxidized in the Glover tower. The gaseous mixture of SO_2, SO_3, N_2, O_2, NO, NO_2, N_2O_3, and steam leaves a Glover tower at a temperature of from 70 to 110°C. and is sucked to the chamber by means of a fan.

Chambers. It is in the chambers that the greatest proportion of sulfur dioxide is oxidized to sulfur trioxide and hydrated to sulfuric acid. The chambers consist of a large steel framework with an interior of lead sheets which are "burned" or welded together with lead. These lead chambers are generally built about 10 ft. above the ground so that leaks in the bottoms may be easily detected and cooling may be facilitated. The reactions in the chamber generate much heat which must be removed continuously if the rate of sulfuric acid production is to be maintained. Under the ordinary condition of construction for chambers, this heat is dissipated slowly. Also some of the reactions proceed at a low rate. Thus, ordinarily, considerable space is needed in the chambers amounting to from

---

[1] FAIRLIE, *op. cit.*, Chap. 8, p. 159, heat balance, p. 170.

[2] PERRY, *op. cit.*, p. 709.

7.5 to 10 cu. ft. per lb. of sulfur burned per 24 hr. This can be much reduced by special cooling and mixing devices. The chambers may be enclosed in a building that is usually air-cooled. With good operation the average chamber set lasts over 20 years. Although, formerly, steam was introduced into the chambers, with the present excellent atomizing equipment water is used almost universally.

Gay-Lussac Tower and Recovery of Nitrogen Oxides. The function of the Gay-Lussac tower[1] is to recover the nitrogen oxides (catalyst) from spent gases. This is accomplished by washing these gases which should not be warmer than 60°C. with cold strong (60°Bé.) Glover acid in packed towers. There results the nitrous vitriol or Gay-Lussac acid containing 1 to 2 per cent of oxides of nitrogen, calculated as N_2O_3. The modern Gay-Lussac towers are constructed of masonry with acidproof cement. They are much taller and narrower and have thinner walls than the Glover tower. In the bottom of the tower is a pan of lead to collect the nitrous vitriol from which it is pumped over the Glover tower. The packing of the Gay-Lussac tower, like that of the Glover tower, is made of special shapes of hard-burned ceramic material.

Concentration of the Acid. The acid issuing from the Glover tower is usually between 60 and 61°Bé. in strength, and from the chambers, 50 to 55°Bé. For many purposes it is desired to concentrate these acids. Much process sulfuric acid must be reconcentrated after use. This is true of denitrated spent acids from making nitro compounds or nitrate esters, and of the sulfuric acid used to manufacture strong (95 per cent) nitric acid. These spent acids illustrate the important dehydrating action of strong sulfuric acid. Other acids that must be recovered and reconcentrated are sludge acids from petroleum purification and the sulfuric acid from the viscose rayon coagulation bath.

Sulfuric acid may be concentrated to around 66°Bé. by heat. Any further fortification is usually done by the addition of oleum or sulfur trioxide. Two types of equipment for concentrating dilute acid operate under a vacuum while the third under atmospheric pressure using airblown combustion gases.

The air-blown concentrator is exemplified by the Chemico[2] *drum-type concentrator* which is shown in Fig. 4. The burner supplies the hot gases at about 1100°F. by the combustion of oil or fuel gas. These hot combustion gases are blown countercurrent to the sulfuric acid in two compartments in the concentrating drum and remove water as they bubble up through the acid. The off gases at 440 to 475°F. from the first compartment of the drum pass to the second compartment along with a portion of the hot gases from the combustion furnace. They leave at 340 to

[1] FAIRLIE, *op. cit.*, Chap. 10, p. 223.

[2] BERGER and GLOSTER, The Chemico Drum Type Sulfuric Acid Concentrator, *Chem. Eng. Progr.*, **43**, 225 (1947).

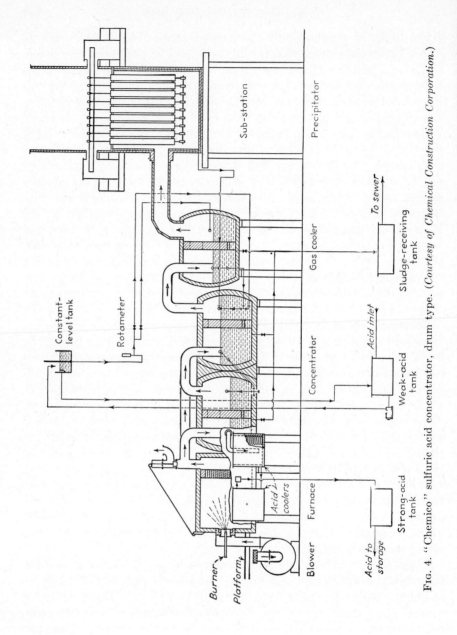

FIG. 4. "Chemico" sulfuric acid concentrator, drum type. (*Courtesy of Chemical Construction Corporation.*)

378

360°F. to enter a gas-cooling drum where they are cooled to 230 to 260°F. in raising the dilute acid to its boiling point. Since some sulfuric acid is entrained as a mist, the hot gases then pass through a Cottrell-type precipitator[1] for the removal of the acid mist before discharge to the atmosphere. A venturi scrubber with cyclone separator is also giving competitive results in removing acid mist by washing with feed acid (Chemico Pease-Anthony design). This procedure will give an acid with a final concentration of 93 per cent or slightly higher. The hot gases also burn out any impurities that may be in a spent acid being concentrated. Hence such concentrators are being extensively employed in the concentration of spent nitrating acids from munition works. If sludge acid from petroleum purification is being handled, the flow of acid from rear to front compartment is passed through an intermediate storage tank where a skimmer removes most of the nonvolatile carbonaceous impurities. The front and rear concentrating compartments of the steel drum are lined with lead and acidproof masonry. The repairs are remarkably low.

Vacuum concentrators (27 to 29.6 in. Hg) may be exemplified by the Simonson-Mantius[2] concentrators made by National Lead Co. There are five types which will permit concentration of practically any acid, though clean acid is preferred to avoid fouling of interfaces. The necessary heat is supplied by high-pressure steam or Dow-therm. The Type E concentrator is the largest and desirable for high concentrations. For the latter reason, this type of concentrator is employed only on relatively clean acids such as some nitration acids. It is a vertical steel shell lined (Fig. 5) first with lead followed by acidproof brick. The metallic tubular heaters inserted through the vertical wall of the vessel are constructed of Duriron or Hastelloy D. Usually there are two or more units in series. The Type D concentrator is a small batch unit with vertical tubes in a vertical cylindrical tank, suitable for acid concentrations up to 93 per cent. The Type C unit consists of many small compartments with individual heaters in series through which the acid to be concentrated flows continuously. The Type B concentrator, a batch unit, is a vertical tank with lead heating coils used mainly for acid concentration up to 80 per cent. The Type A unit can be operated continuously or batchwise. This special corrosion-resistant, high-circulation evaporator is used quite often for the removal of sodium sulfate from the waste acid liquor being discharged from the viscose spinning bath, as well as reconcentrating the remaining acid values. Types C and E have a practical concentration limit of 95 per cent acid.

The central section of the Du Pont[3] falling-film concentrator, shown

---

[1] PERRY, *op. cit.*, pp. 1039–1045.

[2] BURKE and MANTIUS, Concentration of Sulfuric Acid under Vacuum, *Chem. Eng. Progr.*, **43**, 237 (1947). Excellent tables and diagrams are presented.

[3] CHAMBERS and PETERSON, Sulfuric Acid Concentration by the Falling Film Process, *Chem. Eng. Progr.*, **43**, 219 (1947).

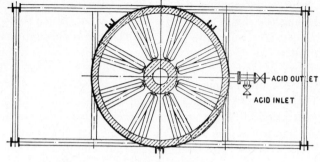

SECTIONAL PLAN

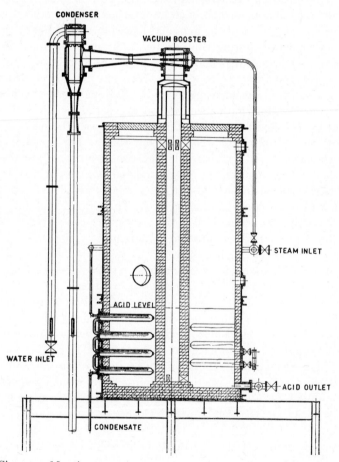

FIG. 5. Simonson-Mantius vacuum concentrator for sulfuric acid. Type E. (*Courtesy of National Lead Company.*)

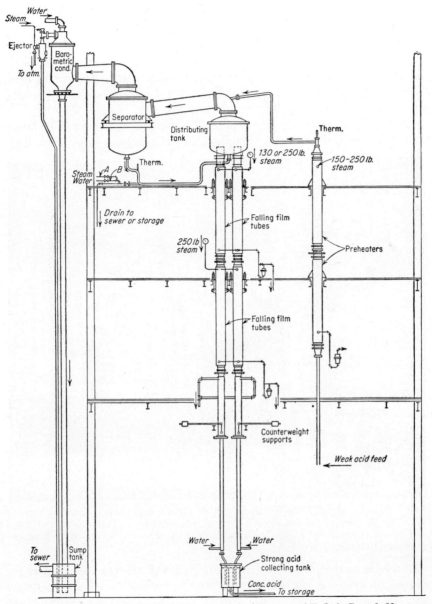

Fig. 6. Du Pont falling-film sulfuric concentrator. (*Courtesy of E. I. du Pont de Nemours & Co., Inc.*)

in Fig. 6, is a vertical steam-jacketed, high-silicon iron tube. The dilute acid is preheated and distributed around the internal periphery of the tube as a falling film. A vacuum of 25 mm. Hg is employed in this concentrator to remove water at the lowest possible temperature. The heating medium is steam at 250 lb. per sq. in. to give a 92 to 94 per cent acid. The heat-transfer rates vary with the temperature differential in the tube as well as the cleanliness of the tube surface.

Improved Chambers.[1] About 140 Mills-Packard chambers (Fig. 7) are in use in the United States though other designs have been tried. This

FIG. 7. World's largest Mills-Packard chamber sulfuric acid plant, located at Tampa, Fla. The 20 lead chambers have a total of 440,000 cu. ft. There are two Glover and three Gay-Lussac towers. (*Courtesy of U.S. Phosphoric Products Division, Tennessee Corporation.*)

chamber is in the form of a truncated cone and the reaction heat is removed by a film of water flowing down the outside. The chambers consist of a large steel framework with an interior of lead sheets which are "burned" or welded together with lead. Some conventional box chambers, which are air-cooled, are still used, but these are mostly being re-

<hr />

[1] JONES, *op. cit.;* FAIRLIE, Development Continues in Chamber Acid Plants, *Chem. Eng.,* **55** (7), 108 (1948). For earlier improvements in both America and Europe, see FAIRLIE, "Manufacture of Sulfuric Acid," Chap. 9, etc., Reinhold Publishing Corporation, New York, 1936.

placed. Mills-Packard chambers of small size are operating at 2.0 cu. ft. per lb. of sulfur, and large ones at 3.5 cu. ft. These rates correspond to approximately 0.5 and 0.7 sq. ft. per lb. of sulfur, and thus have one-half to one-third the surface of conventional box chambers.

MANUFACTURE BY THE CONTACT PROCESS

Until 1900 no contact plant had been built in the United States, although this process had become very important in Europe because of their need for oleums and high-strength acid for sulfonation, particularly in the dye industry. About 1930, American practice demonstrated that the contact process could compete with the chamber process in producing such acid as oil of vitriol. Since the Second World War, most of the new facilities built use the contact process with vanadium catalyst.[1] Probably no new installations employ platinum catalysts, and several existing units have been converted to vanadium catalysts. Except for the new Chemico[2] process, which will be discussed at the end of this chapter, the contact process is based on the same principles as when introduced over 50 years ago. Naturally there have been many improvements in heat exchangers, sulfur burners, instrumentation, size, and catalysts. A typical flow sheet is shown in Fig. 8 (see also Fig 2).

Unit Operations, Unit Processes, and Energy Changes. The flow sheet of Fig. 8 can be divided into the following *unit sequences:*

Transportation of sulfur (or sulfides) to plant (Op.).
Melting of sulfur (Op.).
Pumping and atomizing of melted sulfur (Op.).
Burning of sulfur (or sulfide) (Pr.).
Drying of combustion air (Pr.).
Recovery of heat from or cooling of hot SO_2 gas (Op.).
Purification of SO_2 gas (Op.).
Oxidation of SO_2 to SO_3 in converters (Pr.).
Heat transfer to secure good yields of SO_3 (Op.).
Absorption of SO_3 in strong acid, 98.5 to 99 per cent (Pr.).
Cooling of acid from absorbers (Op.).
Pumping of acid over absorption towers (Op.).

The energy evolved by the oxidation of sulfur to sulfur dioxide and from sulfur dioxide to sulfur trioxide has frequently been partly wasted in air coolers and partly utilized to raise the sulfur dioxide to reaction temperature in the converters. In Fig. 8, the heat of combustion of sulfur is partly utilized by a waste-heat boiler to generate steam for melting

[1] KASTENS and HUTCHINSON, Contact Sulfuric Acid from Sulfur, *Ind. Eng. Chem.*, **40**, 1340 (1948).
[2] OLIVE, Modern Chemical Engineering Revamps Conventional Contact Process, *Chem. Eng.*, **57** (10), 102 (1950).

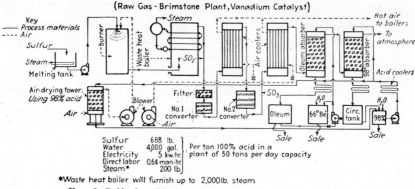

(Raw Gas - Brimstone Plant, Vanadium Catalyst)

Sulfur	688 lb.	Per ton 100% acid in a
Water	4,000 gal.	plant of 50 tons per day capacity
Electricity	5 kw.-hr.	
Direct labor	0.64 man-hr.	
Steam*	200 lb.	

*Waste heat boiler will furnish up to 2,000 lb. steam

FIG. 8. Sulfuric acid manufacture by the contact process.

the sulfur and for power purposes around the plant. In some other plants (Monsanto particularly) that part of the heat of reaction not required for converter temperature control is saved by "inter" and "after" cooling in waste-heat boilers, thus replacing the air coolers shown in Fig. 8.

Reactions. The reactions are

$$S(c) + O_2(g) \rightarrow SO_2(g); \quad \Delta H = -70,900 \text{ cal.}$$
$$SO_2(g) + \tfrac{1}{2}O_2(g) \rightleftarrows SO_3(g); \quad \Delta H = -23,000 \text{ cal.}$$

The oxidation of sulfur dioxide in the converters of the contact plant is a very good example of the many industrial applications of the principles of physical chemistry. As shown above, the reaction from SO_2 to SO_3 is an exothermic reversible reaction. The equilibrium constant for this reaction calculated from partial pressures according to Guldberg and Waage's law of mass action may be expressed as

$$K_p = \frac{p_{SO_3}}{p_{SO_2} \times p_{O_2}^{\frac{1}{2}}}$$

Values for this expression have been calculated based on p in atmospheres and are presented here in Table 4, and are constant for any given temperature.

From these values and from Fig. 9, it is apparent that the conversion of the sulfur dioxide decreases with an increase in temperature. For that reason it is desirable to carry out the reaction at as low a temperature as practicable. At 400°C., where from Fig. 9 the *equilibrium* condition is seen to be very favorable, being almost 100 per cent, the *rate* of attainment of this equilibrium is slow. The rate at 500°C. is 40 times as fast as that at 400°C.; at 550°C. it is much faster. Since the reverse reaction, $SO_3 \rightarrow SO_2 + \tfrac{1}{2}O_2$, does not become appreciable until 550°C., it would seem advisable to run the reaction initially at this temperature in order

TABLE 4. EQUILIBRIUM CONSTANTS FOR SULFUR DIOXIDE OXIDATION[a]

Temperature, °C.	K_p
400	397
500	48.1
600	9.53
700	2.63
800	0.915
900	0.384
1000	0.1845
1100	0.0980

[a]BODENSTEIN and POHL, Gleichgewichtsmessungen an der Kontaktschwefelsaure., *Z. Elektrochem.*, **11**, 373 (1905); FAIRLIE, "Manufacture of Sulfuric Acid," p. 42, Reinhold Publishing Corporation, New York, 1936. See "Rogers' Manual of Industrial Chemistry," 6th ed., pp. 269–276, 311–321, D. Van Nostrand Company, Inc., New York, 1942.

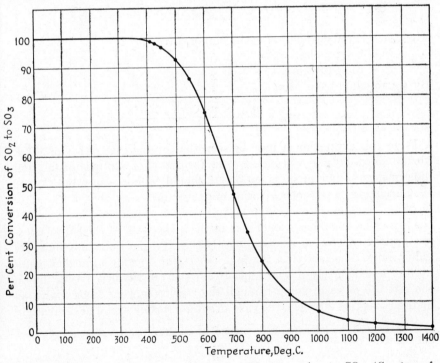

FIG. 9. Equilibrium-temperature relation for SO_2 conversion to SO_3. (*Courtesy of International Correspondence Schools.*)

to get as much conversion as possible to take place quickly.[1] There is here a conflict between the favorable conversion equilibriums at lower temperatures and the favorable rates at higher temperatures.

The actual procedure in a contact plant takes advantage of both the rate and equilibrium considerations by first passing the gases over a part of the catalyst at about 575°C. where the rate is high until about 80 per cent of the sulfur dioxide is converted. Then the gas, before it passes over the remainder of the catalyst, is cooled in a heat exchanger or in a waste-heat boiler, until the temperature of the gases passing over the last portion of the catalyst is only around 450°C. The yields using this procedure are over 97 per cent and the reaction rate is very rapid. Figures 10, 11, and 12 illustrate how these conditions are applied in practice and how the heat of reaction is used.

By rewriting the expression for K_p in terms of mole fractions and total pressures, for the equation $2SO_2 + O_2 \rightleftarrows 2SO_3$ we have

$$K_p = \frac{N \times n_{SO_3}^2}{n_{SO_2}^2 \times n_{O_2} \times P}$$

where n = number moles of each component.
    N = total moles.
    P = total pressure.
By rearranging, we obtain

$$n_{SO_3}^2 = \frac{n_{SO_2}^2 \times n_{O_2} \times K_p \times P}{N}$$

From this expression it may be seen that an increase either of sulfur dioxide or of oxygen[2] will increase the formation of sulfur trioxide, thus illustrating the law of mass action. It should be borne in mind that in the burner gas, if the concentration of oxygen increases, that of the sulfur dioxide decreases and vice versa. An increase of pressure, according to the law of Le Châtelier, would also increase the yield of the sulfur trioxide, but the effect is so small and costly that it is not taken advantage of industrially. The fact that the moles of sulfur trioxide formed at equilibrium are inversely proportional to N, the total moles, shows that if the mixture of gases going through the converter were diluted with an inert gas, such as nitrogen, the yield of sulfur trioxide would be decreased.[3]

[1] LEWIS and RIES, Influence of Reaction Rate on Operating Conditions in Contact Sulfuric Acid Manufacture, *Ind. Eng. Chem.*, **17**, 593 (1925).

[2] MILES, "Manufacture of Sulphuric Acid (Contact Process)," D. Van Nostrand Company, Inc., New York, 1925; FAIRLIE, "Manufacture of Sulfuric Acid," p. 341.

[3] As is true with all phases of sulfuric acid manufacture, FAIRLIE, *ibid.*, should be consulted; Chaps. 12 and 14 partly elaborate on the subject here presented. For a most excellent presentation of the theory of the contact reaction see pp. 269–276, 311–321, of FURNAS, editor, "Rogers' Manual of Industrial Chemistry," Vol. 1; this reference is written by GROSVENOR and PHILLIPS.

Catalysts. It should be remembered that in all catalytic reactions, the only function of the catalyst is to *increase the rate* of the reactions. The catalysts that are of interest for the production of contact sulfuric acid are platinum and vanadium pentoxide. For many years platinum was the only catalyst used industrially, but shortly after the First World War, vanadium gained much ground and there soon arose a sharp rivalry between the advocates of these two. It was not until 1929, however, that many plants began operating on the vanadium catalyst mass. Since that time vanadium has become the more popular and during and since the Second World War has replaced platinum in many installations.

Platinum Catalysts. Platinum is applied as a catalyst on several carriers, the most important being silica gel, calcined magnesium sulfate, and asbestos. The carriers for this catalyst must be porous, have a large surface area, be chemically inert to the gases at high temperatures, be refractory enough to stand the high temperatures, and be strong enough to resist the jars and strains placed on them.

Platinized asbestos is prepared by impregnating specially treated asbestos with a solution of platinic chloride to give a mass that contains from 6 to 10 per cent platinum. The usual platinized asbestos requires 5 to 7 troy ounces of platinum per ton of 100 per cent sulfuric acid per 24 hr. Recently there has been produced a special type of "low-ignition" platinized asbestos which is capable of producing the same amount of sulfuric acid with only 2 to 3 troy ounces of platinum. The impregnation of calcined magnesium sulfate with platinic chloride is done in analogous manner and requires about the same amount of platinum as the ordinary platinized asbestos.

One of the most recent contact catalysts is platinized silica gel. This catalyst usually contains about 0.1 per cent platinum, gives conversion efficiencies of about 96 per cent, and requires only from 1.5 to 3.5 oz. of platinum per daily ton of 100 per cent sulfuric acid.

Vanadium Catalysts. Soluble compounds of vanadium deposited on a carrier were proposed as a catalyst for production of sulfuric acid as early as 1895, but it was not until 1926 that a catalyst of vanadium was used in the American sulfuric industry. The early vanadium catalysts, known as *Monsanto mass* and the *Selden mass*, are prepared from ammonium vanadate or vanadium pentoxide and a carrier such as a zeolite, other base exchange substances, or kieselguhr.[1] The vanadium catalysts give high conversions of 97 to 98 per cent.

The advantages[2] claimed for platinum are that 90 per cent of the

---

[1] Patent and literature references to catalysts, together with abstracts therefrom, and testimony in the various lawsuits are summarized by FAIRLIE, *op. cit.*, Chap. 17.

[2] THOMPSON, Platinum vs. Vanadium Pentoxide as Catalysts for Sulfuric Acid Manufacture, *Trans. Am. Inst. Chem. Engrs.*, **27**, 264 (1931); also FAIRLIE, *op. cit.*, Chaps. 17 and 18.

original metal may be recovered, the operating cost is less (mainly owing to the fact that there is a royalty charge for the vanadium catalyst), and the initial capital cost of the plant is less because gases with higher proportions of sulfur dioxide (8 to 10 per cent) may be used. The disadvantages of platinum are that it suffers a decline of activity with use, the life of the catalyst is shorter, it is subject to poisoning under some conditions, and it is very difficult to handle because it is so fragile. The advantages claimed for vanadium masses are that they have a higher conversion efficiency maintained for a longer period than platinum, the catalysts are immune to poisoning (not now of any great importance), the vanadium mass is less troublesome during operation, it is easier to handle, and has a lower initial cost. The disadvantages of vanadium are that it handles a lower sulfur dioxide (7 to 8 per cent) content gas, it cannot be overloaded as can platinum and it has no salvage value when worn out.

CONTACT PROCESS EQUIPMENT

Fairlie, in his book on sulfuric acid manufacture, details the many variations in the equipment employed that appeared to his date of publication (1936).

Lee[1] lists more recently the materials of construction. Probably the major innovation in the design of new plants is the "outdoor" type of construction, which saves initial capital investment. In almost all parts of the country, new plants are completely exposed to the elements with only the control room, blower, and feed-water pumps enclosed.

Treatment of the Burner Gas. The sulfur dioxide burner gas for the contact process may contain, in addition to dust, carbon dioxide, nitrogen, and oxygen, such impurities as arsenic, chlorine, and fluorine. The last three impurities are present only when pyrite is burned. To prevent corrosion from the burner gases and to add the water more advantageously to the absorber acid, it is now customary, as shown in Fig. 8, to dry the air for burning the sulfur or a sulfide. Such drying is done in towers usually with 95 to 98 per cent sulfuric acid. The burner gas has much of its heat removed in waste-heat boilers for the generation of steam. If a sulfide is burned, an efficient dust collector and acid washing towers may be added. The sulfuric acid wash removes halogens.

Preheaters and Coolers. Before the gases can be taken to the converter, they should be heated to increase the speed of the reaction. Since the converted gases should be cooled on issuing from the converter, all plants use the heat from these gases to preheat the gases traveling to the converter. These heat exchangers usually consist of large vertical cylin-

---

[1] LEE, "Materials of Construction for Chemical Process Industries," McGraw-Hill Book Company, Inc., New York, 1950.

ders containing many small tubes. The sulfur trioxide gas passes downward through the tubes while the sulfur dioxide gas surrounds the tubes and passes upward against them. In some cases baffles are provided to change the direction of the gases so that better heat transfer will be obtained. Several heat exchangers may be used and many complicated designs have been introduced.

Converters. Converters[1] are of two broad types: two-stage or multipass converters with outside heat exchangers or by-product boilers (Figs. 8 and 12), and a converter that is a combination converter and heat exchanger (Figs. 10 and 11). The first stage or the first converter operates at a higher temperature up to from 500 to 600°C. to ensure a rapid attainment of a moderate conversion equilibrium. The second stage or the second converter is controlled to a lower temperature of around 400 to 450°C. where the rate is slower but the conversion is higher. This combination results in a high over-all efficiency. Other factors in the conversion are the time of contact of the gas with the catalyst and the activity of the catalyst.

The multipass type generally consists of a primary converter which contains about 30 per cent of the total amount of catalyst. The secondary has the remaining portion of the catalyst divided into several layers. These are usually operated in conjunction with two heat exchangers or two by-product boilers. Burner gas, partly cooled by the by-product boiler, passes downward and in the top of the primary converter. The gas is about 80 per cent converted here and is heated to the higher temperature. It flows to the intercooler or heat exchanger and enters the top of the second converter at the lower temperature passing through the catalyst layers where the conversion is brought to about 96 or 97 per cent (see Fig. 8). The gas passes through the aftercooler or heat exchanger and then to the absorber.[2]

The second type of converter passes the incoming sulfur dioxide gas entering at about 260°C., upward through inner pipes and downward through the outer concentric pipes embedded in a deep layer or 60 per cent of the catalyst as shown by Figs. 10 and 11. This lower catalyst bed is maintained at 570 to 595°C. and accomplishes 85 per cent of the conversion. The sulfur dioxide first has its temperature raised in the outer pipe; it then enters the catalyst bed, oxidizes, and liberates heat with a further rise in temperature. This rise is checked and reduced by the continued upward flow through the catalyst bed and above it of the partly converted sulfur dioxide (counter to the downflow of the incoming sulfur dioxide in the pipes). The partly converted sulfur dioxide con-

---

[1] DuBois and HARNEY, Contact Sulfuric Acid Converters, *Ind. Eng. Chem.*, **24**, 1091 (1932).

[2] *Cf.* ANON., Contact Acid from Pyrites, *Chem. & Met. Eng.*, **46**, 477 (1939) for a pictured flow sheet of a multipass plant with different arrangement of gas treatment.

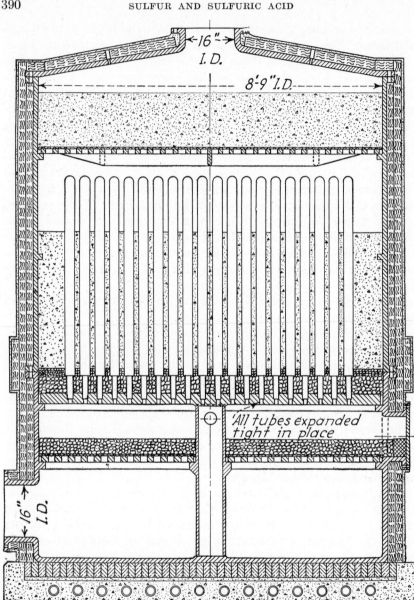

Fig. 10. "Chemico" Selden converter for sulfur trioxide using vanadium pentoxide. (*Courtesy of Chemical Construction Corporation.*)

tinues to rise upward at its lowered temperature through the second layer of catalyst, maintained at 460 to 475°C., and is there converted to sulfur trioxide up to 97 per cent. This hot gas passes to the aftercooler or boiler and then on to the absorbers at a temperature of around 140°C. The figures, just cited, are for a Chemico vanadium converter which has an ignition temperature of about 400°C.; hence the gases must contact the catalyst above this temperature to avoid cold spots.

The advantages[1] of the first type are the lower cost of construction, greater accessibility for repair, the use of less catalyst, less power for the movement of gases, and ease of adaption to gases of varying sulfur dioxide content. The advantages of the other type are that it occupies less ground space and that the heat-exchanger tubes are not subject to rupture by buckling or stretching.

Sulfur Trioxide Absorbers. It has been known for a long time that a concentration of acid between 98.5 and 99 per cent sulfuric acid is the most efficient agent for absorption, probably because acid of this strength has a lower vapor pressure than any other concentration. Hence acid of this strength is used for the final absorber before the waste gas is vented to the atmosphere. Water cannot be used because an acid mist is formed by the direct contact with the sulfur trioxide which is almost impossible to absorb. Since the absorbing acid is continuously becoming more concentrated, it is necessary to provide some means for diluting that part of the acid discharged from the final absorber which is to be recirculated. Also, the absorbing acid must be cooled. The diluting of the recirculating acid is done by adding spent or dilute sulfuric acid or water in the amount required, withdrawing from the system any excess acid for sale.

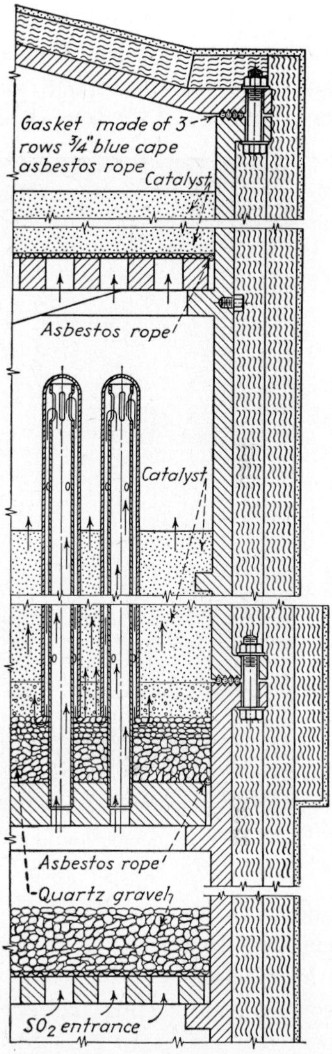

The 20 per cent oleum is made in the oleum absorber, as shown in Fig. 8, by passing cooled 99 per cent acid over this tower. If an oleum of 60 to 70 per cent is wanted, it may be prepared by distilling the 20 per cent oleum in steel vessels. The trioxide driven off is absorbed in 20 per cent oleum in water-cooled vessels equipped with a mechanical stirrer.

FIG. 11. Detail of heat exchange in "Chemico" converter. (*Courtesy of Chemical Construction Corporation.*)

[1] FAIRLIE, *op. cit.*, p. 382, also pp. 365–383, quoting DuBois and HARNEY, *op. cit.*

Although bubble-cap towers have been used to absorb sulfur trioxide, the most common type is the packed steel towers lined with acidproof masonry. Unlined towers are now being employed where cast iron is used for the 98 to 99.5 per cent acid and steel for the oleums. The packing generally consists of chemical stoneware,[1] though at times lumps of quartz or coke have been used. The gas enters the bottom and leaves by a flue out of the top. It has been found that a tower 6 ft. in diameter

FIG. 12. Heat exchanger and secondary converter of the Monsanto multipass system. (*Courtesy of Monsanto Chemical Company.*)

and 24 ft. high will absorb ¼ ton of sulfur trioxide per hour while recirculating 10 tons of acid. Newer developments in the latest plants are towers capable of absorbing 4 tons of sulfur trioxide while fed with 110 tons of recirculating acid per hour. At least two absorbers are used, connected in series. In the first tower 20 per cent oleum is usually made. In the second tower, 98 per cent sulfuric acid is made.

New Type Contact Process.[2] This new process, designed and built by the Chemical Construction Corp. at Hamilton, Ohio, in 1950, represents the first real change in the contact process for over 50 years. The process is conventional up to the converter except that the combustion air is not dried. From the converter on, all the steps are new. Table 5 sum-

[1] PERRY, *op. cit.*, p. 685.

[2] OLIVE, Modern Chemical Engineering Revamps Conventional Contact Process, *Chem. Eng.*, **57** (10), 102 (1950), including a comparison flow sheet of the old and new.

marizes the equipment changes. This process claims a marked increase in conversion efficiency, greatly simplified plant, and decreased investment and physical size. However, this plant is not recommended at present for acid over 95 per cent.

TABLE 5. COMPARISON OF EQUIPMENT USED IN THE CONVENTIONAL AND NEW CONTACT PROCESS

Equipment	Conventional	New
Converter	Usually in 2 stages, with each stage in a separate vessel	Four stages in a single vessel
Heat exchangers	Shell-and-tube heat exchangers to cool the gas from each stage	No heat exchangers. Cools by direct injection of air into the gas stream between converter stages
Absorber	Packed tower	Horizontal vessel similar to drum concentrator (shown in Fig. 4) which achieves direct contact of gas and absorption
Final SO₃ cooler	Used. Large amount of water needed. New process eliminates this, reducing cooling water needs 90 per cent or more	Not used. Absorber has dual function. Also cools by evaporating water from the absorption acid
Acid-mist cleanup	Great care taken to avoid acid-mist formation, i.e., air drying. Usually no need to clean up exit gases	Produces a great deal of acid mist. Pease-Anthony venturi scrubber combined with a small cyclone scrubber efficiently removes the mist

SELECTED REFERENCES

Fairlie, A. M., "Manufacture of Sulfuric Acid," Reinhold Publishing Corporation, New York, 1936.

Haynes, W., "The Stone That Burns," D. Van Nostrand Company, Inc., New York, 1942. Book on sulfur.

De Wolf, P., and E. Larison, "American Sulfuric Acid Practice," McGraw-Hill Book Company, Inc., New York, 1921.

Wells, A. E., and D. E. Fogg, The Manufacture of Sulfuric Acid in the United States, U.S. Bur. Mines Bull. 184, 216 pp., 1920.

Miles, F. D., "The Manufacture of Sulfuric Acid (Contact Process)," Gurney & Jackson, London; D. Van Nostrand Company, Inc., New York, 1925.

Furnas, C. C., editor, "Rogers' Manual of Industrial Chemistry," 6th ed., 2 vols., D. Van Nostrand Company, Inc., New York, 1942.

"Chemical Plant Control Data," 4th ed., Chemical Construction Co., New York, 1935.

Kreps, T. J., "Economics of the Sulfuric Acid Industry," Stanford University Press, Stanford University, Calif., 1938.

Symposium, Sulfur, Ind. Eng. Chem., 42, 2186–2302 (1950).

CHAPTER 20

NITROGEN INDUSTRIES

Man must feed nitrogen back into the soil or face a decrease in his supply of food. However much this latter was feared at one time, the chemists and the chemical engineers found out how to make nitrogen derivatives out of air in an economical way. The first successful process—the arc process—required much cheap electrical energy. However, the present solution of the nitrogen-fixation problem came from reacting nitrogen with low-cost hydrogen to make ammonia under conditions requiring low power demands and low conversion expense. This made the arc process obsolete. Ammonia has now become one of our heavy chemicals produced in an enormous tonnage throughout the globe and at such low prices as to dominate the world supply of nitrogen fertilizers and most nitrogen compounds. It is probable that this is one of the most important chemical engineering achievements of history.

Historical. Priestley observed that an electric spark passed through air confined over water caused a lessening in gas volume and acidification of the water. A few years later, in 1780, Cavendish repeated Priestley's experiments and found that nitrites and nitrates were formed if the experiment was carried out over an alkaline solution. With the lowered cost of electrical energy which came with the use of water power, interest in the arc method of nitrogen fixation was revived and was accompanied by the establishment of a successful arc process in Norway in 1904, known as the *Birkeland-Eyde* process. Here air was passed through a flaming electric arc at a very high temperature when a small percentage of the nitrogen was burned to NO. This nitric oxide was rapidly cooled successively in brick-lined iron pipes, steel boilers, and aluminum coolers, being oxidized to NO_2 at the lower temperatures. The initial cooling was rapid to prevent reversal. Other arc furnaces rapidly followed, but today the arc method is competitively uneconomical and is obsolete.

Attempts to produce cyanides of the alkaline earth metals as substitutes for the more costly alkali cyanides resulted in the discovery of the calcium cyanamide method of fixing nitrogen. The cyanamide, as such, is a fertilizer but, by further treatment, may be transformed into a cyanide or into numerous other nitrogen-containing chemicals such as guanidine.

394

The direct ammonia method was long in developing but it now holds the paramount position. It was the researches of Haber, Nernst, and their coworkers that laid the real foundation for the present exceedingly important synthetic ammonia industry and, in the years 1904–1908, equilibrium data for the ammonia-nitrogen-hydrogen system were established with fair accuracy over considerable ranges of temperatures and pressures. The development of a practical synthetic ammonia process was carried out through the efforts of Haber and Bosch with their coworkers, and the growth of this industry has continued since this beginning.

Curtis[1] describes various processes not now economical, such as the arc,[2] cyanide, and Serpek aluminum nitride procedure. The cyanamide and the ammonia manufacturing procedures are the present ones of technical importance for supplying the world with fixed nitrogen, although

TABLE 1. UNITED STATES NITROGEN STATISTICS, 1947–1953[a]
(In thousands of short tons)

	1943–1947 over	1948	1950	1953
Ammonia:				
Synthetic, anhydrous....................	695	1,090	1,565	2,288
By-product (NH₃ content):				
Aqua ammonia.......................	28	25	23	25
Ammonium sulfate...................	190	208	208	237
Ammonium sulfate:				
Synthetic.............................	119	264	1,138	576
By-product............................	759	831	831	946
Sodium nitrate, total synthetic and by-product	. . .	210		
Ammonium nitrate, 100 per cent solution......	744	988	1,214	1,558

[a] "Minerals Yearbook." Many company details are given.

thermal fixation may develop into technical importance. The only plant in North America producing calcium cyanamide is at Niagara Falls, Canada, and is owned and operated by the American Cyanamid Company. It has an annual capacity of about 235,000 tons of calcium cyanamide.

Uses and Economics. The chemical nitrogen industries include not only the nitrogen fixed by man, but also the by-product ammonia from coke ovens and such natural nitrogen deposits as Chile saltpeter, all subjected to manufacturing processes. Table 1 summarizes the statistics in the United States while Table 2 illustrates the world nitrogen fertilizer situation only. Nitrogen for fertilizers is still in short supply and plants are

[1] CURTIS, "Fixed Nitrogen," Reinhold Publishing Corporation, New York, 1932. This is an excellent book for this field and will be referred to frequently in this chapter.
[2] Cf. PERRY, op. cit., p. 1820, for a short presentation of the arc processes.

now building to increase the nitrogen production to 3,500,000 short tons (nitrogen) by Jan. 1, 1957 (see Tables 1 and 5). To do this, as of April, 1954, 30 new or enlarged plants were under way, to cost 270 million dollars and to yield about 1,000,000 more tons of nitrogen as NH_3. Although Table 3 is old, it still illustrates the tremendous importance of natural sources of nitrogen. According to Soday,[1]

Approximately 50 per cent of the plant food originally present in the soils of this country has been removed by continued cropping, and the removal of nitrogen by harvested crops each year still exceeds the amount added by fertilizers and manures by 80 per cent. The net loss of plant food each year in this country is estimated at 40,000,000 tons.

TABLE 2. WORLD PRODUCTION OF FERTILIZER NITROGEN COMPOUNDS, FISCAL YEARS, 1948–1953[a]
(In metric tons of contained nitrogen)

Producing country	1948–1949	1949–1950	1950–1951	1952–1953
Austria................	59,000	67,820	74,900	100,700
Belgium..............	152,130	174,985	173,357	215,000
Canada..............	175,420	143,676	149,208	161,208
Chile................	275,270	241,823	242,583	234,660
Czechoslovakia........	29,950	30,000	30,000	30,300
Egypt................	....	....	....	31,000
France..............	187,500	214,000	259,030	305,000
Germany:				
Federal Republic....	327,600	431,405	464,677	520,000
Soviet Zone........	110,000	130,000	205,000	213,000
India................	12,630	9,200	8,417	71,120
Italy................	104,330	136,905	177,301	225,000
Japan................	274,070	378,481	414,595	480,000
Korea, South........	....	....	....	1,122
Netherlands..........	85,080	112,557	189,053	245,000
Norway..............	107,500	150,040	160,747	164,795
Peru................	22,210	34,159	35,440	36,000
Poland..............	55,080	60,000	65,000	65,000
Spain................	....	....	6,600	7,000
Sweden..............	21,540	23,397	25,426	24,659
Taiwan (Formosa)....	....	....	6,112	14,320
United Kingdom......	280,800	275,282	245,000	286,000
United States........	975,000	1,048,000	996,000	1,202,000
Total[b]..............	3,310,900	3,707,000	4,011,103	4,705,864

[a] "Minerals Yearbook," 1952–1953 preliminary; cf. "Nitrogen Fertilizers, A World Report on Production and Consumption," Agricultural Organization, United Nations, Rome, Italy, 1952.

[b] Exclusive of U.S.S.R.

[1] SODAY, Future Trends in the Chemical Industry, *Ind. Eng. Chem.*, **45**, 325 (1953).

TABLE 3. NITROGEN: BALANCE SHEET FOR THE UNITED STATES[a]
(Based on a total acreage of harvested crops in 1930 of 366,505,000 acres)

Nitrogen	Short tons	Nitrogen	Short tons
Losses from		Gains by	
Harvested crops.........	5,500,000	Bacterial fixation.........	3,000,000
Pasturage..............	1,500,000	Rainfall................	1,300,000
Drainage..............	900,000	Fertilizers..............	400,000
Erosion................	500,000	Total gain.............	4,700,000
Total loss............	8,400,000	Annual deficit..............	3,700,000

[a] Data from G. H. Collings, "Commercial Fertilizers," 1st ed., p. 14, Blakiston Division, McGraw-Hill Book Company, Inc., New York, 1934.

CYANAMIDE

The major use of cyanamide is agricultural. Although it has a higher cost per unit of fixed nitrogen than other common fertilizers, its high alkalinity and its ability to speed equilibration in mixed fertilizers make it economical. It is also a herbicide and a much used defoliant especially for cotton plants to permit machine picking. However, its employment as a chemical raw material is becoming increasingly important, with the largest chemical use being for the preparation of the dimer dicyandiamide. Most of this dimer is polymerized to produce the trimer melamine which has many applications especially in plastic resins. Many of the other commercial derivatives are produced by way of a crude calcium cyanide[1] (48 to 50 per cent expressed as NaCN) from a high-temperature melt of cyanamide with excess carbon and NaCl. This is used directly for cyanidation of ores to manufacture ferrocyanides or acidified to yield HCN gas. Hydrocyanic acid has many important derivatives, of which acrylonitrile is probably the most promising commercially.

Reactions and Energy Changes.[1] The essential reactions for the production of calcium cyanamide are as follows:

$$CaCO_3(s) \rightarrow CaO(s) + CO_2(g); \quad \Delta H = +43,500 \text{ cal.} \quad (1)$$
$$CaO(s) + 3C(amorph.) \rightarrow CaC_2(s) + CO(g); \quad \Delta H = +103,000 \text{ cal.} \quad (2)$$
$$CaC_2(s) + N_2(g) \rightarrow CaCN_2(s) + C(amorph.); \quad \Delta H = -68,000 \text{ cal.*} \quad (3)$$

[1] KASTENS and McBURNEY, Calcium Cyanamide, *Ind. Eng. Chem.*, **43**, 1020 (1951). This excellent article with many pictures should be freely consulted. *Cf.* KIRK and OTHMER, *op. cit.*, Vol. 4, pp. 663*ff.*; pp. 708–712 for calcium cyanide. See Chap. 17 for more details on calcium carbide manufacture.

* The heat of this reaction as given in the literature varies considerably. Studies at American Cyanamid indicate a ΔH of 68,500 cal. at 1100°C.

Various catalysts or fluxes are used to increase the rate of reaction or cause it to proceed at lower temperatures. American Cyanamid uses calcium fluoride, and reaction-rate studies have shown that it reduces the temperature of optimum reactivity and increases the velocity of the reaction by 4.5 times at 1000°C. Reaction (3) takes place at 900 to 1000°C. Reaction (2) at Cyanamid is carried out in a battery of two 20,000- and

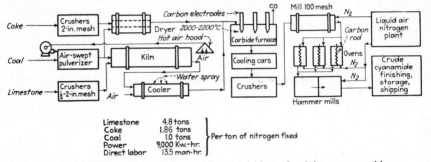

Limestone	4.8 tons	
Coke	1.86 tons	
Coal	1.0 tons	Per ton of nitrogen fixed
Power	9,000 Kw.-hr.	
Direct labor	13.5 man-hr.	

Fig. 1. Flow sheet for making calcium carbide and calcium cyanamide.

two 10,000-kw. furnaces at about 2000 to 2200°C. Under normal conditions reaction (2) yields up to 90 per cent calcium carbide. Considerable over-all energy is needed, principally to secure the high temperature for (3) to start when it is self-sustaining and for making the calcium carbide (2). The source of carbon is usually coke. The coal is required to burn the limestone and to dry the raw materials (Fig. 1).

The following *unit operations* (Op.) and *unit processes* (Pr.) are needed to commercialize[1] the reactions on which Fig. 1 is based.

Limestone, coal, and coke are pulverized, separately (Op.).
Limestone is calcined to quicklime (Pr.).
Coke is pulverized, dried, and mixed with quicklime (Op.).
Carbide is formed in an electric furnace at nearly 2000 to 2200°C. and run out molten (Pr.).
Carbide is cooled, crushed, and finely ground (Op.).
Air is liquefied by compressing, cooling, and expansion (Op.).
Nitrogen is separated from oxygen by liquid rectification (Op.).
Calcium carbide is nitrified over the course of 40 hr. with 99.9 per cent nitrogen around 1000°C. (Pr.).
Calcium cyanamide is pulverized and treated with a small amount of water to hydrate residual CaO and CaC_2. It may be oiled to reduce dust (Op. and Pr.).

Ovens of the discontinuous type are the most common for the nitrification. They consist of a cylindrical steel shell, lined with refractory tile or firebrick. The steel cover, also lined with firebrick, has a hole to permit the escape of inert gas. The carbide is charged in paper-lined, perforated

[1] Anon., Pictured Flow Sheet, *Chem. & Met. Eng.*, **47**, 253 (1940).

steel baskets or the oven may be lined with paper and the carbide charged directly. Nitrogen is admitted through the bottom and the sides near the bottom. A carbon rod placed in the center of the oven serves as an electric resistance element to bring the carbide adjacent to it to the reaction temperature. After this the exothermic nature of the reaction maintains the necessary temperature. In most ovens a single electrode is used, but in some of the larger furnaces there are as many as eight. The ovens range in size from 1 to 8 tons capacity with the corresponding time for nitrification ranging from 30 hr. to 1 week. The treatment of the crude cyanamide depends upon the end usage. For the manufacture of calcium cyanide no further treatment is given. For chemical purposes sufficient water is added to eliminate residual calcium carbide. The product for agricultural purposes goes to a more elaborate milling system where water and sometimes milling oil are added.

SYNTHETIC AMMONIA

Uses and Economics. Ammonia is one of the truly fundamental raw materials for modern civilization. In total chemical tonnage in this country, it is exceeded only by that of H_2SO_4, Na_2CO_3, NaOH, and Cl_2. The largest peacetime consumer of anhydrous ammonia is the fertilizer industry; in the production of calcium and sodium nitrate, ammonium sulfate, nitrate and phosphate, ammoniated superphosphates, urea, and aqueous ammonia. When applied by special machines, anhydrous ammonia has become a very important fertilizer. For this *direct* application to soils, the Department of Agriculture estimates that in 1953–1954, about 325,000 short tons of nitrogen as NH_3 will be available. Ammonia is the starting point of nearly all military explosives. Scarcely an industry is untouched as ammonia is required for the making of soda ash, nitric acid, nylon, plastics, lacquers, dyes, rubber, and other products.[1]

The product is handled and shipped in two forms: ammonia liquor and ammonia anhydrous. Commercial grades of the liquor usually contain 28 per cent ammonia. Shipment of anhydrous in this country is largely done in 26-ton special tank cars and in cylinders of 25, 50, 100, or 150 lb. See Tables 1 and 2 for statistics.

Reactions and Equilibriums. For the reaction

$$\tfrac{1}{2}N_2 + \tfrac{3}{2}H_2 \rightleftarrows NH_3$$

the equilibrium constant is expressed as

$$K_p = \frac{p_{NH_3}}{p_{N_2}^{1/2} \times p_{H_2}^{3/2}}$$

[1] Anon., Ammonia, *Chem. Eng. News*, **28**, 3104 (1950).

The equilibrium constant can be calculated from known partial pressures as exemplified by Perry.[1] Since the volume of ammonia obtained is less than the combined volume of the nitrogen and hydrogen a pressure increase, according to the *principle of Le Châtelier*, will give a higher percentage of ammonia at equilibrium. The conversion percentage increases several fold as the pressure increases from 100 to 1,000 atm., but the percentage of ammonia in equilibrium with the reacting gases decreases continually with the temperature rise up to 1100°C., reaches a minimum at

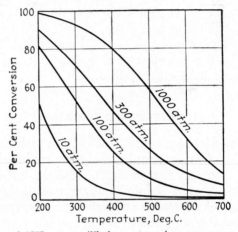

FIG. 2. Percentage of NH₃ at equilibrium at various pressures and temperatures. (*After data in Table 16, p. 152 of Curtis, "Fixed Nitrogen," Reinhold Publishing Corporation, New York, 1932.*)

this temperature, and increases again at higher temperatures. While it amounts to only 0.003 volume per cent at 1100°C., it is 1.23 volume per cent at 2400°C. While operating below 1100°C. (see Fig. 2), the lower the temperature for a given pressure at which an ammonia converter can be run, the larger the possible percentage of ammonia in the ammonia-nitrogen-hydrogen mixture, but the longer the time required to attain equilibrium. Accordingly, temperatures in the converters are kept as low as is consistent with a sufficiently rapid reaction rate to be economical on the catalyst used and with the investment required.

Rate and Catalysis of the Reaction. To be economical, the rate of this reaction must be increased because hydrogen and nitrogen of themselves react very slowly. The solution of the commercial synthesis of ammonia rests upon efficient catalysts to speed up the reaction rate to an econom-

[1] PERRY, *op. cit.*, pp. 350, 356. See LEWIS and RANDALL, "Thermodynamics and the Free Energy of Chemical Substances," p. 557, McGraw-Hill Book Company, Inc., New York, 1923, for plot of log K against reciprocal of absolute temperature and for general free-energy equation.

ical degree. Such catalysts[1] have been found in iron whose rate is promoted by the addition of small amounts of oxides of aluminum and potassium.

Space velocity is the number of cubic feet of exit gases, corrected to standard conditions (0°C. and 760 mm.), that pass over 1 cu. ft. of catalyst space per hour. The space velocity used in commercial operation differs considerably in different processes and in different plants using the same process. Although the percentage of ammonia in the gas stream issuing from a converter goes down as the space velocity goes up, the amount of ammonia per cubic foot of catalyst space per hour increases. However, a too high space velocity disturbs the thermal balance of a converter, involves increased cost of ammonia removal because of the smaller percentage present in the exit gases, and makes necessary the recirculation of large volumes of gas. Most commercial units use a space velocity between 20,000 and 40,000.

Many reactions are known which occur as a result of one reacting constituent combining with the catalyst to form an intermediate compound that is capable of reacting with the second reacting constituent to form the product of the catalytic reaction and to regenerate the catalyst. Thus it is postulated that nitride formation is possible on the active iron atoms on the surface of the ammonia catalyst. Iron seems to be by far the most satisfactory *catalyst* material, though it seems to lose its activity rapidly if heated to temperatures above 520°C. The catalyst is promoted by metallic oxides, the activity being increased most by adding both an amphoteric oxide of a metal such as aluminum, zirconium, or silicon and an alkaline oxide such as potassium oxide. As P. H. Emmett[2] summarizes this, "The percentage ammonia in a gaseous mixture of pure 3:1 hydrogen-nitrogen gas passed over such a doubly promoted catalyst at 100 atm. pressure, 5,000 space velocity, and at 450°C., is 13 to 14 for the doubly promoted catalyst in contrast to 8 or 9 for the singly promoted one and to 3 or 5 per cent for the pure iron catalyst." Many methods of preparing promoted iron catalysts are found in the patent literature; however, practically all the catalysts now used commercially are made by melting iron oxide together with the desired promoter ingredients upon a protecting bed having the same composition as the catalyst material. This is done in an electric furnace in which the iron oxide itself acts as the resistor. After cooling, the material is crushed to the desired particle size. These catalysts are ruined by contact with many substances like

[1] EMMETT and KUMMER, Kinetics of Ammonia Synthesis, *Ind. Eng. Chem.*, **35**, 677 (1943). This article includes the newer Russian equations of Temkin and Pyzhev with many data and literature references.

[2] CURTIS, *op. cit.*, p. 156. From, p. 154 to p. 206, this book contains a most excellent summary of the theoretical and laboratory studies pertaining to the catalysis of nitrogen and hydrogen to form ammonia. *Cf.* EMMETT, Studies on the Mechanism of Ammonia Synthesis over Iron Catalysts, *J. Chem. Educ.*, **7**, 2571 (1930).

phosphorus, arsenic, and sulfur; carbon monoxide greatly reduces their activity. Hence, much money must be spent in purifying the hydrogen and nitrogen for the ammonia synthesis.

Manufacturing Procedures. There are numerous variations in pressure, temperature, catalyst, and equipment from the original Haber procedure, that have been put into practice in plants throughout the world. Table 4 summarizes these and includes the procedure for obtaining the hydrogen.

There is as much difference in the economic sources of hydrogen as in any other variable. The principal hydrogen-manufacturing processes that are in use for synthetic ammonia production are the steam–water gas process, the steam-hydrocarbon (natural gas) process, the coke-oven gas process, and the electrolysis of water[1] (see Chap. 8, pages 134 to 138). According to van Krevelen[2] about 50 per cent of the nitrogen production of the world in 1948 derived its hydrogen from water gas, 25 per cent from coke-oven gas, 15 per cent from electrolysis, and the remaining 10 per cent primarily from natural gas. Now (1955) in the United States it is estimated that hydrogen sources for ammonia are natural gas (81 per cent), coke (13 per cent), electrolytic cells ($4\frac{1}{2}$ per cent), and catalytic reforming of refinery gas ($1\frac{1}{2}$ per cent). However, much research work is still directed to find cheaper manufacturing methods for hydrogen from coke and even from charcoal by using oxygen instead of air in the reactions. Many new plants use ethanolamine to remove CO_2 from the gas streams instead of high-pressure water.

In addition to its production by the electrolysis of water, hydrogen is also obtained as a by-product in other electrochemical processes. In smaller installations the electrolytic or by-product plant is the only one that has been employed to any extent. In medium-sized plants all methods are used, and in large-scale plants primarily only coke and natural gas methods. The electrolysis method is competitive in countries where cheap water-power electricity is available (Norway, Italy, Japan). In producing hydrogen from coke-oven gas or by electrolysis methods nitrogen required for the synthesis gas is obtained usually from an air liquefaction plant. In water-gas and natural-gas processes, nitrogen is obtained in the same manufacturing procedure as hydrogen. Air is added in the secondary reformer of the natural-gas process and reacts with CO to furnish CO_2 and N_2.

Nitrogen Engineering Corp. System. The system for ammonia synthesis developed by the Nitrogen Engineering Corp. (now a part of the Chemical Construction Corp. of the American Cyanamid Company) is shown

---

[1] For reactions and details on hydrogen manufacture, see Chap. 9; *cf.* KIRK and OTHMER, *op. cit.*, Vol. 1, pp. 771*ff.*; ANON., Synthetic Ammonia Produced from Natural Gas, *Chem. Eng.*, **52** (12), 92 (1945), with a pictured flow sheet on pp. 134–137; COPE, Ammonia, *Chem. Inds.*, **64**, 920 (1949).

[2] VAN KREVELEN, A Few Aspects of the Development and Technology of the Nitrogen Industries, *Chem. Weekblad*, **44**, 437 (1948).

in the flow sheet of Fig. 3. Like all these ammonia syntheses, this one is based on the following reaction:[1]

$$N_2(g) + 3H_2(g) \rightarrow 2NH_3(g); \qquad \Delta H_{18°C} = -22,000 \text{ cal.}$$
$$\Delta H_{659°C} = -26,600 \text{ cal.}$$

This reaction is highly exothermic and, consequently, the design of the converter should be such as to control the temperature at the point desired for the conversion deemed economical for the particular conditions chosen by the chemical engineers (cf. Fig. 2).

The Nitrogen Engineering Corp.'s system is a modified and improved Haber-Bosch system (cf. Table 4), and can best be presented by breaking

TABLE 4. SYNTHETIC AMMONIA SYSTEMS

Designation	Pressure, atm.	Temperature, °C.	Catalyst	Conversion percentage	Recirculation	Hydrogen and nitrogen
Haber-Bosch.......	200	550	Promoted iron	8	Yes	Water gas and producer gas
Modified Haber....	250	550	Doubly promoted iron	20	Yes	
Nitrogen Engineering Corp., or American, or F.N.R.L.[a]	200–300	500	Doubly promoted iron	20–22	Yes	Natural gas or water gas with producer gas or electrolytic by-product
Modifications of above and Kellogg	300–350	500–525	Doubly promoted iron	24–32	Yes	
Claude............	900–1,000	500–650	Promoted iron	40[b]–85	No	Liquefaction of coke-oven gas and air
L'air liquide.......	900–1,000	500	Promoted iron			
Du Pont..........	1,000	500	Promoted iron	.....	Yes	Natural gas
Casale............	600–610	500	Promoted iron	15–25	Yes	Various methods
Fauser............	200–240	500	Promoted iron	12–23	Yes	Electrolytic, special cell
Mont Cenis........	100	400–425	Iron cyanide	9–20	Yes	Electrolytic by-product or natural gas

[a] F.N.R.L., Fixed Nitrogen Research Laboratory.

[b] Conversion upon passage through a single converter. The 85 per cent is for conversion after passage through the series of converters.

[1] PERRY, op. cit., pp. 347, 350 (equilibrium).

down this flow sheet (Fig. 3) into the following coordinated sequences of *unit operations* (Op.) and *unit processes* (Pr.):

Coke is made into blue water gas by steam as the source of the hydrogen (Pr.).

Coke is converted by a little steam and air into producer gas as the source of the nitrogen (Pr.). The exothermic producer gas reaction permits, to a slight extent, the endothermic water-gas reaction. An alternate source of nitrogen is the "blow gas" from the water-gas generator. The proportions are properly adjusted to the desired ratio.

Heat is saved from hot gases (see Fig. 3) in waste-heat boiler (Op.).

After passing through waste-heat boiler, gases are further cooled and analyzed; gases are warmed and saturated with water vapor in a hot-water scrubber, treated with steam, heated further in exchangers, and passed over iron oxide catalyst to convert[1] $CO + H_2O$ into $CO_2 + H_2$; $\Delta H = -9,800$ cal. (Pr.).

The CO_2 and H_2 are cooled in the heat exchanger and cooling towers and conducted to gas holder which "floats" on the line (Op.). (Not shown in Fig. 3.)

To remove CO_2 from the original gas reactions and from the catalytic CO shift reaction, the gases are compressed to about 25 atm. and washed with water under this pressure (Op.). About 50 per cent of the energy required for this operation of raising the water pressure is recovered as shown in Fig. 3 in a water turbine and used over again for the same purpose. (The "mountain system" of energy recovery is shown in Fig. 4.)

The mixture of 3 parts of H_2 and 1 part of N_2 with residual CO (usually 2 per cent) is compressed with cooling to 200 atm. (Op.).

The CO and any small amount of O_2 are removed (to be put back into start of system) by solution in an ammoniacal cuprous formate solution which is regenerated by heat at atmospheric pressure and reused (Pr.).

The 3 to 1 hydrogen-nitrogen mixture, freed of its CO, is raised to the full compression of 300 atm. and mixed with the recompressed, recirculated gases. The gases then are passed through the oil filter and to the water-ammonia cooler-condenser for removal of residual ammonia (Op.).

In the converter, the gases are raised in a countercurrent heat exchanger to the reaction temperature and caused to react in the presence of the catalyst, after which the gases are cooled and some of the ammonia liquefied (Pr.).

Part of the gases is purged to prevent undue accumulation of diluents, such as methane or argon, and the rest is recompressed for recirculation (Op.).

The purge gas is burned.

One of the plants of the Nitrogen Engineering Corp. in the United States on by-product hydrogen experienced a catalyst life of about 3 years operating at 515°C. and 4,400 lb. pressure. The gas charged analyzed 72 to 73 per cent H_2, and from 15 to 24 per cent was converted to NH_3 per pass. A total of 80,000 cu. ft. of hydrogen was needed for 1 ton of ammonia.

In a modified Nitrogen Engineering Corp. system, Charles O. Brown[2]

---

[1] *Cf.* PERRY, *op. cit.*, p. 350, for equilibrium calculations of this *shift* reaction.

[2] Consulting chemical engineer, New York City, and one of the original group that started the Nitrogen Engineering Corp.

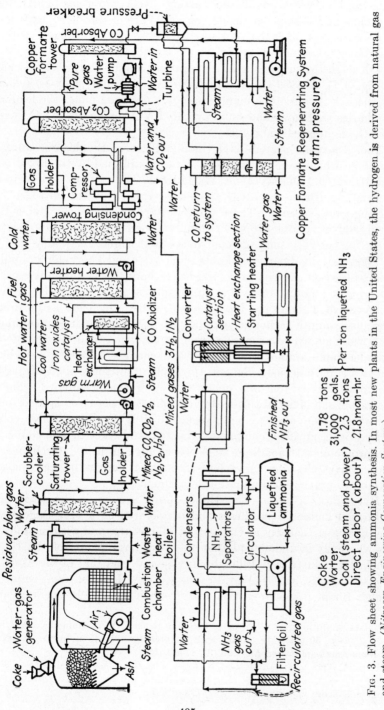

FIG. 3. Flow sheet showing ammonia synthesis. In most new plants in the United States, the hydrogen is derived from natural gas and steam. (*Nitrogen Engineering Corporation System.*)

Coke	1.78	tons
Water	31,000	gals.
Coal (steam and power)	2.3	tons
Direct Labor (about)	21.8	man-hr.

Per ton liquefied NH₃

runs the blue water gas of the "make" cycle into a gas holder, for its hydrogen and carbon monoxide content. Part of the blow gas from the same water-gas set is led to a smaller holder for its nitrogen (with carbon dioxide) content. The two are metered in the proper proportion and put through the succeeding unit operations and unit processes as charted in Fig. 3. A *detailed* description with pictured flow chart is available[1] for the T.V.A. ammonia plant which was designed under the leadership of Charles O. Brown and built by the T.V.A. engineers. The converter is of the laminated-wall type.

The *American* system is a modified Haber-Bosch procedure, the details of which were researched and fully published by the Fixed Nitrogen Research Laboratory[2] at Washington, D.C. Much of the findings associated with the F.N.R.L. have been applied by the Nitrogen Engineering Corp.'s system. These work at 100 atm. above the Haber-Bosch or at 300 atm. and 475°C. A doubly promoted iron catalyst is used operating on very pure gas and hence with a relatively long life. This catalyst contains 1 per cent of potassium oxide and 3 per cent of aluminum oxide, based on the iron oxide originally charged. The promoters prevent sintering. A unique feature is the employment of an initial ammonia converter at a somewhat higher temperature, which has as its function the conversion of carbon-oxygen or carbon-oxygen-hydrogen compounds into water or hydrocarbons, as well as the removal of any sulfur compounds. Some ammonia is formed and condensed, taking out the impurities simultaneously. Several small plants in the United States have employed this system and operate on hydrogen by-product from electrolysis of salt. Part of this hydrogen (about 15 per cent) is used to burn the oxygen from air, leaving nitrogen which is mixed with three volumes of hydrogen, purified, compressed, heated, and reacted. The converter is of chrome-nickel-vanadium steel containing the heat interchanger and the catalyst chamber. A certain amount of the gas in recirculation is purged to prevent accumulation of argon.

Haber-Bosch System. The Haber-Bosch system is the basis of the industrial ammonia syntheses and is operated on a very large scale in Germany, particularly at Oppau and Merseburg, and with modifications elsewhere. It is understood that the very large plants of the Imperial Chemical Industries at Billingham, England, and that of the Allied Dye and Chemical Corp. (Solvay Process Co.) at Hopewell, Va., employ the Haber-Bosch procedures with minor modifications. It operates at the

[1] MILLER and JUNKINS, Nitrogen Fixation at the T.V.A. Ammonia Plant, *Chem. & Met. Eng.*, **50** (11), 119 (1943), with pictured flow sheet, p. 152; *cf.* ANON., Anhydrous Ammonia, *Chem. Eng.*, **58** (8), 174 (1951).

[2] ANON., The American Process Nitrogen Fixation, *Chem. & Met. Eng.*, **30**, 948 (1924); CURTIS, *op. cit.*, pp. 237–239; ERNST, REED, and EDWARDS, A Direct Synthetic Ammonia Plant, *Ind. Eng. Chem.*, **17**, 775 (1925).

comparatively low pressure of 200 atm. (and 550°C.) with from 5 to 10 per cent conversion (*cf.* Fig. 2). It has been fully described[1] and proceeds somewhat as the system depicted in Fig. 3. The catalyst is a promoted iron oxide. Because of the low pressure, the ammonia is somewhat more difficult to remove as a liquid so the reaction gases are washed with water, producing initially aqua ammonia from which anhydrous is manufactured.

Claude and Casale Systems. In 1927 the first Claude units, with modifications from the Casale process, were installed in the United States by the Du Pont Company at Belle, W. Va. A few plants constructed during the Second World War utilized a modified Claude process, which is principally characterized by operating pressures near 1,000 atm. The newest adaptation of the Claude process[2] is by the Mississippi Chemical Corp. at Yazoo City, Miss. Besides high pressures in both the methane reforming and synthesis reaction, an iron catalyst in the reforming step, rather than nickel, is used and temperatures are 730 to 930°F. Because of this only about half as much catalyst is necessary and its life is twice as long as compared with conventional processes. Carbon monoxide impurity, another important factor, is low enough to be practically insignificant.

The synthesis reaction takes place in two converters in series with gas-steam recirculation. The temperature in the first converter will vary from 900 to 1150°F. depending on catalyst activity. The conversion is about 80 per cent per pass, which is high. Other advantages are that only about one-seventh as much catalyst is needed to produce the same amount of ammonia and only about one-fifth as much gas must be handled on the basis of actual volume at synthesis conditions. The catalyst is a purified magnetic iron oxide, doubly promoted with small percentages of aluminum and potassium oxides. The catalyst life is short, about 3 months, but the small volumes used help offset this loss.

The Casale system (*cf.* Table 4) is characterized chiefly by the design of the converter and condenser wherein some of the ammonia is left in the recirculated gases to temper or slow down the initial reaction in the catalyst chamber. Also, the entering gases are passed down in contact with the outside wall of the converter in order to keep its temperature below 400°C.

Du Pont System. The Du Pont much modified Claude-Casale system is outlined in Fig. 4. The plant is located at Belle, W. Va., on the banks of the Kanawha River where plentiful supplies of water and cheap coal are available. The coal is delivered by river barges. The Du Pont engineers

---

[1] CURTIS, *op. cit.*, p. 229; PARTINGTON, The Haber Process at Merseburg, *J. Soc. Chem. Ind.*, **40**, 144R (1921); WARDENBURG, High Pressure Synthesis Applied to Manufacture of Things in Everyday Use, *J. Franklin Inst.*, **221**, 449 (1936).

[2] SHEARON and THOMPSON, Ammonia at 1000 Atmospheres, *Ind. Eng. Chem.*, **40**, 254 (1952).

until the Second World War used hydrogen produced by the water-gas reaction from coke. Expansion marked the advent of natural gas, and now all ammonia at this plant is made from hydrogen derived from natural gas. The hydrogen from the water-gas reaction is used for "impure" hydrogenations such as in the manufacture of nylon intermediates, long chain alcohols, ammonium carbonate, urea, and dozens of other chemicals (see Fig. 1 in Chap. 39). A description of this older process follows, since it is a unique development requiring a great deal of intelligence and stern vigilance and a great monetary outlay for automatic instruments and devices.

The ignited coke in the gas generators is blown with air, furnishing "blow-run gas" or "blow gas" rich in nitrogen and carbon dioxide. When this white-hot coke has steam and some air passed through it, "blue gas" is made, rich in hydrogen and carbon monoxide with some nitrogen. As this latter is an endothermic reaction (cf. Chap. 7), it must be succeeded by a "blow run." Thus alternately blowing air and steam through coke, the four gases are produced. These gases are proportioned to get the mixture required for the product desired. However, the blue gas analyzing about 50 per cent CO, 40 per cent H_2, and 10 per cent N_2 must be purified of its sulfur. This is done by the Thylox process (see Chap. 7).

As shown in Fig. 4 the Du Pont engineers remove the CO_2[1] by washing with water under 30 atm. pressure. They, however, have developed an economical method of recovering about 60 per cent of the energy in this high-pressure aqueous solution of the carbon dioxide. This is the so-called *mountain recovery* procedure in which the pressure in the water forces it 600 ft. up to the top of the mountain adjoining the Belle plant. When at the top of the mountain, the pressure having been expended in the work done, the CO_2 mostly escapes, the residual being blown out with air. This denuded water flows down again to the pumps but possessed of nearly 300 lb. actual pressure. Such a procedure also saves something in the cost in water purifying as the water is used over and over again.

Before Second World War demands required an enlargement of this Du Pont plant, it had a gas plant sufficient in size to supply a city of over 2,000,000 inhabitants. It is obvious that it would not be economical to store more than a few minutes' supply. However, the various processes are so rapid, the coordination so accurate, and the control so exact, that

. . . only thirty minutes are required for a unit of hydrogen leaving the coke bed in the water-gas generators to appear as its equivalent of ammonia or alcohols coming from the synthesis units. During the thirty minutes' ride taken by the gases in their journey at Belle, they are heated to 2400°F., washed and rewashed with water and other liquids, cooled to −350°F., expanded to atmospheric pressure, compressed to 12,000 pounds per square inch, and passed over various catalysts.

[1] ANON., The Pressure Synthesis of the Du Pont Ammonium Corp., *Ind. Eng. Chem.*, **22**, 433 (1930).

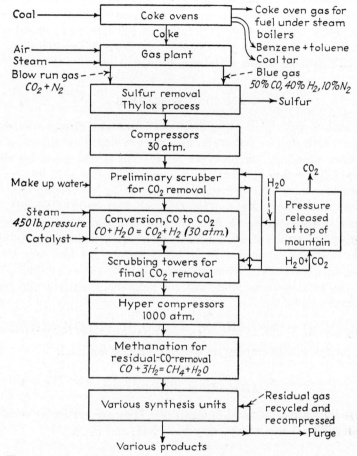

FIG. 4. Flow chart for Du Pont hydrogen manufacture from coal, air, and water. The blowrun gas and the blue gas are made from the coke by alternately blowing with air and steam.

Miscellaneous Ammonia Systems. The Italian Fauser[1] procedure employs an electrically controlled converter at 200 atm. and 500°C. and works on electrolytic hydrogen generated in a special cell. For some of the foreign plants, the nitrogen is obtained by purification of the nitrogen from the exit gases arising from the air-ammonia oxidation procedure for nitric acid. At Trail, B.C., Claude liquid-air units furnish the nitrogen.

[1] For a flow sheet, see *Chem. Met. Eng.*, **38**, 628 (1931). This article describes with considerable exactness the procedures operating at Trail, B.C.

This being a low-pressure system, the ammonia is frequently removed by water scrubbing, though the Trail plant employs pressure cooling first by water and next by ammonia refrigeration. The lowest pressure system is the *Mont Cenis* one, operating at 100 atm. and somewhat over 400°C. The catalyst is an iron-cyanide complex. This system is used by the Shell Chemical Co. at Pittsburg, Calif.

AMMONIUM SULFATE

Ammonium sulfate has long been an important nitrogen carrier for fertilizers, although its industrial uses are growing. Less than half of its more than a million ton per year production is still made by the old process of recovering ammonia from coal gas (*cf.* Chap. 7) by scrubbing with sulfuric acid.[1] The greater part is made by converting anhydrous ammonia into the sulfate. The General Petroleum Corporation at Torrance, Calif., makes 11 tons per day and simultaneously solves a waste-disposal problem at a profit. They react refinery-waste sludge sulfuric acid and ammonia from a by-product gas from cracking, to make ammonium sulfate. Another process is in operation at Sindri, India, where the principal raw materials for ammonium sulfate are gypsum and coke:[2]

$$(NH_4)_2CO_3(aq) + CaSO_4 \cdot 2H_2O(s) \rightarrow CaCO_3(s) + 2H_2O + (NH_4)_2SO_4(aq)$$

Many foreign plants employ anhydrite as a raw material.

AMMONIUM PHOSPHATES

These salts are considered in Chap. 18. They are particularly valuable in the fertilizer field as they carry both NH_3 and P_2O_5.

AMMONIUM NITRATE

Ammonium nitrate is the most important nitrogen fertilizer (see Table 5) because of the high nitrogen content (35 per cent) and the simplicity and cheapness of manufacture. It is a vital ingredient in the so-called "safety" type explosives, *e.g.*, dynamite, and is blended with TNT to form Amatol. About 200,000 tons of ammonium nitrate are consumed in these nonfertilizer channels. A minor, but important, application is in the manufacture of nitrous oxide, an anesthetic in extensive use. This gas is formed by heating ammonium nitrate under controlled conditions at temperatures above 200°C.

[1] Kirk and Othmer, *op. cit.*, Vol. 1, p. 778.
[2] Anon., Ammonium Sulfate from Gypsum, *Chem. Eng.*, **59** (6), 242 (1952), a pictured flow sheet.

Ammonium nitrate is simply made by neutralizing nitric acid, oxidized from ammonia, with ammonia:[1]

TABLE 5. NITROGEN FOR FERTILIZER PURPOSES[a]
(Short tons of nitrogen)

	1952–1953 supply	1953–1954 est. supply
Ammonium nitrate, all grades...................	428,600	464,000
Ammonium sulfate and nitrate.................	401,500	375,000
Other solids[b].....................................	250,700	255,000
Natural organics..............................	40,000	39,000
Compound ammoniating solution................	361,900	385,000
NH₃ for ammoniation........................	83,500	73,000
NH₃ for direct application....................	237,800	325,000
Total.......................................	1,804,000	1,916,000

[a] Department of Agriculture and *Ind. Eng. Chem.*, **46**, 1120 (1954).
[b] Ammonium phosphates, sodium nitrate, urea, calcium nitrate, cyanamide, and nitraphosphates.

$$NH_3(g) + HNO_3(aq) \rightarrow NH_4NO_3(aq); \qquad \Delta H = -20{,}600 \text{ cal.}$$

The neutralization is generally carried out batchwise.[2] A continuous neutralization may be accomplished by introducing ammonia vapor at the bottom of a neutralization tower with make-up nitric acid added at the top. The product is taken off at a plate slightly below the middle and the heat of the reaction evaporates a portion of the water leaving a solution of approximately 82 per cent strength. The Stengel[3] process, installed by Commercial Solvents Corp., reacts ammonia and nitric acid between 180 and 250°C., furnishing a solid product in one step. To lessen the deliquescence and caking and to obtain the best physical characteristics in the final product, the ammonium nitrate is grained or prilled. Graining involves batch evaporation of the ammonium nitrate solution to about 98 per cent. By cooling under proper agitation small rounded pellets or grains result with relatively less surface. While these grains, after coating, are suitable for dynamite, this product has less than the minimum size preferred for fertilizer use. Prilling consists in spraying hot concentrated ammonium nitrate solution from the top of a tower and allowing the droplets to descend against a countercurrent stream of air at a lower temperature, forming solid particles (called "prills") about $\frac{1}{16}$ to $\frac{3}{32}$ in. in diameter. After drying and screening,

[1] MITCHELL, Ammonia, *Petroleum Refiner*, **25** (6), 245 (1946); SHEARON and DUNWOODY, Ammonium Nitrate, *Ind. Eng. Chem.*, **45**, 496 (1953); *cf.* KIRK and OTHMER, *op. cit.*, Vol. 1, p. 820.
[2] For a flow sheet with materials of construction, see *Chem. Eng.*, **57** (11), 115 (1950).
[3] U.S. Pat. 2568901 (1951).

the prills or grains are conditioned against moisture pickup by coating them with a material such as diatomaceous earth and are bagged for sale.

UREA

The synthesis of urea by Wöhler in 1828 by heating ammonium cyanate had a profound influence upon chemistry and upon civilization. It was the first time that a substance produced by life had been prepared in the laboratory, thus opening up the entire realm of synthetic organic chemistry. For 100 years, this epoch-making compound was relatively unimportant industrially and was made by the acid hydrolysis of calcium cyanamide. In 1933 Du Pont began production at Belle, W. Va., and remained the sole domestic producer until 1950 when Solvay opened their plant at South Point, Ohio. The most important uses of urea are those in nitrogen fertilizers[1] and in plastics in combination with formaldehyde and furfural. Urea also finds extensive applications in adhesives, coatings, textile antishrink compounds, and ion-exchange resins. It is an intermediate for ammonium sulfamate, sulfamic acid, and phthalocyanine pigments. In 1952, production was 200,000 tons. Approximately two-thirds was the crystal form with the remainder divided nearly even between solid and solution products.

The commercial processes in current use are based on two reactions:[2]

$$CO_2 + 2NH_3 \rightarrow NH_4CO_2NH_2; \qquad \Delta H = -67,000 \text{ B.t.u. per lb.-mole}$$
$$\text{Ammonium carbamate}$$

$$NH_4CO_2NH_2 \rightarrow NH_2CONH_2 + H_2O;$$
$$\Delta H = +18,000 \text{ B.t.u. per lb.-mole}$$

Since both reactions are reversible, the equilibrium depends on the temperature, pressure, and concentration of the various components. The conversion ratio increases with rising temperature; however, urea is formed only in the liquid (solution) or solid phase making it necessary to maintain the liquid phase by pressure. Because the pressure increases rapidly with rising temperature, reaction temperatures over 210°C. are rarely exceeded in commercial practice. This temperature corresponds to a conversion ratio of about 0.55. Because the combined reactions are highly exothermic, this makes cooling necessary.

The Du Pont process continuously reacts purified carbon dioxide and excess ammonia (3 to 5 moles) in the liquid (solution) phase in autoclaves at 200 to 210°C. The NH_3 and CO_2 as an aqueous solution of the ammonium carbamate are recycled, and because of the presence of so much

[1] SKEEN, Urea, *Chem. Eng.*, **56** (6), 319 (1949).

[2] ROOSEBOOM, Urea: A Process Survey, *Chem. Eng.*, **58** (3), 111 (1951). This article contains excellent physical data and process descriptions.

water in the system the above severe conditions necessitate a reactor pressure of about 400 atm. The liquid reaction mass has a urea concentration of about 75 per cent after NH_3 stripping and may be used for making urea-ammonia liquor (U.A.L.) without further concentration. Although silver- or lead-lined equipment is used, corrosion is still a major problem.

Solvay employs a once-through process feeding in a constant molar ratio of 1 part compressed CO_2 to 2 or more liquid NH_3 at 150 to 200 atm. and with the temperature controlled at 160 to 180°C. The liquid reaction mass passes into a flash stripper where the carbamate is dissociated into NH_3 and CO_2 and these gases are removed, recovered, and reused. In both cases, "crystal" urea results from purifying and filtering the crude urea.

The Pechiney process, to be used in the John Deere plant in Oklahoma, differs in that it recycles solid carbamate as a slurry in a neutral mineral oil. This is pumped into a reactor which operates at 180°C. and 200 atm. The oil helps control the temperature in the reactor; and because of the solid and lower reactor temperature corrosion in the lead-lined shell is at a minimum.

NITRIC ACID

Historical. For many years nitric acid was made from Chile[1] saltpeter according to the following reaction:

$$NaNO_3 + H_2SO_4 \rightarrow NaHSO_4 + HNO_3$$

The present almost invariably more economical process involves the commercialization of the oxidation reaction of ammonia with air or oxygen. This has become economical because of the decreasing price of ammonia and of the great savings of the plants in comparison with the old sodium nitrate procedure. Not only is the capital investment in the original plant less, but the maintenance expense and repair are greatly reduced.

The newest process of nitrogen fixation, although still experimental, consists of oxidizing nitrogen with air to nitric oxide in a furnace at 4000°F.[2] Upon cooling the oxide is further oxidized to nitrogen tetraoxide which dissolves in water to give nitric acid.

Uses and Economics. Nitric acid has some direct application as an oxidizing acid in the parting of gold and silver, in the pickling of brass, and in photoengraving. However, its chief function is to make nitrates

[1] Fuller descriptions of this process are found in the older books where details are given of the equipment required.

[2] GILBERT and DANIELS, Fixation of Atmospheric Nitrogen in a Gas Heated Furnace, *Ind. Eng. Chem.*, **40**, 1719 (1948).

in both the inorganic and the organic fields as well as nitro derivatives in all branches of the organic division. The inorganic nitrates important commercially are those of ammonia, sodium, copper, and silver, the first being the most important outlet for nitric acid. A growing and potentially very important use for nitric acid is to replace sulfuric acid in acidulation of phosphate rock. Many of the nitrate or nitro compounds are used directly especially in the explosives industry as is true of ammonium nitrate, nitro-glycerine, and nitro-cellulose (really glyceryl trinitrate and cellulose polynitrate). The nitro aromatic compounds, ammonium picrate and T.N.T. as well as tetryl, are most important explosives. However, quite frequently the nitro group is used as an entering step into hydrocarbons of either aliphatic or aromatic divisions, in order to act as the steppingstone to more technically useful derivatives. This is exemplified by nitro-benzene in the manufacture of aniline (cf. Chap. 38 on intermediates and dyes) and the nitro-paraffins in leading to amines and amino-alcohols in the paraffin series (Chap. 39). For these purposes, there was consumed in 1953 1,764,363 tons of 100 per cent nitric acid.

Commercial grades[1] of nitric acid are

36°Bé. or 1.330 sp. gr	52.3 per cent HNO_3
40°Bé. or 1.381 sp. gr	61.4 per cent HNO_3
42°Bé. or 1.408 sp. gr	67.2 per cent HNO_3

Raw Materials. The essential raw materials for the modern manufacture of nitric acid are anhydrous ammonia, air, and water. Because of the low molecular weight of the ammonia, it can be shipped economically from the large primary nitrogen-fixation plants to various oxidation plants at the consuming centers. This effects a great saving in freight as well as in equipment, because the anhydrous ammonia can be shipped in steel cars in comparison with shipping aqueous nitric acid in stainless-steel tank cars weighing five or six times the weight of the ammonia. To these basic raw materials should be added the stainless-steel alloys[2] required for the nitric acid part of the oxidation plant.

Reactions and Energy Changes. The essential reactions for the production of nitric acid by the oxidation of ammonia may be represented as follows:

$$4NH_3(g) + 5O_2(g) \rightarrow 4NO(g) + 6H_2O(g); \quad \Delta H = -216{,}600 \text{ cal.} \quad (1)$$
$$2NO(g) + O_2(g) \rightarrow 2NO_2(g); \quad \Delta H = -27{,}100 \text{ cal.} \quad (2)$$
$$3NO_2(g) + H_2O(l) \rightarrow 2HNO_3(aq) + NO(g); \quad \Delta H = -32{,}200 \text{ cal.} \quad (3)$$

There are several by-reactions which reduce somewhat the yield of reaction (1).

---

[1] PERRY, op. cit., pp. 38, 180. The data given are for 60°F. (15.5°C.).

[2] ANON., Nitric Acid, Chem. Eng., **57** (11), 726 (1950).

$$4NH_3(g) + 3O_2(g) \rightarrow 2N_2(g) + 6H_2O(g); \qquad \Delta H = -302,700 \text{ cal.} \quad (4)$$
$$4NH_3(g) + 6NO(g) \rightarrow 5N_2(g) + 6H_2O(g); \qquad \Delta H = -431,900 \text{ cal.} \quad (5)$$

Reaction (1) is essentially a very rapid catalytic one, carried on by passing about 10.6 per cent of ammonia by volume, mixed with preheated air through the multilayered, silk fine, platinum gauze, at a temperature of approximately 920°C. (see Fig. 5), and here, once ignited, the stream of ammonia continues to burn. The yield is above 90 per cent. Formerly the temperatures were lower, about 750°C., where the platinum loss by volatilization is much less, but also so is the production rate. Catalyst temperatures in Europe are about 850 to 875°C. This reaction is usually carried out at a pressure of 100 lb. per sq. in.

Much work has been done on the study of the conditions surrounding these reactions.[1] As can be seen from reaction (1), there is only a small increase in volume, so that the principle of Le Châtelier does not affect the equilibrium very substantially. However, the increase in pressure, by compressing the reactants, enables a greater space velocity to be maintained with a consequent saving in plant until such a pressure is reached that the cost of the increased thickness of the stainless steel required more than counterbalances the saving in volume of the equipment per pound produced. Pressure oxidation also furnishes a nitric acid containing 61 to 65 per cent HNO_3 in comparison with the 50 to 55 per cent HNO_3 obtained from atmospheric oxidation. The speed of ammonia oxidation is extraordinarily high, giving an excellent conversion in the short contact time of 3×10^{-4} sec. at 750°C. with a fine platinum gauze catalyst. Hence in the industrial procedure it has been found economical to mix initially with the ammonia all the air needed for reactions (1) and (2).

The oxidation of the nitric oxide, NO, to nitrogen dioxide, NO_2, is the slowest reaction, but the equilibrium is more favorable at lower temperatures. Hence this reaction is carried out in absorbers of considerable capacity and provided with cooling. Because of a decrease in volume, this reaction is favored under pressure according to the principle of Le Châtelier. While these factors raise the cost of the equipment for carrying out the oxidation of the nitric oxide, they increase the conversion. It is necessary in the design of a plant to know how long[2] this reaction

[1] ANDRUSSOW, Catalytic Ammonia Oxidation, *Z. angew. Chem.*, **39**, 321 (1926); *cf.* Chap. 14 by KRASE in CURTIS, *op. cit.*, pp. 366–408*ff.*, for very full description of all factors pertaining to the basic physical chemistry surrounding the reactions, as well as the equipment necessary for its commercialization, together with copious references to the original literature.

[2] KRASE, pp. 384*ff.* in CURTIS, *op. cit.*, reviews the work of many researchers and presents equations and curves derived therefrom pertaining to the velocity of the reaction. For the calculation of time of this reaction as equaling 142 sec. at 25°C., see KRASE in CURTIS, *op. cit.*, p. 390.

will take, in order to calculate the volume necessary for the equipment.

$$3NO_2 + H_2O \rightleftarrows 2HNO_3 + NO \tag{3}$$

Equation (3) is really an absorption phenomenon.[1] This reaction, in the opinion of Taylor, Chilton, and Handforth,[2] is the controlling one in making nitric acid and its rate was increased by employing an absorption tower under pressure and cooling and with countercurrent graded strengths of acid for the absorption. Cold air is introduced into a short raschig ring packed section between the tower and acid trap. This provides for the reoxidation of the NO formed and also desorbs (bleaches) the dissolved nitrous oxides which would color the acid. Chemical engineers have developed a tower 5½ ft. in diameter and 40 ft. high with a capacity of about 55 tons of nitric acid per 24 hr. (*cf.* Fig. 5).

Manufacturing Procedures. Commercialization of these oxidation reactions, from ammonia leading to nitric acid, are exemplified by the flow sheet given in Fig. 5, which depicts the present-day procedure

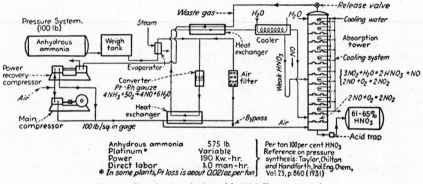

FIG. 5. Synthetic nitric acid (100 lb. pressure).

under 100 lb. pressure. Small-scale plants without any absorption and final oxidation steps are employed to supply the nitric oxide needed as a catalyst[3] in the chamber sulfuric acid procedure. The energy changes involved in these reactions are given with the reactions themselves. Much of the power required for compressing the air to 100 lb. pressure can be regained by expanding the waste gas, mostly nitrogen, from the top of the absorption tower, through a compressor for part of the needed air. Naturally the drive cylinder of this power-recovery compressor

[1] PERRY, *op. cit.*, pp. 706–707. The entire section on gas absorption should be studied.

[2] TAYLOR, CHILTON, and HANDFORTH, Manufacture of Nitric Acid by the Oxidation of Ammonia, *Ind. Eng. Chem.*, **23**, 860 (1931).

[3] SPANGLER, Ammonia Oxidation Replaces Niter for Chamber Acid Plants, *Chem. & Met. Eng.*, **35**, 342 (1928).

should be larger in diameter than the air cylinder. Actually per ton of 100 per cent nitric acid, the saving thus effected is 200 kw.-hr.

Unit Operations and Unit Processes. Figure 5 can be separated into the following coordinated sequences:

Anhydrous ammonia is evaporated continuously and uniformly in an evaporator, using steam to supply the necessary heat of evaporation (Op.). Air for all reactions shown on Fig. 5 is compressed in power recovery compressor and in motor-driven compressor to 105 lb. per sq. in. gage and passed through heat exchangers and air filter (Op.).

Ammonia gas is oxidized with air to nitric oxide at 100 lb. pressure in a converter, by passing through a platinum gauze at 920°C. (Pr.).

Then nitric oxide with the excess air necessary for the succeeding oxidizing steps is cooled in two heat exchangers and a water cooler, and conducted to the bottom of the absorption tower (Op.).

The successive oxidations and hydrations of the nitric oxide are carried out with continuous water cooling in a stainless-steel absorption tower (Pr. and Op.).

The nitric acid (61 to 65 per cent HNO_3) is drawn off through an acid trap (Op.).

The waste gas from the top of the absorption tower is heated in an exchanger counter to reaction gases and expanded through a compressor for part of the air, before being exhausted to the atmosphere (Op.).

Concentration of Nitric Acid. Water and nitric acid form an azeotrope which makes it impossible to get higher than 68 per cent acid from dilute acid by distillation. The 95 to 99 per cent nitric acid, often required by industry, is usually concentrated by mixing 98 per cent sulfuric acid with the 60 per cent nitric acid resulting from the above oxidation and absorption. The mixed acid is pumped to a dehydrating tower heated by steam. The 99 per cent nitric acid vapors leave the top of the tower, are condensed and stored. High-silicon iron is the material of construction used throughout. The aqueous sulfuric acid is concentrated and recirculated, but even so the process adds about $10 per ton to the cost of manufacturing.

SODIUM NITRATE

In recent years large tonnages of sodium nitrate[1] have been made both in America at Hopewell and in Europe by reaction of sodium chloride and soda ash from ammonia-soda or Solvay process, with nitric acid from ammonia oxidation. This is a high-grade product and is sought after for both industrial and fertilizer demands. Such sodium nitrate is particularly excellent in the making of dynamite. See Chap. 15, Chlorine, for reactions.

The Chilean nitrate industry was, until the rise of the synthetic ammonia industry, the dominating factor in the world's nitrogen supply.

[1] CURTIS, *op. cit.*, pp. 54–70, 415–416.

The 50-year-old Shanks process for obtaining the nitrate was inefficient and could not meet the competition. So following the First World War, lean years came to Chile, which had depended on the export tax upon its nitrate for its financial mainstay (42.8 per cent of total revenue or over 1 billion dollars from 1880 to 1930). Also 10 per cent of the total population of Chile had been directly connected with this industry.

These Chilean deposits occur in a desert area at an elevation of from 4,000 to 9,000 ft. and extending some 400 miles north and south with a width of from 5 to 40 miles. The crude salt deposit is called *caliche* and has the following typical analysis, according to Curtis:

	Per cent		Per cent
Sodium nitrate...............	17.6	Magnesium sulfate...........	3.9
Potassium nitrate............	1.3	Calcium sulfate..............	5.5
Sodium chloride..............	16.1	Sodium iodate...............	0.11
Sodium sulfate..............	6.5	Sodium borate...............	0.94
Potassium perchlorate.........	0.23		

The *caliche* usually worked varies in thickness from 8 in. to 14 ft. with an overburden of from 1 to 4 ft. There are still enormous deposits available.

In 1920 the Guggenheim Brothers of New York, owners and developers of large copper-mining operations, started to study the obtaining of sodium nitrate from *caliche*. By applying modern chemical-engineering knowledge of the *unit operations* of mining, transportation, crushing, selective leaching, crystallization, and heat transfer, the Guggenheim process has resulted. This has been applied (1) in the Oficina Maria Elena, which produces 520,000 metric tons of sodium nitrate per year and cost $43,000,000, and (2) in the Pedro de Valdivia plant, which produces 750,000 tons of finished nitrate per year and cost $32,000,000.

The Guggenheim process as perfected consists of improved leaching and crystallization operations on a very large scale using modern labor-saving machinery and various heatsaving devices. The leaching is countercurrent at 40°C. with crystallization down to 5°C. The heat required for the 40°C. level is from heat exchangers in connection with the ammonia condensers and from the exhaust gases and cooling water from the large Diesel engines which supply the plant with electric power. The 5°C. level is attained (1) to 15°C. in heat interchangers counter to the nitrate mother liquor and (2) to 5°C. by ammonia refrigeration. This results in an increased production[1] of from 25 to 30 tons of nitrate from a ton of fuel for the Guggenheim process in comparison with 6 to 7 tons by the Shanks process. The Chilean nitrate industry produces as

[1] Chemical Nitrogen, *U.S. Tariff Comm. Rept.* 114, p. 112, 1937. For numerous flow sheets covering the Guggenheim process, see CURTIS, *op. cit.*, pp. 64–67.

by-products the world's main supply of iodine and also substantial quantities of potassium nitrate.

SELECTED REFERENCES

Curtis, Harry A., "Fixed Nitrogen," Reinhold Publishing Corporation, New York, 1932. This book is a most excellent presentation and has a bibliography of 778 references.

Chemical Nitrogen, *U.S. Tariff Comm. Rept.* 114, 1937, bibliography, pp. 298–300.

Waeser, B., "The Atmospheric Nitrogen Industry," Blakiston Division, McGraw-Hill Book Company, Inc., New York, 1926. German, 2d ed., published by Otto Spamer in Leipzig, 1932.

Lewis, G. N., and Merle Randall, "Thermodynamics and the Free Energy of Chemical Substances," McGraw-Hill Book Company, Inc., New York, 1923.

Taylor, H. S., "Industrial Hydrogen," Reinhold Publishing Corporation, New York, 1921.

Badger, W. L., and E. M. Baker, "Inorganic Chemical Technology," 2d ed., McGraw-Hill Book Company, Inc., New York, 1941.

Sherwood, Thomas K., and R. L. Pigford, "Absorption and Extraction," 2d ed., McGraw-Hill Book Company, Inc., New York, 1952.

Bone, W. A., High Pressure Reactions, *Trans. Inst. Chem. Engrs.*, **8**, 98–106 (1930).

Tongue, Harold, "The Design and Construction of High Pressure Chemical Plant," D. Van Nostrand Company, Inc., New York, 1934.

Ullmann, Fritz, "Enzyklopaedie der technischen Chemie," 2d ed., Urban & Schwarzenberg, Berlin and Vienna, 1928–1932; 3d ed., 1950–.

Newitt, D. M., "The Design of High Pressure Plant and the Properties of Fluids at High Pressure," The Macmillan Company, New York, 1940.

Bridgman, P. W., "The Physics of High Pressures," Oxford University Press, New York, 1931.

Kirk, R. E., and D. F. Othmer, "Encyclopedia of Chemical Technology," 15 vols., The Interscience Encyclopedia, Inc., New York, 1947–1956.

CHAPTER 21

HYDROCHLORIC ACID AND MISCELLANEOUS INORGANIC CHEMICALS

The manufacture of many inorganic chemicals has been subjected to much new study in the past few years, with the result that new processes are in use for old chemicals or that improvements have been made in old processes. An example of a new process is the recovery of bromine and magnesium from sea water and of an improvement is the employment of structural carbon as a material of construction in hydrochloric acid plants.

HYDROCHLORIC OR MURIATIC ACID

Hydrochloric acid, although not manufactured in such large quantities as sulfuric acid, is an important heavy chemical. Manufacturing techniques have changed and improved in recent years and new procedures are employed such as the burning of chlorine in hydrogen.

Hydrogen chloride, HCl, is a gas at ordinary temperatures and pressures. Aqueous solutions of it are known as *hydrochloric acid* or, if the hydrogen chloride in solution is of the commercial grade, as *muriatic acid*. The common acids of commerce are 18°Bé. (1.142 sp. gr.) or 27.9 per cent HCl, 20°Bé. (1.160 sp. gr.) or 32.0 per cent HCl, and 22°Bé. (1.179 sp. gr.) or 35.8 per cent HCl.[1] Anhydrous hydrogen chloride is available in steel cylinders at a very considerable increase in cost, owing to the cylinder expense involved.

Historical. Hydrogen chloride was discovered in the fifteenth century by Basilius Valentinius. Commercial production of hydrochloric acid began in England when legislation was passed prohibiting the indiscriminate discharge of hydrogen chloride into the atmosphere. This legislation forced manufacturers, using the LeBlanc process for soda ash, to absorb the waste hydrogen chloride in water. As more uses for hydrochloric acid were discovered, plants were built solely for its production.

[1] PERRY, *op. cit.*, pp. 38 and 179; "The Condensed Chemical Dictionary," p. 348, 4th ed., Reinhold Publishing Corporation, New York, 1950.

Uses and Economics. The largest users of hydrochloric acid are the petroleum, chemical, food, and metal industries.[1] Industry experts estimate that activation of oil wells consumes about 30 per cent of the acid sold. A breakdown of the remaining uses is: chemical production, 23 per cent; metal production, 13 per cent; food industry including the production of monosodium glutamate and starch hydrolysis, 12 per cent; metal and general cleaning, 10 per cent; and miscellaneous uses, 13 per cent. Since muriatic acid is a relatively cheap chemical, the producing units are usually close to the consuming sources with the exception of by-product which often is transported longer distances.

Manufacture. Hydrochloric acid is obtained from four major sources: as a by-product in the chlorination of both aromatic and aliphatic hydrocarbons, from reacting salt and sulfuric acid, from the combustion of hydrogen and chlorine, and from Hargreaves-type operations ($4NaCl + 2SO_2 + O_2 + 2H_2O = 2Na_2SO_4 + 4HCl$). As can be seen from Table 1, by-product operations furnish most of the acid. The old salt–sulfuric acid method and the newer combustion method each supply about 20 per cent. The Hargreaves process is used by only one company, although a modified Hargreaves process is in operation at another plant.

Reactions and Energy Requirements. The basic steps in the production of by-product acid include the removal of any unchlorinated hydrocarbon followed by the absorption of the HCl in water. A typical chlorination for illustration follows:

$$C_6H_6 + Cl_2 \rightarrow C_6H_5Cl + HCl$$
$$\text{Benzene} \qquad \text{Chlorobenzene}$$

Since the chlorination of aliphatic and aromatic hydrocarbons evolves large amounts of heat, special equipment is necessary for control of the temperature of reaction.[2]

The reactions of the salt-sulfuric acid process are endothermic.

$$NaCl + H_2SO_4 \rightarrow HCl + NaHSO_4$$
$$NaCl + NaHSO_4 \rightarrow HCl + Na_2SO_4$$

Summation:

$$2NaCl(s) + H_2SO_4(l) \rightarrow 2HCl(g) + Na_2SO_4(s); \qquad \Delta H = +15,800 \text{ cal.}$$

The first reaction goes to completion at relatively low temperatures while

[1] WILSON, Now By-product Hydrochloric Rules the Roost, *Chem. Eng.*, **58** (7), 284 (1951).

[2] OLDERSHAW, *et al.*, Absorption and Purification of Hydrogen Chloride from Chlorination of Hydrocarbons, *Chem. Eng. Progr.*, **43**, 371 (1947).

the second approaches completion only at elevated temperatures.[1] The reactions are forced to the right by the escape of the hydrogen chloride from the reaction mass.

The reaction between hydrogen and chlorine[2] is highly exothermic and goes spontaneously to completion as soon as it is initiated.

The absorption of the HCl, made by any process, liberates around 700 B.t.u. per lb. of HCl absorbed. This heat must be taken away in the absorber or the efficiency will be low. Figure 1 illustrates the design of a hydrogen chloride absorber made from Karbate carbon.

Figure 2 illustrates the essential steps in the production of hydrochloric acid using the salt process and the synthetic process. The by-product process differs from these in the variable conditions employed for the production and separation of the hydrogen chloride. The *salt process* may

TABLE 1. PRODUCTION OF HYDROCHLORIC ACID[a]
(In short tons of 100 per cent acid)

Source	1947	1950	1951	1952
Salt...........................	173,541	165,053	174,994	162,411
Chlorine.......................	87,112	111,539	123,063	140,595
By-product and other..........	181,905	342,192	397,534	380,753
Total.....................	442,558	618,784	695,591	683,742

[a] Annual Survey of Manufactures, 1952. The production in 1953 was 773,500 tons.

be divided into the following *unit operations* (Op.) and *unit processes* (Pr.):

Sulfuric acid (or niter cake if available) and salt are roasted in a furnace to form hydrogen chloride and sodium sulfate (salt cake) (Pr.).

The hot hydrogen chloride, contaminated with droplets of sulfuric acid and particles of salt cake, is cooled by passing it through a series of S-shaped Karbate coolers, cooled externally by water (Op.).

The cooled gas is then passed upward through a coke tower to remove suspended foreign materials (Op.). (This equipment is omitted in some plants.)

Purified hydrogen chloride from the top of the coke tower is absorbed in water in a tantalum or Karbate absorber (Op.).

Finished hydrochloric acid is withdrawn from the bottom of the absorber, and any undissolved gas passing out the top of the absorber is scrubbed out with water in a packed tower (Op.).

[1] PERRY, *op. cit.*, pp. 697–698; BADGER and BAKER, "Inorganic Chemical Technology," 2d ed., Chap. V, pp. 111–117, with references on p. 133, McGraw-Hill Book Company, Inc., New York, 1941, is particularly good in presenting diagrams of furnaces and conditions for absorption.

[2] MAUDE, Synthetic Hydrogen Chloride, *Chem. Eng. Progr.*, **44**, 179 (1948); BRUMBAUGH, *et al.*, Synthesis and Recovery of Hydrogen Chloride Gas, *Ind. Eng. Chem.*, **41**, 2165 (1949).

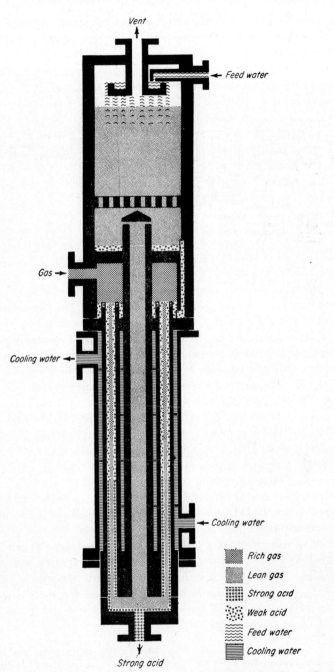

FIG. 1. Diagram of an all-carbon hydrochloric acid cooler-absorber. (*Courtesy of National Carbon Company.*)

The most important of the salt furnaces in operation is the Mannheim furnace. This consists of a cast-iron muffle, composed of a dish-shaped top and bottom bolted together and equipped with plows to agitate the reaction mixture. The rotary furnace is growing in usage. Here sulfuric acid and salt are continuously mixed and heated.

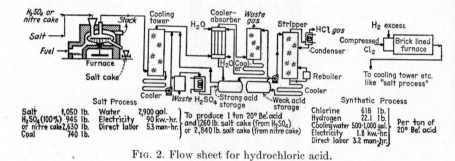

FIG. 2. Flow sheet for hydrochloric acid.

The *synthetic process* generates hydrogen chloride by burning chlorine in a few per cent excess of hydrogen. The purity of the ensuing acid is dependent upon the purity of the hydrogen and chlorine. However, as both of these gases are available in a very pure state as by-products of the electrolytic process for caustic soda, this synthetic method produces the purest hydrogen chloride of all the processes. The cooling and absorption are very similar to that employed in the salt process.

Over 250,000 tons per year of *anhydrous hydrogen chloride* are needed for making methyl chloride, ethyl chloride, vinyl chloride, and other such compounds. This is generally manufactured[1] by burning Cl_2 in excess of H_2, absorbing the HCl in water. The aqueous solution is stripped of HCl under slight pressure, giving strong gaseous HCl which is dehydrated to 99.5 per cent HCl by cooling to 10°F.

Hydrochloric acid is extremely corrosive to most of the common metals and great care should be taken to choose the proper materials for the plant construction. This acid is usually shipped by rail or barge and stored in rubber-lined steel tanks. Although absorbers were made of silica, in recent years tantalum and structural carbon have largely replaced fused silica. Indeed, the installation of Karbate structural carbon heat interchangers and condensers has characterized the recent hydrochloric acid plants because of higher rates of heat transfer and greater strength and resistance to corrosive attack.[2]

[1] ANON., Anhydrous HCl, *Chem. Eng.*, **58** (10), 208 (1951), a pictured flow sheet.

[2] LIPPMAN, Solving the Heat Exchange Problem in Cooling Hot HCl, *Chem. & Met. Eng.*, **52** (3), 112 (1945); LIPPMAN, New HCl Rectifier Can Make C.P. Acid, Dry Gas, Solutions, *Chem. Eng.*, **56** (11), 110 (1949).

BROMINE

Bromine is a member of the halogen family and is a heavy dark-brown liquid. It is much less common and more expensive than chlorine.

Historical. In 1826, 15 years after the discovery of iodine, bromine was discovered by Balard, a French chemist, who obtained it from the mother liquor left after separating the salt from evaporated sea water. Its manufacture from the Stassfurt deposits of carnallite was begun in 1865, from the $MgBr_2$ in the liquors left after working up $MgCl_2$ and KCl. The larger Ethyl Dow plant at Freeport, Tex. (Fig. 3), was built during the Second World War.

Uses and Economics. About 90 per cent of the domestic bromine output is used in the manufacture of ethylene "bromide" (dibromide) for antiknock fluids.[1] Most of the remaining bromine is converted into organic or inorganic compounds. The demand for bromine in liquid form is limited mostly to laboratory reagents and small specialty uses. Among the major inorganic compounds are the alkali bromides which are widely employed in photography and as comparatively safe sedatives in medicine. Hydrobromic acid resembles hydrochloric acid but is a more effective solvent for ore minerals, *i.e.*, with higher boiling point and stronger reducing action. Methyl bromide (insecticide, rodenticide, methylating agent) and the bromoindigo dyes are important organic compounds. Bromine is also employed in the preparation of dyes, disinfectants, war gases, and other compounds.

Prior to the First World War, Germany supplied approximately three-quarters of the total world production (1,250 tons). By 1929 the total United States production was 3,207 tons plus $8\frac{1}{2}$ tons imported. Since 1938 no imports have been received. In 1952, 78,101 tons (value 30 million dollars) were produced in this country.

The price of bromine has varied greatly from 10 cents per pound in 1908 to $1.31 per pound in 1916. Since the First World War, however, it has been somewhat stabilized, being 17 cents in 1923, 27 cents in 1929, and 19 cents in 1954. The major part of the bromine is shipped as ethylene dibromide.

Manufacture. In the United States the chief raw material is sea water in which bromine occurs in concentrations of 60 to 70 p.p.m. It is also manufactured from natural brines, where its concentration may be as high as 1,300 p.p.m. In Germany it is produced from waste liquors resulting from the extraction of potash salts from the carnallite deposits of Stassfurt, which were formerly the chief source of bromine in the world. Various other countries have the following sources of bromine: Italy extracts it from one of the largest inland lakes of the country; Russia from

[1] KIRK and OTHMER, *op. cit.*, Vol. 2, pp. 645–659.

the water of Saksky Lake in the Crimea district; France from deposits in Alsace; Palestine from the Dead Sea, the richest source known.

Bromine from Sea Water. A process was worked out for the removal of this small quantity of bromine by adding aniline to chlorinated sea

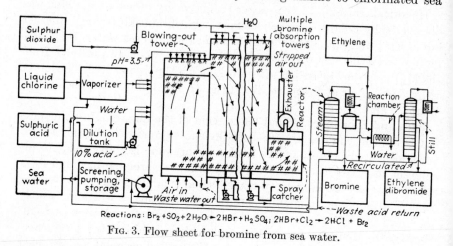

Reactions: $Br_2 + SO_2 + 2H_2O \rightarrow 2HBr + H_2SO_4$; $2HBr + Cl_2 \rightarrow 2HCl + Br_2$

FIG. 3. Flow sheet for bromine from sea water.

water according to the equation:

$$3NaBr + 3Cl_2 + C_6H_5NH_2 \rightarrow C_6H_2NH_2Br_3 + 3NaCl + 3HCl$$

The process was operated on board a floating chemical factory, the *S.S. Ethyl*. The Dow Chemical Company succeeded in devising a more economical process, without the use of aniline. By this process, the bromide-containing brine is (1) oxidized with chlorine, (2) blown with air to free bromine, and (3) the bromine is reacted with sulfur dioxide and absorbed. The process has been made a commercial success by the Ethyl-Dow Corporation. This "blowing-out" process functions according to the flow sheet of Fig. 3 which can be broken down into the following coordinated sequences[1] of *unit operations* (Op.) and *unit processes* (Pr.):

Sea water is allowed to flow into a settling basin, thence over a traveling screen and into a pond, from which it is pumped into the extraction plant (Op.).

The water from the pond is sent into a 42-in. rubber-lined pipe where acid from the end of the process, supplemented by a dilute sulfuric acid, is added to reduce the pH to 3 and to suppress subsequent reaction of the chlorine (Pr.).

The sea water is pumped to the top of the blowing-out tower after having had chlorine added through a rubber-lined pipe (Op. and Pr.).

$$2NaBr + Cl_2 \rightarrow 2NaCl + Br_2$$

Air, sucked up through the wood-packed tower by powerful fans, blows out the freed bromine from the sea water which is returned to the sea (Op.).

[1] See also pictured flow sheet, *Chem. & Met. Eng.*, **46**, 771 (1939). Old soda ash absorption is described. KIRK and OTHMER, *op. cit.*, Vol. 2, pp. 637–643.

The moist bromine-containing air plus a small amount of remaining chlorine is mixed with sulfur dioxide and conducted to an adjacent absorption tower where fans draw it through downcoming water or circulating solution.

$$Br_2 + SO_2 + 2H_2O \rightarrow 2HBr + H_2SO_4$$

The tower may be divided into multiple chambers connected in series. The water or recirculated solution enters through nozzles at the top and flows down through the chamber into a receiving tank, from which it is recirculated until a strong bromine–hydrobromic acid solution is obtained (Op. and Pr.).

Bromine dissolves in hydrobromic acid solution. This strong solution also containing a little HCl is pumped to storage (Op.).

After the bromine–hydrobromic acid–hydrochloric acid solution has been collected, it is reacted with chlorine and the free bromine vapors are steamed out of solution and collected in liquid form (Op. and Pr.).

It is then used to manufacture ethylene dibromide through reactions with ethylene (Pr.).

The residual acid, H_2SO_4 + HCl, solution is pumped to the start of the process to reduce the pH of the entering sea water (Op. and Pr.). Over-all plant efficiency is 90 per cent plus.[1]

Manufacture from Salt Brines.[2] In ocean water where bromine is relatively dilute, air has proved to be the most economical blowing-out agent. However, in the treatment of relatively rich bromine sources such as brines, steaming out the bromine vapor is the more satisfactory. The original steaming-out process was developed by the Germans for processing the Stassfurt deposits and with modifications is still used there, as well as in Palestine and this country. This process involves preheating the brine to 90°C. in a heat exchanger and passing down a chlorinator tower. After partial chlorination, the brine flows into a steaming-out tower where steam is injected at the bottom and the remaining chlorine is introduced. The halogen-containing vapor is condensed and gravity separated. The top water-halogen layer is returned to the steaming-out tower. The crude halogen (predominantly bromine) bottom layer is separated and purified.

Crude bromine from any of the foregoing processes can be purified by redistillation or by passing the vapors over iron filings which hold back the chlorine impurity. The alkali bromides account for an important proportion of the bromine produced. They cannot be made by the action of caustic soda on bromine, since hypobromites and bromates are produced also. The approved method consists in allowing bromine to trickle into a mixture of water and iron borings until a heavy sirup of ferrous bromide has formed. This is siphoned off, treated with the desired alkali carbonate, filtered to remove the precipitate of iron hydroxides, evaporated, and recrystallized.

[1] HEATH, U.S. Pat. 2143223 (1939); HOOKER, U.S. Pat. 2143224 (1939); HART, SO_2 Control Problem Solved in Sea Water Bromine Plants, *Chem. Eng.*, **54** (10), 102 (1947).

[2] For flow sheet, see KIRK and OTHMER, *op. cit.*, Vol. 2, p. 639.

IODINE

Historical and Raw Materials. It was in 1811 that M. Courtois, a salt-peter manufacturer of Paris, obtained a beautiful violet vapor from the mother liquors left from the recrystallization of certain salts. This iodine was later found to exist almost universally in nature. It is present as iodates (0.05 to 0.15 per cent) in the Chilean nitrate deposits. It occurs in sea water from which certain seaweeds extract and concentrate it within their cells. The iodine has been made from these weeds by the kelp-burning process[1] which has been practiced for years in Scotland, Norway, Normandy, and Japan. The present sources of the element, as far as the United States is concerned, however, are the nitrate fields of Chile, the oil-well brines of California, and the seaweed process of Japan.

Uses and Economics. Iodine is used as a catalyst for the chlorination of organic compounds and in analytical chemistry for the determination of so-called *iodine numbers* of oils. The iodine for medicinal, photographic, and pharmaceutical purposes is usually in the form of alkali iodides, pre-pared through the agency of ferrous iodide. In addition to the above, the element is also employed for the manufacture of certain dyes and as a germicide. The simple iodine derivatives of the hydrocarbons, such as iodoform, have antiseptic action. For years, Chilean-produced iodine dominated the market and controlled the price, which was set at $4.65 per pound. World production was about 1,000 tons, 70 per cent from Chile. Upon development of the iodine from the oil-well brines of the Southwestern United States, the price of iodine was reduced to approxi-mately $3.50 per pound in 1932. A year later domestic production had risen to 200 tons, a little over 22 per cent of the annual consumption then. Since there are only two domestic producers, actual statistics are not given. They supply an ever-increasing proportion of the iodine con-sumed domestically, which is about 500 tons annually. Import prices de-clined slowly to a low of 81 cents per pound in 1937, but in 1954 the price per pound was $1.75. Iodine imports in 1950 amounted to 724,858 lb. with a valuation of $1,055,946.

Manufacture. The major sources for the production of industrial iodine are from Chilean nitrate mother liquor and from oil-well brines of Cali-fornia. The Chilean process is the more important from the standpoint of world production.

Chilean Iodine. Figure 4 shows the essential steps in the production of Chilean iodine. The initial concentration of iodine, usually as iodate, in the nitrate liquor is 6 to 12 grams per liter. The liquor runs down a tower and meets a stream of ascending sulfur dioxide which liberates the

---

[1] DYSON, Chemistry and Chemotherapy of Iodine and Its Derivatives, *Chem. Age*, **22**, 362 (1930).

iodine according to the reaction:[1]

$$2NaIO_3 + 4H_2O + 5SO_2 \rightarrow Na_2SO_4 + 4H_2SO_4 + I_2$$

The iodine is filtered in canvas bags, which are pressed to remove water. The resulting cake, containing approximately 80 per cent iodine, is put into cement-lined retorts and sublimed. The vapors are condensed in earthenware pipe sections 2 ft. in diameter by 4 ft. long, jointed with

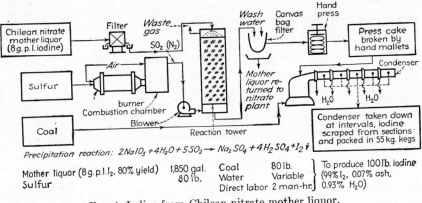

Precipitation reaction: $2NaIO_3 + 4H_2O + 5SO_2 \rightarrow Na_2SO_4 + 4H_2SO_4 + I_2$ ↓

Mother liquor (8g. p.l.I₂, 80% yield)	1,850 gal.	Coal	80 lb.	To produce 100 lb. iodine
Sulfur	80 lb.	Water	Variable	(99% I₂, 0.07% ash,
		Direct labor	2 man-hr.	0.93% H₂O)

FIG. 4. Iodine from Chilean nitrate mother liquor.

mud and jute. The water in the vapor condenses and runs down the granules of iodine which collect on the sides. The iodine is packed in kegs covered with fresh cowhide and is 99 to 99.5 per cent pure. The average over-all yield from mother liquor is 70 per cent, which represents an extraction of only 25 to 30 per cent of the iodine present in the original raw material.

In addition to the foregoing process, iodine was also made (1) by reduction with sodium thiosulfate and sulfuric acid and (2) by the reaction of sodium bisulfite either prepared at the plant by reacting soda ash with sulfur dioxide or imported.

American Iodine (from oil brines). Certain California oil wells are producing by-product brines containing 10 to 135 p.p.m. iodide ion. The extraction of this iodine has been attempted by various processes: (1) extraction with kerosene, (2) silver iodide process, (3) activated carbon process, (4) Turrentine process, (5) precipitation by cuprous and mercurous salts, (6) blowing out by air after chlorinating and SO₂ absorption. The first, second, and sixth are of present-day importance.[2] The brine is first cleaned and freed of oil and dirt in sand filters operating in series. The iodine may then be recovered by the *silver iodide process* as depicted

---

[1] HOLSTEIN, Fortunes and Misfortunes in Iodine, *Chem. & Met. Eng.*, **39**, 422 (1932); FAUST, The Production of Iodine in Chile, *Ind. Eng. Chem.*, **18**, 808 (1926).

[2] SAWYER, *et al.*, Iodine from Oil Well Brines, *Ind. Eng. Chem.*, **41**, 1547 (1949).

in Fig. 5. The iodine is precipitated by treatment with a 2 per cent silver nitrate solution, in the presence of ferric chloride solution as a coagulant. A wooden tub is used. The mixed AgI-$Fe(OH)_3$ precipitate settles and is treated with concentrated hydrochloric acid to dissolve the iron precipitate. Steel scrap is added, forming ferrous iodide and silver metal, the

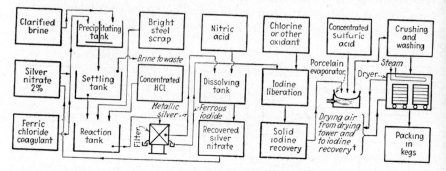

Certain details of process are not available and cannot be shown on this flow sheet
† Air dried over $CaCl_2$, vaporized iodine recovered in tower irrigated with alkali solution

FIG. 5. Iodine from oil brines by the silver iodide process.

reaction being completed within about an hour. The silver is filtered and reoxidized to silver nitrate, while the ferrous iodide solution is treated with an oxidant, Cl_2, HNO_3 or $Na_2Cr_2O_7$ and H_2SO_4, to precipitate the iodine. This iodine is melted under concentrated sulfuric acid and the purified iodine taken off. The resulting cake is washed and dried in a special drying chamber. It is not sublimed but is shipped in 200-lb. kegs as a 99.8 per cent pure product.

In addition to the silver iodide process operated by Deepwater Chemical Company, Dow Chemical Company[1] operates three plants using an *SO_2 process* in southern California at Venice, Inglewood, and Seal Beach. The first two plants do no iodine finishing, the finishing for all three being done at Seal Beach. The latter's operations will be described (Fig. 6) in the following coordinated steps of *unit processes* and *unit operations:*

A composite brine (62 to 67 p.p.m. of I_2) is passed through a series of skimming tanks to remove the oil (Op.).

Ferric chloride solutions are used to flocculate remaining oil, silt, and other impurities (Pr.).

Sulfuric acid is added to the clarified brine for pH control (under 3.5) and to precipitate the barium (Pr.).

The clarified brine is filtered in wooden sand filters (Op.).

Chlorine gas, somewhat in excess of the theoretical ration of 0.28 lb. chlorine per lb. iodine, is added to the filtered brine en route to the steel, acidproof brick-

[1] SAWYER, *op. cit.*

lined blowing-out tower where the brine is stripped by a countercurrent flow of air (Op. and Pr.).

The iodine-laden air stream enters the bottom of the packed absorption tower where the absorbing liquor (HI and H_2SO_4 in a water solution) passes countercurrent. Water and sulfur dioxide are added continuously to this solution to reduce the free iodine (Op. and Pr.).

$$I_2(\text{air}) + SO_2 + 2H_2O \rightarrow 2HI + H_2SO_4$$

The iodine is precipitated by chlorine from the HI-H_2SO_4 liquor. The precipitate is filtered, dried with strong H_2SO_4, and heated to melt the iodine which is withdrawn and solidified (Op. and Pr.).

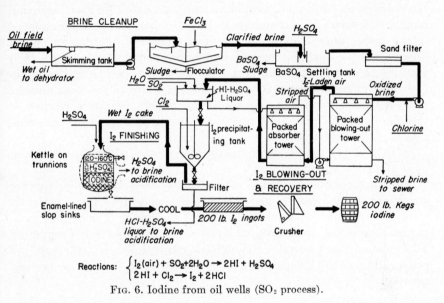

FIG. 6. Iodine from oil wells (SO_2 process).

The approximately 200-lb. ingots are cooled, crushed, and packaged in 200-lb. wooden kegs for shipping (Op.).

FLUORINE AND FLUORO-CHEMICALS

Fluorine, a pale, greenish-yellow gas of the halogen family, is the most chemically active nonmetal element. It occurs in the combined form and second only to chlorine in abundance among the halogens. The chief fluorine-containing minerals of commercial significance are fluorspar, fluorapatite (see superphosphates), and cryolite.

Historical. Fluorine was discovered by Scheele in 1771, but not isolated until 1886 by H. Moissan after a period of more than 75 years of intensive effort by many experimenters. The Freon refrigerants developed in 1930 fostered the commercial development of anhydrous hydro-fluoric acid and stimulated the growth of this new industry which came into its own at the beginning of the Second World War[1] largely because of demands for UF_6 for isotope separation and for Freons.

Uses and Economics. Elemental fluorine is costly and has a compara-tively limited usage. The element is employed in making sulfur hexa-fluoride, SF_6, for high-voltage insulation[2] and for uranium hexafluoride. Fluorine is used directly or combined with higher metals (Co, Ag, Ce, etc.) and halogens (Cl and Br) for organic fluorinations and the produc-tion of fluorocarbons.[3]

The largest production of fluorine compounds is of hydrofluoric acid (anhydrous[4] and aqueous), used in making "alkylate" for gasoline manu-facture and Freon for refrigerants and Aerosol bombs. It is also employed in the preparation of inorganic fluorides, elemental fluorine, and many organic fluorine- and non-fluorine-containing compounds. Aqueous HF is used in the glass, metal, and petroleum industries, besides in the manu-facture of many inorganic and acid fluorides. Three of the most unusual plastics known (see Chap. 35) are Teflon, a polymerization product of tetrafluorethylene, and Kel F and Fluorothene, products by polymeriza-tion of chlorofluorethylenes.

In 1939, 7,421 tons of hydrofluoric acid were produced as compared with 51,845 tons in 1953.

Manufacture. *Fluorine gas* is generated by electrolysis under varying conditions of temperature and electrolyte composition. These variables often require cells constructed of different materials.[5] The process men-tioned here is the one employed by the Pennsylvania Salt Company.[6] This company now operates commercial cells of 1,500 to 2,000 amp. per cell at 105 to 110°C. capable of producing 60 to 80 lb. fluorine per cell per day.

[1] Symposium Fluorine Chemistry, *Ind. Eng. Chem.*, **39**, 236 (1949). This is a com-prehensive compilation of 53 papers considering all phases of fluorine; its generation, handling, and disposal; industrial development of fluorocarbon processes; and the chemistry of fluorine and fluorine compounds. See following years *Ind. Eng. Chem.* for subsequent symposia; FINGER, Recent Advances in Fluorine Chemistry, *J. Chem. Educ.*, **28**, 49 (1951); KIRK and OTHMER, *op. cit.*, Vol. 6, pp. 656–771.

[2] MILLER and GALL, Inorganic Compounds Containing Sulfur and Fluorine, *Ind. Eng. Chem.*, **42**, 2223 (1950).

[3] Symposium, *op. cit.*, pp. 289–359, entitled Industrial Scale Development of Fluoro-carbon Processes; SIMONS, The Fluorocarbons, *Chem. Eng.*, **57** (7), 129 (1950).

[4] FINGER and REED, Fluorine in Industry, *Chem. Inds.*, **64**, 51 (1949).

[5] Symposium, Fluorine Chemistry, *Ind. Eng. Chem.*, **39**, 244–289 (1947). This sec-tion is entitled Fluorine Generation, Handling and Disposal and should be freely consulted.

[6] PORTER, Fluorine Production Paves Way for New Chemical Industry, *Chem. Eng.*, **53** (7), 106 (1946); Fluorine Progress, *Chem. Eng.*, **55** (4), 102 (1948); ANON., Fluorochemicals Go Commercial, *Chem. Eng.*, **58** (12), 215 (1951).

Both *aqueous* and *anhydrous hydrofluoric acid*[1] are prepared in heated kilns by the following reaction:

$$CaF_2(\text{fluorspar}) + H_2SO_4 \rightarrow CaSO_4 + 2HF$$

Aqueous acid is the older product and is formed by absorbing the HF gases in lead cooling and absorbing towers. By recycling absorption liquors, various strengths of acid are obtained, although the most common strengths are 60 and 65 per cent. Since concentrations of 60 per cent and above can be handled in steel compared with lead and hard rubber for lower acid strengths, the shipping trend is more to the stronger or anhydrous acid.

For anhydrous HF, finely ground fluorite is mixed with a slight excess of sulfuric acid in a hopper and fed into a heated kiln (300 to 800°C.). A large vent pipe conducts the HF and other gaseous products countercurrently into sulfuric acid absorption towers for dehydration. After distillation, the HF is condensed to a liquid by refrigeration. The corrosive problem has been fairly well solved.[2] Carbon, lead, Durimet 20, Monel metal, and coated and uncoated mild-carbon steel, depending upon concentration and temperature, are recommended.

Freons or *Genetrons* are trade names for important fluorine-containing refrigerants (33,000 tons consumed in 1945), made by the replacement of chlorine in a suitable organic chloride with fluorine supplied by means of a metallic fluoride or HF. These fluoro-compounds are safe solvents and pressure generators for the very widely used aerosol bombs. For Freon-12 (dichlorodifluoromethane) the reactions are

$$3CCl_4 + 2SbF_3 \xrightarrow{\text{SbCl}_5} 3CCl_2F_2 + 2SbCl_3$$
$$2SbCl_3 + 6HF \longrightarrow 2SbF_3 + 6HCl$$

In this case HF is continuously added to the mixture to regenerate the antimony trifluoride.

Fluorosilicates or Silicofluorides. The wet process for superphosphates (Chap. 18) evolves a toxic gaseous mixture of fluorine compounds predominantly silicon tetrafluoride, hydrofluoric acid, and fluorosilicic acid (H_2SiF_6). This mixture is passed through water absorption towers yielding fluorosilicic acid and a silica precipitate. The H_2SiF_6 liquor is concentrated to commercial strengths (generally 30 to 35 per cent) by recycling or distillation. A large use for this acid is in the brewing industry as a disinfectant for copper and brass vessels. It is also employed as a preserv-

---

[1] ZABEL, New Pennsalt HF Plant, *Chem. Inds.*, **66**, 508 (1950); FINGER and REED, *op. cit.;* for a pictured flow sheet on manufacturing acid-grade fluorspar, see *Chem. & Met. Eng.*, **52** (8), 130 (1945).

[2] ANON., Hydrofluoric Acid, *Chem. Eng.*, **57** (11), 124 (1950).

ative, in electroplating, as a concrete hardener, and in the manufacture of silicofluoride salts.

The most common salt, *sodium silicofluoride* (Na_2SiF_6), is prepared by the reaction of NaCl or soda ash on the acid. It is consumed to the extent of 10,000 tons per year as an insecticide, laundry sour, fluxing and opacifying agent, and as a protective agent in the casting of light metals. Other salts such as ammonium, magnesium, zinc, copper, and barium are also prepared by neutralization and find many uses in industry.

ALUMINA

Alumina, Al_2O_3, is an important chemical because it is the raw material for metallic aluminum (*cf.* Chap. 16).

Uses and Economics. Large quantities of alumina are produced yearly for the manufacture of metallic aluminum. In 1954, 7,297,789 long tons

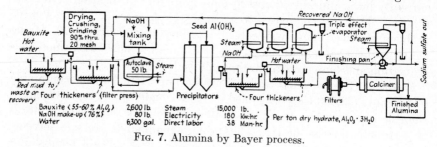

FIG. 7. Alumina by Bayer process.

of bauxite (dried bauxite equivalent) were imported (73 per cent) or mined. Most of this went for the production of about 2,600,000 short tons of Al_2O_3 (as 100 per cent) for conversion to the metal. Of the total bauxite consumption, the alumina industry used approximately 90 per cent, the abrasive industry 4 per cent, the chemical industry 4 per cent, the refractory industry 1 per cent, and all other industries 1 per cent.

Manufacture. Figure 7 shows the essential steps in the production of alumina from bauxite by the Bayer process.[1] The steps involved may be divided into the following *unit operations* (Op.) and *unit processes* (Pr.):

Bauxite, a mineral containing about 55 per cent aluminum oxide and less than 7 per cent silica, is crushed and wet ground to 100 mesh (Op.).

The finely divided bauxite is dissolved under pressure and heat in digesters with concentrated spent caustic soda solution from a previous cycle and sufficient lime and soda ash (Pr.). Sodium aluminate is formed and the dissolved silica is precipitated as sodium aluminum silicate.

The undissolved residue (red mud) is separated from the alumina solution by filtration and washing and sent to recovery (Op.). Thickeners and Kelly or Oliver filters are used.

[1] KIRK and OTHMER, *op. cit.*, Vol. 1, pp. 600–603.

The solution of sodium aluminate is hydrolyzed to aluminum hydroxide by cooling and by dilution with wash waters; the aluminum hydroxide is induced to crystallize by seeding with the finest of the aluminum hydroxide from last thickener (Op. and Pr.).

The precipitate is separated from the liquor and clarified in four thickeners and washed with hot water. It is filtered in Dorrco or Vallez filters (Op.).

The aluminum hydroxide is calcined up to 1150°C. to alumina in a rotary kiln (Pr.).

The alumina is cooled and shipped to the reduction plants (Op.).

The dilute caustic soda filtered from the aluminum hydroxide is concentrated for reuse (Op.).

The red mud may be reworked for recovery of additional amounts of alumina (Pr. and Op.).

While many other processes and raw materials have been investigated none of these has proved to be commercially feasible except the red mud process[1] for treating red mud or low-grade bauxites, i.e., those containing up to about 15 per cent silica. In this process, the red mud from the Bayer digestion is mixed with soda ash and limestone and sintered. This sinter is reacted with water to form a sodium aluminate solution leaving the silica combined as an insoluble dicalcium silicate. After separation from the insoluble residue, the sodium aluminate solution is recycled to the Bayer digester.[2]

ALUMINUM SULFATE AND ALUMS

The manufacture of alums entails just one step additional to the aluminum sulfate process. This, along with the fact that the uses of aluminum sulfate and alums are similar and the compounds are largely interchangeable, justifies their concurrent discussion. The term *alum* has been very loosely applied. A true alum is a double sulfate of aluminum or chromium and a monovalent metal (or radical, such as ammonium). Aluminum sulfate is very important industrially and while it is not a double sulfate it is often called either "alum" or papermakers' alum. Alum has been known since ancient times. The writings of the Egyptians mention its use as a mordant for madder and in certain medical preparations. The Romans employed it to fireproof their siege machines and probably prepared it from alunite, $K_2Al_6(OH)_{12}(SO_4)_4$, which is plentiful in Italy.

Uses and Economics. Alums are used in water treatment and somewhat in dyeing. They have been replaced to a large extent in these applications by aluminum sulfate which has a greater alumina equivalent per unit weight. Pharmaceutically, aluminum sulfate is employed in di-

[1] Editors, Bayer Process Red Mud Treated for Alumina Recovery, *Chem. & Met. Eng.*, **52** (1), 106 (1945); GOULD, Alumina from Low-grade Bauxite, *Ind. Eng. Chem.*, **37**, 796 (1945).

[2] FRARY, Adventures with Alumina, *Ind. Eng. Chem.*, **38**, 129 (1946).

lute solution as a mild astringent and antiseptic for the skin. The most important single application of it is in clarifying water, more than half of the total amount manufactured being so consumed. Sodium aluminate, which is basic, is sometimes used with aluminum sulfate, which is acid, to produce the aluminum hydroxide floc.

$$6NaAlO_2 + Al_2(SO_4)_3 + 12H_2O \rightarrow 8Al(OH)_3 + 3Na_2SO_4$$

Second in importance is the application of aluminum sulfate to the sizing of paper. It reacts with sodium resinate to give the insoluble aluminum resinate. For the sizing of paper, aluminum sulfate must be free from ferric iron or the paper will be discolored. The ferrous ions do no harm since they form a soluble, practically colorless resinate which, however,

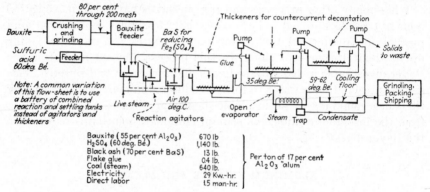

Bauxite (55 per cent Al_2O_3)	670 lb.	
H_2SO_4 (60 deg. Bé.)	1,140 lb.	
Black ash (70 per cent BaS)	13 lb.	Per ton of 17 per cent
Flake glue	0.4 lb.	Al_2O_3 "alum"
Coal (steam)	640 lb.	
Electricity	29 Kw.-hr.	
Direct labor	1.5 man-hr.	

FIG. 8. Manufacture of aluminum sulfate by the Dorr procedure.

would represent a loss of the resinate. A small amount of aluminum sulfate is consumed by the dye industry as a mordant. Soda alum or aluminum sulfate is used in some baking powders. In 1953, 731,039 tons of aluminum sulfate and 38,229 tons of iron-free aluminum sulfate (both 17 per cent Al_2O_3) were produced in the United States. In addition, municipally owned plants made about 13,600 tons of aluminum sulfate for their own use.

Manufacture. Practically all alums and aluminum sulfate are made now from bauxite by reaction with 60°Bé. sulfuric acid. However, potash alum was first prepared from alunite by the ancients. Other possible sources of alums are shales and other alumina-bearing materials such as clay. Figure 8 illustrates the manufacture of aluminum sulfate.[1] The bauxite is ground until 80 per cent passes 200 mesh; next it is conveyed to storage bins. The reaction occurs in lead-lined steel tanks where the reactants are thoroughly mixed and heated with the aid of agitators and live steam. These reactors are operated in series. Into the last reactor

[1] Cf. Alum, *Chem. Eng.*, **57** (12), 172 (1950), for a pictured flow sheet of American Cyanamid plant at Mobile, Ala.

barium sulfide is added in the form of black ash to reduce ferric sulfate to the ferrous state and to precipitate the iron.

The mixture from the reactors is sent through a series of thickeners, operated countercurrently, which remove undissolved matter and thoroughly wash the waste so that when discarded it will contain practically no "alum." The clarified aluminum sulfate solution is concentrated in an open, steam-coil-heated evaporator from 35°Bé. to 59 or 62°Bé. The concentrated liquor is poured into flat pans where it is cooled and completely solidified. The solid cake is broken and ground to size for shipping. Another slightly modified procedure uses, instead of reactors and thickeners, combined reaction and settling tanks. The Dalecarlia rapid-sand filter plant which supplies water to Washington, D.C., makes its own filter alum. In this case concentration of liquor would be an unnecessary expense; therefore, the aluminum sulfate is made and used in water solution.[1]

To make the various true alums, it is necessary only to add the sulfate of the monovalent metal to the dilute aluminum sulfate solution in the proper amount. Concentration of the mixed solution, followed by cooling, yields the alum crystals.

ALUMINUM CHLORIDE

Aluminum chloride is a white solid when pure. In the presence of moisture, anhydrous aluminum chloride partly decomposes with the evolution of hydrogen chloride. This salt was first prepared in 1825 by H. C. Oersted who passed chlorine over a mixture of alumina and carbon and condensed the vapors of the aluminum chloride formed. Essentially the same process is used today in the commercial preparation of aluminum chloride. The price in 1913 was $1.50 per pound, while the present price is below 8 cents per pound in carload lots.

Uses. Since modern methods of manufacture have reduced the price of aluminum chloride, it has found increasing application in the petroleum industries and various phases of organic technology. It is used to a considerable extent in certain petroleum processes. Aluminum chloride is a catalyst in alkylation of paraffins and aromatic hydrocarbons by olefins and also in the formation of complex ketones, aldehydes, and carboxylic acid derivatives. In 1953, 48,434 tons of liquid, crystal and anhydrous, were manufactured.

Manufacture.[2] There are three important methods for the preparation of anhydrous aluminum chloride. One of these is the direct reaction of liquid or gaseous chlorine with metallic aluminum; the second consists of

[1] LAUTER, Manufacture of Aluminum Sulfate at the Dalecarlia Filter Plant, Washington, D.C., *Ind. Eng. Chem.*, **25**, 953 (1933).

[2] KIRK and OTHMER, *op. cit.*, Vol. 1, p. 633.

the simultaneous reduction by carbon and chlorination by gaseous chlorine of alumina-bearing materials; and the third consists of the action of hydrogen chloride on alumina. The reaction between aluminum and chlorine is exothermic. Enough heat is given off to vaporize the aluminum chloride continuously as it is formed. The reaction between carbon, bauxite, and chlorine, however, is endothermic and heat must be supplied to cause the reaction to take place. In the United States bauxite is calcined, mixed with a carbonaceous residue, briquetted, and recalcined to drive off all hydrocarbons that would form corrosive hydrogen chloride later on. This material in a shaft kiln is heated up to 1600°C. by a blast of air and chlorinated, the aluminum chloride being volatilized and condensed. The reaction of HCl on alumina produces Al_2Cl_6 which sublimes off and must be condensed. The product made from aluminum metal is of a very high purity but may be resublimed for the highest-purity material available.

FERROUS SULFATE

Ferrous sulfate (copperas) is the most abundant of the iron compounds as it is the waste product of the pickling processes in which steel surfaces are cleaned preparatory to electroplating, tinning, galvanizing, or enameling operations. Between 500,000,000 and 800,000,000 gal. of waste liquor, containing on the average 15 per cent ferrous sulfate, are produced annually.[1] This can be evaporated to furnish the ferrous sulfate whenever the market warrants. Unfortunately, no large-scale use has been found for this salt though it has been employed for water clarification by certain cities like St. Louis, Mo. (see Fig. 6, Chap. 24).

COPPER SALTS

Copper sulfate[2] is the most important compound of copper and over 72,000 tons were produced in 1953. Commonly known as *blue vitriol*, it is prepared by the action of sulfuric acid on cupric oxide or sulfide ores. Its poisonous nature is utilized in the insecticide, Bordeaux mixture, which is formed upon the mixing of copper sulfate solution with milk of lime. Copper sulfate is added to water reservoirs occasionally to kill algae. It is employed in electroplating and finds minor applications as a mordant, germicide, and agent in engraving. Certain copper compounds are added to antifouling paints used on ship bottoms.

[1] HODGE, Waste Problems of the Iron and Steel Industries, *Ind. Eng. Chem.*, **31**, 1364 (1939); VAN ANTWERPEN, Utilization of Pickle Liquor, *Ind. Eng. Chem.*, **34**, 1138 (1942); TREFFLER, Manufacture of Ferrous Sulfate, *Chem. Inds.*, **54**, 70 (1944), flow chart.

[2] KIRK and OTHMER, *op. cit.*, Vol. 5, pp. 474–478; a flow sheet is given in *Chem. Eng.*, **57** (11), 119 (1950).

MOLYBDENUM COMPOUNDS

Molybdenum compounds are not consumed in large tonnage in the process industries, but they are important in conjunction with hydroxyl compounds like pyrogallol in dyeing furs, feathers, hair, and skins; as lake-forming substances with basic dyes; as pigments; and to produce adherence of porcelain enamels to steel. The compounds used for dyes are sodium, potassium, or ammonium molybdates. With basic dyes phospho-molybdic acid is employed. The pigment known as *molybdenum orange* is a mixed crystal of lead chromate and lead molybdate. The compounds used to produce better adherence of enamels are molybdenum trioxide, ammonium, sodium, calcium, barium, and lead molybdates. The mineral raw material is molybdenite, MoS_2, which by roasting furnishes a technical grade of molybdenum trioxide, MoO_3, of 80 to 90 per cent purity.

BARIUM SALTS

The most common naturally occurring barium compounds are the mineral carbonate or witherite, which is fairly abundant in England and the sulfate or barite which is common in certain sections of the United States. The greatest source of barite is Arkansas.

Uses. The applications of barium compounds are varied and important. In 1953, 97,508 tons of barium compounds and 52,439 tons of lithopone were sold. *Barium carbonate* is sometimes employed as a neutralizing agent for sulfuric acid and, because both barium carbonate and sulfate are insoluble, no contaminating barium ions are introduced. The foregoing application is found in the synthetic dyestuffs industry. Barium carbonate is a component in some rat poisons and is a minor constituent in crown glass. Witherite is used chiefly to prepare other compounds. *Barium sulfate* is a useful white pigment (see Chap. 24) particularly in the precipitated form, blanc fixe. It is used as a filler for paper, rubber, linoleum, and oilcloth. Because of its opacity to X rays, barium sulfate, in a purified form, is important in contour photographs of the digestive tract. The paint industry is the largest single consumer of barium compounds. Barium sulfide and zinc sulfate solutions are mixed to give a precipitate of barium sulfate and zinc sulfide, which is given a heat-treatment to yield the cheap but good pigment, *lithopone*, as described in Chap. 24. Barium chlorate and nitrate are used in pyrotechnics to impart a green flame. Barium chloride is applied where a soluble barium compound is needed. Barium saccharate is used by a large beet-sugar group for sugar recovery from discard molasses (Chap. 30).

Manufacture. The preparation of soluble barium salts is simple where witherite is available. The only steps necessary are treatment with the proper acid, filtration to remove insoluble impurities, and crystallization of the salt. Since there is little witherite in the United States, barium salts are prepared from barite. The high-temperature reduction of barium sulfate with coke yields the water-soluble barium sulfide which is subsequently leached out. The treatment of barium sulfide with the proper chemical yields the desired barium salt. Purification of the product is complicated by the impurities introduced in the coke. Pure barium carbonate and barium sulfate are made by precipitation from solutions of water-soluble barium salts. Much barite is ground,[1] acid-washed, lixiviated, and dried to produce a cheap pigment or paper or rubber filler or changed to blanc fixe by action of $CaCl_2$.[2]

STRONTIUM SALTS

Uses are small in tonnage but important; these are in red-flame pyrotechnic compositions, such as truck signal flares and railroad "fusees," tracer bullets, and military signal flares. Low-grade strontium deposits are available in this country, but a high-grade celestite is imported from the United Kingdom. This ore (strontium sulfate) is finely ground and converted to the carbonate by boiling with 10 per cent sodium carbonate solution; giving almost a quantitative yield

$$SrSO_4 + Na_2CO_3 \rightarrow SrCO_3 + Na_2SO_4$$

By reaction of the strontium carbonate with appropriate acids, the various salts result.[3]

LITHIUM SALTS

Since the Second World War lithium compounds have become of some importance. During the Second World War, lithium hydride, produced from metallic lithium, when reacted with sea water provided a convenient lightweight source of hydrogen for the inflation of emergency balloons used to raise antenna from aircraft disabled at sea. By 1951 expansion resulted in shipments of 12,897 tons of lithium-bearing ores and compounds containing 956 tons of lithium oxide. Lithium is recovered from the brine of Searles Lake in California as a concentrate of lithium-sodium phosphate (Li_2NaPO_4) (see Chap. 13). Three domestic ores are mined for lithium: spodumene ($Li_2O \cdot Al_2O_3 \cdot 4SiO_2$), lepidolite, and amblygonite. Over 50 per cent of the world's production of ores is centered in this country.

Uses. Lithium-base greases, often the stearate, are the largest outlet (about 44 per cent). These lubricants are efficient over the extremely

---

[1] See KIRK and OTHMER, *op. cit.*, Vol. 2, pp. 307–323; WHITE, The Plant That Barite Built, *Chem. Eng.*, **56** (4), 90 (1949), with a pictured flow sheet on pp. 128–131.

[2] FARR, U.S. Pat. 1752244(1930); SHREVE, *et al.*, U.S. Pat. 2030659(1936).

[3] ANON., Strontium Chemicals, *Chem. Eng.*, **53** (1), 152 (1946), a pictured flow sheet.

wide temperature range of -60 to $320°F$. Lithium carbonate is the most significant lithium compound currently produced, since it is widely used per se in the ceramics industry. It is also the starting material for a wide variety of other lithium chemicals, including metallic lithium. Both the hollowware industry and the porcelain-enamel field consume amounts approaching that of the greases. Lithium hydroxide is a component of the electrolyte in alkaline storage batteries. Welding fluxes and alloys are also avenues of consumption. Lithium chloride is in demand for low-temperature batteries and for aluminum brazing.

Manufacture.[1] Since spodumene is by far the most important ore, the manufacture of lithium carbonate from it will be presented. Spodumene ore (beneficiated to 3 to 5 per cent Li_2O) is converted from the alpha form to the beta form by heating to over $1000°C$. The latter is treated as follows:

$$Li_2O \cdot Al_2O_3 \cdot 4SiO_2 + H_2SO_4 \xrightarrow[250–300°C.]{} H_2O \cdot Al_2O_3 \cdot 4SiO_2 + Li_2SO_4$$

The water-soluble lithium sulfate is leached out and reacted with sodium carbonate to yield lithium carbonate. Various salts are derived from the carbonate as follows:

$$Li_2CO_3 + Ca(OH)_2 + 2H_2O \rightarrow CaCO_3 + 2LiOH \cdot H_2O \xrightarrow{\Delta} 2LiOH$$

$$Li_2CO_3 + 2HCl \rightarrow H_2O + CO_2 + 2LiCl(\text{soln.}) \xrightarrow{\Delta} 2LiCl(\text{anhyd.})$$

$$2LiCl(\text{anhyd.}) \xrightarrow{\text{electrolysis}} 2Li + Cl_2\uparrow \xrightarrow{H_2} 2LiH \xrightarrow{2NH_3} 2LiNH_2 + 2H_2\uparrow$$

BORON COMPOUNDS

The important naturally occurring ores of boron have been colemanite, $Ca_2B_6O_{11} \cdot 5H_2O$; tincal, $Na_2B_4O_7 \cdot 10H_2O$; and boracite, $2Mg_3B_8O_{15} \cdot MgCl_2$. However, boron-containing brines and kernite or rasorite, $Na_2B_4O_7 \cdot 4H_2O$, are the present sources in the United States.

Uses. The most important compound for industrial use is borax, $Na_2B_4O_7 \cdot 10H_2O$. It is widely used as a flux, in the manufacture of Pyrex glass, in the making of glazes and enamels, in the preparation of soaps, and other miscellaneous processes. Boric acid, H_3BO_3, is a weak acid that is applied medicinally as a mild antiseptic and also finds some consumption in the manufacture of glazes and enamels for pottery. Boron carbide, B_4C, is the hardest artificial abrasive known.

Manufacture. Most of the borax in the United States is prepared either from the mineral kernite found in the Mojave Desert of California or from the saline brines of Searles Lake. As mined, kernite contains

[1] HADER, et al., Lithium and Its Compounds, *Ind. Eng. Chem.*, **43**, 2636 (1951), a most excellent article with flow sheet.

considerable clay which is removed by dissolving in water, filtering, and crystallizing. Borax is recovered along with potassium chloride from the brines of Searles Lake.[1]

SILVER NITRATE

Silver nitrate (lunar caustic) is used in surgery, as a laboratory reagent, in hair dyes, and in laundry marking inks. When it is allowed to come in contact with skin, hair, or cloth, it is reduced to metallic silver, thus leaving a gray to black stain. The largest consumption is, however, in the photographic industry where silver nitrate is the source of the various sensitive silver halides of the emulsion. It is prepared by dissolving metallic silver in dilute nitric acid in porcelain or stainless steel vessels, evaporating, and crystallizing.

RADIUM AND URANIUM SALTS

Radium. The discovery of radium and its isolation by the Curies was one of the greatest events of all time. Marie Curie noticed that certain samples of uranium ore exhibited greater radioactivity than was to be expected from the uranium content. After a long series of concentrating operations based upon partial crystallization, the Curies discovered and isolated polonium first and then, in 1898, radium.

Uses. The most important single application of radium has been medical. Its valuable curative properties on cancerous growths and in certain other morbid conditions are well known even to the layman. To a certain extent other radiations have been substituted for radium. The discovery of radium and its properties completely transformed the fundamental concepts of chemical elements and, hence, affected the philosophical view of the universe.

Manufacture. Radium occurs with uranium of which it is a disintegration product. The Curies isolated radium from the mineral pitchblende, where it is found in the proportion of 1 part of radium to each 3,000,000 parts of uranium occurring as uraninite, U_3O_8. Pure uraninite, therefore, would yield 1 gram of radium for each 3.88 tons. The separation of radium from uranium is usually by an acid sulfate treatment yielding a relatively small precipitate of alkaline earth, lead, and radium sulfates. This is further processed to radium.[2]

Uranium.[3] Until about 1940, uranium-bearing ores were processed for their radium content; the uranium was considered a less useful by-prod-

---

[1] See Chap. 13 for description and flow chart; *cf.* KIRK and OTHMER, *op. cit.*, Vol. 2, pp. 588–622, particularly pp. 611–614.

[2] VIOL, The Commercial Production and Uses of Radium, *J. Chem. Educ.*, **3,** 757 (1926); KIRK and OTHMER, *op. cit.*, Vol. 11, p. 446, flow sheet; *cf.* this book, 1st ed., p. 435, for flow sheet of radium from pitchblende.

[3] KATZ, J. J., and E. RABINOWITCH, "The Chemistry of Uranium," McGraw-Hill Book Company, Inc., New York, 1951; KIRK and OTHMER, *op. cit.*

uct. However, with recent innovations in the field of nucleonics, the importance of radium has been overshadowed by that of uranium.

Uses. Uranium gained increasing importance during the Second World War as a fissionable material for use in weapons (see Atomic Bombs, Chap. 22). Postwar interest, although still along those lines, has broadened in scope to include use of the heat produced by nuclear decomposition of uranium for raising steam to drive turbines for locomotion or production of electricity. This is called *nuclear engineering*.

Manufacture. The ores commonly processed for their uranium content are pitchblende, carnotite, and autinite. Prior to final chemical separa-

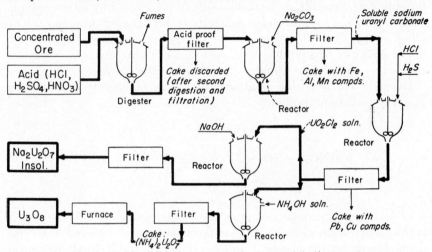

Fig. 9. Schematic outline of a process for uranium recovery.

tion and purification of the uranium, initial concentrations are performed for removal of sands and clays, and such impurities as silver, gold, vanadium, and copper. The concentrates can then be treated by the scheme outlined in Figure 9, for recovery and final purification of the uranium.

The process involves a preliminary double digestion of the concentrate with hydrochloric, sulfuric, or nitric acid to solubilize the uranium. The leach filtrates from this slurry are treated with carbonate to form the soluble uranyl carbonate complex and to remove such things as iron, aluminum, and manganese by precipitation. Subsequent treatment of the filtrate of the carbonate slurry with hydrochloric acid and hydrogen sulfide removes lead and copper. Final treatment includes alkaline precipitation of the uranium as either $(NH_4)_2U_2O_7$ or $Na_2U_2O_7$.

Further processing of the metal can be accomplished by four general routes: (1) reduction of uranium oxide with carbon in a graphite crucible using a high-temperature arc; (2) reduction of uranium oxides with calcium, magnesium, or aluminum at elevated temperatures in an evacuated steel crucible; (3) reduction of uranium halides by alkali or alkaline earth metals in an iron crucible lined with a fused salt; and (4) cathodic reduction of uranium halides in molten salt baths.

Most of the above procedures yield the metal powder; however, massive metal was first successfully prepared by reduction of uranium tetrachloride with sodium metal in a sealed iron crucible lined with fused sodium chloride. In general, reduction of the halides with alkali or alkaline earth metals appears more promising than the reduction of uranium oxides. The slags produced from the halide reductions are relatively low melting, producing molten reaction mixtures in which slag and metal separation is more complete. Heats of reaction indicate that uranium tetrafluoride, tetrabromide, or tetrachloride can be reduced by either sodium, calcium, or magnesium. Small amounts of high-purity uranium can be obtained by thermal decomposition of uranium tetraiodide. Although metal purity of this product surpasses that of metal from other types of reductions, the process would not be economically feasible on large scale.

Recently the following reactions have been published[1] as indicating one way to obtain uranium:

$$U_3O_8 + HNO_3 \rightarrow NO_3\!-\!\overset{\overset{\displaystyle O}{\|}}{\underset{\underset{\displaystyle O}{\|}}{U}}\!-\!NO_3 \cdot 6H_2O \rightarrow UO_3 \rightarrow UF_4 \rightarrow U$$

Concerning these reactions more data were published[2] in 1954 and it is "the story of the highest degree of purification ever achieved on a commercial scale by the chemical industry—i.e. by Mallinckrodt Chemical Works (St. Louis), whose task this was."

For atomic bombs or other chain reactions uranium must be *extremely pure* with "nearly all possible impurities—below 100 ppm," and with boron which absorbs the split-off neutrons so readily that "even 1 ppm will seriously hamper the efficiency of an atomic pile."

The process described digests the ore and, for the most part, dissolves this in a hot nitric acid–sulfuric acid mixture.

The insoluble portion (including radium sulfate), is removed by a rotary filter. . . . After treatment with $BaCO_3$ to precipitate sulfates, the filtrate is essentially uranyl nitrate. . . . To obtain the high degree of purity required, the uranium compound is then continuously extracted from the aqueous filtrate, with ether. . . . Fortunately the uranyl nitrate dissolves more readily in ether than do the impurities and so can be separated from contaminants. . . . From the ether solution, the highly purified uranyl nitrate is reextracted with water. . . . The uranyl nitrate is converted into uranium trioxide by thermal denitration, then reduced to uranium dioxide by heating in hydrogen.

[1] *Fortune Magazine*, January, 1954.
[2] Anon., Assignment to Unknown, *Chem. Week*, **75**, 50 (Oct. 23, 1954).

The dioxide is treated with HF and converted into UF_4. The UF_4 product stream then takes one of two directions: either it is reduced to uranium metal for pile slugs or to UF_6 for separation into the isotopes, U^{235} and U^{238}.

At Geneva, Switzerland, in the summer of 1955, very many important technical papers[1] were presented covering hitherto unpublicized aspects of the behavior of uranium, its reaction products, and nucleonics in general. H. A. Wilhelm made the statement that UF_4 in a steel crucible lined with hard-packed, sifted, electrothermally fused, and pure dolomitic oxide can be reduced by finely divided magnesium, furnishing U reguli. The reguli can be melted in a graphite crucible in an induction-heated vacuum furnace, the molten uranium being cast into ingots in graphite molds.

The following reactions are of interest in connection with a method to prepare uranium metal:

$$U_3O_8 + 8HNO_3(aq) \rightarrow 3UO_2(NO_3)_2(aq) + 2NO_2 + 4H_2O; \quad \Delta H = -41,400 \text{ cal.}$$
$$UO_2(NO_3)_2 \cdot 6H_2O \rightarrow UO_3 + 2NO_2 + \tfrac{1}{2}O_2 + 6H_2O(g); \quad \Delta H = +134,600 \text{ cal.}$$
$$UO_3 + H_2 \rightarrow UO_2 + H_2O; \quad \Delta H = -35,000 \text{ cal.}$$
$$UO_2 + 4HF \rightarrow UF_4 + 2H_2O; \quad \Delta H = -64,000 \text{ cal.}$$
$$UF_4 + 2Mg \rightarrow U + 2MgF_2; \quad \Delta H = -83,000 \text{ cal.}$$

Freshly polished uranium metal is silver-bright but quickly tarnishes in air. There are three crystalline forms of the uranium: (1) the alpha or low-temperature form, which is considered semiplastic because of its poor elasticity, (2) the beta or medium-temperature form, which is brittle, and (3) the gamma or high-temperature form, which is plastic. It can be forged, drawn, or extruded at high temperatures.

Isotope Separation.[2] Separation of U^{235} (0.7 per cent) and U^{238} can be realized by either the gaseous-diffusion or the electromagnetic method, both of which make use of the difference in mass of these isotopes.

The gaseous-diffusion method involves passage of vaporized UF_6 under pressure through a series of separators consisting essentially of containers each divided in half by a permeable barrier. The U^{238}, because of its higher mass, lower velocity, and relatively lower incidence of collision with the barrier, passes through the barrier more slowly than U^{235}. A cascade of separators is used, allowing stepwise purification of both the U^{235} and U^{238} streams.

The electromagnetic method employs a very large mass spectrograph which operates on the principle that high-speed charged particles of dif-

---

[1] TOWNSEND, OLIVER and J. R. BARLOW, "World Development of Atomic Energy," Atomic Industrial Forum, Inc., 260 Madison Avenue, New York, 1955, with special supplements on U.S. bilateral agreements and the U.N. Geneva Conference. Titles are given for the more than 1,000 technical papers presented in Geneva orally or by title; one of these was WILHELM, H. A., The Preparation of Uranium Metal by Reduction of Uranium Tetrafluoride with Magnesium.

[2] SMYTH, "Atomic Energy for Military Purposes," Official report, Princeton University Press, Princeton, N.J., 1945.

ferent mass travel in different paths in a uniform magnetic field. A uranium (VI) halide is vaporized in a furnace and is bombarded by a stream of electrons from a heated filament. The ions formed are drawn by a series of electrodes maintained at a potential negative with respect to the ion source into an evacuated chamber pervaded by a magnetic field. After traveling through a 180-deg. arc, the U^{235} and U^{238} can be collected separately.

Nuclear Properties of the Isotopes. U^{238} undergoes thermal neutron (n) capture with subsequent beta decay (here loss of negative electron) to Np^{239} and then to Pu^{239}:

$$_{92}U^{238} + _{0}n^1 \rightarrow {}_{92}U^{239} \xrightarrow[\substack{23 \\ \text{min.}}]{\beta-} {}_{93}Np^{239} \xrightarrow[\substack{2.3 \\ \text{days}}]{\beta-} {}_{94}Pu^{239}$$

The plutonium isotope has a reasonably long half life (24,000 years) and is quite important since it will undergo fast fission, a property essential in military application. U^{235} undergoes fast fission and is separated from the more abundant U^{238} by gaseous diffusion for military and other reactor application. U^{234} is present in natural uranium in extremely small proportions. This isotope is the daughter product of U^{238}.

Nucleonic engineering[1] is important for military weapons and for industrial power. With the removal of many restrictions (summer, 1954) more industrial efforts will supplement the splendid accomplishments of the Atomic Energy Commission, and both will establish the conditions for practical energy from nucleonic reactions. As this field is in a complicated state of development in 1954, information should be obtained from the latest literature. One type of reactor design will absorb the heat of nuclear fission by a molten liquid like sodium, using this in a boiler to generate steam for heat or electricity.

RARE-EARTH COMPOUNDS

The rare earths comprise a series of 15 elements so nearly identical in properties that they are separated only with difficulty. Cerium and thorium are the most important commercially. Although rare earths occur in certain minerals native to the Carolinas, these minerals have not been able to compete with the richer monazite sands found in Brazil. Preliminary separation is accomplished by the use of jigging, where the valuable material is denser than the worthless fraction. The concentrates

[1] MURRAY, R. L., "Introduction to Nuclear Engineering," Prentice-Hall, Inc., New York, 1954; STEPHENSON, RICHARD, "Introduction to Nuclear Engineering," McGraw-Hill Book Company, Inc., New York, 1954; A.I.E.E. Nucleonics Committee, "Elements of Nucleonics for Engineers," American Institute of Electrical Engineers, New York, 1950.

are leached with hot sulfuric acid of strength greater than 66°Bé. The rare-earth metal compounds are precipitated by dilution of the sulfuric acid solution. The usual practice is to isolate thorium and cerium hydroxides, the latter containing all the other rare earths except thorium unless careful and tedious purifications are carried out.

Crude cerium hydroxide is employed in flaming arc carbons, and the purified form imparts a yellow color to glass. A large use for thorium and cerium is in gas mantles. Metallic cerium alloyed with iron gives pyrophoric alloys.[1] Thorium is of interest in nuclear reactions.

SODIUM DICHROMATE

The starting material for the manufacture of sodium dichromate and other chromium compounds is chromite, a chromium iron oxide contain-

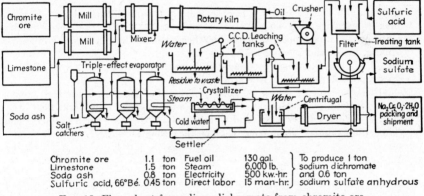

Chromite ore	1.1	ton	Fuel oil	130 gal.	}	To produce 1 ton
Limestone	1.5	ton	Steam	6,000 lb.		sodium dichromate
Soda ash	0.8	ton	Electricity	500 kw.-hr.	}	and 0.6 ton
Sulfuric acid, 66°Bé.	0.45	ton	Direct labor	15 man-hr.	}	sodium sulfate anhydrous

Fig. 10. Flow chart for sodium dichromate from chromite ore.

ing approximately 50 per cent Cr_2O_3, the balance being principally FeO, Al_2O_3, SiO_2, and MgO. There are no high-grade chromite deposits in the United States, and most of the ore used in the chemical industry is imported from South Africa. In war years it was proposed that domestic ore[2] should be used. Much sodium dichromate is consumed as the starting material for making, by glucose reduction, the solutions of chromium salts employed in chrome leather tanning (Chap. 25) and in chrome mordant dyeing of wool cloth. Certain pigments, as the yellow lead chromate, are manufactured basically from sodium dichromate as are also the green chromium oxides for ceramic pigments. Over half of the chromium enters the metal field as stainless steel and other high-chromium alloys and for

[1] KUEBEL, Extraction of Radium from Canadian Pitchblende, *J. Chem. Educ.*, **17**, 417 (1940).

[2] ANON., Producing Chromate Salts from Domestic Ores, *Chem. & Met. Eng.*, **47**, 688 (1940), flow chart; McBERTY, F. H., and B. H. WILCOXON, Bichromate Manufacture, OTS report, PB-22627, Hobart Publishing Co.

chromium plating of other metals, the balance being about equally divided between chrome refractories and chrome chemicals.

The ore is ground to 200 mesh, mixed with ground limestone and soda ash, and roasted at approximately 2200°F. in a strongly oxidizing atmosphere. The sintered mass is crushed and leached with hot water to separate the soluble sodium chromate. The solution is treated with enough sulfuric acid to convert the chromate to dichromate with the resulting formation of sodium sulfate. Most of the sodium sulfate crystallizes in the anhydrous state from the boiling-hot solution during acidification, and the remainder drops out in the evaporators on concentrating the dichromate solution. From the evaporator the hot saturated dichromate solution is fed to the crystallizer, then to the centrifuge and drier (see Fig. 10).

SELECTED REFERENCES

Kirk, R. E., and D. F. Othmer, "Encyclopedia of Chemical Technology," 15 vols., The Interscience Encyclopedia, Inc., New York, 1947–1956.

Ullmann, Fritz, "Enzyklopaedia der technischen Chemie," 3d ed., Urban & Schwarzenberg, Berlin and Vienna, 1952–.

Furnas, C. C., editor, "Rogers' Manual of Industrial Chemistry," 2 vols., D. Van Nostrand Company, Inc., New York, 1942.

National Nuclear Energy Series, 60 vols. (projected) of the work of the U.S. Atomic Energy Commission, McGraw-Hill Book Company, Inc., New York, 1948–.

Yost, D. M., Horace Russell, Jr., and C. S. Garner, "The Rare-earth Elements and Their Compounds," John Wiley & Sons, Inc., New York, 1947.

CHAPTER 22

EXPLOSIVES, PYROTECHNICS, AND CHEMICAL WARFARE

INDUSTRIAL AND MILITARY EXPLOSIVES

Many professional chemists and chemical engineers tend to view the subject of explosives from a purely military standpoint. It should always be remembered that, although explosives have contributed much to the destruction of man, they have also enabled him to perform many great engineering feats which would have been physically or economically impossible without their use. The building of such large engineering projects as Hoover Dam and the Holland Tunnel would have taken hundreds of years if performed by hand labor alone. Explosives are among the most powerful slaves that man has learned to employ. Mining of all kinds depends on blasting, as does such a prosaic but necessary act as the clearing of stumps and large boulders from land. Even the digging of holes for tree planting and ditches for drainage is quickly, efficiently, and cheaply done by means of dynamite—and with less effort than by any other method. Even truck brakes are relined and airplanes are constructed with rivets which have an explosive in the shank that is fired by heat with the consequent saving of much time and effort.

Uses and Economics. In peacetime large quantities of explosives are consumed for normal technical operations as listed in Table 1; in times of war tremendous quantities are required.

Classification. An explosive is a material which, under the influence of thermal or mechanical shock, decomposes rapidly and spontaneously with the evolution of a great deal of heat and much gas. The hot gases cause extremely high pressure if the explosive is set off in a confined space. Explosives differ widely in their sensitivity and power. Only those of a comparatively insensitive nature, capable of being controlled and having a high energy content, are of importance commercially or in a military sense.

For purposes of classification it is convenient to place explosives in three distinct divisions:

1. Initiating or primary explosives (detonators)—lead azide, mercury fulminate, diazodinitro-phenol, lead styphnate (lead trinitro-resorcinate).

2. High explosives—trinitro-toluene (T.N.T.), amatols, pentaerythritol-tetranitrate, cyclonite (hexogen or R.D.X.), tetryl,[1] dynamites, nitro-starch.

3. Low explosives or propellants—colloided cellulose nitrate (smokeless powder), black powders.

TABLE 1. INDUSTRIAL EXPLOSIVES MANUFACTURED AND SOLD IN THE
UNITED STATES, 1953[a]
(In thousands of pounds)

Use	Total	Permissible explosives	High explosives, other than permissibles	Black blasting powder	Liquid-oxygen explosives
Coal mining............	250,578	88,810	134,483	4,868	22,417
Metal mining...........	167,419	73	167,294	52	
Quarrying and nonmetallic mining.............	176,985	819	175,188	930	48
Railway and other construction work.........	181,856	94	178,988	2,774	
All other purposes.......	13,973	83	12,999	891	
Total.................	790,811	89,876	668,952	9,515	22,465

[a] U.S. Bureau of Mines, Mineral Market Report MMS2273, 1954.

Initiating or *primary explosives* are quite sensitive materials which can be made to explode by the application of fire or by means of a slight blow. They are very dangerous to handle and are used in comparatively small quantities to start the explosion of larger quantities of less sensitive explosives. Initiating explosives are generally used in primers, detonators, and percussion caps.

High explosives are materials which are quite insensitive to both mechanical shock and flame but which explode with great violence when set off by an explosive shock such as that which would be obtained by detonating a small amount of an initiating explosive in contact with the high explosive. In the case of high and primary explosives, decomposition proceeds by means of a detonation, which is a rapid chemical destruction progressing directly through the mass of the explosive. This detonation is thought to be a chain reaction and proceeds at rates that are frequently as high as 20,000 ft. per sec. for high-velocity dynamites. It is this high rate of energy release rather than the total energy given off that makes a product an explosive. Nitro-glycerine has only one-eighth the potential energy of gasoline. On the other hand, most high explosives, when unconfined or unshocked, will merely burn if ignited.

Low explosives, or *propellants*, differ in their mode of decomposition from the two other types; they only burn. Burning is a phenomenon that

---

[1] Because of higher brisance, tetryl also is used as a booster between the initiating and high explosive.

proceeds not through the body of the material but in layers parallel to. the surface. It is quite slow in its action, comparatively speaking, rarely exceeding 0.25 m. per sec. The action of low explosives is, therefore, less shattering. Low explosives evolve large volumes of gas on combustion in a definite and controllable manner.

The industrial classification used in Table 1 is that of the U.S. Bureau of Mines where *black blasting powder* refers to all black powder having sodium or potassium nitrate as a constituent. Here *permissible explosives* include ammonium nitrate explosives, hydrated explosives, organic nitrate explosives, and certain nitro-glycerine explosives that contain an excess of free water or carbon. The permissible explosives must pass certain tests[1] to ensure a minimum of flame and temperature to reduce fires in coal mines where 99 per cent of the permissibles are employed. Ammonium nitrate constitutes over 65 per cent of the weight of the permissibles. The *high explosives* used in industries are the usual dynamites.

Properties of Explosives. In order to compare explosives, certain standard tests have been worked out to measure their properties. These tests are empirical and are of value only for purposes of comparison. The results of some of these tests are shown in Table 2 and include also military explosives.

The *power* or *brisance* of an explosive may be measured by exploding a small quantity of it in a *sand bomb*, which is a heavy-walled vessel designed to resist the explosion without being ruptured. It contains 200 grams of Ottawa silica sand,[2] all of which passes through a 20-mesh sieve and all of which is retained on a 30-mesh sieve. The explosive is immersed in the sand and the bomb closed. After the explosion, the sand is sieved and the weight of sand passing through the 30-mesh screen is taken as a measure of the power of the explosive being tested. Another test of a somewhat similar nature is the *Trauzl block test*. This test measures the power of the explosive by measuring the ballooning of a soft lead cylinder in which the explosive is inserted and exploded. The standard Trauzl block is 200 mm. in diameter and 200 mm. high with a central hole 25 mm. in diameter and 125 mm. deep. Ten grams of the explosive is used in making the test and the results are reported in terms of the cubic centimeters of increase in volume caused by detonation of the explosive. Both of these tests furnish an indication of the *brisance* (from French *briser*, to shatter) or shattering power of the high explosive being tested. This *brisance*, or shattering effect, is probably a combination of the strength and the velocity.

[1] U.S. Bureau of Mines, Explosives Division, Active List of Permissible Explosives and Blasting Devices, *U.S. Bur. Mines, Rept. Invest.* 3910, 1946.

[2] This sand is selected for its uniformity. It is mined at Ottawa, Ill. For details of testing explosives, see references at end of this chapter, particularly the book by Meyer for an over-all presentation.

The *sensitivity* of an explosive to *impact* is determined by finding the height from which a standard weight must be allowed to fall in order to detonate the explosive. This test is of greatest importance in the case of initiating explosives.

The heat of explosion is given in Table 2 as Qv. This is the heat evolved at constant volume. In comparison with heats of combustion of ordinary fuels, this is comparatively small in the number of calories. An explosive,

TABLE 2. SUMMARY OF CHARACTERISTICS OF EXPLOSIVES[a]

Name	Formula	Products per formula weight	Qv, Cal. per kg.	Te, °C.	f, kg. per sq. cm.	V, m. per sec.	Trauzl expansion, cc. per 10g.	Potential $\times 10^5$ kg.-m.
Gunpowder.......	$2KNO_3 + 3C + S$	$N_2 + 3CO_2 + K_2S$	501	2090	2,970	.....	30	2.1
Nitro-cellulose.....	$C_{24}H_{29}O_9(NO_3)_{11}$	$20.5CO + 3.5CO_2 + 14.5H_2O + 5.5N_2$	1,250	2800	10,000	6,100	420	5.3
Nitro-glycerine....	$C_3H_5(NO_3)_3$	$3CO_2 + 2.5H_2O + 1.5N_2 + 0.25O_2$	1,526	3360	9,835	8,500	590	6.5
Ammonium nitrate	NH_4NO_3	$2H_2O + N_2 + 0.5O_2$	384	1100	5,100	4,100	300	1.6
T.N.T............	$C_7H_5(NO_2)_3$	$6CO + C + 2.5H_2 + 1.5N_2$	656	2200	8,386	6,800	260	2.8
Picric acid.......	$C_6H_2(OH)(NO_2)_3$	$6CO + H_2O$ $0.5H_2 + 1.5N_2$	847	2717	9,960	7,000	300	3.6
Ammonium picrate	$C_6H_2(NO_2)_3ONH_4$	$6CO + H_2O + 2H_2 + 2N_2$	622	1979	8,537	6,500	230	2.6
Tetryl...........	$C_7H_5N_5O_8$	$7CO + H_2O + 1.5H_2 + 2.5N_2$	908	2781	10,830	7,229	320	3.9
Mercury fulminate	$Hg(ONC)_2$	$Hg + 2CO + N_2$	420	4105	5,212	3,920	213	1.8
Lead azide........	PbN_6	$Pb + 3N_2$	684	3180	8,070	5,000	250	2.9

[a] By permission, from p. 439 of MEYER, "The Science of Explosives," Thomas Y. Crowell Company, New York, 1943.

however, exerts all this energy extremely rapidly. In the same table, Te is the *explosion temperature*. The *specific pressure*, designated in the table as f, signifies the pressure exerted by 1 kg. of explosive in volume of 1 l. at the explosion temperature of Te. *Potential* equals $425Qv$ kg.-m. where 425 is the mechanical equivalent of heat. This measures the total capacity for work in units of mechanical energy.

The *velocity* (V in the table) of the *detonation wave* in a column of explosive may be determined by threading wires across the column. These wires are connected through an electrical circuit in such a manner that, when they are broken by the moving wave, they cause a spark to jump onto the surface of a sooted drum revolving at a high, constant speed. The distance between the marks made by the sparks on the rotating drum, the distance between the wires inserted in the column of explosive, the diameter and speed of rotation of the drum all being known, it is a simple matter to calculate the velocity of detonation. Recently, methods have been developed for determining the velocity of detonation by means of high-speed photography. The velocity of detonation is dependent on many factors including the composition of the explosive, the density at which it was loaded before firing, and the degree of confinement. It is, however, constant for a given explosive under fixed conditions.

Certain accelerated aging tests are frequently run to determine the *stability* of explosives on storage. The time required for the evolution of traces of oxides of nitrogen at a comparatively high temperature is most frequently used for this purpose. Such tests are difficult to correlate with storage life.

It is important that explosives for use in mines, particularly coal mines, be of such a type that they evolve no poisonous gases on explosion and

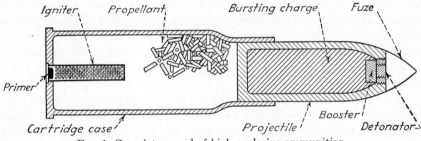

FIG. 1. Complete round of high explosive ammunition.

produce a minimum of flame. This latter requirement is necessary in order that the explosive be incapable of igniting mixtures of air and coal dust, or air and methane (firedamp), which inevitably occur in coal mines. Explosives for mine use are tested and their properties specified by the U.S. Bureau of Mines and are commonly known as *permissibles*. Permissibles differ from other explosives, particularly black powder; most markedly in the fact that they produce a flame of small size and extremely short duration. Permissibles contain coolants to regulate the temperatures of their flames and hence further reduce the possibility of their ignition of combustible mixtures. Permissibles are tested by explosion in a long gallery filled with coal dust, air, and methane. They should not explode this mixture.

MILITARY EXPLOSIVES

As the requirements for military explosives are extremely strict, only a few of them have survived the competitive testing. In this connection it is fundamental to understand the construction of a high-explosive artillery shell as depicted in Fig. 1. Such a shell consists of a thin brass or steel cartridge case holding the primer, igniter, and propellant charge.

This case is designed to fit smoothly into the gun and, on explosion, to expand (obdurate), sealing the breech of the gun so that the escape of gases from the burning of the propellant charge is prevented and thus allowing the full effect of the propellant to be exerted on the projectile or destructive half of the shell.

The *primer* contains a small amount of a primary explosive or sensitive mixture (*e.g.*, lead azide or a mixture such as $KClO_3 + Pb(CNS)_2 + Sb_2S_3 + T.N.T. +$ ground glass). This mixture explodes under the impact of the firing pin and produces a flame which ignites the black powder[1] charge in the *igniter*, which in turn ignites the *propellant* charge of smokeless powder. The burning of the smokeless powder causes the rapid emission of heated gas which ejects the *projectile* from the gun. On impact with the target, the mechanism of the *fuze* sets off a small quantity of a primary explosive (*detonator*) which causes the explosion of the *booster*—an explosive of intermediate sensitivity (between that of a primary explosive and the bursting charge), which picks up the explosive wave from the primary explosive, amplifies it, and ensures the complete detonation of the bursting charge. The *bursting charge* or high explosive is usually T.N.T. alone or in admixture with, for example, P.E.T.N., R.D.X., or tetryl.

Projectiles designed for *armor piercing* must have heavy walls and contain an explosive so insensitive to impact that it can withstand the passage of the shell through the armor plate and not explode until the shell has penetrated it. Ammonium and guanidine picrates are the two explosives most suitable for this purpose. Special projectiles loaded with lead balls embedded in a matrix of rosin or bakelite and equipped with a time fuze causing them to explode in mid-air are known as *shrapnel*.[2] Some projectiles contain toxic gas in place of the bursting charge. In this case the special elongated and strengthened burster acts to break open the shell case and scatter the chemical casualty-producing agent.

Nitro-cellulose.[3] The explosive properties of nitrated cotton were recognized at an early date and attempts were made to adapt this material as a military propellant. These early attempts were abortive, for, because of the large amount of surface of the nitrated cotton, the combustion was far too rapid and uncontrollable for propellant use. Many lives were lost during these early experiments. The discovery of methods of

---

[1] Black powder is easy and smokeless powder difficult to ignite; therefore, black powder is frequently used to ignite smokeless powder.

[2] The original shrapnel is considered obsolete. Popular opinion now applies the name *shrapnel* to any type of high-explosive shell fragmenting in mid-air, *e.g.*, anti-aircraft shell.

[3] Although the word *nitro-cellulose* is commonly used for nitrated cellulose fiber, it should be noted that the material is not a nitro compound but a true nitrate ester. The name *cellulose nitrate* is therefore chemically more proper, but nitro-cellulose is much more widely employed in technical spheres.

colloiding the material into a dense uniform mass of resinous appearance removed this difficulty and, with the discovery of suitable stabilization methods to prolong its storage life, nitro-cellulose soon pushed black powder out of use as a military propellant.

The cellulose molecule is a highly complicated[1] one with a molecular weight that is frequently as high as 300,000. Any given sample of cellulose will contain a wide distribution of molecular weights all having the empirical formula $[C_6H_7O_2(OH)_3]_n$. There are thus three hydroxyl groups per fundamental (glucose) unit that may be esterified with nitric acid, indicating a possible nitrogen content of 14.16 per cent which

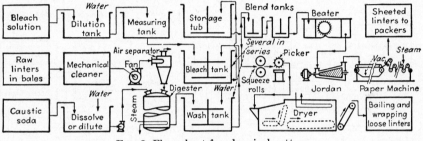

FIG. 2. Flow sheet for chemical cotton.

is higher than any commercially used product. The reaction may be formulated:

$$C_6H_7O_2(OH)_3 + 3HONO_2 + H_2SO_4 \rightarrow C_6H_7O_2(ONO_2)_3 + 3H_2O + H_2SO_4$$

Celluloses that have not been nitrated completely to the trinitrate are used for the various industrial cellulose nitrates as shown in Fig. 3. In addition to the nitrate esters, some sulfate esters are formed by the sulfuric acid which is added to tie up the water resulting from the nitration reaction and to permit the reaction to progress to the right. These sulfate esters are unstable, and their decomposition would give rise to a dangerous acid condition in the stored powder if not removed. These sulfate esters are decomposed in the poaching process. A recent proposal used cold, dilute NH_4OH solution to attain the same net effect of the poaching step.

The finished nitro-cellulose should not be allowed to become acid in use or storage as this catalyzes its further decomposition. A stabilizer is, therefore, added which reacts with any trace of nitrous, nitric, or sulfuric acid that may be released due to the decomposition of the nitro-cellulose and thus stop further decomposition. For smokeless powder diphenylamine is used (diphenylurea in Great Britain) and for celluloid, urea.

[1] *Cf.* Whitmore, "Organic Chemistry," 2d ed., p. 496, D. Van Nostrand Company, Inc., New York, 1951; Kirk and Othmer, *op. cit.*, Vol. 3, pp. 342*ff*.

The diphenylamine forms a series of innocuous compounds[1] with the evolved gases of which the following are examples:

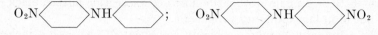

The commercial manufacture of cellulose nitrate is illustrated in Fig. 3 where the following *unit operations* (Op.) and *unit processes* (Pr.) are involved:

Cotton linters, or specially prepared wood pulp,[2] are purified by boiling in Kiers (vats) with dilute caustic solution (Pr.). See Fig. 2 for purification details.

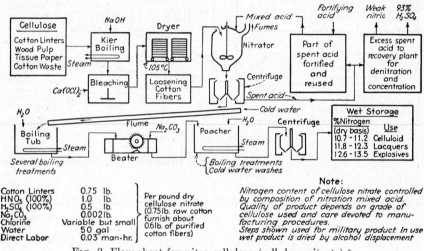

Cotton Linters	0.75 lb.	Per pound dry cellulose nitrate (0.75 lb. raw cotton furnish about 0.6 lb. of purified cotton fibers)	Note:
HNO₃ (100%)	1.0 lb.		Nitrogen content of cellulose nitrate controlled by composition of nitration mixed acid.
H₂SO₄ (100%)	0.5 lb.		Quality of product depends on grade of cellulose used and care devoted to manufacturing procedures.
Na₂CO₃	0.002 lb.		Steps shown used for military product. In use wet product is dried by alcohol displacement
Chlorine	Variable but small		
Water	50 gal		
Direct Labor	0.03 man-hr.		

FIG. 3. Flow sheet for nitro-cellulose (cellulose nitrate).[3]

Bleaching is effected with CaCl·OCl or NaOCl or Ca(OCl)₂ (Pr.).

The cotton is dried, fluffed, and weighed (Op.).

Mixed acid is made up from fortifying acid and spent acid, brought to proper temperature and run into the nitrator (Op.).

Nitration (esterification) is usually conducted under carefully controlled conditions in a "mechanical dipper" nitrator (Pr.).

32 lb. of purified and dried cotton linters form one nitrator charge. The cotton

[1] SCHROEDER, *et al.*, Chromatographic Investigations of Smokeless Powder, *Ind. Eng. Chem.*, **41**, 2818 (1949).

[2] Cotton linters are considered to be the purest form of cellulose fiber available and hence are most desirable for a starting material. Other cellulose material is nitrated, including waste cotton and specially purified sulfite pulp or paper. A pictured flow sheet for linters production is given by *Chem. & Met. Eng.*, **48** (4), 108 (1941), and a pictured flow sheet for smokeless powder by *Chem. & Met. Eng.*, **49** (4), 76, 110 (1942).

[3] For the materials of construction used in this particular flow sheet, see *Chem. Eng.*, **57** (11), 119 (1950); *cf.* ANON., Progress in Solvent Recovery, *Chem. Eng.*, **54** (1), 98 (1947) with pictured flow sheet on p. 138.

is agitated with approximately 1,500 lb. of mixed acid at 30°C. for about 25 min. The composition of the acid used averages: HNO_3, 21 per cent; H_2SO_4, 63 per cent; N_2O_4, 0.5 per cent; H_2O, 15.5 per cent.

The entire nitrator charge is dropped into a centrifugal where the spent acid is centrifuged from the nitrated cellulose (Op.).

The spent acid is partly fortified for reuse and partly sold or otherwise disposed of as by denitration and concentration of the sulfuric acid (Op. and Pr.).

The nitrated cotton is drowned with water, washed by boiling and again washed in a beater (Op.).

In order to produce a smokeless powder more stable on storage, the following purification is employed in these two steps and the poaching, to destroy unstable sulfate esters and completely to remove free acid: (1) 40 hr. of boiling with at least four changes of water, (2) pulping of fiber by means of a beater or a Jordan engine followed by

Poaching of the washed nitrated cotton by boiling first with a dilute Na_2CO_3 solution (5 lb. soda ash per ton of the cellulose nitrate) and then with many washes of boiling pure water (Pr.).

The poached nitro-cellulose is freed of most of its water by centrifugation. This usually results in a water content of approximately 28 per cent (Op.).

At this point the nitro-cellulose is usually stored until desired and the complete laboratory examination can be made (Op.).

The water content of the nitrated cotton is reduced to a low figure by alcohol percolation under pressure dehydration (Op.).

The nitrated cellulose is disintegrated, then "colloidized" by mixing with alcohol, ether, diphenylamine, and other modifying agents (Op.).

Grains are formed by extrusion through dies and these are dried and blended to form smokeless powder (Op.), see Fig. 4.

The nitro-cellulose produced in this manner contains about 12.6 per cent nitrogen and is known as *pyrocotton*. By using a stronger acid, the nitrogen content may be made as high as 13.6 per cent nitrogen. Cotton nitrated to contain 13.2 per cent nitrogen or greater is known as *guncotton*. Modern military smokeless powder contains about 13.15 per cent nitrogen and is made from a blend of pyro- and guncotton.

Smokeless powder is colloided nitro-cellulose containing about 1 per cent of diphenylamine to improve its storage life and a small amount of a plasticizer (*e.g.*, dibutyl phthalate). The manufacturing sequences are given by Fig. 4. Modifying agents such as dinitro-toluene and certain inorganic salts are sometimes added in order to reduce the flash of the gun in which the powder is used and to minimize the hygroscopicity of the powder. In the United States the colloiding is usually accomplished by pumping ethyl alcohol through the wet nitro-cellulose in a hydraulic press to remove the water (this makes a drying process unnecessary), adding ether, and macerating in a dough mixer. This combination of alcohol and ether reduces the nitro-cellulose to a pulpy mass which may be extruded into rope and cut to a definite length to give powder grains. It should be noted that neither alcohol nor ether alone will colloidize the nitro-cellulose, but the combination (1 part alcohol to 2 parts ether) is most effective, yielding a hard horny product that is very tough. The remaining solvent is removed from the grains by heating in vats under water, and the small amount of water remaining behind is removed by air drying.

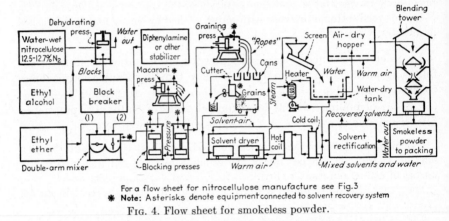

For a flow sheet for nitrocellulose manufacture see Fig.3
❋ **Note:** Asterisks denote equipment connected to solvent recovery system

FIG. 4. Flow sheet for smokeless powder.

The solvent should be removed slowly in order to avoid warping of the grains. The British form their colloided double-base powder (Cordite) by treating a high or 13 per cent nitrogen nitro-cellulose with a mixture of acetone and nitro-glycerine with some petroleum jelly. The nitro-glycerine increases the heat of burning of the powder and keeps the grains from becoming brittle.

Trinitro-toluene. In spite of other new explosives developed during the Second World War, symmetrical trinitro-toluene (T.N.T.) was still the most important military high explosive used in this country. T.N.T. also has a peacetime application as the basic raw material for phloroglucinol, an important compound in photocopying (black-on-white reproduction), and the dyeing of textiles.[1] Because of the low melting point of commercial

T.N.T. (80.3°C.) it is loaded into shells in the molten state by mechanical devices. It is superior to picric acid from the standpoint of safety by reason of its lower melting point and the fact that it has no tendency to form sensitive salts with metals.

T.N.T. is made by the nitration of toluene with mixed acids in cast-iron or steel nitrators. Before the Second World War the preferred or "indirect" method was the addition of the progressively stronger acid in three steps at progressively higher temperatures to the "oil." A great deal of difficulty was encountered especially in the tri-mix addition

---

[1] KASTENS and KAPLAN, TNT into Phloroglucinol, *Ind. Eng. Chem.*, **42**, 402 (1950), an excellent article with flow sheet and tables.

caused by heat evolution and vigorous foaming. Quite often uncontrollable temperatures necessitated the dumping of the entire mix to avoid possible fire or explosion.

The major change for reducing the time cycle and improving safety and yields was the introduction of the "direct" method, where the organic material is added to each charge of mixed acid for each of the three stages using strong downward agitation. At one time, therefore, only a small amount of nitratable material is present in relation to the nitrating acid. The thorough mixing gives nearly complete nitration in the mono- and bi-stages at the end of the "oil" additions. In the tri-stage it is still necessary to heat the material, but dangerous foaming is eliminated.[1]

The crude T.N.T. or "tri-oil" may be purified by a water and soda ash wash followed by a sellite (acidulated 16 per cent Na_2SO_3) wash. The first two serve to neutralize the excess acid and the sellite reacts preferentially with the unsymmetrical T.N.T. to produce water-soluble sodium dinitrosulfonates. During the war an ammoniated sellite purification[2] method was developed, but although it is thought to be the cheapest method, several plants still use the old method because of existing equipment. After purification the resulting slurry is filtered, rewashed, remelted, dried, and either flaked or grained. Over-all yields are excellent.

Tetryl. (2,4,6-trinitro-phenyl)-methylnitramine, $C_6H_2(NO_2)_3NCH_3NO_2$ is generally used as the base charge in blasting caps,[3] as the booster explosive in high-explosive shell, and as the sole bursting charge in certain aircraft cannon shell and antiaircraft shell. It is generally prepared by the action of mixed sulfuric and nitric acid on dimethylaniline in a multiple-stage nitration. The dimethylaniline may be first dissolved in sulfuric acid.

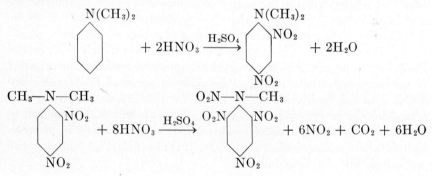

[1] *Cf.* KIRK and OTHMER, *op. cit.*, Vol. 6, p. 45 for more exact conditions of time and composition of the three nitrating acids.

[2] RAIFSNIDER, New Techniques Improve TNT Manufacture, *Chem. Inds.*, **57**, 1054 (1945).

[3] Blasting caps are small metal capsules containing sufficient explosive to ensure the detonation of dynamite. In earlier days they were loaded with mercury fulminate or fulminate-$KClO_3$ mixtures. Many are now loaded with a small charge of azide or dinol, designed to set off a larger charge of tetryl which in turn sets off the dynamite.

It may also be made by alkylating 2,4-dinitro-chloro-benzene with methylamine, then nitrating.[1] This method is calculated to be more economical of raw materials, but the extreme toxicity of the dinitro-chloro-

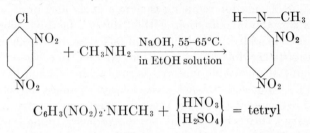

$$C_6H_3(NO_2)_2 \cdot NHCH_3 + \begin{Bmatrix} HNO_3 \\ H_2SO_4 \end{Bmatrix} = \text{tetryl}$$

benzene weighs heavily against it. Tetryl is an extremely powerful high explosive with great shattering power.

Picric Acid. Picric acid is not made directly by the nitration of phenol because too many oxidation by-products are formed. It is manufactured instead by the nitration of mixed phenol-sulfonates. The phenol-sulfonates result from heating 1 mole of phenol with $3\frac{1}{2}$ moles of 66°Bé. sulfuric acid and holding the well-mixed mass at a temperature of 80°C. for about 4 hr. The phenol-sulfonates (mixed mono and di) are then run into nitrators constructed of acidproof brick. The nitration is carried out with mixed sulfuric and nitric acids.[2] After the addition of all the acid, the temperature is held at 100°C. for at least 1 hr.

Ammonium Picrate. Ammonium picrate[3] is made by the neutralization of a hot aqueous solution of picric acid with ammonia water. It is employed for armor-piercing shell.

P.E.T.N. Pentaerythritol tetranitrate, $C(CH_2ONO_2)_4$, is the most brisant and sensitive of the bursting-charge explosives used in ammunition and is loaded as such only in detonators where small quantities are involved. For use as a booster explosive, a bursting charge, or a plastic demolition explosive, it is desensitized by admixture with T.N.T. (called Pentolite) or by addition of wax. P.E.T.N. may be made by the nitration of pentaerythritol with strong nitric acid, 94 per cent HNO_3, at about 50°C. The polyhydric alcohol is made by treating acetaldehyde with formaldehyde in the presence of lime. The lime leaves the reaction as calcium formate. Three aldol condensations occur followed by a cross-Cannizzaro reaction yielding $C(CH_2OH)_4$. It should not be confused with erythritol. The reactions follow:

[1] HILL and KLIPSTEIN, Dinitromethylaniline as an Intermediate in the Manufacture of Tetryl, *Trans. Am. Inst. Chem. Engrs.*, **42**, 527 (1946).

[2] Formerly strong nitric acid alone was used. Mixed acids cut down the health hazard caused by fuming, reduce the amount of acid required, and increase the yield of desired products. The use of mixed acid is now almost universal.

[3] GERBER, Ammonium Picrate Production for Military Explosive Requirements, *Chem. & Met. Eng.*, **51** (3), 100 (1944), flow sheet from dinitro-chloro-benzene.

$$3CH_2O + CH_3CHO \rightarrow (CH_2OH)_3CCHO \qquad (1)$$
$$(CH_2OH)_3CCHO + CH_2O + H_2O \rightarrow C(CH_2OH)_4 + HCOOH \qquad (2)$$
$$C(CH_2OH)_4 + 4HNO_3 \rightarrow C(CH_2ONO_2)_4 + 4H_2O \qquad (3)$$

It is probable that the reaction of decomposition may be expressed:

$$C(CH_2ONO_2)_4 \rightarrow 3CO_2 + 2CO + 4H_2O + 2N_2$$

Cyclonite.[1] Cyclonite or symmetrical cyclo-trimethylene-trinitramine

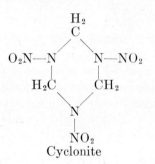

Cyclonite

mostly called R.D.X., is one of the most powerful explosives known at the present time. R.D.X. was used in a mixture with T.N.T. and aluminum known as Torpex for mines, depth charges, and torpedo war heads. It was also employed as an ingredient for explosive for shells and bombs. It is desensitized by wax or oily materials.

The British developed the first practical or Woolwich process, which involved the destructive nitration of hexamethylene-tetramine with concentrated nitric acid:

$$C_6H_{12}N_4 + 3HNO_3 \rightarrow C_3H_6O_6N_6 + 3HCHO + NH_3$$

Although this method was used in this country during the Second World War, it involved a large excess of HNO_3 and the loss of formaldehyde by HNO_3 oxidation. The McGill University process reacted formaldehyde with ammonium nitrate in the presence of a dehydrating agent:

$$3HCHO + 3NH_4NO_3 + 6(CH_3CO)_2O \rightarrow C_3H_6O_6N_6 + 12CH_3COOH$$

In order to obviate the large HNO_3 requirements of the Woolwich process and to reduce the amount of dehydrating agent in the McGill process, the combination process was developed by Bachman at the University of Michigan who utilized the by-products to get a second mole of R.D.X. This method was developed on a continuous scale by Tennessee Eastman

[1] BACHMAN, *J. Am. Chem. Soc.*, **71**, 1842 (1949).

who were able to manufacture it the most cheaply and with the least capital outlay of all.

$$C_6H_{12}N_4 + 4HNO_3 + 2NH_4NO_3 + 6(CH_3CO)_2O$$
$$\rightarrow 2C_3H_6O_6N_6 + 12CH_3COOH$$

Yields on the basis of this equation of 70 per cent are possible.

Lead Azide. $Pb\left(-N\overset{\displaystyle N}{\underset{\displaystyle N}{\diagdown\!\!\!\diagup}} \right)_2$ has almost entirely replaced mercury ful-

minate as the important initiating or primary explosive for blasting caps. The fulminate had less than desirable stability, had to be manufactured in small batches, and involved the strategic raw material, mercury. On the other hand lead azide has remarkable stability, involves no strategic materials, and can be manufactured in large batches by treating sodium azide with lead acetate or nitrate. Sodium azide may be made from sodium amide and nitrous oxide:

$$NaNH_2 + N_2O \rightarrow NaN_3 + H_2O; NaNH_2 + H_2O \rightarrow NaOH + NH_3$$
$$2NaN_3 + Pb(C_2H_3O_2)_2 \rightarrow Pb(N_3)_2 + 2Na(C_2H_3O_2)$$

Silver azide has also been used to a very limited extent.

Dinol. Diazodinitro-phenol or 4,6-dinitro-benzene-1,2-diazooxide, was the first diazo compound ever discovered (Griess, 1858). Its valuable properties as a primary explosive were not generally recognized until recent years. It is made by diazotizing picramic acid. An internal coupling yields the product desired. Although its rate of detonation and brisance (approximately equal to T.N.T.) are greater than lead azide or mercury fulminate, its density is so low that much less dinol can be loaded in a standard equipment even under pressure.

INDUSTRIAL EXPLOSIVES

For blasting purposes large quantities of *black powder* are still used. Black powder is an intimate mixture of KNO_3, charcoal, and sulfur, usually in the approximate proportions 75-15-10. For cheap blasting explosives the less desirable $NaNO_3$ is frequently substituted for KNO_3. $NaNO_3$ is less desirable because of its tendency to absorb water from the air. Thorough mixing is essential for good black powder; consequently, it is customary to work the mixed raw materials under a wheel mill, as is depicted in Fig. 5. Certain observers think that this operation colloids the sulfur and produces a more homogeneous product than would be otherwise obtainable.

Black powder is relatively undesirable for use in mines because of the persistent flame produced on explosion and the ability of this flame to ignite gas and coal-dust mixtures. The fact that considerable quantities of carbon monoxide are evolved on its explosion is also a disadvantage. It remains in use principally because of its cheapness and because of the fact that it is not shattering in its action (very desirable in coal mining). The fact that the properties of black powder can be varied over quite wide ranges by altering the composition and the granulation has also been a deterrent to its replacement by other explosives.

Black powder upon explosion liberates from each gram 718 cal. and about 270 cc. of permanent gases, but about 50 per cent of the products

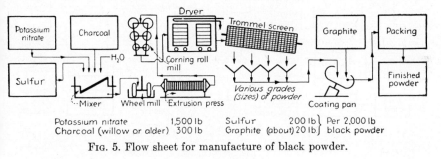

| Potassium nitrate | 1,500 lb | Sulfur | 200 lb | Per 2,000 lb |
| Charcoal (willow or alder) | 300 lb | Graphite (about) | 20 lb | black powder |

FIG. 5. Flow sheet for manufacture of black powder.

are solids. Among these products are CO_2, CO, N_2, H_2S, H_2, K_2CO_3, K_2SO_4, K_2S, and unreacted constituents.

Nitro-glycerine and Dynamite.[1] Nitro-glycerine was the first high explosive to be employed on a large scale. The nitration is effected by slowly adding glycerine of high purity (99.9+ per cent) to mixed acid having the approximate composition: H_2SO_4, 50 per cent; HNO_3, 50 per cent. The nitration is accomplished in from 60 to 90 min. in agitated nitrators equipped with cooling coils carrying brine[2] at 5°C. to maintain a temperature below 10°C. Above this temperature there is great danger that the charge will begin to react very violently, ultimately resulting in explosion. After nitration, the mixture of nitro-glycerine and spent acid is allowed to flow through a trough (a trough is easier to clean completely than a pipe) into separating and settling tanks at some distance from the nitrator. Here the nitro-glycerine, being lighter than the spent acid, rises to the top. The nitro-glycerine is carefully separated from the

---

[1] *Cf.* GROGGINS, "Unit Processes in Organic Synthesis," 4th ed., p. 644, McGraw-Hill Book Company, Inc., New York, 1952; NAOUM (Symmes, *translator*), "Nitro-glycerine and Nitroglycerine Explosives," The Williams & Wilkins Company, Baltimore, 1928.

[2] Brine can be a little cooler than 5°C. but pure nitro-glycerine freezes at 12.8°C. Freezing would be hazardous as it might interfere with the temperature control.

acid and sent to the wash tank where it is washed twice with warm water. After this, it is treated with a 1 per cent sodium carbonate solution to ensure complete removal of any remaining acid. Additional washes with warm water are continued until there remains no trace of alkalinity. After this the material is well settled and sent to storage. The sequences of the *unit operations* and the *unit processes* involved in manufacturing nitro-glycerine and dynamite are shown in Fig. 6, where also the quantities of raw material are listed.[1] The product is really glyceryl trinitrate

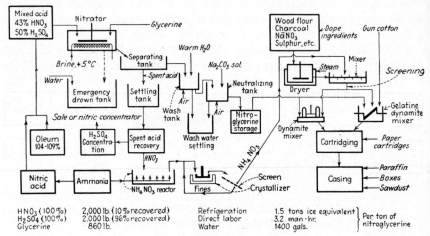

HNO$_3$ (100%)	2,000 lb. (10% recovered)	Refrigeration	1.5 tons ice equivalent	Per ton of
H$_2$SO$_4$ (100%)	2,000 lb. (96% recovered)	Direct labor	3.2 man·hr.	nitroglycerine
Glycerine	860 lb.	Water	1400 gals.	

FIG. 6. Flow sheet for nitro-glycerine and dynamites. Usually an evaporator is needed between the ammonium nitrate reactor and the crystallizer.

and the reaction falls under the (nitrate) esterification classification. The reaction may be formulated:

$$
\begin{array}{l}
CH_2OH \\
| \\
CHOH \\
| \\
CH_2OH
\end{array}
+ 3HNO_3 + (H_2SO_4) \rightarrow
\begin{array}{l}
CH_2ONO_2 \\
| \\
CHONO_2 \\
| \\
CH_2ONO_2
\end{array}
+ 3H_2O + (H_2SO_4)
$$

Nitro-glycerine is a liquid very similar in appearance to the original glycerine. It is quite sensitive to blows and freezes at 56°F.; when solid it is less sensitive. As it has a strong tendency in this state to explode only partly, frozen nitro-glycerine must always be thawed before using.

To make nitro-glycerine easier and safer to handle it is usually manufactured into dynamite. The original dynamite was made by absorbing nitro-glycerine in kieselguhr. Modern dynamites generally use wood flour, ammonium nitrate, or sodium nitrate as the agent employed to absorb the nitro-glycerine. Such a mixture is easy to handle and can be made to con-

---

[1] Further details are available in Chap. 32 of "Rogers' Manual of Industrial Chemistry," 6th ed., D. Van Nostrand Company, Inc., New York, 1942.

tain as much as 75 per cent nitro-glycerine and yet retain its solid form. Nitro-glycerine in such mixtures, however, still freezes at comparatively high temperatures, and dynamite when frozen is relatively insensitive and may not detonate completely when set off. It is quite hazardous to thaw out dynamite rapidly. Because of the demand for a nonfreezing dynamite for work in cold weather, several dynamites containing other material designed to lower the freezing point of the nitro-glycerine have been put on the market. The material most widely used to lower the freezing point of dynamite is ethylene glycol dinitrate. This material is an excellent explosive in its own right. Such nonfreezing dynamites have potentials almost as great as "straight" dynamite. Nitro-cellulose can be gelatinized by nitro-glycerine, and the resulting firm jelly is an exceptionally powerful high explosive commonly known as *gelatine dynamite*.

A wide variety of other explosives have been suggested for both commercial and military use, but most of these have been abandoned because of such properties as poor stability on storage, excessive cost of manufacture, tendency to form very sensitive materials on decomposition, and toxicity. The following materials have been important in the past or enjoy a limited use today: hexanitro-mannite, tetranitro-aniline, starch nitrate, hexanitro-diphenylamine, trinitro-benzene, etc.

D.E.G.N. Diethylene glycol dinitrate was developed by the Germans as a replacement for nitro-glycerine in double-base powders. After field testing in the Spanish Civil War, the Germans concentrated on this explosive as it appeared to be superior to nitro-glycerine. Diethylene glycol is nitrated to the dinitrate in practically the same manner as glycerine nitration (Fig. 6.).

Toxicity. Almost without exception the nitro compounds and nitric acid esters used as explosives are toxic. The degree of toxicity varies widely with the material in question, but most are capable of causing acute distress if taken orally. Some materials used in the past have been extremely toxic; hexanitro-diphenylamine, for example, is an active vesicant. Extremely toxic properties would weigh heavily against any new explosive that might be introduced.

CHEMICAL WARFARE

The field of chemical warfare is generally taken to include those substances which by their chemical action produce powerful physiological effects, screening smokes, or incendiary action. Although it is currently assumed that the employment of such chemicals began with the First World War, the fact is that incendiary and asphyxiating substances have been used over the centuries in warfare, but they only reached a really effective stage on Apr. 22, 1915, with the release by the Germans of 600,000 lb. of chlorine along a 2-mile front against an unprotected enemy.

Although vast preparations for offensive and defensive use of toxic gases were made during the Second World War by all countries, gas warfare was rejected by all for various reasons.[1] Mutual distrust and fear, however, made preparedness a matter of vital importance. In the Second World War screening smokes and incendiaries proved to be extremely valuable.

Toxic Materials. The use of the so-called *poison gases* in warfare[2] is a widely misunderstood and much maligned subject, the major cause of the misunderstanding being unreasoning fear and a lack of knowledge of the physical difficulties incident to establishing high concentrations of casualty-producing[3] agents over wide areas. The requirements which a satisfactory chemical-warfare agent must meet are so rigid that only a small group of compounds possess the necessary properties. Among the more important of these requirements are

1. Volatility should be high enough to allow ready dispersal at temperatures met in both summer and winter warfare, and the material should be readily liquefiable so that it may be loaded into shell and bombs in the liquid state.

2. Stability should be sufficient to withstand storage.

3. The chemical should not readily react with or be decomposed by water, metals, or earth.

4. The chemical should not be decomposed by the shock of explosion.

5. The chemical should be very toxic in small concentrations and should be difficult to protect against.

6. The chemical should be cheap and easy to manufacture from readily available raw materials in enormous quantities without the use of too highly specialized equipment. It is preferable that the toxic properties develop only in the last stages of manufacture.

Contrary to popular opinion, from a military standpoint, it may be undesirable to cause the death of the personnel of the enemy. Deceased personnel may be disposed of in a very short time; incapacitated personnel require the attendance of approximately four persons during the time of their hospitalization. The services of five persons are hence of no military value during this time. In casualty-producing effect the chemical agents have no peer, but they produce a very low percentage of fatalities, as shown by Fig. 7, wherein are charted the comparative disabilities and mortalities caused by gas and other weapons in various wars. The ratio of the mortality percentages shows the relative chances for

[1] For an especially interesting account of gas in the Second World War, see Chap. XVII in BAXTER, "Scientists against Time," Little, Brown & Company, Boston, 1946.

[2] KIRK and OTHMER, *op. cit.*, Vol. 7, pp. 117–145, excellent article with many references.

[3] It should be clearly understood that, in a military sense, a casualty is a disabled person, one who cannot fight. Casualties include both the wounded and the killed.

recovery of those wounded by gas or other weapons and demonstrates that a man injured by gas had a 12 to 1 better chance for recovery than one wounded by other means. A persistent rumor that aftereffects of chemical warfare (tuberculosis, etc.) cause an exceptionally high mortality rate in later years has been disproved.[1] It should never be forgotten that to apply any warfare agent effectively there is always great wastage

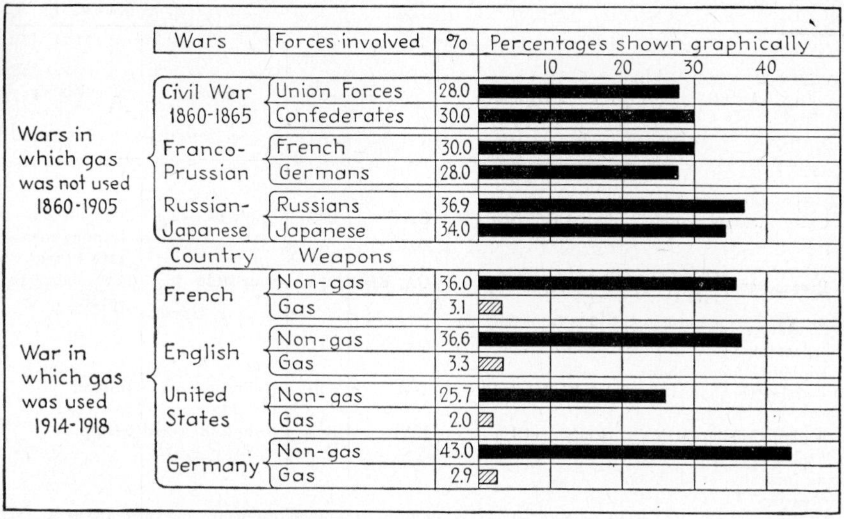

	Wars	Forces involved	%	Percentages shown graphically 10 20 30 40
Wars in which gas was not used 1860-1905	Civil War 1860-1865	Union Forces	28.0	
		Confederates	30.0	
	Franco-Prussian	French	30.0	
		Germans	28.0	
	Russian-Japanese	Russians	36.9	
		Japanese	34.0	
	Country	Weapons		
War in which gas was used 1914-1918	French	Non-gas	36.0	
		Gas	3.1	
	English	Non-gas	36.6	
		Gas	3.3	
	United States	Non-gas	25.7	
		Gas	2.0	
	Germany	Non-gas	43.0	
		Gas	2.9	

Fig. 7. Mortality from gas wounds and wounds produced by other causes in the First World War. (*From Gilchrist, World War Casualties, Chemical Warfare School Edgewood Arsenal, Md., 1928.*)

of material. For example, Kibler[2] states for the First World War, "Casualty records show that for each casualty there were required 23 mustard shells or 60 lb. of mustard, 100 high-explosive shells or 500 lb. of high explosives, or 5,000 rounds of rifle ammunition."

Based on physiological action the chemical agents may be classified as follows and as arranged in Table 3:

1. Lachrymators or tear gases, which produce temporary inability to see.
2. Sternutators,[3] which cause sneezing, nausea, and temporary physical disability.
3. Lung injurants, which, in case of severe contact, cause death from edema of the lungs.
4. Vesicants or blister-producing agents, which act mostly on the skin but also on any part of the body contacted. The effect may be very serious.

[1] KOONTZ, War Gases and Tuberculosis, *Arch. Internal Med.*, **39**, 833 (1927).
[2] From an address by A. L. Kibler, Chief of the Information Division of the Chemical Warfare Service, U.S. Army, given Sept. 11, 1940, at the American Chemical Society meeting at Detroit, Mich., before the Division of Industrial and Engineering Chemistry.
[3] JACKSON, Sternutators, *Chem. Revs.*, **17**, 251 (1935).

5. Nerve gases which are extremely toxic chemicals on nerves and are also vesicants.

The sternutators listed in Table 3 are solids at ordinary temperatures and are dispersed as fine smokes. A modern gas mask gives complete protection against the lethal effects of all of these. For protection against

TABLE 3. CHARACTERISTICS OF IMPORTANT CHEMICAL WARFARE AGENTS

Agent	Formula	Symbol	Boiling point, °C.	Odor	Persistency
Lachrymators or tear gases:					
Chloro-acetophenone....	$C_6H_5COCH_2Cl$	CN	247	Apple blossoms	Solid for days; burning mixture 10 min.
Bromo-benzyl cyanide..	$C_6H_5CHBrCN$	CA, BBC	225	Sour fruit	Few days to several weeks
Sternutators or vomiting gases:					
Diphenylamine-chloroarsine or Adamsite...	$NH(C_6H_4)_2AsCl$	DM	410[a]	Not pronounced (moldy hay)	10 min.
Diphenyl-chloro-arsine..	$(C_6H_5)_2AsCl$	DA	383	Not pronounced (shoe polish)	5–10 min.
Lung injurants or choking gases:					
Chlorine..............	Cl_2	CL	−34.6	Pungent	1–5 min.
Phosgene.............	$COCl_2$	CG	8.3	Ensilage	1–10 min.
Diphosgene...........	$ClCOOCCl_3$	DP	127	Ensilage	30 min.
Chloropicrin[b].........	CCl_3NO_2	PS	112	Fly paper	1 min. to 1 day
Vesicants or blister gases[c]:					
Mustard..............	$(ClCH_2CH_2)_2S$	H	228	Mustard	1 day to weeks
Lewisite..............	$ClCH \cdot CHAsCl_2$	L	190	Geranium	1 day to 1 week
Nitrogen mustards.....	$N(CH_2CH_2Cl)_3$	HN₃	144	Slightly fishy	Less persistent
	$CH_3N(CH_2CH_2Cl)_2$	HN₂	87	or none	than H
	$C_2H_5N(CH_2CH_2Cl)_2$	HN₁	85		
Nerve gases, diisopropyl fluorophosphate	$(iso-C_3H_7O)_2POF$	DFP	65	Practically odorless	

[a] Decomposes; melting point 195°C.

[b] Also causes vomiting and has some lachrymatory action. For more extensive and detailed tabulation of these and other war chemicals see p. 262 of PRENTISS, "Chemicals in War," McGraw-Hill Book Company, Inc., New York, 1937; SARTORI, "The War Gases," Table 13, D. Van Nostrand Company, Inc., New York, 1939.

[c] The term *gas* used by Army Chemical Corps is a very broad one as many of the substances employed are liquids or solids at ordinary temperatures but give off toxic or irritating vapors or gases.

the vesicants, however, somewhat uncomfortable ointments and protective clothing must be worn. Vesicants, therefore, have the highest nuisance value.

Mustard, bis(2-chloro-ethyl) sulfide, $(ClCH_2CH_2)_2S$, is a heavy, oily liquid which freezes at 14.4°C. It has very little odor in the pure state but the technical material smells strongly of mustard or horseradish. It is generally made by the Levinstein process which consists of bubbling dry ethylene into sulfur monochloride at approximately 35°C., some mustard from a previous batch being present in the jacketed reactor. The simplified reaction is

$$S_2Cl_2 + 2CH_2:CH_2 \rightarrow (ClCH_2CH_2)_2S + S$$

After the mustard is made, it is allowed to settle for a while to permit some of the solid impurities to settle out. The resultant oil is a light brownish material. Mustard gas can also be prepared from thiodiglycol.

The sulfur monochloride is made by passing dry chlorine gas into steel tanks containing melted sulfur, $2S + Cl_2 \rightarrow S_2Cl_2$. Once started, the reaction evolves heat and the tanks must be cooled by a water spray. During the First World War the ethylene was prepared by dehydrating ethyl alcohol, but now large amounts are available from the gas from cracking stills in the petroleum industry or by dehydrogenating ethane. Thus enormous amounts of mustard gas were made during the Second World War from these easily available raw materials.

As mustard is readily absorbed by rubber and leather, special protective clothing and ointments are required. Mustard acts in three ways: as a lachrymator in lowest effective concentration, as a lung irritant at slightly higher concentration (0.007 mg. per l.) and as a vesicant or burning agent at enhanced concentrations either as a vapor or as a liquid.

The *nitrogen mustards* are a series of chloroalkyl amines, the most active being tris(2-chloroethyl)amine: $N(C_2H_4Cl)_3$; and methyl-bis(2-chloro-ethyl)amine, $CH_3N(C_2H_4Cl)_2$. These nitrogen analogs of mustard gas are active vesicants. The nitrogen mustards[1] are prepared by the action of thionyl chloride on the appropriate ethanolamine:

$$RN(CH_2CH_2OH)_2 + 2SOCl_2 \rightarrow RN(CH_2CH_2Cl)_2 \cdot HCl + 2SO_2 + HCl$$

The *nerve gases*[2] are generally organic phosphates. Three discovered by the Germans near the close of the Second World War are

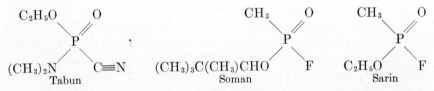

Much of the information relating to these compounds is classified for security reasons. These substances are among the most poisonous synthetical chemicals known and are concerned with the inhibition of vital enzyme activity, specifically cholinesterase which is essential to the proper

[1] For further details, see KIRK and OTHMER, *op. cit.*, Vol. 7, p. 130.

[2] HOLMSTEAD, Nerve Gas Unveiled, *Chem. Eng. News,* **31**, 4676 (1953); ANON., Physiological Effect of G-Gas, *Chem. Eng. News,* **32**, 2000 (1954); ANON., Muscle Shoals Makes G-Gas Basics, *Chem. Eng. News,* **32**, 2886 (1954).

functioning of the nervous system. Diisopropyl fluorophosphate may be regarded as a compound typical of this group. Nerve gases are nearly colorless and odorless liquids, which yield toxic vapors upon evaporation. They vary in specific gravity and are described as persistent as well as relatively nonpersistent types.

Phosgene,[1] carbonyl chloride, $COCl_2$, is made by the union of carbon monoxide and chlorine in the presence of a catalyst, usually carbon granules:

$$CO + Cl_2 \rightarrow COCl_2$$

As much heat is evolved, the reaction is usually started in a reactor which is water-cooled and completed in a similar reactor in which the temperature is allowed to rise slightly. This material is extremely toxic but its persistency is low. It reacts readily with sodium phenate or hexamethylene-tetramine which render it nonpoisonous. During peacetime phosgene is used for organic synthesis of acetyl chloride and Michler's ketone.

Adamsite, diphenylamine-chloro-arsine, is a canary-yellow crystalline solid named after Prof. Roger Adams. This agent is dispersed in the form of a smoke. It has been used during peacetime for dispelling persistent mobs. Adamsite causes acute nausea which persists for some time but leaves no ill effects. It is prepared by the reaction of diphenylamine with arsenic trichloride.

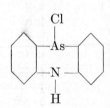

Chloro-acetophenone, phenyl-chloromethylketone is a very effective solid lachrymator (m.p. 54°C.) produced from benzene and chloro-acetyl chloride. For military use it is applied in solution with other agents. One solution is chloroacetophenone, 23.2 per cent; chloropicrin, CCl_3NO_2, 38.4 per cent; and chloroform, 38.4 per cent. It is widely used for training in chemical-warfare work and in protection against prowlers, etc.

Biological Warfare. Biological and bacteriological warfare is being studied exhaustively. This may be the *most humane* method of reducing the will of an enemy to fight without killing.

Defense. Gas masks provide only respiratory and eye protection. They consist essentially of facepieces, canisters, and carriers. It is in the canister that the poisonous gases are removed by adsorption and toxic particulates by filtration. For the latter, most modern military respirators employ filters of fibers of finely subdivided asbestos supported on porous filter paper for strength. The major constituent employed in gas masks is activated charcoal. This material possesses the faculty of adsorbing

---

[1] Editors, Phosgenation Products, Resins to Grass Killers, *Chem. Inds.*, **61**, 805 (1947).

and retaining high-molecular-weight vapors without regard to chemical structure. Low-molecular-weight gases are taken care of by impregnants (various reactants and catalysts) on the charcoal.

TABLE 4. CHARCOAL IMPREGNANTS[a]

Impregnant	Form in granule	Function
Copper...........	Cu, CuO Cu$_2$O, CuS	Reactant: Cu$_2$O + 2HCN → H$_2$O + 2CuCN CuO + COCl$_2$ → CO$_2$ + CuCl$_2$
Zinc..............	ZnO, Na$_2$ZnO$_2$	Catalyst: 2AsH$_3$ + 3O$_2$ → As$_2$O$_3$ + 3H$_2$O Reactant: ZnO + 2HCN → Zn(CN)$_2$ + H$_2$O ZnO + COCl$_2$ → ZnCl$_2$ + CO$_2$
Silver.............	Ag, Ag$_2$O	Catalyst: 2AsH$_3$ + 3O$_2$ → As$_2$O$_3$ + 3H$_2$O
Pyridine..........	C$_5$H$_5$N	Reactant: C$_5$H$_5$N + CNCl + H$_2$O → CHOCH:CHCH:CHNHCN + HCl

[a] KIRK and OTHMER, op. cit., Vol. 7, p. 141.

The activated charcoal used in gas masks is basically the same as described in Chap. 9, but it must meet various special requirements such as either chemical or gas activation. Chemical activation of carbon for military gas masks is practically confined to zinc chloride, potassium thiocyanate, and potassium sulfide. Suitable carbonaceous materials include peat and certain hardwoods. The largest production of military-respirator charcoal utilizes steam for the activating agent. Carbon dioxide has also been successfully used for gas activation. Table 4 lists the most commonly used impregnants. Formerly mixtures of soda lime coated with sodium permanganate and activated charcoal were employed for the highly volatile agents, but present practice mostly utilizes impregnated charcoal.

To protect the body from vesicants the present means of defense are special protective clothing designed to cover the entire body, special ointments, and the gas masks.

Screening Smokes. Various chemical materials have been employed to produce smokes or fogs primarily designed to conceal the movements of troops or installations from enemy observation. Smoke screens[1] are basically of two compositions: (1) dispersions of solid particles in air which correspond to a true smoke or (2) dispersions of minute liquid droplets which resemble natural fogs or mists. One of the important innovations of the Second World War was the use of smokes not dependent on water but prepared by atomization of high-boiling fractions of petroleum. Much

[1] LEVEY, Chemical Smokes and Smoke Screens, *Chem. Inds.*, **58**, 980 (1946).

of the hiding effect of all smokes is due to their ability to scatter light rays by reflection. This is more effective than to obstruct. Smokes may be dispersed by various methods, mechanical, thermal, and chemical, even to screen a whole city.

White phosphorus is loaded in the molten state directly into shells, bombs, and grenades. The material is dissipated by the force of the explosion and immediately burns to P_2O_5 which absorbs water from the air. In terms of pounds of smoke-producing agent this is the most efficient obscuring smoke. The smoke will cause coughing but is harmless. These particles also have some incendiary effect.

Hexachlorethane is employed in mixtures with finely powdered aluminum and zinc oxide, which are started by a fuse.

$$2Al + 3ZnO \rightarrow 3Zn + Al_2O_3$$
$$3Zn + C_2Cl_6 \rightarrow 3ZnCl_2 + 2C$$

The obscuring power here is less than phosphorus. The $ZnCl_2$ which is hygroscopic attracts moisture to form a fog, the finely divided Al_2O_3 deflects the light rays, and the carbon colors the cloud gray. These mixtures are used in shells, grenades, and floating smoke pots.

Sulfur trioxide-chlorosulfonic acid hydrolyzes in air thus:

$$SO_3 + H_2O \rightarrow H_2SO_4$$
$$ClSO_3H + H_2O \rightarrow H_2SO_4 + HCl$$

This liquid, used mainly by low-flying airplanes in spray tanks, was developed to replace the more costly and scarce titanium tetrachloride. The fumes are highly acid and cannot be used over defensive troops and the screening power of the smoke due to hydroscopic action is not nearly so effective as phosphorus.

Fog oils are high-boiling petroleum fractions which when heated and mixed with steam produce finely divided particles of steam and oil, resulting in a very dense white smoke. Fog oils are used in mechanical smoke generators, which are gasoline-operated portable units, capable of screening huge areas for days.

Colored smokes[1] are produced by burning a pyrotechnic mixture of fuel plus various colored organic dyes. Anthraquinone dyes are superior and are dispersed into the air where they act as aerosols of brilliant hue. They are used for signaling purposes.

Incendiaries.[2] The largest single class of supplies in chemical warfare during the Second World War and one of the vital factors in the victory were the incendiaries. Table 5 gives some statistics on this program.

Incendiaries can be divided into two classes, metallic and petroleum,

---

[1] Technical Command, Colored Signal Smokes, *Chem. Eng. News*, **22**, 1990 (1944).

[2] ANON., "The Chemical Warfare Service in World War II," pp. 65*ff.*, Reinhold Publishing Corporation, New York, 1948.

also known as the intensive and scatter types, respectively. Metallic incendiaries include those bombs with metallic cases, usually a combustible
magnesium alloy although a steel-cased bomb was used when Mg became
critically short, filled with a mixture of barium nitrate and some aluminum with four-fifths thermite to ignite the case. Thermite is a mixture
of aluminum powder and iron oxide, which, when ignited, burns fiercely
at a high temperature and *cannot be extinguished by means of water*.

$$3Fe_3O_4 + 8Al \rightarrow 4Al_2O_3 + 9Fe; \qquad \Delta H = -719,000 \text{ cal.}$$

Some readily ignitible material, such as black powder, is employed to
ignite the thermite. Sometimes white phosphorus or a small amount of
tetryl was added as a deterrent to fire fighters.

Petroleum incendiaries are gasoline bombs thickened with various ingredients. The first satisfactory thickener was rubber, but because of the

TABLE 5. EXPENDITURE OF INCENDIARIES (METALLIC AND PETROLEUM) FROM
DEC. 7, 1941, THROUGH AUG. 15, 1945[a]

Type of bomb	Filling	Dropped on Germany		Dropped on Japan	
		Number	Tonnage	Number	Tonnage
M47 (s)..........	IM	758,540	39,927	601,600	30,080
M76 (s)..........	PT	39,370	7,874	37,755	7,151
M50 (c)..........	Mg	27,620,838	67,463	9,649,928	25,171
M69 (c)..........	Napalm	....	......	8,472,880	49,700
M74 (c)..........	PT	....	......	351,000	2,317

[a] Compiled from "The Chemical Warfare Service in World War II," Reinhold Publishing Corporation, p. 74, New York, 1948. The small s denotes those bombs were
dropped singly; c denotes the bombs were dropped in clusters. As incendiary bombing
progressed, clusters of 100 and 500 lb. were developed of the quick-opening type.
Later 500-lb.-size bomb-shaped clusters which could be accurately aimed and caused
to open at predetermined heights were standardized.

critical rubber shortage, other thickeners were sought. One of these was
isobutyl methacrylate polymer which was dissolved in gasoline in combination with calcium soap. This filling was known as IM. A further
refinement was a mixture of isobutyl methacrylate and "goop" known
as pyrotechnic gell or PT. "Goop," an intermediate in one process for
the manufacture of magnesium, is a thick paste of ultrafine magnesium
particles, magnesia, magnesium carbide, and carbon. This was mixed with
naphtha and asphalt. Pyrogel is the most difficult of the gels to extin-
guish because it is mixed with white phosphorus which keeps reigniting
the gel.

Perhaps the most important thickener was *Napalm*.[1] This is a granu-

[1] FIESER, Napalm, *Ind. Eng. Chem.*, **38**, 768 (1946); ANON., How the New Napalm
Process Works, *Chem. Eng.*, **58** (11), 162 (1951); FIESER, U.S. Pat. 2606107(1952).

lar aluminum soap prepared by precipitating aluminum sulfate in excess alkali with two parts of acids from coconut oil, one part of naphthenic acid, and one part of oleic acid. The soap is capable of withstanding elevated temperatures and produces a gasoline jelly at ordinary temperatures by simple mixing. Napalm surpasses rubber gels in effectiveness and is applicable in flame throwers where rubber gels are not. It was due to Napalm that the flame thrower became such an important and formidable weapon.

Peacetime Use of Irritating Chemicals. To control mobs without resorting to firearms, the use of chemical-warfare agents is now standard practice. The desired effect is attained by making the members of any rioting group so uncomfortable that they lose their desire to fight. For this purpose is used chloro-acetophenone, CN, a powerful and instantaneous tear gas, or a mixture of this with diphenylamine-chloro-arsine (Adamsite or D.M.), a sickening gas or sternutator. The latter alone cannot be used effectively in riot work because it does not act at once, but its slightly delayed nausea is a powerful deterrent to rioting. Such lachrymators and sternutators are loaded[1] into short-range shells, grenades, or candles. They are generally dispersed by an explosion in the device with the active agent. Many war items have peacetime[2] applications, too. The flame thrower is widely used for weed and water vegetation control, chemical smokes and fogs for improved crop protection against frost, and modern gas masks for factories and mines.

PYROTECHNICS

Because many states have passed rigid antifireworks laws, the pyrotechnics industry holds at present only a fraction of its former importance. Pyrotechnic mixtures, however, still have a number of fairly spectacular uses in our modern civilization: parachute flares enable airplanes to land safely on strange terrain, marine signal rockets have been much improved by attachment to parachutes, the old red signal flare (fusee) has become almost a requirement for a modern truck as well as for trains, and many pounds of colored light mixtures are being used for military purposes (tracer bullets and Very lights).

Pyrotechnic products, in general, consist of mixtures of strong oxidizing agents, easily oxidizable materials, and various other materials to act as binders and to alter the character of the flame, together with the color-producing chemical itself. A typical composition used in the manufac-

[1] For example, the Federal Laboratories of Pittsburgh, Pa., supply a full line of equipment, for such control, available to the police.

[2] For further details see Chap. XI, By-products from the Implements of War, "The Chemical Warfare Service in World War II," Reinhold Publishing Corporation, New York, 1948.

ture of *parachute flares* contains the following materials for the purposes indicated: barium nitrate, oxidizing agent, 34 per cent; metallic magnesium, grained (to give heat) 36 per cent; aluminum powder (to give strong light) 8 per cent; sodium oxalate (to give a yellow tint) 20 per cent; calcium stearate, castor oil, and linseed oil (as binders) 2 per cent. As this formula does not fire readily, an igniter consisting of a mixture of 75 per cent black powder and 25 per cent of the above formula is always used to start the flame. The tug of the opening parachute actuates a mechanical device which starts the combustion of the formula.

Signal flares contain a pyrotechnic charge and a parachute to float the burning signal in the air. These flares are usually shot into the air from a suitable pistol, using black powder. If a colored fire is desired at the end of the flight, stars, usually chlorate compositions with certain salts added to color the flames, may be added. *Truck flares* are required in many states as warning lights in case of accidents or mechanical failures. Such slow-burning (about 1 in. per min.) mixtures packed in paper tubes are ignited by means of scratch compositions on the head. A typical mixture is the following: $Sr(NO_3)_2$, 68.3; sulfur, 13.0; wood flour, 0.5; $KClO_4$, 7.8; and sawdust, 10.4. *Tracer bullets* contain in their base a light-producing material which makes their path of flight plainly visible to the shooter. Tracer compositions are usually mixed with $Sr(NO_3)_2$ for red color.

MATCHES

The manufacture of matches is an essential industry. In this country it has become almost completely mechanized. At present, practically all matches fall within two classes: strike-anywhere matches and safety matches. Match-head compositions for *strike-anywhere matches* consist essentially of a material with a low kindling point, usually phosphorus sesquisulfide, P_4S_3, an oxidizing agent such as potassium or barium chlorate, ground glass, and glue. Although other oxidizing agents may be used, they are employed in conjunction with a chlorate and never completely replace it. The P_4S_3 has completely displaced yellow phosphorus as the igniting material; many countries even forbid the use of yellow phosphorus. Because the use of yellow phosphorus has been eliminated in matches, the terrible bone disease, phossy jaw, is now practically unknown in the industry.

Safety matches owe their ignition to the generation of heat on the striking surface of the box, the coating of which consists mainly of red phosphorus, ground glass, and glue. No phosphorus sesquisulfide is used in safety matches, but antimony sulfide is used in the heads as a flame-producing agent.

In making matches, the wood sticks are formed by forcing wooden blocks through a steel die which carries the splints so formed through the next operations. They are punched out. The sticks are first coated with paraffin, dipped in the match composition, and allowed to dry.

PROPELLANTS OF ROCKETS AND GUIDED MISSILES

These propellants[1] are related to explosives since they carry their own oxidant or other reactant necessary to cause the planned reaction to take place. The thrust of the escaping hot products of the reaction pushes the device forward under the principle that forces act equally in opposite directions. However, these highly developed and extraordinarily engineered rockets are but an extension of the skyrocket of our fireworks exhibitions.

TABLE 6. SOME ROCKETRY REACTIONS

Reaction	ΔH, cal.	Calories per gram product
Oxidation:		
$C + O_2 \rightarrow CO_2$	$-96,500$	2.2
$C + \frac{1}{2}O_2 \rightarrow CO$	$-28,900$	1.0
$H_2 + \frac{1}{2}O_2 \rightarrow H_2O$	$-57,800$	3.2
Fluorination:		
$\frac{1}{2}H_2 + \frac{1}{2}F_2 \rightarrow HF$	$-64,000$	3.2
$\frac{1}{4}N_2H_4 + \frac{1}{2}F_2 \rightarrow \frac{1}{4}N_2 + HF$	$-67,000$	2.8
Decomposition:		
$H_2O_2 \rightarrow H_2O + \frac{1}{2}O_2$	$-23,000$	0.7

The propellant may be either a liquid or solid system chosen to give the highest practical temperature together with the lowest molecular weight. These factors are the most important ones in the equation[2] defining *specific impulse* or pounds of thrust per pound weight of propellant burned per second, wherein the square root of the absolute temperature (Te) divided by square root of the average molecular weight (M) of the exhaust gases, most greatly influences the value of the specific impulse, e.g., $\sqrt{Te}/\sqrt{M}$.

However, the reaction temperature may be so high that resistant engineering materials are not available, and means must be taken to reduce the temperature. In the V-2 rocket on which Germany spent 1 billion marks in 5 years, the engine burned 123 lb. of fuel (alcohol 75 per cent; water 25 per cent) with 152 lb. of liquid oxygen per second at 215 lb. per sq. in., with the total fuel weight of 18,000 lb. consumed in about 1 min.

[1] TSCHINKEL, Propellants for Rockets, *Chem. Eng. News*, **32**, 2582 (1954), excellent article with equations and tables; KIRK and OTHMER, *op. cit.*, Vol. 11, p. 760, history and details, bibliography, detailed equations.

[2] TSCHINKEL, *op. cit.*; KIRK and OTHMER, *op. cit.*

The water lowered the exhaust velocity 3.5 per cent in comparison with pure alcohol but reduced the chamber temperature by 7 per cent, which aided design. In Table 6 are some of the heat-releasing reactions that are being used or studied in conjunction with rocketry.

Other oxidizers are HNO_3 (fuming), HNO_3 with 12 per cent oleum, N_2O_4; $NaNO_3$, NH_4NO_3; $KClO_4$, NH_4ClO_4. For fuels: hydrides, N_2H_4 gasoline, alcohols, and aniline are used. Asphalt binder with $KClO_4$, and double-base powder both carry their own oxidizer. The latter embodies the largest tonnage of a solid propellant for rockets. Jet-assisted "take-offs" (JATO) for airplanes are analogous to rocket propellants.

ATOMIC BOMBS

The destructive sensation of the Second World War was the "atomic bomb" which released tremendous energy by fission of the atom through nucleonic[1] reactions. Here matter was transformed by a chain reaction into energy according to Einstein's law: $E = mc^2$ where E is the energy from the mass, m, that disappears multiplied by the square of the velocity of light, c. Uranium 235 (see Chap. 21) and plutonium were used for these bombs which exerted initially the destructive force of 20,000 tons of T.N.T. though converting only about 0.1 per cent of the mass of U^{235} or plutonium into energy. This energy released has been much increased by recent developments.

The fission reaction is brought about through bombardment by neutrons of the nucleus of U^{235} (or of plutonium) forming about 25 different radioactive elements of smaller atomic weight together with more neutrons, heat, and radiation. If the amount of the fissionable U^{235} or plutonium is above a minimum critical mass, a chain reaction results from the action of the released neutrons—and instantaneous fission occurs. This nucleonic reaction may be expressed:

$$U^{235} + neutron \rightarrow fission\ products + energy + 2\tfrac{1}{2}\ neutrons$$

Natural occurring uranium contains 0.7 per cent U^{235}, the rest being U^{238} and a small trace of U^{234}. To sustain the chain reaction either for the bomb or in a pile to get usable energy, the U^{235} content must be raised by isotope separation (cf. Uranium, Chap. 21) because the U^{238} absorbs the emitted neutrons.

The "hydrogen" bomb is still covered by restrictions but published releases indicate that this is much more powerful than the bombs wholly dependent upon U^{235} or plutonium. It is said to resemble the synthetic reaction of the sun at very high energy levels whereupon, as in the fission

---

[1] KIRK and OTHMER, op. cit., Vol. 9, p. 515. Here under Nucleonics is a good over-all presentation of the fundamentals of nucleonic reactions, nuclear power, radiation protection, and references.

bomb, matter is converted to energy (Einstein's equation). The sun's energy is derived from the matter lost when hydrogen is converted by thermonuclear or "fusion" reactions at extremely high temperatures into helium (assumed to be through complex reactions involving carbon and nitrogen). Probably in the hydrogen bomb, the thermonuclear synthetic reaction will be detonated by a U^{235} fission reaction.

SELECTED REFERENCES

Explosives:

Davis, T. L., "Chemistry of Powder and Explosives," John Wiley & Sons, Inc., New York, 1941.

Robinson, C. S., "Explosions, Their Anatomy and Destructiveness," McGraw-Hill Book Company, Inc., New York, 1944.

Munroe, C. E. and J. E. Tiffany, Physical Testing of Explosives, *U.S. Bur. Mines Bull.* 346, 1931.

Meyer, Martin, "The Science of Explosives," Thomas Y. Crowell Company, New York, 1943. Bibliography.

"Military Explosives," *U.S. War Dept., Tech. Manual,* TM 9-2900, 1940.

Hessel, F. A., W. J. Martin, and M. S. Hessel, "Chemistry in Warfare," Hastings House, Publishers, Inc., New York, 1942.

Marshall, A., "Explosives," 3 vols., J. & A. Churchill, London, 1917, 1917, and 1932.

Beyling, C., and K. Drekopf, "Sprengstoffe and Zundmittel mit besonderer Beruck-sichtigung der Sprengarbeit unter Tage," Springer-Verlag OHG, Berlin, 1936; lithoprinted in United States by Edwards Bros., Inc., Ann Arbor, Mich., 1943. This book covers particularly the underground use of explosives in the mining industry.

Olsen, A. L., and J. W. Greene, "Laboratory Manual of Explosive Chemistry," John Wiley & Sons, Inc., New York, 1943.

Bebie, Jules, "Manual of Explosives (Pyrotechnics and Chemical Warfare Agents)" (information arranged like a dictionary), The Macmillan Company, New York, 1943.

Chemical Warfare:

Anon., "The Chemical Warfare Service in World War II," Reinhold Publishing Company, New York, 1948.

Gilchrist, H. L., "A Comparative Study of World War Casualties from Gas and Other Weapons," Chemical Warfare School, Edgewood Arsenal, Md., 1928.

"Military Chemistry & Chemical Agents," *U.S. War Dept., Tech. Manual,* TM 3-215.

Prentiss, A. M., "Chemicals in War," McGraw-Hill Book Company, Inc., New York, 1937.

———, "Civil Defense in Modern War," McGraw-Hill Book Company, Inc., New York, 1951.

Hessel, *et al.*, see Explosives.

Jacobs, M. B., "War Gases," Interscience Publishers, Inc., New York, 1942.

Fischer, G. J. B., "Incendiary Warfare," McGraw-Hill Book Company, Inc., New York, 1946.

Sartori, M., "The War Gases," D. Van Nostrand Company, Inc., New York, 1939.

Boyce, J. C., "New Weapons for Air Warfare," Little, Brown & Company, Boston, 1948.

Noyes, W. A., Jr., "Chemistry," Little, Brown & Company, Boston, 1948.

Pyrotechnics:

Reilly, J., "Explosives, Matches and Fireworks," D. Van Nostrand Company, Inc., New York, 1938.

Weingart, C. W., "Pyrotechnics," 2d ed., Chemical Publishing Company, Inc., New York, 1947.

Rockets:

Burchard, J. E., "Rockets, Guns and Targets," Little, Brown & Company, Boston, 1948.

CHAPTER 23

THE PHOTOGRAPHIC INDUSTRY

The importance of photography to our modern civilization is a fact demanding no more proof than the simple statement that vision is the most common method that man has at his disposal for receiving and conveying impressions of the world in which he exists. There is no field of human activity at the present time, whether it be industry, science, recreation, news reporting, printing, or the mere recording of family histories, which is not, in some phase or other, touched upon by the photographic process. About two-thirds of the photographs taken have some connection with the industry[1] or the health of the country.

History. The first recorded use of a lens for image formation occurred in the latter part of the sixteenth century. The effect of light on silver salts was known to the early alchemists, but it was Wedgwood, son of an English potter, at the beginning of the nineteenth century, who first successfully reproduced images, as negatives, on paper or leather impregnated with these silver salts. In 1819, Herschel discovered the fixing properties of sodium thiosulfate, thus paving the way for permanent pictorial reproductions and making possible the first exhibit, in 1839, of so-called *photographs*. The same year, the Frenchman, Daguerre, released to the public his formula for the manufacture of the familiar daguerreotype and the American, Draper, made what was probably the first photographic portrait.

The announcement of these processes created a demand for better lenses, which was soon satisfied. In 1850, Archer improved and perfected the "wet collodion" process, but in the hands of the public all the collodion processes eventually bowed to the superior gelatine dry plate discovered by Maddox. In 1889, George Eastman introduced transparent roll film and popularized the now familiar snapshot camera. Soon after this, Edison and Lumière invented practical methods for producing motion pictures.

Color-sensitized emulsions were used as early as 1904 by the Hoechst Dye Works of Germany, and the famous Wratten panchromatic plates were introduced in 1906. Velox developing-out paper was announced

---

[1] MATHEWS, Photography in Industry, *Science*, American Annual of Photography, 1950.

in America at about the same time, as the result of the discoveries of the late Dr. Leo H. Baekeland. Portrait film was introduced about 1920, and projection printing came into general use about the same time. Since the early twenties developments in all phases of the art have been fundamental and rapid, culminating with the introduction of natural

TABLE 1. VALUE OF PHOTOGRAPHIC PRODUCTS: 1947[a]
(Thousands of dollars)

Items	Totals
Motion-picture equipment, except film	$ 90,102
Cameras: 35 mm.: $1,820; 16 mm.: $5,556; 8 mm.: $14,904	
Projectors: 35 mm. standard: $4,035; sound equipment: $2,822; arc lamphouses: $1,965	
Projectors: 16 mm. sound: $17,906; 16 mm. silent: $4,133; 8 mm. $15,437	
Motion-picture projection screens: $5,599; developing and printing equipment: $1,679; parts, attachments, accessories, etc.: $14,246	
Still-picture equipment, except film	95,822
Still cameras (excluding photocopying and microfilming)	
Hand-type cameras, variable-focus, roll film, 35 mm. or under: $11,075; over 35 mm. and sheet: $11,796	
Hand-type cameras, fixed-focus, roll film, 35 mm.: $934; roll film, over 35 mm.: $15,450	
View and studio cameras: $964; photoengraving and photolithography cameras: $2,147; other still cameras: $1,940	
Photocopying equipment: $3,529	
Blueprinting, Van Dyke, and whiteprinting equipment: $5,773	
Projectors: $5,584; enlargers: $4,482	
Other still-picture equipment, etc.: $32,108	142,773
Film, total	
X-ray film: $31,525; photographic glass plates and slides: $2,479	
Sheet film and pack film: $12,596; graphic arts film: $7,234	
Other film, motion picture, black-white, color, amateur roll, still color, aerofilm, microfilm, etc.: $88,939	60,079
Photographic paper and cloth	
Blueprint type: $5,945; silver halide type: $41,575	
Van Dyke type: $814; Diazo type: $9,276	
Photographic (sensitized) paper and cloth, n.e.c.: $2,469	9,199
Prepared photographic chemicals (developers, fixers, and toners)	
Other photographic equipment and supplies (largely film base, paper base, and other raw materials)	35,832
Entire industry photographic equipment and supplies	$433,807

[a] 1947 Census of Manufactures. No details available for 1955.

color film about 1928 and practical amateur color prints in 1941. It is this latter field, color photography, that now holds the most promise for the future. The present advanced position of the photographic industry was attained as the result of thorough research on the fundamentals in this field and their application.

Statistics and Economics. The value of photographic equipment and supplies manufactured in the United States increased from 126 million dollars in 1939 to 434 million dollars in 1947 and to 638 million dollars for 1952. Table 1 gives the breakdown for the 1947 figure, which is the last year for which any details are available.

Photographic Process. *Cameras.* The essential parts of a camera include (1) a lightproof chamber, (2) a lens for forming the image, (3) a device for supporting the film or plate, (4) a shutter for controlling the quantity of light admitted, and (5) a view finder for determining the area being photographed. Two additional accessories, not absolutely necessary but extremely useful, are a focusing device and a diaphragm. All types of cameras have these parts and differ only in their degree of refinement and method of operation. They may be classified as box cameras, folding cameras, reflex cameras, plate and film-pack cameras, view and studio cameras, miniature cameras, and a group of special varieties which include stereo cameras, panoramic cameras, and recording cameras. In addition to the so-called *still* cameras, there are numerous varieties of motion-picture cameras.

Photographic Materials. A review of materials used for recording the photographic image resolves itself quite logically into three parts: (1) a discussion of the various types of film or plate for the negative image —orthochromatic, panchromatic, infrared, and color, (2) a description of the different papers for the positive image—chloride, bromide, and chloro-bromide, and (3) a brief mention of so-called *transparencies.*

All *films* and *plates* consist essentially of an emulsion on a film support of cellulose acetate or a polyester (related to Dacron fiber), or on glass. The *emulsion* is composed of a suspension of minute silver halide crystals in gelatine, suitably sensitized by the addition of certain dyes or various classes of sulfur compounds. In addition, antifogging agents, hardening agents, and an antihalation backing are also used. The back of the film is generally coated with a layer of hardened gelatine to prevent curling.

Ordinary emulsions, to which no specially sensitizing material has been added, are sensitive only to blue and ultraviolet. Orthochromatic emulsions are sensitive to the above and also to green, while panchromatic emulsions are sensitive to all colors of the visible spectrum. The latter type may be further subdivided into Type A, sensitive highly to blue and with much lower sensitivity to green and red; Type B, or orthopanchromatic with a high green and blue sensitivity and a slightly lower red sensitivity; and Type C, or hyperpanchromatic with a fairly high green sensitivity and an extremely high red sensitivity. Infrared emulsions, as their name implies, are sensitive beyond the visible spectrum and respond to wave lengths as long as 13,000 A. Many organic dyes can be used as sensitizing compounds,[1] but the sensitizers most commonly used today

[1] KORNFELD, The Action of Optical Sensitizers on the Photographic Plate, general summary with 90 references, *J. Phys. Chem.*, **42**, 795 (1938); KIRK and OTHMER,

belong to the cyanines, merocyanines, xanthenes, styryls, or the flavine series. These dyes are essentially transformers of energy, changing the light that they absorb into wave lengths that affect the photographic emulsion.

The support for most photographic papers[1] is made from high-grade sulfite pulp, prepared in both single and double weights and coated with a layer of precipitated barium sulfate in hardened gelatine to present a smooth surface for the light-sensitive emulsion.

Lantern slides that have a glass support and motion-picture film, the base of which is generally cellulose acetate, both constitute the *transparencies* of the photographic industry. Naturally these have an emulsion coating.

Development and Fixing.[2] Modern developing solutions contain mainly four functional constituents: an organic reducing agent, a preservative, an accelerator, and a restrainer. The function of the *reducing agent* is to reduce, chemically, the silver halide to metallic silver at the various points where light has produced the latent image. As this reduction is a rate process, the practical developers are those which reduce the silver halide of the latent image to silver much faster than is the reduction of the silver halide unaffected by light. Chemically they are polyhydroxy, aminohydroxy, or polyamine derivatives mostly of the aromatic series. Less than a dozen different chemicals are in common use today. These include pyrogallol or 1,2,3-trihydroxy-benzene, hydroquinone or *p*-dihydroxybenzene, Pictol, Elon or Metol or sulfate of *N*-methyl-*p*-aminophenol, glycin or Eikonogen or sodium salt of 1-amino-2-naphthol-6-sulfonate, Amidol or the mono-hydrochloride of the 2,4-diamino-phenol, Rodinol or *p*-amino-phenol and *p*-phenylene-diamine.

The *preservatives* guard the developer against aerial oxidation. The most common is sodium sulfite but the bisulfite and metabisulfite are also employed. The *accelerators* increase the alkalinity of the developing solution and hence increase the activity of most of the developing or reducing agents. They include the carbonates of sodium and potassium, sodium metaborate, and borax. In order to control the speed of the alkalized developer it is necessary to employ a *restrainer*, usually potassium bromide. Other agents added to the developing solution in a limited way include various *hardeners* (formaldehyde or chrome alum), citric

---

op. cit., Vol. 10, p. 559. This article by T. H. James with 60 references should be consulted for further information on this entire chapter.

[1] DUTTON, Types of Photographic Papers, *Am. Phot.*, **32**, 872–883 (1938); WHEELER, "Photographic Printing Processes," Chapman & Hall, Ltd., London, 1930.

[2] RABINOWITSCH, The Mechanism of Development, *J. Phys.*, **5**, 232 (1934); "The Chemistry of Photography," Mallinckrodt Chemical Works, St. Louis, 1935; O'HARA and OSTERBERG, "Practical Photographic Chemistry," American Photographic Publishing Company, New York, 1952.

acid for *clarification*, methanol as a *solvent*, and various sugars to control the *rate of diffusion* of the developer into the emulsion.

The theory[1] of the development of the photographic image is connected with the properties of the emulsion. In the emulsion there are sensitive spots where Ag_2S molecules are present (*cf.* Emulsions, page 485). When a minute amount of light energy is absorbed by these supersensitive molecules, a free atom of silver is liberated. These almost infinitesimal nuclei of silver (within the silver halide grains) constitute the latent image that is changed into the visible image by the developer depositing on these nuclei sufficient metallic silver from the silver haloids of the emulsion. In the presence of sufficient sulfite a typical developer: N-methyl-p-amino-phenol (Metol) probably reacts as follows:

$$CH_3NH-\langle\rangle-OH + 2AgBr + Na_2SO_3$$

$$SO_3Na$$
$$|$$
$$\rightarrow CH_3NH-\langle\rangle-OH + 2Ag + HBr + NaBr$$

Modern *fixing agents*[2] are of the nonhardening or acid-hardening type. Their main purpose is to render the silver image permanent by dissolving away the undeveloped silver halide. In addition, the acid-hardening baths neutralize the alkali of the occluded developer and harden the emulsion. The latter type is most commonly employed and includes a silver halide solvent (sodium or ammonium thiosulfate), an antistaining agent (acetic or citric acid), a preservative (sodium sulfite), and a hardening agent (potassium chrome alum or formaldehyde).

The photographic process may be summarized by these steps: exposure of the negative film or plate in a camera followed by development of the latent image, fixing of the image by removal of the unaffected but still sensitive silver halides, and drying of the negative. The negative is used to make a positive usually on paper, which is subjected to the same sequences of development, fixation, and drying.

Manufacture of Films, Plates, and Papers. In the making of photographic films, plates, and papers three distinct steps are carried on: (1) the preparation of the light-sensitive emulsion, (2) the manufacture of the base or support for the emulsion, and (3) the coating of the emulsion on the base. The flow sheet shown in Fig. 1 gives a general representation of the manufacturing steps involved.

---

[1] JAMES and KORNFELD, Reduction of Silver Halides and the Mechanism of Photographic Development, *Chem. Rev.*, **30**, 1–32 (1942), 153 references; MEES, "The Theory of the Photographic Process," The Macmillan Company, New York, 1942; KIRK and OTHMER, *op. cit.*, Vol. 10, pp. 565*ff.*

[2] MEES, *op. cit.*, Chap. XIII.

Emulsions. The so-called photographic *emulsion* is in reality not a true emulsion but rather a dispersion of tiny silver halide crystals in gelatine which serves as a mechanical binder, a protective colloid, and a sensitizer for the halide grains.

Many different types of silver halide emulsions are manufactured, the characteristics of each being dependent upon the silver halide used and the details of manufacture. In slow positive emulsions for photographic papers the bromide, chloride, and chloro-bromide are chosen. Chloro-bromide and pure bromide emulsions are also employed for lantern slides and other very slow plates. All fast emulsions, usually for negatives, contain silver bromide and small amounts of silver iodide. The iodide is essential for high-speed types but seldom exceeds 5 per cent. The finished emulsion generally consists of 35 to 40 per cent silver halide and 65 to 60 per cent gelatine.[1]

The manufacture[2] of the emulsion may be divided into four principal steps: precipitation, first ripening, washing, and second or afterripening. The following presentation will deal with AgBr-AgI emulsion and is further illustrated by Fig. 1.

1. *Precipitation.* The gelatine after soaking in cold water for about 20 min. is dissolved in hot water. The requisite quantities of KBr and KI are dissolved in this solution, which is then ready to receive the $AgNO_3$ solution. In the case of the ammonia process a 10 to 15 per cent excess of KBr is used and the amount of gelatine is 20 to 60 per cent of the total required in the finished emulsion. For neutral or "boiled" emulsions a 2 to 5 per cent excess of KBr is generally used and 10 to 20 per cent of the total gelatine.

In the ammonia process a silver nitrate solution is mixed with concentrated ammonia until the initial precipitate of Ag_2O redissolves. This solution is added slowly, with thorough mixing, to the halide-gelatine solution. The mixing temperature is usually about 40°C.; at 50°C. and higher, fog will appear.

For neutral emulsions no ammonia is used. A 10 per cent silver nitrate solution is added to the halide-gelatine solution at 60 to 80°C.

In this mixing operation an excess of KBr is necessary to produce large grain size and to prevent interaction of silver ions with the gelatine. The KBr solution is prepared with a relatively small part of the total gelatine, as too much of the latter would interfere with grain growth during the ripening step. Moreover, the principal part of the gelatine is protected from the harmful influence of heat and ammonia. However, care should be taken that AgBr does not settle out owing to the smaller quan-

---

[1] CARROLL, The Preparation of Photographic Emulsions, *J. Chem. Educ.*, **8**, 2341–2367 (1931).

[2] ANON., Photographic Sensitizing, *Chem. Eng.*, **60** (5), 274 (1953), pictured flow sheets.

tity of gelatine. Careful control of the mixing process is essential, as the concentrations of the solutions, the temperature, and the manner in which the $AgNO_3$ solution is added all have a pronounced effect on the character of the emulsion.

2. *First Ripening.* The ripening or digesting process is essentially a continuation of grain growth under the influence of heat, the temperature being about the same as that of the mixing step. The excess of KBr in the emulsion increases the solvent capacity for AgBr. The small crystals,

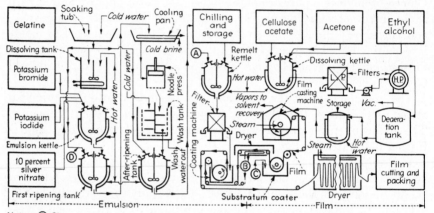

Notes: (A) Chrome alum, preservative, (phenol or thymol), saponin, KBr and sensitizing dyes added here. (B) If special papers are being coated, they enter here. (C) Gelatine and solvent used for substratum coating. (D) Gelatine added at close of ripening period

Potassium bromide	22.5 lb.	Silver nitrate	20 lb	Ethyl alcohol	90 gal.	} Per 10,000 sq. ft.
Potassium iodide	0.6 lb.	Cellulose acetate	450 lb.	Acetone	180 gal.	} of film; solvents
Gelatine	80.0 lb.	Glycerine	50 lb.			} mostly recovered

FIG. 1. Flow sheet for making photographic film and paper. Extreme cleanliness must be practiced and appropriate safety light provided after silver halide has been formed.

being more soluble than the large ones, tend to dissolve and reprecipitate upon the large crystals.[1] Since the sensitivity of the final product is dependent upon the grain size, the ripening step is an important one and warrants careful regulation. If this process is carried too far, the finished plate or film will be subject to fogging. After the first ripening, no more crystal growth takes place.

3. *Washing.* At the close of the first ripening process, the balance of the gelatine, previously soaked in water, is added slowly with thorough stirring. The emulsion is then cooled to about 10°C. to produce a firm jelly. It is important to chill the emulsion as quickly as possible, so that the ripening process is suddenly interrupted at the proper point. In order to attain maximum solidity, the emulsion may be permitted to stand overnight in refrigerated rooms, or it may be chilled in silver-plated

[1] HANSON, The Preparation of Photographic Emulsions, *Am. Phot.*, **35**, 560–566 (1941).

metal pans cooled with brine. The latter method allows the next step to proceed after 2 to 3 hr.

The cold jellied emulsion is shredded into small "noodles," 2 to 5 mm. in diameter. This is accomplished in the noodle press, where a piston operating in a silver-plated cylinder of bronze or nickel forces the jelly through a screen (see Fig. 1). The noodles are dumped into a wire basket set in a wooden or stoneware tank, where they are washed for several hours in cold running water (less than 10°C.) to remove free NH_3, KNO_3, NH_4NO_3, and excess KBr. A careful control of the washing process is essential, as a certain amount of residual KBr is highly desirable in the emulsion to inhibit fogging during development. Some hardness in the wash water is desirable, as bivalent cations inhibit swelling of the gelatine.[1] Consequently a solution of $CaSO_4$ is used frequently for the wash water.

4. *Afterripening (Chemical Sensitizing).* The emulsion noodles are freed as much as possible from mechanically adhering water by drainage. They are next melted at about 45°C. Gelatine may be added to compensate for the water carried by the swollen noodles. The noodles are digested for some time at 50°C. in the afterripening or second ripening tank as depicted in Fig. 1. No crystal growth takes place during this treatment, the chief effect of which is an increased sensitivity due to the formation of minute activated centers of Ag_2S by a reaction of the halide with sulfur-containing substances occurring in the gelatine.[2] These are allyl isothiocyanate (mustard oil) and related compounds. In the case of the ammonia process the afterripening may be omitted, since most of the Ag_2S centers are probably formed during the first ripening, presumably by the following reactions:

$$C_3H_5N\!\!=\!\!C\!\!=\!\!S + NH_3 \rightarrow C_3H_5\!\!-\!\!NH\!\!-\!\!\overset{\overset{\textstyle S}{\|}}{C}\!\!-\!\!NH_2$$

Allyl isothio-   Allyl thiocarbamide
cyanate

$$C_3H_5\!\cdot\!NH\!\cdot\!\overset{\overset{\textstyle S}{\|}}{C}\!\cdot\!NH_2 + 2NH_3 + 2AgBr \rightarrow Ag_2S + 2NH_4Br \\ + C_3H_5\!\cdot\!NH\!\cdot\!C\!\!\equiv\!\!N$$

If the afterripening process is carried too far, a decrease in sensitivity begins to occur. Emulsions containing iodide can be ripened for a longer time without fog formation than can pure bromide emulsions. For this reason a much higher sensitivity can be obtained with the former type.

Before coating the emulsion on the support, it is customary to add chrome alum or formaldehyde as a hardening agent. Phenol or thymol

[1] CARROLL, *op. cit.*

[2] HANSON, *op. cit.*

may be introduced to prevent the growth of mold or bacterial attack. The addition of KBr at this stage is an aid in the prevention of fog. The introduction of amyl alcohol or saponin serves to depress the surface tension of the liquid emulsion, facilitating uniform foam-free spreading on the support. The sensitizing dyes for orthochromatic or panchromatic films are here added to the emulsion. The warm fluid emulsion is filtered and is then ready to be coated on the support.

Preparation of the Support. The support for the photographic emulsion can be of glass, paper, or cellulose acetate or polyester film. The use of nitro-cellulose for photographic film was abandoned about 1951. Before 1888 glass was universally used. In that year George Eastman designed his first roll-film camera. Glass plates are still employed for many scientific and commercial purposes, map making, and some copying and color printing jobs. Glass has the advantages of freedom from distortion and not deteriorating with age. Glass plates are made from high-quality, thin sheet glass. Their preparation for the emulsion includes preliminary inspection and automatic cleaning by revolving brushes in a strong soda solution. They are coated with a thin substratum of gelatine containing chrome alum, dried in ovens, inspected, packed in trays, and transferred to the coating room.

The white flaky cellulose acetate for film has an acetyl content of 39.5 to 42.0 per cent. It is insoluble in chloroform but dissolves in acetone. Chloroform-soluble acetate is not strong enough for photographic film. To decrease the tendency of cellulose acetate to stretch in water and shrink after drying, substances such as triphenyl phosphate are generally added. This highly viscous solution is known as "dope." Filtration, aeration, and temperature adjustment are necessary before sending the "dope" to the film base-coating machines (Figs. 1 and 2). Each machine has a heated, rotating drum 20 ft. in diameter by 4 to 6 ft. wide. It is coated with silver. By the time the drum has made one revolution the solvents have evaporated. The film is stripped off, wound into rolls, and transferred to the cooling rooms. The solvents may be recovered by adsorption on activated carbon.

The acetate film is given a thin undercoat or substratum (the "subbing") of gelatine and chrome alum to increase the adhesiveness of the light-sensitive emulsion. The base for photographic papers is coated with gelatine containing blanc fixe (precipitated barium sulfate) to mask the cellulose impurities from the halide salts. Sometimes china clay or satin white (a coprecipitate of calcium sulfate and aluminum hydroxide) is used instead of blanc fixe.

Coating. Glass plates are coated on a traveling belt, the fluid emulsion flowing onto the glass surface. The coated glass then proceeds onto a belt or rollers which are kept wet with ice-cold water to set the emulsion. The plates are removed, dried, cut into requisite sizes, and packed.

In coating both films and papers,[1] the base moves on rollers into the coating trough containing the liquid emulsion as represented in Figs. 1 and 2. The excess emulsion draining off as the support leaves the trough produces a uniform coat. The coated base passes over a chill roll or into a cooling chamber to set the emulsion. After leaving the chill roll or

FIG. 2. Coating of film base with light-sensitive emulsion. (*Courtesy of Eastman Kodak Co.*)

chamber, the film or paper is automatically looped into festoons 5 to 20 ft. long, which are moved slowly through a drying tunnel supplied with warm, filtered air.

The finished film is spooled for use. Naturally the preparation of the emulsion and its coating onto the base must be conducted in air-conditioned rooms, illuminated only with lights for the particular emulsion being manufactured.

[1] ANON., Photographic Sensitizing, *Chem. Eng.*, **60** (5), 274 (1953), pictured flow sheet for photographic paper.

Color Photography.[1] Natural-color processes can be divided into two classes: additive and subtractive processes. In the former the colored light reflected or transmitted by each image is transferred directly to the observer's eye, independent of the other images; in the subtractive processes the light first passes through a number of the images in succession. Each image subtracts or removes certain of the light components, until the final transmitted total contains only those components necessary

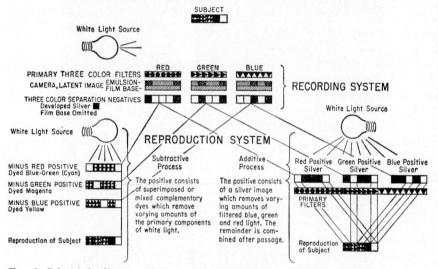

FIG. 3. Schematic diagram of three-color photography. (*Courtesy of Eastman Kodak Co.*)

to reproduce the original colors. Figure 3 presents a schematic outline of three-color photography.

The additive processes of modern importance are the mosaic-screen ones, known as Agfa color, Autochrome, Dufay color, and the Finlay process. In these processes the image plane contains tiny differential areas, each of which acts as a color filter. The sum total of light from all these areas produces, to the eye, a colored image.

In the subtractive processes, the final positive is the composite sum of the effects produced by three (or more) transparencies superimposed one upon the other on the same film. In the reversal subtractive processes (Kodachrome[2]) the color transparency is produced directly. The Ansco

---

[1] HENNEY, "Color Photography for the Amateur," McGraw-Hill Book Company, Inc., New York, 1948; HARRISON, Theory of Additive Three-color Photography, *Phot. J.*, December, 1939, p. 706; SPENCER, Colour Photography in Practice, 3d ed., Sir Isaac Pitman & Sons, Ltd., London, 1948; "Kodak Color Handbook," Eastman Kodak Co., Rochester, N.Y., 1950; EVANS, *et al.*, "Principles of Color Photography," John Wiley & Sons, Inc., New York, 1953.

[2] For detailed description of Kodachrome film and its historical development see "Encyclopaedia Britannica," Vol. 17, p. 816, 1952.

color film is also a multilayer subtractive or complementary type consisting of a "pack" of three color-sensitized emulsion layers and a filter layer coated on acetate film. The total thickness of the pack is only slightly more than that of most black-and-white negative emulsions. The layers are in the following order, top to bottom: blue-sensitive (furnishes yellow dye record); yellow filter (screens blue light from lower layers); green-sensitive (furnishes magenta dye record); red-sensitive (forms cyan dye record); base; antihalation backcoating. Note that the colors of the dye records are complementary to the subject colors. When such a negative is printed on color-positive film, a positive print results reproducing the color and range of light values of the subject.

Kodacolor (Eastman color) film and prints are similar to Ansco color, giving first a color negative from which any number of color positives can be made. In the remaining processes, separation negatives are made which must be printed by one of the color-printing processes, all of which are subtractive. These latter processes include (1) imbibition dye printing, Eastman Dye transfer and Curtis Orthotone; (2) imbibition ink printing, Bromoil Transfer; (3) tricolor pigment printing, Carbro process; and (4) metal toning, Chromatone process.

In addition, there are certain processes in which the reversal emulsion mentioned above is used for printing. These are Kodachrome prints and enlargements, which are Kodachrome emulsions on a white opaque cellulose acetate base.

Pictures in color are extensively employed by the public, especially for the 8- and 16-mm. motion-picture film. This is remarkable in view of the complexity of the manufacturing sequences for color photographs and for their processing. In these color films, the *coupler* method is used to make the dyes, whereby the reduced developer combines to form the desired color, either with constituents in each layer or brought in during the processing.

Although three-color separation negatives can be made in a standard film-pack camera by means of a specially constructed so-called *tripack*, it is much more satisfactory to employ a special single-mirror or double-mirror camera, in which three or more selectively sensitized films are exposed singly, but simultaneously, to record each its special color, the composite of which is the true color reproduction.

Photomechanical Reproduction.[1] Photography finds one of its most important modern applications in the reproduction of photographs on the printed page by means of printing inks. These processes may be classified as (1) relief printing (photoengraving), (2) intaglio printing (photo-

[1] GROESBECK, "The Process and Practice of Photoengraving," Doubleday & Company, Inc., New York, 1924; HACKLEMAN, "Commercial Engraving and Printing," Commercial Engraving Publishing Co., Indianapolis, 1924; MERTLE, et al., "Photolithography and Offset Printing," Graphic Arts Publishing Co., Chicago, 1937.

gravure, rotogravure, and metal engraving), and (3) planographic print-ing (lithography, photolithography).

In *relief* printing the raised portion of a plate receives the ink for transference to the paper. So-called *line* plates and halftone plates are used. The line plates are prepared by exposing a negative against a zinc plate coated with sensitive albumen and ammonium dichromate. The exposed zinc positive plate is coated with greasy ink and washed with warm water to remove the unexposed light-sensitive coating. Topping powder (dragon's blood) is next dusted on the remaining inked areas and burned in to form an acid-resistant layer, after which the plate is immersed in nitric acid to dissolve out the exposed areas, leaving the image in relief upon the plate, to which the ink adheres in printing.

Halftone plates are made by copying the picture on standard photo-graphic film through a halftone screen, which produces a dot pattern of different intensity and then engraving in the manner described above, using, instead of zinc, a copper plate. The halftone screen is made by ruling a series of fine straight lines on a plate of high-grade optical glass and filling the grooves with opaque pigment. The lines are ruled at an angle of 45 deg. with the vertical. Two such plates, with their lines crossing at right angles, are cemented together to produce the "screen." Fidelity of reproduction is controlled by the fineness of the screen used, the coarsest being 55 lines per inch and the finest 400 lines per inch.

With *intaglio* printing, the procedure is reversed from relief printing, the hollow regions of the plate holding the ink. In photogravure intaglio printing, a positive transparency is made and brought in contact with a sheet of dichromated gelatine and exposed to light, insolubilizing the gela-tine in the light areas of the photograph. Meanwhile, a copper plate has been coated with finely powdered resin, which is burned onto the plate. The gelatine sheet is softened in water and placed in contact with the copper plate. It is immersed in water to remove the backing and finally further washed in warm water to dissolve the gelatine that composed the dark portions of the original picture. The plate is now etched with iron perchloride, the insoluble gelatine retarding selectively the rate of etching on the various portions to which it has adhered. The resultant copper image is iron-faced by electroplating.

Rotogravure is similar to photogravure, except that a metal cylinder instead of a plate is used, and a "screen" similar to the halftone screen is employed for the gelatine image described above.

Planographic printing, or *lithography*,[1] makes use of the inability of a water-wet surface to take ink. A zinc or aluminum plate is roughened in order to make it capable of retaining water and coated with dichromated albumen. A line negative, or halftone negative prepared as described

[1] Originally lithography meant engraving on stone and printing therefrom. The employment of stone is not favored now except for small jobs.

above, is exposed in contact with the plate, after which the insolubilized image is coated with a greasy ink and the whole soaked in warm water to remove the soluble albumen. Subsequent etching with acid gum arabic renders the exposed surface repellent to ink but does not attack the metal. A water solution of gum arabic, next added, protects the bare portions of the lithographic plate, which is printed by the so-called *offset printing* process. Lithographic plates are particularly adaptable to illustrative work in color, the usual separation negatives being used in their preparation.

Blueprinting. This widely used reproductive process is dependent on the fact that ferric ions are reduced to ferrous ions in the presence of organic matter and under the influence of strong light. Paper is coated with a solution of ferric ammonium citrate and potassium ferricyanide. If a line drawing is placed over such a prepared paper, exposed to strong light, and treated with water (as both a developing and fixing agent), the blue image appears wherever the light reduced the ferric ion. The image is the insoluble blue ferrous ferricyanide, $Fe_3[Fe(CN)_6]_2$.

SELECTED REFERENCES

Mees, C. E. K., "The Theory of the Photographic Process," The Macmillan Company, New York, 1942. Comprehensive volume of 1,124 pp.

Neblette, C. B., "Photography, Its Material and Processes," 5th ed., D. Van Nostrand Company, Inc., New York, 1952.

Dunn, C. E., "Natural Color Processes," 4th ed., American Photographic Publishing Company, Boston, 1945.

Ullmann, Fritz, "Enzyklopaedie der technischen Chemie," 2 auf., Vol. 8, pp. 392–468, Urban & Schwarzenberg, Berlin and Vienna, 1928–1932.

Meidinger, W., "Handbuch der wissenschaftlichen und angewandten Photographie," Springer-Verlag OHG, Berlin, 1932.

"Encyclopaedia Britannica," 1952 ed., Vol. 17, pp. 800*ff.*

Henney, Keith, "Color Photography for the Amateur," McGraw-Hill Book Company, Inc., New York, 1948.

Quarles, G. G., "Elementary Photography," 2d ed., McGraw-Hill Book Company, Inc., New York, 1949.

Friedman, J. S., "History of Color Photography," 3d printing, American Photographic Publishing Company, Boston, 1947.

Evans, R. M., *et al.*, "Principles of Color Photography," John Wiley & Sons, Inc., New York, 1953.

Baker, T. T., "Photographic Emulsion Technique," 2d ed., American Photographic Publishing Company, Boston, 1948.

James, T. H., and G. C. Higgins, "Fundamentals of Photographic Theory," John Wiley & Sons, Inc., New York, 1948.

CHAPTER 24

PAINT, VARNISH, LACQUER, AND ALLIED INDUSTRIES

The use of organic surface-protecting coatings is of the utmost importance in preserving the country's homes, churches, buildings, and factories from the ordinary attacks of the weather. Uncoated, or as we say "unpainted," wood and steel are particularly susceptible to deterioration especially in the cities where soot and sulfur dioxide accelerate such action. The "paint-up" campaign should be supported by everyone, for it protects the capital of the nation invested in structures.

TABLE 1. VALUE OF SHIPMENTS OF PAINTS, VARNISHES, LACQUERS, AND ALLIED PRODUCTS IN THE UNITED STATES[a]
(Thousands of dollars)

	1952	1947
Paints and varnishes, total..........................	$1,377,374	$1,204,540
Oil and water paints and stains...................	613,280	570,336
Other paint products, n.e.c.......................	....	43,397
Paints not specified by kind......................	....	24,647
Varnishes, lacquers, enamels, thinners, and dopes....	681,074	566,160
Inorganic color pigments...........................	337,403	279,957
Whiting, putty, and wood fillers....................	....	29,007

[a] Annual Survey of Manufactures, 1952. Total sales for 1953 were $1,402,733,000.

Apart from their purely protective action, paints, varnishes, and lacquers, by their decorative effect, greatly increase the attractiveness and aesthetic appeal of a community of homes or the interior of a room. Here is a case where art and utility proceed hand in hand. Indeed some of the research toward obtaining longer-lasting out-of-door paint has enabled the manufacturers of artists' colors to produce more permanent colors for purely artistic purposes.

Historical. The surface-coating industry is indeed an ancient one. The origin of paints dates back to prehistoric times when the inhabitants of the earth recorded some of their activities in colors on the walls of their caves. These crude paints consisted probably of colored earths or clays suspended in water. The Egyptians, starting very early, developed the art of painting and by 1500 B.C. had a wide number and variety of colors.

Around 1000 B.C. they discovered the forerunner of our present-day varnishes, using naturally occurring resins or beeswax for their film-forming ingredient. Pliny outlined the manufacture of white lead from lead and vinegar, and it is probable that this ancient procedure resembles the old Dutch process. It is in more recent years, however, that the surface-coating industry has made its greatest strides owing to the results of scientific research and application of modern engineering.

Uses and Economics. The manufacture of paints, pigments, lacquers, and varnishes is an industry which has an annual production value of well over 1 billion dollars and whose products are of vital importance in our everyday life. Table 1 gives a comprehensive economic picture of the industry. In 1948 latex emulsion paints were developed commercially and now account for over half of the sales of interior paints with a reduction in the oil- and alkyd-based interior flat paints.

PAINTS[1]

A paint is a mixture of usually opaque solids, dispersed in a liquid medium which is used as a protective and/or decorative coating for suitable surfaces, which dries by the oxidation, polymerization, and evaporation of portions of its components, and which contains only a small proportion, if any, of resins.[2]

Constituents. The constituents of paints are outlined in Tables 2 and 3. The *pigment*, while usually an inorganic substance, may also be a pure insoluble organic dye known as a *toner* or an organic dye precipitated on an inorganic carrier such as aluminum hydroxide, barium sulfate, or clay, thus constituting a *lake*. Pigment *extenders* or *fillers* act to reduce the cost of the paint and frequently to increase the durability. The function of the pigments and the fillers is not to provide simply a colored surface pleasing for its aesthetic appeal, important as that may be. The solid particles in the paint reflect much of the destructive light rays and thus help to prolong the life of the entire paint. In general, pigments should be *opaque* to ensure good covering power and be *chemically inert* to secure stability and hence long life. The pigments now acceptable should be *nontoxic* or at least of very low toxicity to both the painter and the inhabitants. Finally the pigments must have *mixing ability* toward the film-forming constituents and be of *low cost*. Different pigments possess different covering power per pound. Table 4 evaluates some white pigments in terms of cost; however, weathering ability is not considered.

Without *film-forming materials*, the pigments would not be held onto

[1] *Cf.* the five volumes under the editorship of the late Joseph Mattiello, entitled "Protective and Decorative Coatings, Paints, Varnishes, Lacquers, and Inks," John Wiley & Sons, Inc., New York, 1941. These should be consulted by anyone wanting detailed knowledge of any phase of this field.

[2] GOLDING AND BRAGE, Lilly Varnish Company.

the surface. These paint films are formed by the "drying" of various unsaturated oils such as are listed in Table 2 and further described in Chap. 28. The drying is a chemical change representing oxidation and polymerization; it is hastened by pretreatment of the oil and by adding *driers*, predominantly heavy-metallic soaps,[1] which are oxygen carriers usually soluble in oil. These driers need be used in only small amounts (1 to 2 per cent by weight) yet about 35,000,000 lb. are manufactured annually. In *emulsion-base* paints, the film-forming materials are the various latices with or without other additions. The film formation takes place largely by coalescence of dispersed resin particles to form a strong continuous film.

As paints are mechanical mixtures, the pigments and extenders are carried or suspended in a *vehicle*. This vehicle is the film-forming oil to which other liquids are added in varying amounts not only in the factory but by the painter on the job. The *diluent* or *thinner* used for this purpose is a volatile liquid like turpentine or turpentine substitute, the latter usually being a petroleum naphtha of the approximate evaporating rate of turpentine. To reduce certain aspects of cracking in paints, *plasticizers* are being introduced into the formulas, largely by proper choice of the oils.

Proper paint formulation centers around the specific requirements in the particular application. These requirements may be listed as hiding, color, weather resistance, washability, gloss, metal anticorrosive properties and consistency as related to type of application (brushing, dipping, spraying, or roller coating). The individual requirements are met by proper choice of pigments, extenders, and vehicles by the paint formulator. Since the techniques of paint formulation are still largely empirical, it is difficult to predict the properties of a specific formulation and this means a considerable number of trials have to be run before the desired properties are obtained.

For the modern paint formulator, some authorities believe the most important concept is that of pigment volume concentration, or P.V.C. It is defined simply as

$$\text{P.V.C.} = \frac{\text{volume of pigment in paint}}{\text{volume of pigment in the paint} + \text{volume of nonvolatile vehicle constituents in the paint}}$$

The P.V.C. largely controls such factors as gloss, rheological properties, washability, and durability. The inherent oil requirements of the pigment-extender combination being used does, however, affect the P.V.C. used in a given formulation.

[1] ELLIOTT, "The Alkaline Earth and Heavy-metal Soaps," Reinhold Publishing Corporation, New York, 1946; KASTENS and HANSEN, Drier Soap Manufacture, *Ind. Eng. Chem.*, **41**, 2080 (1949).

As a consequence there is usually a range of P.V.C. for a given paint, as indicated in the following:

	P.V.C., per cent		P.V.C., per cent
Flat paints..................	50–75	Exterior house paints........	28–36
Semigloss paints..............	35–45	Metal primers..............	25–40
Gloss paints................	25–35	Wood primers..............	35–40

The P.V.C. of a given formulation serves as the guide for reformulation work using different pigment or vehicle combinations, and as such is extremely useful to the paint formulator.

Manufacturing Procedures. The various operations needed to mix paints are wholly physical. These *unit operations* are shown in proper

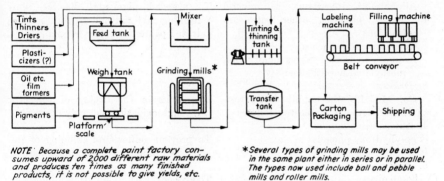

NOTE: Because a complete paint factory consumes upward of 2,000 different raw materials and produces ten times as many finished products, it is not possible to give yields, etc.

*Several types of grinding mills may be used in the same plant either in series or in parallel. The types now used include ball and pebble mills and roller mills.

Fig. 1. Flow sheet for mixing of paint.

sequence in the flow sheet[1] of Fig. 1. Chemical changes or *unit processes* are involved in the manufacture of the constituents of paints as well as in the drying of the film.

A modern paint factory may consume 2,000 raw materials and produce ten times that number of finished products, so great is the variety of surface coatings needed for public demands. The manufacturing procedures illustrated in Fig. 1 and described here are for a mass-production paint. The first operations are housed on the top floor so that, as manufacturing continues, the materials can be transferred easily and economically from floor to floor by gravity. The weighing, assembling, and mixing of the pigments and vehicles are done on the top floor. The mixer may be similar to a large dough kneader, with sigma blades.

The batch masses are conveyed to the floor below, where grinding and further mixing take place. A variety of grinding mills may be used. One of the oldest methods is grinding or dispersion between two buhrstones;

[1] A pictured flow sheet is given in *Chem. & Met. Eng.*, **46**, 157 (1939).

however, steel roller mills using as many as five rolls or ball and pebble mills are generally used now. It is very important to have correct proportions of pigments and vehicles in grinding.

This mixing and grinding of pigments in oil requires much skill and experience to secure a smooth product without too high a cost. Perry[1]

TABLE 2. PAINT CONSTITUENTS, EXCEPT FOR PIGMENTS (TABLE 3)

Ingredient	Function
1. *Film-forming materials:*	
Linseed oil, Soybean-oil	To form the protective film through oxi-
Tung oil, Dehydrated castor oil	dation and polymerization of the un-
Tall oil, Fish oils	saturated constituents of the drying oil
Oiticica oil, Perilla oil	
Casein, Latex emulsions	
Varnishes	
2. *Thinners:*	
Aliphatic hydrocarbons, as mineral	To suspend pigments, dissolve film-
spirits, naphtha, other petroleum	forming material and to thin concen-
fractions	trated paints for better handling
Turpentine, dipentenes	
Aromatic hydrocarbons, as toluol, xylol,	
methylated naphthalene	
3. *Driers:*	
Co, Mn, Pb, Zn naphthenates, resi-	To accelerate the drying of the film
nates, octoates, linoleates, tallates	through oxidation and polymerization
4. *Antiskinning agents:*	
Polyhydroxy phenols	To prevent gelling and skinning of the
	finished product before application
5. *Plasticizers*	
Some oils	To give elasticity to film, thus minimizing
	or preventing cracking

presents these unit operations in a very useful manner with pictures of various mills and tabulations of the engineering factors concerned.

The paint is transferred to the next lower floor, where it is thinned and tinted in large 600-gal. tanks, each equipped with an agitator. The liquid paint is strained into a transfer tank or the hopper of the filling machine on the floor below. To remove nondispersed pigments centrifuges are used. The paint is filled into cans, labeled, packed, and moved to storage, each step being completely automatic.[2]

[1] PERRY, *op. cit.* See following pages for the items noted: p. 1197 for physical factors in mixing with explanation of viscosity and its opposite, fluidity—as well as of plasticity and its opposite, mobility; pp. 1199–1202 for apparent viscosity or consistency with consistency curves for classification of paints; p. 1218 for mixing liquids and solids with various consistencies as measured in centipoises; p. 1206 for pony mixer; p. 1205 for mixers with stationary fingers; p. 1207 for kneaders; pp. 1145 and 1137 for roller mill; pp. 1123 and 1130 for ball and pebble mills; p. 1157 for pigment grinding.

[2] For a somewhat more detailed account of paint manufacture as well as numerous pictures of equipment, see ANON., Modern Equipment—Better Paint, *Chem. & Met.*

Paint Failure. The failure of paints to stand up under wear may be due to several causes and in each case there is a special term used to describe the failure. *Chalking* is a progressive powdering of the paint

TABLE 3. PIGMENTS AND EXTENDERS FOR SURFACE COATINGS

Ingredients		Function
1. Pigments		To protect the film by reflecting the destructive ultraviolet light, to strengthen the film and to impart an aesthetic appeal. Pigments should possess the following properties: opacity and good covering power, mixing ability with oil, chemical inertness, non- or low toxicity, reasonable cost
White hiding pigments:	*Yellow pigments:*	
White lead	Litharge	
Titanium dioxide	Ocher	
Zinc oxide	Lead or zinc chromate	
Lithopone	Hansa yellows	
Zinc sulfide	Ferrite yellows	
Basic lead sulfate	Cadmium lithopone	
Black pigments:	*Orange pigments:*	
Carbon black	Basic lead chromate	
Lampblack	Cadmium orange	
Graphite	Molybdenum orange	
Magnetite black	*Green pigments:*	
Blue pigments:	Chromium oxide	
Ultramarine	Chrome green	
Cobalt blues	Hydrated chromium oxide	
Copper phthalocyanine	Phthalocyanine green	
Iron blues	Permansa greens (phthalocyanine blue plus zinc chromate)	
Red pigments:		
Red lead		
Iron oxides	*Brown pigments:*	
Cadmium reds	Burnt sienna	
Toners and lakes	Burnt umber	
Metallics:	Vandyke brown	
Aluminum	*Metal protective pigments:*	
Zinc dust	Red lead	
Copper powder	Blue lead	
	Zinc, basic lead, and barium potassium chromates	
2. Extenders or inerts		To reduce the pigment cost, and, in many cases, to increase the covering and weathering power of pigments by complementing pigment particle size
China clay	Gypsum	
Talc	Mica	
Asbestos (short fibers)	Barytes	
Silica	Blanc fixe	
Whiting		

film from the surface inward and is caused by continued and destructive oxidation of the oil after the original drying of the paint. Very rapid

Eng., **46**, 157 (1939). For a description of modern paint equipment, see also SHEARON, *et al.*, Paint and Varnish Manufacture, *Ind. Eng. Chem.*, **41**, 1088 (1949). For a very excellent short (47 pp.) presentation of Organic Protective Coatings, see Chap. 19 under this title in LEIGHOU, edited by Warner, "Chemistry of Engineering Materials," 4th ed., McGraw-Hill Book Company, Inc., New York, 1942.

chalking is termed *erosion*. *Flaking*, sometimes called *peeling*, is due to poor attachment of the paint to the surface being covered and is usually attributed to dirt or grease on the surface or to water entering from behind the paint. *Alligatoring* is a form of peeling in which the center portion of the section starting to peel remains attached to the surface. *Checking* denotes a very fine type of surface cracking. As opposed to these methods of paint failure, normal wear is the gradual removal of paint from the surface by the elements, leaving a smooth surface behind.

TABLE 4. COMPARISON OF WHITE PIGMENTS[a]

	Refractive index	Covering power, sq. ft. per lb.	Vehicle reaction	Prices per lb., 1954
Titanium dioxide (anatase)	2.52	115	Inert	$0.225
Titanium dioxide (rutile)	2.71	163	Inert	0.245
Zinc sulfide	2.37	58	Inert	0.25
Lithopone (regular)	1.86	27	Inert	0.075
Lithopone (titanated)	1.96	44	Inert	0.10
Zinc oxide (American process)	2.03	20	Reactive	0.135
White lead	2.09	15	Reactive	0.165

[a] O'BRIEN, Titanium Pigment Industry, *Chem. Eng. Progr.*, **44**, 811 (1948); prices, *Chem. Eng. News*, June 28, 1954.

Paint Application. Much application of paint is still done by hand brushes, but dipping and spray painting are gaining favor with some because of the ease and rapidity of spread, thus saving labor though it may waste a little material. A wide variety of types of atomizers for spraying is available, including internal mixing and the more common external mixing. Spray guns are operated frequently at a pressure of 40 to 60 lb. per sq. in. Four to eight cubic feet of free air per minute are required at 40 lb. per sq. in.[1] A revolutionary development is spray painting by replacing the air pressure with an electrostatic field. A surface that is efficiently painted, varnished, or lacquered generally requires the application of a number of different coats of composition varied to suit the condition. For example, most surfaces require the use of a primer or filler coat to smooth over inequalities and to secure better adherence. This may then be covered with the paint proper in several applications.

Emulsion Paints.[2] Although water-thinned paints date back to antiquity, commercially they were not important until the development of the casein-based paints around 1925. Resin-emulsion paints have been widely used since the Second World War, but the latex or "rubber-base" paints,

[1] PERRY, *op. cit.*, 1173.

[2] Symposium, Emulsion Paints, *Ind. Eng. Chem.*, **45**, 710 (1953).

introduced commercially only in 1948, have had a *spectacular growth*. In 1953 latex paint sales amounted to 40,000,000 gal. compared with 70,000,000 gal. for oil-based paints and more than half of interior paint sales were latex-based paints. This type of paint has been developed to meet demands for greater ease of application, quick drying, low odor, easy cleaning, great durability, and absence of dirt penetration.

Latex paints have as their major film-forming constituent a synthetic resin latex, with or without other film-forming constituents added, in an oil-water emulsion type of system. The continuous phase consists of an alkali-dispersed hydrophilic colloid in water and contains two or more different phases or different types of particles suspended therein. The latex most widely employed is a butadiene-styrene copolymer type, essentially GR-S modified by raising the styrene content and lowering the odor. A typical latex paint may be manufactured as follows:[1]

1. *Protein Dispersion.* The protein (casein or unhydrolyzed soybean proteins are most commonly used) is stirred into water and mixed for 5 mins. An alkali is added (ammonia, triethanolamine, borax) and the mixture is stirred for an hour at room temperature. The protective colloids (protein) furnish body, improve brushing, stabilize the emulsion, and act as a thickener. The alkalies disperse the protein and maintain the pH (about 9.0).

2. *Pigment Dispersion.* The dispersant and ammonia are added to water in a pony mixer followed by pigments and premixed. This is ground in a ball mill. The pigments and extenders most used are water-dispersible grades of titanium dioxide, zinc sulfide, and lithopone and regular grades of barium sulfate, mica, diatomaceous silica, clay, and magnesium silicate. A combination of four or five inerts is generally employed. The usual colored pigments may be used for tinting with certain exceptions such as Prussian blue, chrome yellow, chrome green, and carbon black. The first three are sensitive to alkalies and the last tends to break the emulsion. Also sodium-free alkalies and pigments are preferred as they minimize efflorescence, caused by sodium sulfate on the paint surface.

3. *Paint Manufacture.* The protein dispersion is added to the pigment dispersion followed by the preservative solution (usually chlorinated phenols) and the antifoam (sulfonated tallow or pine oil). The latex emulsion is stirred in slowly, followed by water. The entire paint is mixed, screened, and mixed again before packaging. A typical white-paint formula by weight is: TiO_2, 270; clay, 76.8; tetrasodium pyrophosphate, 1.8; deionized H_2O, 165; 15 per cent casein solution (NH_4OH solubilized), 76.4; 15 per cent sodium pentachlorophenate solution, 17.4; pine oil, 4.2; tributyl phosphate, 13.2; and copolymer latex (45 per cent nonvolatile), 466.

[1] Partly based upon BIXLER, Viscosity Stability of Latex Paints, *Ind. Eng. Chem.*, **45**, 740 (1953).

It has been shown[1] that, in the preparation of the emulsion polymers, copolymer composition, the emulsifying system, and the particle size have a profound effect on such ultimate paint properties as adhesion, gloss, scrub resistance, chemical and mechanical stability, and viscosity. Most butadiene-styrene copolymerizations are made batchwise by charging the ingredients to a jacketed and agitated reactor heating to reaction temperature and cooling after the desired conversion. Acrylic ester polymerizations are carried out in the same manner except under reflux conditions. The pigments must be pure and dispersed compatibly with the latex. The manufacture of these paints presents an excellent example of applied colloid chemistry.

PIGMENTS

Pigments[2] (Table 3) are used very widely in surface coatings but are also employed in the ink, plastic, rubber, ceramic, paper, and linoleum industries. A large number of pigments and dyes are consumed because different products require a particular choice of material to give maximum coverage, economy, opacity, color, and durability. Twenty years ago white lead, zinc oxide, and lithopone were the principal white pigments; colored pigments consisted of Prussian blue, lead chromates, various iron oxides, and a few lake colors. Today we find among the new pigments titanium oxide in many varieties, chromium oxides and hydrates, and a host of organic colors. Table 5 exhibits recent figures on the production of pigments.

WHITE PIGMENTS

White Lead. The oldest and one of the most important of the white pigments is white lead,[3] which has the approximate formula $2PbCO_3 \cdot Pb(OH)_2$. Paints made from white lead are very easily applied and have a high covering power. They have the disadvantages of reacting with sulfur-containing gases and of becoming chalky and wearing off. These disadvantages have been largely overcome by using white lead in balanced formulations with titanium dioxide, magnesium silicate, and leaded zinc oxide.

In the *Dutch process*[4] of manufacture (Fig. 2), lead is melted and cast in the form of 6-in. perforated disks or "buckles," which are placed on a shelf in small earthenware pots containing 3 per cent acetic acid (vine-

---

[1] NAIDUS, Emulsion Polymers for Paints, *Ind. Eng. Chem.*, **45**, 712 (1953).

[2] MATTIELLO, *op. cit.*, Vol. 2, 1942, gives a very full account of pigments in all phases, with full references to the literature. See this reference for further data on any individual pigment.

[3] *Ibid.*, p. 337.

[4] Pictured flow chart, *Chem. & Met. Eng.*, **50** (3), 130 (1943).

gar strength) in reservoirs underneath and not in contact with the lead buckles. The pots are then stacked in tiers, covered with boards, and arranged 10 tiers high. Spent tanbark is placed all around the pots and the rooms are closed off. During a period of about 100 days, the acetic

TABLE 5. PRODUCTION OR SHIPMENT OF SELECTED PIGMENTS IN THE UNITED STATES, 1951, 1953[a]

	Tons	
	1953	1951
White opaque pigments:		
White lead.................................	26,217	35,415
Zinc oxide pigments:		
Lead-free ZnO..............................	148,627	147,716
Leaded ZnO................................	39,712	44,341
Titanium dioxide (100 per cent)...................	314,442[b]	319,139
Lithopone..................................	52,439	102,837
White extender pigments:		
Barium carbonate, precipitate....................	74,122	60,181
Barium sulfate..............................	14,390	14,237
Color pigments (except lakes and toners):		
Chrome colors:		
Chrome green..............................	7,147	7,766
Chromium oxide green........................	9,688	11,599
Chrome yellow and orange.....................	25,518	31,046
Molybdate chrome orange......................	4,138	4,021
Zinc yellow[c]..............................	6,909	8,143
Iron oxide pigments (sales).......................	108,350	126,432
Lead oxide pigments:		
Red lead..................................	31,333	35,352
Litharge..................................	154,518	154,753

[a] Chemical Statistics Handbook, Manufacturing Chemists' Association, Washington, 1955.
[b] 1952.
[c] Zinc chromate.

acid vapors, moisture, and the carbon dioxide gas from the warm fermenting tanbark act on the lead to give the flaky white lead or basic lead carbonate. This is broken away from any unreacted lead, ground, floated in water, and dried to give the product which contains about 70 per cent carbonate and 30 per cent hydroxide.

In the *Carter*[1] or "*quick*" *process* (Fig. 2), the melted lead is atomized by spraying from nozzles by means of air or superheated steam. This finely divided lead is periodically treated or "corroded" with a spray of

[1] U.S. Pat. 2250756 (1941); *Chem. & Met. Eng.*, **50** (3), 130 (1943), pictured flow chart.

acetic acid, purified carbon dioxide gas from coke, and air in a large slowly revolving wooden cylinder to give the white lead after some 5 to 12 days. This material is whiter, finer, and more uniform than the old Dutch lead.

The reactions for the old Dutch and the Carter processes are as follows:

$$Pb + \tfrac{1}{2} O_2 \rightarrow PbO$$
$$PbO + 2CH_3COOH \rightarrow Pb(C_2H_3O_2)_2 + H_2O$$
$$Pb(C_2H_3O_2)_2 + 2PbO + 2H_2O \rightarrow Pb(C_2H_3O_2)_2 \cdot 2Pb(OH)_2$$
$$3[Pb(C_2H_3O_2)_2 \cdot 2Pb(OH)_2] + 4CO_2 \rightarrow$$
$$2[2PbCO_3 \cdot Pb(OH)_2] + 3Pb(C_2H_3O_2)_2 + 4H_2O$$

A third method of manufacture is the *electrolytic process* wherein the reaction is carried out by means of a concrete electrolytic diaphragm cell

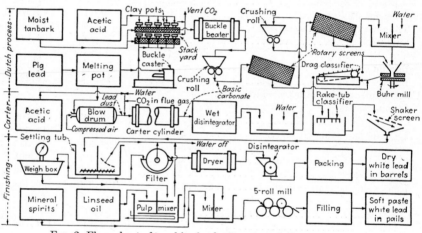

Fig. 2. Flow charts for white lead—Dutch and Carter processes.

made up of lead plates as anodes, suspended in a sodium acetate solution (containing a trace of sodium carbonate), and iron plates as cathodes, suspended in a sodium carbonate solution. The two divisions of the cell are separated by a fabric diaphragm. Upon the application of current, the lead anodes dissolve as lead acetate which almost immediately precipitates as the basic lead carbonate upon meeting carbonate and hydroxide ions migrating toward the anode from the cathode compartment. The white lead is carried out of the cell with the anolyte and is settled, filtered, washed, and dried to give the final product. As the carbonate ions in the catholyte diffuse through the diaphragm and are precipitated, circulation of the catholyte through a carbonating tower is necessary.

Sublimed White Lead (Basic Sulfate). A pigment closely related to ordinary white lead is sublimed white lead or *basic sulfate* as it is sometimes called. It is made by the sublimation of galena ores which are essentially lead sulfide, PbS, together with a small amount of zinc sulfide. The product, mainly basic lead sulfate with a small percentage of zinc oxide, is much more resistant to the action of sulfur than ordinary white lead. The composition is approximately 75 per cent $PbSO_4$, 20 per cent PbO, and 5 per cent ZnO. Basic lead sulfate is used in the form of leaded zinc oxides which are cheap.

Zinc Oxide. Another important white pigment is zinc oxide,[1] ZnO, which has been in use for over a century. Zinc oxide has a higher opacity or covering power than most grades of white lead. It is the truest white that can be obtained and its color is unaffected by gases in the atmosphere. Zinc oxide prevents premature chalking through the formation of zinc soaps and through its high opacity toward ultraviolet rays. Zinc oxide also reacts with the linseed oil to harden the film.[2] The methods employed to produce this pigment are the American or Wetherill process, the older French process, and the electrothermal process. The three processes may be broken down into the following sequences of *unit operations* (Op.) and *unit processes* (Pr.):

American Process	French Process	Electrothermal Process
Reducing of ZnO by CO and C (Pr.)	Vaporization of zinc (Op.)	Roasting to ZnO (Pr.)
Vaporization of zinc (Op.)	Oxidation to ZnO (Pr.)	Sintering (Pr. and Op.)
Oxidation to ZnO (Pr.)	Separating and collecting (Op.)	Sizing (Op.)
Settling, separating, and collecting (Op.)	Revolatilization of coarse oxide (Op.)	Preheating and electrothermal volatilizing of Zn (Pr. and Op.)
Bolting, packing (Op.)	Bolting, packing (Op.)	Oxidizing to ZnO (Pr.)
		Separating and collecting (Op.)
		Bolting, packing (Op.)

The *American* or *Wetherill process*, used where whiteness is not an important factor, produces the zinc oxide directly from the ore, franklinite, which is a zinc oxide with oxides of iron and manganese. This ore is mixed with coal and delivered to a specially designed furnace. Here carbon and carbon monoxide reduce the zinc oxide of the ore to metallic zinc which is vaporized and reoxidized to ZnO upon contact with the air from the furnace, as shown in Fig. 3. The product is collected, the coarse in cyclones and the fines in bag filters. The larger particles are returned to the process. The residue from the furnace contains manganese and iron from the original franklinite, as well as carbon from the coal, and is sometimes used to make spiegeleisen, a manganese alloy. Through the addition of

[1] MATTIELLO, *op. cit.*, Vol. 2, p. 369; NELSON, Zinc Oxide, *Chem. Inds.*, **47**, 508 (1940); see Chap. 25 by SWARD in "Rogers' Manual of Industrial Chemistry," 6th ed., D. Van Nostrand Company, Inc., New York, 1942.

[2] JOACHIM, "Applied Paint and Varnish Chemistry," Vol. I, American Paint Journal Co., St. Louis, Mo., 1934.

galena, PbS, during the process, a content of lead sulfate can be secured, producing the so-called *leaded* zinc oxides, containing up to 35 per cent lead sulfate. This product would have the analysis[1]: ZnO, 65 per cent; PbO, 9 per cent; PbSO$_4$, 26 per cent.

The *French process*, as may be seen from the accompanying flow sheet (Fig. 3), consists in vaporizing zinc (spelter) in a retort with indirect heat and carbon monoxide gas, and then oxidizing both the zinc vapor and the carbon monoxide by meeting a current of preheated air in a combustion chamber. The reducing gas, CO, aids in the volatilization of the zinc. When it burns, it forms carbon dioxide simultaneously with the change

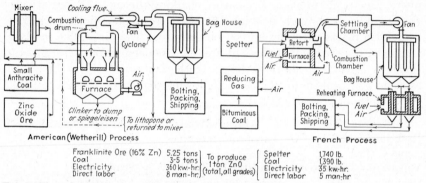

Franklinite Ore (16% Zn)	5.25 tons		Spelter	1,740 lb.
Coal	3–5 tons	To produce	Coal	1,390 lb.
Electricity	360 kw-hr.	1 ton ZnO	Electricity	35 kw-hr.
Direct labor	8 man-hr.	(total, all grades)	Direct labor	5 man-hr

American (Wetherill) Process   French Process

FIG. 3. Flow sheets for zinc oxide by the American (Wetherill) and French processes.

of zinc vapor to zinc oxide. Under these conditions the lead that frequently accompanies the zinc forms white lead. Otherwise yellow PbO would be produced and cause the zinc oxide to possess a yellowish tinge. The larger particles of the oxide are removed in a settling chamber, while the fines are collected in bag filters. After revolatilizing the coarse oxide in the reheat furnace, both products are ready for bolting, packaging, and shipping.

The *electrothermal process*,[2] a modification of the American process, uses sphalerite, a zinc sulfide ore, and produces sulfuric acid as a by-product (Fig. 4). The concentrated ore is first roasted and the sulfur content reduced from 32 to about 1 per cent, sulfur dioxide gas produced being sent to the acid plant. The product from the roaster is mixed with coke, fluxes, and various residues from previous runs and is then fed to a sintering machine. Here the material reaches temperatures as high as 1600°C., following which it is crushed and screened. Carefully sized coke is mixed in and the mass sent through a gas-fired preheater into the electric resistance furnace. These furnaces are around 36 ft. high and 57 in. in internal

---

[1] EIDE and DEPEW, Leaded Zinc Oxide, *Drugs, Oils & Paints*, **54**, 119 (1939).

[2] For a description of this process complete with pictures, see *Chem. & Met. Eng.*, **48** (2), 142 (1941); NAJARIAN, *et al.*, The Josephtown Electro-thermic Zinc Smelter, *Mining & Met.*, **28**, 398 (1947).

diameter and hold 55 tons. Electrodes are inserted in the charge, the charge acting as the resistance and the temperature rising to 1200°C. The gases leaving the furnaces are zinc vapor and carbon monoxide which are oxidized by the air entering at several points up the side of the furnace exit. The product is collected, screened, packed, and shipped.

Lithopone. Lithopone, as originally prepared in 1874, had an incorrect particle size and possessed a tendency to turn temporarily gray on exposure to sunlight. However, it was discovered in 1880 that heating the

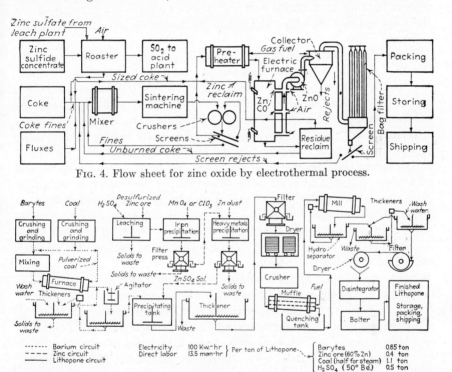

Fig. 4. Flow sheet for zinc oxide by electrothermal process.

Fig. 5. Flow sheet for lithopone.

product to a red heat and plunging it into water remedied the physical defect. This original light-sensitiveness has been overcome by raw-material purification and by such addition agents as polythionates and cobalt sulfate. Lithopone is a brilliantly white, extremely fine, cheap white pigment. It is particularly well adapted to interior coatings.

The manufacture is shown diagrammatically in Fig. 5, where the barium, zinc, and lithopone circuits are represented by different types of lines. The barium sulfide solution is prepared by reducing barite ore, BaSO₄, with carbon and leaching the resulting mass. The equation is

$$BaSO_4 + 4C \rightarrow BaS + 4CO$$

Scrap zinc or concentrated zinc ores are dissolved in sulfuric acid and the solution purified as shown in Fig. 5. The two solutions are reacted and a heavy mixed precipitate results which is 28 to 30 per cent zinc sulfide and 72 to 70 per cent barium sulfate.

$$ZnSO_4 + BaS \rightarrow ZnS + BaSO_4$$

This precipitate is not suitable for a pigment until it is filtered, dried, crushed, heated to a high temperature, and quenched in cold water. This second heating in a muffle furnace at 725°C. produces crystals of the right optical size. Subsequent treatments, as indicated, give the finished product.

Some of the variations of the original lithopone are calcium lithopone in which calcium sulfide replaces the barium sulfide in the precipitation; high-strength lithopone which contains from 50 to 60 per cent zinc sulfide due to the addition of zinc chloride to the sulfate solution; and titanated lithopone which has about 15 per cent titanium dioxide added.

Titanium Dioxide. The most recently introduced and the largest seller of white pigments is titanium dioxide[1] because of its low cost per unit of hiding power. It is marketed in the rutile and anatase crystal forms and as a coprecipitated mixture with either 70 per cent calcium sulfate or 75 per cent barium sulfate. Titanium dioxide is widely employed in exterior paints and also for enamels and lacquers. A typical exterior white paint may contain 15 per cent TiO_2, 25 per cent ZnO, 50 per cent white lead, and 10 per cent extender. Such a formulation has long life through controlled chalking (self-cleaning), and presents a good surface for subsequent repaintings. Approximately 75 per cent of the TiO_2 consumed is in paints, varnishes, and lacquers, while the second important consumer (about 10 per cent) is the paper industry. Other large users of this pigment are the rubber, linoleum, leather, and textile industries. The excellent hiding power of TiO_2 is ascribed to its high index of refraction (2.52 for anatase, 2.71 for rutile) with relation to that of the film-forming oil. Although the more recently developed, more stable rutile form has less chalking tendencies and greater hiding power, it has a yellowish cast which limits its use in certain items.

Domestic ore deposits are worked, but the best grade is imported chiefly from India. Recently the largest deposits in the world were discovered in Quebec and electric smelting furnaces are in operation at Sorel, Quebec, yielding a high-grade melting steel and a titanium-rich slag with low iron content.

The flow sheet depicted in Fig. 6 may be broken down into the following coordinated series of *unit operations* and *unit processes:*

---

[1] MATTIELLO, *op. cit.*, Vol. 2, p. 389; O'BRIEN, Titanium Pigment Industry, *Chem. Eng. Progr.*, **44**, 809 (1948); BURKSDALE, "Titanium—Its Occurrence, Chemistry and Technology," The Ronald Press Company, New York, 1949.

The ground ilmenite ore is digested hot in large conical concrete or heavy steel tanks with 66°Bé.H₂SO₄. The mixture is agitated and steam heated to 110°C. The reaction is exothermic, the heat evaporating the water (Pr. and Op.).

The solid reaction mass is dissolved in water giving a solution of the soluble titanium, ferrous and ferric sulfates (Op.).

The ferric sulfate is reduced by scrap iron (Pr.).

The solution is clarified in thickeners (Op.).

Fifty per cent of the iron is removed from the solution as crystallized ferrous sulfate by cooling, crystallization, and centrifugation (Op.).

A second clarification removes the last traces of residues (Op.).

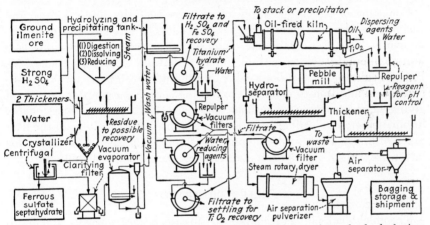

Fig. 6. Flow sheet for titanium dioxide: for reducing, add scrap iron; for hydrolyzing, add seeds of anatase or rutile and water (small amount).

The solution is concentrated in a continuous lead-lined evaporator to equivalent of about 200 grams TiO₂ (Op.) as soluble sulfate.

This strong acid-soluble titanyl sulfate (*probable TiOSO₄*) is hydrolyzed. The hydrolysis reaction is dependent upon many factors, *i.e.*, the quantity and quality of seed (*colloidal suspension TiO₂*), concentration, rate of heating, and pH. Using anatase seeds, 6 hr. of boiling are practiced, while with rutile seeds, 3 hr. are needed (Pr.).

The *precipitate* is vacuum filtered, repulped, and refiltered (Op.). This operation removes the rest of the iron sulfate.

The filter cake is repulped, treated with a conditioning agent, and calcined to TiO₂ for 24 hr. For anatase production, 0.75 per cent K₂CO₃ (based on TiO₂ equivalent pulp content) is used as a conditioning agent (nonfritting) and to develop highest tinting strength and good color. In rutile production certain carbonates such as Na, K, and Li may be used as well as Zn and Mg carbonates to promote rutilization (Pr.).

The hot TiO₂ is pulverized, quenched in water (dispersed), wet ground, hydro-separated, thickened, filtered, dried, and reground (Op.).

In case it is desired to make a pigment containing an extender like barium sulfate or calcium sulfate, the exact amount of a solution of either barium or calcium chloride is added to the hydrolyzing tank. Barium sulfate or calcium sulfate precipitates at once and, in the course of the several hours of the hot hydrolysis, the titanium hydrate precipitates onto the carrier.[1]

Barium Sulfate. Barium sulfate is occasionally used as a pigment because of its great stability. It has, however, very poor covering power. On the other hand, it is widely employed as a filler in rubber, or as a coating material on certain fine papers. It is opaque to X rays and consequently finds application in the form of the so-called *barium meal* for X-ray visualization of the intestinal tract.

For some of its cruder applications it is made by fine grinding and washing of the ore, barite. A better product results by precipitation, known as *blanc fixe*. Blanc fixe made by precipitation[2] of a soluble barium compound, such as barium sulfide or barium chloride, by a sulfate. Barium sulfate, when intended for internal administration for X-ray diagnosis, in addition to being in the form of a very fine powder capable of giving good aqueous suspensions, must also be free from objectionable impurities such as lead, arsenic, sulfide, soluble barium salts, and the like. Since ordinary blanc fixe of commerce is not of a purity suitable for this latter use, this X-ray barium sulfate must be especially manufactured.

BLACK PIGMENTS

The chief black pigments employed are *carbon black, graphite*, and *lampblack*. Their manufacture is discussed under Industrial Carbon, Chap. 9. They retard the oxidation of linseed oil and cause a slow-drying film which under many conditions prolongs the life of paint. Carbon and graphite pigments should not be used in direct contact with iron and steel in primer coatings, for example, as they stimulate metal corrosion. Black dyes are also used as coloring agents; for example, spirit-soluble nigrosine finds extensive use in the formulation of black lacquers.

BLUE PIGMENTS

The most widely used blue pigment today is synthetic *ultramarine blue*. Formerly this was available only to artists as powdered *lapis lazuli*, an expensive mineral. Ultramarine is a complex sodium aluminum silicate and sulfide, made by heating together sodium carbonate, kaolin, charcoal, quartz, sulfur, sodium sulfate, and resin. It is absolutely essential that iron be absent in all the raw materials, as it appreciably dulls the color. The melt is cooled, ground, washed free of water-soluble salts, and

---

[1] BARTON, U.S. Pat. 1236655, 1155462(1914).

[2] FARR, U.S. Pat. 1752244 (1930); SHREVE, *et al.*, U.S. Pat. 2030659(1936); SHREVE and PRITCHARD, New Method for Barium Chloride, *Ind. Eng. Chem.*, **27**, 1488 (1935).

heated with more sulfur at 500°C. until a blue color develops. A darker blue may be produced by substituting sodium sulfate for sodium carbonate. These pigments are stable to light and alkali but are affected by acids owing to the liberation of hydrogen sulfide. Ultramarine because of its sulfide composition should not be employed on iron or mixed with lead pigments. Ultramarine is widely used as bluing in laundering to neutralize the yellowish tone in cotton and linen fabrics. It is also applied for whitening paper and other products.

Cobalt blues are very expensive and not used in paints for ordinary purposes. One is a compound oxide of cobalt (30 to 35 per cent Co_3O_4) and alumina (70 to 65 per cent Al_2O_3); another is a powdered glass colored by cobalt oxide. Another product, erroneously called cobalt blue, is made by the reaction of ammonium chloride on ultramarine at 200°C. The substitution of potash salts for sodium salts in the making of ultramarine gives a blue color somewhat analogous to cobalt. A newcomer in this field with a real future, particularly as a pigment in printing inks, is *copper phthalocyanine*, which is described in Chap. 38.

The various ferric ferrocyanide blues[1] are known as Prussian blue, Chinese blue, milori blue, bronze blue, Antwerp blue, and Turnbull's blue. As these names have lost much of their original differentiation, the more general term of *iron blues* is preferred. These are made in essentially the same manner by the precipitation of ferrous sulfate solutions (sometimes in the presence of ammonium sulfate) with sodium ferrocyanide giving a white ferrous ferrocyanide which is then oxidized to ferric ferrocyanide, $Fe_4[Fe(CN)_6]_3$, or to $Fe(NH_4)[Fe(CN)_6]$ by different reagents such as potassium chlorate, bleaching powder, and potassium dichromate. The pigment is washed and allowed to settle since filtration is extremely difficult because of its colloidal nature. The coloring power of Prussian blue is very great; this pigment is also permanent to light and air. It is decomposed by whiting and basic pigments such as white lead, ferric hydroxide being formed.

RED PIGMENTS

Red lead, Pb_3O_4, has a brilliant red-orange color, is quite resistant to light, and finds extensive use as a priming coat for structural steel, particularly as it possesses corrosion-inhibition properties against iron and steel. The red lead, or minium, is manufactured by oxidizing lead to litharge, PbO, in air, and further oxidizing the litharge to the red lead by heating to around 700°F.

Ferric oxide, Fe_2O_3, is another red pigment that is employed in paints and primers as well as in rubber formulation. It is made by heating the

[1] Callaham, Modernizing Chemical Color Manufacture, *Chem. & Met. Eng.*, **50** (6), 106 (1943), flow charts.

iron sulfate obtained from the pickling vats of steel mills. *Venetian red* is a mixture of ferric oxide with up to an equal amount of the pigment extender, calcium sulfate. This pigment is manufactured by heating ferrous sulfate with quicklime in a furnace. Venetian red is a very permanent and inert pigment particularly on wood. The calcium sulfate content, because of furnishing corrosion-stimulating sulfate ions, militates against the application of this pigment on iron. *Indian red* is a naturally occurring mineral whose ferric oxide content may vary from 80 to 95 per cent, the remainder being clay and silica. It is made by grinding hematite and floating off the fines for use. The basic lead chromate, $PbCrO_4 \cdot Pb(OH)_2$, may also be used as an orange-red pigment; it is also a most excellent corrosion inhibitor. It is manufactured by boiling white lead with a solution of sodium dichromate. *Cadmium reds* are made by roasting the precipitate obtained through mixing cadmium sulfate, sodium sulfite, and sodium selenide. Red pigments include a large variety of insoluble organic dyes, either in the pure state as toners or precipitated on inorganic bases as lakes.

YELLOW PIGMENTS

Ocher is a naturally occurring pigment consisting of clay colored with 10 to 30 per cent ferric hydroxide. It must have been ground and levigated. At best the ochers are very weak tinting colors and are being replaced by synthetic hydrated yellow iron oxides.

Yellow pigments with a wide variety of shades fall in the class known as *chrome yellows;*[1] they are the most popular yellow pigments because of exceptional brilliance, great opacity, and excellent light-fastness. They are produced by mixing a solution of lead nitrate or acetate with a solution of sodium dichromate. Extenders may be present up to an equal weight of gypsum, clay, or barite. The pigment is of high specific gravity and settles out. *Zinc yellow* or *chromate*, while of poor tinting power, is used because of its excellent inhibiting effect both in mixed paints and as a priming coat for steel and aluminum. Zinc yellow is a complex of the approximate composition $4ZnO \cdot K_2O \cdot 4CrO_3 \cdot 3H_2O$.

Litharge, PbO, is made by heating melted lead in a current of air. It is used to some extent in anticorrosion paints.

GREEN PIGMENTS

One of the oldest green pigments is *chromium oxide*, Cr_2O_3. It has many disadvantages such as high cost and lack of brilliancy and opacity. It is

[1] WILLIAMS, Continuous Chrome Yellow Process, *Chem. Eng.*, **56** (3), 121 (1949).

made by fusing a chromate or dichromate with sulfur in a reverberatory furnace.

$$Na_2Cr_2O_7 + S \rightarrow Cr_2O_3 + Na_2SO_4$$

Guignet's green (emerald green) is a hydrated chromic oxide, $Cr_2O(OH)_4$, possessing a much more brilliant green color than the oxide and yet with good permanency. It is prepared by furnacing a mixture of potassium dichromate and boric acid at a dull red heat for several hours. In addition green of good permanency for use in outside-trim paints may be obtained in the intimate mixtures of copper phthalocyanine with zinc chromate or Hansa yellow. The brightest permanent green available, chlorinated copper phthalocyanine, is expensive.

Chrome green, sold under various names, is a mixture or a coprecipitation of chrome yellow with Prussian blue. Inert fillers are used with this pigment in making paints. Unless carefully ground or coprecipitated, the two colors may separate when mixed in a paint.

BROWN PIGMENTS

The carefully controlled heating of various naturally occurring iron-containing clays furnishes the brown pigments known as burnt *sienna*, burnt *umber* and burnt *ocher*. The iron hydroxides are more or less converted to the oxides. The umbers contain the brown manganic oxide as well as the iron oxides. These are all very permanent pigments and very suitable for both wood and iron. *Van Dyke brown* is a native earth of indefinite composition, containing oxide of iron and organic matter.

TONERS AND LAKES

Toners[1] are insoluble organic dyes that may be used directly as pigments because of their durability and coloring power. Lakes result from the precipitation of organic colors usually of synthetic origin upon some inorganic base.

Toners, or organic dyes, are employed in many colors. Some typical examples are given here. Para red is formed by diazotizing *p*-nitro-aniline and coupling it with β-naphthol. Toluidine toner, a better and more expensive red pigment, is made by diazotizing *m*-nitro-*p*-toluidine and coupling it with β-naphthol. Hansa yellow G (lemon yellow) is manufactured by diazotizing *m*-nitro-*p*-toluidine and coupling it with acetoacetanilide. Hansa yellow 10 G (primrose yellow) is made by coupling ortho-chloroacetanilide with diazotized 4-chloro-2-nitroaniline.

The *lakes* are really dyed inorganic pigments. The inorganic part or base consists of such an extender as clay, barite, or blanc fixe and alumi-

[1] MATTIELLO, *op. cit.*, Vol. 2, pp. 3–286; CALLAHAM, *op. cit.*

num hydroxide. The organic dye may be either precipitated onto an already existing base, such as clay or barite suspended in solution, or both the dye and the base may be coprecipitated as onto blanc fixe or aluminum hydroxide. Both toners and lakes are ground in oil or applied like any other pigment. Both should be insoluble not only in water to resist washing away, but in oil to prevent "bleeding." As the latter property is not so easy to attain, an old color frequently will run or bleed into a new coat of another color. This can be prevented by painting over the old color a paint containing as a pigment an absorptive black or a metallic pigment like flake aluminum. However, the toners and lakes are very useful and beautiful pigments for paints and inks.

METALLIC POWDERS

In surface coatings, flaked or finely powdered metals[1] and alloys have come into wide application. This is not only for their appearance as pigments but in many cases for their chemical or anticorrosion effect. Among such metallic substances, bronze and aluminum powders have been employed for years in lacquers. In recent years aluminum flake, or powder in suspension in various media, has given excellent results as a light-reflecting pigment as well as a primer coat. On iron and steel to retard corrosion, pigments containing zinc dust or *powdered* zinc dust and zinc oxide have been demonstrated to possess real value. This latter is also true of powders of lead and lead alloys.

PIGMENT EXTENDERS

There are a number of different substances that may be added to paints as fillers or extenders[2] for the purpose of giving a thicker paint film, providing better weathering properties, furnishing a base for the real pigment, or reducing the cost of the pigment (see Tables 2 and 5). These extenders should not be viewed as adulterants. Quoting from Lewis, Squires, and Broughton,[3]

The properties of such a (paint) film can be still further improved by incorporating a certain percentage of far coarser pigments, which by themselves are practically worthless—the so-called extenders. This calls to mind the well recognized principle of mixing in the case of materials such as concrete, where a mixture containing coarse, skeletal particles has the voids between these filled with

---

[1] MATTIELLO, *op. cit.*, Vol. 2, pp. 555–612.

[2] *Ibid.*, pp. 427–479; HARNESS, Natural Mineral Paint Extenders, *U.S. Bur. Mines, Inform. Circ.* 7264, Washington, 1943.

[3] LEWIS, SQUIRES, and BROUGHTON, "Industrial Chemistry of Colloidal and Amorphous Materials," p. 326, The Macmillan Company, New York, 1942. By permission.

progressively finer particles and the whole mass ultimately bonded together by a suitable matrix. The presence of 10 to 20 per cent of extenders in a paint, rather than being an indication of adulteration, may add materially to quality.

Barium sulfate, in the natural crystalline form of barite but finely ground or in the precipitated form of blanc fixe, is one of the most important of the extenders. Finely ground calcium carbonate, sometimes called *whiting*, is another. Ordinary silicon dioxide, when finely divided, makes a good filler. Magnesium silicate is also widely used—the trade names being *asbestine* and *talc*, the latter being finely ground soapstone.

OILS

Although, in the organic surface-protective industries, oils do serve as part of the vehicle for the carrying of the pigments, their chief function is to form or to help form the protective film. For this, reactive oils[1] are necessary, such as those which are drying or semidrying. The drying or the hardening of these oils involves chemical reactions, rather complex but including oxidation as the initiating step. Some polymerization also occurs and much cross linkage. Those oils which exhibit this phenomenon of drying to a film possess olefinic unsaturation. For example, the acids of linseed oil contain about 9 per cent saturated acids (palmitic and stearic), 19 per cent of oleic acid, 24 per cent of linoleic acid, and 48 per cent of linolenic acid. In drying, these oils at the first stage absorb oxygen from the air forming peroxides or hydro-peroxides at the olefinic bonds. These still liquid products partly decompose, giving the volatile oxidation products, but mainly change in the next stage of the reactions, by cross linkages into the solid though still elastic films through colloidal aggregation. In case of linseed oil, the solid, insoluble, but elastic film is called *linoxyn*. Such films are not permanent as the chemical reactions continue though at a much slower rate until, after the course of years, the film is entirely destroyed. Light, particularly ultraviolet, catalyzes these reactions and one of the functions of the pigment in surface coatings is to reflect the light and thus to help preserve the film.[2]

Drying oils are seldom used unmodified.[3] They may be improved in a number of different ways by (1) the action of driers, (2) oil bodying, (3) fractionation and segregation, (4) isomerization or conjugation, (5) dehydration, and (6) other carbon double-bond reactions. There are also

[1] MATTIELLO, *op. cit.*, Vol. 1, pp. 57–174; KILLEFFER, Drying Oils, *Ind. Eng. Chem.*, **29**, 1365 (1937).
[2] A fuller summary of researches in this matter is presented in LEIGHOU, *op. cit.*, pp. 545, 560–564; LEWIS, *et al.*, *op. cit.*, pp. 323–326.
[3] Symposium, Drying Oils, *Ind. Eng. Chem.*, **41**, 280 (1949); BURRELL, Polypentaerythritol Drying Oils, *Ind. Eng. Chem.*, **37**, 86 (1945); SUTHEIM, Drying Oils, *Chem. Inds.*, **62**, 65, 241 (1948).

the copolymer oils, the polyalcohols such as polypentaerythritol, oil-modified alkyds, and synthetic oils. Bodied oils vary with the oil, but generally have better drying, wetting, and color retention. Bodying may be achieved either by heating in kettles or by blowing air in fine bubbles through oils at 100 to 200°C. for several hours. Solvent or liquid-liquid extraction separates the drying constituents of an oil from the nondry-ing. Isomerization of paint oils, especially popular for linseed and soy-bean oils, involves the partial rearrangement of the isolated double bonds (nonconjugated) into the more reactive conjugated position upon heat-treatment with catalysts, such as certain metal oxides, activated nickel, or SO_2. Dehydration, at present, is applicable only for castor oil and is achieved by heating castor oil in a vacuum in the presence of dehydrat-ing catalysts, as alumina, fuller's earth, silica gel, H_3PO_4, or H_2SO_4. Only 16,000,000 lb. were so made in 1952, marking a sharp decline from a peak of 49,000,000 lb. in 1950. The reaction is probably as follows:

$$CH_3(CH_2)_5CH(OH)CH_2CH:CH(CH_2)_7COOH \rightarrow$$
Ricinoleic acid

$$H_2O + CH_3(CH_2)_4CH:CHCH_2CH:CH(CH_2)_7COOH$$
9,12-Linoleic acid, 59–64 per cent

$$+ CH_3(CH_2)_5CH:CHCH:CH(CH_2)_7COOH$$
9,11-Linoleic acid, 17–26 per cent

It was earlier thought that the 9,11-linoleic acid, with its conjugated double bonds, was formed in the larger amount, but recent investiga-tions show the other isomer to exist in the larger quantity. The composi-tion of the fatty acids in the thoroughly dehydrated castor oil analyzes as follows:

	Per cent		Per cent
Saturated acids	0.5–2.5	9,12-Linoleic acid	59–64
Hydroxyl acids	3–8	9,11-Linoleic acid	17–26
Oleic acid	7.5–10.5		

VARNISHES

A varnish is a colloidal dispersion or solution of synthetic and/or natural resins in oils and/or thinners used as a protective and/or decorative coating for various surfaces and which dries by evaporation, oxidation and polymerization of portions of its constituents.[1]

Varnishes fall into two general classes: oleoresinous varnishes and spirit varnishes. To these is sometimes added a third class, the japans. *Oleoresinous varnishes* are solutions of one or more natural or synthetic resins in a drying oil and a volatile solvent. The oil reduces the natural

[1] GOLDING AND BRAGE, Lilly Varnish Company.

brittleness of the pure resin film. Spirit varnishes are likewise solutions of resins, but the solvent is completely volatile and non-film-forming.

Oleoresinous varnishes are much the more important of the oil varnishes. They may be classified according to oil length as short, medium, or long: the number of gallons of oil used per 100 lb. of resin. The properties of the varnish are largely controlled by this factor. In general, a short varnish will possess faster drying properties to a harder and more brittle film, while the long varnishes possess more weather-resistant, pliable films. Some oil lengths of typical varnishes are as follows:

Short type (6–15 gal.)................ Floor and furniture varnishes
Medium type (20–30 gal.)............ General-purpose varnishes
Long type (35–60 gal.)............... Spar varnishes

Also the properties of the varnish will vary greatly, depending upon the cooking procedure, the type or types of drying oil used, and the types of resins employed. Table 6 gives a summary of varnish constituents.

Manufacturing Procedures.[1] The *oleoresinous varnishes* may be considered solutions of a resin, natural or synthetic, in a drying oil to which has been added driers and thinners. The procedure used in manufacturing varies widely, depending upon the types of oil or resin used. With some natural resins, as, for example, kauri gum, the resin is insoluble in oil and must be depolymerized by heating, a process called "running." This is accomplished by heating with stirring at temperatures of from 300 to 350°C. until the foaming ceases. The preheated drying oil is then added, and the heating continued to the correct viscosity. The mixture is cooled to 200°C. and the thinner and drier added.

In the case of synthetic resins the preheating is not necessary. The oils and resins are heated together until a homogeneous solution of the correct viscosity is obtained. The solution of resin in oils is frequently chilled back with a small amount of oil, cooled, and the thinner and driers added. In either procedure the varnish is clarified by filtration or centrifuging, followed by aging in large tanks to precipitate fine gel particles not removed in the previous operations.

The *spirit varnishes* are solutions of resins in volatile solvents only, usually either methanol or alcohol. Spirit varnishes dry the most rapidly but are likely to be brittle and eventually crack and peel off unless suitable plasticizers are added. The preparation of these products involves active stirring and sometimes heating to bring about the desired solution. The most important example of a spirit varnish is shellac or a solution of the resin shellac in methanol or alcohol. Not being pigmented, varnishes are less resistant to light than are paints, enamels, and pigmented

[1] ANON., Varnish and Paint, *Chem. & Met. Eng.*, **52** (3), 130 (1945), pictured flow sheets.

lacquers. They furnish, however, a transparent film which exhibits the texture of the surface coated.

Japans are of two types: painter's japans and decorative japans. The former, added to paints to give more luster, consist of a resin dissolved in a drying oil to which are added driers and thinners. The latter are

TABLE 6. VARNISH CONSTITUENTS
ᒃ (Enamel if pigmented)

Ingredient		Function
1. *Film-forming Materials*		
Oils:	*Synthetic resins:*	To form a protective film
Linseed oil	Phenol-aldehyde (oil-	and to serve as a binder
Tung oil	soluble)	for pigments upon
Dehydrated castor oil	Alkyd resins	evaporation of solvent
Castor oil	Mannitol esters	or drying of the varnish
Fish oils	Pentaerythritol esters	oil used
Tall oils	and interesters	
Soya oil	Limed rosin	
Cottonseed oil	Ester gum	
Coconut oil	Cumarone-indene	
	Melamine and urea-	
Natural resins:	formaldehyde	
Shellac, insect secretion	Chlorinated rubber	
Rosin	and diphenyl	
East India	Acrylates	
Manila	Vinyl resins	
Kauri, old fossil resin	Silicones	
Copal, fossil resin		
Dammar, recent fossil resin		
2. *Solvents and Thinners*		
Turpentine	Naphthas (aromatic)	To dissolve and control
Kerosene	Xylol	viscosity of film-forming
Dipentene	Toluol	material
Naphthas (aliphatic)	Alcohols	
3. *Driers*		
Co, Mn, Pb, Zn naphthenates, resinates, linoleates, tallates, or 2-ethylhexoates (octoates)		To increase rate of drying or hardening of varnish film
4. *Antiskinning Agents*		
Guaiacol	Tertiary-amyl-phenol	

opaque varnishes to which asphaltum or some similar material has been added for color and luster. They may be subdivided into baking, semi-baking, and air-drying japans according to their method of application.

Resins. The original resins[1] used were the *copals* which consisted of fossil gums from various parts of the world. Another natural but present-day resin widely employed is that from the pine tree, or *rosin* as it is called. When a plant exudes these products, they are called *balsams* and,

[1] MATTIELLO, *op. cit.*, Vol. 1, pp. 175–498.

upon evaporation of the volatile constituents, yield the resin. Thus the long-leaf, yellow, or hard pine of the Southern states upon proper incision yields a balsam which after distillation gives turpentine and a residue called *rosin*. This latter product is essentially abietic acid (see Chap. 32). Most of the natural resins that have been employed are fossil resins that have been buried and gradually changed by the centuries. From the rosin of present days, these resins[1] reach back through dammar, copal, and kauri resins to the oldest of the fossil resins, amber. Some resins like kauri and copal are so ancient that they have changed to insoluble products and must be partly depolymerized by heat before they can be dissolved or blended with the hot oils and other constituents in the varnish kettle. An important resin of the present day is *shellac* or *lac resin*. This, unlike the others, is the product of animal life, from a parasitic female insect (*coccus lacca*) which, feeding upon certain trees in India, secretes a protective exudate that eventually coats the twigs, furnishing the *stick lac*. This is collected and purified to the shellac of commerce by rolling, crushing, separating, washing, and bleaching.

Overshadowing these natural products are the more recently introduced synthetic resins (see Chap. 35). The *phenolic resins* (phenol-formaldehyde) were the first of these to be supplied and are still in wide use as they are very resistant to water and many chemicals. In order to make these materials soluble in the oils and solvents in common use in the varnish industry, it is necessary to modify them. This may be done either by fluxing them with softer materials such as ester gum, or by controlling the reaction by choosing a para-substituted phenol and thus stopping the reaction before a final insoluble, infusible product is obtained. The *alkyd resins*[2] are the most important in the industry today. These are formed by condensing dicarboxylic acids with polyhydric alcohols. When a constituent of varnishes or enamels, they have the distinctive properties of beauty and flexibility which show marked retention upon prolonged weathering exposure. The phthalic alkyds are classified in a manner similar to oleoresinous varnishes as long-, medium-, or short-oil products based, however, on phthalic anhydride content or equivalent. The properties of the alkyd formulation may be varied by use of different fatty acids or oils of both drying and nondrying types, by the use of pentaerythritol for the glycerol, by the use of maleic and other dibasic anhydrides for all or part of the phthalic anhydride, and by modifying with other resins (phenolics, rosin), and the like. As such they find extremely diversified application in various paint formulations. They have largely replaced varnishes of the oleoresinous type for use as paint vehicles. *Ester gum*, the product of the esterification of the abietic acid of rosin with glycerol, is another one of the important raw materials for

[1] For a fuller account, see LEIGHOU, *op. cit.*
[2] Symposium, Alkyd Resins, *Ind. Eng. Chem.*, **41,** 716 (1949).

making varnish. Some of the newer resins that may be mentioned in this connection are the coumarone-indene type, the urea-formaldehyde types, and the melamine-formaldehyde resins. The synthetic resins have numerous advantages over the naturally occurring types such as superior resistance on exposure to weather and chemicals and ability to be baked more rapidly at higher temperatures.

ENAMELS AND JAPANS

Enamels are pigmented varnishes or lacquers and are consequently more resistant to sunlight. Some enamels can be brushed or sprayed on the surface while others are finally hardened by baking, the latter being very durable.

Japans are very closely related to enamels, being pigmented with asphaltum or stearin pitch. For the desirable deep-black japans some carbon black is added. These japans are based on a heavily lead-bodied oil, made by cooking linseed oil and litharge for about 5 hr. at around 230°C. The product is almost a solid mass and is called *lead oil*. To this are added the asphaltum and any necessary thinners (kerosene). These japans[1] are applied and baked at 200°C. for a few hours. The japans are very useful for such products as bicycles, bedsteads, and electrical devices.

LACQUERS

A lacquer is a colloidal dispersion or solution of nitro-cellulose, or similar film-forming compound, resins and plasticizers in solvents and diluents, which is used as a protective and/or decorative coating for various surfaces and which dries principally by evaporation of its volatile constituents.[2]

Table 7 summarizes the constituents of lacquers. Clear lacquers upon the addition of a pigment become lacquer enamels or simply pigmented lacquers. Naturally the latter, because of the light-reflecting pigment, are more permanent to weather. Lacquer is a fairly recent addition to the organic surface-protecting industries, but it has had a phenomenal growth owing to a number of factors such as the enormous quantity of nitrated cellulose recovered from the breakdown of shells of the First World War and the commercial production of a number of new and suitable solvents, both coupled with the development of the automobile industry.

The nitrated cellulose of the variety used as a propellant explosive in shell is not the ideal film-forming material. However, untreated nitrocellulose of any variety upon solution in suitable solvents is too viscous

[1] Many formulas are given by BENNETT, "Chemical Formulary," Vol. 1, p. 241, Chemical Publishing Company, Inc., New York, 1933; see also Vol. 5, p. 430, 1941.

[2] GOLDING AND BRAGE, Lilly Varnish Company.

TABLE 7. LACQUER CONSTITUENTS

Class	Ingredients	Function
1. Film-forming or basic materials	*Cellulose derivatives:* Nitro-cellulose Cellulose acetate Ethyl cellulose *Resins and gums:* Ester gum Dammar Copal *Synthetic resins:* Phenol-aldehyde Alkyd	Cellulose derivatives to furnish waterproofness, hardness, and durability Resins, natural and synthetic, to improve retention of original gloss, adhesion, and water resistance
2. Pigments—omitted in clear lacquers	See Table 3	To impart pleasing color and to improve resistance to light
3. Solvents	*Esters:* Ethyl acetate (rapid) Butyl acetate (slow) Amyl acetate (slow) Ethyl lactate (slow) *Ketones:* Methyl-ethyl ketone (rapid) Cyclohexanone (slow) *Ethers:* Cellosolve (slow) *Alcohols:* Ethyl alcohol (rapid) Butanol (slow) Amyl alcohols (slow)	To dissolve the film-forming substances and to suspend the pigments. Rate of evaporation and solvency is governed by choice of the various solvents. "Rapid" and "slow" refer to rate of evaporation. Ethyl alcohol is a latent solvent becoming an actual solvent in presence of esters and ketones. Usually mixtures give best results
4. Diluents	*Coal-tar products:* Toluol Benzol Solvent naphtha *Petroleum products:* Petroleum naphtha V.M. & P. naphtha	To reduce viscosity and cost
5. Plasticizers	Castor oil, raw and blown Dibutyl phthalate Tricresyl phosphate Certain alkyds	To reduce film brittleness and to improve adherence

to allow sufficient to be dissolved to furnish a lacquer of requisite film thickness and yet be limpid enough for spraying or brushing. The early films were also too brittle and did not adhere well.

The invention of means to reduce viscosity laid the foundation for the rapid development of lacquer. This is now carried out by heating nitro-cellulose, of the nitrogen content to ensure desired solubility, with water in the liquid phase. This is done at about 130°C. by pumping the aqueous suspension of nitro-cellulose through a steel pipe against the pressure of a standpipe at the exit. Such a procedure is safer than the old method of

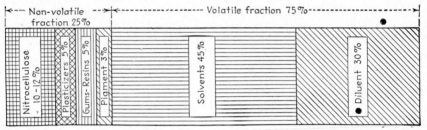

FIG. 7. Approximate composition of lacquers. [*Ind. Bull.* **17**, *No.* **7**, *New York State* (1938).]

heating a large amount of water and nitro-cellulose in a steel tank auto-clave. Chemically, in all probability, the long-chain cellulose ester mole-cules are degraded by hydrolysis to produce this lowering of viscosity. The choice of the solvents also has an effect on the viscosity, this being reduced if a solvent is selected which in itself does not dissolve the nitro-cellulose but yet mixes with the other organic liquids. This is called *desolvation.*[1]

Lacquer formulation is very complex. By reason of the large number of constituents available now numbered in the hundreds, lacquers emi-nently and specifically suitable to a wide variety of different objects whether of metal or of wood are available. These lacquers have greatly decreased the cost of finishing automobiles and given a longer-lasting job. This saving has been passed on to the consumer.

Figure 7 indicates roughly the composition of a typical nitro-cellulose lacquer. There exist considerable variations for individual lacquers. No one can efficiently fit a lacquer formula to a specific application with-out wide training, deep knowledge, and years of experience in this field.[2]

The ordinary lacquer ingredients are tabulated in Table 7, each of which has a definite function and also augments the properties of the others, thereby giving a finished product of desired characteristics. The classes of ingredients and their functions are as follows:

[1] LEWIS, *et al., op. cit.,* p. 318.
[2] MATTIELLO, *op. cit.;* see all volumes.

1. Among *film-forming bases*, nitro-cellulose or cellulose acetate gives waterproofness, hardness, and durability to the coating. The nitro-cellulose or, as it should be called, the *cellulose nitrate*, is an ester of cellulose made by the reaction of mixed nitric and sulfuric acid on cotton linters as is described in Chap. 22. The degree of nitration is closely controlled to give a product with the desired range of solubility. Cellulose acetate, the acetate ester, is made in a similar manner, with acetic anhydride replacing the nitric acid (*cf.* Chap. 34). The acetate has an advantage over the nitrate in that the film formed is nonflammable. The nitro-cellulose comes to the lacquer manufacturer in the form of a white solid moistened with about 30 per cent ethyl alcohol. The solvents, plasticizers, and diluents are blended in using mechanical agitation. The lacquer solution is clarified either by filtration or centrifuging. In case the lacquer is to be colored, the pigments are generally ground in a steel ball mill using a synthetic resin, usually an alkyd, as the vehicle. Another popular method is to mix a very high viscosity nitro-cellulose solution and the pigments in a sigma-blade dough mixer, or to mill a mixture of nitro-cellulose pigment and chemical plasticizer on a two-roll rubber mill.[1] Other film-forming materials are the resins, both natural and synthetic. These are added to supplement the cellulose derivatives and to improve the over-all properties[2] of the film.

2. *Pigments* have been presented in the earlier part of this chapter.

3. *Solvent formulation*[3] is a very complex subject. Bogin lists the following factors to be considered:

1. Rate of evaporation.
2. Solvency relations.
3. Effect on the viscosity of solution.
4. Compatibility with resins and other ingredients.
5. Blushing behavior.
6. Flow and orange peel.
7. Stability.
8. Odor, purity, availability, etc.

As Table 7 points out, mixtures are the rule, the choice of constituents being governed by the film-forming materials and the rate of evaporation desired. It should be noted that the *drying of lacquers is not an oxidation but an evaporation*, with the properties of the film dependent not only on the nature of the film but upon the conditions of the evaporation. Thus

[1] *Cf.* ANON., Ultra-fine Pigment Particles Basis of New Lacquer, *Chem. Inds.*, **59**, 57 (1946).

[2] See the various chapters devoted to particular resins in MATTIELLO, *op. cit.*, Vol. 1.

[3] BOGIN, Lacquer Solvents and Formulation of Solvent Mixtures, Chap. 27, in MATTIELLO, *op. cit.*, Vol. 1. Extensive tables and curves are included, giving evaporation rates, tolerances, and other pertinent chemical and physical properties.

blushing may result in an improperly formulated lacquer; this is a whitish or milky appearance in the film caused by the too rapid evaporation of the solvents and diluents with consequent cooling of the film 30 to 40°F. below the temperature of the atmosphere. This causes a condensation of moisture upon the lacquer and results in a milky aqueous emulsion. Upon drying, the water phase is occupied by air, resulting in the same milky[1] appearance.

4. The *diluents* are of great importance in reducing cost. Tolerance of the various solvents for these diluents is an important property in the choice of the original solvents. The diluents have a real dissolving effect on any gums used.

5. The original nitro-cellulose film was far too brittle for practical application. The *plasticizers* remedy this and also improve adhesion. Dozens of plasticizers are available to the lacquer formulator. Some are really *very-high-boiling* solvents of great chemical stability; others are "soft" resins (alkyds).

PRINTING INKS

Printing inks consist of a fine dispersion of pigments or dyes in a vehicle which may be drying oils with or without natural or synthetic resins and added driers or thinners. Drying oils or petroleum oils and resins are employed, although the newer types based on synthetic resins are finding great favor because they are quick-drying and their working properties are excellent. Printing inks have a wide variety of compositions and a large variation in properties.[2] This is because of the great number of different printing processes and types of papers employed. A very general classification of printing processes would include typographic, lithographic, and intaglio.

The usual paint pigments are also employed in printing ink, although some of the metallic oxides are too coarse and gritty for this use. The driers described under Paints are the ones used in inks as well. Antioxidants are used to counteract pigments which are natural oxidation catalysts. Guaiacol is a typical example.

The actual manufacture of printing inks consists in grinding the pigment in a small amount of vehicle and then mixing in the remainder of the constituents. Details of manufacture will vary greatly with the type of ink being produced.

[1] BOGIN, *op. cit.*, pp. 686–694.

[2] For a complete description of inks see ELLIS, "Printing Inks," Reinhold Publishing Corporation, New York, 1940; HESTER and ALLEN, Peacock Blue, *Ind. Eng. Chem.*, **45**, 1610 (1953).

COATED FABRICS

An industry closely allied to the lacquer industry is the manufacture of coated fabrics.[1] Coated fabrics consist of multiple layers of pigmented nitro-cellulose lacquer or of a vinyl or other dispersion or solution deposited upon a cloth backing, dyed, and embossed.

The basis of this coated fabric is usually cotton cloth which varies in grade according to the product being made. The first step is to remove any loose threads and knots that might cause bumps in the finish. The cloth then runs into a series of dye vats where it is colored the shade desired.

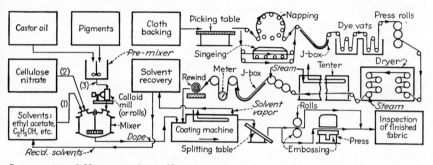

Dope consists of 60 percent solvents, 40 percent pyroxylin. Solvent fraction may consist, for example, of 30 percent ethyl acetate, 40 percent ethyl alcohol and 30 percent naphtha. "Solids" fraction may contain, for example, 25 percent pigment, 25 percent cellulose nitrate and 50 percent castor oil.

FIG. 8.

The drying of the dyed fabric is carried out on a series of steam-heated rolls, followed by a tunnel drier (see Fig. 8).

At the same time the cloth is being dyed, the coating solution or "dope" is being prepared in another part of the plant. For pyroxylin-coated fabrics the ingredients of this substance are nitro-cellulose, castor oil, pigment, and solvents. The castor oil and pigment receive a preliminary mix and are fed to the dispersion mills, which consist of two circular plates, set close together and rotated in opposite directions. This dispersion, plus the nitro-cellulose, more castor oil, and the solvents (a mixture of ethyl acetate, naphtha, and ethyl alcohol) are all mixed in large tanks to give the dope. Care must be taken in these operations to avoid fires and explosions due to the flammability of the nitro-cotton and solvents.

The fabric is coated with the dope in large automatic machines, the thickness of the layer being regulated by doctor knives. These machines are completely enclosed for solvent recovery, steam-heated cylinders causing the evaporation. From 3 to 20 layers of the nitro-cellulose (pyroxylin) material are added before the product is finished. Large

[1] For details of manufacture see CLARK, Leather Cloth from Chemicals, *Chem. & Met. Eng.*, **47**, 544 (1940); KIRK and OTHMER, *op. cit.*, Vol. 4, pp. 134–189.

embossing roll presses or bed presses put on designs such as resemble buckskin or pigskin.

The vapors being drawn off the coating machines contain from 0.7 to 0.9 per cent solvents. These are cooled and the solvents removed by passing through activated carbon adsorbers.[1] When the carbon is 75 to 80 per cent saturated, the solvents are driven off with steam, the vapors condensed, separated, and rectified.

While pyroxylin-coated fabric (artificial leather) embodied the first large production in this field, now other coating agents are employed more extensively, such as acetyl cellulose, vinyl polymers and copolymers, rubber latex and various synthetic rubbers, as neoprene, butyl, butadiene-styrene (GR-S), and others.

LINOLEUM

Linoleum, widely used for floor covering, was introduced in England in 1860. It costs from $1.30 to $3.00 per square yard, and the annual volume is placed around 70,000,000 sq. yd. Vinyl tile and sheet, felt-base flooring, asphalt tile, and rubber tile are the major competitors. In the manufacture of linoleum, linseed oil is oxidized at 50°C. by a stream of air for 4 to 6 days to form linoxyn (oxidized linseed oil), cooled until solid, cut into pieces, and cured at 35 to 40°C. for several days. Then the linoxyn is heated with rosin or other resin until a thermoplastic cement is formed to which fillers and pigments are added. The coating is spread in a uniform layer on canvas or burlap backing, the surface of which may be printed in patterns of different colors. The entire surface is afterward coated or waterproofed with an oil paint. With inlaid linoleum, the pattern goes right through the fabric, the different sections being pieced together and then passed between heated rolls.

SELECTED REFERENCES

Blom, A. V., "Organic Coatings in Theory and Practice," Elsevier Press, Inc., Houston, Tex., 1949.

Mattiello, J. J., editor, "Protective and Decorative Coatings, Paints, Varnishes, Lacquers and Inks," 5 vols., John Wiley & Sons, Inc., New York, 1941. This is a comprehensive treatise with excellent bibliographies.

Krumbhaar, W., "Coating and Ink Resins," Reinhold Publishing Corporation, New York, 1947.

Barry, T. H., "Natural Varnish Resins," D. Van Nostrand Company, Inc., New York, 1932.

Gardner, H. A., and G. G. Sward, "Physical and Chemical Examination of Paints, Varnishes, Lacquers and Colors," 11th ed., Institute of Paint and Varnish Research, Washington, 1950.

[1] See Chap. 9.

Lewis, Warren K., Lombard Squires, and Geoffrey Broughton, "Industrial Chemistry of Colloidal and Amorphous Materials," The Macmillan Company, New York, 1942.

Barry, T. II., and G. W. Dunster, "Varnish Making," Leonard Hill, Ltd., London, 1934.

Durrans, T. H., "Solvents," D. Van Nostrand Company, Inc., 6th ed., New York, 1950.

Heaton, N., "Outlines of Paint Technology," 2d ed., J. B. Lippincott Company, Philadelphia, 1940.

Morrell, R. S., "Varnishes and Their Components," Henry Frowde, and Hodder & Stoughton, Ltd., London, 1923.

Morrell, R. S., and A. De Waele, "Rubber, Resins, Paints and Varnishes," D. Van Nostrand Company, Inc., New York, 1920.

Parry, E. J., "Shellac," Sir Isaac Pitman & Sons, Ltd., London, 1935.

Martin, R. C., "Lacquer and Synthetic Enamel Finishes," D. Van Nostrand Company, Inc., New York, 1942.

Furnas, C. C., editor, "Rogers' Manual of Industrial Chemistry," 6th ed., Chaps. 25 and 26, D. Van Nostrand Company, Inc., New York, 1942.

Von Fischer, W., editor, "Paint and Varnish Technology," Reinhold Publishing Corporation, New York, 1948.

Pratt, L. S., "The Chemistry and Physics of Organic Pigments," John Wiley & Sons, Inc., New York, 1947.

Stewart, J. R., "National Paint Dictionary," 3d ed., Stewart Laboratory, Washington, 1948.

Symposium, Paint, Varnish and Plastics, 25th Anniversary Program, *Ind. Eng. Chem.*, **41**, 252 (1949).

Mellan, Ibert, "Industrial Solvents," 2d ed., Reinhold Publishing Corporation, 1950.

Bidlack, V. C., and E. W. Fasig, "Paint and Varnish Production Manual," John Wiley & Sons, Inc., New York, 1951.

CHAPTER 25

LEATHER, GELATINE, AND GLUE

The chemistry and engineering behind the leather and leather-tanning industry are so complex that scientific control in this industry has developed comparatively slowly. The skins and bones of animals and their products—leather, gelatine, and glue—are mostly colloidal materials and have almost indefinable properties, about which too little is known. The raw skin consists of a number of different complex proteins which vary in structure in different animals and even vary in different parts of the same hide. It has been said by Claflin, "Tanning will ever be an art so long as one animal differs from his fellow and one hide from another." The complexity of the art of leather manufacturing is enhanced by the large number of active substances that affect the skins—enzymes, bacteria, alkalies, acids, tannins, tannin substitutes, oils, fats, and salts. The leather industry is constantly searching for new chemicals with which to make better leathers at a cheaper price. It is already a large chemical consumer (see Table 2) ranking twelfth among industrial markets for chemicals.

LEATHER

Historical. Leather is one of the oldest of the commodities on the present-day world market. It has been called "the most historic of useful materials." The art of leather manufacturing from hides and skin. antedates, by centuries, any of man's scientific knowledge of chemistry Specimens of ancient Egyptian leather have been found which are claimed to be at least 3,000 years old. The color and strength of this leathe are remarkably unimpaired. Judging from these well-preserved leathe products, the origin of the technique must have antedated this time by many centuries. The original primitive methods for preservation of skin probably consisted of simply drying them in air and sunlight. Later th preservative effects of different oils were noted. Still later probably, th accidental discovery of the tanning effects of leaves, twigs, and barks c certain trees soaked in water were observed. It is believed that unti around 1900 the development of the leather industry was chiefly th result of rule-of-thumb discoveries, since it is only within recent time that any of the theory of leather tanning and dressing has been given in chemical terms.

Probably the greatest modern advancement in the leather industry has been the discovery and application of the chrome process of tanning which was first used approximately 45 years ago. Because of the results of this process, more than 90 per cent of the world's output of upper shoe leather is now chrome-tanned. The chrome process has greatly speeded up the tanning operation and gives increased strength. Vegetable tanning takes 2 to 4 months while the chrome process has reduced this interval to 1 to 3 weeks. The chief use of vegetable tanning at present is in the tanning of heavy leathers such as sole leather or leather belting; consequently, this old historical process is still widely employed.

Economics and Uses. According to the 1952 Survey of Manufactures there were 5,012 establishments with 361,873 workers (Table 1) producing an estimated 3½ billion dollars worth of products. Around 85 per cent of all the leather tanned in this country is consumed in footwear. Of the remainder, industrial leather constitutes a large part.

Artificial leather and coated fabrics are making heavy inroads on traditional leather markets. Also nearly 40 per cent of the shoe soling is no longer leather but synthetics. For example, nuclear soles (a combination of synthetic rubber and a special high styrene-butadiene resin) outwear leather by a wide margin but have a cost only about three-quarters that of good leather. Patent leather has mostly been replaced by the superior vinyl plastic and many other examples could be cited where plastics are supplanting leather because of more plentiful supply and superior uniformity at lower cost.[1]

ANIMAL SKINS

The United States is able to produce most of its own hides and skins for leather production. South America is the chief source of hides imported; the Argentine hides are usually of very good quality. Technically, the term *hide* is applied to the skins of larger animals such as bulls, horses, cows, and oxen; the term *skin* refers to skins of goats, sheep, calves, and the smaller animals. Very often the term *kip* is used for the skins of animals smaller than a full-grown calf. The quantities of the various types of raw materials have varied but little in the past decade. In 1949, 23,413 cattle hides, 10,169 calfskins and kips, 34,674 goat and kidskins, and 28,855 sheep and lambskins were consumed. In 1952, the value shipped of leather tanned and finished was 708 million dollars; of cattle hide and kip side leathers 424 million dollars; of calf and whole kip leathers 82 million dollars; and of other leathers tanned and finished 134 million dollars.

[1] Hoover, Synthetics Invade Leather Markets, *Chem. Eng.*, **56** (6), 138 (1949).

TABLE 1. LEATHERS AND LEATHER PRODUCTS, 1947 AND 1952[a]

	No. of estab- lish- ments 1947	No. of employees		Value added by manufacture ($1,000)		Value products shipped ($1,000) 1952
		1947	1952	1947	1952	
Leather tanning and finishing............	561	53,205	44,028	$ 156,540	$ 285,515	$ 796,112
Footwear cut stock....	606	22,077	18,926	47,793	77,154	267,249
Footwear (except rubber)...............	1,500	240,315	231,185	516,879	931,995	1,789,871
Leather gloves and mittens............	341	11,544	6,414	20,710	26,724	
Luggage..............	592	16,099	17,004	41,293	82,848	173,065
Handbags and small leather goods.......	980	25,907	31,131	57,011	110,501	
Miscellaneous leather goods..............	545	9,029	7,617	19,899	37,114	
Leather goods, n.e.c...	405	6,168		13,605		
Totals for industry..	5,308[b]	383,175	361,373	$1,532,803	$1,597,375	

[a] Annual Survey of Manufacturers, 1952.
[b] Number of establishments in 1952 had decreased to 5,012.

TABLE 2. CHEMICALS IN LEATHER MANUFACTURE[a]

	No. of products	Chemicals used in leather industry, million lb. per year	Cost estimate 1946–1948, million dollars
Heavy chemicals...............	31	354	7.4
Vegetable tanning agents........	16	586	41.0
Other tanning agents...........	6	123	8.4
Oils, soaps, fat liquors..........	14	69	8.8
Finishes, pigments, solvents......	15	46	13.0
Enzymes, syntans, moldicides....	6	80	6.2
Dyes........................	n.a.	n.a.	8.7
Total......................	...	...	94.0

[a] BELL and FLINN, Leather Industry Is Big Chemical Consumer, *Chem. Eng.*, 56 (6), 131 (1949). The heavy chemicals consist of such items as sodium sulfide, lactic acid, sulfuric acid, sodium thiosulfate, borax, and salt (largest).

Animal skins as received by the tanner[1] may be divided in three layers: the epidermis, the derma or corium, and the flesh. The epidermis comprising about 1 per cent of the total skin, is the outer layer and con-

[1] McLAUGHLIN and THEIS, "The Chemistry of Leather Manufacture," Reinhold Publishing Corporation, New York, 1945.

sists chiefly of the protein keratin. The hair, which grows through both the derma and the epidermis, is also largely keratin. The derma is the leather-forming part of the skin and consists mainly of the proteins collagen and elastin. This layer is dense and chemically resistant, thus allowing the epidermis to be readily removed by chemical means. Hot water, however, causes a slow solubilization by hydrolysis of the collagen to produce gelatine. The elastin is not affected by this treatment. The flesh is a thin layer, mostly adipose tissue, which must be removed to ensure tannin penetration on both sides of the corium.

MANUFACTURE

Unit Processes and Unit Operations. Figure 1 shows the necessary steps in the manufacture of leather.[1] These steps may be broken down into the following *unit operations* (Op.) and *unit processes* (Pr.):

The skins are opened, examined and, if of foreign origin, disinfected. The hoofs, ears, tails, etc., are trimmed off (Op.).

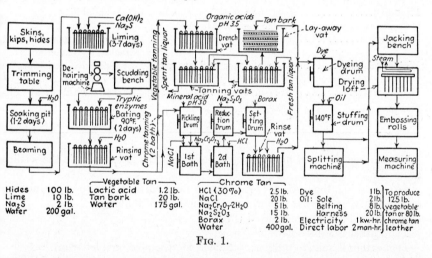

Hides	100 lb.		Vegetable Tan			Chrome Tan				
Hides	100 lb.	Lactic acid	1.2 lb.	HCl (30%)	2.5 lb.	Dye	1 lb.	To produce
Lime	10 lb.	Tan bark	20 lb.	NaCl	20 lb.	Oil: Sole	2 lb.	125 lb.
Na₂S	2 lb.	Water	175 gal.	Na₂Cr₂O₇·2H₂O	5 lb.	Belting	8 lb.	vegetable
Water	200 gal.			Na₂S₂O₃	15 lb.	Harness	20 lb.	tan or 80 lb.
				Borax	2 lb.	Electricity	1 kw-hr.	chrome tan
				Water	400 gal.	Direct labor	2 man-hr.	leather

FIG. 1.

The skins are water-soaked for 12 to 24 hr. and the flesh is removed by a machine equipped with a spiral-bladed cylinder (beaming) (Op.).

The skins are partly dehaired and treated with a saturated lime solution plus certain accelerators, such as sodium sulfide or sulfahydrate and dimethylamine, for 3 to 7 days (Op. and Pr.).

Any hair remaining is removed by machine and hand scraping (Op.).

The clean, dehaired hides are treated with certain enzymatic preparations for 2 days to soften the skin and remove the lime (bating) (Pr.).

After rinsing, the hides are ready for tanning (Op.).

The two principal methods of tanning are shown in Fig. 1.

[1] Pictured flow sheet with more details, *Chem. & Met. Eng.*, **50** (1), 112 (1943).

The vegetable tanning process consists of the following procedures:

The prepared skins are treated with organic acids to neutralize any residual lime (Pr.).

The tanning is carried out in several tanning baths starting very weak to prevent "casehardening" and becoming progressively stronger. This requires about 1 month (Pr.).

The skins are then allowed to rest in a vat containing tanbark for 60 days (Pr.).

The chrome-tanning process is somewhat different from the tanning process as indicated in Fig. 1. The following pertains to the two bath processes.

The prepared skins are pickled in a bath of salt and sulfuric acid (Pr.).

The pickled hides are soaked with a solution of sodium dichromate (Op. and Pr.).

The dichromate saturated skins are treated with sodium thiosulfate in the reduction drum (Pr.).

TABLE 3. COMPARISON OF SKINS AND LEATHER

	Skins or hides	Leather
Pliability.............	Soon lose pliability and become hard and brittle	Retains pliability
Permanence...........	Putresce very quickly	Extremely permanent, not attacked by bacteria
Water resistance.......	Absorb water and are permeated easily by it	Possesses great resistance to water
Boiling water..........	Are converted to gelatine by hydration	Attacked with great difficulty
Mechanical strength....	Fairly good	Very good

The chrome salt is set on the fibers by adding borax to the skins in the settling drum (Pr.).

After washing, the leather is ready for the finishing operations (Op.). Finishing operations are somewhat similar for both methods of tanning.

The tanned hides may be dyed (Pr.).

The leather is stuffed with oil (Op.).

The leather is split to produce a thinner, more supple product (Op.).

Gloss is developed on the surface of this leather by ironing and jacking the leather with a glass cylinder (Op.).

The jacked leather is dried (Op.), embossed (Op.), and measured (Op.).

In industrial application these unit processes and operations are complicated and require experienced men to carry them out. Each important operation or process is given more detailed presentation on the next few pages. The results are tabulated in general in Table 3. However, leather has an outstanding, extremely valuable property that is not duplicated by many of its substitutes, namely, its great permeability to water vapor and therefore its ventilating property.

Preservation and Disinfection of Skins. As the raw skins decay rapidly after flaying, some method of preservation must be used to arrest the bacterial action and subsequent hide disintegration. Standard United States practice piles the hides flesh side up in alternate layers with salt. These packs are arranged for proper drainage of the brine. This method of curing requires a minimum of 3 or 4 weeks at about 13°C., during which the hide loses part of its moisture by dehydration and gains weight through salt absorption. The loss is the greater and the over-all difference is termed the "shrink." Great care must be taken in this operation as many irregularities in the leather may be traced to the curing and storing. Preservation methods predominantly used by foreign countries include air drying, a combination of salting and air drying, and salting with sodium sulfate and other substitutes in those countries where the chloride is not available.[1]

Preparation of Hides for Tanning. The first step in the tanning process is the inspection of the hides for defects as they come into the tannery, cutting off of ears and ends, the cleansing of the hides from dirt, manure, and salt, and restoring the hide to a natural soft hydrated state by paddle washing, drum washing, or soaking in vats.

In the paddle method, the washing is done in a cylindrical wooden vessel, usually about 9 ft. wide and 5 ft. deep, containing a rotor or paddle 5 ft. in diameter. This paddle operates at approximately 15 r.p.m. The equipment is cheap and easy to construct, uses little power, and is not so liable to injure the hides as is the drum method. The chief disadvantages are the necessary high ratio of water to hide (about 3 lb. of water per pound of hide) and the required hand removal of the hides from the paddle.

In the drum method, a cylindrical wooden drum (cypress or fir), about 8 ft. in diameter and internally fitted with wooden pegs or shelves, is used. The drum is rotated and gives the hides a tumbling effect during washing. The chief disadvantage of this method is the danger of damage or rub marks on the hides.

The soaking and washing of the hides are quite important because if the hide is not properly "wet back," it will not respond properly to the different tanning operations. Small amounts of sodium polysulfide and surface-active agents are added which greatly accelerate the soaking. Bactericides in the soak, except sodium bifluoride for pathogenic diseases, are no longer necessary because of the completeness of preservation. If the hide is oversoaked, it will be soft and below par. A properly soaked hide contains about 65 per cent of water.

Liming. Liming is a means of loosening and removing the epidermis and hair from the hide and is usually done in wooden or concrete vats.

[1] McLaughlin and Theis, *op. cit.*

The hides are tied or hooked together and placed in the vats containing water with 10 per cent of the weight of the hides in lime, and 2 per cent of the lime weight in sodium sulfide which acts as an accelerating agent. Dimethylamine and sodium sulfahydrate are also used as accelerating or "sharpening agents." The hides are moved ahead daily in a series consisting of three to seven vats, remain in each one a day, and then enter a fresher lime vat. These vats are drained and the lime charge renewed about every 2 weeks in the summer and every 4 to 5 weeks in the winter.

The epidermis and hair are chiefly composed of keratin. Keratin is a protein containing a cystine residue which is easily attacked by alkali. Lime attacks the disulfide link in the keratin and thus softens the hair and removes the epidermis. This action may be represented[1] as

$$R—S—S—CH_2R + H_2O \rightarrow RSH + RCH_2SOH$$
$$RCH_2SOH \rightarrow RCHO + H_2S$$

After the hides have passed through this series of lime vats, they are usually placed in a vat of warm water which tends to shrink them and permits the easier removal of the hair. The hair and epidermis are removed in a dehairing machine. The skins are brought in contact with a roller set with dull knife blades which rub off the loose hair and epidermis, as represented in Fig. 1.

The great bulk of all skins are depilated by the above practice, although unhairing may also be accomplished by treating the soaked skin with certain enzymes or by "sweating." Here the skin is hung in a warm humid room until the epidermis is digested by the ever-present proteolytic bacteria.

Bating. For centuries bating was one of the most mysterious processes carried out in the tannery and by far the most unpleasant. The old method consisted of placing the limed skins in a warm infusion of the dung of dogs or fowls until the plumpness of the skins disappeared. When pigeon or hen manure was used, the process was called *bating*, and when dog dung was used, it was called *puering*.[2] Later the investigation of the important organic constituents of the dung led to the use of artificial materials and the process became known as *bating*.

Just before immersion of the hides into the tanning liquor, they undergo the bating or deliming process which now uses ammonium sulfate or chloride as the deliming agent, and enzymes derived from bacteria, fungi, or extraction of pancreatic glands for the removal of certain proteins, mainly elastin, and for the improvement of the color of the grain. The ammonium salts dissolve the lime and thus regulate the pH

[1] LEWIS, SQUIRES, and BROUGHTON, "Industrial Chemistry of Colloidal and Amorphous Materials," The Macmillan Company, New York, 1942.

[2] WILSON, "The Chemistry of Leather Manufacture," Reinhold Publishing Corporation, New York, 1928.

of the solution so that the enzymes are activated.[1] Another important reaction in bating is that called *falling* or the reduction in the degree of swelling of the protein constituents of the limed skin previously swollen during the liming process.

Vegetable Tanning. As has been mentioned previously, chrome tanning is for light leathers, and the chief use of vegetable tanning is for heavy leathers used for soles and belting. The active ingredients in vegetable tanning reagents consist of a class of complex organic compounds known as *tannins*, which are found quite abundantly in the vegetable kindgom. The chief sources that have attained commercial importance for supplying tannin for leather manufacture are barks, leaves, twigs, fruits, pods, and roots of various trees, shrubs, and plants.

Chestnut and quebracho account for approximately 80 per cent of the natural tannin consumption in this country, with about a third of domestic origin and the rest from imports. Quebracho from Argentina and Uruguay is the most important while wattle bark from South Africa is second. In smaller quantities, but essential for providing certain leather qualities are valonia from Turkey, myrobalan nuts from India, and mangrove bark from Borneo. Approximately 90 per cent of the domestic tannin supply is obtained from the uncut stand of dead chestnut trees in the southeastern Appalachian forest. Since this source will be depleted in 10 to 15 years, the tanning industry is vigorously exploring other natural sources of tannins or true synthetic replacement materials. Many attempts[2] have been made to classify natural tannins because they do not behave similarly in their action on the skin or in their response to various reagents. Perhaps the earliest classification was to divide them into *catechol* or *pyrogallol* tannins. This was based upon the fact that when the natural tannins were heated to 200°C. they yielded one or the other. Unfortunately some commercial tannins of today yield both groups, but the classification is still popular. Oak, hemlock, chestnut, and quebracho are commonly known as catechol tannins, while tanning reagents from wattle trees, myrobalan nuts, and gambier trees are often called pyrogallol tannins. Although some tanneries extract their own tannin from raw materials, the manufacture of tanning extracts has now become a separate industry of considerable size.

The open-vat leaching method of natural tannins is one of the oldest but perhaps still the most commonly used. The tannin-containing bark, wood, or other material is chopped into small pieces, shredded in a bark mill, and placed in leaching tanks equipped with false bottoms and heating coils and usually arranged in batteries of eight. The bottom of each tank is fitted with a pipe through which the liquor may be pumped from one tank to another. Leaching of the bark is accomplished by countercurrent

[1] BELL, Leather, *J. Chem. Educ.*, **19**, 340 (1942).
[2] McLAUGHLIN and THEIS, *op. cit.*, pp. 515*ff*.

extraction with water. The bark is then dumped and discarded. The fresh water enters at its boiling point and, by means of heating coils in the vats, the temperature can be controlled so that it cools slowly and is about 16°C. for the last leach. Usually the extract is muddy and contains suspended insoluble matter. The extract is then clarified by filter pressing, settling, and decanting or centrifuging. The liquid is concentrated in vacuum evaporators or specially constructed vacuum driers.

Tannins are complex mixtures of glucosides of various polyphenols. Their action on skin is to combine with the protein. The tannins act as negatively charged colloids. The proteins in the skins are positively charged if in acid media. Thus the tannins neutralize the charge on the proteins and coprecipitation or combination of the tannins and proteins occurs. Other complex processes also take place. As the proteins have a negative charge when in alkaline media, it is necessary to neutralize all of the lime from the liming process before tanning. During the tanning process the tannins liberate sugars which are oxidized to acids and thus keep the liquor acidic. These changes may be represented schematically as follows:

$$\text{Skin} + \text{tannin} \rightarrow \text{leather} + \text{sugar}$$

$$\text{Sugar} \xrightarrow{\text{oxidation}} \text{acid}$$

After complete precipitation of the protein the aggregate has the capacity to absorb large quantities of the tannin. Skins may increase in weight as much as 300 per cent during the tanning operation. This combined and absorbed material fills up the holes and stiffens the leather.[1]

Synthetic tanning agents, or *syntans,* are gaining in use as evidenced by present production of nearly 20,000,000 lb., although vegetable tanning extracts are still widely employed. Syntans are condensation products of sulfonated phenols (or higher homologs) and formaldehyde capable of converting animal skin into leather.[2] Comparatively few syntans exist which do not possess a sulfonic acid group. Syntans may be classified according to use as auxiliary, complimentary, or replacement tannins. Until 1945 and the introduction of the first replacement tannin in America (Orotan TV by Rohm & Haas Co.), all syntans belonged to the first two classes. There they functioned as adjuncts and dye mordants and for bleaching chrome leather, for solubilization of vegetable tans, and for increasing the speed of penetration of the natural tannins into the leather. The first successful replacement tannin was prepared by the Germans by partially sulfonating a phenolic resin of the Novolak type, neutralizing the product, and diluting to proper strength. Replacement syntans[3] are

---

[1] LEWIS, *et al., op. cit.*

[2] CHEN, "Syntans and Newer Methods of Tanning," The Chemical Elements, South Lancaster, Mass., 1950; Staff Report, New Tanning Agents Based on German Technology, *Chem. Eng. News,* **26,** 1980 (1948).

[3] KENNEDY, Leather and National Defense, *Chem. Eng.,* **56** (6), 141 (1949).

very promising because quality can be standardized and synthetics can be tailor-made for a specific task.

Vegetable tanning is usually done in wooden (red pine) vats 8 by 7 by 5 or 6 ft. deep which contain the tan liquors and hides. Since the hides remain in the liquor for 1 or more months, many vats are required, and they must therefore be cheap and durable. Hides first enter the oldest, weakest tanning liquors in order to prevent complete plugging of the surface pores and subsequent poor penetration of the tannins through the skins by a strong liquor. They pass successively through liquors of increasing strength until they leave the freshest and strongest liquor as fully tanned leather. The ratio of liquor to hide is kept as low as possible and is usually 6 to 4 lb. of liquor to 1 lb. of hide. The art in tanning lies in the careful selection and blending in the proper proportions of the various tannins so as to give the desired type and color of leather. Sometimes the hides are placed on rockers or paddles for the first 15 to 20 days to give them a gentle movement in the liquid, which tends to accelerate the tanning and make a more uniform leather.

Many attempts have recently been made to speed up the tanning time and to shorten the expensive and tedious aging and mellowing in tan liquors. Such schemes as immediate introduction of the hide into a strong tanning reagent, use of formaldehyde, use of different solvents, use of alternations of pressure and vacuum, and use of higher temperatures have all been tried, but it is claimed that a poorer fiber, grain, and yield are obtained by these means. The methods seem to have attained no great success.

Since approximately 250 gal. of *iron-free* water are required for each hide produced, water supply and disposal are very important factors in tannery location. As in most other fields of industrial endeavor, there is no standard treatment in the tanning industry of waste disposal because of wide differences in local antipollution regulations as well as in type of processes. Because of the relatively high solids found in tannery wastes, some form of precipitation and sedimentation is usually included. In order to segregate those wastes which did require further treatment from those which did not, one company which produced 750,000 to 1,000,000 gal. effluent per day found the following distribution percentagewise:[1]

	Per cent		Per cent
Soak wash....................	10.0	Pickle.......................	9.5
Soak........................	12.5	Chrome tan..................	2.0
Lime........................	17.5	Vegetable tan...............	2.0
Lime wash..................	5.5	Wash, color, fat liquors.......	31.5
Bate........................	9.5		

[1] SUTHERLAND, Industrial Waste . . . Tanning Industry, *Ind. Eng. Chem.*, **39**, 628 (1947); HARNLY, Tanneries, *Ind. Eng. Chem.*, **44**, 520 (1952).

Chrome Tanning. The uppers of a pair of chrome-tanned leather shoes will outwear two or three pairs of a vegetable-tanned product. For this reason over 90 per cent of the world's production of light leather is chrome-tanned by the one-bath process. To condition hides and skins for subsequent mineral tannage, they undergo a process called *pickling.* This involves treating bated hides and skins with mixed solutions of acid, usually sulfuric, and salt.

In the chrome process, the combination of the chromium salts and hide fibers is much more rapid and takes place without the degree of swelling that occurs in vegetable tanning. Therefore, the chrome leather is more pliable and looser in structure. Fillers are usually added to give water-resistant properties. The chrome leather is characterized by high content of original hide proteins and mineral matter, and by low content of water-soluble materials. The mechanism of chrome tanning has not been well established. The tanning liquor has the same electrical charge as the hide. Therefore, the mechanism of coprecipitation, as given under vegetable tanning, is not applicable. It is possible that the collagen forms a coordination compound with the chromium salts.[1]

Chrome tanning is usually subdivided into two processes: the one-bath process using basic chromic sulfate and the two-bath process using sodium dichromate. However, in each case, chromium salt is used in place of the vegetable tanning agent. The chrome liquor for the one-bath process is usually made by reducing an acidified solution of sodium dichromate by slowly adding a solution of glucose to it or by bubbling sulfur dioxide through the dichromate until the reduction is complete.

$$Na_2Cr_2O_7 + 3SO_2 + H_2O \rightarrow 2Cr(OH)SO_4 + Na_2SO_4$$

There are numerous other methods for reduction, but all involve the change of the chromium ion from the hexavalent to the trivalent state. The preferred one-bath process from the standpoint of quality and control is to add the chrome liquor to the wooden drum containing the pickled skins and the exhausted pickle liquor. Usually mold and mildew inhibitors such as pentachlorophenol are added here. The drum is rotated 5 to 6 hr. until the tanning operation is complete.

Various modifications of the two-bath process are in use, but the process used in Fig. 1 serves as an illustration. After pickling, the hides are placed, successively, in two drums or paddle vats containing about 5 per cent of the weight of the hides in sodium dichromate solution with some hydrochloric acid and salt. The skins are allowed to remain in each liquor overnight and are then pulled out and allowed to drain. After an hour or two, the hides are placed in another paddle vat containing approximately 15 per cent of the weight of the hides in sodium thiosulfate. The hides are left in this liquor overnight, pulled out in the morning,

[1] LEWIS, *et al., op. cit.*

and washed in a drum containing water. Borax is added to reduce the acidity of the leather to the desired extent.

In the chrome process, the properties and composition of the finished leather are greatly influenced by many factors that can be controlled during tanning. Such factors as salt concentration, temperature, agitation, time, and proportion of protein to liquor are very important in the effects on the leather produced. In fact it seems that the number of possibilities of operation and final results in chrome tanning is infinite.

Finishing Operations. After the tanning operation is completed, the leather, if dried rapidly, is quite stiff, will usually break if bent sharply, and is not yet fit for use. The fibers must be lubricated to give them pliability and softness. Actually more work is required in the operations following the actual tannage than in all the preceding operations and processes put together. As each of the numerous kinds of leather requires a special series of operations, details will be impossible here.

If the tanned leather is not smooth, it is shaved by means of a machine with sharp blades. Very often it is split by means of a bandlike knife to obtain the desired thickness. (This may be done later, as shown in Fig. 1.) Vegetable-tanned leathers are sometimes washed, bleached, or scoured. The bleaching or washing is usually done in a revolving drum containing sodium carbonate, sodium hydroxide, or sulfuric acid and water. Other bleaching agents such as sodium bisulfite, sulfurous acid, sulfite cellulose solutions, and various syntans are used.

The next operation involves the incorporation of oils and greases and is called *stuffing* or *fat liquoring*. Sulfonated oils blended with raw oils are the most important fat liquors and have mostly replaced raw oils, natural greases, emulsions of raw oils and soaps, waxes, and resins. The leather, either dry or wet, may be stuffed by hand or in a rotating drum. A more uniform job can be obtained by hand. Sole leathers are usually "loaded" with some material as magnesium sulfate and cellulose to give them desired properties.

The color and shade of the finished leather are produced by a combination of dyeing and finishing operations. Dyeing may be united with the fat-liquoring process, or it may be done before or after it. Most of the dyestuffs used at present are now synthetic coal-tar derivatives. The most common method of dyeing is in revolving drums or vats equipped with rotating paddles.

The finishing series of operations in the production of leather includes both mechanical treatments and applications of finishing materials to the leather. The following classes represent the more common materials used in leather finishing: (1) cellulose ethers, (2) waxes, (3) resins, (4) dyes, (5) pigments, (6) lacquer materials, (7) antiseptics, (8) miscellaneous materials such as solvents, perfumes, soaps, sulfonated oils, metal salts, plasticizers, acids, and alkalies. Mechanical operations carried out in the finishing of leathers include staking (flexing the leather over an edge to loosen fibers and soften it), glazing, buffing, graining, trimming, rolling, brushing, and plating. The finishing operations alone embrace a technique requiring great skill, wide experience, and close attention.

Oil Tanning.[1] From very early times skins have been tanned or preserved by the use of certain drying oils which have been worked into the skins and allowed to oxidize and react, thus becoming fixed. An example of this type of leather is that known as *chamois*. The sheep- or lambskins are subjected to the usual rinsing, liming, trimming, fleshing, and bating. They are then swollen preparatory to splitting, frequently with the aid of an acid such as sulfuric at a pH of around 2.0. The pickled skins in the plumped condition can be split easily, separating the grain from the flesh layer. The former is the skiver while the flesh layer is processed to make chamois leather. After this the depickling is carried out with an alkali such as borax or even soda ash or ordinary chalk with the pH around 7.0. The skins are now in condition to be processed with the oil to make chamois. The damp skins are treated with about 10 per cent of their weight of a suitable oil. The oils generally used are cod oil or linseed although the latest development employs aliphatic hydrocarbon sulfonyl chlorides. The treatment with oil is often carried out in a drum where the revolving action extends over 4 hr. so that the oil can distribute itself and penetrate the skin. The skins are removed and piled in layers during which fermentation and oxidation proceed, evolving a number of reactions that are not now well understood. The skins are hung or hooked for the reactions to proceed. The temperature rises some 20°F. during this maturing process. The oiling and hooking are repeated until 40 to 50 per cent of the oil on the weight of the moist skin has been incorporated. After the oil-tanning process is completed, the chamois leather is washed with warm alkalized water and hydraulically pressed to remove excess oil. Further washing, buffing, and drying complete the operations.

GELATINE

Gelatine[2] is an organic nitrogenous colloidal protein substance whose principal value depends on its coagulative, protective, and adhesive powers. Water containing only 1 per cent high-test gelatine by weight will form a jelly when cold. Glue and gelatine are closely related; indeed, glue may be looked upon as an impure gelatine. Both are derived by hydrolysis from collagen—the white fibers of the connective tissues of the animal body, particularly in the skin (corium), bones (ossein), and ten-

---

[1] BARRETT, Manufacture of Chamois Leather, *Leather Trades' Rev.*, **75**, 1125 (1942).

[2] The spelling gelatine is adopted here because of its very wide usage in the industry although it is recognized that the spelling gelatin is used by *Chemical Abstracts* and the *United States Pharmacopeia*.

dons. These reactions have been formulated.[1] However, these are only indications of the complex changes that take place, proceeding from quite variable raw materials to almost as variable products.

$$C_{102}H_{149}N_{31}O_{38} + H_2O = C_{102}H_{151}N_{31}O_{39}$$

Collagen   Water   Gelatine

$$C_{102}H_{151}N_{31}O_{39} + 2H_2O = C_{55}H_{85}N_{17}O_{22} + C_{47}H_{70}N_{14}O_{19}$$

Gelatine   Water   Semiglutin   Hemicollin

Uses and Economics. The industry recognizes three different kinds of gelatine: (1) edible, (2) photographic, and (3) inedible. In 1952, the United States total production of gelatine was 37,523,000 lb., of which the production of inedible and photographic gelatine was approximately 8,000,000 lb. Gelatine has recently become a widely consumed food. It is a very popular dessert which is easily assimilated and even helps in the digestion of other foods by forming an emulsion with fats and proteins. Gelatine is also used by pharmaceutical houses for making capsules and as an emulsifier. Gelatine has played an important part in the rapid development of the motion-picture and photographic industries. The gelatine is coated on the film base as the sensitized emulsion of the light-sensitive silver salts. Inedible gelatine is quite an arbitrary name and is applied to small amounts of gelatine used for miscellaneous purposes such as for sizing paper, textiles, and straw hats.

The prices of the different gelatines vary considerably. The average price of photographic gelatine is about $1.15 per pound while the average price of edible gelatine is only about half this figure. In 1949 there were 11 producers of gelatine in the United States. It should be noted that a distinction is to be made between producers of gelatine and processors. The producer manufactures the plain clear gelatine which he sells to the processor who makes it up into gelatine-dessert powders and other products.

Manufacture. All three types of gelatine produced are made from calfskin, pigskin, or animal bones. These materials contain approximately one-third collagen by weight. A large amount of the bones is imported chiefly from Argentina, while most of the pig- and calfskins are domestically produced. Approximately 89 per cent of the raw materials consumed are calfskin and pigskin, the remaining 11 per cent bones. Although producers do not agree on which raw material yields the greatest quantity of gelatine, it is known that only the best-grade raw materials, such as calfskins, are used for the production of photographic gelatine. Sheppard found that the presence of traces of mustard oil (allyl isothiocyanate) in gelatine prepared from the skins of calves that had eaten

[1] ALEXANDER, in "Rogers' Manual of Industrial Chemistry," 6th ed., p. 1588, D. Van Nostrand Company, Inc., New York, 1942.

wild carrots was very effective in increasing photographic sensitivity.[1]
The skins used for gelatine are usually imperfect ones, not suitable for
making leather. It should be noted that strict government regulations
and inspections govern the choice of raw materials used for the preparation of edible gelatine.

The bones and skins frequently undergo a *pretreatment* which makes
the gelatine preparation easier. They are usually heated in lime and
water to a temperature of about 70°C. for a short time. If higher temperatures and long heating are used, the gelatine hydrolyzes and loses
part of its jellying properties.

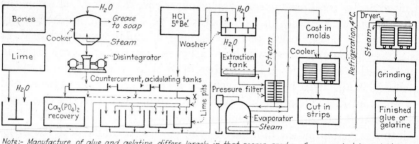

Note:- Manufacture of glue and gelatine differs largely in that poorer grades of raw materials and higher
extracting temperatures are used for the former. Glue is more completely hydrolyzed than gelatine. Instead
of bones, skins, hides, sinews, hide scraps, fleshings, fish stock, etc., may be used, in which case, after washing,
they are introduced at X. Usually three extractions at temperatures from 60 to 75 deg.C. are used. The last
extract requires concentration before molding

Bones	3.03 tons	Steam	400 lb.	To produce
Hydrochloric acid	1.14 tons	Electricity	55 kw.-hr.	Gelatine, 1 ton
Lime	0.76 tons	Direct labor	6 man-hr.	$Ca_3(PO_4)_2$ 1.67 ton
				Grease, 0.08 ton

Fig. 2. Flow sheet for glue and gelatine.

When bones are used as a raw material, they should be *degreased*. This
is done by heating the bones under steam pressure and then running off
the grease layer, or by extracting with a low-boiling petroleum naphtha.
Figure 2 shows the essential steps in the preparation of gelatine and glue
from bones. The bones are then crushed and enter a battery of four or
more wooden tanks in series. Cold 5°Bé. (7.15 per cent) hydrochloric
acid is passed countercurrent to the bones so as to flow into the most
nearly exhausted ones first. The calcium phosphate, carbonate, and other
mineral matter of the bones are dissolved, leaving the organic matter,
collagen, with the residue from the bones. This is now called *ossein*.

It is unnecessary to treat skins used in the manufacture of gelatine
with hydrochloric acid because the collagen of skins is not shielded by
mineral matter such as the calcium salts. The ossein is soaked in concrete
vats containing milk of lime for a period of a month or more. This same
treatment is also given to hides used for gelatine production. The purpose
of this soaking is for *plumping* and to remove and eliminate soluble

[1] SHEPPARD, Photographic Gelatine, *Phot. J.*, **65**, 380 (1925).

proteins (mucin, albumin).[1] When the soaking in the lime is complete, the ossein or hides are washed in a rotary drum or conical-shaped washer, once with fresh water then with slightly acidified water to adjust the pH for optimum hydration of the collagen.

The next step is a series of *extractions*, which are usually performed in wooden tanks equipped with steam coils. The first extraction is made with water kept at 60 to 65°C. by the steam coils. The pH of the hydrolyzing liquid is of importance. The optimum range is 3.0 to 4.0.[2] The water is in contact with the ossein for approximately 8 hr. An 8 to 10 per cent solution of gelatine is obtained which is filtered hot and cooled. Then another extraction is made at a slightly higher temperature. The filtered liquors are run into long steel trays 6 in. wide and 6 in. deep, which are placed in refrigerated rooms to jell the contents. A third extraction of the ossein or hides is carried out at about 75°C. This is darker in color and so dilute that it will not set or jell on cooling. It is, therefore, necessary to evaporate this liquor under vacuum before it is cooled. Very often peroxides of hydrogen or sulfurous acid are used as a bleaching agent.[3] These extractions, usually four or five in number, are run at continually higher temperatures until 100°C. is reached. The extract made at the lowest temperature is of the best quality and usually is used for gelatine for food or photographic purposes. The last extracts yield material suitable only for glue.

The cooled solid gelatine is removed from the mold, cut into slabs ½ in. by 2 in. by 6 ft. These slabs are spread on nets which are stacked on small mobile trucks and pushed into a drying tunnel through which filtered air at about 40°C. is pulled by exhauster fans. On drying, the slabs shrink to a thin strip which may be ground to a powder for further usage.

Although gelatine itself is a by-product of the packing and tanning industries, its manufacture produces several more by-products, as shown in Fig. 3. By-products of gelatine made from pigskin or calfskin are tankage and grease. Gelatine made from degreased bones gives by-products of steamed bone meal which is a valuable stock-feed additive, calcium phosphate for the pottery industry (bone china) and suitable as a fertilizer, and also bone black which is a good decolorizing agent.

The production of edible gelatine must meet the requirements of the Food and Drug Administration and the manufacture of photographic gelatine must undergo very rigid and specialized technical control. The process of making photographic gelatine is much more complicated than

[1] LEWIS, *et al.*, *op. cit.;* PEARSON and SMITH, Gelatine, *Food Manuf.*, **2**, 232, 287; **3**, 427 (1928).

[2] TUPHOLM, The Importance of pH Control in the Manufacture of Gelatine and Glue, *Food Manuf.*, **13**, 46 (1938); *cf.* FRIEDEN, Protein Adhesives, *Chem. Inds.*, **59**, 835 (1946).

[3] RADLEY, Clarification and Bleaching of Gelatine and Glue, *Food Manuf.*, **11**, 242 (1936).

that used for producing other gelatines. It is for this reason that the price of photographic gelatine is nearly twice that of the edible variety. The reagents used must be very pure. For example, lime used in the process must be free from Fe and Mg salts, or else the gelatine cannot be used in photography.[1]

GLUES AND ADHESIVES

Though glues and adhesives[2] are often considered as insignificant materials, they are indispensable and necessary in the production of many of the commonly accepted necessities of life. Strictly interpreted, glue is derived from connective tissues of animals. However, many adhesives, not glues, are commonly called *glues* where they are used as substitutes for glue.

Historical. Animal glue is the oldest type of glue, having been known for at least 3,300 years. It has been an important article of commerce for more than a century, while commercial production of other "glues" is chiefly a recent development. Casein adhesive and starch adhesives became of commercial importance about a generation ago; soybean-protein adhesive in the last 20 years; and synthetic-resin adhesive has been developed only within the last decade. In 1951, 293,000,000 lb. of protein-base adhesives, 369,000,000 lb. of vegetable adhesives, and 290,000,000 lb. of synthetic-resin adhesives were produced (see Table 4).

Protein Adhesives. Because of their stronger, more flexible films, the most popular adhesives of all are *animal glues*. These are made chiefly from waste products of the meat-packing and tanning industries such as fleshings, bones, trimmings, and materials too low in purity for the manufacture of gelatine. Although animal glue is traditionally associated with the woodworking industry, millions of pounds are used annually for rayon sizing and for protective coatings applied to paper, floor coverings, and packaging materials. Sizing paper with animal glue enables it to withstand wear, resist water and ink, and facilitate erasure. *Fish glues*, liquid glues made from waste materials of cod, haddock, cusk, hake, and pollock, have practically the same applications as animal glues. *Casein*, the milk-derived protein, is the basis of another large class of adhesives and can be made both water- and non-water-resistant. Casein adhesives are widely employed in the woodworking industry and in the manufacture of drinking cups, straws, and ice-cream containers. *Soya-protein adhesives* although similar in properties to casein adhesives, are cheaper but not

[1] CHARRIOU and VALETTE, Manufacture of Photographic Gelatine, 15*me. Congr. chim. ind.*, **50** (1936); SHEPPARD, *op. cit.*

[2] FRIEDEN, Modern Methods and Materials for Adhesive Manufacture, *Chem. Inds.*, **59**, 641, 835, 1002 (1946). This excellent article is divided into three parts—starch, protein, and synthetic-resin adhesives.

so good. The two are generally employed in combination, particularly in the veneer field, thus permitting a reduction in glue costs. *Albumin adhesives*, both egg and blood, find specialized uses where low film strength is not of importance yet water resistance is. To adhere the cork pads to crown bottle caps is one of these applications. *Zein*, the protein, is used to a small extent as an adhesive particularly in combination with other bases. *Peanut protein* hydrates are the newest of protein-based adhesives and are suitable for making gummed tape and flexible glues for boxes and books.

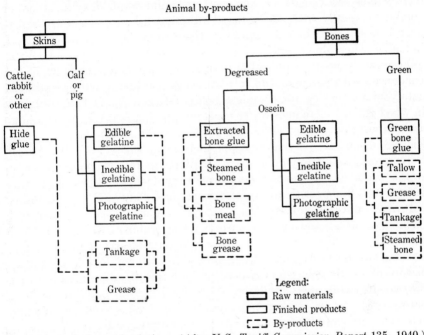

FIG. 3. Animal glue and gelatines. (*After U.S. Tariff Commission Report* 135, 1940.)

Starch Adhesives. Starch adhesives or glues were first found in large-scale industrial application approximately in the 1910's. The chief kinds on the market today are made from corn starch, tapioca flour, wheat flour, cassava starch, and potato starch. Starch adhesives may be applied cold and do not have the undesirable characteristic odors of some animal glues. This is one of the chief advantages of these adhesives over animal glues, although most of them have the disadvantage of less strength and water resistance than animal glues. Starch adhesives are less costly than synthetic-resin adhesives. *Native starch* is widely employed as an adhesive for veneer, plywood, and corrugated and laminated boards where water resistance is not important. Incorporated with 5 to 15 per cent resins such as urea- or melamine-formaldehyde, it is used for cartons where water resistance is important. Through enzyme conversions it is a base for many liquid adhesives. Native starch is the raw material for hydration to dextrins and British gums. *Dextrins* and *British gums* are modified starches important for envelope gums, gummed paper, labeling glues for glass, metal, and wood, cartons, laminated boards, and padding glues. Tapioca dextrin is the adhesive used for postage stamps.

Synthetic Resin Adhesives. These adhesives are desired where water resistance is required and special conditions are to be met. *Urea-melamine resin* adhesives consist of urea- or melamine-formaldehyde alone or combined usually with starch-based adhesives where some water resistance is desirable. The chief outlet of these resins is in the woodworking industry where high water resistance is not essential. *Phenolic-resin*[1] adhesives are based on phenol or derivatives such as resorcinol which are condensed with aldehydes or ketones. They are thermosetting and need catalysts and curing for complete polymerization. Their chief outlet is in wood gluing where high water resistance is required. Vinyls are a large and important class of adhesives which contain water-soluble and insoluble members, polymers, copolymers, emulsions, and dispersions. Polyvinyl alcohol polymers are used along and in combination with starch products, caseins, rubbers, urea-formaldehyde resins, and other vinyl compounds for a variety of applications. Polyvinyl acetate resins, polyvinyl butyral (glass laminations), vinylidene chloride polymer (rubber surfaces), and vinyl chloride polymer (rubber surfaces) complete the picture. *Cellulose adhesives* of particular interest are cellulose acetate, nitrate, and butyrate and ethyl cellulose for solvent-soluble adhesives. Methyl and carboxymethyl cellulose are important for aqueous adhesives. Alkyds, acrylates, methacrylates, allyls, hydrocarbon polymers such as indene, coumarone, styrene polymers, silicone resins, and natural and synthetic rubbers all find application as additives or bases. Because of the limitless variations possible, the manufacture of synthetic-resin adhesives will not be discussed here.[2]

Other Adhesives. There are many more adhesives on the market, such as sodium silicate solutions, mucilage which is a solution of gum arabic or acacia in water, asphalts, waxes, rosin, and shellacs. Except for sodium silicate (see Chap. 14, page 280), the others are more or less specialty adhesives and additives.[3]

[1] SAWYER, *et al.*, Phenolic Resin Glues for Plywood, *Ind. Eng. Chem.*, **40**, 1011 (1948).

[2] See Chap. 35 for the manufacture of the specific resins; *cf.* FRIEDEN, Modern Methods and Materials for Adhesive Manufacture, *Chem. Inds.*, **59**, 1002 (1946); KIRK and OTHMER, *op. cit.*, Vol. 1, pp. 191–205; DELMONTE, "The Technology of Adhesives," Reinhold Publishing Corporation, New York, 1947.

[3] *Cf.* MANTELL, "The Water-soluble Gums," Reinhold Publishing Corporation, New York, 1947.

MANUFACTURE

Animal Glues.[1] The manufacture of glue is almost identical with the manufacture of gelatine. The procedures include grinding bones, cutting hides and scraps into small pieces, degreasing the material by percolating

TABLE 4. GLUES AND ADHESIVES CONSUMED IN THE UNITED STATES, 1947 AND LATER[a]

(All figures in thousands)

	Quantity, lb.[b]	Value
Glues, total...	......	$59,519
Animal glue:		
Hide...	67,386	18,467
Extracted bone.................................	18,114	4,638
Green bone.....................................	69,128	15,244
Vegetable glue.....................................	55,844	4,706
Flexible glue......................................	22,316	4,453
Casein glue.......................................	4,267	1,167
Other glues, including liquid and fish.................	......	10,844
Adhesives and cements, other than glue, total............	......	59,184
Collodion-type adhesives...........................	3,302	1,986
Dextrin-type adhesives............................	76,543	9,314
Fish-glue adhesives................................	287	101
Casein adhesives..................................	26,481	4,515
Synthetic-resin adhesives..........................	35,275	6,074
Furnace cement...................................	12,457	730
Gum-arabic pastes................................	254	69
Mucilage...	......	1,090
Plastic-wood preparations..........................	2,672	1,290
Starch pastes.....................................	63,116	5,323
Other adhesives and cements.......................	......	28,692
Rubber cements, gal...............................	17,650	20,982

[a] 1947 Census of Manufactures. Details are not available for later years, but animal and vegetable glues had a total value of $53,764,000 in 1952 or a decrease from the corresponding figure of $59,519,000 for 1947. Other data, by SKEEN, *Chem. Eng. News*, **30**, 4133 (1952), present an estimate of an annual output for organic adhesives of 200 million dollars per year, but this figure includes about 290,000,000 lb. of synthetic resins not in above table.

[b] All quantities listed are in thousands of pounds, except for rubber cements, which are thousands of gallons.

a grease solvent through it, liming and plumping, washing, making several extractions by hot water, filtering liquors, evaporating, chilling, and drying the jelly slabs in a tunnel. When dry, the slabs of glue are flaked or

[1] Cf. HULL and BANGERT, Animal Glue, *Ind. Eng. Chem.*, **44**, 2275 (1952), for an excellent description accompanied by excellent pictures, tables, and a flow sheet.

ground, blended, graded, and barreled or bagged for shipment (see Figs. 2 and 3).

Variations of this process have been developed which do away with the tunnel drying and considerable hand labor. These consist of forcing the evaporated chilled extraction liquors containing 50 per cent glue through a wire grill or colander instead of placing slabs in a tunnel drier. The glue when forced through the wire grill is cut off into small pellets by knifelike blades. The pellets are dried in a three-stage drying system using bins and rakes to stir the pellets. In some processes the pellets are dropped from the colander or grill into a chilling bath, such as benzene, where they solidify. The adhering benzene evaporates and the pellets are dried. This pellet form of glue is known as *pearl* glue. However, more than three-fourths of the glue produced in the United States is sold in the ground form and the remaining fourth is sold in the flake and pellet form, most of which is mainly flake.

Starch Adhesives. Native starches are prepared from grains or roots. Dextrins are made by heating a dry starch with dilute acid causing partial hydration. British gums result from heating native starch with small amounts of catalysts. British gums are gummier and more adhesive than dextrins. In the manufacture of starch adhesives, rarely are the dextrins, British gums, or starches used alone. Many chemicals may be admixed as indicated. Borax increases viscosity, gumminess, rate of tack, and speed of production. A 50 per cent dextrin solution equals a 25 per cent dextrin solution plus 10 to 15 per cent borax. Sodium hydroxide accentuates borax action and also improves penetration for rosin-sized materials. Other chemicals which function in a like manner but to a lesser degree are Na_2CO_3, KOH, and K_2CO_3. Urea works the opposite of borax, thus enabling manufacturers to use gummy products which would otherwise be unworkable. Other materials used in the manufacture of starch adhesives are plasticizers, defoaming agents, preservatives, "fluidifying agents" (delay viscosity increase upon aging), coloring, flavoring, and emulsifying agents. The latter are used where the surface to be glued is sized with wax or other organic-soluble agents.

SELECTED REFERENCES

Glues, Gelatines and Related Products, *U.S. Tariff Comm. Rept.* 135, 1940.
Lewis, Warren K., Lombard Squires, and Geoffrey Broughton, "Industrial Chemistry of Colloidal and Amorphous Materials," The Macmillan Company, New York, 1942.
Wilson, J. A., "The Chemistry of Leather Manufacture," Vols. 1 and 2, Reinhold Publishing Corporation, New York, 1928, 1929.
———, "Modern Practice in Leather Manufacture," Reinhold Publishing Corporation, New York, 1941.

Smith, P. I., "Glue and Gelatine," Chemical Publishing Company, Inc., New York, 1943.

McLaughlin, G. O., and E. R. Theis, "The Chemistry of Leather Manufacture," Reinhold Publishing Corporation, New York, 1945.

Chen, P. S., "Syntans and New Methods of Tanning," The Chemical Elements, South Lancaster, Mass., 1950.

Delmonte, John, "The Technology of Adhesives," Reinhold Publishing Corporation, New York, 1947.

Woodroffe, David, editor, "Standard Handbook of Industrial Leathers," The National Trade Press, London, 1949.

Alexander, Jerome, "Glues and Gelatines," Reinhold Publishing Corporation, New York, 1923.

National Association of Glue Manufacturers, Inc., "Animal Glue in Industry," New York, 1951.

De Bruyne, N. A., and R. Houwink, "Adhesion and Adhesives," Elsevier Press, Inc., Houston, Tex., 1951.

Herfeld, Hans, "Grundlagen der Lederherstellung," T. Steinkopf, Dresden, Germany, 1950.

CHAPTER 26

PESTICIDES

This chapter covers the important utilization of chemicals to control either plant or animal life disadvantageous to man and his domestic animals. Reliable authorities have carefully estimated[1] the annual loss

TABLE 1. PESTICIDES AND OTHER ORGANIC AGRICULTURAL CHEMICALS[a]

	1953		1954[b]	
	Production 1,000 lb.	Price per lb.	Production 1,000 lb.	Price per lb.
Grand total..........................	355,953	$0.35	418,723	$0.37
Fungicides and seed disinfectants, cyclic total	44,832	0.33	57,993	0.44
Naphthenic acid, copper salt..............	3,268	0.22	3,557	0.22
Phenyl mercuric oleate..................	47	3.95	142	
Herbicides and plant hormones, total........	64,349	0.64	63,462	0.71
2,4-D (2,4-dichlorophenoxyacetic acid).....	49,590	0.48	52,719	0.47
2,4,5-T (2,4,5-trichlorophenoxyacetic acid)	10,667	1.45	6,574	1.22
Phenyl mercuric acetate..................	154	3.73	598	5.48
Insecticides, total........................	187,873	0.28	235,527	0.29
B.H.C. (benzene-hexachloride)............	57,363	0.11	76,934	0.11
Parathion..............................	2,999	.....	3,889	1.32
D.D.T. (dichloro-diphenyl-trichloroethane).	84,366	0.25	97,198	0.24
Fumigants, fungicides, seed disinfectants, herbicides, and insecticides, acyclic total....	58,899	0.40	61,741	0.25
Dimethyldithiocarbamic acid, sodium salt..	538	0.63	471	0.40
Dimethyldithiocarbamic acid, zinc salt (Ziram)...............................	1,152	0.59	1,117	0.53
Tetraethyl pyrophosphate (T.E.P.P.)......	229	0.85	361	0.89

[a] "Synthetic Organic Chemicals," U.S. Tariff Commission, Washington, D.C., printed annually; see preceding for statistics for less important items.
[b] Preliminary.

by agricultural pests to be more than 13 billion dollars. Of this, about 4 billion dollars is caused by insects, the same amount by fungi and plant

[1] Editors, Agricultural Chemicals, *Chem. Eng. News*, **30**, 3078 (1953); WELLMAN, Synthetic Chemicals for Agriculture, *Chem. Ind.*, **62**, 914 (1948); **63**, 223 (1948); *cf.* Symposium on Insecticides in Food Production, *Ind. Eng. Chem.*, **40**, 673 (1948).

diseases, and 5 billion dollars by weeds. The farmer now spends some 300 million dollars annually for pest-control materials; approximately 1 per cent of the cash value of all farm sales (see Table 1). It cannot be stated too strongly that this large loss would be still larger were not these pests kept under some measure of control by the use of chemicals, accompanied by other means, such as the proper cultivation of the soil and the appropriate construction of homes and barns.

Every citizen is concerned with this tremendous loss and should be interested in the chemical warfare directed against man's normal enemies. It is a most important step in the conservation of our resources and in increasing the productivity of our soil. The chemical engineer is called upon to manufacture these domestic chemical warfare agents and in special conditions to assist in their application. This chapter will present, in general, the use of these compounds and, in particular, the means for the manufacture of products for pest control, whether the pests be plants or animals, macro or micro in size, or whether the pests be disturbing our food, our bodies, our clothing, or our habitations.

INSECTICIDES

Insecticides are agents or preparations for destroying insects and are usually classified according to their method of action. *Stomach poisons* are lethal only to insects that ingest them; *contact insecticides* kill following

TABLE 2. INSECTICIDES CLASSIFIED ACCORDING TO METHOD OF ACTION

Stomach poisons	Contact insecticides	Fumigants
BHC, DDT, methoxychlor, Systox, lead arsenate, calcium arsenate, paris green, sodium fluoride, cryolite, fluosilicates, compounds of borax, thallium, phosphorus, and mercury	BHC, DDT, toxaphene, chlordan, dieldrin, aldrin, methoxychlor, nicotine preparations, lime-sulfur, oil emulsions, pyrethrins, rotenone, synthetic thiocyanates, and organic phosphates such as hexaethyl tetraphosphate, parathion, and Systox	BHC, hydrogen cyanide, carbon disulfide, nicotine, sulfur dioxide, p-dichlorobenzene, naphthalene, chloropicrin, ethylene oxide and dichloride, methyl bromide and formate

external bodily contact; and *fumigants* act on the insect through the respiratory system. Table 2 lists some of the principal insecticides in each class. They may be applied as a spray if liquid or in solution, as a dust, or as a gas. The *systemics* are a group of insecticides which, unlike conventional insecticides, are absorbed right into the sap stream and translocated throughout the plant. Thus they render plants toxic to aphids, red spider mites, and other sucking insects that are notoriously hard to kill. This concept of insecticides is very new, but the possibilities could be limitless through proper selectivity, *i.e.*, lethal to harmful insects but harmless to beneficial ones.

History. Records show that insecticides were used as long ago as 1000 B.C. However, they were more often useless than useful as they were based on legend and superstition rather than on scientific knowledge. The essential property of early insecticides was a disagreeable odor rather than a poisonous nature. Although the toxic properties of arsenic were known as early as A.D. 40, it was not employed in the Western world until 1669. About the middle of the last century the use of paris green, lead arsenate, and other really poisonous chemicals was started as a general method of insect control.[1]

Inorganic Insecticides. In recent years inorganic compounds for insecticides have been displaced by organic compounds in many applications. However, they are still the mainstays of the agricultural chemicals industry. Arsenicals, fluorine,[2] and phosphorus compounds are among the sufficiently toxic practical insecticides. Their major disadvantage is their comparable toxicity to man and other warm-blooded animals by handling and residues on food products.

The arsenates, because of their greater safety and versatility, have almost completely displaced the more insect-toxic arsenites. *Paris green,* $Cu(C_2H_3O_2)_2 \cdot 3Cu(AsO_2)_2$, was the first commercially prepared arsenical to come into use. It is made by treating copper arsenite with dilute acetic acid.[3] It is not so widely used as some of the other arsenicals because of its burning effect on plant foliage and because certain organics are more effective. Its principal uses are for the potato beetle and as a sulfur-combined dust against cotton insects.

The *lead arsenate* commonly used as an insecticide is an acid lead arsenate, $PbHAsO_4$. Many other lead arsenates, $Pb_2As_2O_7$, $PbH_2As_2O_7$, etc., are known and occasionally employed for this purpose. Acid lead arsenate may be prepared by the following series of reactions:[4]

$$3PbO + 2CH_3CO_2H \rightarrow (CH_3CO_2)_2Pb \cdot 2PbO + H_2O$$
$$(CH_3CO_2)_2Pb \cdot 2PbO + 2H_3AsO_4 \rightarrow Pb_3(AsO_4)_2 + 2CH_3CO_2H + 2H_2O$$
$$Pb_3(AsO_4)_2 + 2HNO_3 \rightarrow 2PbHAsO_4 + Pb(NO_3)_2$$
$$Pb(NO_3)_2 + H_3AsO_4 \rightarrow PbHAsO_4 + 2HNO_3$$

The actual manufacture of acid lead arsenate is much simpler than the equations indicate. Litharge is dissolved in the calculated quantities of

[1] SHEPARD, "The Chemistry and Action of Insecticides," McGraw-Hill Book Company, Inc., New York, 1951.

[2] NORTON, Inorganic Insecticides, *Ind. Eng. Chem.*, **40**, 619 (1948).

[3] For further details, see the 1st ed. of this book.

[4] ALLEN, U.S. Pat. 1427049(1922).

acetic acid and nitric acid. The theoretical quantity of arsenic acid is added, the precipitated lead arsenate removed by filtration, and the mixture of acetic and nitric acids in the filtrate used over again. Three precipitations of lead arsenate can be made before the spent acid has to be strengthened or discarded. The yields range from 95 to 97 per cent. The commercial product contains 31 to 33 per cent arsenic trioxide and is colored pink to safeguard against confusion with foods such as flour and baking powder. Lead arsenate is widely used, chiefly for the potato beetle and for the codling moth in apple orchards.

Calcium arsenate is cheaper than lead arsenate but does not adhere so well to leaves, thus rendering it less effective. Three calcium arsenates are known, $CaH_4(AsO_4)_2$, $CaHAsO_4$, and $Ca_3(AsO_4)_2$. Both the monocalcium arsenate and dicalcium arsenate are too soluble in water to be used as insecticides. The commercial insecticidal product is usually a mixture of tricalcium arsenate, $Ca_3(AsO_4)_2$, and lime, called *basic* calcium arsenate. The manufacture of basic calcium arsenate may be carried out by adding a dilute solution of arsenic acid to a saturated solution of hydrated lime.[1] To prevent the formation of crystals of soluble dicalcium arsenate coated with insoluble tricalcium arsenate, the arsenic acid solution is atomized into the lime solution and the mixture vigorously agitated. The chief use of calcium arsenate is to control the cotton boll weevil, although it is being displaced by other organic compounds.

Fluorine compounds are important stomach-poison insecticides as substitutes for the arsenicals. As they are also extremely poisonous to man, caution should be observed in their application and handling.

The fluorides are too water-soluble to be used on plants, but sodium fluoride is widely employed to control roaches and poultry lice. Some of the fluosilicates and fluoaluminates may be applied to crops because of their decreased solubility. The principal compounds that are suitable are barium fluosilicate and sodium fluoaluminate (cryolite). Cryolite is a natural mineral although synthetic cryolites are available. Its use as an insecticide is very minor compared with its consumption in the manufacture of aluminum (see Chap. 16). Sodium aluminum fluosilicate is extensively sold today as a mothproofing compound.

Sulfur and *sulfur compounds* are employed to some extent as contact insecticides for the control of mites, spiders, and other insects of that type, but their chief use is as fungicides.[2] In 1951 sulfur (see Chap. 19) alone accounted for over one-third of the total production of all pesticides. Suitable forms, *i.e.*, degrees of fineness, of the element are obtained by milling to 325 mesh or finer, emulsifying molten sulfur, heating mixtures of sulfur with Bentonite, and using flotation sulfur obtained from the

---

[1] NELSON, Preparation of Calcium Arsenates of Low Solubility, *J. Econ. Entomol.*, **32**, 370 (1939).

[2] BALDWIN, Sulfur in Fungicides, *Ind. Eng. Chem.*, **42**, 2227 (1950).

recovery of the element from hydrogen sulfide from petroleum and coal gases. Finely ground sulfur may be employed for dusting without any additives, but wetting agents are needed for the preparation of suspensions for spray purposes.

The lime-sulfurs are widely applied for the control of scale insects. These may be prepared by adding water to a dry mixture of lime and sulfur and using the heat of reaction from slaking the lime, to accelerate the reaction between calcium hydroxide and sulfur to give a self-boiled lime-sulfur; by boiling a mixture of lime, sulfur, and water with external heat; or by evaporating the water from the boiled mixture to furnish a dry mix. Although the reaction is complex it is believed that the pentasulfide is the most active fungicidally.

Sulfur dioxide is the oldest known fumigant. It is usually made *in situ* by burning candles of molded sulfur. Although it is injurious to living plants and so cannot be applied on trees, it is effective for the fumigation of homes and granaries.

Hydrocyanic acid is an efficient fumigant for many pests, especially insects. Large quantities are used in the citrus fruit industry and smaller amounts for greenhouse and household fumigation. When applied on a small scale, the gas is generated as needed by adding sulfuric acid to "eggs" of sodium cyanide. The citrus fruitgrowers, however, use a commercially manufactured liquid product that contains up to 98 per cent hydrocyanic acid, the rest being water. To fumigate a citrus grove, each tree is covered with an airtight cotton tent. The liquid hydrocyanic acid is vaporized or sprayed inside the cover to produce an effective concentration. Care must be taken in handling this material as it is not only a powerful insecticide but also an extreme poison to men and animals.

The steps in the manufacture[1] are as follows, as shown in Fig. 1. An aqueous solution of sodium cyanide (Chap. 14) is mixed with concentrated sulfuric acid and allowed to react. Most of the hydrocyanic acid is expelled by the heat of the reaction. The remainder is removed by heating the residual solution of sodium sulfate with live steam to 103 to 104°C. The mixture of hydrocyanic acid and steam is passed through a cooler where some of the steam condenses and the vapors are sent to a still. Water, almost free of hydrocyanic acid, is collected at the bottom of the still and the vapor is fairly pure hydrocyanic acid. The vapors are conducted through two condensers. The first is cooled with water and about 30 per cent of the acid is liquefied. The second condenser is cooled with brine to liquefy the remainder of the acid. The liquid hydrocyanic acid is degassed to remove carbon dioxide impurity and is adjusted to

[1] CARLISLE, The Manufacture, Handling and Use of Hydrocyanic Acid, *Trans. Am. Inst. Chem. Engrs.*, **29**, 113 (1933). See ANON., Hydrocyanic Acid, *Chem. Eng.*, **57** (11), 127 (1950); the materials of construction are listed for flow sheet.

standard concentration (97 per cent), stabilized with 0.005 per cent by weight of sulfuric acid and packed into tinned steel drums.

Hydrogen cyanide is employed in the production of chemical intermediates for acrylic resins and other products. This has stimulated direct synthesis.[1] When ammonia, air, and natural gas are passed over a red-hot platinum catalyst, they react, probably, as follows:

$$NH_3 + CH_4 + 1\tfrac{1}{2} O_2 \xrightarrow{Pt} HCN + 3H_2O$$

The product gases are scrubbed free from the unconverted ammonia and passed to an absorber where the HCN is removed. The HCN is distilled,

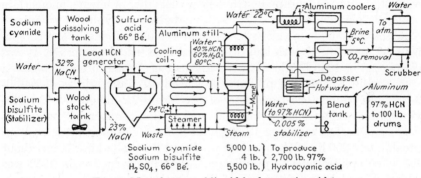

Sodium cyanide   5,000 lb. ⎱ To produce
Sodium bisulfite   4 lb. ⎰ 2,700 lb. 97%
H₂SO₄, 66° Bé.   5,500 lb. ⎰ Hydrocyanic acid

Fig. 1. Manufacture of liquid hydrocyanic acid.[1]

condensed, and handled by refrigeration to avoid losses by evaporation. In one plant the HCN is combined with acetone or ethylene glycol for the plastics intermediates: acetone cyanhydrin or ethylene cyanhydrin, respectively (see Chap. 35). Hydrogen cyanide is also obtained from coke-oven gas on a commercial scale.[2]

Plant Derivatives. Many of the plant derivatives used as insecticides depend for toxicity upon the alkaloids that they contain. These insecticides constitute only a small amount, around 3 per cent for 1944, of the total tonnage consumed annually.[3] As is true of the inorganic insecticide industry, many of the plant-derived insecticides are being supplanted by the synthetic organics.

Pyrethrum. Flowers of the pyrethrum plant (a type of chrysanthemum) contain toxic, nonnitrogenous organic esters (pyrethrins). The principal sources are Kenya, Japan, Belgian Congo, and Brazil. The bales of com-

---

[1] Lee, Hydrogen Cyanide Production, *Chem. Eng.*, **56** (2), 134 (1949). A flow sheet is included.

[2] Kastens and Barraclough, Cyanides from the Coke Oven, *Ind. Eng. Chem.*, **43**, 1882 (1951); *cf.* Chap. 7.

[3] Seiferle and Frear, Insecticides Derived from Plants, *Ind. Eng. Chem.*, **40**, 683 (1948).

pressed flowers are broken up, ground to a fine powder, and extracted several times with kerosene or other organic solvent. The extract is concentrated by removing the solvent in a vacuum still below 60°C., and the resulting oleoresin is employed to prepare the finished insecticide.[1] Pyrethrum is important because of its quick "knockdown" power against flies and nontoxicity to man and warm-blooded animals. The widespread use of pyrethrins in aerosol bombs for household use has led to the preparation of highly concentrated extracts free from precipitated metals to avoid clogging the nozzle. Nitromethane is a satisfactory solvent for this use. *Synergists* or activators (substances which increase the insecticidal efficiency) are employed with pyrethrum. The most important are sesame oil, isobutylundecyleneamide, ethylene glycol ether of pinene, and certain synthetic piperonyl[2] derivatives with methylene dioxyphenyl groupings.

Allethrin is the name given to the allyl homolog of cinerin I, a component of pyrethrum, with almost identical insecticidal properties. It was discovered in 1949 by the U.S. Department of Agriculture and within a year was in commercial production. Chemically, allethrin is *dl*-2-allyl-3-methyl-cyclopentene-1-one ester of *dl-cis-trans*-2,2-dimethyl-3-(2-methylpropenyl)cyclo-propanecarboxylic acid.[3] The commercial process is very complicated requiring 12 steps, 11 different intermediates, and approximately 200 lb. of chemicals to produce 1 lb. of allethrin. It has about the same applications as pyrethrum. Allethrin production in 1952 was 60,000 lb. which was about half of the pyrethrum imports.

Nicotine is a volatile alkaloid obtained by treating by-products of the tobacco-processing industry, *i.e.*, stems and damaged leaves, with an aqueous solution of alkali, followed by steam distillation. Because of its volatile nature, most of the nicotine is converted to the sulfate and sold as a 40 per cent nicotine solution. Nicotine sulfate solutions are employed against aphids, leafhoppers, and thrips. Nicotine preparations are used as fumigants.

Rotenone is the poisonous principle of the roots of several tropical and subtropical plants, chief among which is derris. It is a nonnitrogenous complex organic heterocyclic compound, $C_{23}H_{22}O_6$. The rotenone is obtained by extracting the ground derris roots with chloroform or carbon tetrachloride. Other compounds related to rotenone, but not so toxic, are also present in the extract. However, no attempt is usually made to separate the rotenone from these materials. The solvent is removed and the residue is dissolved in water-soluble solvents such as acetone.

Rotenoid compounds are effective stomach and contact poisons. They

[1] GNADINGER and CORL, Manufacture of Concentrated Pyrethrum Extract, *Ind. Eng. Chem.*, **24**, 988 (1932).

[2] FREAR, "Chemistry of Insecticides and Fungicides," 2d ed., D. Van Nostrand Company, Inc., New York, 1948.

[3] ANON., Carbide Makes Allethrin, *Chem. Eng.*, **57** (6), 11 (1950).

have long been used as fish poisons by natives of the East Indies and Japan, but their chief applications in the United States are as insecticides.

Synthetic Organics. The phenomenal increase in synthetic organic compounds for insecticides since the Second World War has revolutionized this industry. In 1940 the combined output of synthetic organic insecticides was but a few million pounds per year, yet in 1953 the annual production capacity was over 261,000,000 lb.

D.D.T., or Dichloro-diphenyl-trichloroethane. This was first made by Zeidler in Germany in 1874, but its insecticidal properties were not discovered until 1937. It was extensively used during the Second World War to control body lice and as a mosquito larvicide. It was the first chemical to have *great enough residual contact action to be useful, i.e.,* an insect can be killed by simply walking over a dried, sprayed surface. It is widely employed as a household insecticide, against leafhoppers on potatoes, in combination with benzene hexachloride and sulfur in cotton insect control, and for the codling moth in apple orchards (see Table 1 for statistics). However, D.D.T. has shortcomings which naturally accelerated the development of other insecticides. Although not so toxic as some insecticides to man and warm-blooded animals, it can be stored in harmful concentration in animal fatty tissues. It can be transmitted through cow's milk, and D.D.T. residues are not readily removed from fruits by washing. Two other major difficulties are the development of D.D.T.-resistant strains of pests, and the appearance of new pests when one is controlled. For example, in the apple industry, the codling moth has been a problem for years. Now D.D.T. gives excellent control, but the European mite and the red-banded leaf roller are increasing. This is probably due to the killing of the natural predators by D.D.T. which is ineffective on the new pests. The problems discussed here are much the same with all the synthetic organics and have led to the development of many new types.

There are several commercial methods of manufacture for D.D.T. The usual method[1] is the exothermic condensation of chloral and chlorobenzene in the presence of oleum:

$$2C_6H_5Cl + OCHCCl_3 \rightarrow (C_6H_4Cl)_2CHCCl_3 + H_2O$$

The process as depicted in Fig. 2 can be broken down into the following coordinated *unit processes* (Pr.) and *unit operations* (Op.).

Alcohol is chlorinated to chloral-alcoholate in a 750-gal. glass-lined chlorinator, first at below 30°C., but eventually up to 75°C. and 90°C. (Pr.). This takes place

[1] Anon., DDT, *Chem. Eng.*, **57** (11), 204 (1950), with pictured flow sheet; Cook, *et al.*, Synthesis of DDT with Chlorosulfonic Acid as a Condensation Agent, *Ind. Eng. Chem.*, **39**, 868 (1947); Anon., DDT Eyes Fluosulfonic Process, *Chem. Eng.*, **59** (2), 247 (1952); Lee, "Materials of Construction for Chemical Process Industries," p. 114, McGraw-Hill Book Company, Inc., New York, 1950.

over the course of 60 to 70 hr. with the temperature controlled through water in either coils or a jacket (Op.).

The overhead (excess alcohol and HCl) is conducted to a partial condenser (dephlegmator or scavengar) which condenses the alcohol, from the HCl which is absorbed and the small amount of ethyl chloride which is vented (Op.).

The chloral-alcoholate is decomposed by H_2SO_4 into chloral and alcohol (Pr.) and purified by distillation (Op.).

The chloral and chlorobenzene are condensed using strong H_2SO_4 (100 per cent) or oleum in a glass-lined 1,000-gal. reactor (Pr.). Reaction takes 5 to 6 hr. and is controlled at 15 to 30°C. by the brine or steam coils (Pr.).

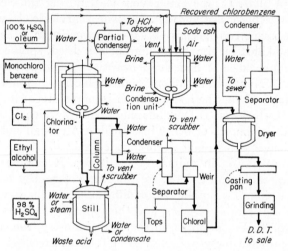

FIG. 2. Flow sheet for manufacture of D.D.T. [*Modified from Chem. Eng.*, **57** (11), 204 (1950).]

The spent acid is withdrawn (Op.) and the D.D.T. is water-washed several times (Op.) and neutralized with soda ash (Pr.). The D.D.T. and chlorobenzene mixture is dropped to a 500-gal. drier where steam melts the D.D.T. and distills any unreacted chlorobenzene overhead (Op.).

The molten D.D.T. is run to casting pans to solidify and to be ground (Op.).

D.D.T. can exist in a number of isomers. The p,p' isomer is the most potent, and manufacturing procedures are conducted to give a maximum of this isomer. However, technical grades contain considerable amounts of the o,p' isomer as an impurity. For use in aerosol bombs, D.D.T. is purified.

B.H.C., or Benzene Hexachloride. This compound exists in a number of stereoisomers, the gamma being by far the most toxic. Because of this remarkable specificity, the insecticidal value was not discovered until 1942 in England although the compound was first prepared by Faraday in 1825. B.H.C., or correctly, 1,2,3,4,5,6-hexachlorocyclohexane is made by the chlorination of benzene in the presence of actinic light:

$$C_6H_6 + 3Cl_2 \rightarrow C_6H_6Cl_6$$

Widely used to control boll weevil in cotton, B.H.C., unless purified, is generally unsuitable for food crops because of its strong musty odor. *Lindane*, a refined material containing at least 99 per cent of the gamma isomer of B.H.C., has largely overcome the odor. It may be used on food crops and is increasingly employed to combat insects that have developed immunity to D.D.T.

Methoxychlor or bis(methoxyphenyl)trichloroethane. This compound has —OCH_3 groups substituted for the —Cl groups of D.D.T. Methoxychlor has high insecticidal efficiency, low toxicity to warm-blooded animals, and safety to plants. It also has greater knockdown power than D.D.T. It is used safely on cattle, vegetable and forage crops, and household pests. Methoxychlor can be made by reacting methyl chloride or dimethyl sulfate with sodium phenate to produce anisole which is then reacted with chloral:

$$CH_3Cl + NaOC_6H_5 \rightarrow CH_3OC_6H_5$$
$$2CH_3OC_6H_5 + OCHCCl_3 \rightarrow (CH_3OC_6H_4)_2CHCCl_3 + H_2O$$

Chlordan is 1,2,4,5,6,7,8,8-octachloro-4,7-methano-3a,4,7,7a-tetrahydroindane. This insecticide is very successful against cricket and locust plagues, cockroaches, and ants. It is employed with D.D.T. against bedbugs. *Heptachlor*, or specifically 1,4,5,6,7,8,8-heptachloro-3a,4,7,7a-tetrahydro-4,7-methanoindene was first isolated from chlordane for study. Because of its similar applications and efficacy against cotton pests, heptachlor is now made by a commercial process based on the Diels-Alder reaction of hexachloro-cyclo-pentadiene and cyclopentadiene.

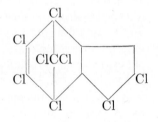

Toxaphene, an important chlorinated camphene insecticide, kills all common cotton pests and is officially recommended by Federal and many state authorities for 74 destructive insects. It is made by chlorinating camphene to 67 to 69 per cent chlorine. Camphene is produced by isomerizing α-pinene, a major constituent of turpentine. The conditions of manufacture are both corrosive and toxic. Toxaphene has the approximate empirical formula $C_{10}H_6Cl_8$. It is a yellow waxy solid (m.p. 65 to 90°C.) with a mild piny odor. It is sold in large amounts.

Tetraethyl pyrophosphate or T.E.P.P. has been found to be the principal active ingredient[1] of the *hexaethyl tetraphosphate* mixtures which replace nicotine for the control of aphids, thrips, and mites. The commercial product is an amber hygroscopic liquid that can be prepared by:

$$5(C_2H_5)_3PO_4 + POCl_3 \rightarrow 3C_2H_5Cl + 3(C_2H_5)_4P_2O_7$$

---

[1] HALL and JACOBSON, Hexaethyl Tetraphosphate and Tetraethyl Pyrophosphate, *Ind. Eng. Chem.*, **40**, 694 (1948).

Manufacturing processes are now so conducted to obtain a maximum yield of T.E.P.P. The above reaction does not yield the pure chemical, but a mixture.

Parathion is another organic phosphate that is five to twenty times as toxic to insects as D.D.T. Chemically it is *O,O*-diethyl-*p*-nitrophenyl thiophosphate. It is made as follows:

$$2C_2H_5ONa + PSCl_3 \rightarrow (C_2H_5O)_2PSCl + 2NaCl$$

Sodium   Thiophosphoryl   Diethyoxy
ethylate   chloride   thiophosphoryl
                            monochloride

$$(C_2H_5O)_2PSCl + NaOC_6H_4NO_2 \rightarrow (C_2H_5O)_2PS\text{-}O\text{-}C_6H_4NO_2 + NaCl$$

Parathion is highly toxic to a very wide range of insects at concentrations that are almost fantastically low. It is also a systemic, but the most prominent systemics are *O,O*-diethyl-*O*-2-(ethylmercapto)-ethyl thiophosphate (*Systox*) and octamethyl pyrophosphoramide (schradan, OMPA, or Pestox 3). The former is the only systemic approved by the U.S. Department of Agriculture for the control of aphids and mites on cotton as of 1952. The use of the latter is being confined to greenhouse aerosols.

Dichloro-diphenyl-dichlorethane is less injurious to corn than D.D.T. and is used for control of the corn borer. It may be prepared by passing chlorine into ethanol, forming a mixture which is directly condensed with chlorobenzene. *Aliphatic thiocyanates* are employed particularly for greenhouse pests or flies. *Phenothiazine*, $C_{12}H_9NS$, is a heterocyclic compound prepared by the fusion of sulfur and diphenylamine, extremely effective as an antihelmintic for worms in livestock. *Diphenylamine* and *diphenyl* are the active ingredients in smears for livestock screwworms. For this use alone, they have saved the farmers millions of dollars. *Naphthalene* is one of the principal hydrocarbons from coal tar (Chap. 6). It has been consumed for many years as a repellent for clothes moths, although it is not usually employed in concentrations strong enough to be fully effective. An ordinary trunk requires about 2 lb. of naphthalene to protect the contents. Ortho- and *p*-dichloro-benzene, by-products in the making of monochloro-benzene, have limited insecticidal application. However, the para compound is used in large volume for moth protection.

Fumigants and Miticides. For the protection of grains, tobacco, and other farm products during storage and for the control of soil-infesting insects, a number of compounds are employed. These include carbon disulfide, hydrogen cyanide, methyl bromide, ethylene dibromide, chloropicrin, and others. The manufacture of all these chemicals is described elsewhere in this book. Chemicals for mite control are enjoying a major boom since insecticides have eradicated the natural enemies of mites while leaving the mites themselves unharmed. A broad range of miticides are available including parathion, 2-(*p-tert*-butylphenoxy)isopropyl

2-chloro-ethyl sulfite, bis(p-chlorophenoxy)methane, di(p-chlorophenyl)-methylcarbinol, and O-ethyl-O-p-nitrophenyl benzenethiophosphonate.

RODENTICIDES

Certain pest animals such as mice, rats, squirrels, ground hogs, and field rodents must be controlled because of their ability to do extensive property damage and to spread diseases. Rodents alone caused property damage in the United States of 500 million dollars annually. The most prominent rodenticides for rats and mice are the following new synthetic organic chemical compounds: *warfarin*, 3-(α-acetonyl-benzyl)-4-hydroxy-coumarin; *ANTU*, α-naphthylthiourea; and Compound 1080, *sodium fluoracetate*. The last is deadly to everything including man and should be handled only by experts. It is made by reacting ethyl chloroacetate[1] and potassium fluoride in an autoclave at 200°C. The resulting ethyl fluoroacetate is saponified with a methanol solution of NaOH, and the sodium fluoroacetate crystallizes out. Because of the high toxicity of ethyl fluoroacetate, extreme caution must be observed in this process. For field-rodent control, the old compounds such as thallium sulfate, zinc phosphide, and strychnine are still favored.

FUNGICIDES

Fungi are parasitic plants comprising the molds, mildews, rusts, smuts, mushrooms, and allied forms that are capable of destroying higher plants, fabrics, even glass, thus depriving man of valuable food or materials. They may attack seeds, the growing plant, plant material or, under proper conditions, finished products such as adhesives, leather, paints, and fabrics. Fungicides fall into two general classifications:[2] agricultural and industrial. Fungicides for plants act by direct contact and often injure the host as well as the fungus.[3]

History. The use of an effective fungicide was probably discovered by accident. It was common practice in the eighteenth and early nineteenth centuries to cover grapevines along the road with a poisonous powder such as copper sulfate and lime, to discourage thievery. In 1883 it was noticed that this substance controlled the downy mildew of the vines. Until the 1930's elemental sulfur and compounds of heavy metals such as copper and mercury dominated the field. However, in the 1940's organics were tried and now, although very large dollarwise, constitute

---

[1] JENKINS and KOEHLER, Making 1080 Safe, *Chem. Inds.*, **62**, 232 (1948).

[2] For further details on industrial fungicides, see KIRK and OTHMER, *op. cit.*, Vol. 6, pp. 991ff.; BLOCK, Chemicals for Fungus Control, *Chem. Week*, **70** (4), 21 (1952).

[3] HORSFALL, Fungicides in Food Production, *Ind. Eng. Chem.*, **40**, 681 (1948).

only about 2 per cent of the fungicide production which in 1952 was about 600,000,000 lb., mainly sulfur.

Inorganic Fungicides. The greater part of all inorganic fungicides used at present are compounds of copper and sulfur while other heavy metals, particularly mercury and zinc, still play an important part.

Bordeaux mixture, an important fungicide, is simple to make at home and is employed in several formulations. The 4-4-50 formula[1] consists of 4 lb. of copper sulfate, 4 lb. of hydrated lime, and 50 gal. of water. The copper sulfate is dissolved in one vessel, the lime in another. Each is diluted to 25 gal. and poured simultaneously through a strainer into a third container. Properly made, Bordeaux mixture consists of a light blue, gelatinous precipitate suspended in water. It is effective for most of the common molds and mildews and most common fruits and vegetables can be safely treated with it.

Mercury Chlorides. Both mercurous and mercuric chlorides are effective fungicides. Mercurous chloride (Hg_2Cl_2, calomel) is prepared by heating 4 parts of mercuric chloride with 3 parts of metallic mercury in an iron pot until a white mass is formed. The temperature is raised to sublime off the mercurous chloride which is further purified by washing. Mercuric chloride ($HgCl_2$, corrosive sublimate, bichloride of mercury) is made by heating mercury in the presence of chlorine gas or by heating equal parts of mercuric sulfate with common salt. The mercuric compound is still extensively used for fungicidal treatment of seeds. In general, these compounds are too injurious to plants to be applied similarly to Bordeaux mixture.

Organic Fungicides. The organic fungicides vary in composition, but most of the new fungicides fall into these chemical classifications: dithiocarbamates, chlorinated quinones, chlorinated phenols, glyoxalidine derivatives, and organic mercury compounds. While chlorination is very important in insecticides, it is much less so in fungicides. Next to sulfur, nitrogen appears to be the most effective constituent element of an organic fungicide other than carbon and hydrogen. The first successful organic fungicide formaldehyde is sold as a 40 per cent solution in water called *Formalin.* Because of its volatility it is still an extensively employed fumigant for seeds, soil, and greenhouses.

Coal-tar creosote has long been the standard substance for wood preservation. It is effective, permanent, and inexpensive, but it is sticky and has a penetrating odor. Because of the dark stain it imparts, wood so treated cannot be painted. However, for many purposes, such as creosoted fence posts and railroad ties, these disadvantages are not of importance. Other developments in wood preservation are the *chlorinated phenols:* tetra and pentachlorophenol, chloro-*o*-phenylphenol and β-naphthol. These are applied in 5 per cent solutions in organic solvents. Generally,

[1] FREAR, *op. cit.,* p. 212.

these phenols are not so powerful as creosote but they do not possess its disadvantages.

The *dithiocarbamates* are the most used of the new fungicides. They are made by reacting carbon disulfide with an amine to form a dithiocarbamic acid. The acid is reacted with a metal hydroxide to give a stable salt:

$$H_2NCH_2CH_2NH_2 + 2CS_2 \rightarrow HSCSNH(CH_2)_2NHCSSH$$
$$HSCSNH(CH_2)_2NHCSSH + 2NaOH \rightarrow$$
$$NaSCSNH(CH_2)_2NHCSSNa + 2H_2O$$

This sodium salt of ethylene bisdithiocarbamate is employed with zinc sulfate and lime and probably reacts to form the zinc salt. These salts are used to combat vegetable blights, particularly potato. Ferric dimethylthiocarbamate is the oldest of these compounds and particularly effective for apple rust. Zinc dimethylthiocarbamate is important for anthracnose diseases on vegetables, *i.e.*, bitter rot.

The only two commercial compounds of the *chlorinated quinones*[1] are tetrachlorobenzoquinone, called *chloranil*, and 2,3-dichloro-1,4-naphthoquinone. The former is applied to leguminous seeds; the latter has a wide range of fungitoxicity, but there is a narrow safety margin without resulting plant injury. Zinc trichlorophenate and 2,4,5-trichlorophenyl acetate are the two significant *chlorinated phenols* finding extensive employment for seed treatment, especially cotton. The important *glyoxalidine derivative* so far is 2-heptadecylglyoxalidine which is used for cherry leaf spot and apple scab. It is prepared by reacting the acid with ethylenediamine.

The *organic mercury compounds* were among the first organic fungicides to be developed. Their main use is in the treatment of seeds. Ethyl mercuric chloride and phosphate and phenyl mercuric oleate seem to be the best antimildewing agents for paints. *Ethyl mercuric chloride* is prepared by treating tetraethyl lead with mercuric chloride:

$$Pb(C_2H_5)_4 + 4HgCl_2 \rightarrow 4C_2H_5HgCl + PbCl_2 + Cl_2$$

These compounds are sold as dusts or solutions under various trade names and are used to treat seeds, to prevent the formation of lumber sap stain, and as general garden sprays.

HERBICIDES

Although it has been estimated[2] that the 1951 consumption of weed killers was 122,000,000 lb., weeds still cause an annual loss of 5 billion

[1] KIRK and OTHMER, *op. cit.*, Vol. 6, p. 988.
[2] FRISSELLE and STILLMAN, Herbicides, *Chem. Eng. News*, **31**, 1175 (1953).

dollars in the United States. Yet the introduction of hormone-type weed killers in the early 1940's stimulated this whole field. Until then only soil sterilants and nonselective contact sprays such as sodium chlorate, sodium arsenite, various borate compounds, industrial waste products, and oil sprays were used mostly for the clearance of utility, railroad, and highway rights of way. Sodium chlorate (see Chap. 16) still plays a major role for this, and another inorganic, ammonium sulfamate, has grown from nothing in the early 1940's to a current consumption of several million pounds per year. The latter is a foliage spray which eliminates woody growths but does not prevent a regrowth of grass. The two most important selective weed killers are 2,4-dichlorophenoxyacetic acid (2,4-D) and 2,4,5-trichlorophenoxyacetic acid (2,4,5-T). For statistics on these two compounds, see Table 1. These hormone-type weed killers act by disrupting the normal growth cycle of certain plants without harming grasses and are effective at such low concentrations that the cost of treatment is small.

The manufacture of 2,4-D begins by chlorinating phenol (from benzene) to 2,4-dichlorophenol. The reaction product is distilled to procure pure 2,4-dichlorophenol. After chlorinating acetic acid to monochloroacetic, it is converted to the sodium salt. This is reacted with the 2,4-dichlorophenol and aqueous caustic to give the sodium salt of 2,4-dichlorophenoxyacetic acid and sodium chloride. Hydrochloric acid is employed to liberate the acid from solution. 2,4,5-T is made by hydrolyzing 1,2,4,5-tetrachlorobenzene with caustic, because phenol cannot be chlorinated to the 2,4,5 position. Hydrolysis yields 2,4,5-trichlorophenol directly. This is purified and converted to 2,4,5-trichlorophenoxyacetic acid by a process similar to that for 2,4-D. Both acids are usually marketed in herbicide formulations as amine salts or as alkyl esters as they are more effective as herbicides than either the straight acid or the various salts. The alkyl esters of the above acid are manufactured by reacting the appropriate alcohol with the acid following the classical method. For the manufacture of alkanolamine salt formulations, the acid is dissolved in an aqueous solution of an alkanolamine.

Other organic compounds of herbicidal interest include isopropyl N-phenyl carbamate (I.P.C.), sodium trichloroacetate (sodium T.C.A.), 3-p-chlorophenyl 1,1-dimethylurea (C.M.U.), isopropyl-N-(3-chlorophenyl)-carbamate (C.I.P.C.), sodium 2,4-dichlorophenoxyethyl sulfate (S.E.S.), and 2-methyl-4-chlorophenoxyacetic acid (M.C.P.). Some of these compounds, such as 2,4-D and 2,4,5-T, are able to act as both plant-growth regulators and weed killers, depending upon the concentration used. Other compounds such as maleic hydrazide and phenoxy compounds are primarily growth regulators otherwise known as plant hormones or auxins and are capable of producing in a great variety of ways profound changes in the basic life processes of plants. Clearly, growth regulators, now only just beginning to be explored, represent one of the most challenging fields for agricultural chemicals today.

GERMICIDES, ANTISEPTICS, DISINFECTANTS

A germicide is anything that destroys germs (pathogenic microorganisms); an antiseptic is a substance that prevents or arrests the growth or action of microorganisms; a disinfectant is an agent that frees from infection.[1] These terms are often used interchangeably. Strictly speaking, the use of *antiseptic* should be restricted to living tissue and *disinfectant* to inanimate objects. The effectiveness of these types of materials is usually expressed in terms of the *phenol coefficient*. The killing power of pure phenol on pure cultures of *Eberthella typhosa* and *Staphylococcus aureus* is arbitrarily set as unity, and the unknown material is rated in comparison. Table 3 lists the phenol coefficients of some of the common germicides, antiseptics, and disinfectants.

TABLE 3. PHENOL COEFFICIENTS[a]

Compound	*Staphylococcus aureus*	*Eberthella typhosa*
Phenol	1	1
Chloramine	133	100
Dakin's solution	......	0.78
Lysol	3.2	5.0
Hexylresorcinol	150	72
Mercurochrome	1.7	
Merthiolate	40–50	40–50
Metaphen	1500	
Tincture of iodine, U.S.P	38	

[a] LANGE, "Handbook of Chemistry," 7th ed., p. 1720, Handbook Publishers, Inc., Sandusky, Ohio, 1949.

The use of germicides began with the discovery of the effectiveness of phenol (carbolic acid) by Lister in 1867. While efficient, it caused serious injury to body tissues when applied in too strong concentrations. It also was a powerful poison to man. Consequently the less toxic germicides are being favored. Most of the important germicides are organic compounds, the well-known tincture of iodine being the chief exception.

Nonmetallic Compounds. Nonmetallic germicides can be highly efficient (see Table 3). They differ widely in chemical structure.

Tincture of Iodine. Tincture (meaning alcoholic solution) of iodine (Chap. 21) has been the standard household germicide. However, more

[1] PATTERSON, Meaning of "Antiseptic," "Disinfectant" and Related Words, *Am. J. Public Health*, **22**, 465 (1932).

effective compounds have been made available that eliminate some of the disadvantages of this solution. Unless the containers are kept tightly capped, part of the alcohol evaporates leaving a more concentrated iodine solution from which serious burns have resulted.

Phenol and *cresols* (Chap. 6 and 38) are effective germicides. Care should be taken in the use of phenol because of its caustic nature. Cresols (especially *m*-cresol) are not soluble in water and are usually sold in the form of emulsions. The emulsions are less caustic and less toxic than phenol.

Dakin's Solution and Chloramine. Dakin's solution is a 0.45 per cent solution of sodium hypochlorite prepared by the action of chlorine on sodium carbonate. It is effective as a surgical germicide and was used extensively in the First World War. Chloramine (chloramine T, Chlorazene) is sodium *p*-toluene-chlorosulfonamide.

Hexylresorcinol is a powerful germicide with a high phenol coefficient (Table 3). It is made by the condensation of resorcinol and caproic acid and subsequent reduction.[1]

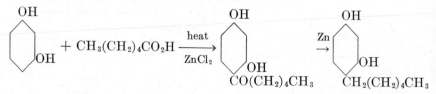

Sulfa Compounds. The group of sulfur compounds familiarly known as *sulfa* drugs possess unique properties that make them especially valuable. The sulfa drugs may be administered internally. The more important members of this group are sulfonamide derivatives of aniline, pyridine, and thiazole and are prepared by a variety of methods.

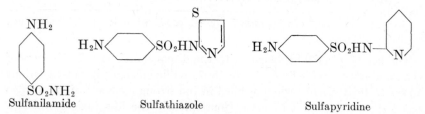

Sulfanilamide   Sulfathiazole   Sulfapyridine

Quaternary ammonium compounds are cationic surface-active agents with marked antibacterial effectiveness.[2] The nitrogen in these amines has a valence of 5 and the hydrogen atoms of the ammonium radical are replaced by other groups. The more important members are cetylpyri-

[1] GROGGINS, "Unit Processes in Organic Synthesis," 4th ed., p. 839, McGraw-Hill Book Company, Inc., New York, 1952.

[2] LAWRENCE, "Surface-active Quaternary Ammonium Germicides," Academic Press, Inc., New York, 1950.

dinium chloride, p-tertiaryoctyl-phenoxy-ethoxyethyldimethylbenzylammonium chloride and mixtures of alkyl dimethylbenzylammonium chlorides in which the alkyl groups vary from C_8 to C_{18}. Cetyldimethylbenzylammonium chloride may be prepared:

$$C_{16}H_{33}OH \xrightarrow{HCl} C_{16}H_{33}Cl \xrightarrow{NH(CH_3)_2} C_{16}H_{33}N(CH_3)_2$$
$$+H_2O \qquad\qquad +HCl$$

$$\xrightarrow{C_6H_5CH_2Cl} C_{16}H_{33}\overset{CH_3}{\underset{CH_3}{N}}(Cl)CH_2\langle\!\!\bigcirc\!\!\rangle$$

Metallic Compounds. Only a few of the metals find use in germicidal compounds. Mercury and silver are the most widely employed. Arsenic compounds which were important for syphilis have been replaced mostly by penicillin.

Mercury Compounds. Two of the more important mercurials are Merthiolate and Metaphen,[1] both of which are excellent germicides. Merthiolate is sodium ethyl-mercurithiosalicylate and is made[2] as follows:

$$C_2H_5MgBr + HgCl_2 \rightarrow C_2H_5HgCl + MgBrCl$$
$$C_2H_5HgCl + NaOH \rightarrow C_2H_5HgOH + NaCl$$

$$C_2H_5HgOH + \overset{COONa}{\underset{}{\langle\!\!\bigcirc\!\!\rangle}}SH \rightarrow \overset{COONa}{\underset{}{\langle\!\!\bigcirc\!\!\rangle}}SHgC_2H_5 + H_2O$$

Silver Compounds. Silver compounds are often employed as germicides. The application of a dilute solution of silver nitrate in the eyes of newborn babies is required by law in most states. Argyrol, a silver protein preparation, is used extensively for eye, ear, nose, and throat infections.

SELECTED REFERENCES

Frear, D. E. H., "Chemistry of Insecticides, Fungicides and Herbicides," 2d ed., D. Van Nostrand Company, Inc., New York, 1948.

de Ong, E. R., "Chemistry and Uses of Insecticides," Reinhold Publishing Corporation, New York, 1948.

Symposium, Insecticides in Food Production, *Ind. Eng. Chem.*, **40**, 673–717 (1948).

Shepard, H. H., "The Chemistry and Action of Insecticides," McGraw-Hill Book Company, Inc., New York, 1951.

Brown, A. W. A., "Insect Control by Chemicals," John Wiley & Sons, Inc., New York, 1951.

[1] RAIZISS, U.S. Pat. (reissue) 17563; Can. Pat. 264444(1926).

[2] KHARASCH, U.S. Pat. 1589599(1926); 1672615(1928); for more details, see GROGGINS, *op. cit.*, p. 842.

PESTICIDES

Skoog, Folke, editor, "Plant Growth Substances," University of Wisconsin Press, Madison, Wis., 1951.

West, T. F., and G. A. Campbell, "DDT and Newer Persistent Insecticides," 2d ed., Chapman & Hall, Ltd., London, 1950.

Ahlgren, G. H., D. E. Wolf, and G. C. Klingman, "Principles of Weed Control," John Wiley & Sons, Inc., New York, 1951.

Metcalf, C. L., R. L. Metcalf, and W. P. Flint, "Destructive and Useful Insects," 3d ed., McGraw-Hill Book Company, Inc., New York, 1951.

Lawrence, C. A., "Surface-active Quaternary Ammonium Germicides," Academic Press, Inc., New York, 1950.

Mitter, M. N., "Manufacture of Disinfectants and Antiseptics," Chemical Publishing Company, Inc., New York, 1941.

CHAPTER 27

PERFUME AND FLAVORING INDUSTRIES

The particular cells that *perceive odors* are located near the top of the nasal cavity, quite close to the septum. As the ordinary process of breathing does not draw air over these regions, only strong odors are perceived. By flaring the nostrils and sniffing, however, the inspired air is passed directly over the olfactory region where the conditions are optimum for discriminatory smelling. Since smell is a chemical sense, a contact is necessary for perception; and the substance, either gaseous or particulate, to be smelled must impinge on the moist surface of the region and dissolve. Since olfactory nerves are quickly fatigued, protracted smelling of any one substance will exhaust the power to recognize it, but the nerve endings may be easily rehabilitated by the breathing of fresh air again. Each odor has a *threshold value* depending on its intensity and volatility. Because of this, civet, when strong, has the disagreeable fecal odor of skatole but, upon dilution, the skatole passes below its threshold intensity and the warm flowery note of the civetone becomes apparent. Some odors that may appear intense are not so at all, as ammonia and formic acid; these compounds produce a sensation that may be likened to a mild pain and not to a true odor.

Perfume gains its name from the fact that in its original form it was incense in the Egyptian temples (*perfumare*—to fill with smoke). The early incenses were merely mixtures of finely ground spices held together by myrrh or storax. The next advance was the discovery that, if certain spices and flowers were steeped in fat or oil, the fat or oil would retain a portion of the odoriferous principle. Thus were manufactured the ointments and fragrant unguents of Biblical fame. To Avicenna, the Arabian physician, must go the honor of discovering steam distillation of volatile oils. During his search for medical potions, he found that flowers boiled in an alembic with water gave up some of their essence to the distillate.

Historical. The returning Crusaders brought to Europe all the art and skill of the Orient in perfumery as well as information relating to the sources of gums, oils, and spices. René, perfumer to Catherine de'Medici, invented many new confections to delight the queenly nose and, in his spare time, was one of the cleverest and deadliest of the famous de'Medici poisoners. The two main changes that have taken place in the perfume and flavoring industries since de'Medici's time are the introduction of synthetics and the improved methods of obtaining the true oils.

Uses and Economics. The perfume and flavoring industries, although seemingly small, are vital because they are necessary components of countless goods whose annual turnover involves billions of dollars. The use of these materials for masking agents of disagreeable odors in manufactured goods is an ever-growing field ranging from adhesives to rubber articles. Synthetic flavoring and perfume materials had an annual sales value in 1953 of 46.5 million dollars. No figures are available on the natural products, but their sales probably involve millions of dollars also.

THE PERFUME INDUSTRY

A perfume may be defined as any mixture of pleasantly odorous substances incorporated in a suitable vehicle. Formerly, practically all the products used in perfumery were of natural origin. Even when man first started imitating Nature and synthesizing materials for use in this field, he endeavored to duplicate the finest in Nature. There has been a marked tendency in recent years, however, to put on the market perfumes which have no exact counterpart in the floral kingdom but which are merely pleasing to the senses. These are the "fantasy" perfumes and have received wide acceptance. The finest modern perfumes are neither wholly synthetic nor yet completely natural. The best product of the art is a judicious blend of the two in order to enhance the natural perfume, to reduce the price, and to introduce new notes of fragrance into the enchanting gamut at present available. A product made solely of synthetics tends to be coarse and unnatural because of the absence of impurities in minute amounts which finish and round out the bouquet of the natural odors. The chemist has also succeeded in creating floral essences of flowers which yielded no natural essence or whose essence was too expensive or too fugitive to make its extraction profitable. Lily of the valley, lilac, and violet are examples.

The constituents of perfumes are threefold: the vehicle or solvent, the fixative, and the odoriferous elements.

VEHICLE

The modern solvent for blending and holding perfume materials is a highly refined ethyl alcohol mixed with more or less water according to the solubilities of the oils employed. This solvent, with its volatile nature, helps to project the scent it carries, is fairly inert to the solutes, and is not too irritating to the human skin. The slight natural odor of the alcohol is removed by deodorizing or "prefixation" of the alcohol. This is accomplished by adding a small amount of gum benzoin or other resinous fixatives to the alcohol and allowing it to mature for a week or two. The result is an almost odorless alcohol, the natural rawness having been neutralized by the resins.

FIXATIVE

In an ordinary solution of perfume substances in alcohol, the more volatile materials will evaporate first, and the odor of the perfume will consist of a series of impressions rather than the desired ensemble. To obviate this difficulty, a fixative is added. Fixatives may be defined as substances which are of lower volatility than the perfume oils and which retard and even up the rate of evaporation of the various odorous constituents. The types of fixative to be considered are animal secretions, resinous products, essential oils, and synthetic chemicals. Any of these fixatives may or may not contribute to the odor of the finished product but, if they do, they must blend with and complement the main fragrance.

Animal Fixatives. Of all animal products *castor* or *castoreum*, a brownish orange exudate of the perineal glands of the beaver, is employed in the greatest quantity. Most castor is obtained as a by-product from the Canadian beaver. Among the odoriferous components of the volatile oil of castor are benzyl alcohol, acetophenone, *l*-borneol, and castorin (the volatile resinous component of unknown structure).

Civet is the soft fatty secretion of the perineal glands of the civet cats which are indigenous to many countries, but developed by Ethiopia. These cats are kept in captivity in pens in which the temperature is higher than normal because of covering and exposure to the hot sun. The heat and also the teasing of the cat increase the yield of the civet. The secretions are collected about every 4 days by spooning and are packed for export in hollowed horns. The crude civet is disagreeable in odor because of the skatole present. On dilution and aging, however, the skatole odor disappears, and the sweet and somewhat floral odor of civetone, a cyclic ketone, appears. The civet is employed as a fixative either in a tincture or as an absolute. Its use along with musk is quite common.

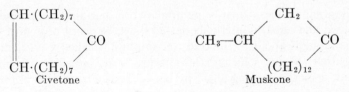

Civetone   Muskone

Musk is the dried secretion of the preputial glands of the male musk deer, found in the Himalayas. The deer are killed and the musk is excised in pods the size of a crab apple and dried. The product in the natural cover is called *pod musk*, while that which has been removed and dried is known as *grain musk*. The odor is due to a cyclic ketone called *muskone*, which is present to the extent of from $\frac{1}{2}$ to 2 per cent. Musk, the most useful of the animal fixatives, will impart body and smoothness to a perfume composition even when diluted so far that its own odor is completely effaced. Musk is used for its own sake in heavy Oriental perfumes.

Ambergris is the least used, but probably best known of the animal fixatives. It is a calculus or secretion developed by certain whales. Ambergris is obtained by cutting open the captured whale, or it is found floating in the ocean or stranded on a beach. It is waxy in consistency, softening at about 60°C., with a color which may be white, yellow, brown, black, or variegated like marble. It is composed of 80 to 85 per cent ambrein,[1] resembling cholesterol and acting merely as a binder, and 12 to 15 per cent of ambergris oil, which is the active ingredient. It is employed as an alcoholic tincture which must be matured before it is used. The odor of the tincture is decidedly musty, and it has great fixative powers.

Musc Zibata is the newest animal fixative. It is derived from glands of the muskrat which is trapped in the United States, especially in Louisiana. It was only during the Second World War that the Musc Zibata was commercialized. About 90 per cent of the unsaponifiable material in muskrat glands consist of large, odorless cyclic alcohols which are converted to the ketones, increasing the characteristic musk odor nearly fifty times. The product is called Musc Zibata, and is a replacement or an addition product to the Asiatic musk.

Resinous Fixatives. The resinous fixatives are normal or pathological exudates from certain plants which are more important historically than commercially. The resins are classified rather arbitrarily as follows:

Resins: hard resins, *e.g.*, benzoin.
Gums: soft resins, *e.g.*, myrrh and labdanum.
Balsams: moderately soft resins, *e.g.*, Peru balsam, Tolu balsam, copiaba, and storax.
Oleoresins: oily materials, *e.g.*, terpenes.
Resinoids: extracts from resins, less viscous, *e.g.*, ambrein.

All these substances, when being prepared for perfume compounding, are dissolved and aged by methods passed down by word of mouth. If solution is brought about in the cold, the mixture is called a *tincture*. If heat is required to give solution, the mixture is an *infusion*. Alcohol is the solvent, sometimes being aided by benzyl benzoate or diethyl phthalate.

The most important of the soft gums is *labdanum*. The leaves of a plant growing in the Mediterranean area exude this sticky substance. In Spain, the branches are boiled in water to remove the gum. In France, the leaves are treated with volatile solvents. An extract from this gum

---

[1] This is a triterpenic tricyclic alcohol, $C_{30}H_{51}OH$, which splits upon oxidation; *cf.* Kirk and Othmer, *op. cit.*, Vol. 10, p. 9.

has an odor suggestive of ambergris and is marketed as *ambrein*, having extremely good fixative value.

Of the harder plant resins used in perfumes, *benzoin* is the most important. The history of chemistry was influenced by this substance. The early source of benzoin was Java, where it was called *Luban Jawi*. Through various contractions and linguistic modifications, it became "banjawi," "benjui," "benzoi," "benzoin," and "benjamin." In early organic chemical history, an acid isolated from this gum became known as *benzoic acid*, from which compound the names of all "benz-" compounds of today are derived.

Essential Oil Fixatives. A few essential oils are used for their fixative properties as well as their odor. The more important of these are clary sage, vetiver, patchouly, orris, and sandalwood. These oils have boiling points higher than normal (285 to 290°C.).

Synthetic Fixatives. Certain high-boiling comparatively odorless esters are used as fixatives, to replace some of the imported animal fixatives. Among them may be mentioned glyceryl diacetate (259°C.), ethyl phthalate (295°C), and benzyl benzoate (323°C.). Other synthetics are used as fixatives although they have a definite odor of their own that contributes to the ensemble in which they are used. A few of these are listed:

Amyl benzoate	Benzophenone[1]
Phenylethyl phenylacetate	Vanillin
Cinnamic alcohol esters	Coumarin
Cinnamic acid esters	Heliotropin
Acetophenone[2]	Hydroxycitronellal
Musk ketone	Indole[3]
Musk ambrette	Skatole

ODOROUS SUBSTANCES

Most odorous substances used in perfumery come under three headings: (1) essential oils, (2) isolates, and (3) synthetic or semisynthetic chemicals.

1. Essential Oils. An essential oil may be defined as a volatile, odoriferous oil of vegetable origin (see Table 1). The distinction should be made, however, between the natural flower oils which are obtained by enfleurage or solvent extraction and the essential oil recovered by distillation. The distilled oils may lack some component which is not volatile enough or which is lost during the distillation. Two notable examples of this are rose oil in which the phenylethyl alcohol is lost to the watery por-

[1] VANDERHOEF, Benzophenone, *Chem. Eng.*, **57** (12), 288 (1950).

[2] Acetophenone should be used with great caution because of its powerful odor which tends to protrude above all others.

[3] TREFFLER, The Synthesis of Indoles, *Chem. Inds.*, **56**, 67 (1943).

TABLE 1. IMPORTANT ESSENTIAL OILS

Name of oil	Botanical source	Important geographical sources	Method of production	Part of plant used	Chief constituents
Almond, bitter	Amygdalus communis, L.	California, Morocco	Steam	Kernels	Benzaldehyde 96–98 %, HCN 2–4 %
Bay	Pimenta acris, Wight	West Indies	Steam	Leaves	Eugenol 50 %
Bergamot	Citrus bergamia, L.	Southern Italy	Expression	Peel	Linalyl acetate 40 %, linaloöl 6 %
Caraway	Carum carvi, L.	Northern Europe, Holland	Steam	Seed	Carvone 55 %, d-limonene
Cassia (Chinese cinnamon)	Cinnamomum cassia	China	Steam	Leaves and twigs	Cinnamic aldehyde 80–90 %
Cedarwood	Juniperus virginiana, L.	North America	Steam	Red core wood	Cedrene, cedral
Cinnamon	Cinnamomum zeylanicum, Nees	Ceylon	Steam	Bark	Cinnamic aldehyde 60 %, eugenol 8 %
Citronella, Java	Cymbopogon Winterianus	Java, Ceylon	Steam	Grass	Geraniol 60–90 %, citronellal
Clove	Caryophyllus aromaticus, L.	Zanzibar, Madagascar	Steam	Buds (cloves)	Eugenol, 85–95 %
Coriander	Coriandrum sativum, L.	Central Europe, Russia	Steam	Fruit	Linaloöl, pinene
Eucalyptus	Several Eucalyptus species	California, Australia	Steam	Leaves	Cineole (eucalyptole) 70–80 %
Geranium	Pelargonium graveolens	Mediterranean countries	Steam	Leaves	Geraniol esters 30 %, citronellol
Jasmine	Jasminum grandiflorum, L.	Grasse	Cold pomade	Flowers	Benzyl acetate, linaloöl, and esters
Lemon	Citrus limon, L.	California, Sicily	Expression	Peel	d-Limonene 90 %, citral (3.5–5 %)
Orange, sweet	Citrus sinensis, L.	Florida, California, Mediterranean area	Expression distillation	Peel	d-Limonene 90 %
Peppermint[a]	Mentha piperita, L.	Michigan, Indiana, etc.	Steam	Leaves and tops	Menthol 45–90 % and esters
Rose	Rosa damascena, alba, L.	Bulgaria, Turkey	Steam solvent, enfleurage	Flowers	Geraniol and citronellol 75 %
Sandalwood	Santalum album, L.	Mysore, East Indies	Steam	Wood	Santalol 90 %, esters 3 %
Spearmint	Mentha spicata	Michigan, Indiana	Steam	Leaves	Carvone 50–60 %
Tuberose	Polianthes tuberosa, L.	France	Enfleurage, solvent extraction	Flowers	
Wintergreen (gaultheria)	Gaultheria procumbens, L.	Eastern United States	Steam	Leaves	Methyl salicylate 99 %
Ylang-ylang	Cananga orodata, Hook	Madagascar, Philippines	Steam, solvent extraction	Flowers	Esters, alcohols

[a] For extraction, see the pictured flow sheet Peppermint Oil. Chem. Eng., **58** (2), 192 (1951).

tion of the distillate, and orange-flower oil in which the distilled oil contains but a very small proportion of methyl anthranilate while the extracted flower oil may contain as much as one-sixth of this constituent. The essential oils are in the main insoluble in water and soluble in organic solvents, although enough of the oil may dissolve in water to give an intense odor to the solution as in rose water and orange-flower water. The oils are flammable liquids which are volatile enough to distill unchanged in most instances. They are also volatile with steam. They vary from colorless to yellow or brown in color. An essential oil is usually a mixture of compounds, although oil of wintergreen is almost pure methyl salicylate. The refractive indexes of the oils are high, averaging around 1.5. The oils show a wide range of optical activity, rotating in both directions.

The compounds occurring in essential oils may be classified as follows:
  1. Esters: Mainly of benzoic, acetic, salicylic, and cinnamic acids.
  2. Alcohols: Linaloöl, geraniol, citronellol, terpinol, menthol, borneol.
  3. Aldehydes: Citral, citronellal, benzaldehyde, cinnamaldehyde, cuminic aldehyde, vanillin.
  4. Acids: Benzoic, cinnamic, myristic, isovaleric acids in the free state.
  5. Phenols: Eugenol, thymol, carvacrol.
  6. Ketones: Carvone, menthone, pulegone, irone, fenchone, thujone, camphor, methyl nonyl ketone, methyl heptenone.
  7. Esters: Cineole[1] (eucalyptole), anethole, safrole.
  8. Lactones: Coumarin.
  9. Terpenes: Camphene, pinene, limonene, phellandrene, cedrene.
  10. Hydrocarbons: Cymene, styrene (phenylethylene).

Although the part played by essential oils in the life of plants is somewhat obscure, they are probably connected with metabolism, fertilization, or protection from enemies. The oils may occur in intercellular spaces or in oil sacs. Any or all parts of the plant may contain an oil. Essential oils are found in the buds, flowers, leaves, bark, stems, fruits, seeds, wood, roots, and rhizomes, and in some trees in the oleoresinous exudates.

The volatile oils may be recovered from the plants by a variety of methods:[2] (1) expression, (2) distillation, (3) extraction with volatile solvents, (4) enfleurage, and (5) maceration. The majority of oils are obtained by distillation, usually steam, but certain oils are adversely affected by the temperature. Distilled citrus oils are of inferior quality; therefore, they are derived by expression. For certain flowers which yield no oil upon distillation or else a deteriorated oil, the last three methods are used. However, extraction with volatile solvents, a comparatively

---

[1] This is an *internal* ether.
[2] GUENTHER, "The Essential Oils," Vol. 1, Chap. 3, Reinhold Publishing Corporation, 1948; for expression, see Vol. 3, pp. 6ff.

recent process, has superseded maceration (extraction with hot fat) for all practical purposes and is replacing enfleurage. Solvent extraction is the most technically advanced process and yields truly representative odors, but is more expensive than distillation. Enfleurage is practiced only in the Grasse region of France and on a much smaller scale than before because it is a delicate and lengthy process, requiring much experience and labor. Yields depend on both the oil and the method. Based on 5 tons of crude material, yields will vary from 5 oz. of violet oil to 1,800 lb. of clove oil.

Distillation, Usually with Steam. In order that the oil may be more easily removed, some treatment of the material may be required. Flowers and grasses are normally charged into the still without preparation. Leaves and succulent roots and twigs are cut into small pieces. Dried materials are powdered. Woods and tough roots are sawed into small pieces or mechanically chipped. Seeds and nuts are fed through crushing rolls which are spaced so as to crack them. Berries are charged in the natural state, as the heat of distillation soon develops enough pressure to burst their integument. The charge should not be too finely comminuted, or it will pack down solidly in the still and the steam applied will channel rather than reach the whole mass evenly.

The stills employed in factories are of copper, tin-lined copper, or stainless steel and of about 600 gal. capacity. They are provided with condensers of various sorts, the tubular ones being the more efficient and with a separator for dividing the oily layer from the aqueous one. Although removable baskets for holding the material to be distilled are used, the better procedure seems to be to construct the still with a perforated false plate, lying just above the bottom. Underneath this false bottom are the steam coils, both closed and perforated. Manholes should be provided at the top and just above the false bottom for an inlet and outlet of the material to be distilled. Such a still will handle from 250 to 800 lb. of material. If the charge is finely ground or easily packed material, the still should be provided with a powerful stirrer, in which case the lower manhole may be omitted and the spent material blown out through a bottom valve. In operating these stills, the charge is heated by steam in both the closed and the open pipes, thus effecting an economical steam distillation. The aqueous layer in the condensate frequently carries, in solution, valuable constituents as from rose and orange-flower oil and is consequently pumped back into the still to supply some of the necessary water. Steam distillation is carried out for the most part at atmospheric pressure. If the constituents of the oil are easily subject to hydrolysis, however, the process may be run in a vacuum.

Much distillation for essential oils is done at the harvest site in extremely crude stills. These stills are converted oil drums or copper pots equipped with pipe condensers running through water tubs. The material and water are charged into the still and a direct fire is built underneath of dried material exhausted in previous distillations. The efficiency is low and the oil is contaminated with pyrolysis products such as acrolein, trimethylamine, and creosotelike substances.

The crude oils obtained from the stills are sometimes further treated before use by rectification under vacuum, fractional freezing (menthol from Japanese peppermint oil), by washing with potassium hydroxide to remove free acids and phenolic compounds, by removal of wanted or unwanted aldehydes and ketones through formation of the bisulfite addition compounds, or by formation of specific insoluble products as in the reaction of calcium chloride with geraniol.[1]

Expression. Only in the last few years has expression by machine made an almost identical oil from the hand-pressed product. Formerly, the hand-pressed oil was superior in quality but more expensive, even though produced in the low-cost labor markets. Of these processes, the "sponge" process is the most important as it produces the highest-quality oil. Here, the fruit is halved, the peel trimmed and soaked in water for several hours. Each peel is pressed against a sponge, ejecting the oil into the sponge which is periodically squeezed dry. One man can prepare only 24 oz. of lemon oil a day by this method, but it is still practiced, especially in Sicily.

Even there machine pressing is replacing hand pressing. Many machines have been invented but only the modern, large-scale process of the American industry will be described here. The expression of citrus oils in this country is a by-product of the canning industry and is centered in California and Florida. The fruit is thoroughly washed and inspected by government inspectors to ensure that no inferior fruit is used. The juice is pressed from the fruit in automatic machines. This juice contains minute quantities of oil which must be eliminated so that the juice will possess a natural flavor and not spoil when canned. This "deoiling" is by continuous vacuum distillation and produces an oil of good quality. The largest quantity of oil is derived from the peel which is crushed in a special machine. After expression, the peel still contains a substantial quantity of oil in the albedo, or white portion of the rind, which is recovered by steam distillation. As is true of all distilled citrus oils, it is of poor quality. The peel is then soaked in hot lime water to recover pectin, much of which enters the jelly industry. The exhausted peel is submitted to high pressure, expelling a watery liquid and, after dehydration, the peel is sold as cattle food. The watery liquid, containing about 6 per cent sugar, is concentrated for molasses production. During this concentration more oil, called "stripper oil," is recovered. Because of its harsh odor and off flavor, it may be used only in technical products such as insect sprays.

Enfleurage. The enfleurage process is a cold-fat extraction process used on a few types of delicate flowers (jasmine, tuberose, violet, etc.) which

[1] JONES and WOOD, Preparation of Pure Geraniol, *Ind. Eng. Chem.*, **34**, 488 (1942).

yield no direct oil at all on distillation. Especially in the case of jasmine and tuberose, the picked flowers continue to produce perfume as long as they are alive (about 24 hr.) which is utilized by this process. The fat or base consists of a highly purified mixture of 1 part of tallow to 2 parts of lard with 0.6 per cent benzoin added as a preservative. The process is carried out on the *chassis* which is a rectangular wooden frame 2 in. high, 20 in. long, and 16 in. wide supporting a glass plate coated on both sides with the fat mixture. The chassis is spread with fresh flowers about every 24 hr., the old ones being removed by hand. The frames are stacked vertically forming airtight compartments. At the end of the 8- to 10-week harvest, the fat, which is not renewed during the process, has become saturated with flower oil. This saturated fat is called a *pomade*. The fat is removed from the frames and extracted with alcohol to recover the perfume. This alcoholic solution is cooled and filtered to remove the slight amount of fat that has dissolved. The alcohol solution is the *extract* and the residue after evaporation of the solvent is the *enfleurage absolute* similar to the products in the old maceration process.

Extraction with Volatile Solvents. The most important factor in the success of this practice is the selection of the solvent. The solvent must: (1) be selective, *i.e.*, quickly and completely dissolve the odoriferous components but only a minimum of inert matter, (2) have a low boiling point, (3) be chemically inert to the oil, (4) evaporate completely without leaving any odorous residue, and (5) be low-priced and, if possible, nonflammable. Many solvents have been used, but highly purified petroleum ether is the most successful, with benzene ranking next. The former is specially prepared by repeated rectification and consists of saturated paraffins, mainly pentane and hexane, with a boiling point not higher than 75°C. When benzene is employed, it is specially purified by repeated crystallization.

The extraction equipment is complicated and relatively expensive and consists of stills for fractionating the solvent, a few batteries for extracting the flowers, and stills for concentrating the flower-oil solutions. A battery consists of three or four extractors, four or five metal tanks for solvents and solutions, and an evaporator for concentrating the oil solutions. The two types of extractors employed are the stationary and rotary types. Although the rotary type is more popular because of higher yields and less solvent loss, the stationary type is still important. For example, voluminous plant material such as lavender cannot be easily charged and discharged in a rotating drum. Most batteries provide for solvent recovery, usually by adsorption on activated carbon. All extractors and stills are now constructed of heavily tinned sheet iron because copper is too expensive.

The stationary extractors are vertical cylinders of 1,200 liter capacity provided with several perforated metal grids. The flowers are charged directly upon these grids, and the extractor is closed. Each batch is extracted three times with solvent, the third washing serving as the second washing for the next batch, then as the first washing, after which it is concentrated in evaporators. The recovered solvent from the evaporators serves as the third washing, and so on. After the third washing, the solvent is recovered by blowing live steam through the discharged, exhausted flowers. Water-solvent separation is effected automatically in specially constructed Florence flasks.

In the rotary process the oil is also extracted on the *countercurrent principle*. These 350-gal. steam-jacketed drums revolve around a horizontal axis and are divided into compartments by perforated plates at right angles to the axis. About 300 lb. of flowers are charged into the first drum along with 150 gal. of petroleum ether which has already come through the other two drums. The drum and its contents are rotated for an hour cold and for an additional half hour with steam in the jacket. The saturated solvent is pumped to the recovery still, the flowers in the drum are treated twice more, the second time with once-used solvent and the last time with fresh solvent from the recovery still. The exhausted flowers are blown with steam to recover the adhering solvent. About 90 per cent of the solvent is boiled off at atmospheric pressure and the rest is removed under vacuum.

After the solvent is removed in either process, the semisolid residue contains the essential oil along with a quantity of waxes, resins, and coloring material from the blossoms. This pasty mass is known as the *concrete*. It, in turn, is treated with cold alcohol in which most of the wax and resin is insoluble. The small amount of unwanted material that does dissolve is removed by cooling the solution to $-20°C$. and filtering it. The resulting liquid contains the essential oil and some of the ether-soluble color of the flower and is known as an *extract*. When the alcohol has been removed, an *absolute* remains. As might be expected, there is considerable difference among the absolutes prepared from the same flower by either enfleurage or extraction with a volatile solvent. For each flower, there is an optimum method that produces the best absolute for any given purpose.

In some oils there is a large quantity of terpenes. This is especially true in the case of lemon and orange oils with as much as 90 per cent *d*-limonene in their normal composition. Not only are terpenes and sesquiterpenes of *exceedingly* little value to the strength and character of the oils, but they oxidize and polymerize rapidly on standing to form compounds of a strong turpentinelike flavor. Furthermore the terpenes are insoluble in the lower strengths of alcohol used as a solvent and make cloudy solutions which are cleared up only with difficulty. For these reasons it is desirable to remove terpenes and sesquiterpenes from many oils. Such an oil, in the case of orange, for example, is forty times as strong as the original and makes a clear solution in dilute alcohol. The oil has now very little tendency to rancidify, although it has not quite the freshness of the original. These treated oils are labeled "t.s.f." (terpene and sesquiterpene free).

Because each oil has a different composition, *deterpenation* requires a special process. Generally speaking only two methods are involved, either the removal of the terpenes, sesquiterpenes, and paraffins by fractional distillation under a vacuum, or extraction of the more soluble oxygenated compounds (principal odor carriers) with dilute alcohol or other solvents. In many cases, especially true for citrus oils, both methods are employed.

Because of the complex nature and the high price commanded by so many of the essential oils, there is a great deal of *adulteration* or sophistication practiced. These additions are extremely hard to detect in most cases as, whenever possible, a mixture of adulterants is used that does not change the physical constants of the oil. Common agents used are alcohol, cedar oil, turpentine, terpenes, sesquiterpenes, and the low-specific-gravity liquid petroleums. The advent of so many esters of glycol and glycerol on the market has increased the difficulty of detection as these are colorless, practically odorless, and in the right combination can be made to simulate almost any specific-gravity and refractive-index specifications set up for the oil they are intended to adulterate. Rose oil is sophisticated with geraniol or a mixture of geraniol and citronellol; wintergreen and sweet birch oil are mixed with large amounts of synthetic methyl salicylate; and lemon oil is often "stretched" considerably with citral from lemon-grass oil.

2. Isolates. An isolate is a pure chemical compound whose source is an essential oil or other natural perfume material. Notable examples are eugenol from clove oil, pinene from turpentine, anethole from anise oil, and linaloöl from linaloa oil (bois de rose).

3. Synthetics and Semisynthetics Used in Perfumes and Flavors.[1] More and more important constituents of perfumes and flavors are being made by the usual chemical synthetic procedures. Some constituents are being chemically synthesized from an isolate or other natural starting materials and are classed as semisynthetics. Examples are vanillin prepared from eugenol from clove oil, ionone prepared from citral from lemon-grass oil, and terpineols from turpentine and pine oil. The following embrace some of the significant synthetics of this field. The better to correlate the manufacturing methods and apparatus with other like processes, the examples here presented are grouped under the most important unit process.

---

[1] For a most excellent book on this topic, see BEDOUKIAN, "Perfumery Synthetics and Isolates." D. Van Nostrand Company, Inc., New York, 1951.

CONDENSATION PROCESSES

Coumarin occurs in tonka beans and 65 other plants, but the economical source is the synthetic. It is employed to amplify the flavor of vanillin, as a fixative and enhancing agent for essential oils and tobacco products, and as a masking agent for disagreeable odors in industrial products. The synthetic product may be prepared[1] in a number of different ways. One method utilizes the Perkin reaction:

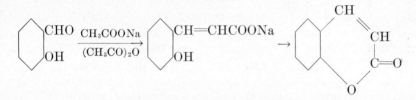

Salicyaldehyde, acetic anhydride, and sodium acetate are refluxed at 135 to 155°C. The reaction mixture is cooled and washed. The coumarin is recovered by solvent extraction or distillation. Other important methods of coumarin preparation utilize *o*-cresol as the starting material or the Haasmann-Reimer synthesis where coumarin-3-carboxylic is produced as an intermediate.

Diphenyl oxide or *ether* is very important in the soap and perfume industries, because of its great stability and strong geranium odor. Very large amounts of this compound are made annually and, although no breakdown is available, most of the diphenyl oxide is used with diphenyl for Dowtherm. Diphenyl oxide is obtained as a by-product in the manufacture of phenol from chlorobenzene and caustic soda.

$$2C_6H_5OH \rightleftharpoons C_6H_5OC_6H_5 + H_2O$$

Ionone and its homologs possess the so-called violet type of odor, thus constituting the base of violet perfumes. However, these compounds are indispensable to fine perfumes and there are but few which do not contain at least a small percentage of ionones. In 1953, 10,000 lb. of α-ionone, 77,000 lb. of methyl ionone, and 111,000 lb. of β-ionone were sold. The sales value of α- and β-ionone mixtures and other ionones was over $500,000. Because of the high price of the natural oil of violet, this was one of the first essential oils synthesized, although it has since been found in certain obscure plants. The olfactory properties of ionone are due to the presence of *dl*-α-ionone and β-ionone. Although the economical commercial methods for the production of these compounds are closely guarded trade secrets, their manufacture involves two steps. First the pseudo-ionone is prepared by the condensation of citral obtained from

[1] KIRK and OTHMER, *op. cit.*, Vol. 4, p. 590.

lemon-grass oil. This is followed by an acid ring closure and the commercial ionone is purified by distillation. Commercial ionones are generally mixtures with one form predominating, although separations are sometimes made through bisulfite compounds.

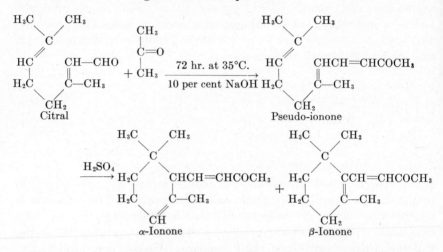

Citral

Pseudo-ionone

α-Ionone

β-Ionone

Cinnamic aldehyde has a cinnamon odor. As it oxidizes in air to cinnamic acid, it should be protected from oxidation. Although this aldehyde is obtained from Ceylon and Chinese cinnamon oils, it is synthesized by action of alkali upon a mixture of benzaldehyde and acetaldehyde.

$$C_6H_5CHO + CH_3CHO \xrightarrow{\text{NaOH}} C_6H_5CH{:}CHCHO + H_2O$$

ESTERIFICATION PROCESSES

Benzyl benzoate has a faint aromatic odor, boils at 323 to 324°C., and is a fixative and a flavoring material. During the Second World War, this ester was used in large quantities[1] as an insecticide to eradicate ticks and mites bearing a typhuslike disease in the South Pacific. It occurs naturally in balsams (Peru, Tolu), but is prepared commercially by the esterification of benzoic acid with benzyl alcohol or by the Cannizzaro reaction with benzaldehyde.

Two esters of *salicylic acid* are very important commercially in the perfume and flavoring industries. Over 300,000 lb. of *amyl salicylate* are used annually in a variety of perfumes because of its lasting quality and low price. Over 3,200,000 lb. of the *methyl salicylate* (synthetic wintergreen oil) are consumed annually as a flavoring ingredient. These are prepared as follows: Carbon dioxide and sodium phenate are reacted under pressure to obtain the salt of phenyl-carbonic acid. This salt is isomerized

[1] In 1952, 1,076,000 lbs. were produced.

to sodium salicylate by heating to 120 to 140°C. The esters are made from the acid and the proper alcohol (see Fig. 8, Chap. 39).

Benzyl acetate, $C_6H_5CH_2OCOCH_3$, is another widely used ester in the perfume industry because of its low cost and floral odor. Over 550,000 lb. are sold annually especially for soap and industrial perfumes. It is prepared by esterification of benzyl alcohol, by heating with either an excess of acetic anhydride or acetic acid with mineral acids. The product is purified by treatment with boric acid and distilled giving a purity of over 98 per cent. *Benzyl alcohol* has annual sales of around 700,000 lb. Large amounts are employed in pharmaceuticals, lacquers, etc. This alcohol has a much weaker odor than its esters. It is made by hydrolyzing benzyl chloride.

GRIGNARD PROCESSES

Phenylethyl alcohol has a roselike odor and occurs in the volatile oils of rose, orange flowers, and others. It is an oily liquid and is much used in perfume formulation, over 700,000 lb. being sold annually. Phenylethyl alcohol can be made by a number of procedures; that employing the Grignard[1] reaction is the most economical and a rare industrial application of this reaction.

$$C_6H_5Br \xrightarrow{\text{Mg(ether)}} C_6H_5MgBr \xrightarrow{\begin{array}{c}CH_2\text{---}CH_2\\ \diagdown O \diagup\end{array}} C_6H_5 \cdot CH_2CH_2OMgBr$$

$$\xrightarrow{\text{Acid}} C_6H_5 \cdot CH_2CH_2OH$$

NITRATION PROCESSES

Artificial musks comprise a number of products that are not identical with the natural musk which derives its odor from macrocyclic compounds. Nitro musks are practical and economical substitutes for this expensive natural fixative and over 170,000 lb. of musk xylene alone are manufactured annually. The reactions for the three important commercial artificial musks follow:

Musk Ambrette:

Musk Xylene and Musk Ketone:

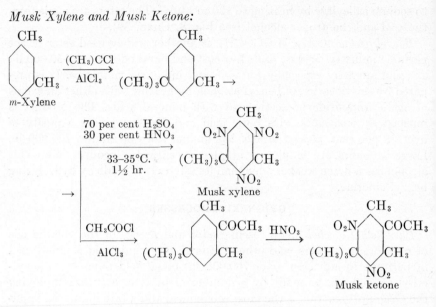

Musk xylene

Musk ketone

OXIDATION PROCESSES

Vanillin is one of the most widely used flavors, being manufactured to the extent of more than 1,000,000 lb. per year. Its characteristic flavor is known to all. It is also used in perfumery and for deodorizing manufactured goods. For its manufacture many processes have been employed of which the following are the most important:

1. From eugenol from oil of cloves, through isoeugenol followed by oxidation to vanillin using nitro-benzene as the oxidizing agent.

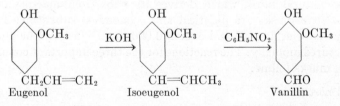

Eugenol   Isoeugenol   Vanillin

2. From lignin[1] through an alkaline pressure cook at 130 to 200 lb. for ½ to 1 hr. of the calcium "ligninsulfonic" acid. The vanillin is purified through the sodium bisulfite compound and extraction with benzene. This process will probably become the most important for making vanillin, although at present more than half is made through guaiacol.

3. From phenol[2] or *o*-chloro-nitro-benzene through guaiacol following the

[1] SANDBORN, U.S. Pat. 2104701(1938); DEVRIS, U.S. Pat. 2399607(1946).

[2] SCHWYZER, "Die Fabrikation pharmazeutischer und chemischtechnischer Produkte," pp. 205–209, 279–288, Springer-Verlag OHG, Berlin, 1931; ULLMANN, "Enzyklopaedie der technischen Chemie," 2 ed., Vol. 8, pp. 815–820, Urban & Schwarz-

procedures and the reactions given in the flow sheet of Fig. 1. This is the usual synthetic procedure. The actual manufacturing steps are quite complicated and are carefully controlled with regard to conditions and apparatus. For these details consult the references, Schwyzer in particular.

Heliotropin or *piperonal* has a pleasant aromatic odor resembling heliotrope. It is produced from safrole by the following reactions:

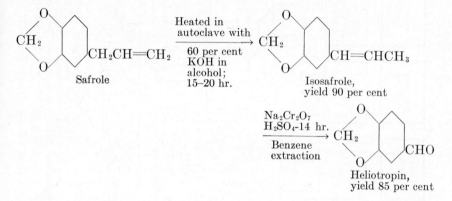

Safrole

Heated in autoclave with 60 per cent KOH in alcohol; 15–20 hr.

Isosafrole, yield 90 per cent

$Na_2Cr_2O_7$ H_2SO_4-14 hr.

Benzene extraction

Heliotropin, yield 85 per cent

Anisaldehyde is a colorless oily liquid with an agreeable odor resembling coumarin which is developed only after dilution and in mixtures. It is made by the oxidation of anethole (the chief constituent of anise, star anise, and fennel oils). Anethole has been obtained recently in this country at very low cost from higher-boiling fractions of pine oil.

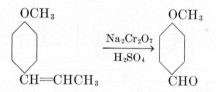

$Na_2Cr_2O_7$
H_2SO_4

Benzaldehyde is used as a flavoring agent, as an ingredient in pharmaceuticals, and as an intermediate in chemical syntheses. Commercially, it is produced by several methods and in two grades, technical and refined. The technical grade is largely used as an intermediate in the synthesis of other chemicals such as benzyl benzoate (page 582), cinnamic aldehyde (page 582), and dyes. Most of the technical grade is made by direct vapor phase oxidation of toluene, although some is made by chlorinating toluene to benzal chloride followed by alkaline or acid hydrolysis.

enberg, Berlin and Vienna, 1928–1932; GROGGINS, "Unit Processes in Organic Synthesis," 4th ed., pp. 431, 829, McGraw-Hill Book Company, Inc., New York, 1952; BEDOUKIAN, *op. cit.*, pp. 401–426; PEARL, Vanillin–Perfumery's First Synthetic, *Am. Perfumer*, **50** (4), 403 (1947).

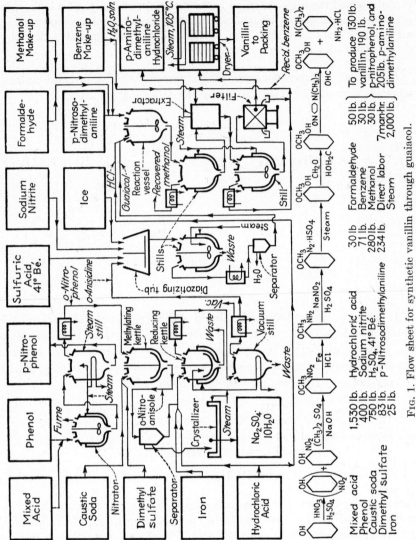

Fig. 1. Flow sheet for synthetic vanillin through guaiacol.

586

For perfume and flavoring use the refined, chlorine free grade is required, which is most economically produced by the direct oxidation of toluene in the vapor phase. This oxidation is sometimes done in the liquid phase.

Vapor phase:

$$C_6H_5CH_3 \xrightarrow[500°C.]{\text{Air, catalyst}} C_6H_5CHO + H_2O; \qquad \Delta H = -91,200 \text{ cal.}$$

It is claimed that a catalyst mixture of 93 per cent uranium oxide and 7 per cent molybdenum oxide gives relative high yields with a low percentage of complete combustion.

Liquid phase:

$$C_6H_5CH_3 \xrightarrow[40°C.]{\text{MnO}_2 \text{ H}_2\text{SO}_4} C_6H_5CHO + H_2O$$

MISCELLANEOUS PROCESSES

About 1,000,000 lb. of *terpineols* are manufactured every year. They are one of the cheapest synthetics and are widely used in soap because of their woodsy and floral odors. Formerly all terpineols were made from turpentine oil which consists largely of α-pinene, but recently pine oil has become an important source. Terpineols may be manufactured directly in a one-step process[1] from pinene by reacting with sulfuric acid and acetone for 6 hr. at 35 to 40°C. The product is purified by fractional distillation. The two-step method has an advantage in that the purification of the intermediate, terpin hydrate, is easier than that of terpineol. Terpin hydrate is formed by reacting pinene with dilute sulfuric acid plus an emulsifying agent.[2] The purified hydrate is then carefully dehydrated to terpineol by using oxygenated carboxylic acids. Terpineols are separated from pine oil by fractional distillation or by the above treatment to the terpin hydrate through 25 per cent sulfuric acid.

Saccharin is a powerful sweetening agent, particularly useful when a sweet flavor is desired without using a carbohydrate. It is manufactured by a series of reactions starting with toluene.[3] This is treated with chloro-

---

[1] SHEFFIELD, U.S. Pat. 2178349(1939).

[2] HASSELSTROM, U.S. Pat. 2330579(1943); SHEFFIELD, U.S. Pat. 2336575(1943).

[3] SCHWYZER, *op. cit.*, pp. 245–249.

sulfonic acid at 0 to 5°C. in cast-iron vessels, the following reactions[1] occurring:

$$\text{C}_6\text{H}_4(\text{CH}_3) + \text{ClSO}_3\text{H} \rightarrow \text{C}_6\text{H}_3(\text{CH}_3)(\text{SO}_3\text{H}) + \text{HCl} \xrightarrow{\text{ClSO}_3\text{H}} \text{C}_6\text{H}_3(\text{CH}_3)(\text{SO}_2\text{Cl}) + \text{H}_2\text{SO}_4$$

An over-all yield of 90 per cent is obtained in these reactions, the product consisting of about 60 per cent of the ortho isomer and 40 per cent of the para isomer. By pouring the products into water and freezing, the undesired para isomer is removed. The o-toluene sulfonyl chloride is treated with concentrated aqueous ammonia solution in enamel-lined autoclaves to give the corresponding sulfonamide in 90 per cent yield:

$$\text{C}_6\text{H}_4(\text{CH}_3)(\text{SO}_2\text{Cl}) + 2\text{NH}_3 \rightarrow \text{C}_6\text{H}_4(\text{CH}_3)(\text{SO}_2\text{NH}_2) + \text{NH}_4\text{Cl}$$

This product is dissolved in sodium hydroxide and oxidized with sodium dichromate and sulfuric acid. The solution is then acidified with HCl, giving the saccharin (benzo-sulfamide) as a precipitate.

$$\text{C}_6\text{H}_4(\text{COONa})(\text{SO}_2\text{NH}_2) + \text{HCl} \rightarrow \text{C}_6\text{H}_4(\text{CO})(\text{SO}_2)\text{NH} + \text{NaCl} + \text{H}_2\text{O}$$

Menthol has long been extracted as the levo- form from oil of Japanese peppermint and used in cigarettes and many other products as an antiseptic cooling flavor. The manufacture of the pure optically inactive form by the hydrogenation of thymol is now being undertaken.[2]

The *acetals* of the *aldehydes* have an odor only slightly modified from that of the aldehydes but have great alkali resistance. Hence these acetals are being used in soaps, which are very difficult to perfume with any lasting odor because the alkaline nature of the soap itself destroys any alkali-sensitive product.

PERFUME FORMULATION

An actual example of a compound perfume, similar to a widely sold product, is given here to indicate the various components that have been

---

[1] Some authorities give this reaction with water splitting off and reacting with the second mole of chloro-sulfonic acid: $\text{C}_6\text{H}_5\text{CH}_3 + \text{ClSO}_3\text{H} \rightarrow \text{C}_6\text{H}_4(\text{CH}_3)\text{SO}_2\text{Cl} + \text{H}_2\text{O}$; $\text{H}_2\text{O} + \text{ClSO}_3\text{H} \rightarrow \text{HCl} + \text{H}_2\text{SO}_4$. ULMANN, *op. cit.*, Vol. 2, p. 247.

[2] BARNEY and HASS, Racemic Menthol, New Synthesis from Thymol, *Ind. Eng. Chem.*, **36**, 85 (1944).

discussed and to show their use in a blended product. The foundation odors are from the eugenols, methyl ionone, and the bergamot oil.

Component	Grams	Component	Grams
Essential oils:		Synthetics:	
Sandalwood oil.............	10	Coumarin................	27.5
Bergamot oil...............	117.5	Vanillin (from guaiacol)....	20
Ylang-ylang oil............	40	Benzyl acetate............	30
Petitgrain oil..............	10	Oleoresins:	
Orange-flower oil..........	10	Opopanax................	2.5
Rose otto.................	15	Balsams (resinoids):	
Jasmine absolute...........	20	Tolu....................	5
Isolates:		Peru....................	7
Eugenol (from clove oil)....	90	Benzoin.................	70
Santalol (from sandalwood)	15	Animal fixatives:	
Semisynthetics:		Castor tincture 1:10.......	12.5
Isoeugenol (from eugenol)...	110	Synthetic fixatives:	
Heliotropin (from safrole)...	15	Musk ketone.............	32.5
Methyl ionone (from citral)	237.5	Musk ambrette...........	12.5
		Vehicle:	
		Ethyl alcohol.............	450 kg.

INDUSTRIAL APPLICATIONS OF PERFUMERY

Perfumes are used industrially in masking, neutralizing, and altering the odor of various products as well as in creating a distinctive aroma for normally odorless objects. "Cashmere" shawls are manufactured in Scotland and given the genuine Hindu touch by a trace of patchouli oil applied to them. Aromatics are added to fabric sizing to disguise the glue or casein smell and leave the finished product with a fine fresh smell. The correct essential oils and fixatives introduced in small quantities to paint will completely mask the usual paint odor during drying. Leather goods and paper are scented delicately to cover up the raw natural smell. A minute amount of bornyl acetate evaporated in an air-conditioning system will impart an outdoor tang to the air. The odor of kerosene in fly sprays is masked and artificial cedarwood is made by coating other woods with cedar oil reclaimed in pencil manufacturing.

The psychological effect of odors is successfully used to increase customer appeal. Perfumed merchandise outsells its odorless counterpart by a large margin. An insurance company boomed its sales of fire insurance overnight by sending out advertising blotters treated to simulate the acrid odor of a fire-gutted building. Newspapers have lately printed advertisements in ink specially mixed with a perfumed oil in order to call attention to a perfumer's product.

THE FLAVORING INDUSTRY

There are only four basic flavors which the nerve endings in the taste buds on the tongue can detect: *sweet, sour, salty,* and *bitter.* The popular conception of flavor, however, involves the combination of these four basic stimuli with the concurrent odor sensations. Apple, for instance, tastes merely sour with a trace of bitterness from the tannins present. The main concept received of an apple is due to the odor of acetaldehyde, amyl formate, amyl acetate, and other esters present in the volatile portion.

The principles of perfume blending also hold good for flavor manufacturing. The best flavoring essences are natural products altered and reinforced where necessary by synthetics. In addition to alcohol as a vehicle, glycerine and isopropyl alcohol are used for the liquid preparations with emulsions of bland gums such as tragacanth and acacia (gum arabic) for pastes. The same fixatives are employed, although the animal types are used more sparingly. Vanillin, coumarin, and heliotropin are used more liberally for this purpose.

Many of the essential oils find application in the flavor industry, the more common being the spice oils, the citrus oils, peppermint, and spearmint. Almost all the perfume synthetics find acceptance plus a number made especially for flavors. The esters of ethyl, methyl, amyl, propyl, butyl, and benzyl alcohols with acetic, propionic, butyric, salicylic, caproic, formic, valeric, and anthranilic acids are widely used to characterize the fruit flavors. As with the flower perfumes, many chemical specialties keynote individual fruit aromas. The gamma lactone of undecylenic acid is a very true representation of the fresh odor of a cut peach. A strawberry base is the ethyl ester of methylphenylglycidic acid, although it is not a true effect and partakes of a somewhat unnatural tone. Propyl succinate and ethyl butyrate are part of the make-up of many pineapple compositions.

NATURAL FRUIT CONCENTRATES

Although the essential oils used in flavoring are of the same grade and source as those used for perfumes, the fruit flavors are handled in a somewhat different manner. Owing to the large percentage of water in most of the common fruits (from 75 per cent in the banana to 90 per cent in the strawberry) and the presence of considerable amounts of sugar and other easily fermented materials, special processes must frequently be employed, such as the following:

Distillation and Extraction of the Fruit. The ripe fruit is stoned and comminuted. It is then subjected to steam distillation and rectification until all the aroma is concentrated in a small portion of the aqueous distillate. This portion is then extracted with low-boiling petroleum ether and the ether removed under vacuum to leave an *essence* or *quint-essence* of the fruit used. Cherry, apple, strawberry, and raspberry are treated by this method.

Extraction of the Juice. In this system the expressed and filtered juice is extracted directly without previous distillation. Occasionally the juice is allowed to ferment slightly before extraction. This is supposed to result in a fuller flavor.

Concentration of the Juice. The expressed and filtered juice is concentrated in vacuum evaporators with a low degree of heat until the water is largely driven off and the sugar concentration is high enough to inhibit bacterial growth (60 per cent). This type of concentrate often has a "jam" or cooked flavor, especially in the case of the strawberries. An alternate method of concentration is by freezing. After reducing the temperature sufficiently, the mush of practically pure water ice is filtered off, and the partly concentrated juice is refrozen and refiltered until the requisite strength is obtained. This is the optimum method of producing concentrates, as there is little injury from heat and the slight off flavors from oxidation can be avoided by running the process in an atmosphere of carbon dioxide.

Vanilla. The vanilla bean is grown principally in Madagascar, Bourbon, and Mexico. It is the immature fruit of the orchid, *Vanilla planifolia* and is cultivated as a vine on trees which support it. The pods are picked when they are just starting to turn from a uniform green to yellow at the tip and have rather a disagreeable odor. The green pods undergo a curing treatment of from 3 to 5 months' duration. In Mexico, the beans are spread out on mats in the heat of day for an hour, after which they are packed into an insulated sweatbox to ferment for 2 days. After drying on open frames for several days, the process is repeated until the bean is cured. Variations of this method include the use of ovens in the initial step and a preliminary dipping into almost boiling water. The cured bean is pliant, shiny, and dark-colored. The odor has become full and rich, and the sweating may have left white aromatic crystals on the outside of the bean. What has happened in substance is that the glucoside, glucovanillin, present in the bean has been acted upon by a ferment and split into glucose, vanillin, and other aromatics. Substances identified in the vanilla bean are anisic acid, alcohol, and aldehyde; vanillic acid and alcohol; cinnamic acid and its esters; vanillin, ethyl vanillin, and possibly other homologs of vanillin.

Preparation of Vanilla Extract. One hundred pounds of a blend of Mexican and Bourbon beans are finely cut up and macerated cold with three successive portions of 35 per cent ethyl alcohol of 100 lb. each. These extracts are combined to make a fine vanilla extract. Other solvents may be used and the extraction carried further, but the product is coarser and less desirable as a fine flavor.

Chocolate and Cocoa.[1] The cacao bean, the seed of *Theobroma cacao L.*, grows on the tree in pods of from 30 to 60 beans. The tree, which when mature is about 20 ft. tall, is grown in Ecuador, West Indies, Brazil, Venezuela, Central America, the African Gold Coast, and other equatorial areas of lesser importance. The pods are gathered twice a year and are split open, and the watery pulp containing the seeds is allowed to ferment in boxes. This fermentation takes from 2 to 7 days and, in addition to liquefying the pulp, kills the embryo (115°F.), reduces the toughness of the bean, frees theobromine from the glucoside, and reduces the astringent tannin content. This fermentation is necessary for flavor in the final product. The moisture in the fermented beans, which is about 30 per cent, is reduced to 5 to 6 per cent by sun or oven drying. The bean is shipped in this condition to manufacturing centers.

The beans are heated in rotary roasters between 220 and 250°F., which develops the true chocolate flavor and aroma, removes unpleasant tannins and volatile matter (butyric and acetic acid, organic bases, and amines), dextrinizes the starch, and embrittles the husk. The roasted beans are quickly cooled to prevent overroasting, cracked in a conical mill, dehusked by a winnowing air stream, and degerminated. This product is known as *cacao nibs*.

Two common methods are used to work the cacao product into chocolate. In the first and older way, the nibs are ground on two or three buhr-stone mills, sugar is added, and the mixture is transferred to a melangeur, which is a mill consisting of a revolving stone on a horizontal revolving heated bed. It merely serves to blend the coarsely ground cacao and the sugar. The paste from the melangeur is fed to a water-cooled grinder with five differentially speeded polished hard cast-iron rollers. This is a refiner and turns out a paste fine enough for *conching*. The newer method is to grind the sugar in a closed-circuit disintegrator and the nibs in a separate water-cooled two-stage disk mill with closed-circuit removal of fines. The two are then mixed. This method takes much less power than the older one and produces a finer and more uniform product in less time. In either method, the paste is run through a concher, which is a granite bed with reciprocally acting granite rollers. It reduces the particle size to an average of less than 1 micron. It is steam-heated to run at 135°F. or can be allowed to heat itself by friction (122°F.). Milk chocolates are prepared by adding condensed fresh milk or milk powder to the melangeur. The finished product has a cocoa butter content of 30 to 35 per cent and not less than 12 per cent of milk solids. Conching heat-treats, aerates, and kneads the mass, producing mellow flavor, extreme smoothness, and lower viscosity in the finished chocolate.

For cocoa, the roasted and ground beans are subjected to pressure in hydraulic presses to remove some of the fat content. Whereas originally

[1] KIRK and OTHMER, *op. cit.*, Vol. 3, pp. 889*ff.*

roasted beans contain 55 per cent of fat, the product remaining after this treatment has the fat reduced to 20 per cent and is known as *cocoa*. The removal of fat makes a beverage that is not too rich and one in which the fat does not separate on top. Some cocoa is treated in between the first and second pressings with alkali solutions. This darkens the cocoa and is supposed to make a more soluble product. Cocoa so treated is known as *Dutch-process* cocoa.

Monosodium Glutamate.[1] Although known in the Orient for many centuries, the growth of monosodium glutamate (M.S.G.) in this country since the Second World War has been spectacular. In 1953, 14,738,000 lb. were sold for $24,419,100. This compound is an important flavoring agent yet has no flavor of its own. It accentuates the hidden and little known flavors of the food where it is used.

Glutamic acid exists in three forms, but only the monosodium salt of *l*-glutamic acid has the flavor-accentuating capacity. Although glutamic acid is a constituent of all common proteins, the economic sources are: wheat gluten, corn gluten, and Steffens filtrate resulting from the desugaring of beet-sugar molasses (Chap. 30). Where the wheat or corn gluten is involved, generally two types of processes are employed, depending on whether the glutamic acid is obtained first as the hydrochloride or as the acid itself. The gluten is hydrolyzed in glass-lined, steam-jacketed autoclaves with 34 per cent HCl. This reaction is completed in several hours at 130°C. This hydrolysis breaks down the protein and produces a considerable amount of *humin*, the name given to the interaction and degradation products of the amino acids and carbohydrates. If the glutamic acid is to be removed as the hydrochloride, the hydrolysate is cooled slightly, filtered for humin removal, and the glutamic acid hydrochloride is crystallized out and separated by filtration. The hydrochloride is converted to glutamic acid. Where the glutamic acid itself is recovered, the hydrolysate is partially neutralized, cooled, and filtered. The filtrate is acidified to a pH of 3.2 (isoelectric point of glutamic acid) and the solution is placed in rubber-lined crystallizers for 5 to 6 days for the glutamic acid to crystallize. The crystals are removed by filtration and repulped with water to remove the inorganic salts, mainly NaCl. The M.S.G. is made by dissolving glutamic acid in a solution of caustic soda, adding filter aid and activated carbon for decolorizing. The solution is filtered, concentrated, and the M.S.G. crystals are centrifuged and dried.

When beet-sugar wastes are used, the principal steps involved are: (1) the concentration and collection of the Steffens filtrate, (2) its hydrolysis, usually with caustic soda, (3) neutralization and acidification of the

---

[1] Manning, *et al.*, Manufacture of Monosodium Glutamate, *Chem. Eng. Progr.*, **44**, 491 (1948); Manning, Food Flavor from Beet Sugar Byproduct, *Chem. Eng.*, **55** (4), 100 (1948), with a pictured flow sheet on p. 136.

hydrolysate, (4) partial removal of the inorganic salts, and (5) crystallization, separation, and purification of the glutamic acid. The M.S.G. is made from the acid as described above.

FLAVOR ESSENCE FORMULATION

A formula is given here for a type of apricot flavoring to be used in candy manufacture. This will indicate in general how a well-balanced flavor is made up of natural products reinforced with suitable synthetics. Many formulas are to be found in print which consist mainly of esters of synthetic origin. These are harsh and unnatural and in many cases the only resemblance to the original is in the designation of the flavor.

APRICOT ESSENCE

	Grams
Apricot extract (a natural product)	1,000
Gamma lactone of undecylenic acid (persicol)	10
Nonyl aldehyde (apricolin)	1
Vanillin	0.5
Ethyl vanillin (bourbonal)	0.2
Ethyl cinnamate	0.2
Benzyl cinnamate	0.2
Tannic acid	0.1

SELECTED REFERENCES

Guenther, Ernest, "The Essential Oils," 6 vols., D. Van Nostrand Company, Inc., New York, 1948. A most excellent series. Many references.

Poucher, W. A., "Perfumes, Cosmetics, and Soaps," 2 vols., 6th ed., D. Van Nostrand Company, Inc., New York, 1942.

Clarke, A., "Flavoring Materials, Natural and Synthetic," Hodder & Stoughton, Ltd., London, 1922.

Naves, R., and G. Mazuyer, "Les parfums naturels," Gauthier-Villars & Cie, Paris, 1939. Translated by E. Sagarin, Reinhold Publishing Corporation, New York, 1947.

DeNavarre, M. G., "The Chemistry and Manufacture of Cosmetics," D. Van Nostrand Company, Inc., New York, 1941.

The American Perfumer (periodical), The Robbins Perfumer Company, Inc., New York.

Tressler, D. K., M. A. Joslyn, and G. L. Marsh, "Fruit and Vegetable Juices," Avi Publishing Co., Inc., New York, 1939. Excellent with regard to equipment and conditions for manufacture.

Bedoukian, P. Z., "Perfumery Synthetics and Isolates," D. Van Nostrand Company, Inc., New York, 1951. An excellent book with many references.

Sagarin, Edward, "The Science and Art of Perfumery," McGraw-Hill Book Company, Inc., New York, 1945. An interesting general account, mostly nontechnical.

Jacobs, M. B., "Synthetic Food Adjuncts," D. Van Nostrand Company, Inc., New York, 1947.

Crocker, E. C., "Flavor," McGraw-Hill Book Company, Inc., New York, 1945.

Kirk, R. E., and D. F. Othmer, "Encyclopedia of Chemical Technology," 15 vols., The Interscience Encyclopedia, Inc., New York, 1947–1956. See specific compound or general headings, i.e., Flavor, Perfume, etc.

CHAPTER 28

OILS, FATS, WAXES

There are, at present, about 13 billion pounds of animal and vegetable fats and oils consumed in the United States each year, of which 80 per cent are of domestic production and the rest imported. Figure 1 depicts the relative consumption for food, soap, and paint of the various oils and fats. It also shows the direct competition of the chemical, soap, and paint industries with basic food products. Fats and oils are found widely

TABLE 1. FATTY ACID CONTENT OF VARIOUS OILS AND FATS[a]
(The figures under the various oils express per cent present)

No. of C atoms	Acid	Formula	Cotton-seed oil	Soy-bean oil	Corn oil	Men-haden oil	Whale oil	Lin-seed oil	Coco-nut oil	Mut-ton tal-low
8	Caprylic	$C_7H_{15}COOH$	....	....	....	....	....	....	7.9	
10	Capric	$C_9H_{19}COOH$	....	....	....	....	....	....	7.2	
12	Lauric	$C_{11}H_{23}COOH$	....	....	....	....	....	....	48.0	
14	Myristic	$C_{13}H_{27}COOH$	1.4	0.4	0.1	5.9	9.2	....	17.5	4.6
14	Unsaturated	$C_{13}H_{25}COOH$	....	....	....	....	2.5			
16	Palmitic	$C_{15}H_{31}COOH$	23.4	10.6	8.1	16.3	15.6	6.3	9.0	24.7
16	Unsaturated	....	2.0	1.0	1.2	15.5	13.9			
18	Stearic	$C_{17}H_{35}COOH$	1.1	2.4	2.5	0.6	1.9	2.5	2.1	30.4
18	Oleic	$C_{17}H_{33}COOH$	22.9	23.5	30.1	....	....	19.0	5.7	36.0
18	Linoleic	$C_{17}H_{31}COOH$	47.8	51.2	56.3	....	....	24.1	2.6	4.3
18	Linolenic	$C_{17}H_{29}COOH$	....	8.5	....	....	....	47.4		
18	Unsaturated	....	....	....	....	29.6	37.2			
20	Arachidic	$C_{19}H_{39}COOH$	1.3	2.4	1.7	1.4	0.6	0.5		
20	Unsaturated	....	....	....	....	19.0	12.0			
22	Unsaturated	....	....	....	....	11.7	7.1			
24	Lignoceric	$C_{23}H_{47}COOH$	....	....	....	....	....	0.2		

[a] Data compiled from KIRK and OTHMER, op. cit., Vol. 6, pp. 142–146, and GUILLANDEU, Ind. Eng Chem., 31, 158 (1939), for mutton tallow.

distributed in nature, in both the plant and the animal kingdoms. Waxes likewise are natural products but differ slightly from the fats and oils in their basic composition. Whereas the fats and oils are mixtures of the glycerides of various fatty acids, the waxes are mixed esters of higher polyhydric alcohols other than glycerol with fatty acids.

Table 1 indicates the characteristic composition of various important oils in regard to their fatty acid content. These acids fall within (1) the saturated series as exemplified by stearic acid and are the basis for the nondrying oils, (2) monoolefinic series with one double bond between carbons as illustrated by oleic acid, and (3) polyolefinic series with more than one such double bond as exemplified by linoleic and linolenic acids. The latter two classes of acids, being unsaturated, furnish the semidrying and drying oils, according to the amounts of unsaturation present. It is of interest to note that the chief constituents of the vegetable oils are the 16 and 18 carbon acids, while the 20, 22, and 24 carbon acids predominate in the fish oils. Coconut oil is unique in that it consists of esters of much shorter carbon chain acids, the 12 and 14 carbon acids being present in greatest amounts.

The degree of unsaturation of the acids involved affects the melting point of the ester mixture, the more unsaturated acids giving esters with lower melting points, these being the chief constituents of the oils. The more saturated esters, on the other hand, are constituents of the fats. Thus, we see that the factor determining whether one of these compounds is termed a *fat* or an *oil* is merely its melting point. These oils are called *fixed oils* in distinction from the essential or *volatile* oils described in Chap. 27. The fixed oils cannot be distilled without some decomposition under ordinary atmospheric pressure. Differentiation should also be noted from petroleum oils discussed in Chap. 37.

Historical. Since ancient times man has known how to remove oils and fats from their natural sources and fit them to his own uses. The animal fats were first consumed as food, but it was not long before the burning of the oils for light and heat was learned. The obtaining of oils from vegetable sources is of ancient origin, for the natives in the tropical regions of the globe have long been removing these oils from various nuts after drying them in the sun. The utilization of marine oils began with the whaling industry, which was started by the Basques in the Bay of Biscay in the fifteenth century.

The first chemical reaction applied to fats and oils (excluding oxidation in burning) was that of saponification to give soap. The early raw materials were mainly of animal origin, the rendering of animal flesh being an old art.

Industrialization of oils and fats began with the erection of a cottonseed mill in South Carolina about 1826. The methods were crude and the product impure. The industry did not expand very rapidly until after 1865. In 1850, the use of caustic soda to remove free acids from the oil was introduced from France. About this time, the millers became aware of the value of the linters that clung to the hulls and also of the hulls themselves for cattle feed. By 1887 more scientific methods of refining had been introduced.

The beginning of the oleomargarine industry in Chicago in 1885 gave a large impetus to the cottonseed-oil industry, since it was found that the oil could be used as a thinning agent in oleomargarine.[1] The higher quality demanded by this new market produced several processing improvements. Fuller's earth was used to decolorize the oil. In 1893 it was learned that the oil could be deodorized by blowing steam through it at high temperatures. Later it was found that deodorization under reduced pressure bettered both flavor and odor.

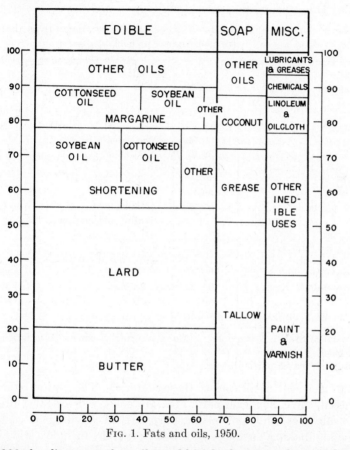

FIG. 1. Fats and oils, 1950.

In 1900 the discovery that oils could be hydrogenated to produce fats revolutionized the entire oil and fat industry and led to our modern hydrogenated shortenings. This discovery also made marketable many of the lesser known oils, which up to that time had not been usable. This phase of the industry has advanced rapidly, until (1953) there are 1,674-702,000 lb. of shortening and 3,097,000,000 lb. of hydrogenated oils produced in the United States each year.

[1] Margarine is now the accepted term. In the beginning this product contained beef fat from whence the term oleo was derived. Now in the United States it is strictly a vegetable-oil product.

Uses and Economics. The fats and oils have always had an essential role as food for mankind. In addition, however, our modern industrial world has found many important applications for them. The uses are summarized in Fig. 1. The oils are saponified, hydrogenated, and sulfonated to a great number of usable products.

There are two broad classifications for the fats and oils: edible and inedible. The consumption of fats and oils in *edible* products represents

TABLE 2. FACTORY PRODUCTION OF FATS, OILS, AND DERIVATIVES IN 1953[a]
(In thousands of pounds)

Vegetable:		Animal:	
Cottonseed..............	1,868,469	Lard..................	2,123,000
Peanut................	58,179	Tallow, edible..........	174,616
Corn..................	259,181	Tallow, inedible........	1,690,973
Soybean...............	2,515,497	Grease, other than wool..	598,330
Olive.................	6,596	Wool grease............	9,041
Coconut...............	422,277	Neat's-foot oil..........	2,158
Linseed...............	503,108	Fish:	
Tung.................	43,153	Cod and cod-liver........	1,095
Castor................	69,190	Other liver oil..........	302
Other vegetable.........	27,272	Menhaden.............	125,154
		Sardine and herring......	4,629
Derivatives:[b]		Other fish oil...........	8,120
Winterized oil...........	609,813	Tallow oil...............	9,315
Deodorized oil..........	279,706	Hydrogenated oils and fats:	
Stearin, vegetable oil.....	120,612	Edible................	3,097,000
Stearin, animal..........	54,092	Shortening..............	1,674,702
Oleo, oil...............	55,565	Margarine..............	1,291,803
Grease and lard oil.......	60,476		

[a] "Chemical Statistics Handbook," Manufacturing Chemists' Association, Washington, 1955.

[b] Naturally, only a partial listing.

about 67 per cent of all uses of these materials. The various edible oils, cottonseed, olive, soybean, corn, etc., are employed for salad dressings, other table uses, and for cooking purposes. The hydrogenated fats for cooking and baking, such as Crisco and Spry, may include a wide variety of vegetable oils, such as cottonseed, peanut, and soybean, since the hydrogenating process removes the color, flavor, and odor of the original source. The various fish-liver oils are used in the medicinal field for their vitamin content and in the paint industry as drying oils. Castor oil is a well-known cathartic.

In 1950 about 33 per cent of all oils and fats consumed in the United States were for *inedible* purposes, as shown by Fig. 1. Around 50 per cent of these inedible oils were used in the soap industry. These include tallow, coconut oil, palm oil, and certain greases. Others were slightly hydrogenated to make them suitable for soapmaking.

The drying-oil industries (including paints and varnishes) consume 12 per cent of all inedible oils. The major oil is still linseed, with tung, soybean, and castor in smaller demand. These drying oils are essentially unsaturated and produce films or coatings upon drying. They are also employed with synthetic resins and cellulose derivatives to give special types of films. Castor oil, linseed, soybean, rapeseed, and cottonseed oils are being used to some extent as plasticizers for nitro-cellulose lacquers.

Other miscellaneous uses include the oilcloth and linoleum industry, the chemical industry for the manufacture of fat and oil derivatives, the manufacture of lubricants and greases, the printing industry, and the tin-plate industry. A wide variety of oils form an integral part of various polishes, creams, and emulsions. Large quantities of sulfonated glycerides and sulfated fatty alcohols and derivatives serve as wetting agents and detergents. Table 2 details the statistics of the principal fats and oils together with some of their important derivatives. It should be compared with Fig. 1.

The *waxes*,[1] carnauba, beeswax, and sperm wax, enter into the manufacture of various polishes for floors, shoes, automobiles, and furniture. Other outlets include the making of carbon paper, candles, electrical insulation, waterproof textiles, and phonograph records.

VEGETABLE OILS

For purposes of discussion of the various technical aspects, the three classical divisions of the general subject of oils, fats, and waxes will be retained: vegetable oils, animal oils and fats, and waxes. Under each

TABLE 3. APPROXIMATE OIL YIELDS OF CERTAIN VEGETABLE OIL MATERIALS[a]

Raw material	Per cent	Raw material	Per cent
Babassu kernels	63	Palm kernels	45
Castor beans	45	Peanuts in the shell	30–35
Corn kernels	4.5	Peanuts shelled	45–50
Copra	63	Perilla seed	37
Cottonseed	15.5	Rapeseed	35
Flaxseed	34	Sesame seed	47
Hempseed	24	Soybeans	18
Kapok seed	18	Tung nuts	50–55

[a] Mostly taken from U.S. Tariff Commission, "Fats, Oils, and Oil-bearing Materials in the U.S.," Washington, Dec. 15, 1941.

of these headings the general methods of manufacture will be discussed, after which the most important of the individual members will be presented. Table 3 indicates the yields of vegetable oils from some of the

[1] MARSEL, Waxes, *Chem. Inds.*, **67**, 563 (1950).

usual sources. The two general methods employed in obtaining vegetable fats and oils are expression and solvent extraction.

Manufacturing Cottonseed Oil[1] by the Expression Process. The obtaining of crude vegetable and animal oils involves almost altogether only the *physical* changes or unit operations, but the *chemical* changes or unit processes are concerned in the refining and the hydrogenation of such oils. Figure 2 presents flow sheets for crude, refined, and hydrogenated

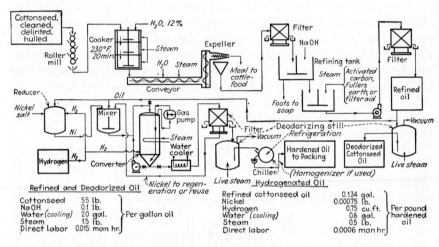

Note: This flow sheet combines processes not ordinarily performed in the same plant. The first processor may produce crude oil, for example, while a second will refine and hydrogenate it. Oils hydrogenated for food are deodorized after hardening.

FIG. 2. Flow sheet for cottonseed oil, refined and hydrogenated. Hydraulic pressing (Fig. 3) now more used than expeller.

cottonseed oils. The flow sheet for crude oil can be broken down into the following sequences of *unit operations* (Op.) (hydrogenation will be considered under its own special heading):

The cottonseeds are cleaned, delinted, and dehulled (Op.).

The kernels are rolled into thin flakes (about 0.010 in.) to make them easily permeable to the steam in the cooking operation (Op.).

All flaked meats are now cooked before expression to precipitate the phosphatides, to detoxify the gossypol, to reduce the moisture content of the flakes, and to coagulate the proteins. For hydraulic pressing, "stack" cookers are the most common and the moisture content is reduced from 12 to 5 per cent. For expellers, the cooker is usually integrated with the press (Op. and Pr.).

Hydraulic pressing (see Fig. 3) has become the most common method of cottonseed-oil recovery, with expeller or screw presses (see Figs. 2 and 4) accounting for a smaller portion of the expression process (Op.). Since the late 1940's, solvent extraction is now practiced in many cottonseed plants, mostly with, but

[1] BAILEY, "Cottonseed and Cottonseed Products," Interscience Publishers, Inc., New York, 1948.

sometimes without, a preliminary expression. These plants are essentially the same as those used for soybean extraction (Fig. 5).

The cooked meal is formed into cakes and placed in the hydraulic press (Fig. 3). The pressure is applied gradually to an ultimate of 1,700 to 2,000 lb. per sq. in. After the oil begins to flow, the press is drained for 20 to 45 min., the cakes are discharged and the cycle repeated. The oil-rich edges of the cakes are trimmed off and reprocessed. One press will handle about 7 tons of cooked meats (equivalent to 12.5 tons of whole seed) per day (Op.). A continuous expeller or screw press

FIG. 3. Hydraulic press removing oil from cottonseed. (*Courtesy of National Cottonseed Products Association.*)

(Figs. 2 and 4) consists of powerful, motor-driven worms operating inside perforated barrels. They exert a pressure of 10 to 12 tons per sq. in., discharging the oil through the barrel spacings and the spent cake through a cone-shaped orifice at the end of the final barrel (Op.). Although the resulting cake contains only 4.0 to 4.5 per cent oil, the equipment and its upkeep are greater and power consumption is high.[1]

The yields from 1 ton of crude cottonseeds average: oil, 310 to 320 lb.; cake, 900 lb.; hulls, 500 lb.; linters, 160 to 200 lb.; loss (chiefly moisture), 100 lb. Virtually the entire cottonseed-oil production is used by edible-oil

[1] KIRK and OTHMER, *op. cit.*, Vol. 4, pp. 579–588.

processors for shortenings, margarine, and salad or cooking oils. The cake is broken or ground and used for cattle feed. The hulls provide roughage for livestock feeding. The linters, with an α-cellulose of 70 to 85 per cent, are utilized as a cellulose source of high purity for rayon, plastics, lacquers, etc.

Fig. 4. Expeller pressing oil out of cottonseed. (*Courtesy of National Cottonseed Products Association.*)

Manufacture by Solvent Extraction. Solvent extraction can recover up to 98 per cent of oil compared with about 80 and 88 per cent from hydraulic and screw expression. The soybean, whose physical structure is particularly suited to solvent extraction, has been responsible for this development. But solvent extraction is assuming importance in virtually all vegetable-oil recovery alone or in combination with a prepressing. High-oil-content seeds, such as cottonseed, usually utilize both expression and extraction in their recovery systems for higher yields.[1]

In 1951–1952 solvent extraction accounted for 70 per cent of the oil recovery from soybeans, while practically all the rest was obtained from screw presses. Because of the efficiency of oil yields (hydraulic press, 8.67

---

[1] Moore, More Oil from Cottonseed, *Chem. Eng.*, **57** (6), 106 (1950); Tray and Bilbe, Solvent Extraction of Vegetable Oils, *Chem. Eng.*, **54** (5), 139 (1947), with a pictured flow sheet.

lb. per bu.; screw presses, 9.16 lb. per bu.; solvent extraction, 10.94 lb. per bu.) virtually all new soybean installations today are solvent extractors.[1]

The preliminary operations of cleaning, hulling, and milling are the same as for expression (Figs. 2 and 5), but the heat-treatment is milder and varies widely with the extraction method. The basic principles of solvent extraction have been well outlined by Cofield and Perry.[2] Although milling releases some of the oil which is immediately dissolved in the solvent, the greater portion of oil is removed by *diffusion of the solvent* through the cell walls until equilibrium is reached. By replacing the equilibrium solution with solvent of lesser oil content, the diffusion process is again resumed. Economic limit to this procedure is about 0.5 per cent oil remaining in the seed mass. The rate of diffusion is directly proportional to the surface area of the seed particle and inversely proportional to its thickness with free circulation of the solvent.

Batch extraction is widely practiced in Europe, but *continuous-extraction* methods based on *countercurrent solvent flow* are the preferred methods here. Many kinds of continuous extractors are used. The original German Bollman[3] extractor (see Fig. 5) with its American modifications, is a conventional basket-type extractor and accomplishes 80 per cent of soybean solvent extraction. Other large-scale extractors are the Hildebrandt, Allis-Chalmers, Anderson, Kennedy, Sherwin Williams, Rotocel,[4] and Bonnoto. The usual solvents are a light petroleum fraction, consisting chiefly of *n*-hexane. Several small extractors employ nonflammable but somewhat toxic trichloroethylene.

After extraction, the meal is steamed to remove all solvent. If to be sold for cattle feed, the meal is toasted to increase its nutritive value. The solvent is stripped from the oil-solvent known as the *miscella*, as shown in Fig. 5.[5]

Purification. Crude oils, obtained by either of the processes outlined above, should be purified. The recently developed liquid-liquid extraction processes for refining of vegetable and animal fats and oils is superseding the once widely used alkali purification. In the *alkali method*, the free

---

[1] ANON., Oilseed Solutions, *Ind. Eng. Chem.*, **43** (2), 15A (1951); ANON., Sans Presses, *Chem. Inds. Week*, **68** (14), 15 (1951); KENYON, *et al.*, Solvent Extraction of Oil from Soybeans, *Chem. Inds.*, **60**, 186 (1948); COFIELD, Solvent Extraction of Oilseed, *Chem. Eng.*, **58** (1), 127 (1951).

[2] COFIELD, *op. cit.*; PERRY, *op. cit.*, pp. 713*ff*.

[3] KENYON, *op. cit.*; COFIELD, *op. cit.*, for drawings, pictures, and brief descriptions of most of the important extractors; *cf.* MARKLEY and Goss, "Soybean Chemistry and Technology," Chemical Publishing Company, Inc., New York, 1944.

[4] KARNOFSKY, The Rotocel Extractor, *Chem. Eng.*, **57** (8), 108 (1950); McCUBBEN and RITZ, New Glidden Soybean Plant First to Use the Rotocel Extractor, *Chem. Inds.*, **66**, 354 (1950).

[5] *Cf.* CROCKIN, Water Injection Streamlines Miscella Classification, *Chem. Eng.*, **57** (11), 160 (1950).

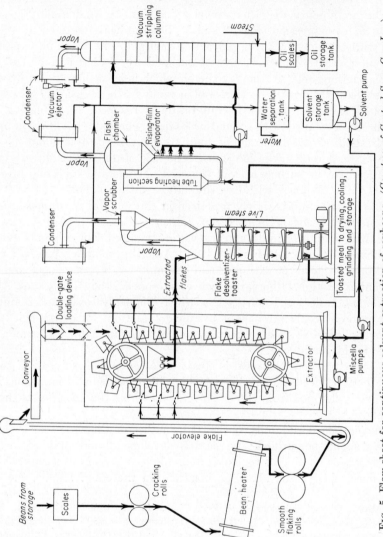

FIG. 5. Flow sheet for continuous solvent extraction of soybeans. (*Courtesy of Central Soya Co., Inc.*)

fatty acids are neutralized with caustic soda or soda-ash-forming soaps, commonly called *foots* (see Fig. 2), which are removed by centrifuges or filters and the fatty acids recovered. The oils are bleached with adsorbent clay either batchwise or in a continuous[1] process. For salad oils, the bleached oil is subjected to a *winterizing* treatment before deodorization, which consists of cooling the oil to low temperatures and filtering the solid stearin that crystallizes out. For shortening, the bleached oil is hydrogenated and bleached again before deodorization. Deodorization in both cases may be either batchwise or continuous[2] and is accomplished by blowing superheated steam through the oil (with the hydrogenated oil still hot and in the liquid stage) under a high vacuum of about 28 in. Hg.

The *liquid-liquid extraction systems* have many advantages over the alkali purification as they involve no chemical reactions for the removal of color bodies, odorous constituents, etc., to provide upgraded and new products. The Solexol continuous-extraction process[3] employs propane under pressure and at low temperatures, when the propane mixes in all proportions with the glyceride oils. By raising the temperature this ability to mix is reduced and the heavier oils precipitate out. Thus, a *selective extraction* of as much material as is desired can be achieved by selectively raising the temperature (critical temperature of propane is 206°F.) and bringing the oil-propane mixture to the desired equilibrium. For example, 100 lb. of crude soybean oil may be extracted yielding 98.5 lb. refined oil and 1.5 lb. pigment lecithin. A great advantage is that, after preliminary refining, the oil may be further extracted yielding an edible glyceride portion and the industrial highly unsaturated glyceride portion. Further extraction of the 98.5 lb. refined soybean oil yields 67.5 lb. edible oil, 30.0 lb. paint oil (see Chap. 24), and 1.0 lb. sterol concentrate. The latter contains tocopherols and sterols useful for synthesis of hormones and other pharmaceuticals. Marine oils provide vitamin A and D sources. Another liquid-liquid process, developed by the Pittsburgh Plate Glass Company, utilizes furfural as the selective solvent.[4]

Linseed Oil. The flaxseed produced in this country is grown largely in the Midwest, south Texas, and the Far West. The production and refining are carried out similarly to the process for cottonseed oil depicted in Fig. 2, either hydraulic presses or Anderson expellers being employed. The average oil content of the flaxseed is about 40 per cent, which would indicate a yield by expression of about 34 per cent on the weight of the

[1] HIGHTOWER, Better Way to Bleach Vegetable Oils, *Chem. Eng.*, **56** (9), 102 (1949).

[2] See ANON., Deodorizing Edible Oils, *Chem. Eng.*, **53** (9), 134 (1946), for pictured flow sheets of both processes; SHEARON, *et al.*, Edible Oils, *Ind. Eng. Chem.*, **42**, 1266 (1950), including flow sheets.

[3] VON BERG and WIEGANDT, Liquid-liquid Extraction, *Chem. Eng.*, **59** (6), 189 (1952); *private communication.*

[4] GLOYER, Furans in Vegetable Oil Refining, *Ind. Eng. Chem.*, **40**, 228 (1948); Goss, Processing Edible Fats, *Ind. Eng. Chem.*, **40**, 2247 (1948).

seeds, leaving about 6 per cent oil in the press cake. Newer and improved installations combine screw pressing with solvent extraction, reducing the residual oil in the cake to about 0.75 per cent.

Soybean Oil. Soybeans are the principal oil source in this country and are grown largely in the corn belt region. An average yield from 1 ton of soybeans is about 360 lb. of oil and 1,640 lb. of cake.

Coconut Oil. The raw material for the production of coconut oil[1] is all imported from various tropical countries, a large part coming from the Philippines. The raw material is brought in as copra, which is coconut kernel that has been shelled, cut up, and heat-dried at the point where grown. This treatment not only avoids the cost of shipping excess moisture but also prevents deterioration of the oil. The coconuts, as they come from the tree, contain from 30 to 40 per cent oil, while the copra contains from 65 to 70 per cent oil. The copra is expressed in expellers or screw presses. A ton of copra yields about 1,250 lb. of oil and 720 lb. of cake. The oil is refined and contains from 1 to 12 per cent free fatty acid depending on the quality of the copra meats. Only oil of low free fatty acid content is employed for edible purposes, while the rest (about 75 per cent of the total receipts) is used for the production of soap and alcohols.

Corn Oil. The production of corn oil differs from some of the others in certain respects. After cleaning, the corn is placed in large tanks and steeped with warm water containing SO_2, thus loosening the hull from the kernel. The steeped corn is run through the "attrition" mills, which break the germ away from the rest of the kernel. The separation of the germ and the kernel is accomplished by running the mixture into a tank of water, where the germ floats, owing to its oil content, and is skimmed off. Before going into the ordinary grinding and expelling apparatus, the germ should be washed and thoroughly dried. The crude oil from the expellers (see Fig. 4) is given the usual purification treatment, such as that described under Cottonseed Oil. The oil content of the corn kernel, exclusive of the hull, is about 4.5 per cent. This oil is used almost exclusively as a salad oil.

Palm Oil. Palm oil is prepared from the fruit of the palm tree, which has been cultivated on plantations in the Dutch East Indies, the Malay Peninsula, and elsewhere. The palms grow naturally on the west coast of Africa. The fruit is 1 to 2 in. long, oval-shaped, and weighs, on an average, about 6 to 8 grams. The oil content ranges from 40 to 50 per cent of the kernel or seed. The oil is obtained in two separate procedures. In the first, the oil is removed from the fruit and in the second from the kernels, or seeds. The former is done at the place where the fruit is grown. The procedure consists in cooking the fruit in large steam-pressure digesters equipped with agitators. From the steaming, the charge goes to basket

---

[1] Anon., Copra Refining, *Chem. & Met. Eng.*, **52** (2), 148 (1944), with a pictured flow sheet.

centrifuges, where a 10-min. treatment, accompanied by blowing with live steam, separates the oil. The residual fiber and kernels are dried in a rotary continuous drier and separated by a screening operation. The nuts or kernels are bagged and shipped to the United States, where they are processed by the previously described methods for oil removal. The fibers are burned under the boilers of the first processing plant. Most of this oil in the United States goes into soap manufacture.

Peanut Oil. Peanut oil is produced by either the hydraulic press or the Anderson expeller, from the peanuts grown in the various Southern states. The yield from 1 ton of peanuts is about 600 lb. of oil and 700 lb. of cake. The oil is hydrogenated and refined for use in the manufacture of margarine, salad and cooking oils, and in some vegetable shortenings. Inedible grades of the oil are consumed by the soapmaker.

Tung Oil. Tung or China wood oil is obtained from the fruit of the tung tree which grows extensively in China. Since 1923 large-scale planting has been carried out in Florida and has become one of the prime industries of that state. Owing to the large demand for fast-drying finishes and the difficulties in obtaining this oil from China, various modifications of other oils (see Chap. 24) for drying purposes are employed. As of now, this oil is superior but unavailable. The oil is obtained by expression and the cake, unfit for stock feeding, is used as fertilizer because of its high nitrogen and phosphorus content.

Castor Oil. This well-known oil is obtained from the seeds or beans of the castor plant found in most tropical regions. The beans contain 35 to 55 per cent oil and are expressed or solvent-extracted.[1] The finest grade of oil is reserved for medicinal purposes. The lower grades are used in the manufacture of transparent soaps, flypaper, typewriter inks, and as a motor lubricant. Large quantities of the oil are sulfonated to produce the familiar Turkey-red oil long employed in dyeing cotton fabrics, particularly with alizarin. Dehydrated castor oil, a very important drying oil, is described in Chap. 24. This manufactured product compares quite favorably with tung oil previously imported.

ANIMAL FATS AND OILS

There is no particular method common to the manufacture of all animal oils and fats.

Lard and Lard Oil. Lard is produced by the rendering of hog fat and is used for food. Lard oil is the most important of the animal oils and is expressed from "white grease," an inedible lard. The white grease is prepared by a circulating rendering process such as that of Wurster and

---

[1] Editorial Staff Report, Now Castor Oil by Solvent Extraction, *Chem. Inds.*, **64**, 926 (1949).

Sanger,[1] wherein the ground fat is rendered or sharply separated into the lard or pure fat, and the nonfat or cracklings. This circulating process involves a low-temperature heating under circulation and a vacuum wherein the lard is removed as a liquid fat more quickly than usually, thus avoiding its yellowing. The white grease is seeded with stearin and held at 50°F. to allow the stearin to crystallize out (graining). After the graining process is completed, the grease is wrapped in duck, stacked in a hydraulic press, and expressed. The oil is used for illumination and in the textile industry. The stearin is employed for the manufacture of soap.[2]

Neat's-foot Oil. The skin, bones, and feet of cattle (exclusive of the hoofs) are cooked in water for 10 hr. to separate the fat. This is skimmed off the top of the water and, after filtering through cloth, heated in a kettle to 250°F. for several hours. The kettle is cooled, the contents are settled, the oil is drawn off, filtered through flannel bags, and sent to the refinery. Here the oil is "grained" in the manner described above for lard oil. This requires about two weeks at 34°F. The product is pressed once, yielding pure neat's-foot oil. The stearin from the first pressing is re-pressed to yield a second grade of oil. The pure variety is used for oiling watches and other fine machinery, the latter in the textile and leather industries. The stearin from the second pressing is consumed in soap.

Whale Oil. This oil is now obtained from modern floating factory ships which catch, butcher, and process the mammals at the scene of the catch. To prepare the oil, the blubber is stripped from the flesh and boiled in open digesters. The finest grade of oil separates first. It is practically odorless, very pale in color, and contains very little free fatty acids. Upon continued boiling a second grade is obtained and, if the residue from this operation is cooked under pressure, a third grade is made available. All grades are centrifuged further to clarify and dry them before being placed in storage. The oils obtained are used in the manufacture of lard substitutes and in soapmaking.[3] Both fish and whale oils contain unsaturated fatty acids of 14 to 22 carbon atoms, and as many as 6 double bonds.

Cod-liver Oil. This oil, whose value was known long before the discovery of vitamins, was originally prepared by storing the fish in barrels and allowing them to rot until the oil floated to the top. It is now manufactured by live steam cooking of the livers (and other parts) of the cod and halibut, until a white scum floats to the top. This usually requires about 30 min., after which the mass is settled for 5 min., decanted, and strained. The oil desired for medicinal purposes is filtered, bleached, and wintered. It is rich in vitamins A and D.

Shark-liver Oil. Recent investigations have shown that the oil obtained from the liver of the shark, *Galeorhinus zyopterus*, contains more vitamins

---

[1] Circulars, Wurster & Sanger, Inc., Chicago, Ill.
[2] LEVITT, Industrial Uses of Animal Oils, *Chem. Inds.*, **42**, 419 (1938).
[3] RADCLIFFE, The Whaling Industry, *Ind. Eng. Chem.*, **25**, 764 (1933).

A and D than cod- or halibut-liver oils. It is rapidly becoming the most important of the fish-liver oils for use in supplying these two vitamins, although the others are used.[1] However, in 1950 vitamin A was commercially synthesized[2] and this process is making a sizable dent in the market formerly held by fish-liver oils. This 12-step synthesis process is based on citral, formaldehyde, and acetic acid as raw materials.

Fish Oils. Fresh menhaden, sardine, and salmon are cooked whole by steam for a short period and pressed. The oil is settled (or centrifuged) and wintered. The remainder of the fish is dried, pulverized, and sold as meal for feed. Each fish contains, on the average, 20 per cent oil by weight.[3] The oils are consumed in paints, as lubricants, in leather and soft-soap manufacture, and sulfonated to give a variety of Turkey-red oil.

The tremendous quantities (Fig. 1) of *butter* and *tallow* produced for food in the United States might logically warrant discussing with the other animal oils. Their methods of processing, however, are fairly well known.

WAXES[4]

There are animal, vegetable, mineral, and synthetic waxes, depending upon their source. The animal waxes are secreted as protective coatings by certain insects. The vegetable waxes are found as coatings on leaves, stems, flowers, and seeds. The mineral waxes are the paraffin waxes obtained from petroleum and such waxes as are yielded by coal, peat, and lignite. The mineral waxes from petroleum are not true waxes (esters) but are so classified because of their physical characteristics.

Beeswax. This is probably the best-known wax. It is made from the honeycomb by solvent extraction, expression, or by boiling in water.

Carnauba Wax. This wax is obtained from the carnauba palm which grows in Brazil. The leaves are cut, dried for 3 days, and sent to the beater house. The drying loosens the wax which can be easily beaten from the slashed leaf and falls to the floor, where it is gathered at the end of the day and melted. Five gallons of powdered wax yield less than 1 qt. of molten wax. This is filtered hot through cheesecloth, allowed to harden, and sold. Five palm trees will produce about 1 lb. of wax per year. The product is used as a constituent of floor, automobile, and furniture polishes, in carbon paper, candles, and certain molded products.

Sperm Oil. The oil removed from the head cavity and parts of the

[1] GRANBERG, Automatic Handling Marks Vitamin Oil Extraction, *Chem. Inds.*, **65**, 41 (1949).

[2] O'CONNOR, Synthetic Vitamin A, *Chem. Eng.*, **57** (4), 146 (1950).

[3] ANON., Menhaden's Fame, *Chem. Inds. Week*, **68** (4), 13 (1951).

[4] WARTH, "The Chemistry and Technology of Waxes," Reinhold Publishing Corporation, New York, 1947.

blubber of the sperm whale is in reality a wax, owing to its chemical composition. Sperm oil is important for lubricating. The head oil upon chilling and setting yields spermaceti, a solid wax. This constitutes about 11 per cent of the original oil and is largely cetyl palmitate. It is melted, treated with hot, dilute caustic soda solution, washed with water, and run into molds to solidify. It is translucent, odorless, and tasteless and is used chiefly as a base for ointments.

Ozocerite is the name given to certain naturally occurring mineral waxes. The ozocerite known commercially is the particular earth wax that is mined in eastern Europe, but important similar waxes are mined elsewhere. One variety, mined in Utah, is known as Utahwax or Utah ozocerite. This can be substituted to a great extent for the other and is chiefly employed for electrical insulations, waterproofing and impregnating. Paraffin wax is concentrated in certain lubricating-oil fractions as the result of distillation and is separated by chilling and filter pressing (see Chap. 37). The name *montan wax* generally applies to the wax obtained from a bituminous wax, solvent extracted from bituminous lignite or shale, but a similar wax may be obtained from peat or brown coal. Its important applications include electrical insulations, polishes, and pastes. *Synthetic waxes*, developed especially by the Germans, offer some of the same physical properties, but are not waxylike in appearance. Many types are now on the market.[1]

HYDROGENATION

Hydrogenation,[2] or hardening as applied to fats and oils, might be defined as the conversion of various unsaturated radicals of fatty glycerides into more highly or completely saturated glycerides by the addition of hydrogen in the presence of a catalyst. This constitutes one of the chief commercial examples of the unit process of hydrogenation.[3] Various fats and oils, such as soybean, cottonseed, fish, whale, and peanut, are converted by partial hydrogenation into fats of a more suitable composition for shortenings, margarine, and edible purposes, as well as for soapmaking and numerous other industrial uses. The object of the hydrogenation is not only to raise the melting point but greatly to improve the keeping qualities, taste, and odor of many oils.

The application of the unit process of hydrogenation to oils has been more important and far-reaching than any other improvement in this industry.

[1] MARSEL, Waxes, *Chem. Inds.*, **67,** 563 (1950); an excellent table on synthetic and blended natural waxes is included.

[2] WURSTER, Hydrogenation of Fats, *Ind. Eng. Chem.*, **32,** 1193 (1940); ARMSTRONG, Fat Hydrogenation, *Chemistry & Industry*, **51,** 92 (1932).

[3] GROGGINS, "Unit Processes in Organic Synthesis," 4th ed., p. 488, but pp. 513–530 particularly, McGraw-Hill Book Company, Inc., New York, 1952.

Reaction and Energy Changes. As the reaction itself is exothermic, the chief energy requirements are in the production of hydrogen, warming of the oil, pumping, and filtering. The reaction may be generalized:

$$(C_{17}H_{31}COO)_3C_3H_5 + 3H_2 \xrightarrow{Ni} (C_{17}H_{33}COO)_3C_3H_5$$
$$\text{Linolein} \qquad\qquad\qquad \text{Olein}$$

Manufacture of Hydrogenated Oils. The hydrogenation plant consists of hydrogen-generating equipment, catalyst equipment, equipment for refining the oil prior to hydrogenation, a converter for the actual hydrogenation, and equipment for posthydrogenation treatment of the fat. These are all included in the lower part of the flow sheet of Fig. 2. One type of converter is pictured in Fig. 6.

The *hydrogen* needed may be manufactured by a number of methods,[1] *i.e.*, electrolytic, steam-iron, water-gas, and hydrocarbon-steam processes, depending upon local cost and purity. Since traces of gaseous sulfur compounds (H_2S, SO_2, etc.) are strong catalyst poisons, as is also, to a lesser degree, carbon monoxide, it is essential that the hydrogen be completely free of these poisons as well as taste-producing substances. The amount of hydrogen necessary is a function of the reduction of unsaturation, as measured by the decrease in the iodine number during hydrogenation. The theoretical quantity to reduce the iodine number 1 unit is about 30 cu. ft. (s.t.p.) of H_2 per ton of oil. Weighted averages at one plant[2] show a consumption of 0.604 cu. ft. of H_2 per pound of oil hydrogenated.

The *catalyst* used commercially is nickel. It may be manufactured by a number of processes. Nickel made by the liquid or *wet-reduced process* is the most used.[3] Two to four parts of a highly saturated oil or the oil to be hydrogenated and 1 part of nickel formate are introduced into a specially designed closed vessel equipped for accurate temperature control. The charge is heated as quickly as possible to as high as 464°F., but 375°F. is a more common temperature. At about 300°F. the nickel formate begins to reduce

$$Ni(HCOO)_2 \cdot 2H_2O \rightarrow Ni + 2CO_2 + H_2 + 2H_2O$$

The charge is held at the maximum temperature upward of 1 hr., then cooled. During the reduction and cooling period, hydrogen is bubbled through the oil solely to sweep decomposition products from the oil. Upon completion of the reduction, the charge may be pumped directly to the converter or formed into blocks, flakes, or granules for later use.

The *dry-reduced* catalysts are prepared by precipitating nickel carbonate or nickel hydroxide on diatomaceous earth, drying and grinding

---

[1] See Chap. 8 for details on these various processes.

[2] SHEARON, *et al.*, *op. cit.*

[3] See Hydrogenation and Hydrogenolysis Reviews annually in September issue, *Ind. Eng. Chem.*; Symposium, Nickel Catalysts, *Ind. Eng. Chem.*, **44**, 977 (1952).

the precipitate, and reducing the resultant powder at a high temperature with a current of hydrogen. A relatively new type of dry catalyst is prepared by adsorbing nickel hydroxide formed by anodic corrosion of nickel on kieselguhr, and reducing. *Raney's nickel* or sponge nickel is employed not only for hydrogenation of fats but for various other hydrogenation processes. In its manufacture, the nickel is first alloyed with aluminum in a proportion of about 1 to 1 by weight. The alloy is cooled

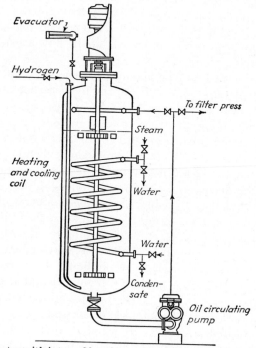

FIG. 6. Hydrogenator with internal heating and cooling coil, oil and catalyst circulating pump, and turbine-type mechanical agitator. (*Courtesy of O. H. Wurster.*)

and marketed in the form of a powder. For use, this powder is treated with an excess of strong NaOH. After the initial exothermic reaction the products are heated to 250°F. for 2 or 3 hr. The resulting sludge, almost entirely metallic nickel, is subjected to repeated washings to remove all traces of sodium aluminate and alkali. The residual sludge is covered with oil to supply a protective coating and heated. The finished catalyst is in the form of relatively large particles as compared with the wet-reduced nickel, thus filtering out more easily.

Hydrogenation of the Oil. Although many continuous processes for oil hydrogenation have been patented none is known to be in operation in this country. The present commercial hydrogenators range in capacity from 5 to 20 tons of oil per batch, are usually made from carbon steel, and can withstand pressures from 100 lb. per sq. in. gage to full vacuum. They may be divided into two types. The *hydrogen-recirculation* type (see Fig. 2) is a tall cylindrical vessel, often without mechanical agitation, provided with a hydrogen distributor in the bottom through which the hydrogen in excess of the amount required is blown during the reaction. The unabsorbed hydrogen at the top is recirculated from the headspace by means of a blower. The *dead-end system* (see Fig. 6) employs a vertical, cylindrical pressure vessel with a mechanical agitator of the gas-dispersion type. It is supplied with only enough hydrogen from high-pressure tanks to be absorbed by the oil.

The usual range of temperatures is about 250 to 375°F., but all the variables will depend upon the type of product desired. Margarine and shortening stocks are generally hydrogenated 1 to 2 hr. Since margarine must resemble butter, *i.e.*, a firm but low-melting product, it is hydrogenated very selectively at relatively low pressures and high temperatures. Shortenings, however, are hydrogenated mainly to olein but with moderate

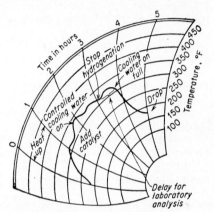

FIG. 7. Typical hydrogenation operating chart. [*Courtesy of Industrial and Engineering Chemistry. Ind. Eng. Chem.*, **42**, 1266 (1950).]

selectivity at lower temperatures and higher pressures to obtain the proper high- and low-temperature consistency coupled with maximum stability and the minimum iodine value. A melting-point range of 95 to 97°F. and iodine number of 65 is common.

Although the procedure varies from one plant to another, a typical hydrogenation will be described.[1] The oil is first charged to the converter and heated sometimes under vacuum to drive off any air or moisture present. Then the catalyst is pumped in and thoroughly mixed with the oil. Catalyst concentrations are held fairly constant and range from 1/2 to 1 1/2 lb. of nickel per 100 lb. of oil. The hydrogen is introduced and, since the reaction is exothermic, the steam is now turned off. See Fig. 7 for a typical hydrogenation curve. When the desired degree of hardness is attained, the oil is cooled and filtered. The press cake is the catalyst, which is used over and over, either alone or with the addition of small quantities of fresh catalyst from time to time, until no longer active. For shortenings and margarine the finished oil is again bleached and deodorized.

[1] SHEARON, *et al.*, *op. cit.*

SELECTED REFERENCES

Hilditch, T. P., "The Chemical Constitution of Natural Fats," 2d ed., John Wiley & Sons, Inc., New York, 1947.

Bailey, A. E., "Oil and Fat Products," 2d ed., Interscience Publishers, Inc., New York, 1951.

———, "Cottonseed and Cottonseed Products," Interscience Publishers, Inc., New York, 1948.

———, "Melting and Solidification of Fats," Interscience Publishers, Inc., New York, 1950.

Markley, K. S., "Soybean and Soybean Products," 2 vols., Interscience Publishers, Inc., New York, 1950.

———, "Fatty Acids," Interscience Publishers, Inc., New York, 1947.

Kirk, R. E., and D. F. Othmer, "Encyclopedia of Chemical Technology," 15 vols., The Interscience Encyclopedia, Inc., New York, 1947–1956.

Journal of the American Oil Chemists' Society, a monthly publication. Printed by Garrard Press, Champaign, Ill. For Edible Fats, see *ibid.*, **XXVI** (10), 547–635 (1949) and for Drying Oils, *ibid.*, **XXVI** (11), 433–544 (1950).

Daubert, B. F., "Fats-Oils-Detergents," A loose-leaf abstract service, monthly by Interscience Publishers, Inc., New York, since 1944.

Treybal, R. E., "Liquid Extraction," McGraw-Hill Book Company, Inc., New York, 1951.

Levitt, Benjamin, "Oil, Fat, and Soap," Chemical Publishing Company, Inc., New York, 1951.

Schwitzer, K. M., "Continuous Processing of Fats," Leonard Hill, Ltd., London, 1951.

Warth, A. H., "The Chemistry and Technology of Waxes," Reinhold Publishing Corporation, New York, 1947.

Root, H. H., "Beeswax," Chemical Publishing Company, Inc., New York, 1951.

Eckey, E. W., and L. P. Miller, "Vegetable Fats and Oils," Reinhold Publishing Corporation, New York, 1955.

CHAPTER 29

SOAP, DETERGENTS, AND RELATED COMPOUNDS

Soap comprises the sodium or potassium salts of various fatty acids, but chiefly of oleic, stearic, palmitic, lauric, and myristic acids. For generations its use has increased until its manufacture has become an industry essential to the comfort and health of civilized man. We may well gage the advance of modern civilization by the per capita consumption of soap. Although soap may be classified as a detergent, a *synthetic detergent* in present-day usage connotes synthetic surface-active agents derived from a wide variety of materials, particularly petroleum. The spectacular growth of these compounds may be illustrated by stating that for 1953 detergents exceeded soaps for the first time, the estimate being 20+ lb. detergents per capita vs. 20− lb. for soaps, or a production of 2,134,000,000 lb. for detergents and 1,948,000,000 lb. for soap. Contrast these figures with the 1935–1940 average of 10,000,000 lb. of detergents and 3,044,000,000 lb. of soap.

Historical. Soap itself was never actually "discovered," but instead gradually evolved from crude mixtures of alkaline and fatty materials. Pliny the elder described the manufacture of both hard and soft soap in the first century. Although a fully equipped soap factory was found in the ruins of Pompeii, it was not until the thirteenth century that soap was produced in sufficient quantities to call it an industry. Up to the early 1800's soap was believed to be a mechanical mixture of fat and alkali; then Chevreul, a French chemist, showed that soap formation was actually a chemical reaction. Domeier completed his researches on the recovery of glycerine from saponification mixtures in this period. Until LeBlanc's important discovery of producing lower-priced sodium carbonate from sodium chloride, the alkali required was obtained by the crude leaching of wood ashes or from the evaporation of the naturally occurring alkaline waters, such as from the Nile River.

The basic process for soapmaking has remained practically unchanged for 2,000 years! This is by batchwise saponifying the oils and fats with an alkali and salting out the soap. The major changes have been in the pretreatment of the fats and oils, in actual plant procedure, and in the processing of the finished soap. Hydrogenation, liquid extraction, and solvent crystallization of various fats and oils provide newer and better raw materials. Better control methods and spray drying are important examples of the latter two.

Continuous processes in plant stage in this country date from 1937 when Procter and Gamble installed a high-pressure-hydrolysis continuous-neutralization process at Quincy, Mass. The next development was a continuous-saponification process jointly developed by Sharples and Lever Brothers and first installed at the latter's plant at Baltimore in 1945. Since then, there have been many installations of both types. These

TABLE 1. TOTAL SOAP SALES[a]
(By kinds of products. In millions of pounds)

Year	Granulated, powdered, and sprayed, package and bulk	Chips and flakes, package and bulk	Washing powder, package and bulk	Bar toilet	Bar laundry white	Bar laundry yellow
1935	502.6	458.4	216.9	345.3	420.5	701.4
1939	891.4	417.3	239.8	396.1	660.7	566.1
1943	1,120.0	386.3	258.7	497.8	493.8	669.4
1945	1,276.5	481.7	245.6	510.1	360.1	784.7
1947	1,538.4	415.0	187.3	548.8	406.6	340.6
1949	1,356.2	308.8	113.2	515.8	301.6	257.6
1951	964.0	286.0	89.1	514.0	252.2	304.8

[a] NEIDIG and HERSBERGER, Organic Synthetic Detergents, Chem. Eng. News, **30**, 23611 (1952).

continuous processes, although extremely important technological developments, have been partially eclipsed by synthetic detergents. The relatively low labor ratio to the product stabilizes old processes in the soap industry. As one soapmaker said,[1] "It does not pay us to scrap our kettles to install a continuous system, but on any expansion or replacement basis, only such a method will be considered."

Uses and Economics. The soap industry is a large one, embracing 249 plants in the United States, with products valued by the U.S. Bureau of the Census at $1,085,789,000 in 1947, and giving employment to 27,660 people. Table 1 gives a breakdown of the principal sales items. It is a matter of common information that the chief use of soap is as a cleansing agent in the home. Although synthetic detergents have been making inroads into traditional industrial markets such as textile finishing and dyeing, laundries, and dairies, soap is still an important industrial chemical. Bulk consumption is estimated at 300,000,000 to 400,000,000 lb. annually of which 136,000,000 lb. are used in the manufacture of synthetic rubber.[2] Other important applications are emulsification, particu-

[1] McCUTCHEON, Soap Progress Since 1900, Soap Sanit. Chemicals, **27** (1), 27 (1951).

[2] FLETT, What's Ahead for Soap and Synthetic Detergents, Soap Sanit. Chemicals, **27** (3), 35 (1951).

larly of cold cream and cosmetic preparations, and for textile processing. Although we shall be concerned here with the alkali-metal soaps, *i.e.*, those showing pronounced water solubility, heavy metal salts of non-volatile fatty acids[1] and organic nitrogen-base soaps also have important industrial applications. The latter class, of which triethanolamine oleate is a good example, is used in dry cleaning and cosmetics. Zinc and magnesium stearates are constituents of face powder. Calcium and aluminum soaps are insoluble in water (Table 2) and, indeed, are water repellents, being consequently employed for waterproofing textiles and walls. Rosin soap is a widely consumed sizing for paper.

TABLE 2. SOLUBILITIES OF VARIOUS PURE SOAPS
(At 25°C. Grams per 100 g. of water)

	Stearate	Oleate	Palmitate	Laurate
Sodium	0.1^a	18.1	0.8^a	2.75
Potassium	. . . . .	25.0	. . . . .	70.0^a
Calcium	0.004^b	0.04	0.003	0.004^b
Magnesium	0.004	0.024	0.008	0.007
Aluminum	i	i	d	

^{a} Approximate.
^{b} Solubility given at 15°C. only.
i indicates that the compound is insoluble.
d indicates decomposition.

SOAP MANUFACTURE

The basic chemical reaction in the making of soap may be expressed as *saponification*:[2]

$$3NaOH + (C_{17}H_{35}COO)_3C_3H_5 \rightarrow 3C_{17}H_{35}COONa + C_3H_5(OH)_3$$

Caustic   Glyceryl   Sodium stearate   Glycerine
soda   stearate

In recent years the tendency has been to split or *hydrolyze* the fat and then, after separation from the valuable glycerine, *neutralize* the fatty acid with caustic soda or soda ash solution.

$$(C_{17}H_{35}COO)_3C_3H_5 + 3H_2O \rightarrow 3C_{17}H_{35}COOH + C_3H_5(OH)_3$$

Glyceryl   Stearic acid   Glycerine
stearate

$$C_{17}H_{35}COOH + NaOH \rightarrow C_{17}H_{35}COONa + H_2O$$

Stearic acid   Caustic   Sodium
      soda   stearate

[1] ELLIOTT, "The Alkaline Earth and Heavy-metal Soaps," Reinhold Publishing Corporation, New York, 1945.
[2] Although stearic acid is written in these reactions, oleic, lauric, or other constituent acids of the fats could be substituted. See Table 1, Chap. 28 for fatty-acid composition of various fats and oils.

It should be pointed out that the usual fats and oils of commerce are not composed of the glyceride of any one fatty acid, but of a mixture. However, some individual fatty acids of 90 per cent purity or better are available by special processing. Since the solubility and hardness of the sodium salts (Table 2) of the various fatty acids differ considerably, the soapmaker chooses his raw material according to the properties desired, with due consideration to the market price.

Raw Materials. *Tallow* is the principal fatty material in soapmaking, the quantities used representing 51.5 per cent of the total oils and fats consumed by the soap industry as shown by Fig. 1, Chap. 28. It contains the mixed glycerides obtained from the solid fat of cattle by steam rendering. This solid fat is digested with steam, the tallow forming a layer above the water where it can easily be removed. Tallow is usually mixed with coconut oil in the soap kettle in order to reduce the hardness and to increase the solubility of the soap. *Greases* (20.8 per cent) are the second most important raw material in soapmaking. They are obtained from hogs and the smaller domestic animals or from garbage, and are an important source of glycerides of fatty acids. They are refined by steam rendering or by solvent extraction and seldom used without blending with other fats. In some cases, they are treated so as to free their fatty acids which are used in soap instead of the grease itself. *Coconut oil* ranks third, representing 15 per cent of the total fats and oils consumed in this industry. This oil is almost always an important constituent of household soap, as the soap from coconut oil is firm and lathers well. It contains large proportions of the very desirable glycerides of lauric and myristic acids, as well as smaller amounts of oleic, stearic, palmitic, and similar acids. The crude oil is treated with NaOH solution, settled, separated, and bleached. *Palm oil* resembles tallow. *Palm-kernel* and *Babassu-nut oils* are very similar to coconut oil and upon saponification produce very similar soaps. *Fish oils*, although once important by hydrogenation for soap raw materials, are now mostly utilized through better processing techniques where unsaturation is important, *i.e.*, drying oils. Denatured *olive oil* is used for soap, but most of it is sold undenatured for edible purposes.

The soapmaker is also a large consumer of chemicals, especially caustic soda, salt, soda ash, and caustic potash as well as sodium silicate, sodium bicarbonate, and trisodium phosphate. The inorganic chemicals added to the soap, the so-called *alkalinity builders*, decrease the cost of the soap product without decreasing its efficiency.

Free fatty acids are not only a raw material for soap, but are becoming an ever-increasing source of raw materials for other chemicals. Fatty acid derivatives include the nitrogen-containing chemicals (amines, amides, and nitriles), the fatty-acid esters (glycerine monostearate, ethylene glycol monostearate), and the metallic stearates (Al, Zn, Ca, Mg). Free fatty acids are utilized in the soap, detergent, cosmetic, paint, textile, and many other industries. Although fatty acids have been synthesized commercially in Germany, most of the commercial fatty acids are produced by the *hydrolysis* or *splitting* of naturally occurring fats and oils. Acidification of "foots," or stock resulting from alkaline refining of oils, also produces fatty acids. The important general methods of splitting are outlined in Table 3. The Twitchell process is the oldest. Continuous countercurrent processes are found in two modifications; one of these is known

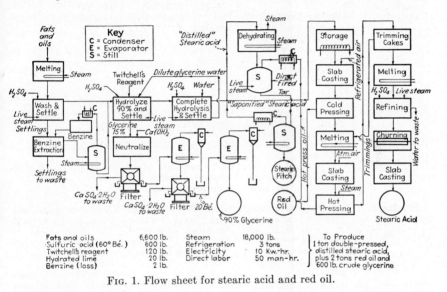

Fats and oils	6,600 lb.	Steam	18,000 lb.	To Produce
Sulfuric acid (60° Bé.)	600 lb.	Refrigeration	3 tons	1 ton double-pressed,
Twitchells reagent	120 lb.	Electricity	10 Kw.-hr.	distilled stearic acid,
Hydrated lime	20 lb.	Direct labor	50 man-hr.	plus 2 tons red oil and
Benzine (loss)	2 lb.			600 lb. crude glycerine

FIG. 1. Flow sheet for stearic acid and red oil.

as the Colgate-Emery Process, the other as the Procter and Gamble process. The *Twitchell process* is an acid hydrolysis of the fats in the presence of Twitchell's reagent. This is illustrated in Fig. 1, which also shows the steps leading to the separation of the mixed free fatty acids into a double-pressed stearic acid, red oil (mainly oleic acid), and stearin pitch. The latter is employed for roofing and other coatings. The glycerine resulting is free from salt and is higher in concentration (15 per cent) than in spent soap lye (5 to 8 per cent). Compare Table 3.

In outline, the purified fats and oils are hydrolyzed by boiling 12 to 48 hr. in lead-lined tanks with ¾ to 1¼ per cent of Twitchell's reagent, on weight of fat, and some 66°Bé. sulfuric acid diluted 1 to 1 with water. As shown in the flow sheet (Fig. 1), this hydrolysis is carried out countercurrently in two stages. After settling and skimming off the fat, the aqueous liquor is neutralized with slaked lime, the calcium sulfate filtered off, and the glycerine liquor evaporated. It should be noted from the flow sheet that more calcium sulfate crystallizes out as the evaporation proceeds and must be filtered off. The 90 per cent glycerine is refined, as

TABLE 3. TABULAR COMPARISON OF THE VARIOUS FAT-SPLITTING PROCESSES[a]

	Twitchell[b]	Batch autoclave		Continuous countercurrent[c]
Temperature, °F	212–220	300–350	450	485 approx.
Pressure, lb. per sq. in. gage	0	75–150	425–450	600–700
Catalyst	Alkyl-aryl sulfonic acids or cycloaliphatic sulfonic acids, both used with sulfuric acid 0.75–1.25 per cent of the charge	Zinc, calcium, or magnesium oxides, 1–2 per cent	No catalyst	Optional
Time, hr	12–48	5–10		2–3
Operation	Batch	Batch		Continuous
Equipment	Lead-lined, copper-lined, Monel-lined, or wooden tanks	Copper or stainless-steel autoclave		Type 316 stainless tower
Per cent	85–98 per cent hydrolyzed	85–98 per cent hydrolyzed		97–99 per cent
Hydrolyzed	5–15 per cent glycerol solution obtained depending on number of stages	10–15 per cent glycerol depending on number of stages		10–25 per cent glycerol
Advantages	Low temperature and pressure; adaptable to small scale; low first cost because of relatively simple and inexpensive equipment	Adaptable to small scale; lower first cost for small scale than continuous process; faster than Twitchell		Small floor space; uniform product quality; high yield of acids; high glycerine concentration; low labor cost; more accurate and automatic control; constant utility load
Disadvantages	Catalyst handling; long reaction time; fat stocks of poor quality must often be acid-refined to avoid catalyst poisoning; high steam consumption; tendency to form dark-colored acids; need more than one stage for good yield and high glycerine concentration; not adaptable to automatic control; high labor cost	High first cost; catalyst handling; longer reaction time than continuous processes; not so adaptable to automatic control as continuous; high labor cost; need more than one stage for good yield and high glycerine concentration		High first cost; high temperature and pressure; greater operating skill

[a] MARSEL and ALLEN, Fatty Acid Processing, *Chem. Eng.*, **54** (6), 104 (1947).
[b] See Fig. 1.
[c] See Fig. 3.

outlined in flow sheet on Fig. 5. The fatty acids are washed free of sulfuric acid and sent to the soap plant, or distilled under low vacuum, or purified by pressing, as shown in the flow sheet to furnish the various fatty acids of commerce.

In *continuous, countercurrent* splitting the fatty oil is deaerated under a vacuum to prevent darkening by oxidation during processing. It is charged at a controlled rate to the bottom of the hydrolyzing tower through a sparge ring which breaks the fat into droplets. These towers, around 70 ft. high, 3 ft. in diameter, are built of stainless steel Type 316 (see Fig. 3). The oil in the bottom contacting section rises because of its lower density and extracts the small amount of fatty material dissolved in the aqueous glycerine phase. At the same time deaerated and demineralized water is fed to the top contacting section where it extracts the glycerine dissolved in the fatty phase. After leaving the contacting sections, the two streams enter the reaction zone.[1] Here they are brought to reaction temperature by direct injection of high-pressure steam and the final phases of splitting occur. The fatty acids are discharged from the top of the splitter to a decanter where the entrained water is separated. The glycerine-water solution is discharged by an automatic interface controller to a settling tank. See Fig. 5 for glycerine processing.

Purification of Fatty Acids. Although the crude mixtures of fatty acids resulting from any of the above methods may be used as such, usually a separation into the more useful components is made. The composition of the fatty acids from the splitter depends upon the fat or oil from which they were derived. Those most commonly used for fatty-acid production include beef tallow and coconut, palm, cottonseed, and soybean oil.

Probably the most used of the older processes is "panning and pressing" (see Fig. 1). This fractional crystallization process is limited to those fatty-acid mixtures which solidify readily such as tallow fatty acid. The molten fatty acid is run into pans, chilled, wrapped in burlap bags, and pressed. This expression extracts the liquid *red oil* (mainly oleic acid) leaving the solid stearic acid. The total number of pressings indicates the purity of the product, although purer products may be derived from any of the following. A more recent method is fractional crystallization of the acid from solvents. The solvent may be polar or nonpolar (see Solexol process, page 605). One polar solvent process uses an acetone-water mixture, another a 90-10 per cent mixture of methanol and water.[2] In the latter, known as the Emersol process, the distilled fatty acid is

---

[1] ALLEN, *et al.*, Continuous Hydrolysis of Fats, *Chem. Eng. Progr.*, **43**, 459 (1947); ANON., Fatty Acids, *Chem. Eng.*, **57** (11), 118 (1950).

[2] DEMMERLE, Emersol Process, *Ind. Eng. Chem.*, **39**, 126 (1947). This article contains an interesting table on comparative cost data for the mechanical pressing vs. Emersol process. ANON., Continuous Separation of Fatty Acids, *Chem. Eng.*, **53** (11), 168 (1946).

dissolved in the methanol solution along with a small amount of glyceride as a crystal promoter. This mixture is chilled in a multitubular agitated crystallizer. The crystallized stearic acid is separated on a continuous rotary vacuum filter, melted, and charged to a still for solvent recovery. The oleic acid solution from the filter is similarly stripped of solvent.

The above methods separate fatty acids of different degrees of saturation. To separate fatty acids of different chain lengths, distillation[1] is used with vacuum distillation the most widely used. Three fractionating towers of the conventional tray type are operated under a vacuum. Preheated, crude fatty-acid stock is charged to the top of a stripping tower. While flowing downward, the air, moisture, and low-boiling fatty acids are swept out the top of the tank. The condensate, with part redrawn as a reflux, passes into the main fractionating tower where a high vacuum is maintained at the top. A liquid side stream also near the top removes the main cut (low-boiling acids), while overheads and noncondensables are withdrawn. The liquid condensate (high-boiling acids) is pumped to a final flash tower where the overhead distillate is condensed and represents the second fatty-acid fraction. The bottoms are returned to the stripping tower, reworked, and removed as pitch. The fatty acids may be sold as such or converted into many new chemicals.[2]

Energy Changes, Unit Operations, Unit Processes. The energy requirements that enter into the cost of producing soap are relatively unimportant in comparison to the cost of raw materials, packaging, and distribution. The energy required to move some of the fats and oils to the soap factory is occasionally considerable. The reaction that goes on in the saponification kettle is exothermic, but much steam is employed to raise and maintain the entire mass at boiling temperature and to ensure an efficiently rapid reaction. However, in large-scale saponifications employing appreciable quantities of coconut oil, comparatively small amounts of steam are required. See Figs. 2 and 3 for electricity and steam required.

The following are the principal *unit operations* (Op.) and *unit processes* (Pr.) into which the making of laundry bar soap can be divided:

Transportation of fats and oils (Op.).
Transportation or manufacture of caustic soda (Op. or Pr.).
Melting of fats and pumping to soap kettle and charging of 12 per cent NaOH (Op.).

[1] Anon., Fatty Acid Distillation, *Chem. Eng.*, **55** (2), 146 (1948), with pictured flow sheets of both straight and fractional distillation; *cf.* Marsel and Allen, Fatty Acid Processing, *Chem. Eng.*, **54** (6), 104 (1947); Kirk and Othmer, *op. cit.*, Vol. 6, pp. 235ff.; Kenyon, *et al.*, Chemicals from Fats, *Ind. Eng. Chem.*, **42**, 202 (1950).

[2] Kenyon, *op. cit.*; Potts and McBride, Armour's Star, *Chem. Eng.*, **57** (2), 124 (1950), with a pictured flow sheet, p. 172; Williams, Versatility in Fatty Acids, *Chem. Eng.*, **56** (7), 92 (1949), with a pictured flow sheet, p. 128.

Saponification of fatty acid glyceride, forming soap and glycerine, usually conducted hot and under agitation (Pr. and Op.).

Soap salted out and grained (Pr.).

Lyes separated and soap washed (Op.).

Rosin, sodium silicate, etc., mixed with soap (Op.).

Soap cooled and solidified in frames (Op.).

Soap put through finishing procedures (Op.): drying, cake forming, wrapping, and packaging.

Methods of Manufacture. The manufacture of soap will be discussed under the following general headings: full-boiled process, semiboiled process, cold-made process, neutralization processes, and other processes.

Full-boiled Process. The full-boiled procedure is the one most generally employed in soapmaking. It is represented by the flow sheet of Fig. 2,

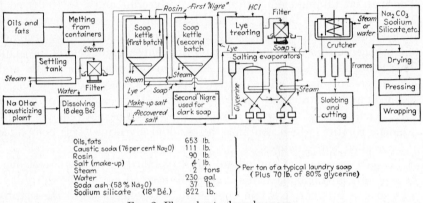

Oils, fats	653 lb.	
Caustic soda (76 per cent Na₂O)	111 lb.	
Rosin	90 lb.	
Salt (make-up)	4 lb.	Per ton of a typical laundry soap
Steam	2 tons	(Plus 70 lb. of 80% glycerine)
Water	230 gal.	
Soda ash (58% Na₂O)	37 lb.	
Sodium silicate (18° Bé.)	822 lb.	

FIG. 2. Flow sheet—laundry soap.

and consists of a series of so-called *changes*, or steps, including several brine changes, a "strengthening" change (also known as a *strong* change), and a finishing change. These changes may be broken down into unit operations or unit processes as outlined above. Most toilet soaps and laundry soaps are made by this process, which is distinguished from the half-boiled process by the fact that it is carried out in *several* boiling stages, or changes, and with eventually an excess of alkali which enters the following batch. In this procedure the required mixture of fats and oils is melted, settled, filtered, and pumped to the kettle, as detailed in the flow sheet on Fig. 2. Naturally the proportions of fats, oils, and other constituents vary with the soap.

The soap kettles are 15 to 30 ft. in diameter and may be twice as deep, with a capacity of up to 150 tons. To lessen discoloration of soap, they usually have at least their top sections lined with Monel, nickel-clad steel,[1] or stainless steel. They are equipped with both open and closed

[1] Cox, Corrosion of Metals in the Soap and Allied Products Industries, *Ind. Eng. Chem.*, **30**, 1349 (1938).

steam coils, a bottom liquor outlet, and a swing pipe for pumping out the soap. The open steam coil is for agitation and the closed one for the boildown on the strong change.

After the mixture of fats is melted, the caustic soda solution (18°Bé.)[1] is added followed by agitation and heating with an open steam jet. Small portions of caustic are added from time to time, as long as the fats will react with them. After 3 or 4 hr. the paste becomes smooth and creamy and is ready for graining. This is done with recovered and more often make-up salt, NaCl, either granular or as a strong brine solution. The salt is added to the boiling soap until a sample on a trowel separates distinctly into soap and spent lye. About 10 to 12 per cent sodium chloride concentration is usually necessary. The steam is turned off and the kettle settled. This operation requires at least 3 hr. and frequently many more. The lyes, containing from 1 to 8 per cent glycerine and 5 to 15 per cent NaCl, settle to the bottom and are drawn off. The soap is heated and boiled once more. Water is added gradually until the kettle mass becomes smooth again, thus dissolving any glycerine and salt retained by the soap. This condition is known as *closed* soap. Further quantities of fats and caustic are sometimes added at this point. If so, they should be boiled, grained, and separated as described above. After adding any needed caustic and boiling, the kettle mixture is settled to permit removal of the aqueous solution which contains the residual glycerine. This completes the so-called *brine* changes.

The last traces of fat and oil are now saponified by means of a strong, or strengthening, change. This is generally carried out on the third day. The soap is brought to a boil once more, water added until the soap is closed, and then lye of about 25°Bé.[2] run in at such a rate as not to cool the mass. The soap is not soluble in the strong alkali. After it has become "grainy" once more, the steam is shut off and the kettle settled for 3 or 4 hr. The lye is run off and used in the initial saponification of a new batch of fats and oils.

The mixture is ready for the finishing change on the fourth day. The soap is heated again and water added until the mass "closes." Boiling is continued until the soap, when tested with a heated trowel, flows off in a thin, transparent sheet. This indicates that the boil is in such condition that the soaps of the higher fatty acids will separate from those of the lower fatty acids. The mass is then settled, during which time it separates into three layers. The top layer is neat soap, the intermediate layer is nigre which is a dark, strongly alkaline soap, and the lower layer is a mixture of soap and lye. The upper layer is removed by pumping out the soap through a skimmer pipe. The nigre may be degraded and incorporated in cheaper, darker grades of soap, but it generally enters into the

[1] 18°Bé. caustic soda is equivalent to 12.6 per cent NaOH.

[2] Equivalent to 18.6 per cent NaOH.

next batch. The small bottom layer follows the nigre. The neat soap is now ready for further treatment. This finishing change frequently consumes several days' time to ensure complete separation.[1]

Soap can be made continuously by the full-boiled process by the *Sharples* process by means of centrifugal separation. This new method requires only 2 hr. to change the fat to neat soap as compared with several days for the kettle process.[2] The flow through the continuous process is divided into four stages, corresponding essentially to the changes of the kettle process, except the flow of lye is countercurrent to the flow of fat. The heart of the process is the centrifuges which operate at 15,000 r.p.m. and develop a centrifugal force of 13,200 times gravity. In them the grained soap of the first three stages and the melted neat soap of the fourth stage are quickly and completely separated from their respective spent lyes. Many advantages are claimed, such as reduction in amount of process water, less degradation of soap color and quality, nigres are recycled, smaller lye ratio, and higher glycerine content of the spent lye.

Soap from the full-boiled or continuous processes is finished in many ways, *e.g.*, bars, flakes, granules, or milled toilet soaps. The continuous making of soap is shown in Fig. 2. The soap for some bars, such as white laundry, is still finished batchwise (see Fig. 2). Here soap is run through a crutcher, which is a special type of steam-jacketed agitator, and poured into great oblong iron boxes or *frames* mounted on wheels. Each frame holds around 900 lb. of soap. After aging for several days, the sides of the frame are removed, the soap trimmed, cut into bars, dried, stamped with a trade-mark, and wrapped.

For milled toilet soap bars, the kettle soap is processed into pellets containing the perfumes, medicinals, and other added materials. The pellets are milled on iron and granite rolls which knead the soap into thin, smooth ribbons. These are dropped to the plodders, where a spiral screw forces the soap to the nozzle at the far end. The plodder is water-cooled, except for the very end of the nozzle, which is heated to give a slight polish to the soap. The soap emerges as a long, continuous bar which is cut into the desired blanks and pressed with a trade-mark into small bars. All scrap soap is reworked and reprocessed.

Soap is flaked by pouring the warm soap, which has previously been mixed, between two steel rolls. The small upper roll is steam-heated while the large lower roll is ice cold causing the soap to stick to it in a thin film.

---

[1] For a study of the troublesome *middle soap* sometimes formed in the soap-boiling process, *cf.* FERGUSON and RICHARDSON, *Ind. Eng. Chem.*, **24**, 1329 (1932). Neat soap, middle soap, and nigre are different phases of the three-component system of soap, water, and salt.

[2] SMITH, Centrifugal Separation Permits Continuous Production of Soap, *Chem. Inds.*, **63**, 787 (1948).

The filmy sheet is cut into ribbons which are scraped off by a long blade and dried in large steam-heated ovens. The ribbons are cut into flakes and packaged.

Spray-drying to form fast-dissolving, sneezeproof granules or beads is the most widely used treatment for both soaps and synthetic detergents and is classed as one of the four most important developments in the soap industry since 1900.[1] The soap from the crutcher is atomized into the top of a tower up to 100 ft. in height. The heated air (about 500°F.) may be blown countercurrent or concurrent to the hot sprayed soap particles. The former is most popular as the drying is gradual with less puffing and the density of the resulting granule is higher. Bulk density is the most important property. These compounds show a marked increase in bulk density with increase in solids concentration of the feed material. They may contain up to 70 per cent solids and still be fluid enough to atomize, but 62 to 66 per cent is average. Another way of increasing bulk density is by adding inorganic salts such as sodium chloride. The finished product drops to hoppers where it is removed by a conveyer. Any finely divided soap that is carried along by the hot air current is reclaimed and added to the fresh soap for recirculation.

Semiboiled Process. By means of this process the fats and oils are heated with just the required amount of alkali and the saponification is allowed to go to completion. All glycerine formed remains in the soap. The nigre is not separated out. The product is inferior to full-boiled soap but more economical to manufacture. Pumice soaps, some floating soaps, and certain soft potash soaps can be prepared by this process.

Cold-made Process. This is undoubtedly the simplest method of making soap. It is very similar to the semiboiled process, any differences being largely a matter of temperature. The fats used must, however, be purer, the lye of *exactly* the correct proportion and concentration, and the temperature control rigid. Some potash soft soaps are prepared by this process, but it is generally used to produce cold-made coconut-oil and olive-oil soaps. A typical batch follows: 700 lb. of preheated coconut oil are sent to a crutcher maintained at 80 to 90°F., and 400 lb. of 36°Bé. caustic added. The resulting creamy mass is crutched anywhere from 10 to 60 min. Perfume and sodium hydrosulfite (an antioxidant) are added, and the mixture is run into frames, where saponification is completed. The frames are maintained at a temperature of around 110°F. After 24 hr. the frames are removed from the hot room and cooled for 72 to 96 hr. at room temperature. There are several major objections to this process: none of the glycerine can be recovered, all scrap soap must be discarded, and discolored soaps often occur, as the result of incomplete saponification.

Neutralization Process. This method neutralizes with alkali the free

---

[1] McCUTCHEON, *op. cit.;* for a most excellent article, see MARSHALL and SELTZER, Principles of Spray Drying, *Chem. Eng. Progr.*, **46**, 501, 575 (1950).

fatty acids obtained by the processes outlined in Table 3. The majority of soapmakers neutralize with NaOH rather than Na_2CO_3. The most important source of the fatty acids is the continuous countercurrent hydrolysis of fats which is the basis of one of the continuous soap processes. The main advantages of soap manufactured by this process as compared with the kettle process are:[1] (1) improved soap color from a crude fat

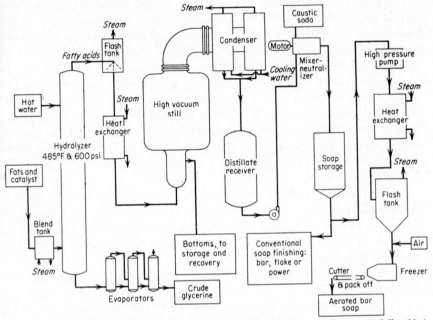

FIG. 3. Continuous process for fatty acids and soap. (*Courtesy of Procter and Gamble.*)
Based on 100 lb. of finished toilet soap of 20 per cent moisture

85 lb. fat	10 gal. new water
23.6 lb. lye, 50°Bé. caustic	150 lb. steam
0.67 lb. salt	2½ kw.-hr. electricity
0.5 lb. silicate of soda 49°Bé.	

without extensive pretreatment; (2) improved glycerine recovery; (3) flexibility in control; and (4) less space and manpower.

The raw fats and the catalyst, zinc oxide, are blended and introduced to the bottom of the hydrolyzer or splitting tower (Fig. 3). After water removal by flashing, the crude fatty acids are purified continuously by dry vacuum distillation. The distillate is neutralized with a proportional quantity of NaOH solution in a high-speed mixer to yield neat soap. The soap is discharged at 200°F. into a blending tank where it is slowly mixed by a vertically mounted worm in case any minor variation in pumping rate or caustic concentration should occur. The free caustic content is limited

[1] McBRIDE, Continuous Process for Soap, *Chem. Eng.*, **54** (4), 94 (1947), with a pictured flow sheet.

to 0.02 to 0.10 per cent Na_2O, the salt content is about 0.3 to 0.6 per cent, and the water content is approximately 30 per cent at this point. This neat soap, like that obtained from the kettles, may be extruded, milled, framed, flaked, or spray-dried depending upon the product desired. This flow sheet of Fig. 3 depicts the finishing operations of a floating bar soap.

The pressure on the neat soap is raised to 700 lb. per sq. in. and the soap is heated to about 400°F. in a high-pressure steam exchanger. This heated soap is released to a flash tank at atmospheric pressure where a partial drying (to about 20 per cent) takes place because the soap is well above its boiling point at atmospheric pressure. This viscous, pasty soap is mixed with the desired amount of air in a Votator, a mechanical heat exchanger, where the soap is also cooled by brine circulation in the outer shell from 220 to 150°F. At this temperature the soap is continuously extruded in strip form and is cut into three-bar lengths. Further cooling, cutting, stamping, and wrapping complete the operation. This entire procedure requires only 24 hr. as compared with several days for the kettle process.

Typical Soaps. The three main classes of soap are: toilet soaps, household soaps, and industrial soaps. The household soaps comprise the various laundry soaps and many varieties of soap chips and powders. These different soaps can frequently be made by one or more of the previously described procedures.

Except for the purest of toilet soaps, various chemicals are added as "builders" economically to improve their over-all cleansing quality. Practically all soap as merchandised contains from 10 to around 30 per cent of water. If soap were anhydrous, it would be too hard to dissolve easily. Almost all toilet and household soaps contain perfume, even though it is not apparent, serving merely to disguise the original soapy odor. Toilet soaps are made from selected materials and usually contain only 10 to 15 per cent moisture with very little added material except for the perfume and perhaps a fraction of a per cent of titanium dioxide as a whitening agent.

A typical composition of a laundry soap can be inferred from the materials given on the bottom of Fig. 2. These soaps contain up to 30 per cent moisture. Household chipped or flaked soaps are generally a little lower in moisture content than the corresponding bar soaps; a representative composition would be as follows: moisture, 10 to 20 per cent; soap, 50 to 60 per cent; tetrasodium pyrophosphate, 15 per cent; sodium metasilicate, 7 per cent; soda ash, 8 per cent.

Shaving soaps contain a considerable proportion of potassium soap with an excess of stearic acid, the combination giving a slower-drying lather. The "brushless" shaving creams contain stearic acid and fats with much less soap. The soft or liquid soaps at one time were almost all potash soaps. Now they are mostly soda soaps with the proper choice of the fatty acid to give the desired fluidity.

DETERGENTS OR SURFACE-ACTIVE AGENTS
(Other than Soaps)

The modern concept of surface-active agents[1] includes soaps, detergents, emulsifiers, wetting agents, and penetrants. These all owe their activity to a modification of the properties of the surface layer between two phases in contact with another. Most of the surface-active agents are a combination of water-attracting or hydrophilic groups on one end of the molecule, with water-repelling or hydrophobic groups on the other. The detergents possess these special properties to effect soil removal.

Historical. The consumer packaged powders and liquids which now account for the great majority of the synthetic detergents[2] produced are actually the incidental result of the search for new compounds to overcome difficulties, *i.e.*, acidity and hard water encountered in textile processing. Until the 1920's *Turkey-red oil*, a sulfated castor oil, was the best commercial product for textile users, but a poor one at best. At that time the Germans began to search for a "universal soap" and in 1930 the Igepon A series, sulfonated fatty acid esters, and Gardinol, a sulfated fatty alcohol, were marketed. In 1931 the Igepon T[3] series, taurine derivatives, were introduced which overcame some of the difficulties of Igepon A in textile processing. Since these synthetics used vegetable oils which were relatively expensive, the search began for cheaper starting materials such as petroleum. The first cyclic derived detergent, an alkyl-naphthalene sulfonate, was Nacconol which was introduced in 1933. The alkyl-aryl sulfonates are the largest class of synthetic detergents today.

Uses, Economics, and Classification. Many detergents with their different trade names can be grouped into five main chemical classes. The first three of these are anionic detergents which ionize in water to give a negatively charged organic ion. The fourth group comprises the cationic detergents which ionize in water to give a positively charged ion. The last group is the nonionics which do not ionize. Cationics and anionics are not compatible as they combine into an insoluble precipitate. For this same reason cationics are not compatible with soap. Compounds of the

---

[1] McCutcheon, Synthetic Detergents, *Chem. Inds.*, **61**, 811 (1947); Schwartz and Perry, "Surface Active Agents," Interscience Publishers, Inc., New York, 1949; Niven, Jr., "Fundamentals of Detergency," Reinhold Publishing Corporation, New York, 1950.

[2] For a more detailed historical discussion, see Kastens and Ayo, Pioneer Surfactant, *Ind. Eng. Chem.*, **42**, 1626 (1950).

[3] Only the principal trade-marks will be used here. Hundreds of trade-marked surface-active compounds are on the market today.

last group, nonionics, are naturally compatible with the other groups and this growing field shows much promise. The five groups[1] are:

1. *Sulfated Fatty Alcohols.* (Orvus, Dreft, Duponol, etc.) These are strong competitors to soap because they are stable in acid, alkaline, or hard water. Sodium lauryl sulfate, prepared from coconut oil, represents the bulk of the sulfated fatty alcohols. It is believed that sulfated fatty alcohols accounted for 19 per cent of the synthetic detergents sold in 1952.

2. *Alkyl-aryl Sulfonates.* (Oronite, Ultrawet, Santomerse, Tide, Fab, Surf, Cheer, etc.) Because of their low price, this group is extensively used in both the home and industry. Sales in 1952 accounted for 58 per cent of the synthetic detergents (see Table 4). Their stability and soil-suspending power is not so good as Group 1, but by adding sodium carboxymethyl cellulose, the suspending power can be increased.

3. *Miscellaneous Sulfates and Sulfonates.* (a) Alkyl sulfonates, as Merpols, MP-189. (b) Sulfated esters and acids, as Artic Syntex, Vel, Igepon A. These detergents, although unaffected by hard water, lack stability in strong acids or alkaline solutions. (c) Sulfated and sulfonated amides, as Igepon T. These detergents have excellent stability and soil-removing properties. (d) Sulfated and sulfonated oils, fats, and waxes, as Turkey-red oil.

4. *Cationic Agents.* These are not normally classified as detergents as their uses are not comparable with soap. Their chief value is their germicidal properties. The quaternary ammonium compounds are the most important members.

5. *Nonionic Agents.* (Spans, Tweens, Glim, Triton, etc.) These products possess excellent soil removal and grease emulsification accompanied by low foam. The ethers are extremely stable in acid and alkaline solutions. The nonionics may be further subdivided into these principal types: (a) alkyl phenol-ethylene oxide type, (b) aliphatic polyhydric alcohol esters, and (c) fatty-acid amides.

The packaged-detergent market is by far the most important. Another large outlet is in scouring powders where 3 to 7 per cent of the active ingredients may be a synthetic detergent. Synthetics are used in many different textile applications including wool scouring, dye leveling, kier boiling of cottons, and as auxiliaries in other applications. Substantial quantities are consumed industrially in dairies and metal cleaning and polishing. Synthetic detergents are employed as an entraining agent in portland cement and as frothing agents in the manufacture of wallboard.

Manufacture. For retail trade the detergent contains around 20 to 40 per cent active material, the rest being builders, fillers, dyes, and other materials. Builders increase detergency. Sodium tripolyphosphate and tetrasodium pyrophosphate are the most outstanding alkaline builders.

[1] HERSBERGER and NEIDIG, Present Status of Organic Synthetic Detergents, *Chem. Eng. News,* **27,** 1646 (1949).

The amount of these used varies from 30 to 50 per cent. Small percentages (1 to 3) of sodium carboxymethyl cellulose markedly improve the soil-suspending power of detergents and prevent the redeposition of dirt. Brightening agents (fluorescent dyes) are sometimes incorporated in amounts of 0.01 to 0.05 per cent. Sodium silicate lessens corrosion of aluminum washing machines. The analysis of the largest-selling heavy-duty household detergent by weight per cent is: 7 per cent keryl-benzene sodium sulfonate, 5 per cent sodium lauryl sulfate, 20 per cent Na_2SO_4, 10 per cent tetrasodium pyrophosphate, 40 per cent sodium tripolyphosphate, 3 per cent sodium silicate, and 3 per cent sodium carboxymethyl cellulose, water being the rest.

Sulfated Fatty Alcohols. The two most important fatty alcohol sulfates are made from mixtures of fatty alcohols derived from coconut oil, predominantly lauryl alcohol, and oleyl alcohol. These high-molecular-weight alcohols are usually prepared either by sodium reduction or by catalytic hydrogenation of the fatty glycerides. The hydrogenation processes manufacture the higher alcohols by both continuous and batchwise reaction in the liquid phase at temperatures of 200 to 300°C., pressures of 100 to 220 atm., with copper chromite or other catalysts. The sodium-reduction process[1] is the more important method at present because it seldom affects unsaturation as does hydrogenation. Although the raw material costs are higher, smaller plant investment and the recovery of glycerine and sodium hydroxide make it competitive to hydrogenation. For each batch of coconut oil, 1 ton of molten sodium is dropped into the reactor which already contains 1 ton of toluene, the latter acting as a solvent for the reaction mass and as a dispersing medium for the sodium. Forty-eight hundred pounds of hydrogenated coconut oil and 6,800 lb. of solvent mix, 4,400 lb. of which is the reducing alcohol such as methyl amyl, the remainder toluene, are fed to the reactor. The rate is so controlled that only a slight excess of unreacted ester is present in the reactor at any time. After the reaction is completed, the mixture is dropped into water where hydrolysis occurs. The mixture settles into three layers, the top containing the product alcohol and the regenerated reducing alcohol. This crude product is separated by continuous distillation. The pure coconut-oil mixture may be fractionated into cuts or all used for the sulfation.

The saturated fatty alcohols are usually treated with an excess of concentrated sulfuric acid under moderate conditions, producing the sulfate which is then converted to the corresponding sodium salt with alkali. The excess sodium sulfate may be separated or left in, where it acts as a filler or inert, and the whole mixture dried. Molar quantities of chlorosulfonic acid are often used as a sulfating agent. The advantage here is that the resultant sulfuric ester may be neutralized directly giving a product of

[1] KASTENS and PEDDICORD, Alcohols by Sodium Reduction, *Ind. Eng. Chem.*, **41**, 438 (1949).

very low inorganic salt content. When oleyl alcohol is treated with sulfuric acid, both the double bond and the terminal hydroxyl group react. Because the terminal sulfate with an unaffected double bond is the more valuable, certain special sulfation methods are used:[1]

1. Sulfating with the SO_3-dioxane complex.
2. Sulfating with the SO_3-pyridine complex.
3. Sulfating with sodium or potassium chlorosulfonate.
4. Sulfating with H_2SO_4 and urea, or other acid amide.
5. Sulfating with the addition complex of SO_3 and $NaNO_2$.

Purification for any compound depends upon the amount of impurities present and the amount desired in the final product.

TABLE 4. STATISTICS OF SURFACE-ACTIVE AGENTS (DETERGENTS) 1954[a]
(100 per cent active basis)

	Quantity (1,000 lb.)	Unit value per lb.
Cyclic compounds, total	640,222	$0.21
Esters and ethers, nonsulfonated	42,089	0.34
Quaternary ammonium	7,215	0.84
Sulfated and sulfonated, total	590,918	0.19
Alkyl benzenoid	388,959	0.22
Alkyl naphthalenoid	7,332	0.36
Petroleum aromatic, sulfonated	142,782	0.14
Acyclic compounds, total	385,614	0.23
Nitrogen-containing, nonsulfonated	56,777	0.32
Phosphorus-containing, nonsulfonated	586	0.63
Esters and ethers, nonsulfonated	88,478	0.25
Salts of fatty acids	21,129	0.10
Sulfated and sulfonated	218,644	0.20
Acids	3,665	0.33
Alcohols, esters	129,503	0.20
Oils, fats, waxes	76,910	0.17
Nitrogen-containing	8,566	0.40
Total, cyclic and acyclic	1,025,836	0.22

[a] Synthetic Organic Chemicals, 1954, *U.S. Tariff Comm.*, Washington, D.C., Many more details in these yearly reports.

Alkyl-aryl Sulfonates.[2] Alkyl-aryl is used to designate those sulfonatable hydrocarbons which contain an aromatic nucleus, usually alkylated benzene. By sulfonating this water-insoluble hydrocarbon, there is provided the necessary water solubility. The alkyl group, which consists of a more

[1] SCHWARTZ and PERRY, *op. cit.*, p. 58.
[2] SITTENFIELD, Petroleum Chemical Detergents, *Chem. Eng.*, **55** (6), 120 (1948); KIRCHER, Sulfonation of Alkyl Aryls, *Soap Sanit. Chemicals*, **26** (12), 48 (1950).

or less straight or branched carbon chain (C_{10} to C_{16}) functions as the oil-soluble portion of the compound. The flow sheet illustrated in Fig. 4 may be divided into three parts: (1) combining the alkyl group with the aromatic hydrocarbon, (2) sulfonating the resulting compound, and (3) neutralizing the sulfonic acid.

The alkyl portion is derived from a kerosene distillate fraction obtained from the refining of paraffinic crudes or from polypropylene tetramer (Chap. 37). When kerosene is used, it is chlorinated at 60 to 70°C. in a

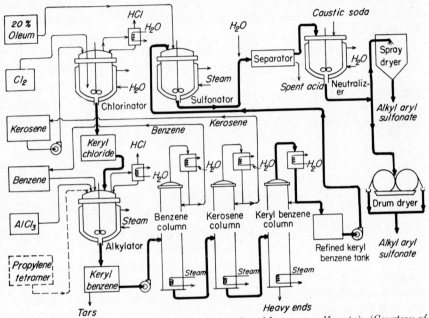

FIG. 4. Flow sheet for alkyl-aryl sulfonate (or keryl-benzene sulfonate). (*Courtesy of Petroleum Refiner.*)

lead-lined, agitated, jacketed reactor with a catalyst added, usually iodine. The monochlorinated kerosene is reacted with an excess of benzene in the presence of $AlCl_3$ in a glass-lined, agitated, jacketed reactor. One part of chlorinated kerosene to 6 parts of benzene to 0.1 parts of $AlCl_3$ are the approximate molar ratios used in this Friedel-Crafts reaction. The alkyl-benzene crude is purified by distillation and then sulfonated. Sulfonation procedures may vary in each plant. For 100 per cent H_2SO_4, the reaction temperature and time would be, respectively, 65 to 80°C. and 1 hr. Usually the alkyl-benzene is mixed with about 1.25 times its weight of acid. The reaction temperature is closely controlled. After sulfonation the mass is allowed to settle, and the spent H_2SO_4 and unreacted hydrocarbon layers are removed. The sulfonated material is drowned in ice water and neutralized with NaOH in a stainless-steel agitated tank provided with cooling coils. After neutralization it may be dried, depending on the finished product.

Miscellaneous Sulfates and Sulfonates. The *alkyl sulfonates* differ from the alkyl sulfates in having no oxygen linkage between the carbon and the sulfur atoms. They are manufactured by neutralizing an alkyl sulfonyl derivative with caustic soda.

The most important products of the *sulfated ester group* are the sulfated monoglycerides of coconut fatty acids, which are sold as Artic, Syntex, and Vel. The fatty monoglyceride may be prepared by the direct reaction of a fatty acid with an excess of glycerine under esterification conditions, after which it is sulfated.

Igepon T is representative of the *amide sulfate class* of detergents. It is the product[1] derived from oleic acid chloride and N-methyltaurine:

$$CH-(CH_2)_7-CH_3 + HN(CH_2)_2-SO_3Na + NaOH \rightarrow$$
$$CH(CH_2)_7-COCl \quad\quad CH_3$$

$$CH-(CH_2)_7-CH_3$$
$$CH(CH_2)_7-C-N-(CH_2)_2-SO_3Na + H_2O + NaCl$$
$$O \quad CH_3$$

Sulfated or *sulfonated* oils are sulfated aliphatic esters which may be obtained by treating castor, mustard seed, soybean, peanut, coconut, and lard oil with 27.5 per cent sulfuric acid, employing so-called high sulfonation, quick sulfonation, or low-temperature sulfonation. These products have long been known as *sulfonated oils*, but the bond is mostly through the oxygen of a sulfate group.[2] Turkey-red oil, a sulfated castor oil, has the following formula for one-third of its molecule:

$$CH_3(CH_2)_5CH \cdot CH_2CH = CH(CH_2)_7COOCH_2R$$
$$\qquad\qquad | \qquad\quad \text{Glyceryl-triricinoleyl sulfate of soda}$$
$$OSO_3Na$$

Tallow, neat's-foot oil, and several fish oils are also so treated.

Nonionic Agents. This group contains large numbers of compounds which are not as yet fully studied. Most of the principal liquid detergents, including the household field, contain some nonionics. The best-known series is made by reacting either a phenol or an alcohol with several moles of ethylene or propylene oxide. Ethylene oxide adds to hydroxyl groups under moderate conditions of temperature and pressure in the presence of alkaline catalysts:

---

[1] KASTENS and AYO, *op. cit.*, a most excellent article.
[2] For more details, see 1st ed. of this book, p. 612; also see GROGGINS, *op. cit.*, p. 338.

$$\text{ROH} + \text{CH}_2\!-\!\!-\!\text{CH}_2 \rightarrow \text{R}\!-\!\text{O}\!-\!\text{C}_2\text{H}_4\!-\!\text{OH}$$
$$\diagdown\!\!\diagup$$
$$\text{O}$$

$$\text{R}\!-\!\text{O}\!-\!\text{C}_2\text{H}_4\!-\!\text{OH} + \text{CH}_2\!-\!\!-\!\text{CH}_2 \rightarrow \text{R}\!-\!\text{O}\!-\!\text{C}_2\text{H}_4\!-\!\text{O}\!-\!\text{C}_2\text{H}_4\!-\!\text{OH}, \text{etc.}$$
$$\diagdown\!\!\diagup$$
$$\text{O}$$

The fatty acid esters of polyhydric alcohols, such as glycerol, glycol, sorbitol, and mannitol are prepared in the usual esterification manner.

GLYCERINE

Historical. Glycerine[1] is a clear, nearly colorless liquid, having a sweet taste but no odor. K. W. Scheele first prepared glycerine in 1779 by heating a mixture of olive oil and litharge. On washing with water, a sweet solution was obtained, which on evaporation of the water gave a viscous heavy liquid, which the discoverer called "the sweet principle of fats." In 1846 Sobrero produced the explosive nitro-glycerine for the first time, and in 1868 Nobel, by absorbing it in kieselguhr, made it safe to handle as dynamite. These discoveries increased the demand for glycerine. This was in part satisfied by the development in 1870 of a method for recovering glycerine and salt from spent soap lyes.

Uses and Economics. In 1954 the production of crude glycerine was approximately 205,000,000 lb. Synthetic glycerine producers supplied more than 20 per cent of the market, an equal amount from the producers of fatty acids and fatty alcohols, the rest coming from the soapmakers. Glycerine is supplied in several grades. U.S.P. or c.p. grade is chemically pure and contains not less than 95 per cent $C_3H_8O_3$. High-gravity glycerine contains not less than 98.7 per cent of glycerol and is suitable for resins and other industrial products. Yellow distilled is taken for certain processes where the higher-purity types are not essential, such as a lubricant in tire molds. Dynamite, saponification crude, and soap lye crude grades complete the list.

Glycerine is employed for the making, preserving, softening, or moistening of a great many products. About 30 per cent of the glycerine is consumed in the manufacture of alkyd resins. In explosives and as a humectant in tobacco are the next two largest outlets. This is followed by its use as a plasticizer in cellophane, then by cosmetics and dentrifices, corks and gaskets, and pharmaceuticals.

GLYCERINE MANUFACTURE

Glycerine may be produced by a number of different methods, among which the following are important: (1) the saponifaction of glycerides

---

[1] The term *glycerine* is chosen because it is the technical spelling most used for the trihydroxy alcohol, *glycerol*. The spelling *glycerin* is employed by the United States Pharmacopeia.

(oils and fats) to produce soap; (2) the splitting of fats and oils to produce soap; (3) the chlorination and hydrolysis of propylene from cracked still gases.

Energy Changes, Unit Operations, and Unit Processes. In recovering glycerine from the soap plants the energy requirements are mostly concerned with heat consumption involved in the unit operations of evaporation and distillation, as can be seen by the steam requirements tabulated on the flow sheet on Fig. 5. The breakdown of two procedures for glycerine is listed in the following columns:

Glycerine from spent lye:
Chemical purification with filtration (Pr. and Op.)
Evaporation (multiple effect) for concentration and for salt recovery (Op.)
Steam vacuum distillation (Op.)
Concentration (Op.)
Decoloration (Op.)
Redistillation (Op.)

Glycerine from petroleum:
Purification of propylene (Op.)
Chlorination to allyl chloride (Pr.)
Purification and distillation (Op.)
Chlorination with HOCl (Pr.)
Hydrolysis to glycerine (Pr.)
Distillation (Op.)

Glycerine from Spent Soap Lyes. The spent soap lyes are by-products and must be purified before recovery[1] of glycerine. A typical spent lye contains about 3 to 8 per cent glycerine, 5 to 15 per cent sodium chloride and water, together with small quantities of caustic soda, sodium carbonate, soap, fatty acids, and other organic impurities. After cooling and settling to remove much of the soap, the lye is treated to reduce the alkalinity and to remove organic impurities, in accordance with the flow sheet on Fig. 5. The lye is pumped to the first treatment tank where ferric chloride is added, in the amount determined by previous experience as being required to give maximum precipitation of hydroxyl ions and of soap. About 2.5 lb. of ferric chloride per 1,000 lb. of lye is usually required. Low-grade lyes need an additional 0.5 lb. of aluminum sulfate for 1,000 lb. of lye in order to produce a more complete removal. Since the ferric chloride used is strongly corrosive to iron and steel, it is dissolved in stoneware crocks or glass-lined tanks and added in solution to the treatment tank. Steel treatment tanks are satisfactory. A little hydrochloric acid is added to bring the lye just on the acid side to cause precipitation of metallic soap.

After thorough agitation in the first treatment tank the lye is filter-pressed warm and then run into the second treatment tank, where a little caustic soda is added until the lye is alkaline. This lye, filtered again, has a glycerine content of from 4 to 10 per cent, and a salt concentration of from 11 to 18 per cent. The glycerine lyes are concentrated in a single-

[1] WURSTER, The Recovery of Crude Glycerol, *Oil & Soap,* **13,** 246 (1936); for pictured flow sheet, see *Chem. & Met. Eng.,* **50** (9), 132 (1943).

or preferably in a double-effect evaporator. The former is used when it is desired to have a minimum amount of equipment. A double effect is preferred because the exhaust steam and water requirements are approximately half those of the single effect.

As the evaporation proceeds and as the concentration of glycerine increases, the solubility of the salt decreases and it crystallizes out. This salt, collecting in the cone of the evaporator, is periodically dropped into the empty one of the two salt catchers. The catchers, or chambers, are provided with false bottoms that catch the salt. The glycerine liquor is drained off and returned to the vacuum evaporator (by a pipe not shown in Fig. 5), after the main valve between the evaporator and the salt

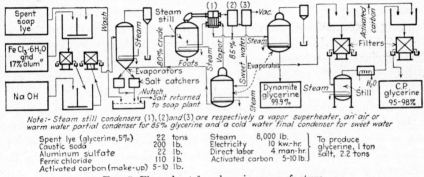

Note:- Steam still condensers (1),(2)and(3) are respectively a vapor superheater, an air or warm water partial condenser for 85% glycerine and a cold water final condenser for sweet water

Spent lye (glycerine,5%)	22 tons	Steam	8,000 lb.
Caustic soda	200 lb.	Electricity	10 kw.-hr.
Aluminum sulfate	22 lb.	Direct labor	4 man-hr.
Ferric chloride	110 lb.	Activated carbon	5-10 lb.
Activated carbon (make-up)	5-10 lb.		

To produce glycerine, 1 ton salt, 2.2 tons

Fig. 5. Flow sheet for glycerine manufacture.

chamber has been closed and a vent opened to the atmosphere. The salt is removed from the catcher, centrifuged, washed, and returned to the soap plant. In some plants a large suction filter box, known as a *nutsch*, is used instead of the centrifuge. Eventually the evaporator contains the crude glycerine (80 per cent) which is either sold by small plants to refiners or refined at once.

Refining of Crude Glycerine. The impurities present in crude glycerine include 0.1 per cent fatty acids (as soap), from 4 to 11 per cent salt, and organic impurities. These are separated by steam vacuum distillation after being made strongly alkaline with caustic soda in order to hold back fatty acids and other impurities. The 80 per cent crude is first heated to boiling with superheated steam, after which low-pressure steam is turned directly into the charge and the glycerine steam distilled under vacuum. The vapors are passed through a series of air-cooled condensers, which remove most of the glycerine and then through a water-cooled condenser, where the water and remaining glycerine are condensed (see Fig. 5). In a continuous system the procedure is similar, except that crude is fed to the evaporator and salt is continuously removed. This continuity of operation permits standardization of operating conditions and perhaps greater uniformity of product. The latest development in crude[1] glycerine purification is by ion exchange[2] which eliminates distillation although not evaporation. This work is based on removal of impurities and ionized solids from aqueous solutions of valuable nonionized constituents. The crude glycerine is purified through successive beds of regenerated cation- and anion-exchange resins. No heat is required or excessive amounts of NaOH as for distillation. C.p. glycerine is derived by evaporation of the glycerine-water solution, provided there is no excess of nonionized material such as polyglycerides in the original material.

Synthetic Glycerine from Petroleum. The growing market for glycerine, together with the fact that it is a by-product of soap and dependent upon the latter's production, has been the incentive for research into synthetic methods for producing this trihydroxy alcohol. The process of making glycerine from propylene from the debutanizers of the petroleum industry procured for the Shell Development Company the 1948 Chemical Engineering Achievement Award.[3] The propylene is chlorinated at 510°C. at 1 atm. to produce allyl chloride in amounts greater than 85 per cent of theory (based on the propylene). Vinyl chloride, some disubstituted olefins, and some 1:2- and 1:3-dichloro-propanes are also formed. (The reaction producing allyl chloride is new to organic synthesis, involving as it does the chlorination of an olefin by substitution instead of addition.) Treatment of the allyl chloride with hypochlorous acid at 38°C. produces the glycerine dichlorohydrin, $CH_2Cl\cdot CHCl\cdot CH_2OH$, which can be hydrolyzed by caustic soda in a 6 per cent Na_2CO_3 solution at 96°C. The glycerine dichlorohydrin can be hydrolyzed directly to glycerine but this takes two molecules of caustic soda; hence a more economical procedure may be to react with the cheaper calcium hydroxide, taking off the epichlorohydrin as an overhead in a stripping column. The epichlorohydrin is easily hydrated to monochlorohydrin and then hydrated to glycerine[4] with caustic soda. The reactions follow:

$$CH_3\cdot CH{:}CH_2 + Cl_2 \rightarrow CH_2Cl\cdot CH{:}CH_2 + HCl$$

(85 per cent yield)

$$CH_2Cl\cdot CH{:}CH_2 + HOCl \rightarrow CH_2Cl\cdot CHCl\cdot CH_2OH$$

(95 per cent yield)

$$CH_2Cl\cdot CHCl\cdot CH_2OH + 2NaOH \rightarrow CH_2OH\cdot CHOH\cdot CH_2OH + 2NaCl$$

The over-all yield of glycerine from allyl chloride is above 90 per cent.

[1] STROMQUIST and REENTS, C. P. Glycerol by Ion Exchange, *Ind. Eng. Chem.*, **43**, 1065 (1951); ANON., New Units Deionize Glycerine, *Chem. Eng.*, **59** (5), 260 (1952).

[2] STOCKMAN, Glycerine Distillation Greatly Improved by High Vacuum, *Chem. & Met. Eng.*, **52** (4), 100 (1945).

[3] HIGHTOWER, Glycerine from Petroleum, *Chem. Eng.*, **55** (9), 96 (1948); ANON., Synthetic Glycerine, *Chem. Eng.*, **55** (10), 100 (1948) with pictured flow sheet on pp. 134–137.

[4] KIDOO, Petrochemical Processes, *Chem. Eng.*, **59** (9), 164 (1952).

A recent announcement (Shell) indicates another process for glycerine from propylene. In the following reactions, isopropyl alcohol and propylene furnish acetone and glycerine (through acrolein) and in good yields.

$$CH_3 \cdot CHOH \cdot CH_3 + air \xrightarrow[\text{alyst}]{\text{Cat-}} CH_3 \cdot CO \cdot CH_3 + H_2O_2$$

$$CH_3 \cdot CH{:}CH_2 + air \xrightarrow[\text{alyst}]{\text{Cat-}} CHO \cdot CH{:}CH_2 + H_2O$$

$$CHO \cdot CH{:}CH_2 + H_2O_2 \rightarrow CHO \cdot CHOH \cdot CH_2OH$$
$$\xrightarrow{H_2} CH_2OH \cdot CHOH \cdot CH_2OH$$

SELECTED REFERENCES

Martin, Geoffrey, "The Modern Soap and Detergent Industry," Vol. 1, "Theory and Practice of Soap Making"; Vol. 2, "Manufacture of Special Soaps and Detergent Compositions," 3d ed., The Technical Press, Ltd., London, 1950.

Wigner, J. H., "Soap Manufacture," Reinhold Publishing Corporation, New York, 1940.

Thomssen, E. G., and J. W. McCutcheon, "Soaps and Detergents," MacNair-Dorland Co., New York, 1949.

Leffingwell, G., and M. Lesser, "Soap in Industry," Chemical Publishing Company, Inc., New York, 1946.

Niven, Jr., W. W., "Fundamentals of Detergency," Reinhold Publishing Corporation, New York, 1950.

Young, C. B. F., and K. W. Coons, "Surface Active Agents," Chemical Publishing Company, Inc., New York, 1945.

Moilliet, J. L., and B. Collie, "Surface Activity," E. F. N. Spon, Ltd., London, 1951.

McCutcheon, J. W., "Synthetic Detergents," MacNair-Dorland Co., New York, 1950.

Schwartz, A. M., and J. M. Perry, "Surface-active Agents; Their Chemistry and Technology," Interscience Publishers, Inc., New York, 1949.

Ralston, A. W., "Fatty Acids and Their Derivatives," John Wiley & Sons, Inc., New York, 1948.

Markley, K. S., "Fatty Acids," Interscience Publishers, Inc., New York, 1947.

Elliott, S. B., "The Alkaline-earth and Heavy-metal Soaps," Reinhold Publishing Corporation, New York, 1946.

Miner, Carl, and N. N. Dalton, "Glycerol," Reinhold Publishing Corporation, New York, 1953.

Leffingwell, G., and M. Lesser, "Glycerin, Its Industrial and Commercial Applications," Chemical Publishing Company, Inc., New York, 1945.

Soap and Sanitary Chemicals, MacNair-Dorland Co., New York.

Price, Donald, "Detergents," Chemical Publishing Company, Inc., New York, 1952.

CHAPTER 30

SUGAR AND STARCH INDUSTRIES

The carbohydrates, sugar and starch, are products of our soils. They serve as man's principal energy foods and enter into countless manufacturing sequences. The present virile chemurgic movement seeks to broaden the application of these and other farm products into an ever-increasing tide of raw materials through the country's factories into manufactured consumers' goods.

SUGAR

Nature has always provided foods from her ample stores in the vegetable kingdom to supply the sweetness that man requires in his diet. The average person in the United States eats his own weight in sugar about every year and a half.[1] The world average is only one-third of this. This is due not solely to his liking for the sweet taste but to the demands of an active body for fuel, since sugar supplies man with about 13 per cent of the energy required for existence. As a result, sugar refining is an enormous industry, representing in the United States alone an investment of more than $250,000,000 and paying about $100,000,000 in annual Federal taxes.

Historical.[2] It is difficult to discover just when sugar was first known to mankind, but it seems to be generally agreed that it occurred in India many centuries before Christ. Methods for extracting and purifying the sugar from the cane were very slow in being developed, but we find record of crude methods having been brought from the East to Europe about 1400. The sugar trade between Asia and Europe was one of the most important commercial items in the early centuries. Later, cane plantations were established in northern Africa and in the West Indies.

Sugar was first extracted in North America in 1689, using cane from the West Indies, while in 1751 cane was grown on the continent. From this time on, the industry increased steadily, both in size and in quality of product. Steam-driven crushing and grinding roller mills were introduced in the latter part of the eighteenth century; the vacuum pan was

---

[1] A more exact figure is 93.3 lb. per capita per year, based on 1949 consumption.

[2] HORNE, et al., Sugar Chemistry, *Ind. Eng. Chem.*, **43**, 804 (1951).

invented by Howard about 1824; bone-black filtration was employed for the first time in 1812. Multieffect evaporation was proposed about 1834, and the first suspended centrifugal was developed by Weston in 1852. A recent development has been the use of decolorizing carbons, which in several plants has been replaced by treatment with bauxite, followed by calcium hypochlorite.

Evaporation, adsorption, centrifugation, and filtration were early important and necessary steps in the manufacturing sequences for sugar, and much of our knowledge of these steps came from their application to the industry. We may say that this study of the functioning of evaporation, adsorption, centrifugation, and filtration as exemplified in sugar making helped to establish the generalized concept of unit operations.

In 1747 beet sugar was discovered, but it was not introduced into the United States until 1830, and no successful plants were operated until 1870. A great deal of time, effort, and money was expended in bringing the more complicated beet-sugar industry to the point where it could compete with cane sugar. The various tariffs imposed on raw cane-sugar imports, among other things, are responsible for the continuance of the beet-sugar industry.

The first preparation of dextrose in 1811 led to the development of the corn-sugar industry in this country. The first manufacturing began about 1872, the product being liquid glucose. It was not until 1918, however, that appreciable quantities of pure, crystalline dextrose were produced.

At the start of the present century, the Bergius process for the production of sugar by saccharification or hydrolysis of wood received its first industrial trial. A small plant for the production of alcohol was erected in South Carolina in 1910. In 1916 Bergius and Hagglund, in Germany, undertook the development of the present Bergius process, employing hydrochloric acid. In 1930 Scholler began operations with sulfuric acid, at Tornesch, Germany. As far as the United States is concerned, these processes, although chemically feasible, have generally proved economically unsound, owing to the abundance and low price of starch and sugar; however, they seem to be finding their place in the countries of Europe, where the scarcity of food supplies gives the products a higher value.

Uses and Economics. Over 9,000,000 tons of refined sugar are consumed in the United States. Of this total about 75 per cent is of cane origin and the remainder is from beet. Exports are around 60,000 tons. About 50 per cent of the sugar consumed annually is sold for household use in the United States; the remaining 50 per cent goes to various industries where baking leads. The soft drink, candy, and condensed-milk industries are also large consumers. Nonfood uses of sugar are very few and constitute only a small amount of the total output. They include the use of sugar as a strengthening agent in lime-sand mortar, in leather tanning, in paper softening, as calcium saccharate in whipping cream and ice cream, as copper saccharate insecticide, and as sucrose octaacetate, a denaturant in ethyl alcohol. Histadine and histamine are made with sugar as a raw material. Dextran,[1] the polysaccharide produced from sucrose by certain bacteria, is a very effective plasma volume expander. Administered by intravenous infusion, it relieves shock and prevents loss of body fluids after extensive burns or other wounds.

Probably no other organic product of comparable purity (99.5 per cent) is offered on the retail market for so low a price as sugar. This, however, is merely a reflection of the progress and growth in refining methods due to applied chemical engineering within the industry, which has succeeded in reducing the price from the $4 a pound prevailing during the administration of John Adams to its present low level of about 9 cents per pound.

MANUFACTURE OF SUGAR

Cane. Sugar cane is a member of the grass family. It has a bamboolike stalk, grows to a height of from 8 to 15 ft., and contains 11 to 15 per cent sucrose by weight. The source of the raw cane refined in the United States is portrayed in Table 1. The cane is usually planted with cuttings

TABLE 1. PRODUCTION OF CENTRIFUGAL SUGAR (RAW) IN PRINCIPAL AREAS
SUPPLYING THE UNITED STATES MARKET[a]
(In thousands of short tons)

Area	1935–1939 average	1940–1944 average	1950	1954
United States (beet)	1,518	1,451	1,950	2,037
United States (cane)	474	429	525	610
Puerto Rico	974	961	1,275	1,200
Virgin Islands	6	4	4	10
Hawaii	980	880	1,085	1,092
Philippine Islands	1,058	320	1,000	1,405
Cuba	3,183	3,686	6,300	4,998
Total	8,193	7,731	12,139	11,354

[a] The world total for 1954 was 24,690,000 short tons. Data are from Sugar Research Foundation and U.S. Department of Agriculture.

from the mature stalk, which sprouts and produces a number of new stalks. As many as 20 successive crops or "ratoons" may be obtained from a single planting, provided conditions are favorable. The approximate period of growth of the cane is 12 to 15 months in Cuba, while

[1] BIXLER, HINES, McGEE, and SHURTER, Dextran, Ind. Eng. Chem., **45**, 692 (1953), flow sheet.

nearly twice this time is required in Hawaii. Harvesting is done by hand with machetes or by mechanical cutters. The workmen cut off the stalks close to the ground and then remove the top sections and leaves, which are used as cattle food or fertilizer. The remainder of the stalks is loaded on trucks or large wagons which may be taken to a railroad siding. The trucks or railroads take the cane to the raw-sugar plants, or *centrales* as they are called in Cuba. There can be no delay in getting the freshly cut cane to the factory, because failure to grind it in less than 2 days after cutting causes much of the sucrose to be lost by inversion into glucose and fructose.

The production of raw cane sugar at the factory is illustrated in Fig. 1 and may be divided into the following *unit operations* (Op.) and *unit processes*[1] (Pr.):

The cane is torn and shredded by crushers in preparation for removing the juice (Op.).

The juice is extracted by passing the crushed cane through a series of mills, each of which consists of three grooved rolls that exert a heavy pressure. Water and weak juices may be added to help macerate the cane and aid in the extraction. About 95 per cent of the juice is extracted from the cane (Op.). The spent cane (bagasse) is either burned for fuel or used to manufacture insulating material.

The juice is screened to remove floating impurities and treated with lime to coagulate part of the colloidal matter, precipitate some of the impurities, and change the pH (Op. and Pr.). Phosphoric acid may be added because juices that do not contain a small amount of phosphates do not clarify well. If acid is added, an excess of lime is used. The mixture is heated with high-pressure steam and settled in large tanks called *clarifiers* or in continuous settlers or thickeners (Op.).

To recover the sugar from the settled-out muds continuous rotary drum vacuum filters are generally used although plate-and-frame presses may be employed (Op.). The cake constitutes 1 to 4 per cent of the weight of cane charged and is used as manure.

The filtrate, a clarified juice of high lime content, contains about 85 per cent water. It is evaporated to approximately 40 per cent water in triple- or quadruple-effect evaporators[2] (Op.).

The resulting dark-brown, viscous liquid is crystallized in a single-effect vacuum pan. The sirup is concentrated until crystal formation begins (Op.).

The mixture of sirup and crystals (massecuite) is dumped into a crystallizer which is a horizontal agitated tank equipped with cooling coils. Here additional sucrose deposits on the crystals already formed, and crystallization is completed (Op.).

[1] See also the pictured flow sheet, Raw Sugar from Cane, *Chem. & Met. Eng.*, **48** (7), 106 (1941); Process Flow Sheet for Raw Sugar House, "Rogers' Manual of Industrial Chemistry," 6th ed., p. 1340, D. Van Nostrand Company, Inc., New York, 1942.

[2] For vacuum evaporation equipment and accessories, heat-transfer data, and condenser water, see section by Badger, pp. 500–522, in Perry, *op. cit.* On p. 505, types of evaporators are presented, and on pp. 516–518 consideration is given to calculations for the economical number of effects.

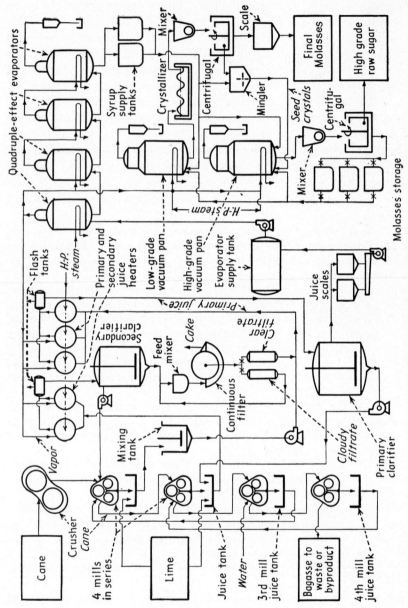

Fig. 1. Flow sheet for raw cane sugar.

The massecuite is then centrifuged to remove the sirup. The crystals are high-grade raw sugar, and the sirup is retreated to obtain one or two more crops of crystals. The final liquid after reworking is known as *blackstrap* molasses (Op.). The raw sugar (light brown in color), containing approximately 97 per cent sucrose, is packed in bags and shipped to the refinery (Op.).

The molasses[1] is shipped to the United States and other countries in full tank steamers and is used as a source of carbohydrates for fermentation and for cattle feed (Op.).

Cane Sugar. The sacks of raw sugar, weighing 300 to 330 lb., are unloaded from the ships at the refinery dock and are sampled both by the chemists and the customs inspector. The bags are then stored and emptied as needed into the raw-sugar dump, whence the raw sugar is transported to the raw-sugar bin of the refinery by means of bucket elevators and screw conveyers. The jute bags are given a water wash or brushed to remove the adhering sugar, dried, and sold. The wash water is evaporated to sirup, which then undergoes the usual refinery operations.

Figure 2 illustrates the following sequence of *unit operations* (Op.) and *unit processes* (Pr.)[2] in the refining of cane sugar:

The first step in refining is called *affination*, wherein the raw-sugar crystals are treated with a heavy sirup (60 to 80° Brix)[3] in order to remove the film of adhering molasses. This strong sirup dissolves little or none of the sugar but does soften or dissolve the coating of impurities. This operation is performed in *minglers* which are heavy scroll conveyers fitted with strong mixing flights (Op.).

The resulting sirup is removed by a centrifuge and the sugar cake is sprayed with water[4] (Op.).

The crystals are dumped into the melter, where they are dissolved in about half their weight of hot water, part of which is sweet water from the filter presses (Op.). The sirup from the centrifugals is divided, part being diluted and reused as mingler sirup while the remainder is diluted to about 54° Brix with sweet waters and sent to the defecators.

Defecation is the preparation of the raw liquor for filtration and clarification by removing solid impurities. During the operation a flocculent precipitate is formed which entangles the suspended matter and colloids; at the same time the acidity of the solution is reduced. So-called *blow-ups* (Pachuca tanks), which are circular tanks with conical bottoms fitted with steam and air connections, are used. The sirup is first neutralized with lime to a pH of 7.0 to 7.3, and diatomaceous earth is added as a filter aid (Pr. and Op.). However, a new defectant[5] made from specially processed alkaline earth metals (the principal one, mag-

[1] See Chap. 31.
[2] For pictured flow sheet, see *Chem. & Met. Eng.*, **47**, 119 (1940); SHEARON, *et al.*, Cane Sugar Refining, *Ind. Eng. Chem.*, **43**, 552 (1951). This is a most excellent article.
[3] The degree Brix is the percentage, by weight, of sucrose in a pure-sugar solution; commercially it is the approximate percentage of solid matter dissolved in a liquid.
[4] PERRY, *op. cit.*, pp. 997–1000 for centrifugals.
[5] ANON., Sugar Takes a Giant Step, *Chem. Eng.*, **58** (10), 224 (1951).

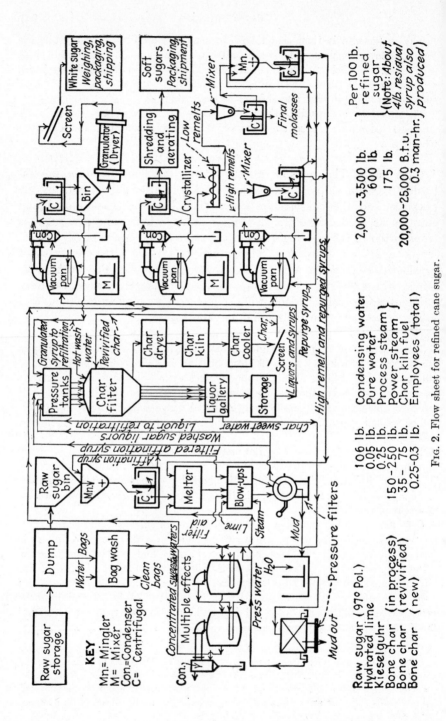

FIG. 2. Flow sheet for refined cane sugar.

		Per 100 lb. refined sugar
Raw sugar (97° Pol.)	106 lb.	
Hydrated lime	0.05 lb.	
Kieselguhr	0.25 lb.	
Bone char (in process)	150–250 lb.	
Bone char (revivified)	35–75 lb.	
Bone char (new)	0.25-0.3 lb.	
Condensing water	2,000–3,500 lb.	
Pure water	600 lb.	
Process steam	175 lb.	
Power steam		
Char kiln fuel	20,000–25,000 B.t.u.	
Employees (total)	0.3 man-hr.	

(Note: About 4 lb. residual syrup also produced)

646

nesium) is showing promise as a lime replacement. Already used commercially, it yields an improved product in less time.

The mixture is filtered and the effluent liquor from the filter presses, now free of insoluble material, still retains a large amount of dissolved impurities.[1] These impurities are removed by percolation through bone char[2] (Op.). The char tanks

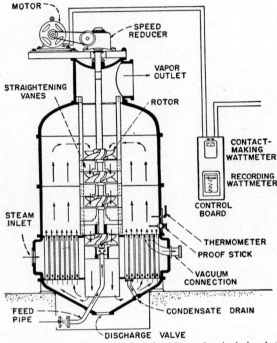

FIG. 3. Cross section of vacuum pan equipped with mechanical circulator. The sirup is heated by passage upward through the tubes of the steam chest or "calandria" near the bottom. The liquid boils at the upper surface, vapor being drawn out through the large central pipe. A set of screw impellers forces the liquid back through the central downtake pipe. The stirrer is motor driven, with recording and controlling wattmeters in its circuit. (*Courtesy of Esterline-Angus Company.*)

are about 10 ft. in diameter and 20 ft. deep. From 24 to 36 char filters are required per 1,000,000 lb. of melt. The percolation is carried out at about 180°F. and the product is a clear, water-white sirup.

After a certain amount of use, the char loses its decolorizing ability and must be *revivified*. This is done approximately every 32 hr. by first washing free of sugar and then removing the char and roasting it at 1000 to 2000°F. in retorts (Pr.).

The sirups from the bone-char filters are piped to the *liquor gallery* where

[1] Symposium, Filtration and Clarification, *Ind. Eng. Chem.*, **34**, 403 (1942); Symposium, Purification of Sugar Juices, *Ind. Eng. Chem.*, **43**, 603 (1951); MINDLER, Demineralization of Sugar Cane Juice, *Ind. Eng. Chem.*, **40**, 1211 (1948).

[2] PERRY, *op. cit.*, p. 897; LEWIS, SQUIRES, and BROUGHTON, "Industrial Chemistry of Colloidal and Amorphous Materials," The Macmillan Company, New York, 1942.

they are graded according to purity and strength, there being four classes: 99 to 99.7 deg. purity, 90 to 93 deg. purity, 84 to 87 deg. purity, and 75 to 80 deg. purity (Op.).

The lower grades are too dark to make granulated sugar directly and are given a triple filtration and then sometimes used for soft-sugar production (Op.).

The higher grades are sent to different vacuum pans and concentrated under reduced pressure to produce various types of sugars (Op.).

Figure 3 shows a cross section of the crystallizing or "strike" vacuum pan. Here the sugar sirup is concentrated to crystallization or "seeds." These small crystals are grown to a merchantable size by a properly regulated rate of boiling

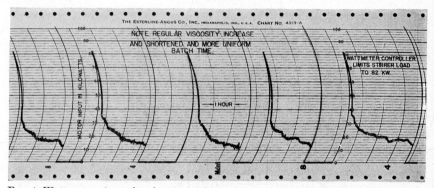

Fig. 4. Wattmeter chart showing power input to stirrer after perfection in instrument control method. The controlling wattmeter was set to cut off the stirrer at 82 kw. Note the uniform processing time, the uniform rise in viscosity during the boiling operation, and the lack of necessity for addition of water. The average boiling time was only 2¾ hr. as compared with 4 hr. before installation of instrument control. (*Courtesy of Esterline-Angus Company.*)

or evaporation as well as of agitation. This rate should not be too rapid or new crystals (false grains) will be formed and not have time to grow, with consequent loss through the screen of the centrifugal. This operation therefore requires careful control which may be secured by charting the power consumption of the stirrer as depicted in Fig. 4.

The purest sirups are used for cubes, cut-loaf, confectioner's, and granulated sugar, and the second and third grades for "off-granulated" sugar, which is gradually mixed with the better strikes.

The pan is discharged into a mixer which keeps the whole mass from sticking together, then sent to centrifuges where the crystals are separated from the sirup, washed, and dropped to the wet sugar storage bin (Op.).

The sirup is returned to the process for further recovery of sugar (Op.).

When the purity of the sirup becomes too low, it is used for blended table sirups, with the poorer lots going for animal feed or alcohol manufacture.

The wet sugar is dried in a granulator, which is a horizontal rotating drum about 6 ft. in diameter and 25 ft. long, having a series of narrow shelves (flights) attached to its inner surface. These lift the sugar and allow it to fall through the stream of hot air flowing countercurrent to it (Op.).

The dried crystals pass over a series of screens where they are graded according to size (Op.).

Various automatic packing and weighing machines put up the sugar in barrels, sacks, and boxes (Op.).

The powdered sugars are made by grinding the granulated sugar in mills (Op.). Cube and cut-loaf sugars are prepared by mixing certain types of granulated sugar with a heavy white sirup to form a moist mass which is then molded and dried (Op.).

The soft or brown sugars are not dried but are packed directly from the centrifugals. They are graded according to color, running from No. 1 which is nearly white to No. 4 which is dark (Op.).

The yield of refined sugar obtained, based on raw sugar of 96° polarization, is usually about 93 to 94 per cent, sirup 5 per cent, with mechanical and wash losses 0.7 per cent.

In handling sugar, some inversion takes place according to the following reaction:

$$C_{12}H_{22}O_{11} + H_2O \rightarrow C_6H_{12}O_6 + C_6H_{12}O_6$$

	Sucrose	d-Glucose	d-Fructose
Polarization	+66.6°	+52.8°	−92.8°

The product is called *invert sugar*, but the polarization of the pure sucrose of +66.6° (+ to the right) now reads −20.0° (− to the left) for the resulting mixture.

$$\frac{+52.8° - 92.8°}{2} = -20.0°$$

In some important installations, sugar refineries have turned to processes employing activated carbon, rather than the older bone-char process.[1] The difference in the two processes lies in the purification step. The bone-char process requires a filtration of the insoluble materials in a filter followed by the decolorization in the bone-char filters. The activated carbon requires mixing tanks to mix in the activated carbon, followed by specially designed filters. The fact that the activated carbon is a much better filtering product and a much more powerful decolorizing agent than the bone char permits the substitution of one-thirtieth to one-fortieth of weight of bone char. There results, naturally, a saving in time, fuel, wash water, building space, and investment in equipment. In addition, the fact that the new-type plants can operate economically on a smaller scale than the old, combined with the water and fuel savings, allows these plants to be built in the tropics right alongside the raw-sugar mills. This, in turn, saves on transportation and sacking of the raw sugar. This new development in sugar refining seems to be taking hold rapidly and may someday force some of the bone-char plants into obsolescence

[1] PERRY, *op. cit.*, pp. 901,903 (flow sheet).

provided the cost of the decolorizing carbon can be considerably reduced. However, today, an *established* bone-char refinery can produce sugar more cheaply because the bone char can be used many times over again and reactivated at a low cost.

Manufacture of Celotex.[1] In the United States it has been found much more profitable[2] to make insulating board from the bagasse from cane mills than to burn it under the boilers. Besides finding use here, it is also employed as a plastics filler and as a source of furfural. The bagasse is baled at the raw-sugar mill and shipped to the board plant. Here the bales are broken open by hand and the material conveyed by an endless belt to the rotary digesters, which are 14 ft. in diameter. The liquor is cooked under pressure in order to render the fibers pliable, loosen the incrusting material, dissolve organic material, and sterilize the fiber. The resulting pulp, in a 2 to 3 per cent suspension, is pumped to swing hammer shredders and washed in specially designed rotary washers in order to remove dirt, soluble compounds, and some pith. From the washers, the pulp enters half stock chests, where the sizing, usually papermakers' rosin and alum, is added and the mass stirred with powerful agitators to remove any irregularities. The fibers are refined in conical-revolving Jordans,[3] to give optimum fiber size. The refined fiber goes to stock chests, from which it is fed, as an approximately 2 per cent suspension, to the head box of the board machine. In the head box it is diluted to about 0.5 per cent.

The board machines, although of special design, are somewhat similar to Fourdrinier machines. The stock is fed onto forming screens, led to drying felts, and finally to press rolls. The sheets do not appear laminated but are felted together to give the required thickness. The board from these machines is 13 ft. wide, contains 50 to 55 per cent water, and is produced at the rate of 200 ft. per min. It is dried in a continuous sheet, at 300 to 450°F., in a gas- or steam-heated drier 800 to 1,000 ft. long. The product is practically bone dry and must be sprayed with water as it leaves the drier in order to bring it up to its normal water content of approximately 8 per cent. The board is now cut and fabricated into the forms in which it is used. The dust from these operations is used as a filler in plastics.

Beet Sugar. The familiar sugar, sucrose, can be obtained from many sources, other than cane, such as maple sirup and palm sugar. However, the great commercial sources are the sugar cane and the sugar beet. Only a skilled chemist can tell whether a sample of refined sugar originated from the tropical cane or the beet grown in the temperate zone. Ordinarily speaking, there is no distinction.

The sugar beet differs from the ordinary table beet in that it is much

---

[1] LATHROP, The Celotex and Cane-sugar Industries, *Ind. Eng. Chem.*, **22**, 449 (1930).
[2] This use of the bagasse pays the sugar mill enough money for it to buy other fuel.
[3] Figure 7, Chap. 33.

larger and is not red. Sugar beets are an important crop in many sections of the world, not only because of their sugar value but also because they enrich the soil for other crops. The mills begin operation in early September, the farmer harvesting his crop with machines that uproot the beets. Field workers follow the machines, remove the dirt and leaves from the beets, and load them for shipment to the factory. The beets, containing from 13 to 17 per cent sucrose and 0.8 per cent ash, enter the factory by way of flumes, small canals filled with warm water, which not only transport them but wash them as well.

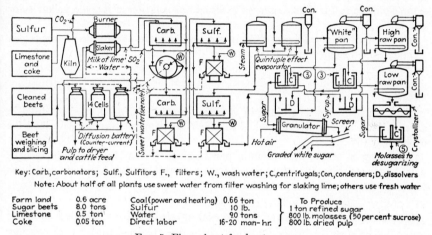

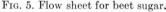

Key: Carb., carbonators; Sulf., Sulfitors F., filters; W., wash water; C., centrifugals; Con., condensers; D., dissolvers

Note: About half of all plants use sweet water from filter washing for slaking lime; others use fresh water

Farm land	0.6 acre	Coal (power and heating)	0.66 ton		To Produce
Sugar beets	8.0 tons	Sulfur	10 lb.		1 ton refined sugar
Limestone	0.5 ton	Water	90 tons		800 lb. molasses (50 per cent sucrose)
Coke	0.05 ton	Direct labor	16-20 man-hr.		800 lb. dried pulp

FIG. 5. Flow sheet for beet sugar.

Figure 5 illustrates the essential steps in the making of beet sugar. This manufacture may be divided into the following *unit operations* (Op.) and *unit processes* (Pr.):[1]

The beets are rewashed, weighed, and sliced into long narrow strips called *cossettes* (Op.).

The cossettes are dropped into large tanks or cells, 12 or 14 of which are connected in series to form a diffusion[2] battery. The sugar is extracted countercurrently with water at 160 to 175°F., the water being in contact with each cell for 6 to 8 min. (Op.). The resulting sirup contains 10 to 12 per cent sucrose, a small amount of invert sugar, and 2 to 3 per cent ash. The pulp remaining contains 0.1 to 0.3 per cent sugar (based on the beets). This pulp is dried and sold as cattle feed (Op.).

The sirup is given a rough screening to remove foreign materials (Op.).

Milk of lime is added until the concentration is equivalent to about 2 to 3 per cent. The lime aids in the precipitation of undesirable impurities. Any calcium

[1] See also pictured flow sheet, Beet Sugar Production, *Chem. & Met. Eng.*, **49** (6), 110 (1942); McDILL, Beet Sugar Industry—Industrial Wastes, *Ind. Eng. Chem.*, **39**, 657 (1947); McGINNIS, "Beet Sugar Technology," Reinhold Publishing Corporation, New York, 1951.

[2] ANON., New Diffuser Proves Its Worth, *Chem. Eng.*, **58** (11), 238 (1951).

saccharate formed is decomposed in carbonators by passing carbon dioxide through the sirup for 10 to 15 min. The foaming that occurs at this stage is reduced by adding a small quantity of castor oil and/or tallow (Pr.).

The sludge produced by the lime is equal to 4 or 5 per cent of the weight of the beets charged. This is removed by filtering the mixture on Oliver filters (Op.).

Lime is added again until the concentration is equivalent to 0.5 per cent and the mixture again carbonated, this time hot (Pr.).

It is then filtered on a plate-and-frame press (Op.).

The resulting filtrate contains a large concentration of calcium ions, which are removed by bubbling sulfur dioxide through the sirup in sulfitors. At the same time the sulfur dioxide serves to *bleach* the solution of its pale yellow color (Pr.).

The precipitate of calcium sulfite is removed on plate-and-frame presses (Op.).

The purified sugar is concentrated from 10 to 12 per cent sugar to about 55 per cent sugar in multiple-effect evaporators (Op.). This increases the concentration of calcium ions again and necessitates retreatment with sulfur dioxide and another filtration (Op. and Pr.).

The resulting sirup is grained in vacuum pans,[1] centrifuged, washed, dried in a granulator, screened, and packed in much the same manner as described for cane sugar (Op.).

The sirup from the first vacuum pan is given further treatment to recover more sugar crystals, but they are not pure enough for market and are sent back to the process for further purification (Op.).

The sirup remaining after the several crystallizations is called *molasses* and may be sold to the various industries as explained under Cane Sugar. Processes for the recovery of the remaining sugar have been worked out and are used commercially. Initial recovery is obtained by the Steffen process.

In the *Steffen process* the molasses from the centrifugals is cooled to 10°C., and finely ground quicklime added. A precipitate of tricalcium saccharate is formed and filtered off. This "saccharate cake" is washed and returned to the process, where it is mixed with the juice from the diffusion battery, thereby clarifying it in the same manner as the lime which this tricalcium saccharate partly replaced. The molasses remaining, so-called *discard molasses*, contains about 60 to 63 per cent sugar, 2 to 5 per cent raffinose, 14 to 16 per cent ash, and 5 per cent sugar, based on the dry material. It is sold as livestock feed or processed for the recovery of monosodium glutamate and other amino compounds.

Ion exchange is a recent development in beet-sugar manufacture.[2] It has been tried or proposed for the treatment of process liquors at several

---

[1] McGinnis, Moore, and Alston, Low-purity Beet Sugar Factory Materials, *Ind. Eng. Chem.*, **34**, 171 (1942).

[2] Michener, *et al.*, Ion Exchange in Beet Sugar Factories, *Ind. Eng. Chem.*, **42**, 643 (1950); Mandru, Ion Exchange in Beet Sugar Manufacture, *Ind. Eng. Chem.*, **43**, 615 (1951).

places in the manufacturing procedure. At present, deionization is used commercially on the second carbonation juice and gives, compared with the previously described process, greater recovery of white sugar, better color removal, lower ash, and crystallization of two or three strikes of white sugar instead of one. The beets are sliced and diffused in the usual manner. The diffusion juice is carbonated to free it of colloids which cause trouble in the presently used ion-exchange equipment. Also non-sugar solids in the raw juice, removable by lime, may be eliminated more cheaply by lime than by ion exchange. One commercial ion-exchange unit consists of four pairs of cells, each consisting of a cation and an anion exchanger. At any one time only one pair of cells is used in the cycle, while the other pairs are in various stages of regeneration or other preparation.

In operation, the juice is pumped first into the cation cell of a freshly regenerated pair and is passed through the pair until breakthrough occurs. The breakthrough is determined by pH meters on both cation and anion effluents. Breakthrough occurs when the latter pH attains 7.0, at which time the former is about 3.0. The amounts of regenerating chemicals used are regulated so that breakthrough on both cells occurs at approximately the same time. After completion of this so-called juice cycle, the juice flow is transferred to another pair and water is introduced into the original pair to displace the juice. This is called *sweetening off* and is continued until the Brix reaches some low figure, about 1.5. The cells are back-washed with raw water which removes mechanically held impurities and reclassifies the resins, thus reducing the pressure drop through the beds during the service cycle. After draining, the cation bed is regenerated[1] with 5 per cent sulfuric acid. Usually 200 to 300 per cent of the stoichiometric amount is used. The anion bed is regenerated with 2 per cent aqua ammonia. Both cells are rinsed to remove excess regenerant and then are ready for use again. A typical time cycle in minutes is: juice, 45; sweetening off, 17; backwash, 15; drain, 7; regeneration, 30; and rinse, 20. Ion exchange requires a large amount of water for the various procedures outlined above. Besides this, the main disadvantages are the large capital cost of the outlay, the acidproofing of all exposed surfaces, and the high price of the regenerating chemicals.

Energy Requirements. In the direct manufacture of sugar there are few or no chemical changes that require energy. Almost all the steps in the manufacturing sequences involve physical changes or unit operations. These consume energy in the form of *power* for crushing, pumping, and centrifugation, and *heat* for solution, evaporation, and drying. On the bottom of the flow sheets for refined cane sugar and for beet sugar (Figs. 2 and 5) are given some average figures for energy material (steam or coal) requirements. The steady improvement by chemical engineers of the equipment necessary to make these various unit operations function

---

[1] See Chap. 4 for more details on ion exchange.

efficiently has gradually reduced the energy requirements to the reasonable amounts given.

Although bagasse is used for fuel in most raw-sugar mills, bagasse is becoming a more important raw material yearly (Celotex, chicken litter, stock feed); hence, other fuel may be employed. In fact, only 8 per cent of the total weight of sugar cane is obtained as raw sugar, and recovery of such potential by-products as allyl sucrose, lactic acid, sorbitol, furfural, and wax from the cane pulp, cuticle wax, and molasses should be profitable.

In all sugar-manufacturing establishments, there is an economical dual use of steam (see Chap. 5) wherein high-pressure steam from the boiler is expanded through a reciprocating engine or a turbine to furnish power and wherein the exhaust steam is condensed to secure heat for evaporation of the juices and sirups. The condensed steam resulting is pumped back to the boilers or is employed for making sirups.

In beet-sugar refining, Fig. 5 indicates 0.66 tons of coal for 1 ton of refined sugar or 10,000 B.t.u.[1] per lb. of sugar. Some plants now produce 1 lb. of refined beet sugar with only 6,000 B.t.u.[2]

Miscellaneous Sugars. Lactose or milk sugar is presented in Chap. 39 under Milk Chemicals, while sorbitol and mannitol are now made by hydrogenation. Much molasses serves as the carbohydrate raw material in the fermentation industries (Chap. 31) or as cattle feed.

STARCHES AND RELATED PRODUCTS

Although starch is known to have the approximate formula $(C_6H_{10}O_5)_n$, its exact structure is still unsolved. It may be regarded as a chain polyglucosidic macromolecule. It is one of the most common substances existing in nature and is the major basic constituent of the average diet. Industrially, its applications are numerous, being used in more than 300 modern industries, including the manufacture of textiles, paper, adhesives, insecticides, paints, soaps, explosives, and such derivatives as dextrins, nitrostarch, and corn sugar. Starch has been the object of a large amount of research in recent years, covering such products as heat-resistant adhesives, esters comparable to the cellulose esters, oxidation of dextrose to carboxylic acids, and the preparation of wetting agents.

Historical.[3] It is a well-known fact that the ancients used starch in manufacturing paper (as an adhesive and stiffener) as early as 3500 B.C.

[1] PERRY, op. cit., p. 1561, for B.t.u. in typical coals.

[2] SHAFOR, Process Economy Emphasized in Recent Beet Sugar Developments, Chem. & Met. Eng., **47,** 464 (1940); DANIELS and COTTON, Reburning of Defecation Lime Cake, Ind. Eng. Chem., **43,** 624 (1951).

[3] RADLEY, "Starch and Its Derivatives," D. Van Nostrand Company, Inc., New York, 1940.

The Egyptians of this period cemented papyrus together in this manner. Between A.D. 700 and 1300 most paper was heavily coated with starch but the practice was abandoned toward the end of the fourteenth century and was not revived until our modern era. The use of starch in textiles began during the Middle Ages, when it was very common as a stiffening agent. By 1744 the English were using it in sizing and warp glazing.

Textile demands soon brought about the introduction of potato starch to supplement the wheat starch solely available up to this time. In 1811 the discoveries of Kirchhoff with respect to glucose and the thinning of starches by enzymatic action gave great impetus to starch manufacture through the increased fields of application which they created. The use of roasted starch did not begin until 1821, its usefulness being discovered as the result of a textile fire at Dublin, Ireland. It had, however, been prepared by LeGrange as early as 1804.

The first starch produced in this country was white-potato starch, made at Antrim, N.H., in 1831. In 1842, Kingsford began the production of corn starch, which became increasingly popular until by 1885 it had risen to the position of the leading textile starch in the field. It was in this period also that the manufacture of dextrins (roasted starches) was begun in the United States.

Uses and Economics. In 1954 nearly 2 billion pounds of starch were produced in the United States, for all purposes, including conversion into sirup and sugar. Of this total about 95 per cent was corn starch. Some statistics on corn are presented in Table 2. Imports, consisting principally of tapioca, sago, and arrowroot starches, totaled about 63,000,000 lb., and exports, principally corn starch, totaled about 100,000,000 lb.

The largest single use for *corn starch* is as a food,[1] about 30 per cent being thus consumed. Industrial uses account for the remaining 70 per cent with the cotton textile industry and domestic and commercial laundry trade the largest consumers. The third largest is the paper industry which utilizes corn starch as a filler and sizing material. Following in importance are the explosives, cosmetics, and adhesive industries. Adhesives requiring a starch base are used in making an almost countless number of products, as is discussed more fully in Chap. 25. *White-potato starch* can be employed for almost every one of the uses outlined for corn starch. Approximately 8,250 tons of starch were made in 1949 requiring 3,000,000 bu. of potatoes for production. It has the advantage of a large granule size and more desirable phosphoric acid content, but it is more expensive than corn starch.

Wheat, rice, arrowroot, and *cassava (tapioca) starches* also have many of

---

[1] ANON., "The Story of Corn and Its Products," Corn Industries Research Foundation, New York, 1949.

the same applications as corn starch. Rice starch is particularly preferred for laundry purposes. Tapioca starch is very common as a food.

In addition to the starches themselves, many further reaction products are made. These include the following: *Dextrin*, or "roasted starch," which is available in more than 100 different blends and types, varying from pure white to light yellow in color; they are used to make a great number of different pastes, gums, and adhesives. *Corn sirup* is a combination of dextrose, maltose, dextrin, and water. Approximately 1.9 billion pounds a year, or 95 per cent, are used for food, largely as sweeteners.

TABLE 2. SALE OF SPECIFIED CORN PRODUCTS FROM WET-PROCESS GRINDINGS[a]
(For 1954)

Product	1,000 units	Product	1,000 units
Starch..............	1,905,586 lb.	Corn oil, crude.........	53,394 lb.
Sugar.............	745,112 lb.	Corn oil, refined........	176,986 lb.
Sirup, unmixed......	1,559,594 lb.	Corn oil meal..........	945 tons
Dextrins...........	168,958 lb.	Gluten feed and meal....	46 tons

[a] U.S. Department of Agriculture, Washington, 1955.

Nonfood or industrial applications are small but important, such as in the textile, leather tanning, adhesive, pharmaceutical, paper, and tobacco industries. *Corn sugar*, or dextrose, is the sugar found in the blood. It has many food uses dependent upon its lower rate of crystallization, lesser sweetness, and different crystal formation. It is widely employed by the medical profession for infant feeding and prescriptions in sirup form. Industrially, it is important as a constituent of the viscose-rayon spinning bath, in leather tanning, tobacco conditioning, and fermentation. Important by-products of the starch industry are corn gluten, feed and meal, corn-oil meal, and corn oil. Virtually all the gluten and meal is used as feed, but a specially prepared gluten, very high in protein, is employed as a material for plastics and lacquers. Zein, concentrated from the gluten fraction, is used as the raw material for Vicara. Over 12,000,000 lb. of *steep water* are consumed annually in the growing of penicillin and streptomycin (Chap. 31). Inositol,[1] or hexahydroxy-cyclohexane, a sugar substance and a member of the vitamin B complex, is made from corn steep water.

Manufacture of Starch, Dextrin, and Dextrose from Corn. Corn refining is an enormous industry, consuming (in 1954) 130,940,000 bu. of corn, and at one time (1947) as high as 140,000,000.

[1] ANON., Up Output Tenfold, *Chem. Eng.*, **58** (7), 200 (1951), including a flow sheet; *cf.* GREENFIELD, *et al.*, Industrial Wastes Cornstarch Process, *Ind. Eng. Chem.*, **39**, 583 (1947).

Chemically, the corn kernel consists of from 11 to 20 per cent water and the following nonaqueous constituents, expressed in per cent:[1]

Starch..................	60.0–65.0	Oil.....................	3.0–4.5
Proteins................	8.0–10.0	Fiber..................	1.2–1.5
Pentosans..............	7.0– 7.5	Ash....................	1.2–1.3

On this basis, 1 bu. of corn yields about 30.8 lb. of starch, 23.5 lb. of by-products (gluten meal, corn bran, germ-oil meal, and steep water), and 1.7 lb. of corn oil.

The sulfurous acid method of refining is employed, using shelled corn as raw material[2] and the following *physical changes* or *unit operations* (see Fig. 6).

The first operation consists of cleaning the corn by means of screens, compressed air, and electromagnets. The cleaned corn is steeped for 2 days in warm water (115 to 125°F.) containing about 0.30 per cent sulfur dioxide. The latter prevents fermentation during the soaking period. Large, hopper-bottomed, wood-steeping vats are employed for this operation which softens the gluten and loosens the hull. The steep water dissolves salts, soluble carbohydrates, and protein.

The cleaned and softened kernels are degerminated between two studded steel plates, one rotating and one stationary, which tear the kernels apart and extricate the corn germs without crushing them. The latter is liquid-separated from the hull in so-called *germ separators*, which are large agitated tanks. The germ, because of its oil content, is floated away from the rest of the kernel and carried off in the overflow. It is washed, dried, ground, and put through expellers (see Chap. 28).

The remainder of the corn kernel contains the starch, gluten, and cellulose. It is wet-ground in buhrstone mills and passed through a series of hexagonal reels open at both ends and covered with nylon bolting cloth. Water washes the starch and gluten through the nylon sides while the hull and fiber particles tumble out the lower end. The last bits of hull and fiber are removed on rectangular shaker screens covered with nylon bolting cloth, after which the starch-gluten suspension flows into the centrifugal separators. Figure 6 shows the still widely used screens and starch tables.

Centrifugal separators are a recent innovation[3] to improve the old-time starch tables. They require less space, are cleaner because they are completely enclosed, show a marked reduction in start-up and shut-down

[1] WALTON, "A Comprehensive Study of Starch Chemistry," Vol. 1, pp. 130–139, Reinhold Publishing Corporation, New York, 1928.
[2] STARR, Making the Most from Corn, *Chem. Eng.*, **56** (8), 93 (1949), with a pictured flow sheet on p. 140.
[3] TAYLOR, Centrifugals Replace Tables for Separation of Starch and Gluten, *Chem. Inds.*, **62**, 54 (1948).

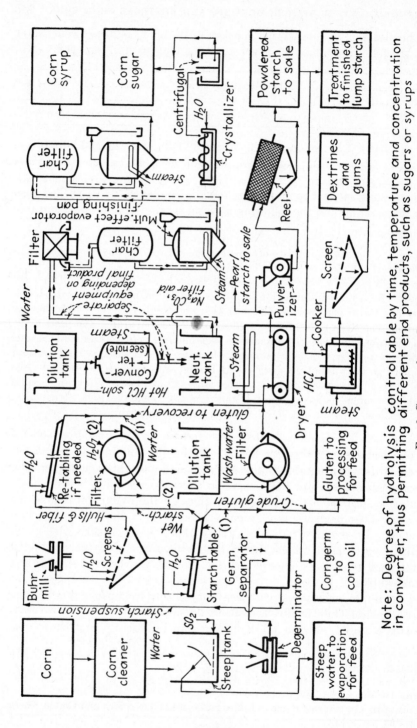

Note: Degree of hydrolysis controllable by time, temperature and concentration in converter, thus permitting different end products, such as sugars or syrups.

Fig. 6. Corn products flow sheet.

time, and give a satisfactory separation of starch and gluten. A starch recovery of 85 to 90 per cent of theoretical was the best available on the tables, while centrifugals recover 95 per cent or better. The starch and gluten suspensions are passed through two centrifugals operated in series. The starch, being the heavier, leaves the underflow from the first centrifugal and is further separated from the gluten in the second stage. After centrifuging, the last traces of soluble materials are removed from the starch slurry by continuous vacuum filters. The washed starch cake is removed from the drums by either a "doctor blade" or string-discharge arrangement. The starch is reslurried and processed into a finished dry starch product or converted into other products. The *gluten*, obtained from overflow in the centrifugal separators, is partially dehydrated by centrifugal force, dried, and sold as adhesive or food.

If *commercial starch* is to be made, the starch is removed from suspension with a vacuum string-discharge filter. The cake is broken and dried in a continuous-tunnel drier traveling countercurrent to the air. The starch enters with a moisture content of 44 per cent and exits at 10 to 14 per cent. This form is sold as *pearl starch*. Powdered starch is ground and screened pearl starch. *Lump* or *gloss starch* is made from powdered starch containing a slightly higher per cent of moisture. Precooking the starch yields *gelatinized starches*. For *thick-boiling starch*, alkali conversion is used; for *thin-boiling starch*, mild-acid conversion.

Another product of corn refining is *dextrin*, or "roasted starch." Starch itself is not soluble in water, but its derivative, dextrin, dissolves readily to give various commercial adhesives, pastes, and gums. Conversion is carried out in round wood tanks equipped with a scraper and open at the top. The scraper prevents sticking during the heating period which may vary from 2 hr. for some white dextrins to 15 hr. for certain gums. The temperature also influences the kind of dextrin being prepared.

When starch is *hydrolyzed* in the presence of acid, the product is either *corn sirup* or *corn sugar* (dextrose), depending upon the extent of the conversion. Hydrochloric acid is the hydrolyzing agent employed almost exclusively in the United States and sulfuric acid in Europe. A green starch suspension is pumped into a cylindrical bronze converter and heated to 270 to 280°F. over a period of 15 to 20 min. If corn sugar (dextrose) is being prepared instead of the sirup, a slightly stronger acid (0.2 per cent) and a longer conversion period are necessary. The converter mixture is adjusted to a pH of 4.5 to 5.5 with soda ash, filtered, and concentrated to 30°Bé. The resulting sirupy liquid is decolorized with activated carbon and evaporation continued, now under vacuum, until the concentration has reached 42 to 45°Bé. The resulting sirup, containing dextrose, maltose, dextrin, and water, is cooled, packaged, and sold as corn sirup or glucose. The sirup may be dried between two steam-heated chromium-plated rolls where the moisture is reduced to less than 5 per

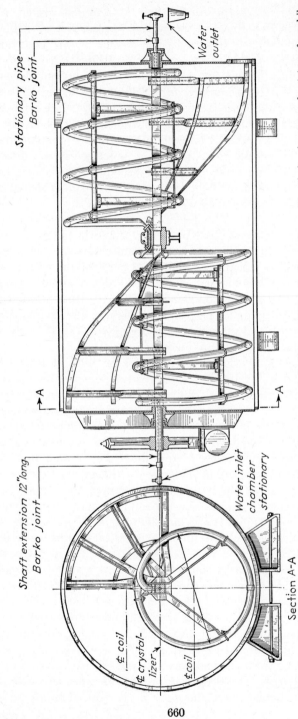

FIG. 7. Sugar crystallizer provided with scraper and eccentric coil crystallizer. Such cooling with stirring improves heat transfer while maintaining uniformity in temperature drop. Rotation ⅛ r.p.m. Crystallization time is about 100 hr. for dextrose. Water is passed through coil for cooling. (*Courtesy of Kilby Manufacturing Company.*)

cent. The dried material is scraped off the heated drum rolls and ground. If pure corn sugar is desired, the hydrolysis is carried farther so that little or no starch and dextrin are in the sirup. This sirup, concentrated to 42°Bé., containing about 80 per cent corn sugar, is cooled, seeded, and crystallized slowly with gentle agitation in closed horizontal cylindrical vessels during 100 hr. (see Fig. 7). This sugar is separated from its mother liquor in centrifuges, washed, and dried. Three types of corn sugar, known as crude, pressed, and refined, are available. The commercial product is usually sold as dextrose or corn sugar but chemically this is the mono-saccharide d-glucose. Lactic acid may be and is produced from the fermentation of dextrose by lactobacilli in wooden fermentors.

A new plant, in fact the first plant processing starch[1] from grain built in the United States since 1922, was completed in 1949. This plant was specifically *designed to process starch from grain* sorghums as milo maize. Although the chemical composition of milo maize is about the same as corn, milo maize differs in practically every other respect. This plant employs continuous and fully automatic operation, and since it is located at Corpus Christi, Tex., utilizes partly "outdoor" type of construction. The processes used are very similar to those described under wet-milling of corn.

MISCELLANEOUS STARCHES

Two varieties of potato starch are manufactured at present: white-potato starch and sweet-potato starch.

White-potato Starch.[2] White potatoes contain 10 to 30 per cent starch. The starch may be recovered either batchwise or continuously, with the trend definitely toward the economical continuous processing. Upon being received at the factory, the potatoes are washed and disintegrated to a watery pulp. Formerly for disintegration a rasping machine was used, but newer practice utilizes a hammer mill. The pulp is treated with sulfur dioxide gas, in the ratio 0.5 lb. per lb. of starch and sent to a continuous horizontal centrifuge with an imperforate conical bowl and continuous spiral ribbon starch remover. The protein-water mixture is separated from the starch, cellulose, and skins, and the latter resuspended in water as a milk. The suspension is sieved, the pulp from the sieves is reground and resieved. The milk from the second sieving is again passed through a cen-

---

[1] TAYLOR, Starch and Sugar from Milo Maize, *Chem. Inds.*, **64**, 932 (1949); HIGH-TOWER, The New Corn Products Plant: It Makes Wet Milling History, *Chem. Eng.*, **56** (6), 92 (1949), with a pictured flow sheet. This plant may be of particular interest because the literature contains accounts of the laboratory and pilot-plant studies which may be compared with the actual plant practice. See ROGGE, Dextrose from Cornstarch, *Ind. Eng. Chem.*, **41**, 2070 (1949).

[2] HOWERTON and TREADWAY, Manufacture of White Potato Starch, *Ind. Eng. Chem.*, **40**, 1402 (1948); REICHENBERG, Potato Starch Comeback, *Chem. Eng.*, **56** (6), 120 (1949).

trifuge, suspended in water, and sent to the tables for separation. From this point on operations are similar to those used for the manufacture of corn starch.

Wheat Starch.[1] In the manufacture of this cereal starch, the major difficulty encountered is the separation of the starch and gluten. This may be accomplished by fermentation or Martin's process. In the fermentation process the grain is steeped until soft, a mash made which is left to ferment for 7 to 30 days. The gluten is solubilized, and the remainder of the grain loses its adhesive properties. At the proper point the starch is washed from the mixture in a washing drum. The process is but rarely used because of its objectionable odor, low yield, and wastage of now valuable gluten. In the Martin process, wheat is ground to flour, made into a dough with about 40 per cent of its weight of water and stored for 1 hr. The resulting mass is divided into small lumps and placed in a semicircular sieve where a traveling roller presses out the starch, which is removed by a fine water spray. The resulting liquor is treated in much the same manner as corn-starch liquor.

Rice Starch. This is made from "cargo rice" which still has the brown, outer cuticle attached, or from the broken white grains rejected as foodstuff. The rice is steeped for 24 hr. with caustic soda solution (specific gravity 1.005) in cement or iron tanks with perforated false bottoms. At the end of the period the liquor is withdrawn, the rice washed, fresh liquor added, and steeping continued for another 36 to 48 hr. The resulting softened grains are ground with a caustic solution to a specific gravity of 1.24 and the mash is centrifuged. The solids obtained include all sorts of fibrous material, starch, and gluten. These are resuspended, a small amount of formaldehyde is added to inhibit fermentation, and they are recentrifuged and washed. A bleaching or bluing agent may be added at this point. The liquor is screened, adjusted to a specific gravity of 1.21, and sent to draining boxes having perforated bottoms covered with cotton fabric. Settling is aided by applying suction through the box bottom. The resulting starch blocks are cut and placed on porous plates in a crusting stove, where they are allowed to dry for 2 days at 50 to 60°C.

Cassava (Tapioca) Starch. This starch is obtained from the roots and tubers of the manioc plant, which grows in the East Indies, West Indies, and South America. The average starch content varies from 20 to 30 per cent. In general, the roots are pulped and washed on sieves to obtain the starch. In the West Indies, the pulp is squeezed through coarse bags to expel the starch milk. Separating and purifying operations are similar to those described for potato starch.

Sago Starch. This is obtained from the pith of the sago palm, and also from yams in the East Indies and Borneo. Pearl sago starch is made by

[1] KERR, "Chemistry and Industry of Starch," 2d ed., Academic Press, Inc., New York, 1950.

drying the starch so as to form a plastic dough, which is then forced through sieves and dried in the air.

SELECTED REFERENCES

Sugar:

Sugar, monthly journal, 339 Carondelet St., New Orleans, La.

Tromp, L. A., "Machinery and Equipment of the Cane Sugar Factory," Norman Rodger, London, 1936.

Spencer, G. L., and G. P. Meade, "Handbook for Cane Sugar Manufacturers," John Wiley & Sons, Inc., New York, 1929.

Davies, J. G., "Principles of Cane Sugar Manufacture," Norman Rodger, London, 1938.

Browne, C. A., "Physical and Chemical Methods of Sugar Analysis," 3d ed., John Wiley & Sons, Inc., New York, 1940.

Lyle, O., "Technology for Sugar Refinery Workers," Norman Rodger, London, 1941.

U.S. Tariff Commission, "Sugar and Reciprocal Trade Agreements," Washington, April, 1940.

Furnas, C. C., editor, "Rogers' Manual of Industrial Chemistry," 6th ed., Chap. 35, pp. 1335–1377, D. Van Nostrand Company, Inc., New York, 1942.

Sugar Bibliography, pp. 1373–1377 in "Rogers' Manual of Industrial Chemistry," 6th ed., D. Van Nostrand Company, Inc., New York, 1942.

McGinnis, R. A., "Beet Sugar Technology," Reinhold Publishing Corporation, New York, 1951.

Starch:

Walton, R. P., "A Comprehensive Study of Starch Chemistry," Reinhold Publishing Corporation, New York, 1928.

Radley, J. A., "Starch and Its Derivatives," 3d ed., Vols. I and II, John Wiley & Sons, Inc., New York, 1954.

U.S. Tariff Commission, "Starch and Dextrins and Reciprocal Trade Agreements," Washington, September, 1940.

Furnas, C. C., editor, "Rogers' Manual of Industrial Chemistry," 6th ed., Chap. 36, pp. 1378–1406, D. Van Nostrand Company, Inc., New York, 1942.

Kerr, R. W. E., "Chemistry and Industry of Starch," 2d ed., Academic Press, Inc., New York, 1950.

CHAPTER 31

FERMENTATION INDUSTRIES

The employment of microorganisms to convert one substance into another is a science that man is assiduously studying and is energetically applying. Although the fermentation of fruits to alcohol was known to primitive man and although the making of various beverages out of fruits and grains has been well established for centuries, it is only during the past generation that the wider application of this procedure has been recognized. Now, man is directing the life processes of yeasts, bacteria, and molds to the production of chemicals. Alcohol can be viewed as having been produced in this way from the earliest times, but the making of acetone and butanol, of acetic acid, lactic acid, citric acid, and the many antibiotics is a recent technical accomplishment.

The foundation of the scientific understanding of fermentation, indeed of the action of all microorganisms and hence of their economic control, rests firmly upon the genius of one man, Louis Pasteur.[1] He showed that fermentation is directly caused by the life processes of minute organisms. By understanding how these microorganisms function and by the recognition that varieties of yeasts, for instance, act differently and that environment fundamentally affects even a given strain, one can control these processes of fermentation in an exact scientific manner.

The fungi are a branch of the nongreen plants and include bacteria, yeasts, and molds. These feed upon organic materials. It is this feeding that interests the manufacturer; for if he supplies to certain yeasts, bacteria, or molds the necessary fundamental energy food, together with the other needed nutrients, then these microvegetative organisms will not only grow and multiply but will change the food into other chemical substances.

Yeasts and bacteria are unicellular and of very small dimensions. The yeasts are irregularly oval and perhaps 0.004 to 0.010 mm. in diameter. The bacteria are smaller, mostly less than 0.007 mm. in the longer dimension and more diverse in shape. Many of them, the bacilli, are rod-shaped. The yeasts multiply by budding, and the bacteria by binary fission. The molds are multicellular filaments and increase by vegetative growth of the

[1] For further historical background, see BORUFF and VAN LANEN, Fermentation, *Ind. Eng. Chem.*, **43**, 574 (1951).

filament. Sporulation provides for the next cycle, as it does also with many bacteria. The vegetative reproduction cycle of these bacteria and of the yeasts is short—measured in minutes. Because of this, they multiply exceedingly fast.

Many microorganisms have been brought into useful service to man. One of the striking developments since the 1920's has been the extension to the making of chemicals, other than alcohol, of the life processes of these minute vegetative organisms. Table 1 lists some of these performances, which, in larger industrial scale, embrace the manufacture of antibiotics, acetone, butanol, acetic acid, lactic acid, and citric acid. This table shows the importance of fermentation in foods and feeds. Several of the older laboratory procedures, such as the making of citric and gluconic acids, have been developed to the industrial stage. One of the outstanding developments of the Second World War was the making of penicillin which stimulated further important discoveries in the field of antibiotics. Many fermentation processes are frequently in direct competition with strictly chemical syntheses. Alcohol from fermentation and from ethylene compete. Acetone, butanol, and acetic acid by fermentation have largely been superseded by their synthetic counterparts. However, the antibiotics have paced a recent fermentation revival and with the exception of one, chloramphenicol, all the major antibiotics are obtained exclusively from fermentation processes. Dextran[1] is another fermentation product which, because of its possible use as a plasma volume expander, has gained prominence. The microbiological production of vitamins has also become economically important.

Actually fermentation under controlled conditions involves many *chemical processes*. Some of the more important ones are: *oxidation*, *e.g.*, alcohol to acetic acid, sucrose to citric acid, and dextrose to gluconic acid; *reduction*, *e.g.*, aldehydes to alcohols, as acetaldehyde to ethyl alcohol and sulfur to hydrogen sulfide; *hydrolysis*, *e.g.*, starch to glucose or sucrose to glucose and fructose; and *esterification*, *e.g.*, hexose phosphate from hexose and phosphoric acid.

However, many of the chemical reactions caused by microorganisms are very complex and cannot easily be classified; so the concept of fermentation itself as a unit process has been developed. According to Silcox and Lee[2] the five basic prerequisites of a good fermentation process are:

1. A microorganism that forms a desired end product. This organism must be readily propagated and be capable of maintaining biological uniformity, thereby giving predictable yields.

[1] BIXLER, et al., Dextran, *Ind. Eng. Chem.*, **45**, 692 (1953).

[2] SILCOX and LEE, Fermentation, *Ind. Eng. Chem.*, **40**, 1602 (1948); LEE, et al., *Ind. Eng. Chem.*, **41**, 1868 (1949); **42**, 1672 (1950); **43**, 1948 (1951); **44**, 1996 (1952); PERLMAN, et al., **45**, 1944 (1953). The fermentation section of these annual unit-process *reviews* should be especially consulted.

2. Economic raw materials for the substrate.
3. Acceptable yields.
4. Rapid fermentation.
5. A product that is readily recovered and purified.

According to Lee, certain factors should be stressed in relation to the fermentation unit process concept, such as microorganism, equipment, and the fermentation itself. Certain critical factors of the fermentation are the pH, temperature, aeration-agitation, pure-culture fermentation, and uniformity of yields.

In understanding, and hence in correctly handling microorganisms, a sharp differentiation should be made usually between the initial growth of a selected strain of these organisms to a sufficient quantity; and the subsequent processes whereby, either through their continued *living* or as a result of *enzymes* previously secreted, the desired chemical is manufactured. To get a maximum chemical yield it is frequently advisable to suppress additional increase in quantity of the microorganism. Highly specialized mycologists[1] working in well-equipped laboratories are engaged in selecting and growing the particular strain of the organism that experiment has shown to produce the chemical or chemicals wanted and with the *greatest yields* and the *least by-product*.

No longer will just any yeast do to make industrial alcohol or a fermented beverage; not only are wild yeasts excluded, but a special strain must be used.

The yeasts, bacteria, and molds employed require specific environments and foods to ensure their activities. The concentration of the sugar or other food affects the product. The temperature most favorable varies (5 to 40°C.). The pH also has great influence. Indeed, the bacteriologist has developed some acid-loving yeasts, so that the *wild yeasts*, not liking this condition, do not flourish. Some microorganisms require air (aerobic), and others go through their life processes without air (anaerobic). Certain anaerobes will neither grow nor function in the presence of air. In directing these minute vegetative organisms, conditions can be controlled to encourage the multiplication of the organism first and then its functioning either directly or through the enzymes secreted. How important this is can be seen from the knowledge that to grow 1 gram of yeast (dry basis) requires 1.5 to 2.0 grams of monosaccharide per day, and 6 grams to maintain the yeast. By virtue of this growth organic catalysts or enzymes are formed frequently that directly cause the desired chemical change. During the growth period, in addition to the primary or energy food, such as monosaccharides for yeast, there are needed various nutrients, such as small amounts of phosphates, nitrogenous compounds, as well as the favorable pH and temperature. Finally, certain substances will poison

[1] Those skilled in dealing with bacteria, yeasts, and molds. Industrially, one laboratory will frequently control the use of only one species of bacteria, for example.

these useful little vegetables and their enzymes. Even the alcohol formed by the yeasts will eventually reach a concentration (varying with the yeast from about 2 to 15 per cent) that will suppress the activity of the organism and of the enzymes. We are, furthermore, recognizing the im-

TABLE 1. SURVEY OF IMPORTANT FERMENTATIONS[a]

Food and feed	Industrial, pharmaceutical	Laboratory
Bread (Y.)	Alcohol (Y.)	Succinic acid (M., Y., and B.)
Cheese (M. or B.)	Yeast (Y.)	Fumaric acid (M.)
	Enzymes (M., Y., and B.)	
Vinegar (B. and Y.)	Carbon dioxide (Y.)	Kojic acid (M.)
Sauerkraut (B.)	Lactic acid (B.)	Butyric acid (B.)
Koji (M. and Y.)	Gallic acid (M.)	Propionic acid (B.)
Tea (B.)	Glycerine (Y.)	Malic acid (M. and Y.)
Coffee (M.)	Acetic acid (B.)	Fuel gas, H_2 (B.)
Cocoa (B. and Y.)	Acetone-butyl alcohol (B.)	Dihydroxy-acetone (B.)
Pickles (B. and Y.)	Citric acid (M.)	Acetic acid from cellulose (B.)
Olives (B.)	Gluconic acid (M.)	
Yeast (Y.)	Penicillin (M.)	
	Sulfuric acid from sulfur (B.)	
Beer (Y.)	Precipitation iron (B.)	
Wine (Y.)	Nitrogen fixation (B.)	
Whisky (Y.)	Fusel oil (Y.)	
Vitamins	2,3-butanediol (B.)	Various antibiotics
Riboflavin (B. and Y.)	Itaconic acid (M.)	
Vitamin B_{12} (B. and M.)	2-Ketogluconic acid (B.)	
Ergosterol (Y. and M.)	5-Ketogluconic acid (B.)	
Vitamin B_1 (Y.)	Penicillin (M.)	
Antibiotics	Streptomycin (M.)	
Penicillin (M.)	Chloramphenicol (M.)	
Aureomycin (M.)	Aureomycin (M.)	
Terramycin (M.)	Terramycin (M.)	
Bacitracin (M.)	Bacitracin (B.)	
	Neomycin (M.)	
	Dextran (B.)	

[a] Y. stands for yeast; B. for bacteria; M. for molds.

portance of the life processes of the microorganisms in making vitamins, some of which are being recovered and sold in a concentrated form.

INDUSTRIAL ALCOHOL

Industrial alcohol was an outgrowth of alcoholic beverages, but now it has become important by virtue of its economically useful properties as a solvent and for synthesis of other chemicals. Alcohol is sold as tax-paid[1] alcohol or, much more widely, as nontaxed denatured alcohol. There are two classes of the latter: completely denatured and specially denatured alcohol. The *completely denatured* formulas comprise admixtures of substances which are difficult to separate from the alcohol and which smell and taste bad, this all being designed to render the alcohol nonpotable. Such completely denatured alcohol is sold widely without bond. The public uses it as an antifreeze and the factories find it an essential raw material. A typical completely denatured alcohol formula follows:

Formula No. 12. To every 100 gal. of ethyl alcohol of not less than 160 deg. proof add:

4.0 gal. of ST-115[2] or a compound similar thereto.

1.0 gal. of Dehydrol-0 or a compound similar thereto.

0.5 gal. of acetaldol (hydroxy-butyraldehyde) or 1.5 gal. of methyl isobutyl ketone.

1.0 gal. of kerosene.

The Federal government has recognized the needs of industry for alcohol in such form that it can enter into specialized manufacturing processes where the denaturants used in the completely denatured alcohols would interfere. So, since 1906, when the first United States denatured alcohol law was passed, many formulas, of *specially denatured* alcohol, have been approved by the Federal authorities. Such special formulas are limited to certain designated processes and are manufactured, stored, and used under bond, to ensure such specially denatured alcohols from unlawful consumption. However, the 57 approved special formulas under their authorized uses enter into an exceedingly broad section of the entire industrial life of the nation.[3] Typical specially denatured formulas are:

[1] The Federal tax is $10.50 per proof gallon and hence $19.95 on a gallon of 190-proof alcohol. To this the state may add its own tax. The total sum collected by the Federal Alcohol Tax Unit was $2,549,119,689 during the fiscal year 1952, largely from beverages. A *proof gallon* (tax gallon) signifies a gallon containing 50 per cent alcohol by volume; 100 volumes of 100-proof alcohol contain 50 volumes of absolute alcohol and 53.73 volumes of water, owing to volume contraction. Ordinary alcohol of 95 per cent strength is thus 190-proof alcohol, and pure anhydrous alcohol is 200-proof. It is interesting to observe that 100-proof alcohol is about the lower limit of burning for alcohol dilutions by direct ignition at ordinary temperatures. A *wine gallon* is a measure of volume (231 cu. in.) of any proof.

[2] The denaturants added to make completely denatured alcohol are frequently commercial mixtures. Full specifications are given in the pamphlet entitled "Formulae for Completely and Specially Denatured Alcohol," published by the U.S. Bureau of Internal Revenue, Appendix to Regulations, No. 3, revised, 1942. ST-115 is an impure pyroligneous product, free from wood alcohol, but produced from destructive distillation of wood. Dehydrol-0 is a compound petroleum product.

[3] Formulas 1, 2B, and 29 accounted for approximately 80 per cent of the withdrawals during the fiscal year 1952 of 489,788,861 proof gal. (455,999,873 in 1951).

To every 100 gal. of ethyl alcohol, add for the designated number:
No. 1. five gal. approved wood alcohol. Withdrawals for 1950: 25,272,168 wine gal.
Authorized uses: lacquers and other surfaced coatings, dyes, chemicals, etc.
No. 2B. One-half gal. benzol.
Withdrawals for 1950: 20,013,497 wine gal.
Authorized uses: plastics, dehydrations, explosives, food products, chemicals, etc.
No. 29. One gal. of 100 per cent acetaldehyde.
Withdrawals for 1950: 94,430,664 wine gal.
Authorized uses: manufacturing acetaldehyde, acetic acid, esters, ethers, etc.

In industrial nomenclature *alcohol* means ethyl alcohol or ethanol with the formula C_2H_5OH. It is sold by the gallon which weighs 6.794 lb. and contains 95 per cent C_2H_5OH and 5 per cent H_2O both by volume and at 15.56°C.[1] No distinction is made as to the source of the alcohol, whether it be from fermentation or from synthesis.

Uses and Economics.[2] Tax-paid pure alcohol is used only for medicinal, pharmaceutical, flavoring, or beverage purposes. The large consumption and the wide field of industrial application have arisen only since the availability of the low-priced tax-free denatured alcohols. Completely denatured alcohol is consumed chiefly as an antifreeze. The trend has been toward the use of specially denatured alcohols for industrial applications. Alcohol is second only to water in solvent value and is employed in nearly all industries. In addition it is the raw material for making hundreds of chemicals. Most important of these are acetaldehyde, ethyl acetate, acetic acid, ethylene dibromide, glycols, and ethyl chloride. During the Second World War when tremendous quantities of butadiene and styrene were needed for the synthetic-rubber program, alcohol was used as a supplemental raw material for butadiene although petroleum is the cheaper raw material. In fact, in 1945, 75 per cent of the specially denatured alcohol entered into synthetic-rubber manufacture.

In petroleum-poor countries it is economical to mix alcohol (frequently absolute) in with the gasoline in order to conserve the petroleum products. For such mixtures, if the alcohol is not anhydrous, a blending agent is needed. These procedures have been carried out quite extensively in Europe and in some tropical sugar-growing countries where from 10 to 20 per cent alcohol may be in the motor fuel, the higher amount having been employed in Sweden for many years. Similar proposals have been made for the United States and even tried in localized areas but were uneconomical.

The cost of alcohol is largely that of the raw material, although steam,

[1] This corresponds to 92.423 per cent of ethyl alcohol by weight. However, when alcohol percentage strength is given, it refers to percentage by volume.

[2] Staff Report, Industrial Alcohol, *Chem. Eng. News*, **29**, 4932 (1951); "Ethyl Alcohol," U.S. Tariff Commission, Industrial Materials Series, M-1, 1951.

overhead, labor, and other factors vary as to location. Raw materials from which ethyl alcohol may be made fall into four general classifications: (1) saccharine materials (molasses from sugar beets and sugar cane), (2) starchy materials (cereal grains, potatoes), (3) hydrocarbon gases, and (4) cellulosic materials (wood, agricultural residues, and waste

TABLE 2. ETHYL ALCOHOL: COMPARATIVE STATISTICS, FISCAL YEARS 1951 AND 1954[a]

(In thousands)

	1951	1954
Materials used:		
Total grain, lb.	1,310,874	96,614
Corn and products, lb.	273,139	59,988
Rye and products, lb.	701	2,072
Malt and products, lb.	109,646	3,314
Wheat and products, lb.	63	31,165
Sorghum grain and products, lb.	930,681	
Ethylene gas, lb.	72,409	117,259
Molasses, wine gal.	128,536	80,916
Ethyl sulfate, wine gal.	148,393	189,423
Sulfite liquors, wine gal.	256,238	250,546
Domestic undenatured alcohol, proof gal:		
Production	444,935	378,444
Withdrawals from bond, total.	536,524	410,634
Tax-paid withdrawals.	42,824	15,225
Tax-free withdrawals.	499,699	395,410
For denaturation.	456,000	386,229
All other.	38,553	8,982
Denatured alcohol, wine gal.:		
Completely denatured alcohol:		
Production	1,438	625
Withdrawals.	1,456	621
Specially denatured alcohol:		
Production	243,998	207,921
Withdrawals.	237,192	207,353

[a] "Chemical Statistics Handbook," Manufacturing Chemists' Association (published annually).

sulfite liquors). Until 1935, blackstrap molasses from cane sugar was used more than any other material because of its cheapness, availability, and easy conversion into alcohol. Blackstrap molasses contains from 50 to 55 per cent of fermentable sugar consisting mainly of 70 per cent sucrose and 30 per cent invert (glucose-fructose mixture) sugar. A high-test molasses was used extensively from 1935 to 1941 for alcohol production and was a product of cane sugar which has been partly hydrolyzed, usually by acid treatment. It contains about 70 to 78 per cent total fermentable sugars, mostly invert. Molasses being almost unobtainable during the Second World War, manufacturers turned to corn and wheat as the demand was urgent and cost secondary.

Since that time, the economics of the situation have varied so that fermentors use the cheapest raw material, although a long-term trend indicates that fermentation is to occupy a place of less importance as a source of industrial alcohol. The year 1950 was the first year that fermentation accounted for less than 50 per cent of the alcohol produced, the greater part being synthetically derived. The beverage laws specify the use of grain alcohol in certain beverages (whisky), and custom demands it for some tax-paid solvent uses (see Tables 2 and 3). Thus a

TABLE 3. RAW MATERIALS USED IN ETHYL ALCOHOL MANUFACTURE[a]
(Per cent of total output)

Raw material	1945	1946	1947	1948	1949	1950	1951[b]	1952[c]
Molasses.	29.2	26.4	21.7	42.8	36.3	31.5	23.9	26.3
Grain.	43.3	31.8	16.0	10.4	3.3	0.7	25.7	18.2
Ethylene.	17.2	38.6	53.5	42.1	46.9	57.5	48.5	48.7
Other.	10.3	3.2	8.8	4.7	13.5	10.3	1.9	5.5
Sulfite liquor.								1.2

[a] KUHN and HATCHESON, Ethylene Chemicals, *Chem. Week*, **69** (13), 24 (1951).
[b] Staff Report, Industrial Alcohol, *Chem. Eng. News*, **29**, 4932 (1951).
[c] Annual Report, Internal Revenue, 1952, Table 16.

demand is created for this higher-priced grain alcohol which means that lower-priced synthetics under these conditions will not entirely displace fermentation alcohol.

MANUFACTURE OF INDUSTRIAL ALCOHOL

Raw Materials. The manufacture of alcohol from ethylene or other synthetic manufacturing procedures, now the most important source, is discussed in Chap. 37. Alcohol from cellulosic materials, wood, wood wastes, and sulfite liquors is considered in Chap. 32. This last is not competitive except under special conditions, largely because of the cost of converting the cellulosic material to fermentable sugars.

Reactions. The principal reactions in alcohol fermentation are *Equation of inversion:*[1]

$$C_{12}H_{22}O_{11} + H_2O \rightarrow C_6H_{12}O_6 + C_6H_{12}O_6$$
Sucrose d-Glucose d-Fructose

[1] In commercial parlance, reducing or invert sugars are fermented and include the scientific d-glucose and d-fructose. The product sold commercially as glucose is usually a sirup of d-glucose with some dextrin and maltose, while dextrose U.S.P. is d-glucose.

Equations of fermentation:[1]

$$C_6H_{12}O_6 \rightarrow 2C_2H_5OH + 2CO_2; \quad \Delta H = -31,200 \text{ cal.} \quad (1)$$
Monosaccharide   Alcohol

Toward the end of a fermentation, the acidity and glycerine increase. Neuberg's third equation may account for this.

$$2C_6H_{12}O_6 + H_2O \rightarrow C_2H_5OH + CH_3COOH + 2CO_2 + 2C_3H_8O_3 \quad (2)$$
Monosaccharide   Alcohol   Acetic   Glycerine
                          acid

There is always found in alcohol fermentations a small amount of glycerine.

Energy Requirements, Unit Operations, Unit Processes. The shipment of raw material may involve tank-car movement of molasses to the Cuban

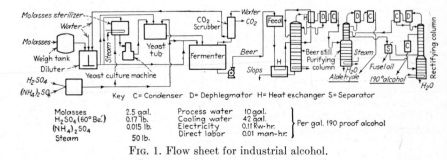

Molasses	2.5 gal.	Process water	10 gal.	
H_2SO_4 (60° Bé.)	0.17 lb.	Cooling water	42 gal.	
$(NH_4)_2SO_4$	0.015 lb.	Electricity	0.11 kw-hr.	Per gal. 190 proof alcohol
Steam	50 lb.	Direct labor	0.01 man-hr.	

FIG. 1. Flow sheet for industrial alcohol.

or Puerto Rican shore, steamer to an American (or other) port, and barge or tank-train[2] transshipment to a plant, if inland. The plant procedures require steam heating for distillation, power for pumping, and water for condensation and occasionally for cooling during the exothermic

---

[1] This is the classic Gay-Lussac equation for alcohol formation. It is the principal equation in acid or low pH medium. When growing yeast for sale as such or for inoculation, usually with some air blown in, the yield of alcohol is lower, it being partly changed to CO_2 and H_2O. However, this fermentation, like so very many industrial reactions, is very much more involved than these simple reactions indicate. Probably the first step is a phosphate hexose ester formation, followed by a split in the six-carbon chain. *Cf.* MICHAELIS, Chemistry of Alcoholic Fermentation, *Ind. Eng. Chem.*, **27**, 1037 (1935). The fusel oil (mixed amyl alcohols with some propyl, butyl, and hexyl alcohols and esters), amounting to 3 to 11 parts per 1,000 of alcohol, obtained from yeast fermentations, is held to be furnished by the protein materials in the *mash* fermented. *Cf.* PRESCOTT and DUNN, "Industrial Microbiology," 2d ed., Chap. IV, McGraw-Hill Book Company, Inc., New York, 1949; UNDERKOFLER, L. A., editor, "Commercial Fermentations," Chemical Publishing Company, Inc., New York, 1952.

[2] The U.S. Interstate Commerce Commission allows the railroads to make special (low) freight charges for entire trainload shipments of tank cars of molasses.

fermentation. The heat evolved by this fermentation reaction calculates to 88,940,000 kg.-cal., or 353,000,000 B.t.u. per 1,000 gal. of 95 per cent alcohol. Its evolution is usually spread over several days.

The manufacture of alcohol, as presented in Fig. 1, can be broken down into the following principal *unit processes* (Pr.) and *unit operations* (Op.). The main steps in the competitive manufacture of alcohol from petroleum cracking (*cf.* flow sheet, Fig. 19, Chap. 37) are shown in parallel comparison.

Fermentation Alcohol	*Alcohol from Ethylene*
Transportation of molasses or corn (Op.).	Liquefaction of the petroleum gases containing ethylene (Op.).
Storage of molasses or corn (Op.).	Rectification to produce pure ethylene and pure ethane (Op.).
Grinding, etc., of corn (Op.).	
Hydrolysis by heating of cornmeal with malt or acid to make mash (Pr.).	Dehydrogenation of ethane to ethylene (Pr.).
Growth of inoculating cultures (Pr.).	Esterification of strong sulfuric acid by ethylene (Pr.).
Fermentation of diluted inverted molasses or of corn mash (Pr.).	Hydrolysis of diluted ester to alcohol and diluted sulfuric acid (Pr.).
Distillation of alcohol from "beer" (Op.).	Distillation of alcohol from acid (Op.).
Rectification and purification of alcohol (Op.).	Rectification and purification of alcohol (Op.).
Recovery of by-products, *e.g.*, CO_2, feed, potash salts (Op.).	Concentration of diluted sulfuric acid to strong acid (Op.).
	Recovery of by-products, *e.g.*, ether (Op.).

Making of Industrial Alcohol. The flow sheet in Fig. 1 shows the various operations and processes involved in changing molasses into salable alcohol. Molasses, because of the strong concentration of sugar, does not support direct yeast fermentation.[1] It must be diluted first to a concentration of about 10 to 14 per cent sugars. This is called the *mash* and represents the carbohydrate ready for yeast inoculation. It is pumped to a large steel fermentor (60,000 to 500,000 gal.), closed in modern plants to collect the carbon dioxide evolved and to afford easier conditions for cleaning and sterilizing. An ammonium salt and sulfuric acid are added, the one to furnish a nutritive constituent deficient in molasses, and the other the right environmental pH (4.0 to 5.0) to facilitate the activity of the selected yeast and to suppress the multiplication of wild yeasts or bacteria. Magnesium sulfate is also added, when deficient.

In the meanwhile a charge of the selected yeast (about 5 per cent of the total volume) has been growing in the yeast tub. All this is under exact laboratory supervision, including the selection of the inoculating yeast

[1] Indeed strong sugar sirup is a *preservative;* witness the preserving of fruits with it.

strain, the sterilization of the diluted molasses, the addition of the nutrients, the pH, the temperature (76°F.) and finally the cleaning and sterilizing of the yeast culture machine in readiness for the next batch. The bacteriologists have been able to cultivate a strain of yeast that thrives under these acid conditions, while wild yeast and bacteria do not. As the reaction study indicates, the fermentation is exothermic and so cooling by outside sprays is frequently used; hence one advantage of the steel fermentor. Although the most favorable temperature varies, it is usually around 70°F. for starting and under 100°F. at the end. Four days are allowed by governmental regulations for a fermentation cycle, though usually 36 to 50 hr. are used. As alcohol is formed by yeast only from monosaccharides, it is necessary to split the sucrose, $C_{12}H_{22}O_{11}$, into d-glucose and d-fructose.[1] In alcohol fermentation by yeast, this microorganism furnishes an organic catalyst, or enzyme, known as *invertase* which effects this hydrolysis. The yeast also produces another and more important enzyme, *zymase*, which changes the monosaccharides into alcohol and carbon dioxide. The flow sheet of Fig. 2, Chap. 8, outlines the procedure for purification of the carbon dioxide from fermentation. Such recovery is practiced from a number of different fermentations—industrial alcohol, whisky, and butanol-acetone.

When *starchy materials* are used for industrial alcohol, it is first necessary to convert the starch to monosaccharides. This can be done with either malt or various mold processes. The *malt process* except for emergency periods is too expensive for industrial alcohol. *Fungal amylase*, an enzymatic material produced by the fermentation of *Aspergillus niger*, has been found to be an economical[2] replacement of malt for industrial alcohol. However, grain alcohol made by this method is still not competitive with that produced by synthesis or by fermentation of blackstrap molasses. In addition fungal amylase cannot replace barley malt for beverage production, since the flavor is not the same and because of Federal regulations. During the Second World War, grain processing changed from batch operations to continuous cooking and hydrolyzing processes.[3] Two types of such cookers were used commercially: a pipe-line cooker operated at 350°F. with a holding time of 1 to 2 min.; and a vertical tower, embodying a lower temperature and longer holding time.

---

[1] An equimolecular mixture of these is known as *invert* sugar and results by the action of heat, acids, or enzymes.

[2] ANON., Grain Alcohol without Malt, *Chem. Week*, **68** (3), 19 (1951); ANON., Methods and Costs of Producing Alcohol from Grain by the Fungal Amylase Process on a Commercial Process, *U.S. Dept. Agr. Tech. Bull.* 1024; *cf.* KIRK and OTHMER, *op. cit.*, Vol. 1, pp. 252–286.

[3] STARK, KOLACHOV, and WILKIE, Wheat as a Raw Material for Alcohol Production, *Ind. Eng. Chem.*, **35**, 133 (1943); ANON., Continuous Cooking of Cereal Grains, *Chem. & Met. Eng.*, **51** (10), 142 (1944), a pictured flow sheet; ANON., Recent Advances in Fermentation, *Chem. Eng.*, **54** (12), 141 (1947).

The liquor in the fermentors after the action is finished, is called a *beer*.[1] The alcohol is separated by *distillation*.[2] In such fermentation as pictured in Fig. 1, the beer, containing about 6.5 to 8.5 per cent alcohol by volume, is pumped to the upper sections of the beer still, after passing several heat exchangers. As the beer passes down the beer column, it gradually loses its lighter-boiling constituents, namely, alcohol and a small amount of aldehydes. The liquid discharged from the bottom of the still through a heat exchanger is known as *slop* or *stillage*.[3] It carries proteins, some residual sugars, and, in some instances, vitamin products so that it is frequently evaporated and used as a constituent of animal feed. The overhead containing alcohol, some water, and the aldehydes passes through a heat exchanger to the partial condenser or dephlegmator, which condenses sufficient of the vapors to afford a reflux and also to strengthen the vapors that do pass through to the condenser where about 50 per cent alcohol, containing the volatiles or aldehydes, is condensed. This condensate, frequently known as the *high wines*, is conducted into the aldehyde or heads column, from which the low-boiling impurities, or aldehydes, are separated as an overhead. The effluent liquor from part way down the aldehyde column flows into the rectifying column.

In this third column the alcohol is brought to strength and finally purified in the following manner: The overhead going through a dephlegmator is partly condensed to keep the stronger alcohol in this column and to provide reflux for the upper plates. The more volatile products, which may still contain a trace of aldehydes and of course some alcohol, are totally condensed and carried back to the upper part of the aldehyde still. Near the top of the column 95 to 95.6 per cent alcohol is taken off through a condenser for storage and sale. Farther down the column, the higher-boiling fusel oils are run off through a cooler and separator to a special still where they are rectified from any alcohol they may carry, before being sold as an impure amyl alcohol for solvent purposes. The bottom of this rectifying column[4] discharges water.

Alcohol-water mixtures are rectified to increase the strength of the alcohol component by virtue of the composition of the vapors being stronger in the more volatile constituent than the liquid from which these vapors arise. This is shown quantitatively by the curves of Fig. 2 where

---

[1] This is a general term applied to the result of any such fermentation, whether it results finally in industrial alcohol or the beverage beer, or whisky, or butanol and acetone.

[2] For an excellent series of diagrams of various types of distillation units, see KIRK and OTHMER, *op. cit.*, Vol. 1, pp. 264*ff.*

[3] REICH, Molasses Stillage, *Ind. Eng. Chem.*, **37**, 534 (1945).

[4] Further details with excellent pictures of a somewhat similar plant to that of Fig. 1 are given by REICH, Modern Molasses Distillery, *Chem. & Met. Eng.*, **41**, 64 (1934); ANON., Modern Molasses Distillery, *Chem. & Met. Eng.*, **46**, 365 (1939), pictured flow sheet.

the composition of the vapor in equilibrium with the liquid is on a horizontal line. However, alcohol cannot be made stronger by rectification than 95.6 per cent because, as can be seen from Fig. 2, water forms a binary constant boiling mixture of this composition which boils slightly lower than absolute or anhydrous alcohol. The principles shown here

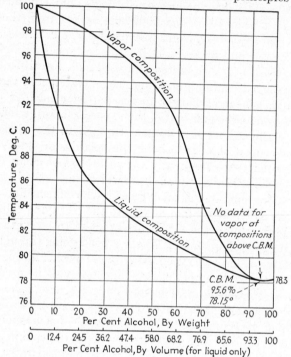

Fig. 2. Temperature vs. composition of vapor and liquid for alcohol—water at 760 mm.

are the basis of the strengthening of the more volatile constituent of any liquid mixture by distillation.

ABSOLUTE OR ANHYDROUS ALCOHOL[1]

Anhydrous alcohol was made by absorbing the 5 per cent of water present in 95 per cent industrial alcohol, using quicklime, with subsequent distillation. This process was expensive and, although it produced a very high quality of anhydrous alcohol, it has now been superseded largely by improved chemical engineering unit operations of distillation and extraction involving a third component. This has led to lower cost of dehydrating operations, mostly of a continuous nature using preferably all liquids or solutions, and has resulted in reducing the price of anhydrous alcohol to a figure only slightly in excess of the usual selling value of the

[1] This is practically 100 per cent ethyl alcohol and is frequently known as *absolute* alcohol but, as the absence of water is more notable than that of other impurities, the term *anhydrous* alcohol is preferred by some.

alcohol contents. These newer procedures involve improvements both in dehydrating agents and in the continuous columns used.

According to D. B. Keyes,[1]

. . . the basic principle of a dehydrating agent, when used in a fractionating column to produce anhydrous alcohol from wet alcohol, is the effect of the dehydrating agent on the partial pressure of the alcohol and of the water. In other words, there are two classes of dehydrating agents used in fractionating columns for this purpose. One depresses the partial pressure of the water more than the alcohol and the other depresses the partial pressure of the alcohol more than the water. In the first instance, the alcohol goes out of the top of the column, and in the second instance, out of the bottom. The dehydrating agent functions according to the above-mentioned ·principle. For example, lime, anhydrous calcium sulfate,[2] or any solid dehydrating agent will naturally come out of the bottom of the column and must carry the water with it, forcing the alcohol to come out of the top. Glycerine and ethylene glycol being high-boiling constituents have a tendency to be removed at the bottom of the column and are useful because they depress the partial pressure of the water more than the alcohol and, therefore, carry the water with them, permitting the alcohol to come out at the top of the column. Ether, benzene, ethyl acetate, toluene, hexane, or carbon tetrachloride,[3] on the other hand, are much more volatile constituents than the glycerine and glycol and also have a tendency to depress the partial pressure of the alcohol more than the water. Therefore, they are removed with the water at the top of the column and the anhydrous alcohol leaves at the bottom.

The water in 95 per cent alcohol is removed technically by either of two principal methods: (1) Dehydration by *distillation with a third component*[4] which forms a minimum constant boiling mixture in the system, boiling at a lower temperature than the 95 per cent alcohol (78.15°C.) or the water. Here (a) the minimum is a binary one, of which water-ethyl ether is an example,[5] or (b) the minimum is a ternary one of which alcohol-water-benzene is an example. In such instances anhydrous alcohol is obtained at the bottom of the distilling column, because its vapor pressure is relatively lower than that of the constant boiling mixture removing the water. (2) Dehydration by *countercurrent extraction*[6] usu-

[1] *Private communication; cf.* KEYES, The Manufacture of Anhydrous Ethyl Alcohol, *Ind. Eng. Chem.*, **21**, 998–1001 (1929); OTHMER, Partial Pressure Processes, *Ind. Eng. Chem.*, **33**, 1107 (1941).

[2] WALLIS, Absolute Alcohol, *Intern. Sugar J.*, **38**, 217–219 (1936). This process used a solid absorbent $CaSO_4$ changing to the hemihydrate.

[3] Other withdrawing agents employed are trichloro-ethylene or a petroleum fraction, or other liquid fairly insoluble in water and boiling in the range 30 to 120°C.

[4] This third component is frequently called a *dehydrating* or *withdrawing agent* or simply an *entrainer*.

[5] OTHMER and WENTWORTH, Absolute Alcohol, *Ind. Eng. Chem.*, **32**, 1588–1593 (1940). Here the water is removed overhead by ether, the system being under 100 lb. pressure.

[6] OTHMER and TRUEGER, Recovery of Acetone and Ethanol by Solvent Extraction, *Trans. Am. Inst. Chem. Engrs.*, **37**, 597–619 (1941).

ally also in a continuous column with a third component which depresses the vapor pressure of water more than it depresses the vapor pressure of alcohol, *e.g.*, glycerine, ethylene glycol, glycerine or glycol with dissolved salts, molten eutectic mixture of Na and K acetates. Anhydrous alcohol comes out the top of the extraction column.[1]

The basic principle of the process using benzene as a withdrawing agent is illustrated[2] by Fig. 3. There are three binary minimum constant

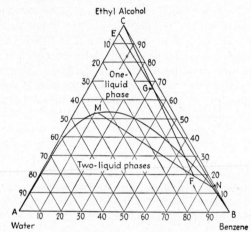

Fig. 3. Ternary diagram of liquid system. Water-alcohol-benzene.

boiling mixtures in the system, two homogeneous ones and one heterogeneous one (between water and benzene), and a ternary minimum constant boiling mixture which is the lowest-boiling composition in the system, boiling at 64.85°C.

In Fig. 3 the composition of the ternary[3] minimum constant boiling mixture is represented by point *F*. In order that the removal of the c.b.m. from the starting mixture shall leave anhydrous alcohol in the still, the starting composition must lie on the straight line *CF*. If the starting mixture is to be made up by adding benzene to 95 per cent alcohol, the starting composition must also lie on the line *EB*. Therefore, the intersection *G* represents the starting composition. If enough benzene is added to 95 per cent alcohol to bring the total composition to point *G*, continuous distillation gives the ternary constant boiling mixture (boiling point, 64.85°C.) at the top of the column and absolute alcohol (boiling point, 78.3°C.) at the bottom of the column in a simple distillation.

---

[1] The use of a solid dehydrating agent, such as quicklime or calcium sulfate, may be looked upon as an extreme case of this method, though usually run in a discontinuous manner because of the solid involved.

[2] A somewhat similar procedure is the ether pressure system of OTHMER and WENTWORTH, *op. cit.*

[3] See PERRY, *op. cit.*, pp. 718*ff.*, for triangular phase diagrams.

An important[1] feature of the process is the separation of the condensate into two liquid layers, represented in Fig. 3 by points M and N.

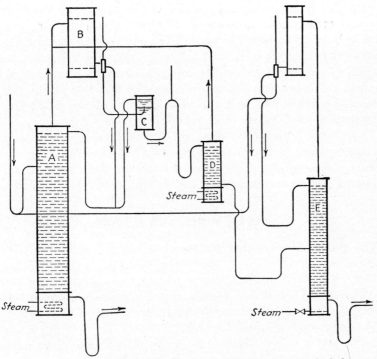

Fig. 4. Manufacture of absolute alcohol from 95 per cent alcohol.

The ratio of the top layer N to the bottom layer M is equal to MF/FN. The compositions involved are

Ternary distillate:
  18.5 per cent alcohol.
   7.4 per cent water.
  74.1 per cent benzene.
Top layer of condensate at 20°C., representing 84 per cent by volume:
  14.5 per cent alcohol.
   1 per cent water.
  84.5 per cent benzene.
Bottom layer of condensate at 20°C., representing 16 per cent by volume:
  53 per cent alcohol.
  36 per cent water.
  11 per cent benzene.

Figure 4 illustrates how this process functions. The 95 per cent alcohol with the requisite amount of benzene[2] is introduced continuously into

---

[1] GUINOT and CLARK, Azeotropic Distillation in Industry, *Trans. Inst. Chem. Engrs.* (London), **16**, 189 (1938).

[2] This withdrawing agent is used over and over again with a loss that should not exceed 0.05 per cent on the volume of the anhydrous alcohol produced.

column A heated at the bottom by a closed steam coil. The ternary goes overhead through the condenser B to the separator and decanter C, or is partly returned as reflux. From the decanter, the top layer, rich in withdrawing agent, is returned to the main column A and the lower layer, rich in water, is run to the smaller column D, from which the overhead as the ternary c.b.m. is passed to the main condenser B. From the bottom of the small column D, aqueous alcohol is obtained which is rectified to 95 per cent alcohol in column E and returned to the main column. From the base of E the water flows to the sewer. The product, anhydrous alcohol, passes from base of main column A.

These same principles of distillation in multicomponent systems, involving constant boiling mixtures, are used for dehydrating other organic liquids such as propyl alcohol and for removing the water formed in sulfonations (benzene-sulfonic acid) and esterifications (ethyl acetate).[1]

BEERS, WINES, AND LIQUORS

The making of fermented beverages was discovered by primitive man and has been practiced as an art for thousands of years. Within the past century and a half this has become a highly developed science. As Muspratt writes, "There is no department of the arts and manufactures where chemistry has exerted a more decided influence than in brewing." But E. A. Siebel adds to this, "A modern brewer has to be an engineer, a chemist, and a bacteriologist." In common with other food industries, the factors of taste, odor, yes, and of almost individual preference exist, to force the manufacturer to exert the greatest of skill and experience in producing palatable beverages of great variety. In the last analysis, the criterion of quality, with all the arts of modern science, still lies in the human sensory organs of taste, smell, and sight.

Uses and Economics. As Table 4 indicates, many millions of barrels of alcoholic beverages are manufactured in the United States each year.

Raw Materials. Grains and fruits supplying carbohydrates are the basic raw materials. The variety of grains and fruits employed is wide, changing from country to country or from beverage to beverage. Russia ferments potatoes and by distillation obtains vodka; similar treatment of the sap of the maguey in Mexico yields pulque; but the world's chief raw materials for fermentations are the cereals, corn, barley, and rice, together with the grape.

Making of Beer.[2] Beer and allied products are beverages of low alcoholic content (2 to 7 per cent) made by brewing various cereals with hops, usually added to impart a more or less bitter taste, followed by

---

[1] GUINOT and CLARK, op. cit.; OTHMER, op. cit.

[2] SHEARON and WEISSLER, Brewing, *Ind. Eng. Chem.*, **43**, 1262 (1951), many excellent pictures, tables, and diagrams.

fermentation. The cereals employed are called *brewers' grains* and are barley, malted to develop the necessary enzymes and the desired flavor, as well as malt adjuncts: flaked rice, oats, and corn, with wheat used in Germany and rice and millet in China. Brewing sugars and sirups (corn sugar or glucose) and yeast complete the raw materials. For beer the most important cereal is barley, which is converted into malt by partial germination.[1]

TABLE 4. UNITED STATES PRODUCTION OF ALCOHOLIC BEVERAGES, 1939, 1950, AND 1954

Beverage	1939	1950	1954
Still wines, wine gal................	231,986,000	297,857,104	117,133,731
Sparkling wines, half pt.............	6,634,000	21,225,108	31,032,920
Rectified spirits and wines, proof gal..	43,401,000	107,951,272	90,410,552
Fermented malt liquors, bbl.........	53,871,000	88,807,075	85,747,439
Cereal beverages, bbl..............	63,000	45,211	27,473

NOTE: "bbl." contains 31 gal.

The barley is steeped in cold water and spread out on floors, or in special compartments, and regularly turned over for from 5 to 8 days, the layers being gradually thinned as the germination proceeds. At the proper time, when the enzymes are formed, the growth is arrested by heat. During the growth, oxygen is absorbed, carbon dioxide given off, and the enzyme, diastase, formed. This latter is the biological catalyst that changes the dissolved starch into the disaccharide maltose which, after transformation into the monosaccharide, glucose, by the maltase enzyme, is directly fermentable by yeast.

The flow sheet for beer on Fig. 5 may be divided into three groups of procedures: (1) brewing of the mash through to the cooled hopped wort, (2) fermentation, and (3) storage, finishing, and packaging for market. *Mashing* is the extraction of the valuable constituents of malt, malt adjuncts, and sugars by macerating the ground materials with water treated to prevent too high pH, which would tend to make a dark beer. In America, 35 to 38 lb. of barley malt and 12 to 14 lb. of malt adjuncts or unmalted cereals (rice, corn, or carbohydrate) are used per U.S. barrel of 31 gal. These are flaked or ground on rolls. This mixture is added to water in the proportion of 1,000 lb. per 7.5 to 9 bbl. of water. The materials so treated, the converter mash, are heated in the pressure cooker in order to convert insoluble starch into soluble starch, and the soluble malt starch into dextrin and malt sugars. The resulting boiling cooker

---

[1] See ANON., Brewing of Lager Beer, *Chem. & Met. Eng.*, **49** (7), 112 (1942), for pictured flow sheet; *cf.* KIRK and OTHMER, *op. cit.*, Vol. 2, pp. 384–413; Staff Industry Report, Beer, *Ind. Eng. Chem.*, **43**, 1264 (1951).

mash, mixed with the rest of the malt in the mash tub, raising the temperature to 168°F., is used to prepare the brewers' *wort*.[1] This is carried out in the mash tun. After all the required ingredients have been dissolved from the brewing materials, the entire mash is run from the mash tun to the lauter or straining tub, where the wort is separated from the insoluble spent grains through a slotted false bottom and run into the copper wort cooker. For complete recovery of all substances in solution,

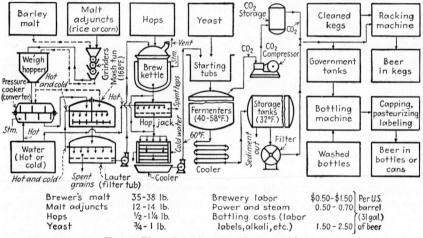

Brewer's malt	35-38 lb.	Brewery labor	$0.50-$1.50	Per U.S.
Malt adjuncts	12-14 lb.	Power and steam	0.50-0.70	barrel
Hops	½-1¼ lb.	Bottling costs (labor		(31 gal.)
Yeast	¾-1 lb.	labels, alkali, etc.)	1.50-2.50	of beer

Fig. 5. Flow sheet for manufacture of beer.

a spray of decarbonated water at 165°F. is rained through the grains. This is called *sparging*.

The wort is cooked for approximately 3 hr., during two of which it is in contact with hops. The purpose of boiling is to concentrate the wort to the desired strength, to sterilize it (15 min.) and destroy all the enzymes, to coagulate certain proteins by heat (180°F.), to modify the malty smell of the wort, and to extract the tannin and aroma from the hops which are added during the cooking process. At the end of the 3 hr., the spent hops are separated from the boiling wort very quickly through a false bottom in the hop jack or strainer underneath the copper cooker. Since the spent hops retain 3 bbl. of wort per 100 lb. of hops, they should also be sparged. The wort is then ready to be cooled.

The cooling step is not only to reduce the temperature but also to allow the wort to absorb enough air to facilitate the start of the fermentation. In addition, the protein and hop resins are precipitated. The hot wort may be first cooled to about 150 to 160°F. in a large shallow cooler

---

[1] The wort is the liquid resulting from the mashing process, *i.e.*, the extracting and solubilizing of the malt and malt adjuncts. Wort composition varies from 17 to 24 per cent solids by weight for the first wort, to approximately 1 per cent solids for the last wort removed by the sparge water.

where certain of the resins precipitate. The wort is then run over the horizontal, brine-cooled copper tubes of the open Baudelot cooler, where aeration also takes place. Slight concentration, due to evaporation, occurs. This operation is performed under controlled conditions to prevent contamination by *wild* yeasts. Frequently, sterilized air is used.

The cooled wort is mixed with selected yeasts in the line leading to the starting tubs, between ¾ and 1 lb. of yeast being used per barrel of beer. The initial *fermentation* temperature is 40 to 43°F. but, as the fermentation proceeds, the temperature rises to 58°F. This is easily explained by the fact that the conversion of the sugar to CO_2 and ethyl alcohol, by the enzymes of the yeast, generates 280 B.t.u. per lb. of maltose converted.[1] The temperature is partly controlled by attemperators inserted in the fermentors. The mixture is skimmed to remove the foreign substances that the evolved carbon dioxide brings to the top. Thus it is quite evident that a steady evolution of gas is necessary to cleanse the beer properly. The CO_2 evolved is collected by using closed fermentors and stored under 250 lb. pressure for subsequent use in carbonating beer.

The yeast gradually settles to the bottom of the tub, so that at the end of 7 to 10 days the fermented beer is ready to be vatted. The liquid is very opalescent in appearance, under a cover of foam. As the beer leaves the fermenting cellar, it contains in suspension hop resins, insoluble nitrogenous substances, and a fair amount of yeast.

The beer is cooled to 32°F. and stored in the cellar for 3 to 6 weeks at this temperature. During this period, clarification, separation, and precipitation of hard resins and improvement in palatability (mellowing) occur. At the end of the period the beer is carbonated[2] and pumped through a pulp filter with or without such nontaste-imparting filter aids as asbestos fiber. In the United States, public demand favors a brilliant beverage.[3] As a result, the beer is sometimes refiltered through cotton pulp, keeping carbon dioxide on the entire system. About 97 bbl. of beer are produced per 100 bbl. of wort in the starting tubs. After bottling, the beer is pasteurized at 140°F.

Making of Wine. Wine[4] has been made for several thousand years by fermentation of the juice of the grape. Like other fermentations, many of the primitive procedures have been supplanted by improved science and engineering, to reduce costs and to make more uniform products.

[1] ROSENBUSCH, Brewing—The Present Situation, *Refrig. Eng.*, **26**, 251–253 (1933).

[2] The carbon dioxide should be kept free from air which would interfere with the stability and quality of the beer. The gas is pumped in close to 32°F. and amounts to between 0.36 and 0.45 per cent of the weight of the beer.

[3] Max and Leo Wallerstein have invented a process for the production of haze-free chillproof beers by adding selective proteolytic enzymes to beer right after fermentation to split the proteins and thus delay or prevent the formation of the protein-tannin haze.

[4] HULL, *et al.*, Modern Winemaking, *Ind. Eng. Chem.*, **43**, 2180 (1951).

But now, as always, the quality of the product is largely related to grape, soil, and sun, resulting in variation in flavor, bouquet, and aroma. The color depends largely upon the nature of the grapes and whether the skins are pressed out before fermentation.

Wines are classified as natural (alcohol 7 to 14 per cent), fortified (alcohol 14 to 30 per cent), sweet or dry, still or sparkling. The fortified wines have alcohol or brandy added. In the sweet wines, some of the sugar remains.

For the manufacture of dry red wine, red or black grapes are necessary. The grapes are run through a crusher which macerates them but does not crush the seeds, and also removes part of the stems. The resulting pulp, or *must*, is pumped into 3,000- to 10,000-gal. tanks,[1] where sulfurous acid is added to check the growth of wild yeast. An active culture of selected and cultivated yeast equal to 3 to 5 per cent of the volume of juice is added. During fermentation, the temperature rises, so that cooling coils are necessary to maintain a temperature of 85°F. The CO_2 evolved carries the stems and seeds to the top, which is partly prevented by a grating floated in the vat. This allows an extraction of the color and the tannin from the skins and seeds. When the fermentation slows up, the juice is pumped out of the bottom of the vat, back over the top. The wine is finally run into closed tanks in the storage cellar where, during a period of 2 or 3 weeks, the yeast ferments the remainder of the sugar. The wine is given a cellar treatment to clear it, improve the taste, and decrease the time of aging. During this treatment the wine is first allowed to remain quiet for 6 weeks to remove part of the matter in suspension, then racked for clarification.[2] Bentonite, or other diatomaceous earth, may be used for clearing, 2 to 16 lb. being stirred into every 1,000 gal. of wine. An insoluble precipitate with the tannin is also formed. Extra tannin may also be added, the wine racked, filtered through diatomaceous earth, asbestos, or paper pulp. The wine is corrected to commercial standards by blending it with other wines and by the addition of sugar, acids, or tannins. It is standard procedure to chill some wines for removal of argols or crude potassium acid tartrate which is recovered and constitutes the commercial source of tartaric acid and its compounds. This treatment also gives a more stable finished wine. By quick aging methods it is possible to put out a good sweet wine in 4 months. These methods include pasteurization, refrigeration, sunlight, ultraviolet light, ozone, agitation, and aeration. The wine may be held at about freezing for 3 weeks to a

[1] In many of the modern American wineries these tanks are even larger and are constructed of concrete.

[2] During this and following periods the new wine undergoes a complicated series of reactions, resulting in the removal of undesired constituents and the development of the aroma, bouquet, and taste. Oxidation takes place, as well as precipitation of proteins and argols, and esterification of the acids by alcohols.

nonth, and a small amount of oxygen gas bubbled in. Then the wine is
·acked, clarified, and further filtered in the usual manner.

Distilled Liquors. Various fermented products, upon distillation and
ιging, yield the distilled liquors. Figure 6 shows the flow sheet for whisky
ιnd gin. Brandy is distilled from wine or from the *marc*, which is the
pulp left by racking or straining. By making a beer[1] from a grain mixture
:ontaining at least 51 per cent of corn and distilling and aging it, bourbon
whisky is yielded. Similarly rye whisky must have started with 51 per
:ent of rye in the grain to be mashed and fermented. By inspecting the

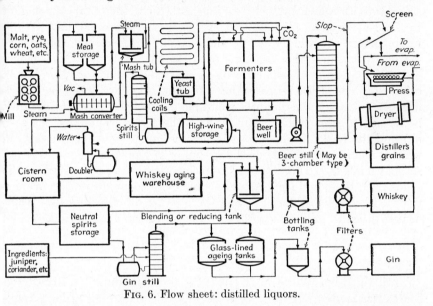

FIG. 6. Flow sheet: distilled liquors.

flow sheet of Fig. 6 in the light of Figs. 1 and 5, and the description
accompanying them, the procedures of Fig. 6 for distilled liquors will be
clear. The equipment,[2] up to the stills, in modern liquor plants is of steel,
with the stills of copper. By law, the aging of bourbon or rye whisky of
claimed age must take place in charred new white-oak barrels of approximately 50 gal. These are kept in bonded warehouses at 65 to 85°F. and at
a preferred humidity of 65 to 70 per cent for 1 to 5 years usually. During
this time an evaporation of the contents takes place, largely through the
ends of the barrel staves. By reason of a more rapid capillary travel and
osmosis of the smaller water molecules in comparison to alcohol molecules,

[1] The yeast in this fermentation is grown in the presence of lactic acid to ensure
proper strain and to secure the desired quality of the product (whisky).

[2] OWEN, Modern Distillery Design, *Sugar*, **37** (3), 26–30 (1942). In *Chem. & Met.
Eng.*, **49** (11), 126 (1942) is a pictured flow sheet of a grain distillery; STALLINGS,
WILLKIE, and HERMAN, Chemical Engineering Developments in a Grain Distillery,
Am. Inst. Chem. Engrs., **38**, 791 (1942).

an increase in percentage of alcohol is found in the barrel contents. The government shrinkage allowance is approximately 8 per cent the first year, 4 per cent the second year, 4 per cent the third year, and 3 per cent the fourth year. If the shrinkages are exceeded (and this is often the case), the manufacturer must pay a tax on the excess but, with the best cooperages under the best conditions, these allowances can just be met. The distillate from the spirit still is under 160 proof and is subsequently diluted upon barreling to 100 to 110 proof. It is *not* pure alcohol but contains small amounts of many different constituents, generally classed together as *congenerics*, which by their reaction with each other or the alcohol, or by their absorption, all catalyzed by the char of the wood, help greatly in imparting the whisky flavor and bouquet.[1] The aging whisky also extracts color and other products from the charred white oak. Changes of a like nature occur similarly on aging brandy and rum. Here, as in other divisions of the fermentation industries, skill and scientific knowledge aid in the production of a palatable product. By law, whisky must be fermented from whole grains, so that the germs (containing the corn oil) and the husks are in suspension in the liquor from the beer still in whisky manufacture. This discharge liquor is known as *slop* or *stillage*. As shown in Fig. 6, this is treated to recover the values by separating the solids from the liquid slop. After vacuum evaporation of the liquid[2] portion, it is added to the solids, and the mixture dried in rotating steam-heated driers to produce *distillers' grains*,[3] a valuable cattle feed.

BUTYL ALCOHOL AND ACETONE

Until the First World War, all the acetone produced in the United States was made by the dry distillation of calcium acetate from pyroligneous acid. Under the stimulus of the wartime demand for acetone for the manufacture of double-base smokeless powder the important process became that developed by Chaim Weizmann[4] for the fermentation of starch-containing grains to butyl alcohol and acetone. The Commercial Solvents Corporation was organized, and it built and operated two plants in the corn belt to ferment corn using *Clostridium acetobutylicum* bacteria. However, this fermentation gave 2 parts of butyl alcohol to 1 part of

[1] LIEBMANN and SCHERL, Changes in Whisky while Maturing, *Ind. Eng. Chem.*, **41**, 534 (1949).

[2] *Cf.* BORUFF, *et al.*, Vitamin Content of Distillers' By-products, *Ind. Eng. Chem.*, **32**, 123 (1940).

[3] For a pictured flow sheet, see Recovery of Grain Alcohol By-products, *Chem. & Met. Eng.*, **52** (6), 130 (1945); BORUFF, Industrial Wastes: Recovery of Fermentation Residues as Feeds, *Ind. Eng. Chem.*, **39**, 602 (1947).

[4] Brit. Pat. 4845 (1915); U.S. Pat. 1315585 (1919). Weizmann used much of his large royalties from this process to help finance his interest in the Zionist movement of which he became the head in 1920.

acetone and until the development of the fast-drying nitrocellulose lacquers particularly for the automotive industry, there was virtually no market for the butyl alcohol produced. Then the conditions became reversed with butyl alcohol becoming the important commodity and acetone the by-product. This better sale of first one product and then another is characteristic of industries in the chemical field, where more than one substance results from a process and reflects the changing demand that accompanies a growing and dynamic industry.

With the advent of the manufacture of butyl alcohol and especially of acetone by chemical processes, competition forced the abandonment of corn in favor of the lower-priced by-product molasses for the monosaccharide raw material for fermentation after new cultures were found which would work well on the molasses, since the Weizmann starch-fermenting bacteria were not satisfactory. These new cultures also gave a more desirable solvent ratio (approximately 3 parts of butyl alcohol to 1 of acetone). Since the early 1930's the molasses process has been in use, except during certain periods of the Second World War when the scarcity of molasses made it necessary for producers in the United States to return temporarily to grain. Higher costs for molasses and grain now have given the synthetic processes dominant positions.

Uses and Economics. The production of normal butyl alcohol and of acetone amounted to somewhat over 194,000,000 and 478,000,000 lb., respectively, during 1954. It is estimated that 40 per cent of the butyl alcohol and 4 per cent of the acetone is produced by fermentation. About 70 per cent of n-butyl alcohol enters directly or indirectly into lacquer solvents. A percentage breakdown of the end use of acetone is approximately as follows: cellulose acetate, 50; acetylene (solvent), 5; chemicals, 15; paint, varnish, and lacquer, 12; drugs, 5; and miscellaneous, 15.

Reactions. The action of the bacteria on starch has been very carefully studied and Fig. 7 gives the best hypothesis as to the course of this fermentation.

Manufacturing Procedure. The flow sheet on Fig. 8 illustrates the fermentation[1] of either starch or sugar, furnishing butanol, acetone, and other products. Most of the apparatus outlined in this flow sheet is made of steel except the stills which are constructed of copper. The process, when starting from corn, goes through the usual operation of separating the corn oil, the germ meal, and the husks from the starch, which is made into mash by mixing with hot water and cooking. The steam cooking not only disperses the starch into a so-called *soluble* form available for

[1] GABRIEL, Butanol Fermentation Process, *Ind. Eng. Chem.*, **20**, 1063 (1928); GABRIEL and CRAWFORD, Development of the Butyl-acetone Fermentation Industry, *Ind. Eng. Chem.*, **22**, 1163 (1930); McCUTCHAN and HICKEY, The Butanol-acetone Fermentations, Chap. 9 in UNDERKOFLER, editor, "Commercial Fermentations," Chemical Publishing Company, Inc., New York, 1952.

the bacteria to act on but at the same time sterilizes it so that the unwanted microorganisms are killed. At one time, the Terre Haute factory became contaminated with other bacteria which grew and multiplied even more rapidly than the Weizmann bacteria, which divided and doubled in 20 min. Thus the available food was consumed by the invaders, and the yield of solvents greatly decreased. Now, complete sterilization following each batch fermentation, coupled with exact selection and

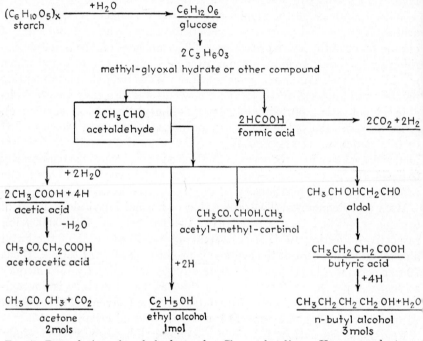

$$(C_6 H_{10} O_5)_x \xrightarrow{+H_2O} C_6 H_{12} O_6$$
starch   glucose

$$2 C_3 H_6 O_3$$
methyl-glyoxal hydrate or other compound

$2 CH_3 CHO$ — acetaldehyde

$2 HCOOH \longrightarrow 2 CO_2 + 2H_2$
formic acid

$+2H_2O$

$2 CH_3 COOH + 4H$ — acetic acid
$-H_2O$
$CH_3 CO.CH_2 COOH$ — acetoacetic acid
$CH_3 CO. CH_3 + CO_2$
acetone
2 mols

$CH_3 CO. CHOH.CH_3$ — acetyl-methyl-carbinol
$+2H$
$C_2 H_5 OH$
ethyl alcohol
1 mol

$CH_3 CH OHCH_2 CHO$ — aldol
$CH_3CH_2 CH_2 COOH$ — butyric acid
$+4H$
$CH_3CH_2 CH_2 CH_2 OH + H_2O$
n-butyl alcohol
3 mols

FIG. 7. Degradation of carbohydrates by *Cl. acetobutylicum*. Known products are underlined. (*After Peterson and Fred.*)

cultivation of only the selected microorganisms, ensures the desired fermentation.

The respective desired bacteria are carefully cultured in the laboratory by skilled and experienced bacteriologists who, after they have secured a pure culture, inoculate the sterile mash in increasing quantities from a test tube up to the 800-gal. seed tank, as shown in Fig. 8. In the meanwhile the main mash has been prepared and pumped into the 50,000-gal. fermentor through a heat exchanger, lowering the temperature to 98°F. for the starch mash, and to about 85°F. for the molasses mash. The fermentation proceeds with the liberation of the hydrogen and carbon dioxide (60 per cent CO_2 and 40 per cent H_2), which are used for the manufacture of methanol or burned for fuel.

After 36 to 40 hr. the fermentation is ended and the *beer*, containing around 1.5 to 2.5 per cent solvents, is pumped to the beer still. The yield of the neutral solvents is 30 per cent and up, on the weight of the starch from corn or of the fermentable sugar in molasses. In addition there is evolved about 1.5 times the weight of solvents in gases (60 per cent CO_2 and 40 per cent H_2 by volume).

The beer still consists of a continuous column containing plates, one on top of the other, yielding as vapor overhead, 50 per cent mixed solvents. The discharge from the beer still is known as *distillers' slop* or *stillage* and, as is true of a number of these fermentation operations, is a

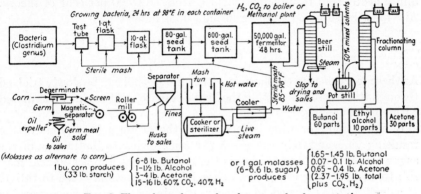

FIG. 8. Flow sheet: butanol and acetone by fermentation.

solution containing a very considerable quantity of proteins, fats, and carbohydrates, of value in animal feeds.

It has been discovered[1] that the butyl-alcohol-producing bacteria in their life cycle synthesize vitamins. The vitamins thus produced are riboflavin (vitamin B_2) and other factors of the original B complex. A riboflavin-containing feed is being manufactured from the butyl fermentation process.

The 50 per cent mixed solvents obtained from the beer still are rectified through careful fractionation, yielding pure butanol, 95 per cent ethyl alcohol, and acetone. This butanol is the normal butyl alcohol. This fractionation furnishes initially fractions rich in acetone, alcohol, and butanol. Careful rectification yields the pure products. The fraction rich in butanol[2] is a mixture of 85 per cent butanol and 15 per cent water (by volume) boiling at 92.25°C. at 760 mm. of Hg. This is introduced into a column still where the take-off is first an azeotrope, containing 37.3 per cent of water by weight. This is condensed, whereupon it separates into two layers: an upper one with some water and a lower one with 4 per cent butanol and 96 per cent water. (This lower layer so rich in water is returned to the beer still.) The upper layer is run back to the

[1] MINER, U.S. Pat. 2202161 (1940).
[2] *Cf.* STEVENS, U.S. Pat. 1394232 (1921).

column still. The net result is a constant withdrawing of water with an enhancement of the butanol percentage up to any desired figure.

VINEGAR AND ACETIC ACID

The aerobic bacterial (*Acetobacter aceti* or *Bacterium aceti*) oxidation of alcohol to dilute acetic[1] acid (8 per cent) is another ancient procedure, furnishing vinegar, a flavored acetic acid solution, fermented from wine, cider, malt, or dilute alcohol. If a pure dilute alcohol is fermented, pure dilute acetic acid results. The yield is from 80 to 90 per cent of theory. Air[2] must be supplied as these formulations indicate:

$$2C_2H_5OH + O_2 \rightarrow 2CH_3CHO + 2H_2O$$
$$2CH_3CHO + O_2 \rightarrow 2CH_3COOH$$

As these reactions are exothermic, either the alcohol can be slowly trickled through the apparatus, letting the heat dissipate, or it can be recirculated with special cooling.

If cider, malt, or wine is fermented, the acetic acid content of the resulting vinegar rarely exceeds 5 per cent, owing to limitations of the sugar content; if dilute alcohol is the raw material, the acetic acid may rise to 12 or 14 per cent, at which acidity the bacteria cease to thrive. If a fruit juice is turned to vinegar, certain esters are formed varying with the raw material, thus imparting a characteristic flavor.

The ancient process consisted in letting alcoholic products like wine or cider stand around in contact with air until the wine or cider *turned to vinegar*. This was a slow procedure, taking many months. The modern *quick* vinegar process, as commercially carried out, trickles the diluted alcohol, usually mixed with vinegar, down tall wooden tanks with false bottoms (20 ft. high by 10 ft. in diameter) packed with beechwood shavings or coke on which the bacteria find lodgment commonly as *mother of vinegar*. The acetic bacteria secrete an enzyme which causes the reaction. Air rises up through the tank.[3] This takes a week or so, but the production amounts to 10 to 16 gal. of 9 to 10 per cent spirit vinegar per 24 hr. from a 200-cu. ft. generator. Acid mashes are favorable to the acetic fermentation and oxidize rapidly; so it is customary to charge the generators with a mixture of vinegar and the alcoholic raw material. When 10 per cent (acetic acid) spirit vinegars are wanted, a mix of 8.2 per cent acetic and 2 to 2.6 per cent by volume of alcohol is charged.[4] This is made by mixing

---

[1] For a description of the largest factory engaged in this process, *cf.* HERRICK and MAY, *Chem. & Met. Eng.*, **42**, 142 (1935).

[2] Too much air will cause losses due to further and undesired oxidation.

[3] By keeping cider or wine casks full, so that no air is present, the vinegar formation cannot take place. Likewise, the fortified wines (above 15 per cent) have so much alcohol present that the *A. aceti* cannot function, so these wines *stay sweet*.

[4] HASSACK, Vinegar Manufacture in the United States, *Chem. Age*, **29**, 105 (1921).

finished vinegar with dilute alcohol or low wines. If a cider vinegar is desired of 5 to 5.5 per cent acetic content, there is fed a mix containing 3.4 to 3.75 per cent acid and 2 to 2.6 per cent alcohol by volume.

Modern chemical engineering has improved the *quick process* by designing apparatus using pumps to circulate rapidly the mash over the packing, and with cooling in the recirculation to control the temperature low enough for favorable action of the acetic bacteria, or with special devices to ensure an adequate air supply.[1] Such designs permit the use of large generators, even up to 10,000 gal. capacity. In line with studies on other fermentations, it has been found that the acetic bacteria also need, for best conversion of alcohol to acetic acid, the proper minor foods or *nutrients* that contain sugars and the necessary inorganic salts, such as phosphates. Commercially, dilute acetic acid (8 to 10 per cent) is made this way. The process is economical if the dilute acetic can be utilized.

CITRIC ACID

Citric acid is one of our widely employed organic acids, its production amounting to around 40,000,000 or 50,000,000 lb. Its major use is as an acidulant in carbonated beverages, jams, jellies, and other foodstuffs. Another large outlet is in the medicinal field, including the manufacture of citrates and effervescent salts. Industrial uses, relatively small, include citric acid as a sequestering agent and acetyl tributyl citrate, a vinyl resin plasticizer.

Except for small amounts (less than 7 per cent) produced from citrus fruit wastes, citric acid is manufactured[2] by aerobic fermentation of crude sugar by a special strain of *Aspergillus niger* following the classical researches by Currie.[3]

The over-all reaction is:

$$\underset{\text{Sucrose}}{C_{12}H_{22}O_{11}} + H_2O + 3O_2 \rightarrow \underset{\text{Citric acid}}{2C_6H_8O_7} + 4H_2O$$

The fermentation changes sugar, a straight-chain compound, into a branched chain.

In the tray process for citric acid, air is circulated for 9 to 12 days over hundreds of shallow pure-aluminum trays (approximately 43 by 43 by 2 in.) filled with a sugar solution. These trays are placed a few inches above each other in a closed cabinet provided with facilities for steriliza-

[1] FRINGS, Manufacture of Vinegar, U.S. Pat. 1880381 (1932); OWENS, Vinegar Generator, U.S. Pat. 2089412 (1937); HANSEN, Making Vinegar by the Frings Process, *Food Industries*, **7**, 277 (1935).

[2] See KIRK and OTHMER, *op. cit.*, Vol. 4, p. 12; for a more detailed presentation of the following reaction and other features of citric acid made by fermentation, see Vol. 6, pp. 364ff.

[3] CURRIE, The Citric Acid Fermentation of *A. niger*, *J. Biol. Chem.*, **31**, 15 (1917).

tion, ventilation, and temperature control. Because of the expense to sterilize, fill, handle, and empty the thousands of trays needed for large-scale production, submerged fermentation was developed.

The essential steps of the submerged process[1] are probably as follows: A medium is prepared from decationized molasses feedstock, decationized well water, and the following nutrients—ammonium carbonate, monobasic potassium phosphate, and magnesium sulfate. The addition of 500 p.p.m. of morpholine to the medium is claimed to increase the efficiency of the fermentation, to stimulate spore germination, and to have a stabilizing effect on the physiological characteristics of the fungus, thereby giving better results. The pH of the medium is adjusted to 2.5 with hydrochloric acid followed by 10 lb. steam sterilization for 20 min. The fermentation is carried out by a special strain of A. niger with sterile air bubbled through for both aeration and agitation for approximately 4 to 9 days at 30 to 32°C. Yields based on the initial sugar are claimed to be approximately 80 per cent.

The citric acid is probably recovered from the converted broth by precipitation of the acid by calcium or barium hydroxide followed by filtering or centrifuging and washing. The citric acid is liberated from the salt by sulfuric acid and is crystallized from the filtered, concentrated liquor.

This development of a process for the production of citric acid in a submerged fermentation is an outstanding recent accomplishment.

LACTIC ACID

Lactic acid, 2-hydroxypropionic acid, is one of the oldest known organic acids. It is the primary acid constituent of sour milk, from whence it derives its name, having been formed by the fermentation of milk sugar (lactose) by Streptococcus lactis. Commercially, lactic acid is manufactured by the controlled fermentation of the hexose sugars from molasses, corn, or milk. Lactates have been made by synthetic methods from acetaldehyde and other starting materials, but such methods are more expensive than fermentation procedures. It has only been since 1930 that lactic acid has been produced commercially from the milk by-product whey. About 12 billion pounds of whey are produced annually from cheese or casein production, but less than 2.5 billion pounds is employed in food, feeds, or the production of lactose, much of the rest being wasted or fed to animals.

Of the 5,000,000 lb. (100 per cent) of lactic acid[2] consumed annually,

[1] U.S. Pats. 2476159 (1949), 2492667 (1949), and 2492673 (1949); cf. WAKSMAN and KAROW, Production of Citric Acid in Submerged Culture, Ind. Eng. Chem., 39, 821 (1947).

[2] PECKHAM, The Commercial Manufacture of Lactic Acid, Chem. Eng. News, 22, 440 (1944); WHITTIER and WEBB, "Byproducts from Milk," Reinhold Publishing Corporation, New York, 1950.

the technical grade accounts for 40 per cent and is employed mainly for deliming leather in tanning. Edible grades are used primarily as acidulants for a number of foods and beverages. The small amount of lactic acid remaining is converted into plastics,[1] solvents, and certain other chemical products. The U.S.P. grade is an old, well-established standard pharmaceutical.

The general course of the fermentation reactions may be expressed as

$$C_{12}H_{22}O_{11} + H_2O \rightarrow C_6H_{12}O_6 + C_6H_{12}O_6$$

| Sucrose or lactose | Glucose | Fructose or galactose |

$$C_6H_{12}O_6 \rightarrow 2CH_3CHOHCOOH$$

The commercial acid is the inactive or racemic form, consisting of a mixture of the dextro and levo forms, usually in equal proportions, and it is therefore inactive.

The procedure consists in fermenting a mash of a carbohydrate substrate together with suitable nutrients in the presence of an excess of calcium carbonate. The lactic acid as formed reacts with the $CaCO_3$, producing calcium lactate and carbon dioxide, thus preventing the pH (general range 5.0 to 6.0) in the fermentation from becoming so low as to inhibit bacterial action. The thermophilic[2] type of *Lactobacillus delbrückii* is generally preferred. This eliminates most contamination problems and permits the use of a medium which is pasteurized rather than sterilized. However, this bacterium will not ferment the lactose or milk sugar where a mixed culture of *L. bulgaricus* and a mycoderm are necessary.[3]

After the fermentation is completed, where yields of 85 per cent lactic acid based on the weight of the fermentable sugar are normal, the calcium lactate is decomposed by sulfuric acid to regenerate the lactic acid. Technical lactic acid is manufactured from the calcium lactate as produced in fermentation or after decolorization. The finer grades are made from calcium lactate that has been crystallized at least once; for making acids from 35 to 50 per cent concentration, the "building up" operation is used. Here crystals of calcium lactate are dissolved in the lactic acid, sulfuric acid added as before, and the $CaSO_4 \cdot 2H_2O$ removed by filtration. Usually two of these operations are necessary for the 50 per cent grade. For stronger acids, a vacuum concentration in stainless-steel or glass-lined evaporators is needed.

[1] FISHER and FILACHIONE, "Lactic Acid—Versatile Intermediate for the Chemical Industry," AIC-178, U.S. Department of Agriculture, Eastern Regional Research Laboratory, May, 1948.

[2] Thermophilic is the term given to high-temperature-thriving bacteria. The general strain used here exhibits optimum activity at 50°C.

[3] See WHITTIER and WEBB, *op. cit.*, pp. 31–41 for a detailed presentation of lactic acid from whey including a flow sheet.

ANTIBIOTICS

The term *antibiotic* is a broad one which has been defined by Waksman[1] as "a substance produced by microorganisms, which has the capacity of inhibiting the growth and even of destroying other microorganisms." Approximately 150 substances, at present, come under this classification,[2] but only a few are accepted by the medical profession as being clinically useful. Penicillin, streptomycin and its derivative, dihydrostreptomycin, head the list which also includes bacitracin, chloramphenicol, aureomycin, and terramycin.

History. It is possible that the field of therapeutic antibiotics was opened by the studies of Pasteur and Joubert in 1877. However, most of the materials proved too toxic for human use. In 1929, Sir Alexander Fleming observed that the growth of *Staphylococcus aureus* on an agar plate was arrested by a mold which had contaminated the plate. He produced a filtrate from this mold, named it penicillin, and suggested it would be a useful antiseptic for infected wounds. It was not until 1941 and the work of Florey and his associates that the true value of penicillin was realized. Since 1942 the growth of this antibiotic has been spectacular.

This success stimulated research and hundreds of thousands of soil samples alone were screened for possible antibiotic activity. Streptomycin (1944) is the result of studies at the Rutgers University Experiment Station by Waksman, Schatz, and their associates of the antibacterial activity of materials obtained from the metabolism of various soil organisms. Chloramphenicol, or Chloromycetin, was originally produced in 1947 from a strain of *Streptomyces* isolated from a soil sample collected in Venezuela. This was the first and the only antibiotic at present, to be produced commercially both by synthetic processes and fermentation. Aureomycin and terramycin were derived from the screening of soil samples and bacitracin is the result of isolating a strain of *Bacillus subtilis* from a dirt-contaminated compound fracture of the leg.

Uses and Economics.[3] Table 5 shows the complete production and price change since the discovery of penicillin, streptomycin, and dihydrostreptomycin. No production statistics are released for the others as the number of producers are too small. It is believed that aureomycin, Chloromycetin, and terramycin are being produced at the rate of several hundred kilograms or more per month. Antibiotics accounted for 56 per cent of the sales of medicinal chemicals with sales of over 231 million

[1] WAKSMAN, An Institute of Microbiology—Its Aims and Purposes, *Science*, **110**, 27 (1949); ANON., This Antibiotic Age, *Chem. Eng. News*, **29**, 1190 (1951).

[2] BARON, "Handbook of Antibiotics," Reinhold Publishing Corporation, New York, 1950; KIRK and OTHMER, *op. cit.*, Vol. 2, pp. 7–37.

[3] LEE, *et al.*, *op. cit.*, p. 1958.

dollars in 1953. In 1953 combined output of all antibiotics for human and veterinary use totaled 1,630,000 lb.

TABLE 5. PRODUCTION AND SALES PRICE OF ANTIBIOTICS[a]

	1953		1954	
	1,000 lb.	Dollars per lb.	1,000 lb.	Dollars per lb.
Bacitracin	6	$358	7	$256
Dihydrostreptomycin	305	82	446	68
Penicillin salts, total	753		631	124
Dipenicillin G dibenzene-ethylene diamine	37			
Penicillin potassium	132		186	
Penicillin procaine	556		378	
Penicillin sodium	28		67	
Streptomycin	125	104	141	73
All other	441	386	597	339
Total	1,630	$158	1,837	$190
Antibiotics for feed supplement	434	50	479	46

[a] "Synthetic Organic Chemicals," U.S. Tariff Commission, Washington, D.C. (published annually). The price of penicillin is about 2 per cent of the 1944 price.

Penicillin.[1] Five different penicillins, differing only in the composition of the R group, have been isolated from the natural media. Penicillin Type F has 2-pentenyl for its R group; dihydro F, *n*-amyl; G, benzyl; X, *p*-hydroxybenzyl; and K, *n*-heptyl. Penicillin G, generally the most clinically desirable, is the type commercially available combined usually with procaine or as a potassium salt. Penicillin is also useful in animal feeds.

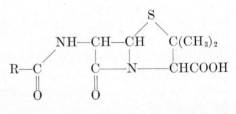

Figure 9 shows how penicillin is made.[2] A special strain of *Penicillin chrysogenum* is grown on media whose main constituents are corn steep liquor and lactose. This aerobic submerged fermentation takes place in 5,000- to 50,000-gal. fermentors. The mass is agitated throughout the

[1] ANON., Penicillin, *Chem. Eng.*, **58** (4), 174 (1951); HAMILTON, The Chemistry and Manufacture of Antibiotic Substances, *J. Chem. Educ.*, **27**, 101 (1950); PETTY, Antibiotics Pace Industrial Fermentation Revival, *Chem. Inds.*, **66**, 184 (1950); KIRK and OTHMER, *op. cit.*, Vol. 9, 922 (1952), many references.

[2] ANON., Penicillin, *Chem. Eng.*, **58** (4), 174 (1951), pictured flow sheet; ANON., Penicillin, Cost vs. Production, *Chem. Eng. News*, **31**, 3057 (1953).

growth cycle and sterile air is used. At 25 to 27°C. the fermentation takes 50 to 100 hr. When the penicillin concentration reaches the optimum the liquor is clarified by filtering out the solids (mycelia, etc.) by means of a rotary vacuum filter (Young type). This antibiotic was recovered from the filtrate by a carbon adsorption and elution, but now the organic solvent extraction method shown in Fig. 9 is employed at a pH of 2.0 to 2.5. The penicillin is quickly extracted from the aqueous phase into the "solvent" such as amyl or butyl acetate or methyl isobutyl ketone. The

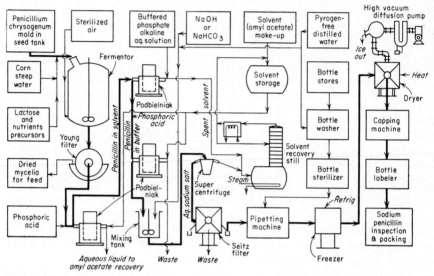

FIG. 9. Flow sheet for penicillin by using solvent extraction (usually butyl or amyl acetate).

reverse takes place at pH of 7.5. However, the penicillin molecule is quite unstable in the acid condition; hence the advantage of the Podbielniak equipment which makes countercurrent contact between the aqueous and the organic solvent rapid and efficient.

Figure 9 depicts the extraction by amyl acetate from the acidified large-volume fermentor filtrate (or "beer"), then into the alkaline buffered phosphate aqueous solution, and thirdly after acidulation into a smaller volume of amyl acetate. This latter has its penicillin extracted into a small volume of alkaline aqueous solution (e.g., NaOH), from which the penicillin is isolated by drying at low temperature through freezing and high-vacuum evaporation. Potassium penicillin or procaine penicillin can be made easily (see Kirk and Othmer reference). The yield is 53 to 60 lb. of penicillin per 10,000 gal. of "beer" or fermentor filtrate. An important improvement in fermentation technology was the use of precursors. When phenylacetic acid, a decomposition product of benzyl-penicillin G, is fed to the mold, a substantial increase in the amount of benzyl-penicillin G is obtained. It has been proved by radioactive-tracer technique that the phenylacetyl groups actually are precursors and supply the acyl group to the molecule and increase the yield.

Streptomycin[1] **and Dihydrostreptomycin.** The commercial method of producing these compounds is also an aerobic submerged fermentation

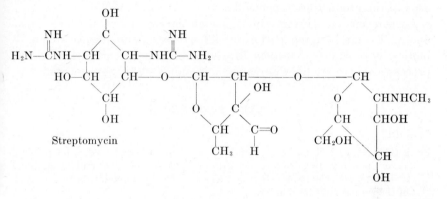

Streptomycin

similar to that used for penicillin production. The medium must be rich in protein, and such sources as meat extracts, fish meal, and soybean meal are commonly used. Probably this antibiotic is recovered from the filtered broth by an ion-exchange process, replacing the old recovery method of adsorption on activated carbon followed by alcoholic hydrochloric acid elution.

Chloromycetin.[2] Chloramphenicol (trade-marked Chloromycetin) is unique among antibiotics, being produced by both submerged-aerobic fermentation and a complicated synthetic process of 10 reactions with about 30 steps. In 1950 it is believed that only 20 per cent or less was produced by fermentation.

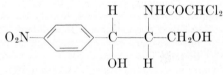

Bacitracin.[3] *Bacillus subtilis* and related bacteria of the gram-positive spore-forming rod type produce a variety of antibiotics[4] of which at present bacitracin is the commercially most important. Not only of thera-

[1] PORTER, Streptomycin Engineered into Commercial Production, *Chem. Eng.*, **53** (10), 94 (1946).

[2] OLIVE, Chloromycetin by Parke, Davis, *Chem. Eng.*, **56** (10), 107 (1949); plus a flow sheet for the synthetic process and a pictured flow sheet for the fermentation process, p. 172.

[3] INSKEEP, *et al.*, Bacitracin, *Ind. Eng. Chem.*, **43**, 1488 (1951). A most excellent article including many pictures, diagrams, and a flow sheet; ANON., Bacitracin, *Chem. Eng.*, **60** (6), 282 (1953), pictured flow sheet.

[4] GARIBALDI and FEENEY, Subtilin Production, *Ind. Eng. Chem.*, **41**, 432 (1949); NELSON, *et al.*, Production of Circulin, *Ind. Eng. Chem.*, **42**, 1259 (1950).

peutic value alone or when mixed with penicillin, bacitracin is of value as a feed supplement where it stimulates the growth and reduces the mortality of poultry and swine. It is produced by a submerged-fermentation process of a mash containing soybean meal, followed by a filtration and solvent extraction (*n*-butyl alcohol) purification quite similar to that used in the production of penicillin.

Aureomycin and Terramycin. Although the commercial method of production has not been reported in detail for these two broad-spectrum antibiotics, it is known that they involve aerobic submerged-fermentation processes. These are likewise valuable in animal-feed supplements.

SELECTED REFERENCES

General:

Prescott, S. C., and C. G. Dunn, "Industrial Microbiology," 2d ed., McGraw-Hill Book Company, Inc., New York, 1949. This book has excellent bibliographies at the end of each chapter. It is also an extensive and fundamental presentation of the subjects of this chapter.

Underkofler, L. A., and R. J. Hickey, editors, "Commercial Fermentations," Chemical Publishing Company, Inc., New York, 1952.

Yeasts:

Jorgensen, A., "Practical Management of Pure Yeast," 3d ed., revised by A. Hansen, Charles Griffin & Co., Ltd., London, 1936.

Walter, F. G., "The Manufacture of Compressed Yeast," Chemical Publishing Company, Inc., New York, 1940.

Underkofler, L. A., and R. J. Hickey, "Industrial Fermentations," Chemical Publishing Company, Inc., New York, 1954.

Annual Unit Process reviews, usually the September issue of *Ind. Eng. Chem.* The excellent presentation with hundreds of references on fermentation is divided into two parts—present or potential commercial fermentations and fermentation as a unit process.

Symposium, Fermentation, *Ind. Eng. Chem.*, **42**, 1769 (1950).

Kirk, R. E., and D. F. Othmer, "Encyclopedia of Chemical Technology," The Interscience Encyclopedia, Inc., New York, 1947–1956.

Industrial Alcohol:

Jacobs, P. B., Industrial Alcohol, *U.S. Dept. Agr. Misc. Publ.* 695, 1950.

Anon., "Ethyl Alcohol (Industrial Alcohol)," Industrial Material Series, Report No. M-1, *U.S. Tariff Commission*, Washington, 1951.

Brewing and Wine:

Babo, A. F. von, and E. Mach, "Handbuch des Weinbaues und der Kellerwirtschaft," 4 vols., Paul Parey, Berlin, 1923–1927.

Vogel, E. H., Jr., F. H. Schwaiger, H. G. Leonhardt, and J. A. Merten, "The Practical Brewer—A Manual for the Brewing Industry," Van Hoffman Press, St. Louis, 1946.

Herstein, K. M., and M. B. Jacobs, "Chemistry and Technology of Wines and Liquors," 2d ed., D. Van Nostrand Company, Inc., New York, 1948.

699

Antibiotics:

Baron, A. L., "Handbook of Antibiotics," Reinhold Publishing Corporation, New York, 1950.
Fleming, Sir Alexander, editor, "Penicillin: Its Practical Application," 2d ed., The C. V. Mosby Company, St. Louis, 1950.
Herrell, W. E., "Penicillin and Other Antibiotic Agents," W. B. Saunders Company, Philadelphia, 1945.
Clarke, H. T., J. R. Johnson, and Robert Johnson, editors, "The Chemistry of Penicillin," Princeton University Press, Princeton, N.J., 1949.
Work, T. S., and E. Work, "The Basis of Chemotherapy," Interscience Publishers, Inc., New York, 1949.

Miscellaneous:

Whittier, E. O., and B. H. Webb, "Byproducts from Milk," Reinhold Publishing Corporation, New York, 1950.
Tauber, Henry, "The Chemistry and Technology of Enzymes," John Wiley & Sons, Inc., New York, 1949.
Foster, J. W., "Chemical Activities of Fungi," Academic Press, Inc., New York, 1949.
Walter, F. G., "The Manufacture of Compressed Yeast," Chemical Publishing Company, Inc., New York, 1940.

CHAPTER 32

WOOD CHEMICALS

Wood,[1] in general, may be divided into two classes, differing from one another in such physical characteristics as specific gravity, compactness of cell structure, and resistance to mechanical treatment, and in such chemical properties as lignin and resin content. These two classes are known as *hardwoods* and *softwoods*, or as broadleaf (deciduous) and coniferous woods. The former contain larger quantities of "extractive matter," including pentosans, while in the latter the amount of resinous matter present is high. Table 1 shows the average composition of wood, the values

TABLE 1. AVERAGE COMPOSITION OF WOOD[a]
(In per cent)

	Broadleaf or hardwood	Coniferous or softwood
Cellulose........................	56	58
Pentosans.......................	18	7
Gums, resins, and oils..............	2	8
Ash............................	1	1
Lignin..........................	23	26

[a] Adapted from HAWLEY, "Wood Distillation," Reinhold Publishing Corporation, New York, 1923.

for the individual species falling within the ranges indicated. The resin content of the deciduous varieties is usually just high enough to cause difficulty but not high enough to yield any valuable product. Both types of wood (broadleaf and coniferous) are suitable for distillation to produce charcoal but, in the case of the resinous softwoods, prior extraction of oils and resins is desirable before the destructive distillation. However, commercial charcoal is made from hardwoods.

[1] The important uses and treatments of wood as a chemical engineering material of construction are reviewed annually in the October issue of *Industrial Engineering Chemistry;* see Chap. 33 for cellulose.

DISTILLATION OF HARDWOOD

History. The origin of the destructive distillation of wood can be traced back to antiquity. The first chemical process invented by man was probably the making of charcoal by the cave man to provide a smokeless fuel in his caves. In ancient Egypt a process for the distillation of wood was known from which were recovered not only charcoal but fluid wood tar and pyroligneous acid as well. The latter was used for embalming. In early times, however, wood distillation was usually carried out for charcoal alone or, when resinous coniferous wood was used, for tar and pine oil in addition. At one time illuminating gas was manufactured from wood by the English, but the process was soon abandoned in favor of the now-familiar coal process.

Wood spirits, a mixture of acetic acid and wood alcohol, was collected and purified to *wood alcohol*, as it was then called. The demands of the growing intermediate dye and synthetic organic chemical industries for wood alcohol became so great that wood was distilled for the main purpose of obtaining this solvent or reagent. In 1870, the process for the manufacture of acetic acid and acetone via calcium acetate from wood was developed. This caused marked advances in wood distillation processes all over the world, particularly in the United States and Hungary, where wood was cheap.

For many years the wood distillation industry was the only source of acetic acid, methanol, and acetone. In addition it furnished considerable quantities of tar, pitch, methyl acetate, and wood oil to the trade. During the First World War, however, a process for producing acetone by fermentation was worked out, as described in Chap. 31. This process effectively removed the acetone produced by the pyrolysis of calcium acetate from wood distillation as a competitor. The introduction, in 1928, of acetic acid from calcium carbide and of acetone from propylene further decreased the wood distiller's market. The manufacture and importation from Germany of synthetic methanol a short time later were further shocks to this industry. In 1953–1954 was introduced another source of by-product acetone—that from the cumene phenol process (see page 887).

Now faced with business ruin, some wood distillers became conscious of the gross inefficiency of many of their operations and applied sound chemical engineering to their problems, but competition has closed all but the better plants. From 100 hardwood-distillation plants, the number in operation dropped to 46 in 1932. In 1947 all but 15 of those had been shut down permanently[1]—and as of 1954 this number has been reduced. While the distillation by-products can be made synthetically, there is no

[1] Wood Distillation, *Northeast. Wood Utilization Council Bull.* 15, New Haven, Conn., 1947.

synthetic counterpart for charcoal, a product of steadily increasing importance but of enhanced price.

Products and Economics. It was estimated in 1947 that 1,200 cords of wood were processed daily by the hardwood-distillation industry. That year saw a total product value of $13,415,000 with a product breakdown of 26,600,000 lb. of acetic acid, basis 100 per cent; 156,577 gal. of crude methanol and 2,552,574 gal. of refined methanol, both on a 100 per cent basis; and 373,362,654 lb. of charcoal. The methanol produced represented approximately 3 per cent of the total production for that year,

TABLE 2. COST PER CORD OF WOOD PROCESSED[a]

Item	Amount
Wood	1947: $8–$12; 1954: $12–$20
Fuel equipment	1,000 lb. bituminous coal (actually wood gas, wood waste, natural gas, and tar are also burned)
Labor	0.5–0.7 man-day
Water	14,000 gal.
Power	15 kw.-hr.
Capital investment	$5,000 per cord capacity (not including chemical-recovery plant)

[a] Wood Distillation, *Northeast. Wood Utilization Council Bull.* 15, New Haven, Conn., 1947.

TABLE 3. PRODUCTS FROM ONE CORD (4,000 LB.) HARDWOOD[a]

Product	Per cent	Product	Per cent
Charcoal	25.2	Tar, oil	5.0
Crude methanol	1.9	Gas	18.3
Acetic acid, or equivalent	2.9	Water, etc	46.7

[a] *Chem. & Met. Eng.*, **39**, 534 (1932).

82,900,000 gal. being manufactured synthetically. Hardwood distillation is practiced principally in Pennsylvania, Michigan, New York, Arkansas, and Tennessee, where the wood is grown as a crop, being harvested after a sufficient period of years to furnish merchantable timber, the scrap going into retorts.

The major items of plant cost per cord of wood processed are given in Table 2. The products from a cord of hardwood, on a weight basis, are shown in Table 3. These products given in Table 3 have a wide variety of applications, some of which are described below:

Charcoal.[1] About half of the charcoal produced is used in the metallurgical industries, chiefly electrometallurgical, where its function is that of both a reducing agent and a fuel. Wood charcoal is the source of

[1] LADOO and STOKES, Industrial Carbon, *Chem. Inds.*, **63**, 609 (1948).

carbon considered essential for the manufacture of carbon disulfide. Fuel uses rank third in quantities consumed.

Methanol. This aliphatic alcohol is employed as a denaturant for ethyl alcohol, an antifreeze for automobiles, a solvent, as a methylating agent, and for formaldehyde.

Acetic Acid. The applications of acetic acid are too numerous to mention completely. It is used in the preparation of a great number of the products of the process industries, including acetic anhydride, sodium acetate, cellulose acetate, ethyl acetate, butyl acetate, amyl acetate, white lead, and for dyeing, and souring agent in textiles.

Methyl Acetone. This is a ternary azeotropic mixture of 21 per cent methanol, 28 per cent methyl acetate, and 51 per cent acetone and is sold as such by the refiners as a solvent to the paint and lacquer manufacturers. However, the composition in practice runs between the limits of 25 to 30 per cent methanol, 40 to 50 per cent acetic esters, and 25 to 45 per cent acetone.

Tar and Oil. The tar produced yields pitch, useful as a rubber softener on electrical insulation, and widely sold gasoline oxidation inhibitor oils.[1] Various grades of wood oils are employed as solvents, in wood preservation, and as insecticides. Some are purified and redistilled to yield guaiacol and wood creosote. Any residue is burned under the plant boilers.

Gas. The gas evolved contains 53 per cent carbon dioxide, 27 per cent carbon monoxide, and 15 per cent methane. It is burned to heat the retorts and to furnish part of the fuel for the boilers. It has an average heat content of 150 to 250 B.t.u. per cu. ft.

MANUFACTURE

Raw Materials. The hardwood distillation industry pyrolyzes all varieties of woods which are commonly classed as members of the broadleaf or deciduous species; *i.e.*, oak, ash, birch, beech, hard and soft maple, hickory, cherry, eucalyptus, and chestnut. As stated previously, only wood wastes are commonly employed, *i.e.*, second-growth timber, branches, twisted trunks, and unmarketable lumber.

Energy Requirements, Unit Operations, Unit Processes. The principal unit process is *pyrolysis* or destructive distillation. In this industry, although the pyrolytic reactions require considerable energy in the form of heat to reach the temperature of reaction, certain later stages are exothermic. Many unit operations are involved to make the unit process of pyrolysis function and to separate and purify the products of the pyrolysis. Among these are *heat transfer, condensation, distillation,* and *extraction (liquid-liquid).* Much energy, mainly as steam heat, is required

---

[1] Universal Oil Products Co., Chicago, Ill.; *cf.* Goos and REITER, New Products from Wood Carbonization, *Ind. Eng. Chem.,* **38,** 132 (1946).

to carry on these operations. The modernization and improving of the wood-distillation industry have largely been concerned with a chemical engineering study of the various unit operations involved in the separation and purification of the crude pyroligneous acid with the object of reducing cost, both capital and operating.

Pyrolysis and General Treatments. Except in the continuous retorts of the plant of the Kingsford Chemical Co. at Iron Mountain, Mich., all United States plants producing wood chemicals by the destructive distillation of hardwood char the wood in batches loaded on steel buggies on standard-gage railroad tracks, in steel retorts holding from 6 to 10 cords, operating on about a 24-hr. cycle. The retorts are hung in firebrick settings, heated by coal or natural gas, sometimes supplemented by the wood gas or tar obtained in the procedure of a previous batch. Some plants cut the wood into short blocks; some char 52-in. billets. Some predry wood for 2 or 3 days, using waste heat from retort or boiler furnace stacks; some dry wood out of doors for 3 to 18 months; but all produce about the same quality and quantity of charcoal and raw pyroligneous acid liquor (see Table 3).

Most plants settle and decant raw retort or pyroligneous liquor to separate clear liquor from settled tar, then give this clear decanted raw liquor a preliminary plain distillation to help free it from "soluble" or polymerized tar, thus producing so-called *boiled liquor*. Some plants, representing a very small proportion of the total cordage pyrolyzed, still neutralize acids in boiled liquor with lime, distill off "weak alcohol" from this neutralized liquor, and evaporate to dryness the remaining acetate liquor to produce "gray" calcium acetate. This process is obsolete and it is believed this practice has been almost discontinued in this country.

Acetic Acid Separation and Purification. The greatest differences in the processes are in the methods of concentration or recovery of acetic acid. Any process for the direct recovery of acetic acid from pyroligneous acid must accomplish two things: (1) remove the many organic substances present and (2) economically concentrate a dilute acetic acid solution.

Concentration of the acid by straight rectification is impractical because the vapor composition never differs greatly from the liquid composition, and the curve even becomes concave as it approaches low concentrations of the acid.[1] Therefore a very long distilling column with a heavy reflux would be required to remove the acetic acid from dilute solutions. The three processes developed, although subordinate in commercial importance to the synthetic methods, are good illustrations of new solutions that have been developed for the problems in chemical engineering. The Suida extractive-distillation process is not widely used (only two plants), because of the process requirements, relatively expensive equipment which does not produce anhydrous acid. The liquid-

[1] PERRY, *op. cit.*, p. 573.

liquid extraction process using ethyl acetate (or ether) is more important. The Othmer azeotropic-distillation process is popular because of the minimum of equipment required and economical operation.

Liquid-Liquid Extraction Process. The liquid-liquid extraction process, as illustrated by Fig. 1, extracts substantially all the acetic acid from the previously distilled liquor with over 95 per cent of the water content flowing to waste without the necessity of reevaporating it. The choice between the two commonly used solvents, ethyl ether and ethyl acetate, depends largely on local fuel costs. Ethyl acetate produces a somewhat drier extract and its vapor pressure is lower, with consequent less tendency

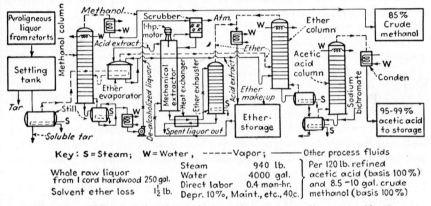

Key: S = Steam; W = Water , -----Vapor; ——— Other process fluids

Whole raw liquor from 1 cord hardwood 250 gal.	Steam 940 lb. Water 4000 gal. Direct labor 0.4 man-hr.	Per 120 lb. refined acetic acid (basis 100%) and 8.5–10 gal. crude
Solvent ether loss 1½ lb.	Depr. 10%, Maint., etc., 40c.	methanol (basis 100%)

Fig. 1. Acetic acid by cold liquid-liquid extraction from pyroligneous acid. (*Courtesy of J. M. Coahran.*)

to solvent loss. Since density, latent heat of vaporization, and boiling temperature are all greater than for ethyl ether and since about the same *volume* of each is required, steam consumption may be somewhat lower for the ether. Further, the greater temperature difference between the boiling points of boiled liquor and ether allows the economical use of liquor vapors from primary stills in an evaporator for the evaporation of ether after extraction (see Fig. 1). In properly designed and operated acetic-extraction plants, ether losses can be kept under 1½ lb. per cord, thus providing a very satisfactorily low solvent cost. The extraction processes are not widely used.

Figure 1 is a flow diagram of a typical plant for *ether extraction* of acetic acid from pyroligneous acid liquor. This process may be broken down into the following coordinated sequences of *unit operations* (Op.):

Settled raw liquor (pyroligneous acid after settling out of the insoluble tar) is fed continuously to a primary still for distillation from the soluble tar in order to lessen fouling of subsequent operations (Op.).

Mixed vapors from this still are passed to the heater tube bundle of the ether evaporator and, after partial condensation, to the middle of the methanol column as its feed. Eighty-five per cent crude methanol is the overhead from this column, and dealcoholized liquor is the bottom discharge (Op.).

The latter is cooled and pumped through a vent scrubber into the upper part of the mechanical countercurrent extractor (Op.).

The acetic acid in the dealcoholized liquor is extracted *cold* as the aqueous liquid passes downward in this mechanical extractor, using 2.6 volumes of ether per volume of liquor countercurrent to the rising ether (Op.).

The ether-saturated extracted liquor is conducted through a heat exchanger to the top of a steam-heated ether exhauster column for the recovery of the dissolved ether. The spent liquor flows from the bottom of this exhauster through the heat exchanger to waste, containing less than 0.1 per cent acetic acid (Op.).

The ether solution of the acetic acid (2 to 3 per cent) is piped from the top of the mechanical extractor to the ether evaporator. Here, heated by the vapors from the primary still, the ether is vaporized, along with some acetic acid (Op.).

The acid freed of most of its ether is led to a lower section of this same ether column. The overhead is rectified ether vapor to be condensed and recirculated. The discharged acid collects in an acid extract receiver kept sufficiently warm by steam to remove ether (Op.).

The ether has carried over into this acid extract practically all of the acetic acid, a small amount of wood oils, some polymerized tar, and from 2 to 3 per cent of water—resulting in a 70 per cent dark crude acid. The water content is a distinct advantage as it forms minimum boiling mixtures with the volatile impurities and facilitates their fractional separation. If sufficient water is not present, it is expedient to add it.

The 70 per cent crude acetic may be refined by either continuous or batch distillation. Figure 1 shows a single batch distillation with an oxidizing and purifying treatment with from 2 to 4 lb. of sodium dichromate per ton of acid. Sometimes, double distillation is practiced with the dichromate treatment between (Op.).

The final acetic acid is of any desired concentration from 90 per cent to glacial, of water color, and with a purity dependent upon the design of the fractionating equipment and the care with which it is operated. Final acid condensers are constructed of silver, though aluminum or Duriron can be and sometimes is used. Modern practice inclines to stainless steel throughout (KA2S Mo 317). Other acid-handling equipment is made of copper or copper alloy, and the parts handling strong hot acid are often lined with acidproof brick set in acidproof cement. Strong acid is stored and shipped in aluminum tanks, with an occasional rubber-lined vessel. For acid under 90 per cent, paraffined wood tanks can be used.

Suida Process. In the Suida process (Fig. 2) the upper layer from the initial settling of the crude pyroligneous acid is first treated to remove acetic acid by being vaporized and scrubbed countercurrently with a wood oil, which is obtained by vacuum distillation of the tar from the settlers (see Fig. 1). The oil with acetic acid in solution passes through a dehydrating column into a vacuum stripping column, where the acetic acid is boiled off under vacuum. The oil returns to the system, while the acetic acid is rectified to 92 per cent or higher. Fresh oil is added to the scrubbing column at frequent intervals. The vapors from the scrubbing column, having been stripped of acetic acid by the oil, are sent to methanol recovery, their alcohol content being about 4 per cent. They also contain a small amount of acetone. Subsequent concentration in an exhausting and rectifying system produces 90 per cent methanol or its equivalent. Final rectification yields 99 per cent methanol, allyl alcohol, acetone, and "weak alcohol." The yields of products per cord (4,000 lb.) of wood and resulting 250 gal. of pyroligneous acid are charcoal, 1,330 lb.;

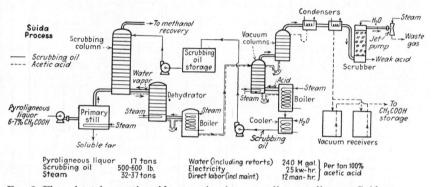

Pyroligneous liquor	17 tons	Water (including retorts)	240 M gal.	Per ton 100%
Scrubbing oil	500-600 lb.	Electricity	25 kw.-hr.	acetic acid
Steam	32-37 tons	Direct labor (incl maint.)	12 man- hr.	

FIG. 2. Flow sheet for acetic acid extraction from pyroligneous liquor—Suida process.

oil, 4.5 gal.; tar, 40 to 45 gal.; acetic acid (100 per cent basis), 120 lb.; and methanol (100 per cent basis), 9 gal.,[1] based on cordwood 60 in. long (vs. usual 52-in. sticks).

Othmer or Azeotropic Distillation Process. The various steps may be divided into the following *unit operations* (Op.) and *unit processes* (Pr.):

Hardwood, previously dried so that moisture content is about 25 per cent, is loaded on "buggies," which hold about 2 or 2½ cords of wood, rolled into a steel retort 50 to 55 ft. long, and heated for about 20 hr. at 600 to 700°F. (Pr.). In order to avoid warping, the doors of the retort are not heated. The initial temperature may be maintained at about 500°F. for 4 hr. to distill out the water, and then raised to 700°F. for 4 to 6 hr. more. At the end of this time the reaction becomes exothermic and little or no external heat is needed to maintain the desired temperature.

Charcoal is removed from the retorts and cooled out of contact with air for 48 hr., placed in open sheds for 2 days, and shipped to consumers (Op.).

The vapors formed by the heat-treatment are passed through water-cooled copper condensers (Op.).

[1] POSTE, Suida Process for Acetic Acid Recovery, *Ind. Eng. Chem.*, **24**, 722 (1932); KRASE, Solvent Extraction Obviates Waste in Acetic Acid Production, *Chem. & Met. Eng.*, **36**, 657 (1929).

The wood gas produced is conducted to a scrubbing system and sent to the distributing pipes leading to the burners (Op.). The gas has a fuel value of 150 to 250 B.t.u. per cu. ft.

The condensed vapors, known as *pyroligneous acid* or liquor, are sent to settling tanks for 24 hr. Here the insoluble tars settle out and are removed (Op.).

Liquid from the tar still is pumped to the demethanolizing column and the crude methanol distilled (Op.). This distillation is a continuous operation. The

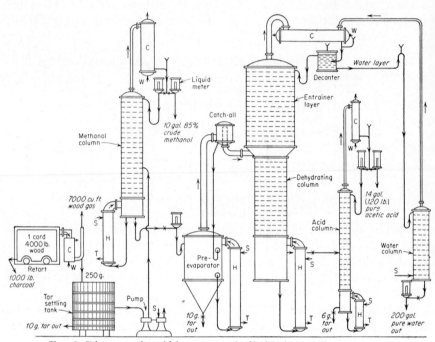

FIG. 3. Direct acetic acid by azeotropic distillation—Othmer process.

plates in the column below the feed plate are of a special perforated design to permit removal of tar deposits (see Fig. 3).

"Crude methanol," containing some acetone and methyl acetate and about 15 per cent water, is fractionated off the top of the column and condensed (Op.).

Dealcoholized liquor from the bottom of the column is metered and sent to a preevaporator (Op.). This evaporator has a conical bottom to permit removal of the tars that passed the previous treatments.

The remaining volatile materials (acetic acid and water) are distilled in the evaporator, pass through a catchall to remove any suspended matter and then to the azeotropic dehydrating column (Op.). Water cannot be removed practically from acetic acid by simple distillation because of the excessive number of plates required in the column and the prohibitive heat requirements. The water is removed in the dehydrating column by adding a water-insoluble "withdrawing" liquid such as butyl acetate.[1] This method of removing water from acetic acid is the Othmer process. Ethylene chloride or various other solvents, some of which may be fractions of oils present in wood distillation, may also be used for this purpose. The butyl acetate or other withdrawing liquid distills with the water as a minimum boiling azeotrope and thus removes the water from the acid (Op.).

The vapors of butyl acetate and water are condensed and cooled. Separation into two layers takes place (Op.).

Butyl acetate is returned to the top plate of the column as reflux and the water containing a small amount of butyl acetate is distilled to recover all the acetate (Op.). The water discharges from the bottom of this water column and contains about 0.01 per cent acetic acid.

The crude acetic acid from the dehydrating column contains some formic, propionic, and butyric acids, a little tar, and not more than 0.5 per cent water. This is rectified in one or sometimes two continuous columns to produce glacial acetic acid, a formic acid fraction, and a fraction of higher acid homologs.

Continuous Hardwood Distillation. The plant of the Kingsford Chemical Company at Iron Mountain, Mich., continuously feeds dry wood to Badger-Stafford retorts at 302°F., the wood entering at the top and being heated as it sinks, until it distills. Retort temperature is 1004°F., maintained (after initial heating of the retort to this point by gas) entirely by the exothermic reaction accompanying distillation. These retorts, which are 40 ft. high and 10 ft. in diameter, discharge into rotary coolers lined with water-cooled tubes and externally sprayed with water. From the coolers the charcoal passes to rotary conditioners, which permit absorption of oxygen. Complete conditioning of the charcoal in 5 hr. is possible by this method.[2]

The wood gas and pyroligneous acid are taken off the retorts and the acid is condensed. The gas is scrubbed and used for fuel. Every two weeks the stills are taken off the line, and the tar is removed. This latter is sent to the pitch department where creosote oil and pitch are recovered. The pyroligneous acid is settled to remove tar.

This plant produces various esters of acetic acid and not the free acid as its products. The distillate from the primary tar stills is distilled in a continuous system to yield 95 per cent *crude* methanol overhead and 15 per cent acetic acid at the base of the column. The crude wood alcohol, containing allyl alcohol, methyl acetate, and acetone, is refined in discontinuous stills, yielding refined allyl alcohol in addition to several

---

[1] OTHMER, Acetic Acid and a Profit from Wood Distillation, *Chem. & Met. Eng.*, **42**, 356 (1935); OTHMER, Dehydrating Aqueous Solutions of Acetic Acid, *Chem. & Met. Eng.*, **40**, 631 (1933); pictured flow chart, *Chem. & Met. Eng.*, **47**, 349 (1940); numerous patents.

[2] NELSON, Waste-wood Utilization by the Badger-Stafford Process, *Ind. Eng. Chem.*, **22**, 312 (1930). RIEGEL, "Industrial Chemistry," 5th ed., pp. 319–321, Reinhold Publishing Corporation, New York, 1949, gives a flow sheet for this process.

fractions that yield pure methanol, 75 per cent methyl acetone, and 75 per cent methyl acetate upon further refining. The 15 per cent acetic acid initially obtained is esterified to ethyl acetate.

PRODUCTS FROM SOFTWOOD

The term *naval stores* is usually applied to the group of products made by the distillation or extraction of softwood or from the oleoresin that exudes therefrom. These products are turpentine, rosin, pine oil, rosin oil and spirit, pine tar, and pitch. These products were used by the Navy in the days of wooden ships. Turpentine and rosin are complex mixtures of organic compounds obtained from pine wood or sap. The destructive distillation of wood yields turpentine but does not produce rosin, while reclaimed gum residues yield rosin but not turpentine (Table 4).

History. Turpentine and rosin are produced from the longleaf pine. This tree flourishes particularly in the Southeast and Southern parts of the United States; in fact, in the early days of America the forests in this region were said to extend in a belt approximately 200 miles deep and 1,000 miles long. The earliest records show that turpentine was being made in 1606 in Maine. In 1608 what was probably the first cargo of American naval stores was shipped to England. Pine-tar manufacture became one of the first industries of the New England colonies, flourishing as early as 1650.[1] By 1750, North Carolina had been settled and had established a growing trade in naval stores. By 1860, South Carolina, Georgia, and Florida had begun production and by 1900 Georgia was the chief producing state. The same year, H. T. Yaryan of Toledo, Ohio, began a series of experiments which resulted in the erection of a plant at Gulfport, Miss., to obtain turpentine and pine oil from the logging waste and also to attempt the removal of the rosin present. Plant production by the steam distillation method rose to 1,700 bbl. of turpentine, 14,000 bbl. of rosin, and 700 bbl. of pine oil per annum. Florida and Georgia produce 95 per cent of today's gum turpentine and rosin. The industry has offered new products and grades of old products to the consumer.

Products and Economics. The production of rosin and turpentine is shown in Table 4. The apparent United States consumption during 1953–1954 was 25,248,000 gal. of turpentine and 626,200,000 lb. of rosin. "Gum" turpentine or rosin refers to that obtained by exudation from incisions in trees of the longleaf or slash pine varieties, while "wood" turpentine or rosin indicates those products obtained from the destructive distillation, steam distillation, or extraction of *wood* or stumps.

Although turpentine and rosin are available from different methods of production (Table 4), the uses of each product from the various sources

[1] PALMER, Naval Stores, *Ind. Eng. Chem.*, **27**, 741 (1935).

are generally interchangeable; hence, no attempt will be made to distinguish between these sources in the list that follows. The major products of the naval-stores industry are the turpentines, rosins, pine oils, rosin oils, spirits, and pine-tar pitches and tars. The tabulation at the bottom of Fig. 4 shows the products obtained from 1,000 tons of white-pine chips, while Table 5 represents the consumption of turpentine and rosin in various industries.

TABLE 4. UNITED STATES PRODUCTION OF ROSIN AND TURPENTINE, 1950–1954[a]

Crop year, April 1–March 31	Turpentine, 50-gal. bbl.		Rosin, 520-lb. drums	
	1953–1954	1950–1951	1953–1954	1950–1951
Gum..........................	177,680	271,880	531,620	797,620
Wood........................	....	....	1,213,340	1,339,410
Wood: Steam distilled.........	193,090	237,080		
Sulfate...............	164,220	194,180		
Destructively distilled...	2,860	5,410		
Total production......	537,850	708,550	1,744,960	2,137,030

[a] U.S. Department of Agriculture.

Turpentine is a mixture of organic compounds known as *terpenes*. The principal constituent is α-pinene:

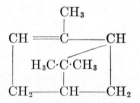

Turpentine as a household paint and varnish thinner accounts for a large part of the present consumption. Important chemical uses have increased the outlets for turpentine. These include synthetic camphor, terpineols, pharmaceuticals, insecticide manufacture, and the production of additives for lubricating oil exposed to extremely high temperatures.

Rosin. One of the chief components of rosin is abietic acid (probably the anhydride),

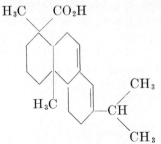

although other acids such as α- and β-pimaric also are present. Many grades of rosin[1] are on the market, largely distinguished by color, clarity, saponification number, and softening point.

The major uses of rosin are for "sizing" or impregnating various types of paper and paperboard; in protective coatings such as varnishes, enamels, and paints; in chemicals and pharmaceuticals; and in yellow laundry soap. Rosin enters into insecticides and germicides because of its adhesiveness, a property that enables it to be used in such widely diversified products as can label cement, linoleum, and sealing wax. The esters of rosin are also quite useful. Methyl and ethyl abietates[2] are employed as plasticizers and cosolvents, while the glycerol ester, widely known as *ester gum*, is applied with tung oil in making water-resistant varnishes. Ester gum is important in synthetic resin and nitro-cellulose coatings.

TABLE 5. PERCENTAGE CONSUMPTION OF TURPENTINE AND ROSIN BY VARIOUS INDUSTRIES IN 1951[a]

Industry	Turpentine	Rosin
Chemicals and pharmaceuticals...........	70.3	26.6
Ester gum and synthetic resins...........	13.9	21.1
Linoleum and floor covering.............	0.0	2.5
Paint, varnishes, lacquers...............	9.0	6.8
Paper and paper size...................	0.0	30.3
Soap.................................	0.0	6.1
Other industries.......................	6.8	6.6

[a] 1950–1951 Annual Naval Stores Report, U.S. Department of Agriculture, Washington, 1951.

Rosin Oils. These oils are used in printers' inks and in varnishes. They are rather high-boiling oils obtained by destructively distilling rosin and are of higher molecular weight and of greater chemical complexity than the terpene hydrocarbons.

Pine Oils. These are mixtures of terpene alcohols, terpenes, aldehydes, and ketones. They do not occur naturally but arise by distillation of wood. They have been fractionated to yield α-terpineol, fenchyl alcohol, borneol, and anethole. Industrially, pine oil itself is used in the flotation of lead and zinc ores, industrial detergents, in textile scouring, and as a cleanser, disinfectant, and deodorant.

Dipentene. Commercial dipentene is a mixture of dipentene (or limonene), terpinene, and terpinolene. These compounds are isomeric *p*-terpadienes.

[1] "Rogers' Manual of Industrial Chemistry," 6th ed., Chap. 17, p. 691, D. Van Nostrand Company, Inc., New York, 1942; HUMPHREY, Solvent Refining of Wood Rosin, *Ind. Eng. Chem.*, **35**, 1062 (1943).

[2] LEE, Hercules Makes Resins from Rosin, *Chem. Eng.*, **55** (11), 129 (1948), with a pictured flow sheet on p. 158 on hydroabietyl alcohol.

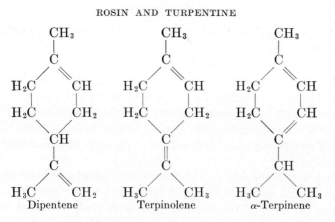

Dipentene Terpinolene α-Terpinene

Dipentene is a solvent, widely used because of its ability to prevent, or at least retard, the formation of surface skins in cans of paint, printing ink, or varnish. It is also employed as a solvent in reclaiming rubber from old tires.

MANUFACTURE

The *raw materials* for the production of naval stores include those species of wood commonly classed as coniferous. Either the gum that flows from the living longleaf or slash pine, or the stumps from the cut-over pine forests, together with other resinous wood wastes, form the source of raw material for the various processes employed.

Processing of Gum.[1] The processing of gum for naval stores products is the older procedure. Originally, all gum was produced in the old, direct-fired copper still. The turpentine was distilled off with the water and separated by gravity; the rosin remained in the kettle and was removed in a molten and impure condition at the end of the run and strained to remove wood chips, pine needles, dirt, etc. Fire stills have largely been supplanted in this country by large steam stills operated either batchwise or continuously in what is known as a central plant. In 1951, over 90 per cent of the gum naval stores products were produced in 29 such plants. Since the advent of these central stills, the owners of pine stands are largely gum farmers instead of processors. They obtain the gum by chipping or wounding longleaf and slash pines and collecting the exudate by means of gutters or cups. A 40 to 60 per cent sulfuric acid spray on the streak increases the yield. The oleoresin so obtained is collected every 3 to 4 weeks and delivered to central gum-cleaning plants.

Although the steam still was developed first, it was not entirely

[1] For a most excellent article see SHEARON, *et al.*, Continuous Distillation of Gum Turpentine, *Ind. Eng. Chem.*, **40**, 1695 (1948); *cf.* POOLE and PATTON, Pine Gum-processing Labor and Fuel Costs, *Chem. Eng.*, **54** (8), 102 (1947); COLLINS and PATTON, A New Tack for Gum Naval Stores, *Chem. Eng.*, **58** (9), 154 (1951).

successful, until the development of the Olustee process of gum cleaning in 1938. Here the crude gum is diluted with turpentine, heated with steam, screened and filtered, and washed with hot water before distillation. There are other methods of gum cleaning,[1] but the Olustee process accounts for approximately 75 per cent of today's cleaning. All central stills clean the gum before processing in order to upgrade and increase the amount of rosin recovered. Turpentine is usually about the same quality, if properly distilled, regardless of the gum cleanliness or method of processing.

The batch still consists of a stainless-steel cylindrical tank containing steam coils and spargers to which gum and water are charged. The turpentine is distilled, condensed, and separated from the water by gravity. The final traces of water are removed in a dehydrator, a receiver containing 4-mesh rock salt, through which the turpentine passes upward. At the end of the charge, the rosin is drawn off the bottom and packaged.

Continuous distillation of gum turpentine was first patented in 1944, and the system departs considerably in both design and operation from the batch steam still. It also differs from the continuous processes of distillation used in the wood naval-stores industry for two reasons— simplicity and operation at atmospheric pressure. Basically, the still embodies a standard 12-in. pipe or upright column about 20 ft. high with a flash chamber at the top, a preheating coil for treating the gum, a condensing tank, and pipe outlets. The cleaned gum is preheated to 350°F. and sprayed into the flash chamber where around 75 per cent of the turpentine is flashed off. The rosin flows downward through the steam-jacketed column, with a current of live steam flowing upward to remove the remaining turpentine. The turpentine is run off continuously from the bottom of the condenser. By adjusting the steam injected into the base of the column, the amount of turpentine in the final rosin may be carefully regulated. Advantages of continuous over batch operation include lower capital investment, lower operating costs, less labor, and greater throughput.

There are three methods for processing wood for naval-stores products, as can be seen from Table 4.

Destructively Distilled Wood Turpentine. This product involves a distillation very similar to that employed for the distillation of hardwood. The pine wood is charged to gas-fired retorts arranged in long rows. The vapors and gases pass through condensers and drain into open tubs. The noncondensable gases are used for retort fuel. The heating period is 16 hr. and the cooling period 8 hr. The lighter oils are condensed first and separated from the pyroligneous liquor which settles to the bottom. During the latter half of the run, heavier oils come over and displace this acid, which rises to the top. The light and heavy oils are filtered,

[1] See Shearon, *et al., op. cit.,* for descriptions.

treated, and combined for steam redistillation in pot stills, the distillate containing turpentine, pine oil, and dipentene. The mixture is bleached with sulfuric acid and subsequently fractionated and refractionated to produce refined dipentene, refined turpentine, and pine oil.[1] The residue in the original pot stills is pine tar. No rosin is produced. As can be seen in Table 4, this process is unimportant.

Steam and Solvent Process. The cutover pine forests of the South provide the raw material, mainly stumps and some other resinous waste

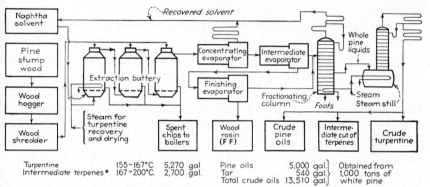

Turpentine	155–167°C.	5,270 gal.	Pine oils	5,000 gal.	Obtained from
Intermediate terpenes*	167–200°C.	2,700 gal.	Tar	540 gal.	1,000 tons of
			Total crude oils	13,510 gal.	white pine

*Included herein are the hydrocarbons: para-menthane, dipentene, para-cymene, terpinene, and terpinolene

FIG. 4. Flow sheet for wood rosin and turpentine by steam and solvent extraction.

wood, for this process. Figure 4 shows the essential *unit operations* (Op.) in this method.[2]

The wood is first ground in a wood hog and then reduced to splinters in a shredder (Op.).

The chips are loaded into a battery of extractors, where they rest upon a false bottom, below which live steam under pressure is admitted at the end of the run for solvent recovery. The extractors are built of acid-resistant stainless alloys and operate at pressures of 65 to 85 lb. per sq. in. gage (Op.).

The solvent (so selected that it is easily separated from turpentine) countercurrently extracts the chips (Op.). This solvent may be naphtha or a petroleum fraction with a boiling range of 200 to 240°F. The hot solvent is drained off, and the residual material on the chips is removed by subsequent steam distillation. The chips are used for fuel (Op.).

Most of the solvent is removed from the turpentine, pine oil, and rosin in a concentrating evaporator (Op.).

The residue from the first evaporator is sent to an intermediate evaporator. The vapors from this evaporator are led into the upper part of the continuous fractionating column, and the residue is sent to the finishing evaporator (Op.).

[1] NEALEY, Distilling Pine Products at New Orleans, *Chem. & Met. Eng.*, **43**, 20 (1936).

[2] HIGHTOWER, From Pine Stumps to Rosin and Terpene Oils, *Chem. Eng.*, **54** (12), 119 (1947), with a pictured flow sheet, p. 150; Naval Stores; New Plant Does Old Job Better, *Chem. Eng.*, **55** (8), 108 (1948).

Vapors from this final evaporator are combined with those of the intermediate evaporator before entering the fractionating column (Op.).

Residue from the third evaporator is whole wood rosin and may be treated by selective solvents and certain adsorbents such as fuller's earth and light rosins[1] (Op.).

The continuous fractionating column separates the pine oils and turpentine from the last of the solvent (Op.).

Pine liquids from the continuous column are separated into three fractions in a batch still: crude pine oil, an intermediate cut of terpenes, and crude turpentine (Op.).

Careful fractionation of these three cuts produces many marketable products (Op.).

Sulfate Pulp Turpentine. The relief gases from the digesters for sulfate (or kraft) pulp contain turpentine and pine oil. Upon condensation, a crude oil is found floating on top of the condensate. There are 2 to 10 gal. of oil per ton of pulp produced. This oil contains 50 to 60 per cent turpentine and 10 to 20 per cent pine oil; and these may easily be separated by fractional distillation. The resulting turpentine contains offensive mercaptans which must be removed by hypochlorite solution or ethylene diamine.[2] Another by-product of the process is tall oil, a so-called *liquid* rosin obtained upon acidification of the digester liquor. It might be classed as a sulfate rosin.

"Sulfite turpentine" is another kind of turpentine available from the paper industry and consists chiefly of *p*-cymene rather than of α-pinene. It is obtained from the pulping of spruce by the sulfite process. To date the actual recovery in the pulp industry is unimportant.

* * * * * *

The increased use of chemicals from wood is dependent upon a solution of the problem as to what their various chemical components are. This is being solved and new derivatives are being made; such a result is stimulating to the entire naval stores industry. *There is ample evidence to predict that the component products of this industry can be developed by research to form the basis for a group of allied industries similar in interdependence to coal tar and its related drug and dye industries.*

HYDROLYSIS OF WOOD

Although such cellulosic materials as corncobs, cottonseed hulls, peanut shells, and bagasse have all been proposed as potential sources of alcohol, following hydrolysis of cellulose to sugar—and its fermen-

---

[1] HIGHTOWER, *op. cit.*

[2] "Pulp and Paper Manufacture," Vol. III, 3d ed., Sec. 5, p. 192, McGraw-Hill Book Company, Inc., New York, 1937; *cf.* Lee, Closer Fractionation, Finer Chemicals *Chem. Eng.*, **58** (3), 142 (1951).

tation—only wood pulp and wood wastes have ever gained even minor status.

History. The saccharification of wood received its first industrial trial at the beginning of the present century. During the first World War, two American plants manufactured alcohol from sawdust using dilute sulfuric acid as the hydrolyzing agent. Because of the low yields, approximately 22 gal. of 100 per cent alcohol per ton of dry southern pine, the plants could not compete and were closed 2 years after the war. At the same time Scholler was trying to produce alcohol from wood in Germany. Using about the same methods, he attained yields of a 3 per cent sugar solution, representing 60 to 70 per cent of theory. Also Willstätter and Zechmeister published the discovery that, at ordinary temperatures, 40 per cent hydrochloric acid easily puts cellulose into solution. It was not until 1916, however, that Bergius and Haaglund undertook the development of a process employing hydrochloric acid and not until 1930 that Scholler began operations with sulfuric acid at Tornesch.[1] By 1941, 30 foreign plants were in successful commercial operation. During the Second World War, two plants were built in this country. The plant at Bellingham, Wash., utilizes waste liquors from the sulfite pulping process in which hydrolysis of cellulose to sugar had occurred. During the fiscal year 1951 it produced 2,900,000 gal. of alcohol, which was about 1 per cent of the total United States production. The alcohol-from-wood-waste plant at Springfield, Ore., employed a modified Scholler process developed by the Department of Agriculture's Forest Products Laboratory at Madison, Wis. This plant was not completed until the summer of 1947 and after a brief run was shut down.

Manufacture. In the sulfite process for the manufacture of pulp, sugars are formed by the hydrolysis of wood constituents that are dissolved out to produce usable fibers. Approximately 65 per cent of these sugars is capable of being fermented to alcohol. This is equivalent to about 1 to 2 per cent of the sulfite waste liquor. First, the sulfite waste liquor is separated from the pulp and conditioned for fermentation.[2] After cooling to 30°C. and adding lime to adjust the pH to 4.5 and urea nutrient, the liquor is pumped into the first of a series of seven fermentors. The yeast, reclaimed from a previous fermentation, is added and fermentation occurs for a period of 20 hr. Each of the tanks is agitated and the flow is continuous. After fermentation the yeast is separated from the beer in centrifugal separators. The yeast is recycled and the alcohol is stripped from the beer before entering the rectifying column. In this column,

[1] Bergius, Conversion of Wood to Carbohydrates, *Ind. Eng. Chem.*, **29**, 247 (1937); The Utilization of Wood for the Production of Food-stuffs, *Trans. Inst. Chem. Engrs.* (London), **11**, 162 (1933).

[2] Ericcson, Alcohol from Sulfite Waste Liquor, *Chem. Eng. Progr.*, **43**, 165 (1947), including a flow sheet.

operating under substantial reflux, the alcohol is concentrated to 190 proof or higher and then purified to remove the low-boiling contaminants. After vaporization, the cooled condensate is deposited to alcohol storage.

In Sweden all the alcohol (and many derivatives therefrom) come from waste sulfite liquors. This includes all beverage spirits and during the war, alcohol for motor fuel.

The Oregon plant was designed to hydrolyze 221 tons per day of Douglas-fir sawmill waste. The process wood is shredded to proper size and packed in five 2,000 cu. ft. percolators by steam shocking to a controlled density. Dilute (0.4 to 0.8 per cent) sulfuric acid is added to the percolator which hydrolyzes the hemicellulose and cellulose of the wood to sugars and other by-products, mostly lignin. After flashing, lime is added to neutralize the excess sulfuric acid. The calcium sulfate formed is filtered out. Nutrients and yeast are added to the liquor and it enters a fermentation cycle of 24 hr. at 86°F. After centrifugal separation of the yeast from the beer, the alcohol is separated by a distillation system.[1] Theoretically, 11,500 gal. of 190-proof ethanol should be obtained per day.

CELLULOSE DERIVATIVES

Many cellulose derivatives have attained commercial importance, such as the ethers: ethyl cellulose,[2] methyl cellulose (Dow's "Methocel") and carboxy-methyl cellulose. The latter is frequently known as "CMC" and may be prepared by the following "alkylation" or by a variation in the proportions:

$$[C_6H_7O_2(OH)_3]_x + xNaOH \rightarrow [C_6H_7O_2(OH)_2ONa]_x$$
Cellulose   Alkali cellulose

$$[C_6H_7O_2(OH)_2ONa]_x + xClCH_2COONa \rightarrow [C_6H_7O_2(OH)_2OCH_2COONa]_x$$
Sodium chloro-   Sodium carboxy-methyl cellulose
acetate

Various degrees of etherification are described in the literature and it is probable that several formulations are commercial. The sodium carboxymethyl cellulose[3] is a white powder when dry, though it is generally produced and sold as solutions of varying concentration and viscosity.

In 1953, 20,005,000 lb. were sold valued at $8,512,000. It is physiologically inert, and is employed as a protective coating for textile and

---

[1] U.S. Pat. 2152164 (1939); HARRIS and BEGLINGER, Madison Wood Sugar Process, *Ind. Eng. Chem.*, **38**, 890 (1946); Symposium, Sugars from Wood, *Ind. Eng. Chem.* **37**, 4 (1945).

[2] ANON., Ethyl Cellulose, Flow Sheet, *Chem. & Met. Eng.*, **52** (9), 142 (1945); see Chap. 35 for cellulose derivatives used in plastics.

[3] HADER, Carboxymethylcellulose, *Ind. Eng. Chem.*, **44**, 2808 (1952).

paper, sizing, ice cream, and other emulsion stabilizers and as an additive to impart strength to sausage casings and other films.

SELECTED REFERENCES

Kirk, R. E., and D. F. Othmer, "Encyclopedia of Chemical Technology," Interscience Publishers, Inc., New York, 1947–1956.

Benson, Henry K., "Chemical Utilization of Wood," U.S. Department of Commerce, 22d Rept. Natl. Comm. Wood Utilization, 115 pp., 1932. This is an excellent summary and contains a comprehensive bibliography.

Hawley, L. F., "Wood Distillation," Reinhold Publishing Corporation, New York, 1923.

Klar, M., "The Technology of Wood Distillation," D. Van Nostrand Company, Inc., New York, 1925.

Bunbury, H. M., "The Destructive Distillation of Wood," Ernest Benn, Ltd., London, 1923.

Gamble, T., "Gamble's International Naval Stores Year Book," T. Gamble, editor and publisher, Savannah, Ga., 1940.

Haynes, Williams, "Cellulose, the Chemical that Grows," Doubleday & Company, Inc., New York, 1953.

CHAPTER 33

PULP AND PAPER INDUSTRIES

Cellulose is probably the most versatile raw material known to man, and its conversion to a group of products that are indispensable to modern civilization is the everyday function of the pulp and paper industry. In 1947, there were 226 pulp mills[1] employing over 50,000 persons. That year there were 665 paper and board mills to process the pulp employing over 140,000 people and the value of the products shipped was nearly 3 billion dollars. Our present per capita use of paper is above 350 lb. annually which is more than any other country in the world. The pulp industry also supplies purified cellulose for explosives, rayon, and plastics. The chemicals used in volume in the pulp and paper industry, the third largest customer of the chemical industry, include heavy chemicals, such as lime, soda ash, caustic soda, sodium silicate, sulfur, salt cake, sodium sulfide, chlorine, clay, calcium carbonate, and titanium dioxide; and organics such as paraffin waxes, rosin, glue, casein, starch, formaldehyde, and dyes.

Historical.[2] Man's earliest attempts to record human activities were made on stone. A little later, bark, leaves, and ivory were also used. Between 2500 and 2000 B.C. the manufacture of a writing paper from papyrus, a tall reed growing along the Nile, was begun. It is from this reed that the word *paper* is derived. There were, however, other early writing materials, including dried calf- and goatskin parchment, the wax-covered boards of the Romans, and the clay-brick records of the Babylonians.

The actual manufacture of paper was invented by the Chinese about A.D. 150 but was kept secret until about 700, when the Arabs conquered Samarkand. By the end of the fourteenth century, the process of manufacture had undergone several improvements and was well known in southern Europe. The industry did not obtain a firm foothold in England until the seventeenth century, and it was almost the beginning of the eighteenth century (1690) before America's first paper mill was established.

[1] 1947 Census of Manufactures. See Tables I and II for 1954 consumption and production statistics.

[2] HUNTER, "Papermaking—The History and Technique of an Ancient Craft," 2d ed., Alfred A. Knopf, Inc., New York, 1947.

720

The only raw material used by the early industry was rags, which were washed, stamped into a pulp by water-driven stamping rods, and the resultant mass diluted. A wooden frame with a wire-screen bottom was dipped into the pulp and shaken as the liquor drained through, matting the fibers into a sheet. These sheets were placed on felts, stacked, pressed to remove additional water, and hung up to dry. The product was rag paper.

Between 1750 and 1800 the Holland beater was developed and adopted. In 1799, a Frenchman, Louis Robert, invented a process for forming a sheet on a moving wire screen. He disposed of his invention to M. Didot and John Gamble, who after making additional improvements sold out to the Fourdrinier brothers in 1804. This machine is known today as the *Fourdrinier* machine. In 1809 the cylinder machine was invented by John Dickinson and immediately forced the Fourdrinier into the background, where it remained until about 1830, when its importance was finally realized. It was in this period that the first Fourdrinier was received in America (1827) and that steam cylinders for drying were first used (1826).[1]

The increased production made possible by the Fourdrinier and cylinder machines so greatly increased the demand for rags that a scarcity soon developed. In 1841, however, Keller of Saxony had invented a mechanical process of making pulp from wood. The soda process was developed by Watt and Burgess in the years 1853–1854. In 1866 and 1867 the American chemist, Tilghman, was granted the basic patents (British) for the sulfite process, although the commercialization of the process was carried out independently of Tilghman, by the Swedish chemist, C. D. Ekman, who began the manufacture of sulfite pulp at Bergvik, Sweden, in 1874. The sulfate or kraft process (*kraft* is German for strong) was the result of basic experiments conducted by C. F. Dahl in 1879, at Danzig. In 1908 the sulfate process was introduced into the United States. At that time, pulp production was divided as follows: mechanical, 48 per cent; sulfite, 40 per cent; soda, 12 per cent. Pulp manufacture gradually developed into an industry of its own and served industries other than the paper industry as well.

The manufacture of pulp for rayon manufacture has assumed major importance and become a distinctly specialized division of pulp manufacture. Perhaps the greatest change in the industry in recent years has been the rise of the sulfate process to the position of major importance in the industry, a place held for years by the sulfite process. This situation will undoubtedly continue.

The control and utilization of the industry's by-products have received widespread attention. The creation of useful materials from the lignin and the waste liquors means an increased income for the industry as well

[1] JOHNSEN, The Pulp and Paper Industry, *Ind. Eng. Chem.*, **27**, 514 (1935).

as a partial solution to its major problem, the avoidance of stream pollution.

Uses and Economics. For statistics see Table 1 and Table 2. Over half the world's production of paper is consumed in the United States.

TABLE 1. PRODUCTION AND CONSUMPTION OF WOOD PULP, PULPWOOD, AND OTHER FIBROUS MATERIALS (1,000 short tons) ("Facts for Industry," Bureau of Census, Washington, D.C.)

	Production		Consumption	
	1954 preliminary	1953	1954 preliminary	1953
Wood pulp, total...................	18,341	17,537	19,033	18,681
Special alpha and dissolving grades..........	791	677	58	55
Bleached sulfite.....................	1,800	1,728	2,062	2,067
Unbleached sulfite...................	582	593	892	942
Bleached sulfate....................	2,684	2,389	3,148	2,905
Semibleached sulfate.................	326	302	363	353
Unbleached sulfate..................	6,797	6,752	6,914	7,018
Soda........................	431	427	495	504
Groundwood...................	2,428	2,342	2,634	2,523
Semichemical...................	1,126	1,028	1,121	1,022
Defibrated or exploded...............	1,203	1,153	1,191	1,142
Screenings, damaged, etc..............	169	140	151	144
Other fibrous materials, total..............	......	......	9,275	9,785
Waste paper...................	......	......	8,063	8,530
Straw........'.................	......	......	239	277
Rags......................	......	......	316	325
Cotton fiber..................	......	......	16	13
Manila stock.................	......	......	47	44
All other...................	......	......	591	593
	Cords of 128 cu. ft.—roughwood basis			
Pulpwood, total...................	......	......	29,436	28,150
Softwood...................	......	......	24,635	23,772
Hardwood...................	......	......	4,800	4,377

MANUFACTURE OF PULP FOR PAPER

There are two distinct phases in the conversion of raw wood into the finished paper which is such an integral part of our everyday life. These are (1) the manufacture of pulp from the raw wood as outlined in Table and (2) the conversion of the pulp to paper itself. Papermaking will be presented in a later section.

There are four different kinds of wood pulp: mechanical pulp, sulfite pulp, sulfate pulp, and soda pulp as shown in Tables 1 to 3. The first is prepared by purely mechanical means, the other three by chemical means. The mechanical pulp contains all of the wood except the bark and that lost during storage and transportation. Chemical pulps, however, are essentially pure cellulose, the unwanted and unstable lignin and the other noncellulosic components of the wood having been dissolved away by the treatment. Because of this, chemical pulps are much superior to mechanical (or ground-wood pulp) for fine papermaking

However, owing to the special processing required, they are too expensive for the cheaper grades of paper, such as newsprint.

TABLE 2. PAPER AND BOARD PRODUCTION, 1954 AND 1953 (1,000 short tons) ("Facts for Industry," Bureau of Census, Washington, D.C.)

	1954 preliminary	1953
All types, total..................................	26,656	26,527
Paper, total......................................	11,614	11,405
Newsprint......................................	1,191	1,068
Groundwood paper..............................	807	771
Paper machine-coated............................	1,215	1,182
Book paper.....................................	1,559	1,622
Fine paper.....................................	1,323	1,297
Coarse paper (including shipping sack)...............	3,428	3,398
Special industrial paper (including absorbent paper)....	526	554
Sanitary tissue.................................	1,320	1,277
Tissue paper (except sanitary and thin)..............	240	232
Paperboard, total.................................	12,046	12,274
Liners..	4,335	4,410
Corrugating material.............................	1,816	1,906
Container chip and filler board.....................	280	296
Folding boxboard...............................	2,484	2,428
Special food board..............................	941	967
Other bending board.............................	245	169
Set-up boxboard................................	710	763
Other non-bending board..........................	209	181
Special paperboard stock..........................	944	1,074
Cardboard.....................................	79	75
Wet-machine board..............................	132	151
Construction paper and board, total..................	2,862	2,695
Construction paper..............................	1,355	1,316
Hardboard, density over 26 lb. per cu. ft.............	493	423
Insulating board, density 26 lb. or less per cu. ft.......	1,013	955

Raw Materials. Wood is the principal source of cellulose for paper-making. However, cotton, linen rags, and waste are also used by the mills, as well as the various hemps, their principal source being the cordage and rough waste of the textile industry.[1]

There are two principal methods used for debarking, apart from manual labor. The first method utilizes friction by tumbling or rotating action in a moving mass of pulpwood sticks. The two principal types of equipment, both continuous in operation, are the rotating cylindrical drums and stationary machines with agitating cam equipment to stir

[1] "Pulp and Paper Manufacture," Vol. 1, Chap. 1, Part 1, McGraw-Hill Book Company, Inc., New York, 1950. This is a four-volume detailed treatise on the various phases of the pulp and paper industries, written by a number of experts under the direction of a committee of the paper industry of the United States and Canada.

up the mass of logs. In the case of the drums, still the most common machines in use, the wood is fed into the upper end of a rotating drum immersed in a tank partly filled with water where it is tumbled. The bark is literally rubbed off and the clean wood discharged at the other end.

The second method for debarking uses mechanical friction or high-pressure (about 1,400 lb. per sq. in.) water jets applied to individual logs. Hydraulic barkers direct the water jets against the log in such a way that the bark is broken up and removed.[1] In the Astrom barking machine the log passes through a rotating ring of chain links held in close contact with the log which is prevented from turning.

Mechanical Pulp. This process involves no chemical treatment of the pulp whatsoever. The chief woods employed are spruce and balsam, which are of the soft, coniferous species. They have the advantage that they can be floated in streams to the mill, in contrast to poplar which sinks soon after immersion. After arrival at the mill, the wood is slashed and debarked. It is then ready to be ground, which is done in water to remove the heat of friction and to float the fibers away. The grinding is at an acute angle to the length of the blocks in order to furnish longer fibers by tearing rather than by right-angle cutting.

For small tonnages, the "three-pocket" grinder is very widely used. This consists of a central grindstone mounted on a steel shaft and having three chambers or pockets around its periphery. The top of each chamber is surmounted by a hydraulic cylinder which operates a ram whose purpose is to force the blocks against the revolving, usually artificial, stone. These stones are given a suitable type of burr by properly dressing their surface. Cooling and removal of the product are effected by means of a spray of "white water" which is returned to this point from a later step in the process. For larger tonnages the Roberts and Great Northern grinders are popular, but for the large installations of 200[2] daily tons or more, either the hydraulic or chain-feed magazine type are preferred. These consist of a large vertical, cylindrical chamber filled to the top with logs. The pressure of the wood on the grindstone at the bottom of the chamber is maintained by the weight of the wood in the magazine.

The pulp and water mixture from the grinders is dropped into a stock sewer below the grinders and is passed along to the sliver screen. Here the larger material is retained and discarded by the screen, while the fine material falls into the screened stock pit, from where it is pumped to the fine screens. The fines that pass these screens are concentrated in thickeners to give commercial mechanical pulp. The oversize from the fine screens is treated in refiners and then returned to the screens again. The water overflow from the thickeners contains about 15 to 20 per cent of the original fibers and is the so-called *white water* which is used in

[1] Editorial Staff, Developments that Aid Western Pulp Industry, *Chem. & Met. Eng.*, **51** (12), 96 (1944).

[2] PERRY, Trend in the Manufacture of Groundwood, *Tappi*, **32**, 67 (1949).

TABLE 3. COMPARISON OF THREE TYPES OF CHEMICAL WOOD PULP[a]

Type of process	Sulfate pulp	Sulfite pulp	Soda pulp
Cellulosic raw material	Almost any kind of wood, soft or hard	Coniferous; must be of good color and free of certain hydroxy phenolic compounds	Limited to short-fibered hardwoods because of low yields and pulp strength, e.g., poplar, birch, maple
Principal reaction in digester	Hydrolysis of lignins to alcohols and acids; some mercaptans formed	$RC{=}CR' + Ca(HSO_3)_2$ $\rightarrow RCH{-}CR'{\cdot}SO_3\frac{1}{2}Ca$	Hydrolysis of lignins to alcohols and acids
Composition of cooking liquor	12.5% solution of NaOH, Na_2S, and Na_2CO_3. Typical analysis of solids: 58.6% NaOH, 27.1% Na_2S, 14.3% Na_2CO_3. Dissolving action due to NaOH and Na_2S. Na_2CO_3 inactive and represents the equilibrium residue between lime and Na_2CO_3 in the formation of NaOH	7% by weight SO_2, of which 4.5% is combined as sulfurous acid and 2.5% as $Ca(HSO_3)_2$. Cooking 1 ton of pulp requires 225 to 300 lb. of sulfur and 350 to 400 lb. of lime rock	12.5% solution of NaOH and Na_2CO_3 in the ratio 85 to 15; dissolving action due solely to NaOH
Cooking conditions	Time: 2–5 hr. Temperature: 340–355°F. Pressure: 100–125 lb. per sq. in.	Time: 7–12 hr. Temperature: 265–300°F. Pressure: 70–90 lb. per sq. in.	Time: 6–8 hr. Temperature: 330–340°F. Pressure: 90–105 lb. per sq. in.
Chemical recovery	Chemicals too expensive to discard; therefore, most of process is devoted to recovery of cooking chemicals with incidental recovery of heat through burning organic matter dissolved in liquor	SO_2 relief gas recovered; liquor discarded after wood digestion and pulp washing; little present salvage of chemicals but use of waste liquor being extensively studied	Sodium hydroxide recovered and re-used as in kraft process, but make-up chemical is Na_2CO_3 instead of Na_2SO_4

TABLE 3. COMPARISON OF THREE TYPES OF CHEMICAL WOOD PULP[a] (*Continued*)

Type of process	Sulfate pulp	Sulfite pulp	Soda pulp
	from wood; chemical losses from system are replenished with salt cake, Na_2SO_4		
Materials of construction	Digesters, pipe lines, pumps, and tanks can be made of mild steel or iron because caustic liquor does not readily corrode them	Acid liquor requires digester lining of acid-proof brick; fittings of chrome-nickel steels (Type 316), lead, and bronze	Same as kraft materials
Pulp characteristics	Brown color; difficult to bleach; strong fibers; resistant to mechanical refining	Dull white color; easily bleached; fibers weaker than kraft	Brown color; easily bleached; fibers weaker than kraft or sulfite
Typical paper products	Strong brown bag and wrapping; multiwall bags, gumming paper, building paper; strong white papers from bleached kraft; paperboards such as used for cartons, containers, milk bottles, and corrugated board	White grades: book paper, bread wrap, fruit tissue, sanitary tissue	Usually blended with other pulps; book and magazine grades, coated papers, sanitary tissue

[a] Mostly taken from SAWYER, *et al.*, Kraft Pulp Production, *Ind. Eng. Chem.*, **42**, 757 (1950).

grinding and to aid flow in the stock sewer. As the process continues to operate, it is necessary to add fresh water to the system to keep down the temperature; therefore, some of the white water must be removed. Before being sent to waste, this water has the remaining fibers strained from it. The fiber is returned to the thickeners.

The *energy requirements* are all mechanical and consist chiefly of power for grinding. The only chemical change occurring in mechanical pulp is a slight hydration of the cellulose by long contact with water.

The *uses* of mechanical pulp are for the most part restricted to the cheaper grades of paper and board, where permanency is not required. The eventual deterioration that occurs in paper made from mechanical pulp is due to chemical decompositions of the noncellulosic portions of the wood. In the manufacture of newsprint, cheap manila, wall, tissue, and certain wrapping papers, the mechanical pulp is usually mixed with a small amount of chemical pulp.

Sulfate or Kraft Pulp. This process is responsible for the major part of the pulp manufactured at the present time (see Table 1). Almost any

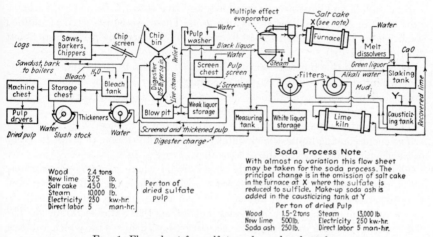

Wood	2.4 tons	
New lime	325	lb.
Salt cake	450	lb.
Steam	10,000	lb.
Electricity	250	kw.-hr.
Direct labor	5	man-hr.

Per ton of dried sulfate pulp

Soda Process Note

With almost no variation this flow sheet may be taken for the soda process. The principal change is in the omission of salt cake in the furnace at X where the sulfate is reduced to sulfide. Make-up soda ash is added in the causticizing tank at Y

Per ton of dried Pulp

Wood	1.5-2 tons	Steam	13,000 lb.
New lime	500 lb.	Electricity	250 kw.-hr.
Soda ash	250 lb.	Direct labor	5 man-hr.

FIG. 1. Flow sheet for sulfate pulp and soda pulp.

kind of wood may be used, hard and soft, although coniferous woods are mostly employed. The process was developed especially to remove the large amounts of oil and resins in these woods. For the production of dissolving pulp for rayon from hardwoods, a modified sulfate process is in use. This involves a prehydrolysis to remove the pentosans and polyoses, followed by the sulfate treatment and multistage bleaching. With softwood supplies becoming more critical, more and more attention will be turned to hardwoods.

The *chemical reactions* are rather indefinite but involve hydrolysis of the lignins to alcohols and acids (see Table 4). This hydrolysis also produces mercaptans and sulfides, which are responsible for the familiar bad odor of sulfate-pulp mills.

The *energy required* is given in Fig. 1 and largely involves mechanical energy to chip the wood and steam to heat up the chips in the digesters to the point where the noncellulosic material is rapidly dissolved.

The steps in the manufacture of sulfate pulp are depicted in the flow sheet of Fig. 1. These may be separated into the following sequences of *unit operations* (Op.) and *unit processes*[1] (Pr.):

The logs are slashed and debarked as previously described and conveyed to the chippers, which are large rotating disks holding four or more long heavy knives to reduce the wood to small chips (Op.).

The chips are screened on either rotary or vibrating screens to separate the oversized chips, the desired product, and the sawdust. The oversized chips and slivers are put through crushers or rechippers to reduce them to the proper size. They are then stored in a large chip bin from where they can be fed to the digesters by gravity (Op.).

The digesters are charged with chips, the cooking liquor containing essentially sodium sulfide and caustic soda is added, and live steam is turned on. Either a stationary or a rotary digester may be used. These are constructed of unlined steel. The pressure is raised to 110 lb. per sq. in. The cooking period lasts about 3 hr. (Op. and Pr.).

At the end of this time the pressure is allowed to drop to 80 lb. and the charge is blown into the pit or into a battery of countercurrent diffusers, which are closed tanks designed to recover through heat exchangers the steam normally wasted in a blow pit; better washing also results.

The pulp after separation from the cooking liquor is washed (Op.).

The spent cooking liquor (black liquor) is pumped to storage to await recovery of its chemicals for reuse in the process (Op.).

The washed pulp is passed to the screen room where it enters the knotters which remove the knots that have failed to disintegrate in the cooking operation, then to screens that sieve out any small slivers of uncooked wood, and finally to filters and thickeners where a greater portion of the water is removed. The thickeners consist of cylindrical frames covered with fine wire screen rotating into the thin pulp. As it emerges, the water passes through the screen, leaving the pulp on the outside (Op.).

The removed knots are wasted, but the screenings are reduced in a refiner, prescreened, and returned to the diffuser chest (Op.).

The thickened pulp is next bleached. Two types of bleaching are employed: a one-stage process which consists of treatment with calcium hypochlorite bleach and produces a cream-colored paper, and a three-stage process which involves treatment with free chlorine, neutralization with milk of lime or caustic soda, and then a bleach with calcium hypochlorite. The bleaching agent in either case oxidizes and destroys the dyes formed from the tannins in the wood and accentuated by the sulfides present in the cooking liquor (Pr.).

After bleaching, the pulp should be washed and rethickened in preparation for making it into sheets dry enough to fold into a bundle called a *lap* (Op.); or it may be run into the charge chest of a paper machine to give dried pulp.

The lapping is done on a wet thickener which consists essentially of a cylinder

---

[1] SAWYER, et al., Kraft Pulp Production, *Ind. Eng. Chem.*, **42**, 756 (1950), with flow sheets; "Pulp and Paper Manufacture," Vol. 1, Chap. 5; PORTER, Bleached Kraft Pulp, *Chem. Eng.*, **55** (6), 123 (1948), with a pictured flow sheet, p. 136; ANON., Sulfate Pulp Bleaching, *Chem. & Met. Eng.*, **51** (3), 132 (1944), a pictured flow sheet.

dipping into a vat filled with stock solution, an endless felt belt which carries the pulp sheet through squeeze rolls, and a series of press rolls. The resulting laps contain 35 to 45 per cent air-dry fiber. These "wet" laps are stacked in hydraulic presses and subjected to pressures up to 3,000 lb. per sq. in. This product contains 50 to 60 per cent air-dry fiber (Op.).

Sulfate pulp, made from coniferous woods, has the longest fibers of all the pulps. This, coupled with the fact that the chemicals used are not so harsh in their action as those employed for the other two chemical pulps, makes possible the production of very strong papers. In the past, the dark

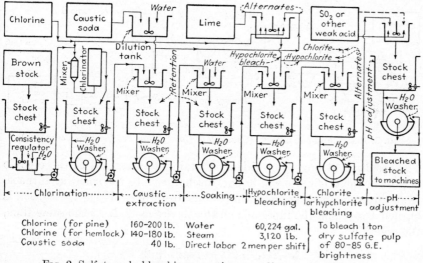

Fig. 2. Sulfate pulp bleaching—continuous sulfate or Kraft process.

Chlorine (for pine)	160–200 lb.	Water	60,224 gal.	} To bleach 1 ton dry sulfate pulp of 80–85 G.E. brightness
Chlorine (for hemlock)	140–180 lb.	Steam	3,120 lb.	
Caustic soda	40 lb.	Direct labor	2 men per shift	

color of the kraft paper has limited its uses mainly to wrapping papers, sacks, and paperboard. However, newer developments in the bleaching treatment have made possible the manufacture of light-colored and white pulps (see Fig. 2). This allows the mixing of this very high strength pulp with other types of pulp to increase the strength of the paper.

Recovery[1] of the Black Liquor. An important factor in the economic balance for the sulfate process has been the recovery of the spent liquor from the cooking process. The black liquor removed from the pulp in the pulp washer or diffuser contains 95 to 98 per cent of the total alkali charged to the digester. Most of the alkali is present as sodium carbonate or as organic compounds with sodium having properties very similar to the carbonate. Appreciable amounts of organic sulfur compounds are present in combination with sodium sulfide. There are also small amounts of sodium sulfate, salt, silica, and traces of lime, iron oxide, alumina, and

---

[1] "Rogers' Manual of Industrial Chemistry," 6th ed., p. 1419, D. Van Nostrand Company, Inc., New York, 1942; SAWYER, *et al., op. cit.*, p. 760.

potash. Total solids usually average about 20 per cent. This black liquor is first concentrated in multiple-effect or cascade evaporators to a concentration between 45 and 70 per cent total solids, depending on the type of recovery unit. This removal of water is necessary in order to produce a liquor that will ignite and burn when sprayed into the furnace.

Figure 3 shows a modern recovery system. Hot, concentrated liquor, to which has been added make-up sodium sulfate, is fed into the disk evaporator, countercurrent to the gas flow. As the charge moves down the furnace, water is evaporated and the organic salts are broken down.

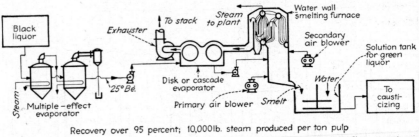

Recovery over 95 percent; 10,000 lb. steam produced per ton pulp

Fig. 3. Black-liquor recovery. (*Courtesy of Combustion Engineering Company.*)

The resulting strong black liquor, containing almost all of the organic matter in the original black liquor, discharges into the smelting furnace. Here any remaining organic compounds are broken down, the carbon is burned away, and the inorganic chemicals are melted. At the same time, the reaction

$$Na_2SO_4 + 2C \rightarrow Na_2S + 2CO_2$$

takes place. The molten chemical "smelt" is allowed to fall into a weak solution of "dissolving liquor" coming from the causticizing plant. The chemicals dissolve immediately to give a characteristic *green liquor*. The insoluble impurities are allowed to settle out and the liquor is then causticized by adding slaked lime prepared from the recovered $CaCO_3$. The reaction

$$Na_2CO_3(aq) + Ca(OH)_2(s) \rightarrow 2NaOH(aq) + CaCO_3(s);$$
$$\Delta H = -2,100 \text{ cal.}$$

occurs quickly. The resulting slurry is separated by rotary continuous filters, using Monel metal screens as a filtering medium. The calcium carbonate sludge is sent to a limekiln to recover the CaO for reuse in the process. The filtrate is the *white liquor* used in the cooking of the fibers. It contains caustic soda, sodium sulfide, and small quantities of sodium carbonate, sodium sulfate, sodium sulfite, and thiosulfate.

Figure 4 shows another method of black liquor recovery. In this process the strong black liquor is sprayed into the furnace. The water is evaporated and the resulting material is heated to 1500°F. to remove organic compounds and melt the inorganic ones. The smelt is dissolved to form green liquor as described above.

Among the by-products from the black liquor recovery plant is tall oil, a black, sticky, viscous liquid composed mainly of resin acids, fatty acids, and methanol.[1] The tall oil may be separated from the weak black liquor by means of centrifuges (in America), or obtained by flotation from the concentrated liquors (in Europe). It is used in the manufacture of soaps and greases and in the preparation of emulsions. Methanol may be recoverd by dry distillation of the pulverized mass obtained by evaporation of the black liquor with barium hydrate. The cost does not

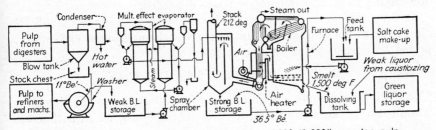

Chemical recovery, 95 percent; Steam production, 10,000-12,000 lb per ton pulp

Fig. 4. Flow sheet for black-liquor recovery from either sulfate or soda pulp—B. & W. Tomlinson process. (*Courtesy of The Babcock & Wilcox Company.*)

permit economical recovery, however. The digester relief gases yield paying quantities of spruce turpentine, from 2 to 10 gal. per ton of pulp produced. This may be refined to produce sulfate turpentine.

Soda Pulp. The manufacture of soda pulp is very similar to that of sulfate pulp, both being alkaline processes. The woods used are of the deciduous or broadleaf variety. Poplar makes up the largest tonnage and is also the easiest to cook. Other woods employed include birch, maple, chestnut, gum, and basswood. Owing to the tendency of broad-leaf woods to sink, it is usually necessary to ship them by rail or truck to the mill rather than to float them in. The preparation of the wood for cooking is similar to that described above under Sulfate Pulp (see notes on Fig. 1). The cooking liquor has a density of 11 to 13°Bé. and contains 6 to 7 per cent caustic soda.

The digesters are very similar to the digesters used in the sulfate process and are constructed of steel or wrought-iron plate, likewise unlined. The cooking time varies from 2 to 3 hr. at a pressure of 110 lb. per sq. in. and a temperature of 344°F. The digesters are usually blown to blow pits which have provisions for heat exchange to utilize the steam. The pulp is washed in an open tank with a false bottom constructed of heavy steel plate covered with a fine wire netting. The plate is perforated

[1] "Pulp and Paper Manufacture," Vol. 1, Sec. 5, pp. 495*ff.*

with ½-in. holes, closely spaced. The remaining operations are very similar to those used for processing sulfate pulp.

The black liquor from the soda pulp contains about 16 per cent total solids and 4.5 per cent total alkali. Most of the latter is sodium carbonate, the remainder being free sodium hydroxide. This liquor is concentrated by multiple-effect evaporation as in the sulfate process (Fig. 1)[1] and fed to either stationary furnaces or rotary driers. No smelting furnace is used ordinarily, the product being a black ash (not fused) containing 20 to 25 per cent free carbon. This ash is charged to a series of leaching tanks equipped with false bottoms. The ash is leached countercurrently with water or weak alkali, the resulting solution being fed to the slaking tanks and the carbon waste discarded.

Recovered lime is added to the liquor in the slaking tank and the slurry fed to the causticizing tanks, where make-up sodium carbonate is added. The reaction taking place is essentially

$$Na_2CO_3 + Ca(OH)_2 \rightarrow 2NaOH + CaCO_3$$

The calcium carbonate sludge is filtered off and sent to the limekilns. The filtrate is the white liquor used in the digesters, all as outlined in Fig. 1.

Since the fibers from broadleaf woods are shorter (1½ mm.) than those from coniferous woods used in the sulfate process (2 to 3 mm.), the product of the soda process is a pulp that makes a weaker paper. Therefore, it is generally used with mixtures of other pulps, serving to fill in the spaces between the longer fibers. The largest tonnage of the pulp enters into the manufacture of book, magazine, and tissue papers.

Sulfite Pulp. On the basis of quantity produced, this process ranks second only to the sulfate process. Although spruce is the wood most commonly employed, appreciable quantities of hemlock and balsam are also used. The wood is barked, cleaned, and chipped as described under Sulfate Pulp, the resulting chips being about ½ in. in length. It is then conveyed to the storage bins above the digesters, preparatory to being cooked.

The chemistry of the sulfite digestion of cellulosic materials is very complicated, and the thermodynamic data are incomplete and not very reliable. The external energy required for the process includes steam for the preparation of the cooking liquor and cooking the pulp, and mechanical energy for chipping the wood and pumping.

The more common sulfite process consists of the digestion of the wood in an aqueous solution containing calcium bisulfite and an excess of sulfur dioxide. The sulfite process involves two principal types of reactions, which are probably concurrent: (1) the reaction of the lignin with the

[1] Cf., ANON., Carbon Recovery from Black Ash, *Chem. Eng.*, **59** (3), 206 (1952), a pictured flow sheet.

bisulfite, and (2) the hydrolytic splitting of the cellulose-lignin complex. The hemicelluloses are also hydrolyzed to simpler compounds, and the extraneous wood components acted on. Since the disposal of waste liquor (more than half of the raw material entering the process appears here as dissolved organic solids) is a serious pollution problem, concerted attention has been turned to its disposal or utilization. Substituting magnesium oxide for lime is being evaluated commercially[1] because chemical and heat recovery is possible accompanied by a solution of the disposal problem of the waste liquor. Sodium and ammonia have also been substituted for calcium as a pulping base and are used in a limited number of commercial plants. So far costly and complicated chemical recovery

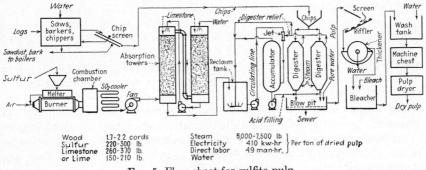

Wood	1.7-2.2 cords	Steam	5,000-7,500 lb	
Sulfur	220-300 lb.	Electricity	410 kw-hr	Per ton of dried pulp
Limestone	260-370 lb.	Direct labor	4.9 man-hr.	
or Lime	150-210 lb.	Water		

FIG. 5. Flow sheet for sulfite pulp.

limits their widespread use. The calcium-based sulfite-pulping process is described below.

Two methods of preparing the cooking liquor (tower and milk of lime) and two methods of cooking (direct and indirect) are widely used. Figure 5 shows the preparation of sulfite pulp using the tower system and direct cooking. The essential reactions involved in the preparation of the cooking liquor are quite simple.

$$S + O_2 \rightarrow SO_2$$
$$2SO_2 + H_2O + CaCO_3 \rightarrow Ca(HSO_3)_2 + CO_2$$
$$2SO_2 + H_2O + MgCO_3 \rightarrow Mg(HSO_3)_2 + CO_2$$

The entire process may be divided into the following *unit operations* (Op.) and *unit processes*[2] (Pr.), as illustrated in Fig. 5.

Sulfur is melted in a tank heated by the rotary burner and then fed to this burner (Op.) for oxidation (Pr.).

Any sulfur that is vaporized in the burner enters a combustion chamber, where

[1] HULL, et al., Magnesia-base Sulfite Pulping, *Ind. Eng. Chem.*, **43**, 2424 (1951), a most excellent article with flow sheets and pictures.

[2] "Pulp and Paper Manufacture," Vol. 3, Sec. 4; ANON., Sulfite Pulp, *Chem. & Met. Eng.*, **48** (8), 106 (1941), pictured flow chart.

it is oxidized to sulfur dioxide. The amount of air in this operation is closely controlled to prevent the formation of sulfur trioxide (Pr.).

The sulfur dioxide obtained is cooled quickly in a horizontal, vertical, or pond cooler consisting essentially of a system of pipes surrounded by water. In all but the pond system the water is sprayed on the outside of the pipes (Op.).

The next step in the process is the absorption of the gas in water, in the presence of calcium and magnesium compounds. This is accomplished in a series of two or more absorption towers packed with limestone. A fine spray of water passes down through the tower system countercurrent to the sulfur dioxide gas, which is blown up through the tower (Op. and Pr.).

The liquor leaving the towers contains a certain amount of free sulfur dioxide, which is enhanced from time to time as the free sulfur dioxide vented from the digesters is bubbled through it in the "reclaiming tower" that follows. The final liquor as charged to the digesters is a solution of calcium and magnesium bisulfites, analyzing about 4.5 per cent "total" sulfur dioxide and about 3.5 per cent "free"[1] sulfur dioxide. The digester is filled with chips and the acid cooking liquor is pumped in at the bottom (Op.). The digesters are cylindrical steel vessels with a capacity of from 1 to 23 tons of fiber and 3,000 to 51,000 gal. of "acid." A special lining of cement, crushed quartz, and acid-resisting brick is used to avoid the corrosive action of the cooking liquor.

The digester is heated with direct steam. In recent years the industry has turned to digesters with forced outside circulation, which heat the cooking liquor in an outside stainless-steel tube heater and circulate it through the charge by means of pumps. This permits a better temperature distribution through the charge and prevents dilution of the liquor with the direct steam formerly used for heating. Conditions of the cook depend on the nature of the wood, the composition of the acid, and the quantity of pulp charged. The pressure varies from 70 to 160 lb. depending upon the construction of the plant. The time and the temperature range from 10 to 11 hr. and 105 to 155°C. (220 to 311°F.) (Pr.).

At the end of the cooking process the digester is discharged by blowing to a blow pit (a large, round tank having a false bottom and equipped with means to wash the pulp with fresh water). The cooking liquor is not recycled (Op.).

The pulp is pumped from the pit to a series of screens where knots and large lumps of fiber are removed (Op.).

The accepted stock from the screens is sent to the rifflers (a series of long felt-lined troughs equipped with cross bars every 6 ft.). The foreign matter in the pulp gradually settles out (Op.).

The relatively pure pulp is concentrated in thickeners which are cylindrical frames covered with 80-mesh bronze wire. The water passes through and the pulp is retained on the screen (Op.).

The pulp is sent to the bleacher, and free chlorine is introduced. After the chlorine has been exhausted, milk of lime is added to neutralize the mass (Pr.).

The stock is washed (Op.), thickened (Op.), and sent to the machine chest.

Pulp from the chest is formed into laps of about 35 per cent dry fiber content

---

[1] In the parlance of the pulp manufacturer, the "free" sulfur dioxide is the sum of that as sulfurous acid and that portion which requires alkali to convert from a bisulfite to a neutral sulfite.

(Op.), and the laps are dried with steam-heated rolls to a product which is 80 to 90 per cent dry fiber (Op.).

The milk-of-lime system of preparing the cooking liquor consists of slaking burnt lime containing a high percentage of magnesia with warm water to produce a 1°Bé. suspension. A high percentage of magnesia is desirable because the magnesium sulfites formed are more soluble than the corresponding calcium compounds. The calcium compounds tend to settle out and clog the pipes. This solution is treated with sulfur dioxide gas to produce the cooking liquor.

The direct process of cooking utilizes a vertical or horizontal digester equipped with hard lead or copper steam coils. The cooking time is about 58 hr., and the maximum temperature and the pressure are 130°C. (266°F.) and 60 lb. per sq. in.

Sulfite pulp is a high-grade type of pulp and serves for the manufacture of some of the finest papers embracing the bond office line. It is used either alone or with some rag pulp to make writing paper and high-grade book paper.

Waste Sulfite Liquor. The disposition of the waste liquors formed in this process has been the subject of much research. Until very recently it was common practice to dump this liquor into a near-by stream, but legislation preventing stream pollution is gradually stopping this. Although preventing stream pollution is now the most important factor, economics emphasizes the importance of the utilization of this vast potential raw material. Among the principal products which have been investigated, proposed, or used are alcohol by fermentation of the waste liquor (see Chap. 32); vanillin from the lignin present (Chap. 27); oxalic acid; tanning material; road binders; special cements; portland cement accelerator; corebinders; plastics from the lignin present; and food yeast.[1] Unfortunately, a great deal of work still remains to be done on this problem—either the disposal or the utilization of the by-product. The latest development for the disposal of waste calcium sulfite liquor is the use of the conkey flat-plate (Rosenblad) evaporator for concentrating the waste liquor to the point where it can be burned. This self-descaling evaporator functions whereas ordinary types of evaporators foul too much.

Rag Pulp.[2] A small but important source of fiber for the manufacture of fine paper is rags. New rags are largely scraps from textile mills and garment factories, while the old rags are collected from the waste disposal from domestic sources. The rags go through a thrasher where dust is removed, before they can be sorted. All are separated according to color. Colors hard to bleach are used in the manufacture of dark papers,

[1] INSKEEP, *et al.*, Food Yeast from Sulfite Liquor, *Ind. Eng. Chem.*, **43**, 1702 (1951); PEARL, Utilization of Sulfite Waste Liquor, *Chem. Eng. News*, **26**, 2950 (1948); ANON., Who'll Take Vanillin Now! *Chem. Week*, **70** (5), 33 (1952).

[2] "Pulp and Paper Manufacture," Vol. 2, Chap. 1.

and the more easily bleached colors are employed for the lighter papers. After being sorted, the rags are cut into small squares, the dust is removed, and the squares are passed over magnets to remove metallic foreign materials. After this they are ready for the cook. In this operation the wax and resins in the fibers are removed, together with additional dirt and grease, and the dyes loosened from the fibers. The cooking liquors include either caustic lime, caustic soda, or a mixture of caustic lime and soda ash. The digester is a cylindrical, horizontal, rotary boiler holding about 5 tons of cloth. Cooking is continued for 10 to 12 hr. at 120°C. The resulting pulp is washed, bleached with chlorine and/or chloride of lime, and rewashed. It is then ready for manufacture into fine writing paper.

MANUFACTURE OF PAPER

The various pulps, even though frequently manufactured in coarse sheets, still lack those properties which are so desirable in a finished paper, such as proper surface, opacity, strength, and feel. Pulp stock is prepared for formation into paper by two general processes: beating and

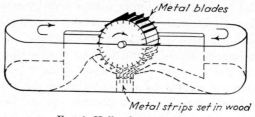

FIG. 6. Hollander or beater.

refining.[1] There is no sharp distinction between these two operations. Mills use either one or the other alone, or both together.

The most generally used type of *beater* (also known as a *Hollander*, Fig. 6) consists of a wooden or metal tank having rounded ends and a partition part way down the middle, thus giving a channel around which the pulp circulates continuously. On one side is a roll, equipped with knives or bars, and directly below this a bedplate consisting of stationary bars. In operation, the circulating pulp is forced between the bars on the revolving roll and the stationary bars of the bedplate. The roll itself may be raised or lowered to achieve the results desired. Beating the fibers makes the paper stronger, more uniform, more dense, more opaque,

[1] "Pulp and Paper Manufacture," Vol. 2, Chap. 3; LEWIS, SQUIRES, and BROUGHTON, "Industrial Chemistry of Colloidal and Amorphous Materials," Chap. XV, The Macmillan Company, New York, 1942; LEE, American Made Papers for Your Cigarettes, *Chem. Eng.*, **53** (6), 94 (1946), a pictured flow sheet on p. 138; ANON., Glassine Paper, *Chem. Eng.*, **54** (11), 148 (1947), a pictured flow sheet.

and less porous. It is in the beater that fillers, coloring agents, and sizing are added. Since the beaters are batch machines, some mills making lower grades of papers have done away with them entirely and use only refiners. The standard practice in making the finer grades of paper, however, is to follow the beaters with the refiners, which are continuous machines.

The *Jordan* engine (Fig. 7) is the standard *refiner* and consists essentially of a conical shell, on the inside of which are set stationary bars. Revolving inside the shell is a core, also set with bars. It is the action between these two sets of bars that produces the desired effect on the

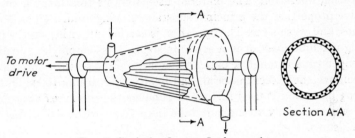

FIG. 7. Conical refiner or Jordan engine.

pulp. The latter enters the small end of the cone and, after being acted upon by the bars, passes out at the other end.

Filler, *sizing*, and *coloring* may be added either in the beater, which is usual practice, in the Jordan, or in both. The order in which these materials are added to the beater may vary in different mills, but generally is as follows: (1) The various pulps are blended to give the desired density and uniformity. (2) The filler is added with or just after the fiber. (3) After sufficient beating the size is put in and mixed thoroughly. (4) The color is added and distributed well throughout the mass. (5) The alum is introduced to produce coagulation and the desired coating of fibers.

All papers except absorbent types, *i.e.*, tissue or blotting paper, must have a *filler*[1] added to them, the purpose of which is to occupy the spaces between the fibers, thus giving a smoother surface, a more brilliant whiteness, increasing printability, and an improved opacity. The fillers are always inorganic substances and may be either naturally occurring materials, such as talc or certain clays, or manufactured products such as suitably precipitated calcium carbonate, blanc fixe, or titanium dioxide. All are finely ground.

Sizing[2] is added to paper to impart resistance to penetration by liquids. Again, the only papers not so treated are blotting and other

---

[1] "Pulp and Paper Manufacture," Vol. 2, Chap. 4.

[2] *Ibid.*, Chap. 5; ANON., Compact Emulsifier Helps Paper Makers, *Chem. Eng.*, **58** (10), 238 (1951).

absorbent papers, where penetration is desired. The sizing may either be added in the beating operation or applied to the surface after the sheet is formed. The process of engine or stock sizing, *i.e.*, adding size in the beater, involves the addition of the sizing agent, consisting of either a soap made from the saponification of rosin with alkali or a wax emulsion, followed by precipitation of the size itself with papermaker's alum, $Al_2(SO_4)_3 \cdot 18H_2O$. This treatment gives a gelatinous film on the fiber, which loses water of hydration and produces a hardened surface.

Tub sizing, on the other hand, is carried out on the dried paper, or surfaces which may or may not have been previously and partly sized in the beating operation. The material used for this treatment must have adhesive properties, the principal substances being animal glue, modified starches, and wash sizes. The operation is carried out either on the paper-making machine itself or in a separate sizing press employing air drying. The paper runs through a bath of the size material, then through rolls that remove the excess material, and finally over drying rolls. This type of sizing operation is used further to enhance the water resistance of the paper and especially to make it take ink evenly without blurring, even after erasures.

Another material that is added to the paper is *coloring*.[1] Approximately 98 per cent of all paper produced has a certain amount of coloring material added to it. Coloring, like sizing, may be added either in the beater or after the paper has been made, although about 95 per cent is added in the former manner. However, surface coloring, the latter method, uses less dye and requires the production of only one type of paper, which may be colored any shade later as needed.

All types of dyes (acid, basic, direct, sulfur) and all types of pigments (both natural and synthetic) are used as coloring agents. The acid dyes have no affinity for the cellulose fibers and must, therefore, be fixed to them by means of mordants. If the paper is colored in the beater, the alum that is added to precipitate the size will also act as a mordant for the dye.

Surface dyeing may be carried out either in the papermaking machine or in a separate piece of equipment. In either case, the process consists in passing the paper through the dye bath, removing the excess dye by means of press rolls, and drying.

The machines used for the actual formation of the sheet are of two general types: the *Fourdrinier machine* and the *cylinder machine*. The basic principles of operation are essentially the same for both machines. The sheet is formed on a traveling wire or a cylinder, dewatered under rollers, dried by heated rolls, and finished by calender rolls.

[1] "Pulp and Paper Manufacture," Vol. 2, Chap. 6.

Fourdrinier Machine.[1] Figure 8 shows the essential parts of a Fourdrinier machine. The stock from the foregoing operations, containing approximately ½ per cent fiber, is first sent through screens to the head box, from which it flows through the sluice onto a moving, endless, bronze-wire screen. The pulp fibers remain on the screen while a great portion of the water drains through. As the screen moves along, it has a sidewise shaking motion which serves to orient some of the fibers and give better felting action and more strength to the sheet. While still on the screen, the paper passes over suction boxes to remove water and under a dandy roll which smooths the top of the sheet. Rubber deckle straps travel

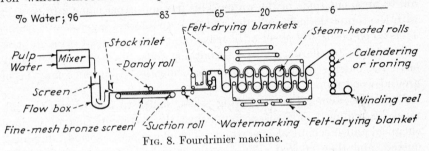

FIG. 8. Fourdrinier machine.

along the sides of the screen at the same speed and thus serve to form the edges of the paper.

From the wire, the paper is transferred to the first felt blanket which carries it through a series of press rolls, where more water is removed and the paper given a watermark if so desired. Leaving the first felt the paper passes through steel smoothing rolls and is picked up by the second felt which carries it through a series of drying rolls heated internally by steam. The paper enters the rolls with a moisture content of 60 to 70 per cent water and leaves them 90 to 94 per cent dry. Sizing may be sprayed on the sheet at this point, in which case it must pass through another series of drying rolls before entering the calender stack which is a series of smooth, heavy, steel rolls which impart the final surface to the paper. The resulting product, finished paper, is wound on the reel. The enormous quantity of water used makes it necessary to recirculate as much of it as possible for economical operation.

The operation of a Fourdrinier is a very complicated procedure. One of the major problems is making suitable allowance in the speed of the various rolls for the shrinkage of the paper as it dries. The operating speeds of the machines vary from 200 ft. per min. for the finer grades of paper, to 1,700 ft. per min. for newsprint.

[1] SAWYER, *et al.*, Kraft Papermaking, *Ind. Eng. Chem.*, **42**, 1007 (1950); SANKEY and COWAN, Problems in Materials Separation on a Fourdrinier Machine, *Chem. Eng. Progr.*, **44**, 745 (1948).

Cylinder Machine. For the manufacture of heavy paper, cardboard, or nonuniform paper, the cylinder machine is employed. It enables several similar or dissimilar layers to be united together into one heavy sheet. The cylinder machine has from four to seven parallel vats into each of which similar or dissimilar dilute paper stocks are charged. A wire-covered rotating cylinder dips into each vat. The paper stock is deposited on the turning screen as the water inside the cylinder is removed. As the cylinder revolves farther, the paper stock reaches the top where the wet layer comes into contact with and adheres to a moving felt. The traveling felt carrying the wet sheet underneath passes on under a couch roll to press out some of the water. This felt and paper come into contact with the top of the next cylinder and pick up another layer of wet paper. Thus a composite wet sheet or board is built up and passed through press rolls and on to the drying and smoothing rolls. Such a composite may have the outside layers of good stock while the inside ones may be of ground-wood pulp.

Paper De-inking. For reworking waste paper to fine papers the ink must be removed. This is accomplished by a combination of various chemical and mechanical operations.[1] The old paper is sorted, shredded, dusted, and then cooked. The digester is either an open cooking tank with fume hood or a rotary boiler, live steam being used in either case. The cooking liquor usually employed is a weak caustic soda solution of about 8 per cent, the cooking time is around 10 hr.; the temperatures are in the neighborhood of 200°F. The purpose of the cooking process is to dissolve out the vehicle from the ink, thus breaking up the ink so that it may be removed. The cooked pulp goes to a series of screen washers similar to thickeners, where dirt and loosened carbon from the ink are removed. It may be necessary to put the pulp through a beater before washing, in order to aid in the loosening of the ink from the fibers. The washed pulp is bleached with either chlorine gas or chloride of lime, yielding in many cases a snow-white product. The recovered pulp is of such a quality that it is used in all fine grades of paper, mixed with new pulp in proportions that vary over a wide range.

Another method of de-inking paper, which has found widespread favor particularly in the utilization of old telephone directories, is based on printing with an ink having an iron lake of hematin as pigment. Paper printed with this special ink is first disintegrated in rod mills and then treated with sulfur dioxide gas in diffusers. The sulfur dioxide serves to discharge the ink from the paper. The gas is added as such, as a strong liquor containing 6 grams of sulfur dioxide per liter, and then as a weak liquor containing 4 grams of sulfur dioxide per liter (see Fig. 9). The

---

[1] WELLS, De-inking and Reprocessing Paper Accomplished by New Methods, *Chem. & Met. Eng.*, **40**, 634 (1933); *cf.* LEE, Paper Mill Goes Modern—Now De-inks with Peroxide, *Chem. Eng.*, **55** (1), 106 (1948), with a pictured flow sheet on p. 146.

de-inked pulp is discharged to a stuff chest and then to a rotary filter and screw press, finally yielding a recovered paper stock. The pigment is recovered from the spent liquor by neutralization with caustic soda and subsequent filtration in a plate-and-frame press. Part of the sulfur dioxide in the waste cooking liquor is recovered in a "SO_2 boiler," a

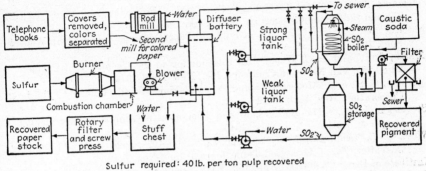

Sulfur required: 40 lb. per ton pulp recovered

Fig. 9. Flow sheet for paper de-inking.

waste containing 2 grams of sulfur dioxide per liter being discharged to the sewer.

PAPERBOARD[1]

The use of waste paper in the manufacture of pulp has reached a very important stage, the reasons being (1) the large supply available, (2) the small cost of making it into pulp, (3) the low original cost, and (4) the grade of product obtained. Over 12,000,000 tons of products from this waste are made yearly, as Table 2 shows. With only mechanical methods, old newspapers, wrapping paper, and boxboard may be made into pulp suitable for roofing paper and new boxboard. Since the product is dark colored, it is not necessary to remove the ink and pigments. Therefore, shredding and beating operations suffice.

SELECTED REFERENCES

"The Manufacture of Pulp and Paper," McGraw-Hill Book Company, Inc., New York: Vol. 1, "Mathematics, How to Read Drawings, Physics," 1921; Vol. II, "Mechanics and Hydraulics, Electricity, Chemistry," 1923; Vols. III, IV, and V of this series are revised under the new title "Pulp and Paper Manufacture," and numbered Vols. 1, 2, 3, and 4: Vol. 1, "Preparation and Treatment of Wood Pulp," 1950; Vol. 2, "Preparation of Stock for Paper Making," 1951; Vol. 3, "Manufacture and Testing of Paper and Board," 1953; Vol. 4, "Auxiliary Paper Mill Equipment," 1955.

[1] Anon., Modern Paperboard Plant, *Chem. Eng.*, **59** (2), 240 (1952), a pictured flow sheet.

Casey, J. P., "Pulp and Paper," 2 vols., Interscience Publishers, Inc., New York, 1952.

Jenness, L. C., and John Lewis, editors, "University of Maine Lectures on Pulp and Paper Manufacturing," Lockwood Trade Journal Company, Inc., New York, 1951.

Clapperton, R. H., "Modern Papermaking," 3d ed., Basil, Blackwell, and Mott, Ltd., Oxford, England, 1947.

Tiemann, H. D., "Wood Technology; Constitution, Properties, and Uses," 3d ed., Pitman Publishing Corporation, New York, 1951.

Sutermeister, C., "The Chemistry of Pulp and Paper Making," 3d ed., John Wiley & Sons, Inc., New York, 1941.

Marsh, J. T., and F. C. Wood, "An Introduction to the Chemistry of Cellulose," 2d ed., D. Van Nostrand Company, Inc., New York, 1942.

Witham, G. S., Sr., "Modern Pulp and Paper Making," 2d ed., Reinhold Publishing Corporation, New York, 1942.

Stevenson, L. T., "The Background and Economics of American Papermaking," Harper & Brothers, New York, 1940.

West, C. J., "Bibliography of Papermaking," 1900–1928, 1928–1935, and annually thereafter, *Tappi*, Lockwood Trade Journal, Inc., New York.

Institute of Paper Chemistry, Appleton, Wis. Various publications.

Ott, Emil, editor, "Cellulose and Cellulose Derivatives," Interscience Publishers, Inc., New York, 1943.

CHAPTER 34

SYNTHETIC FIBERS

The ability of the chemist and the chemical engineer to create, from the test tube through the factory, products that are often superior to naturally occurring materials is one of the outstanding accomplishments of this generation, and nowhere is it so graphically portrayed as by the modern synthetic, or man-made, fibers. These synthetics from their humble beginning in 1900 have grown to a total world production of more than 4.3 billion pounds in 1954. The United States started the manufacture of rayon in 1910 and produced in 1954 about 1.2 billion pounds of rayon and acetate. Over 300,000,000 lb. of other synthetic fibers were made in 1954. The list of synthetic fibers, which in 1900 included only nitro-cellulose, today has many new products, the *more important ones* being viscose rayon, acetate, nylon, and the fibers made from polyacrylonitrile (Orlon), acrylic copolymers (dynel, Acrilan), polyesters (Dacron), vinyls (saran, Vinyon), proteins (Vicara, Ardil), and glass (Fiberglas, Vitron). It is the purpose of this chapter to consider the leading synthetic fibers, their development, methods of manufacture, and uses, thereby presenting a picture of the chemistry and engineering behind our modern "fashions out of test tubes."

Although the word fiber originally referred only to naturally occurring materials (cotton, wool, etc.), it is now used for synthetic products. This latter usage includes both the *semisynthetics* and the *true synthetics*. Semisynthetics result when natural polymeric materials such as cellulose or certain proteins are brought into a dissolved or dispersed state and then spun into fine filaments. Viscose rayon and the various protein fibers are included in this classification. True synthetic polymers as nylon, Orlon, Dacron, etc., result from two methods of forming long-chain molecules: addition polymerization and condensation polymerization. The polymer is then taken from its melt or solution and processed into fiber form. Cellulose acetate really lies between these two classes as here a natural polymer (cellulose) is converted into one of its derivatives (cellulose acetate) which is dissolved and spun into fiber form. From an engineering viewpoint, perhaps the best method of classification for synthetic fibers is by the type of spinning technique—wet, dry, or melt.

Except for the various rayons and acetate, this classification will be used to correlate the manufacturing procedures for the other fibers.

Three of the more important general properties of fibers are length, crimp, and cross section. Concerning length there exist essentially two types of fibers: continuous filaments and staple fibers. *Continuous filaments* are individual fibers whose length is almost infinite. Silk, rayon, nylon, and all other true synthetics are manufactured in this manner. Cotton and wool are examples of natural fibers in the *staple* form, *i.e.*, of short and more or less uniform lengths. Artificial staple fibers such as rayon, acetate, nylon, and Dacron result from the cutting of the tow (untwisted filaments) to uniform lengths usually between 6 and 20 cm. *Crimp* is the curl or waviness placed in synthetic fibers by chemical or mechanical action which is of great importance in the processability of staple fibers. Cotton and wool possess natural crimp. *Cross section* is another important property of all fibers. It is usually measured in *denier*. A fiber has a cross section corresponding to 1 denier, if 9,000 meters of it weighs 1 gram.

RAYON AND ACETATE

The idea of creating synthetic fibers is not new. In 1664, Robert Hooke prophesied that "silk equal to, if not better than that produced by the silkworm will be produced by mechanical means." However, it was not until 1855 that the first patent was issued for the preparation of artificial silk utilizing nitro-cellulose that had been discovered by Schönbein in 1845. Joseph Swan exhibited in London in 1885 fabrics woven from fibers prepared by squeezing collodion through fine orifices. It remained for Count Chardonnet, "father of the rayon industry," to focus and utilize the work of all who preceded him and to establish the first commercial unit for producing artificial silk in 1891.

The basic process of producing cuprammonium rayon was patented in 1890 and the viscose process was discovered in 1892. The first patent for the production of cellulose acetate filaments was issued in 1894. Commercial production in the United States of viscose rayon began in 1910, of nitro-cellulose rayon in 1920, and of cellulose acetate in 1924. By 1926 the production of the various types of rayon and acetate exceeded the consumption of silk. The viscose, cuprammonium, and acetate yarns proved superior to nitro-cellulose which was discontinued here in 1934. Since 1949, nitro-cellulose rayon has not been made anywhere.

Uses and Economics. In 1954, the United States production and consumption of rayon and acetate, the largest man-made fibers, were as shown in Table 1. The 1950 world production of rayon and acetate was percentagewise, according to process: viscose, 73.5; acetate, 23.5; and cuprammonium, 3. Viscose is the largest man-made fiber and its manufacture consumes more than 10 per cent of our entire *industrial chemical* output. High-tenacity viscose yarn is used mainly in tire cords and fabrics for tires, hose, and belting. The difference in strength between ordinary and high-tenacity viscose is conditioned by the amount of

TABLE 1. RAYON AND ACETATE PRODUCTION, 1954[a]

Filament yarn	Million lb.	Staple fiber	Million lb.
Textile, total..............	368	Viscose...................	312
Viscose[b]...............	170	Acetate..................	67
Acetate................	198	Total.................	379
Viscose high tenacity.......	339		
Total................	707	Total rayon and acetate....	1,086

[a] ANON., *Textile Organon*, February, 1955, p. 17.

[b] Cuprammonium-process rayon yarn is combined here, as no separate breakdown is given to avoid disclosure of individual company operations. No cuprammonium rayon is used for the production of staple fiber.

orientation imparted to the fiber molecules when made. The hydroxyl groups in the cellulose molecule allow water absorption to take place in the fiber and also serve to hold molecules together despite strong bending, thus resulting in fibers which tend to maintain their strength better and even at high temperatures. Since early 1950 substantial quantities of

TABLE 2. UNITED STATES TEXTILE RAYON AND ACETATE FILAMENT-YARN SHIPMENTS, 1954[a]
(Million lb.)

	Viscose and cupra yarns	Acetate yarn
Knit goods:		
Hosiery.........................	2.3	1.1
Circular........................	20.8	1.0
Warp...........................	4.7	24.1
Woven goods:		
Broad (over 12 in. wide)............	126.1	167.4
Narrow (less than 12 in.)...........	12.5	0.5
Miscellaneous......................	21.6	3.0
Total textile.....................	188.	197.1

[a] ANON., *Textile Organon*, February, 1955, p. 26.

both viscose and acetate have been blended with wool in carpet manufacture. Table 2 shows the breakdown of the textile consumption according to process. The price of rayon and acetate varies according to the size of the filaments, process of manufacture, and type of finish, but it is around 75 cents a pound for 150 denier viscose and acetate.

Raw Materials. The total cellulose consumption of the United States fiber industry for 1950 was 590,600 short tons of which 77 per cent was wood pulp, the remainder cotton linters. Of the total cellulose employed for the viscose and cuprammonium processes, 87 per cent was wood pulp. The acetate process for its cellulose requirements utilized wood pulp, 61 per cent, and cotton linters, 39 per cent.

Up to a few years ago, the cuprammonium and acetate processes used only cotton linters as their source of cellulose, but recent trends here are toward sulfite-pulp consumption. The viscose process is based on sulfite and some sulfate pulp. The preparation of the wood pulp is described in Chap. 33. The cotton linters are obtained as follows: The seeds from the cotton gin, which have a considerable quantity of short fibers clinging to them, are cleaned to remove any foreign impurities such as leaves and sand, and are sent to the delintering machines. Here the short attached fibers, called *cotton linters*, are cut off by a row of disk saws. First and second cuts are made, the latter fibers being shorter but cleaner. They have the following typical analysis: cellulose (obtainable by caustic soda digestion), 80 to 85 per cent; ash, 1 to 1.5 per cent; iron, 0.06 per cent; ether extract, 1 per cent; lignin (insoluble in H_2SO_4), 3 per cent; moisture, 6 per cent. These linters are graded, examined, and tested by laboratory processing in the solution in which they are eventually to be used.

The purification and conversion to the so-called *chemical cotton* are accomplished as follows: A blend of raw linters is charged to a rotary digester, into which is pumped dilute (1 to 10 per cent) NaOH. Steam is introduced and the cotton cooked under about 20 to 110 lb. per sq. in. for 2 to 6 hr. The mass is dropped into a tank, washed, and bleached. The bleach tanks are preferably of stainless steel, with false, perforated bottoms; here chlorine as such or in the form of hypochlorite is added to the linters and the resulting discolored solution drained off. An acid treatment may then be applied to remove inorganic matter. The cotton is again washed, is pumped over riffles to remove foreign matter and passed through rubber-covered squeeze rolls, which reduce the moisture content to about 50 per cent. The wet lumps are pulled apart in a "picker" and allowed to fall onto a conveyer which carries them through a tunnel drier and to the baler. The resulting product is chemical cotton, 98 per cent α-cellulose (see Fig. 2 of Chap. 22).

If sheet cellulose, the form used in viscose manufacture, is desired, the cotton, after the bleaching treatment has been completed, is blended with several other batches, passed successively through a beater and a refiner (see Manufacture of Paper in Chap. 33), and formed into sheets on a Fourdrinier.[1]

Viscose rayon is a major consumer of sulfuric acid, caustic soda, and

[1] KIRK and OTHMER, *op. cit.*, Vol. 3, p. 352.

carbon disulfide. Titanium dioxide is used in delusterizing, the yarn. Cellulose acetate employs large quantities of acetic anhydride, glacial acetic acid, sulfuric acid, and acetone. In addition to this important consumption of basic chemicals, the fiber industry needs significant quantities of dyes and other chemicals.[1]

The viscose process and the cuprammonium process produce a filament of regenerated cellulose, while the acetate forms a thread that is a definite chemical compound of cellulose, cellulose acetate. Although each of these processes is quite different as far as details of procedure are concerned, they all follow the same general outline: solution of the cellulose through a chemical reaction, aging or ripening of the solution (peculiar to viscose), filtration and removal of air, spinning of the fiber, combining the filaments into yarn, purifying the yarn (not necessary for acetate), and finishing (bleaching, washing, oiling, and drying).

Reactions

Viscose:[2]

$$(C_6H_9O_4 \cdot OH)_x + xNaOH \rightarrow (C_6H_9O_4 \cdot ONa)_x + xH_2O$$
Cellulose   Alkali cellulose

$$(C_6H_9O_4 \cdot ONa)_x + xCS_2 \rightarrow \left(C_6H_9O_4{-}O{-}C{\overset{S}{\underset{SNa}{<}}} \right)_x$$
Cellulose xanthate

$$3\left(C_6H_9O_4{-}O{-}C{\overset{S}{\underset{SNa}{<}}} \right)_x + 2xH_2O \rightarrow \left(C_{18}H_{27}O_{12}(OH)_2O{-}C{\overset{S}{\underset{SNa}{<}}} \right)_x$$
                  Ripened xanthate
$$+ 2xCS_2 + 2xNaOH$$

$$\left(C_{18}H_{27}O_{12}(OH)_2O{-}C{\overset{S}{\underset{SNa}{<}}} \right)_x + \frac{x}{2}H_2SO_4 \rightarrow (C_6H_9O_4 \cdot OH)_{3x} + xCS_2 + \frac{x}{2}Na_2SO_4$$
                              Viscose rayon

Cellulose Acetate:

$$[C_6H_7O_2 \cdot (OH)_3]_x + 3x(CH_3CO)_2O \rightarrow [C_6H_7O_2(O_2CCH_3)_3]_x$$
Cellulose   Cellulose acetate
$$+ 3xCH_3CO_2H$$

[1] ANON., Textiles Emerging from Slump, *Chem. & Eng. News,* **30,** 3620 (1952).

[2] The cellulose molecule is composed of a large undetermined number of glucose units, here represented as $(C_6H_9O_4OH)x$. The value of x does not remain constant throughout these reactions. Each reaction causes a reduction in the molecular weight of the cellulose molecule, so that the viscose-rayon molecule is considerably smaller than the original cellulose fed. Some CS_2 breaks away from the cellulose xanthate during the ripening process.

Cuprammonium:

$(C_6H_{10}O_5)_x$ + $Cu(OH)_2$ + NH_3 + H_2O → solution of cellulose[1]
Cellulose   Schweitzer's reagent
Cellulose solution + NaOH (5%) → partly coagulated cellulose
Partly coagulated cellulose + $H_2SO_4(1\frac{1}{2}\%)$ → $(C_6H_{10}O_5)_x$
                                             Cuprammonium rayon

The main energy requirements for any of these processes are for the mechanical operations of the pumps that force the solutions through the spinnerets and for the multitudinous other mechanical steps of the various processes. Little energy has to be supplied to cause the chemical reactions to occur.

Viscose Manufacturing Process

From the tonnage standpoint, this is the most important of the synthetic processes, representing approximately two-thirds of all the rayon and acetate manufactured in the United States. The finished filament is pure cellulose as shown by the equations but, because it consists of smaller molecules than the cellulose of the original wood pulp or cotton, it possesses different physical properties.

Unit Operations and Unit Processes. The sequences of the process,[2] as shown in Fig. 1, can be broken down into the following *unit operations* (Op.) and *unit processes* (Pr.):

The cellulosic raw material (usually sheets made from wood pulp) is charged to a steeping press containing vertical perforated steel plates; and is steeped in a caustic soda solution (approximately 18 per cent) for 2 to 4 hr. at 56 to 62°F. (Pr.).

The excess liquor is drained off and recovered[3] (Fig. 2). The soft sheets of alkali cellulose are reduced to small crumbs in a shredder (Op.). This requires 2 to 3 hr., and the temperature is maintained at 65 to 68°F.

The crumbs of alkali cellulose are aged for 48 to 72 hr. at 75°F. in steel cans. Some oxidation and degradation[4] occur, although the actual chemical change is unknown (Pr.).

After sufficient aging, the crumbs are charged into the barratte (a hexagonal, horizontal iron drum mixer with a hollow axis). Carbon disulfide in the ratio

[1] This is a chemical reaction but the exact formula of the soluble reaction product is not known.

[2] ANON., Producing Cellophane and Viscose Rayon, *Chem. & Met. Eng.*, **46**, 25 (1939).

[3] See Chap. 4 in LIPSETT, "Industrial Wastes," Atlas Publishing Company, Inc., New York, 1951, for chemical waste recovery in the viscose-rayon industry. The Webcell dialyzer process is also included here.

[4] LEWIS, SQUIRES, and BROUGHTON, "Industrial Chemistry of Colloidal and Amorphous Materials," pp. 360ff., The Macmillan Company, New York, 1942.

of 1 lb. of disulfide per 10 lb. of crumbs is added. The drum is rotated for about 3 hr., during which the crumbs gradually turn yellow and finally a deep orange and coagulate into small balls (Pr.).

The cellulose xanthate balls are dropped into a jacketed mixer (vissolver) containing dilute sodium hydroxide. The xanthate particles dissolve in the caustic and the final product, viscose solution, contains 61 per cent cellulose and 8 per cent sodium hydroxide (Pr.). If desired, delustering agents such as titanium dioxide or organic pigments[1] are added to the viscose solution in the mixer.

Several batches of viscose solution are blended and ripened for 4 to 5 days under rigidly controlled conditions at 66°F. and until the cellulose approaches nearly to the coagulating point. The percentage of combined sulfur decreases as some xanthic acid splits off and part of the cellulose is regenerated (Pr.). During this ripening period the solution is filtered several times to get rid of solid material likely to clog the spinnerets and finally placed under vacuum to remove all bubbles which would break the continuity of the filament (Op.).

The solution is fed to the spinning machine. Two types are in general use: the bucket and the bobbin. Three-quarters of United States production uses the bucket type (see Figs. 3 to 5). The solution is extruded under pressure (gear pumps are used) through the spinneret into the spinning bath (Op.).

The spinnerets are small caps of noble metal, containing minute holes through which the solution is extruded, as depicted in Fig. 3. Just ahead of the spinneret are the candle filters to remove, in a final filtration, any foreign matter that might clog the holes. The spinning solution contains 8 to 10 per cent sulfuric acid to neutralize the caustic, 13.5 to 21.5 per cent sodium sulfate, about 1 per cent zinc sulfate to promote crenellation of the fiber, and 4 to 10 per cent glucose to prevent crystallization of the salts in the filaments. The solution from the spinnerets is coagulated in the bath as a filament of regenerated cellulose (Pr.).

If the bucket machine is used, the spinneret head dips horizontally into the spinning solution, several of the filaments are gathered into a thread and fed down to a small centrifugal bucket spinning at 7,500 r.p.m. (Op.). This is illustrated by Figs. 4 and 5. The bucket imparts one twist to the filaments per revolution and removes a greater portion of the occluded bath liquor through perforations in the periphery (Fig. 3).

If the bobbin machine is used, the spinnerets dip vertically upward into the spinning bath, and the filaments are wound on a revolving bobbin, as shown in Fig. 6 (Op.). No twist is imparted to the thread.

Yarn from either type is washed to remove the spinning liquor (Op.).

The bobbin yarn is dried (Op.), twisted, and skeined (Op.).

The bucket cakes are skeined without drying (Op.).

Both types of yarn are desulfurized by treating with a ¾ to 1 per cent sodium sulfide solution (Pr.).

Both types are washed (Op.), bleached in hydrochlorite solution (Pr.), washed again, dried, and coned (Op.).

[1] BENGER, Economic and Technical Aspects of the Rayon Industry, *Ind. Eng. Chem.*, **28**, 511 (1936).

In the continuous process,[1] the entire treatment of the filament after extrusion, including washing, desulfurizing, bleaching, lubricating, drying, and twisting of the yarn is carried out continuously on one machine, without more than routine attention from the operators. The process

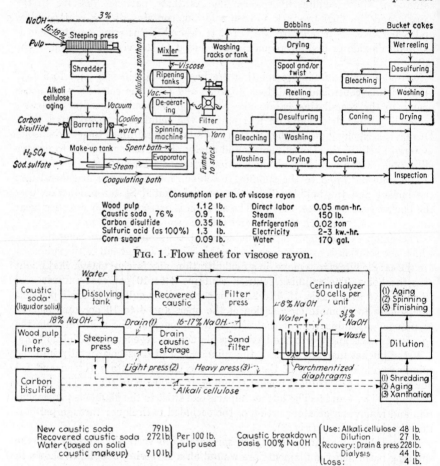

Consumption per lb. of viscose rayon

Wood pulp	1.12 lb.	Direct labor	0.05 man-hr.
Caustic soda, 76%	0.9 lb.	Steam	150 lb.
Carbon disulfide	0.35 lb.	Refrigeration	0.02 ton
Sulfuric acid (as 100%)	1.3 lb.	Electricity	2–3 kw.-hr.
Corn sugar	0.09 lb.	Water	170 gal.

Fig. 1. Flow sheet for viscose rayon.

New caustic soda	79 lb			Use: Alkali cellulose	48 lb.
Recovered caustic soda	272 lb	Per 100 lb.	Caustic breakdown	Dilution	27 lb.
Water (based on solid		pulp used	basis 100% NaOH	Recovery: Drain & press	228 lb.
caustic makeup)	910 lb			Dialysis	44 lb.
				Loss:	4 lb.

Fig. 2. Flow sheet for caustic soda recovery in viscose manufacture—Cerini process.

reduces the entire series of operations, requiring by the old method as high as 90 hr., to about 6 min. and is revolutionizing the entire industry.

Each year more viscose yarn is made into staple fiber. This is manufactured by drawing the filaments from many spinnerets without twisting and cutting them into short, uniform lengths.[2] Filament yarn or fiber,

[1] OLIVE, Viscose Rayon Spun Continuously, *Chem. & Met. Eng.*, **45**, 668 (1938); ANON., Continuous Production of Viscose Rayon, *Chem. & Met. Eng.*, **49** (10), 116 (1942), pictured flow sheet; ANON., Continuous Rayon Spinning Process, *Chem. Eng.*, **54** (11), 103 (1947).

[2] For a pictured flow sheet, see *Chem. & Met. Eng.*, **51** (8), 128 (1944).

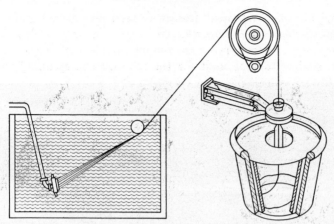

FIG. 3. Spinning in viscose process. (*Courtesy of E. I. du Pont de Nemours & Company, Inc.*)

FIG. 4. General view of bucket type of spinning machine at the Richmond, Va., plant of E. I. du Pont de Nemours & Company, Inc. The white lines up the face of the machine are the rayon threads as they leave the chemical baths. (*Courtesy of E. I. du Pont de Nemours & Company, Inc.*)

described above, is rayon or acetate twisted into a continuous yarn as the filaments leave the spinneret.

Transparent viscose sheeting (cellophane) is manufactured from a solution similar to that used for the rayon.[1] The spinning solution is

FIG. 5. "Threading up" a spinning machine. Pulp used in the manufacture of rayon comes from the barrattes; it is treated chemically and becomes a reddish-brown sirup and is then fed through nozzles called spinnerets into an acid bath that hardens it again. A worker at a rayon plant of E. I. du Pont de Nemours & Company, Inc., near Richmond, Va., picks up the thin thread, passes it over a spinning machine, and guides it into buckets by a stream of water. (*Courtesy of E. I. du Pont de Nemours & Company, Inc.*)

extruded through a narrow slot into the coagulating bath. This may be done in a variety of ways, one of which is to cast the sheet onto a rotating drum, the lower side of which is submerged in the bath. The viscose film formed is transferred to succeeding tanks of warm water to remove the acid. It is desulfurized in a basic solution of sodium sulfide and rewashed. The characteristic yellow tinge must then be removed in a hypochlorite bleach bath, after which the sheet is rewashed. Then, in

[1] HYDEN, Manufacture and Properties of Regenerated Cellulose Films, *Ind. Eng. Chem.*, **21**, 405 (1929); LEVEY, Films and Sheeting from Plastic Products, *Modern Plastics*, **14** (12), 40 (1937); BRANDENBERGER, Notes on Cellophane, *J. Franklin Inst.*, **226**, 797 (1938); a pictured flow sheet for cellophane is given in *Chem. & Met. Eng.*, **46**, 25 (1939).

order to impart softness and pliability to the film, it is passed through a glycerine bath where it absorbs about 17 per cent glycerine, after which it is dried. Much of the cellophane is subsequently made moistureproof by coating it on one side with a suitable lacquer of nitro-cellulose. The development of moistureproofing was due principally to W. H. Charch of the Du Pont Company, to whom has been awarded the 1932 Schoellkopf Medal of the Buffalo Section of the American Chemical Society for this

Fig. 6. A spinning machine of the bobbin type used in the manufacture of rayon. (*Courtesy of E. I. du Pont de Nemours & Company, Inc.*)

achievement. Cellophane may be dyed, either with mordant dyes or direct colors. Owing to its attractive appearance as well as its moisture-proofing, it is widely used as a packaging and wrapping material.

Viscose may be employed to prepare a durable cellulose sponge by introducing a mixture of various sizes of Glauber's salt crystals, hemp or fibrous material, and viscose in a box, which is placed in the coagulating bath to regenerate the cellulose. The blocks are leached with warm water to remove the crystals of salt and cut into small-sized blocks for sale.

CUPRAMMONIUM MANUFACTURING PROCESS

Cuprammonium rayon is represented by the Furness process (Fig. 7), a continuous process that spins, coagulates, decoppers, washes, dries, twists, and spools the yarn in a total time of about 3 min. Bemberg cuprammonium rayon owes some of its desirable properties to "stretch" spinning, wherein the filaments are stretched during the coagulation in the spinning bath. This process can produce extremely fine yarns of as low as 15 denier and of great wet strength. Only one company produces this kind of rayon in this country.

Unit Operations and Unit Processes. The spinning solution is prepared by charging 350 lb. of linters to a double-arm mixer with vacuum connections, as shown in Fig. 7. The ammoniacal copper hydroxide solution (prepared by adding caustic soda to a copper sulfate solution, filtering, and dissolving the precipitate in a solution of 26°Bé. aqua ammonia) is run in and mixed (Op. and Pr.).

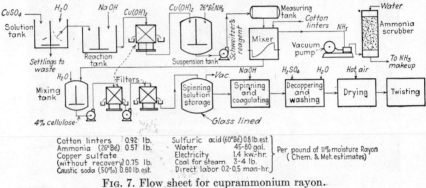

Cotton linters   0.92 lb.
Ammonia (26°Bé) 0.57 lb.
Copper sulfate
(without recovery) 0.75 lb.
Caustic soda (50%) 0.80 lb. est.

Sulfuric acid (60°Bé) 0.8 lb. est.
Water   45-80 gal.
Electricity   1.4 kw.-hr.
Coal for steam   3-4 lb.
Direct labor 0.2-0.5 man-hr.

Per pound of 11% moisture Rayon
(Chem. & Met. estimates)

FIG. 7. Flow sheet for cuprammonium rayon.

The excess ammonia is withdrawn through a vacuum line and the sirupy solution is diluted with water and filtered five times (Op.).

Aging of this solution is not necessary. The solution is forced vertically upward through a nickel spinneret into a coagulating bath of 5 per cent caustic soda (Op.).

The filament is coagulated (Pr.) and passed into a decoppering bath of 1½ per cent sulfuric acid (Pr.).

The yarn is washed (Op.), dried (Op.), and twisted (Op.) continuously by means of a specially designed cylindrical cage.[1]

Recovery of chemicals is very successfully accomplished; 95 per cent of the copper and 40 per cent of the ammonia are obtained again. The caustic soda is not consumed and is recycled.

CELLULOSE ACETATE MANUFACTURING PROCESS

Cellulose acetate (or its homologs) is an ester of cellulose and not regenerated cellulose. The spinning solution may be used to produce fibers, transparent film, photographic film, or precipitated to form molding powder for plastics and the basic constituent of cellulose lacquers.[2]

[1] CHASE, Furness Process Rayon, *Textile World*, **80**, 1888 (1931).

[2] SMITH, Cellulose Acetate Rayons, *Ind. Eng. Chem.*, **32**, 1555 (1940); for a pictured flow sheet on Cellulose Acetate Staple Yarn, see *Chem. Eng.*, **52** (1), 132 (1945).

Unit Operations and Unit Processes. The general sequence of operations (Fig. 8) is essentially the same as those of the other two described processes. The raw material for the spinning solution is prepared by charging 100 lb. of acetic anhydride, 100 lb. of glacial acetic acid, and a small quantity of sulfuric acid as a catalyst to a jacketed, glass-lined, agitated, cast-iron acetylator (Op.). The mixture is cooled to 45°F. and 35 lb. of linters are added slowly. The acetylation requires 5 to 8 hr. and the temperature is maintained below 86°F. (Pr.).

The viscous fluid is diluted with equal parts of concentrated acetic acid and 10 per cent sulfuric acid and allowed to age for 15 hr. at 100°F. Hydration of some of the acetate groups occurs (Pr.). No method has been devised at present

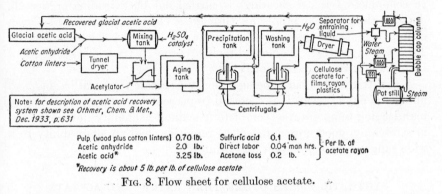

Pulp (wood plus cotton linters) 0.70 lb.   Sulfuric acid   0.1 lb.
Acetic anhydride   2.0 lb.   Direct labor   0.04 man hrs. } Per lb. of acetate rayon
Acetic acid*   3.25 lb.   Acetone loss   0.2 lb.

*Recovery is about 5 lb. per lb. of cellulose acetate

FIG. 8. Flow sheet for cellulose acetate.

whereby cellulose can be converted directly to a product of the desired acetyl content. It is necessary to transform it first to the triacetate and then partly hydrolyze off the required proportion of acetate groups.

The hydration is stopped by running the mixture into a large volume of water and precipitating the secondary acetate (Op.). The secondary acetate is centrifugated to separate it from the still strong acetic acid which is recovered, concentrated, and used over as shown in Fig. 8.

The flakes are washed several times by decantation (Op.) and then centrifuged to remove the remaining liquor (Op.). They are dried (Op.) and then are ready to be used in preparing the spinning solution.

The spinning solution is made by dissolving the dry flakes in acetone in a closed, agitated mixer and, if desired, the delustering pigment is added (Op.).

Several batches are blended, filtered, and sent to the spinning machine (Op.). The solution is forced through the spinnerets into a current of warm moist air (Op.).

The acetone evaporates and is recovered, leaving a filament of cellulose acetate (Op.).

These filaments are twisted and coned in the same manner as those of the previously described rayons (Op.).

Filament yarn is made by twisting the threads before winding on the bobbin. **Tow** consists of threads gathered without twisting and is cut into short lengths for use as staple fiber.

The economical operation of the process depends on the recovery of as many of the chemicals as possible. Dilute acetic acid from various parts of the process is run through a Dorr thickener to remove last traces of acetate and then concentrated in a distilling unit, shown in Fig. 8 of this chapter and described in Chap. 32. The acetone-laden air from the spinning machines may be passed through activated charcoal to adsorb the solvent (which is subsequently recovered by steaming and rectification) or by cooling the air in water towers and simultaneously dissolving out the acetone, the water-acetone mixture subsequently being rectified.

The manufacture of transparent cellulose acetate sheeting comparable to cellophane (viscose sheeting) is carried out by extruding an acetate dope of the required properties through a narrow slot onto a rotating drum where, in the presence of warm air, the acetone solvent evaporates. The resulting sheet is pliable and moistureproof. A trade-marked product is sold under the name Kodapak.

A new triacetate fiber is being spun by Celanese Corporation and sold under the name Arnel. It is reported to possess "resistance to glazing at high ironing temperatures, complete machine washability, low shrinkage in stretching, good crease and pleat retention, and an adaptability to a wide range of colors, designs and prints."[1]

SYNTHETIC FIBERS OTHER THAN RAYON[2] AND ACETATE

All true synthetic fibers first began with the preparation of a polymer which consists of extremely long, chainlike molecules. The polymer is spun in one of the three ways (see below) resulting in a weak, practically useless fiber until it is stretched to orient the molecules and set up crystalline latices. A single-polymer chain is long enough to occupy about four or five crystalline regions. Although the range of any one polymer is always limited, by controlling the degree of orientation and crystallinity a single polymer can be used to make a number of fibers with different mechanical properties. That is, some can be weak and stretchy; others, strong and stiff. The two elements important in determining the range of the polymer's mechanical properties are the attractive forces between the molecules and the flexibility of the molecular chains.

The three spinning procedures are the *melt, dry,* or *wet.* Melt spinning, developed for nylon and also used for Dacron, saran, polyethylene, and others, involves pumping molten polymer through spinneret jets. The polymer solidifies into filaments as it strikes the cool air. In dry spinning,

[1] GROVE, C. S., Jr., R. S. CASEY, and J. L. VODONIK, Fibers, *Ind. Eng. Chem.*, **47**, 1973 (1955).

[2] ANON., Synthetic Fibers, *Chem. Eng.*, **58** (8), 125 (1951); Staff Report, Synthetic Fibers, *Chem. Eng. News*, **29**, 2552 (1951); KIRK and OTHMER, *op. cit.*, Vol. 6, pp. 453–467.

as described under acetate, the polymer is dissolved in a suitable organic solvent. The solution is forced through spinnerets and the filaments result upon the evaporation of the solvent in warm air. Orlon and Vinyon are spun in this manner. Viscose rayon, dynel staple, and Vicara are examples of wet-spun fibers. Here, as the solution emerges from the spinneret, it is coagulated in a chemical bath.

MELT SPUN FIBERS

Nylon. This fiber was truly the first all-synthetic fiber and resulted from the brilliant researches of the late Wallace H. Carothers of the Du Pont Company.[1] It opened the entire field of true synthetic fibers wherein it has a position of commercial superiority. Nylon is commonly produced by reacting hexamethylenediamine and adipic acid to form "nylon salt" or hexamethylene diammonium adipate. This, by removing a molecule of water and polymerization becomes polyhexamethylene adipamide, a linear polyamide. The two intermediates which form the "nylon salt" are currently produced from four different raw materials:

1. Cyclohexane from (coke ovens derived) benzene.
2. Cyclohexane from petroleum.
3. Furfural from oat hulls or corncobs.[2]
4. Butadiene from petroleum.

The first commercial nylon was made from phenol.[3] However, this process was dropped in favor of the one based on oxidation of cyclohexane for adipic acid and of butadiene as foundation for hexamethylenediamine.

The reactions involved may be formulated as follows:

NYLON INTERMEDIATES

A. *Adipic Acid*

$$C_6H_{12} \xrightarrow[\text{Mn-Co-Acetates}]{\text{Air}} C_6H_{11}OH + C_6H_{10}O$$

Cyclohexane from (a) hydrogenation of benzene or (b) petroleum

Cyclohexanol 55% Cyclohexanone 45%

$$\xrightarrow[\substack{\text{Aqueous} \\ \text{HNO}_3}]{80°C.} HOOC(CH_2)_4COOH + xN_2O + yNO$$

Adipic acid

---

[1] BOLTON, Development of Nylon, *Ind. Eng. Chem.*, **34**, 53 (1942).

[2] CASS, Oat Hulls → Adiponitrile → Nylon, *Chem. Inds.*, **60**, 612 (1949).

[3] For reactions and further description of this process, see the 1st ed. of this book, pp. 734–736.

B. *Hexamethylenediamine*

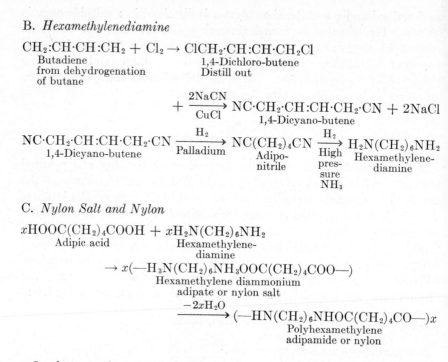

$CH_2:CH \cdot CH:CH_2 + Cl_2 \rightarrow ClCH_2 \cdot CH:CH \cdot CH_2Cl$
Butadiene   1,4-Dichloro-butene
from dehydrogenation   Distill out
of butane

$$+ \xrightarrow[CuCl]{2NaCN} NC \cdot CH_2 \cdot CH:CH \cdot CH_2 \cdot CN + 2NaCl$$
1,4-Dicyano-butene

$$NC \cdot CH_2 \cdot CH:CH \cdot CH_2 \cdot CN \xrightarrow[Palladium]{H_2} NC(CH_2)_4CN \xrightarrow[\substack{High \\ pres- \\ sure \\ NH_3}]{H_2} H_2N(CH_2)_6NH_2$$
1,4-Dicyano-butene   Adipo-   Hexamethylene-
                                                           nitrile   diamine

C. *Nylon Salt and Nylon*

$xHOOC(CH_2)_4COOH + xH_2N(CH_2)_6NH_2$
Adipic acid   Hexamethylene-
                                       diamine

$$\rightarrow x(-H_3N(CH_2)_6NH_3OOC(CH_2)_4COO-)$$
Hexamethylene diammonium
adipate or nylon salt

$$\xrightarrow{-2xH_2O} (-HN(CH_2)_6NHOC(CH_2)_4CO-)x$$
Polyhexamethylene
adipamide or nylon

In the manufacture of the fiber,[1] the nylon salt solution is stored on the first floor. The actual processing starts on the sixth level and the materials move down by gravity through the various steps which may be divided into the following coordinated sequence of *unit operations* (Op.) and *unit processes* (Pr.) as depicted in the flow sheet of Fig. 9. This presents batch processing but continuous procedures have been developed.

The hexamethylene diammonium adipate solution is pumped to the sixth level where the batch is divided equally between two evaporators and concentrated at room temperature (Op.). Acetic acid is added to the evaporator charge to stabilize the viscosity, since any monovalent reaction will interrupt the polymer formation (Pr.).

After evaporation, the salt solution flows into jacketed autoclaves, equipped with internal coils and heated by Dowtherm vapor. Here the rest of the water is removed, the pigment dispersion agent (TiO_2) is added, and polymerization takes place (Op. and Pr.).

After the polymerization is completed, the molten sirupy polymer is forced out of the bottom onto a casting wheel by specially purified nitrogen at 40 to 50 lb. per sq. in. Each 2,000-lb. batch requires approximately 1 hr. to extrude (Op.).

[1] LEE, Nylon Production Technique Is Unique, *Chem. Eng.*, **53** (3), 96 (1946), with a pictured flow sheet, p. 148.

A ribbon of polymer about 12 in. wide and ¼ in. thick flows on the 6-ft. casting drum. Water sprays on the inside cool and harden the underside of the ribbon; the outer is cooled by air (Op.).

The ribbons are cut into small chips or flakes before being blended. Two or more batches are mixed by a screw device in airtight blenders (Op.).

The blenders empty into hoppers on a monorail which supply the spinning area. Special precautions are again taken to keep these and the spinning operations oxygen-free (Op.).

The spinning unit is composed of a metal vessel, surrounded by a Dowtherm vapor-heated jacket which keeps the temperature of the vessel above the melting

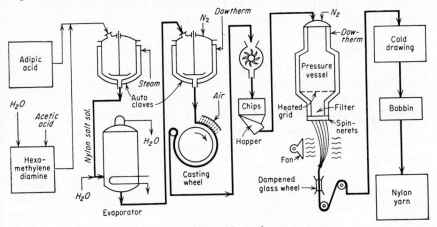

Fig. 9. Flow chart for nylon yarn.

point (263°C.) of the nylon. As the nylon flake enters the vessel it strikes a grid where it melts and dribbles through to the melt chamber below (Op.).

The molten polymer passes through the port holes in this chamber to the gear spinning pumps. They deliver the polymer to a sand filter which is followed by screens and spinnerets (Op.).

The filaments are solidified by air in a cooling chimney and are passed in a bundle through a steam humidifying chamber where the moisture content is brought to equilibrium (Op.).

After lubrication in a glass finish roll, the yarn is stretched or drawn to the desired degree by passing it through a roller system. Here the strength and elasticity characteristics of nylon are developed because the molecules are oriented from their previous helter-skelter arrangement (Op.).

The nylon filament is shipped to the various manufacturers for processing (Op.).

Nylon is also a popular plastic molding powder and bristle material.[1] Like all other synthetic fibers that become competitively popular, nylon in both the filament and staple form must have certain properties that are superior to natural fibers. It is stronger than *any* natural fiber and has a wet strength of 80 to 90 per cent of its dry strength. Its good

[1] WILLIAMS, How Washington Works, *Chem. Eng.*, **55** (9), 118 (1948); *cf.* Chap. 35.

flexing qualities make it popular for stockings and it has excellent stretch recovery. Nylon's high tenacity has made it important in parachute fabrics and related items. Nylon can be dyed by all acid, acetate, pigment, and chrome dyes. It has a low affinity for direct cotton, sulfur, and vat dyes. Probably, as for all other synthetic fibers, its biggest outlet in the future will be in blends with other natural and synthetic fibers.

Dacron. Dacron is a polyester, the condensation product of dimethyl terephthalate and ethylene glycol. The dimethyl terephthalate is oxidized directly from p-xylene in the presence of nitric acid and methanol. About 0.31 lb. glycol and 0.86 lb. ester are added to the reactor for each pound of Dacron. The polymerization is carried out at a high temperature using a vacuum. The reaction releases methanol, and a polymer chain containing about 80 benzene rings is formed. After filtering, the material is melt-spun in a manner similar to that described under nylon. The filaments are stretched about four times their original length. As can be seen from Table 3, some of the interesting properties of this fiber are its resilience, strength, and crease recovery. It is particularly well suited for knit fabrics such as sweaters and socks, men's summer suits, men's shirts, and ladies' blouses. Dacron is also available in both the filament and staple form.

Saran. Saran is the copolymer of vinyl chloride and vinylidene chloride. It is prepared by mixing the two monomers with a catalyst and heating the mixture. Color is added by introducing the pigment in the mass. The copolymer is heated, extruded at 180°C., air-cooled, and stretched. Saran is resistant to mildew, bacterial, and insect attack which makes it suitable for insect screens. Its chemical resistance makes it advantageous for filter-cloth applications; however, its widest use has been for automobile seat covers and home-upholstery uses.

Glass Fibers. Fiber glass was prepared for wearing material as early as 1893, when a dress of fibers about five times the diameter of the present-day product was made by Michael J. Owens. Since that time, however, numerous improvements have been discovered until at present fibers as small as 0.0002 in. in diameter and of indefinite length are possible. The largest and original (1938) producer of glass fibers is the Owens-Corning Fiberglas Corporation which markets under the trade name of Fiberglas. Other companies are in commercial operation.

Glass fibers[1] are derived by two fundamental processes: blowing (glass wool) and drawing (glass textiles). The textile fibers can be made as continuous filaments or staple fibers. In blowing, molten glass at 2800°F. drips through the small holes of a platinum alloy plate, called bushings, at one end of a standard glass furnace. It is caught by high-speed steam jets (72,000 ft. per min.) and the tiny fibers of glass are formed and are ripped off and hurled onto a moving belt. This woolly

---

[1] ANON., Fiber Glass Production, *Chem. Eng.*, **54** (6), 130 (1947), a pictured flow sheet; ANON., Fiberglas, *Fortune Magazine*, **35** (1), 87 (1947).

mass is impregnated with various binders, and is formed into countless shapes for use as insulation or, in the case of fibers coarse as broom straw, set into frames for use as air filters.

In order to use glass in textile manufacture it is necessary to have a material equal in purity to the better grades of optical glass. Also the molten glass must be free of any seeds or bubbles that would tend to break the continuity of the fiber. In the continuous-filament process specially prepared and inspected glass marbles are melted, or a batch of molten glass is particularly purified. Either is allowed to flow through a set of small holes (usually 102 or 204 in number) in a heated platinum bushing at the bottom of the furnace. The fibers are led through an "eye" and then gathered, lubricated, and put on high-speed winders which rotate so much faster than the flow from the bushing that the filaments are drawn down to controlled diameters. These spools can be operated up to 120 m.p.h. The yarn so spun is then put through the finishing operations. It is used for electrical insulation in electric motors and generators, structural reinforcement for plastics, and fireproof wall coverings.

In the production of staple fiber, the glass marbles are automatically fed at regular intervals to a small electrically heated furnace. The molten glass discharges continuously through a spinneret. Directly below the orifice plate is a steam jet discharging high-pressure superheated steam in such a manner as to seize the molten filaments and drag them downward, decreasing their diameters. The individual fibers are projected through the path of a lubricating spray and a drying torch onto a revolving drum. The fibers are directed through guides and wound on tubes, and after drafting and twisting to form yarns, they are sent to weaving and textile fabrication.

Coloring can be achieved through the use of resin-bonded pigments. However, these binders have the disadvantage of not being completely flame-resistant, and the treated fabrics are stiff and won't drape easily. A new process imparts an affinity for vat pigments to glass piece goods by the cross-linking of methyl vinyl ether–maleic anhydride copolymer with polyvinyl alcohol. At the same time, the flame resistance is not impaired, and the fastness to washing, abrasion resistance, and draping qualities are improved.

DRY SPUN FIBERS

Orlon. Polyacrylonitrile is the major component of several new fibers reaching industrial status, but Du Pont's Orlon was the first to attain commercial-scale operation. The name Orlon, like nylon, represents a whole family of fibers. The production in Du Pont's first unit at Camden, S.C., was of a "nondyeable" type. Dyeable Orlon types are generally copolymers.

Orlon is made by polymerizing acrylonitrile.[1] The ivory-white polymer is dissolved in an organic solvent, generally believed to be dimethyl formamide, although it can be dissolved in many concentrated solutions of salts like lithium bromide or sodium sulfocyanide or more successfully in other organic solvents such as dimethoxyacetamide and tetramethylene cyclic sulfone. The solution is filtered and then dry-spun utilizing the spinning technique described under acetate. Unlike nylon which is drawn at room temperature, Orlon is drawn at elevated temperatures[2] in a special machine. It is stretched three to eight times its original length to orient the molecules into long parallel chains for final strength. The continuous-filament yarn is very similar to silk in appearance and feel. The staple fiber has properties like those of wool, as shown in Table 3. Orlon's resistance to chemical attack and especially to weathering makes it highly useful in several fields.

Vinyon. Vinyon is the trade name given to the copolymer of 90 per cent vinyl chloride and 10 per cent vinyl acetate. The copolymer is dissolved in acetone to 22 per cent solids, filtered, and the fibers extruded with the dry-spinning technique. After standing, the fibers are wet-twisted and stretched. Resistance to acids and alkalies, sunlight, and aging make Vinyon useful in heat-sealing fabrics, workmen's clothing, filter cloths, and other related applications.

WET SPUN FIBERS

Dynel.[3] Dynel is the generic name given by Carbide and Carbon to their staple fiber made from acrylonitrile and vinyl chloride. Dynel resin is polymerized from a mixture of monomers that contains 60 per cent vinyl chloride and the remainder acrylonitrile. The resin is converted into staple in a continuous wet-spinning process (cf. viscose rayon). The white resin powder is dissolved in acetone, filtered, and run through a spinneret where the fibers are formed in the aqueous spinning bath. The fiber is dried, stretched, cut, and crimped. After stabilizing and opening, it is packaged and shipped in 300-lb. bales. Dynel is similar to wool in many respects and has some superior characteristics. Its uses include work clothing, water-softener bags, dye nets, filter cloth, blankets, draperies, sweaters, pile fabrics, etc.

Zein Fibers. Vicara is the sole commercial fiber made from the corn protein zein. The zein is removed from the corn meal by solution in

---

[1] See Chap. 36 for the manufacture of this important chemical.

[2] LESSING, Orlon: Case History of a New Fiber, *Fortune Magazine*, **42** (4), 107 (1950); QUIG, "Orlon" Acrylic Fiber—A New Synthetic Textile, *Papers Am. Assoc. Textile Technol.*, **4** (2), 61 (1949).

[3] ANON., Dynel, *Chem. Eng.*, **58** (1), 186 (1951).

alkali, followed by precipitation from an acid solution. The spinning solution is prepared by dissolving in an alkali, extruding the solution into an acid bath where the fibers form. The fiber is cured, stretched, run through several hardening baths, and further treated to improve the resistance to boiling water. After washing, the tow is dried and cut to staple fiber. Unlike most synthetics, Vicara dyes better than wool which it closely resembles (see Table 3). It is used mostly in blends with wool especially, nylon, and rayon. Another protein fiber of interest is Ardil, the Imperial Chemical Industries' (Britain) new fiber from peanut protein made similarly to Vicara.[1] Limited quantities of protein fibers from soybeans and milk are made elsewhere but are not important in this country.

FINISHING OF TEXTILES

The textile industry is second in size to the food industry and many of its mill operations abound in chemical engineering problems.[2] Dyeing, bleaching, printing, special finishing, scouring, water treatment, and waste disposal are outstanding examples of mill treatments where such unit operations as filtering, heating, cooling, evaporation, mixing, and others are involved. Some mill operations are discussed in a general manner elsewhere, e.g., water treatment and waste disposal in Chap. 4, but here brief mention will be given to the use of special finishing agents.

The modification[3] of fibers and fabrics by special treatments to change their properties and to improve their usefulness is increasing yearly. Three important finishes consist of flameproofing or fire retarding, mildew or rotproofing, and water repellency. These are by no means the only lines of treatment. Temporary flameproofing of cellulosic fibers is achieved by the application of ammonium salts or borax and boric acid. Ideal fabric flameproofing which can be cleaned or laundered and yet maintain desirable fabric characteristics is yet to be achieved, although much research is directed to this aim[4] and some processes are finding commercial acceptance. Mildewproofing of cellulosic fabrics may be obtained through the use of many organic and inorganic compounds. Commonly used materials include chlorinated phenols, salicylanilide and organic mercurial

[1] ANON., Garments from Goobers, Ind. Eng. Chem., 43 (9), 11A (1951).

[2] ANON., Chemical Engineering in the Textile Industry, Chem. Eng., 55 (3), 127 (1948).

[3] For an annual résumé of the work done, see the section on Fibers in the annual Materials of Construction review published in the October issue of Industrial Engineering Chemistry; cf. SMITH, Use of Textile Auxiliaries, Chem. Eng. News, 29, 548 (1951); ANON., Chemical Processing, Chem. Eng. News, 30, 4153 (1952).

[4] LITTLE, "Flameproofing Textile Fabrics," Reinhold Publishing Corporation, New York, 1947; Symposium, Flame Retarding of Textile, Ind. Eng. Chem., 42, 414 (1950).

TABLE 3. COMPARISON OF SELECTED SYNTHETIC FIBERS[a]

Fiber	Wool	Orlon	Dynel	Acrilan	Dacron	Vicara	Nylon
Price per lb. staple[b]	$3.00[c]	$1.70	$1.25	$1.85	$2.10	$1.00	$0.70
Tensile strength, gram per denier	1.0–1.7	4.0–5.0	3.0	3.0	4.4–6.6	1.1–1.2	4.7–5.6
Elongation, per cent	25–35	16–21	31	16	18–22	30–35	25–28
Elastic recovery	0.99 at 2%	0.97 at 2%	0.97 at 2%	0.80 at 2%	90–100 at 4%	0.995 at 4%	100 at 8%
Strength, lb. per sq. in.	20M–29M	59M–74M	50M	44M–66M	78M–116M	17M–19M	68M–81M
Stiffness, gram per denier	3.9	24	9.7	30	23–63	2.8	20
Abrasion resistance[d]	0.25	0.61	0.46	0.32	0.49–0.63	0.18	
Water absorbency[e]	21.9% at 90 RH	2% at 95 RH	1% at 95 RH	....	0.5% at 95 RH	64% at 90 RH	8% at 95 RH
Effect of heat	Becomes harsh 100°C. decomposes at 130°C.	Sticking point 235°C.	Sticking point 137°C.	Sticking point 235°C.	Sticking point 240°C.	Weakens 178°C.	Melts 263°C.
Effect of age	Little	Little	Little	Little	Little	Slight	Slight
Effect of sun	Weakened	Very resistant	Slight	Slight	Little	Slight	Weakened
Effect of acids (concentrated, room temp.)	Resistant	Resistant	Resistant	Resistant	Resistant	Resistant	Weakened
Effect of alkalies (weak, room temp.)	Susceptible	Partly resistant	Resistant	Resistant	Resistant	Resistant	Resistant
Effect of organic solvents	Resistant	Resistant	[g]	Resistant	Resistant	Resistant	Resistant
Dyeability[f]	Good	Development	Easily	Development	Development	Easily	Good
Resistance to moths	None	Wholly	Wholly	Wholly	Wholly	High	Wholly
Resistance to mildew	Good	Wholly	Wholly	Wholly	Wholly	High	Wholly

[a] ANON., Wool vs. Synthetics, *Chem. Week*, **69** (3), 11 (1951).
[b] Prices for synthetics in small-scale production may drop as production increases.
[c] *Textile Organon*, February, 1955.
[d] Grams per centimeter divided by denier per centimeter.
[e] RH = relative humidity.
[f] Special specific dyes for some synthetics now in development stage.
[g] Softened by ketones or 5 per cent phenol.

compounds, copper ammonium fluoride, and copper ammonium carbonate. To produce water-repellent finishes durable to the usual cleaning processes, special quaternary ammonium compounds are heat-treated on the fiber.

Shrinkproofing of wool employs various chlorinating processes, especially for socks, shirts, knitting yarns, and blankets. Another method for shrinkproofing woven fabrics is a melamine formaldehyde. Thermosetting resins are being widely used to impart crease or wrinkle resistance to cellulosic fibers. Commonly used products include urea formaldehyde and melamine formaldehyde resins. The fabric is treated with water-soluble precondensates together with a condensation catalyst. The treated fabric is dried and heated at an elevated temperature to develop the resin within the fiber structure. Many other special treatments for fabrics include mothproofing, improving of resiliency, stiffening, softening, eliminating electrostatic charge during processing, sizing, lubricating, and inhibiting atmospheric gas fading.

In recent years chemical finishes are actually being used to react with the fiber material, e.g., cotton, and to thereby change its properties by esterification (carboxymethylation) or amination (2-amino-ethyl sulfuric acid); this is a promising line for research.

SELECTED REFERENCES

Schwarz, E. W. K., and H. R. Mauersberger, "Rayon and Staple Fiber Handbook," 3d ed., Rayon Publishing Corporation, New York, 1939.

Worden, E. C., "Technology of Cellulose Ethers," 5 vols., 3396 pp., Worden Laboratory and Library, Millburn, N.J., 1933.

Ott, Emil, editor, "Cellulose and Cellulose Derivatives," Interscience Publishers, Inc., New York, 1943.

Hermans, P. H., "Physics and Chemistry of Cellulose Fibers," Elsevier Press, Inc., Houston, Tex., 1949.

Robinson, A. T. C., "Rayon Fabric Construction," Thomas Skinner & Co., Ltd., New York, 1950.

Leeming, Joseph, "Rayon," Chemical Publishing Company, Inc., New York, 1950.

Moncrieff, R. W., "Artificial Fibres," John Wiley & Sons, Inc., New York, 1950.

Sherman, J. V., and S. L. Sherman, "The New Fibers," D. Van Nostrand Company, Inc., New York, 1946.

Mauersberger, H. T., editor, "Matthews' Textile Fibers," 5th ed., John Wiley & Sons, Inc., New York, 1948.

Hall, A. J., "The Standard Handbook of Textiles," D. Van Nostrand Company, Inc., New York, 1946.

Harris, Milton, "Handbook of Textile Fibers," Harris Research Laboratories, Inc., Washington, 1954.

Fibers, Annual Review, Materials of Construction, October issue of Industrial and Engineering Chemistry.

Textile Organon, monthly, Textile Economics Bureau, Inc., New York.

Rayon and Synthetic Textiles, monthly, Rayon Publishing Corporation, New York.

Textile World, monthly, McGraw-Hill Publishing Company, Inc., New York.

CHAPTER 35

PLASTICS

The development of plastics from laboratory curiosities to recognized products of industry has brought new and economical materials of construction to the engineer and the designer. Not only may plastics partly replace metals and other materials but they may also be used with them. The common basic raw materials are coal, petroleum, cotton, wood, gas, air, salt, and water. Plastics lend themselves to exceedingly wide application because of their *toughness, water resistance, ease of fabrication, and remarkable color range.* In this chapter the term *plastics* refers to the rigid materials that in their course of manufacture have been *plastic* in some stage but when used are *rigid*, showing no or only a moderate deformation under usage. This excludes the related products known as *rubbers* or *elastomers.*

Plastics and resins may be defined as organic materials that can be easily molded or shaped by mechanical or chemical action to give tough, noncrystalline substances[1] that are solid at ordinary temperatures. These solids may have various substances incorporated with them to impart color and strength. They are resistant to the action of many chemicals and atmospheric conditions.

The use of a plastic material for any specific application is dependent upon its composition, its particular properties, and the design of the part. Synthetic resins are the largest source of plastics with cellulose derivatives ranking next. The great utility of plastics may be shown by reference to a few typical applications in the various fields where these new materials are being applied. In the automotive and airplane industries many different plastics find specific utilization because of beauty, strength, oil and electrical resistance. Their resiliency and strength make them very useful in the manufacture of safety glass, laminated gears, cams, pulleys, self-lubricating bearings, plywood, and the like. In other fields where the plastic cannot be used itself, it is employed in combination with metals, as in the manufacture of steering wheels and plastic-covered dashboards. These combinations develop the best properties of each material.

[1] LEWIS, SQUIRES, and BROUGHTON, "Industrial Chemistry of Colloidal and Amorphous Materials," pp. 140–147, The Macmillan Company, New York, 1942.

In the electrical industries, molded and laminated organic plastics are of real value as solid insulating materials because of their good electrical properties and relatively high mechanical strength. The phenolic resins are used in most of the parts operating under ordinary voltage conditions. For very high frequencies and severe voltage gradients, polystyrene has more desirable characteristics and rivals the best inorganic insulators now available. The civil engineer's investigation of stress analysis has been greatly improved by the aid of transparent plastics that show distortion under stress. By building structural models out of fabricated plastics and by using movie film (plain or color), the effects of applied stress and strain can be studied advantageously for the improvement of structural design. Organic plastics have entered into competition with the older materials for construction in the chemical process industries. Such plastic materials[1] are inherently resistant to corrosive gases, liquids, and chemicals, and they are being used in the form of tubing and piping, plain or laminated piping, tanks, absorption towers, etc.

In the field of the decorative arts plastics have unlimited scope. They have been used to "dress up" all types of articles by eliminating harsh contours and by imparting almost any color combination conceivable.

Classification. Plastics may be classified in various ways. On the basis of raw materials they may be simply grouped as synthetic resins, cellulose derivative plastics, natural resins, and protein products. A raw-material classification[2] shows two main groups of synthetic resins: (1) those derived from coal tar and (2) those utilizing products of non-coal-tar origin. Group (2) may be further subdivided into (a) plastics based on cellulose and plant products, (b) those derived primarily from the hydrocarbons of petroleum, natural gas, and acetylene, (c) the urea resins, and (d) those derived from rubber and alkyl chlorides.

Plastics and resins can best be arranged according to their broad general application into thermosetting, thermoplastic, oil-soluble, and protein products, as presented in Table 1. This arrangement parallels chemical behavior. Plastics and resins may be formed as a result of (1) condensation or polymerization reactions, (2) plasticization of cellulose esters and ethers, and (3) interaction of protein materials with formaldehyde. In general, the synthetic resins of the thermoplastic type are formed by polymerization, and the synthetic resins of the thermosetting type are formed by condensation and polymerization. Proper reaction conditions of time, temperature, catalysts, and concentration of reactants influence the molecular weight which directly affects the physical proper-

---

[1] BRUNER and WAYNE, Industrial Plastics, *Chem. Eng.*, **60** (7), 193 (1953); *cf.* section on plastics in Annual Review of Materials of Construction, October issue, *Ind. Eng. Chem.*

[2] ESSELEN and BACON, Raw Materials of the Plastics Industry, *Ind. Eng. Chem.*, **30**, 125 (1938).

ties of the resin. The cellulose derivatives are thermoplastic materials because of the inherent properties of the long-chain linear molecular structure of cellulose.

The *thermosetting resins* are obtained from fusible intermediates which, under the influence of heat, pressure, and a catalyst, undergo

TABLE 1. CLASSIFICATION AND TYPES OF SYNTHETIC RESINS AND PLASTICS

1. Thermosetting resins (condensation and polymerization):
   Phenolics or phenol (cresol)-aldehyde resins, as Bakelite, Durez, Resinox, Haveg, Catalin, Formica, Indur
   Amino-aldehyde or urea-formaldehyde resins, as Plaskon, Beetle; also melamine-formaldehyde resins
   Alkyd or glyceryl-phthalate resins, as Glyptal, Rezyl, Beckosol, Dulux
   Epoxy resins, as Epon, Araldite
   Polyester (unsaturated) and allyl resins
   Silicone resins
2. Thermoplastic resins (including cellulose derivatives):
   Cellulose derivatives:
   Cellulose nitrate with camphor, as Celluloid, Pyralin, Nitron
   Cellulose acetates, as Lumarith, Kodapak, Tenite, Plastacele
   Cellulose propionates, as Forticel
   Cellulose acetate-butyrates, as Tenite II
   Ethyl cellulose, as Ethocel
   Polymer resins (polymerization):
   Polyethylene and poly-fluoroethylene, as Polythene, Teflon, Kel-F
   Acrylate or polyacrylates, as Plexiglas, Lucite, Acryloid
   Vinyls or polyvinyl resins, as Vinylite, Gelva, Butacite, Koroseal, Alvar
   Polyvinylidine resin, as saran
   Styrenes or polystyrene resins, as Styron, Lustrex
   Coumarone and indene resins, as Cumar, Nevindene
   Polyamides, as nylon (condensation and polymerization)
3. Oil-soluble or modified resins:
   Modified alkyds, as oil-soluble Rezyl
   Modified phenolics, as Albersols, Amberol, Lewisol
   Ester gum (rosin ester of glycerine)
4. Protein substances:
   Casein-formaldehyde, as Galalith, Ameroid, Galorn
   Zein (corn protein)-formaldehyde
   Soybean protein-formaldehyde

chemical changes of condensation and polymerization to form a rigid final shape which is unaffected by heat or solvents. The molded articles, after setting and curing in the molds, may be removed hot without warping. The degree of resistance to heat and solvents may be modified by the addition of materials that cause structural changes. The thermosetting resins owe their heat-resisting properties to a *cross-linked struc-ture*—a three-dimensional molecule.

The *thermoplastic resins* frequently are obtained from substituted derivatives of ethylene which can be made to polymerize under the influence of heat and catalysts. These materials are softened by heat and affected by certain solvents. When molded, they must be cooled in the mold before discharging so that no warping occurs. A notable feature of these resins is the ability of their scrap or rejects to be reworked along with new material. The structure of the thermoplastic resins is that of a *linear* or *string molecule*. Under thermoplastic materials should be included the cellulose derivatives, chiefly plasticized esters and ethers. These compositions, like the synthetic thermoplastic resins, are softened by heat. However, the degree of softening can be controlled by the amount of plasticizer added. The scrap can be reworked also.

Another class of resins becoming more important each year are the modified or *oil-soluble resins*. These are frequently placed as a subclass under thermoplastic resins. Normally, the phenol-formaldehyde type of resins or glyceryl-phthalate resins are not soluble or dispersible in fatty oils to make suitable protective surface coatings. If, during the processing operations, a para-substituted phenol is incorporated with the phenol and formaldehyde, then the normal resin is *modified* to form an oil-soluble material that may be heat-hardened by the addition and use of metal resinates. The para-substituted phenol prevents cross linking of the polymer chains. Straight-chain polymers are usually soluble in oils or other solvents; cross-linked polymers are very insoluble. These resins offer a very wide variety of protective surface coatings that are very hard, nonporous, elastic, and unaffected by heat or the usual solvents.

Protein resins are obtained by treating various protein materials with formaldehyde. This treatment causes a hardening of the protein to form a plastic material and also converts the protein into a material that is not subject to putrefaction. The exact nature of the chemical changes involved is not known definitely. The outstanding characteristic of this type of plastic is its easily polished surface.

Historical and General Description of Various Types. Even though plastic materials had been known for almost 100 years, the industry was not well established until the early part of this century. Numerous investigators studied the phenomena of polymerization and condensation for resin formation, but L. H. Baekeland was the first man to develop scientific control and to produce commercial phenolic resins (1909). His discovery stimulated tremendously the search for new plastics and resulted in an industry which produced in 1953 almost 3 billion pounds of synthetic resins (see Table 2 for a tabulation of the general properties of the principal plastics).

Cellulose nitrate, or pyroxylin, plasticized with camphor and introduced as Celluloid, was the first synthetic plastic of industrial significance.[1] Even though it is a material hazardous to handle, readily decomposed by heat, and unstable to sunlight in the unpigmented form, it has many

[1] Symposium, Cellulose and Cellulose Plastics, *Ind. Eng. Chem.*, **37**, 226 (1945).

TABLE 2. PLASTICS IN CORROSIVE APPLICATIONS[a]

	Temperature, °F.	Phenol formaldehyde (asbestos filled)	Furfuryl-alcohol (asbestos filled)	Polyesters (glass-filled)	Epoxy resins	Poly-ethylene	Polyvinyl (unplasticized)	Polymethyl-methacrylate	Rubber resin blends
Physical Properties									
Specific gravity		1.70	1.70	1.90	1.19	0.92	1.40	1.18	1.07
Tensile strength, lb per sq. in.		4,500	3,500	20,000–30,000	8,500	1,500	9,000	7,500	5,000
Modulus of elasticity (tension), 10⁵ lb per sq. in.		18.8	15.8	20	6.6	0.2	4.5	3.8	2.3
Flexural strength, lb. per sq. in.		6,500	7,500	35,000	21,000	1,800	14,000	16,000	6,600
Impact strength (Izod), ft.-lb. per in.		...	...	20	0.36	>16	1.2	0.5	10
Hardness, Rockwell		R-100	R-100	M-110	M-100	R-11	R-120	M-95	Shore D-75
Thermal expansion, 10⁻⁵ per °C.		3.3	3.3	2.0	6.7	10.0	4.5	4.9	8.2

Chemical Resistance

	Temperature, °F.	Phenol formaldehyde	Furfuryl-alcohol	Polyesters	Epoxy resins	Poly-ethylene	Polyvinyl	Polymethyl-methacrylate	Rubber resin blends
Dilute mineral acids	70	⊙	⊙	⊙	⊙	⊙	⊙	⊙	⊙
	140	⊙	⊙	⊙	⊙	⊙	⊙	⊙	⊙
	200	⊙	⊙	⊙	○	◀	◀	◀	◀
Concentrated mineral acids	70	●	●	○	○	⊙	⊙	○	⊙
	140	●	●	■	○	⊙	⊙	○	⊙
	200	◀	○	●	○	◀	◀	◀	◀
Alkalies	70	◀	⊙	◀	●	⊙	⊙	⊙	⊙
	140	◀	⊙	◀	○	⊙	⊙	○	⊙
	200	◀	⊙	■	○	◀	◀	◀	◀
Salts, acid	70	⊙	⊙	⊙	⊙	⊙	⊙	⊙	⊙
	140	⊙	⊙	⊙	○	⊙	⊙	⊙	⊙
	200	⊙	⊙	⊙	○	◀	●	◀	●
Gases, wet. Cl₂, SO₂, H₂S	70	⊙	⊙	⊙	...	⊙	⊙	○	⊙
	140	⊙	○	○	...	◀	●	○	◀
	200	⊙	◉	○	...	■	◀	◀	◀

⊙ denotes completely resistant.
○ denotes slight attack, but recommended for service.
● denotes some attack—use doubtful.
◀ denotes attack—not recommended.
■ denotes complete decomposition.

[a] Adapted from HIRSCHER, Plastics in Corrosive Applications, Chem. Eng. News, **31**, 863 (1953). See original for more details.

770

unique properties which long made it the best thermoplastic material available for many purposes. Even though the newer thermoplastics have many advantages over pyroxylin, it has shown a steady increase in production. Cellulose nitrate was discovered about the middle of the nineteenth century and was first used as a plastic base in 1869 by John Wesley Hyatt while searching for an ivory substitute.

Cellulose acetate was prepared in 1865 but the first mention in the literature of a plastic from this material did not appear until 1903. In 1906, Miles showed that the triester could be partly hydrolyzed to give an acetone-soluble material with better properties than the triester. No great commercial progress was made until the outbreak of the First World War, when a nonflammable lacquer was used for safe airplane wing coatings. Since 1929 cellulose acetate plastics have been keen competitors with the other plastic materials. The use of propionic, butyric, and other fatty acids higher in the series than acetic acid for esterifying cellulose has also been investigated. In 1938, the Tennessee Eastman Corporation brought out a *cellulose acetate-butyrate* molding compound which is superior in many respects to cellulose acetate. Its applications result from its combination of toughness and resistance to weathering.

Cellulose ethers were initially made and proposed as industrially useful products in 1912 in Germany, Austria, and France. Ethyl cellulose was the first to be manufactured commercially. Others similarly available are methyl cellulose, hydroxyethyl cellulose, carboxymethyl cellulose, and sodium cellulose sulfate (see Chap. 32).

The first commercial synthetic resin, the *phenol-formaldehyde* condensation and polymerization product, was described and patented by Baekeland in 1909[1] in the United States. In 1872, Baeyer had reported that reactions between phenols and aldehydes led to resin formation, but no products of commercial value were obtained until the work of Baekeland. He was the first to control this reaction scientifically. The original Bakelite Company was organized in 1910 and merged with the Condensite Company and the Redmanol Chemical Products Company in 1922 to form the Bakelite Corporation, now a unit of the Carbide and Carbon Chemicals Corporation. After the expiration of the original basic patents in 1926 and 1927, many new companies were formed to make phenolic resins. Furfural is being used in place of formaldehyde giving improved corrosion resistance. When resorcinol replaces phenol, there results a superior adhesive for shipbuilding and aviation-construction industries.

Urea-formaldehyde resinous molding compound first appeared on the United States market in 1929, although the condensation of urea with formaldehyde to form resinous products was discovered in 1897. Their

---

[1] BAEKELAND, Insoluble Products of Phenol and Formaldehyde, U.S. Pats. 942699, 942700, 942808, 942809 (1909).

introduction extended unlimited color possibilities to the field of thermo-setting plastics. The first product was a transparent sheet for glass replacement, but was impractical because of a tendency to crack spontaneously. Research revealed that this cracking could be controlled by the addition of a hygroscopic filler such as wood flour, bleached pulp, or α-cellulose. This yielded a molding composition which could be formed into stable articles.

The *acrylic-type resins* are another example of a synthetic plastic known to chemists for many years, but only available in quantity through present-day industrial research. The polymerization of acrylic acid derivatives was noted as early as 1872, but Röhm did much of the fundamental work on the synthesis and polymerization of the acrylic acid derivatives. In 1931 the Röhm and Haas Company began limited production of acrylates. Methyl methacrylate resin was introduced by them in 1936 in transparent sheet form (Plexiglas) and by the Du Pont Company in 1937 in both the sheet and the molding compound under the trade name Lucite. The polymers of acrylic and methylacrylic acid derivatives are characterized by such important properties as colorless transparency, adhesive qualities, elasticity and stability to light, moderate heat, and weathering and as a result have many applications.

Polyvinyl resins have been known for over 100 years; however their commercial development is recent. The most important resins industrially are polyvinyl chloride, polyvinyl acetate, copolymers of vinyl chloride and vinyl acetate, and the polyvinyl acetals. Not until 1917 was the polymerization of vinyl acetate in the presence of peroxide recorded. Ostromislensky described the preparation of vinyl chloride in 1927, the same year that polyvinyl acetate appeared commercially in Germany. The vinyl acetals, formed by alcoholizing polyvinyl acetate and condensing with aldehydes, were patented in 1934. *Polyvinylidene chloride*, another resin related to this group, was marketed by the Dow Chemical Company under the name saran in 1939 and this has found extensive uses.

Polystyrene is one of the oldest synthetic resins. It was first prepared in 1839. Successful commercial production of this plastic material was begun by the Dow Chemical Company about 1937. Several styrene derivatives and copolymers were introduced during the Second World War which had better heat resistance and impact strength than polystyrene yet retained its excellent electrical characteristics. As an example, an excellent high-impact-strength plastic is obtained by copolymerizing a high proportion of styrene with butadiene and then blending this with natural or synthetic rubber.

Melamine-formaldehyde resins were first made in 1939 by the American Cyanamid Company, although melamine was first synthesized in 1834. Melamine molding compounds, widely used for tableware, are another successful member of the amino plastics.

Nylon,[1] best known as a fiber and the most widely used of the polyamides, is also an important plastic because of its low density, slow burning rate, toughness, flexibility, abrasion resistance, and high tensile strength in oriented monofilaments. Other polyamide resins for use in protective coatings are made by General Mills, Inc., by the condensation of ethylenediamine or diethylenetriamine with a mixture of dimerized and trimerized vegetable-oil fatty acids, *e.g.*, linoleic acid.

Alkyd resins, used extensively in synthetic surface coatings (see Chap. 24), result from the interaction of polybasic acids and polyhydric alcohols.[2] Unless modified by the addition of drying oils or fatty acids derived from such oils, they are unsuitable for use in surface coatings. In 1942, *allyl resins* were introduced which are polyesters with unsaturated ethylenic groups built into them. These unsaturated polyesters undergo a true polymerization in which combination of the monomers occurs through carbon-carbon bonding. The unsaturation is introduced by the use of an unsaturated acid, such as maleic, or an unsaturated alcohol, such as allyl.

Silicone resins were first made available commercially in 1943 by the Dow Corning Corporation. These resins presented a revolutionary advance in the electrical field because of their resistance to heat and low water absorption, combined with excellent electrical insulating properties.

Polyethylene is the simplest member of the large group of thermoplastic resins which are formed by the polymerization of compounds containing an unsaturated bond between two carbon atoms. After several years of development, quantity production was begun in 1943. In 1946 *polytetrafluoroethylene* was made available under the trade name Teflon. It is inert to all types of chemicals except molten alkali metals. It can be molded only by special techniques, but by replacing one fluorine atom with chlorine, monochlorotrifluoroethylene polymer is obtained that has good moldability, general inertness, and high and low temperature resistance.

Epoxy resins based on ethylene oxide or its homologs or derivatives are relatively new. Carbowax, made by the polymerization of ethylene oxide, was the earliest commercial product. Resins made by condensation of epichlorhydrin with bisphenol A [2,2-bis(4-hydroxyphenyl)-propane] have been marketed since 1948 under various trade names. Their major applications are in the field of protective coatings and adhesives which cure at room temperatures.

Cast phenolic resins were introduced about 1929 by the American Catalin Corporation, but it was not until about 1932 that any great production developed. These cast resins offer a wider range of colors than

[1] WILLIAMS, How Washington Works, *Chem. Eng.*, **55** (9), 118 (1948).

[2] ANON., Phthalic Anhydride, *Chem. Eng.*, **59** (9), 208 (1952), a picture flow sheet; ANON., Maleic Anhydride, *Chem. Eng.*, **60** (7), 238 (1953), a pictured flow sheet; HAINES, Resin and Paint Production, *Ind. Eng. Chem.*, **46**, 2010 (1954).

is possible with the regular phenolic resins wherein the reaction is carried further and destroys or masks pastel shades.

Uses and Economics. The uses to which plastics are put depend upon the properties of the various molding compositions. The most important of the multitudinous applications are listed under the manufacture of each type of plastic.

Table 3 shows the relative cost of the various plastics, Tables 4 and 5

TABLE 3. RESINS CLASSIFIED BY COSTS[a]

Type	Average sales price per lb. of net resin	
	1937	1954
Cast phenolic............	$0.41	
Tar acid resins...........	.....	$0.26
For molding...........	0.18	
For laminating........	0.13	
For coatings...........	0.17	
Alkyd...................	0.20	0.30
Urea....................	0.45	0.24
Vinyl...................	0.69	0.41
Acrylate[b]..............	1.66	0.70
Polystyrene..............	0.72	0.31
Polyethylene.............	.....	0.44
Silicone resins...........	.....	3.25
Nylon..................	.....	1.60

[a] U.S. Tariff Commission, "Synthetic Resins," Report 131, 1938; "Synthetic Organic Chemicals, 1954."

[b] In 1938, acrylate molding powder was $0.85 per pound and the cast resin was $1.25 per pound.

the United States production, and Table 6 the estimated consumption for some major resins. Plastics represent one of the fastest-growing industries in the United States.

Raw Materials.[1] The plastics industry has grown so rapidly that the industries supplying the basic and intermediate raw materials have been unable to keep pace with it because of lack of sufficient, ready raw materials and process equipment. These basic and intermediate raw materials come from all parts of the nation—mines, forests, farms, quarries, paper and textile mills, cotton plantations, and natural gas and petroleum

[1] RAYNOLDS, Inter-relationship of Plastics and Chemicals, *Chem. & Met. Eng.*, **51** (3), 109 (1944), very informative; ESSELEN and BACON, *op. cit.*; WEITH, Plastics, *Ind. Eng. Chem.*, **31**, 557 (1939); OTT, Cellulose Derivatives as Basic Materials for Plastics, *Ind. Eng. Chem.*, **32**, 1641 (1940); SWALLEN, Zein, A New Industrial Protein, *Ind. Eng. Chem.*, **33**, 394 (1941); SWEENEY and ARNOLD, Plastics from Agricultural Materials, *Iowa Eng. Expt. Sta. Bull.* 154, 1942.

TABLE 4. SYNTHETIC PLASTICS AND RESINS, UNITED STATES PRODUCTION
AND SALES[a]

Material	Production			Sales, 1954
	1941 1,000 lb.	1953 1,000 lb.	1954 1,000 lb.	Quantity 1,000 lb.
Coumarone-indene and petroleum polymers	....	206,645	219,359	216,462
Phenolic and other tar-acid resins..........	210,838	484,942	433,678	392,089
Molding materials.......................	......	224,364	182,135	171,833
Bonding and adhesive resins................	......	177,652	173,461	145,378
Protective-coating resins..................	......	28,210	22,970	21,644
Resins for all other uses..................	......	34,484	26,145	26,631
Phthalic alkyd resins....................	128,363	390,527	382,367	205,986
For protective coatings[b]..................	......	410,062	....	206,349
For other uses[b].........................	......	8,883	....	2,472
Styrene and styrene-derivative resins......	......	507,962	481,037	458,037
Molding materials.......................	......	324,157	325,910	309,204
Protective-coating resins..................	......	84,247	83,215	80,420
All other uses..........................	......	99,555	71,910	68,416
Nonbenzenoid alkyd resins (maleic, fumaric)	9,474	75,973	71,234	53,411
Rosin and terpene adduct resins............	......	10,430	6,945	6,940
Rosin esters............................	......	56,271	56,867	55,705
Silicone resins..........................	......	2,558	1,851	1,705
Urea and melamine resins...............	34,849	257,310	265,193	244,633
Textile treating and coating..............	......	39,579	44,352	38,640
Paper treating and coating................	......	22,121	20,567	19,672
Bonding and adhesive....................	......	96,192	105,125	98,697
Protective coating......................	......	30,364	27,839	21,603
Other uses, including molding..............	......	69,060	67,311	66,041
Vinyl and vinyl copolymer resins...........	......	515,873	523,605	514,282
Film (under 0.01 gage)...................	......	....	....	68,818
Sheeting (0.01 gage and over)............	......	....	....	54,708
Molding and extrusion....................	......	....	....	146,505
Textile, paper..........................	......	....	....	48,395
Flooring................................	......	....	....	34,497
Protective coatings......................	......	....	....	23,372
Adhesives..............................	......	....	....	28,462
Other uses..............................	......	....	....	109,431
Total...................................	437,800	2,776,627	2,827,803	2,496,597

[a] "Synthetic Organic Chemicals," (published annually), U.S. Tariff Commission;
see original tabulations for many more and individual details.

[b] Includes nonbenzenoid alkyds.

TABLE 5. CELLULOSE PLASTICS, UNITED STATES PRODUCTION[a]

(In thousands of pounds)

Material	Production 1953	Production 1954
Cellulose plastics, total...................	128,963	123,224
Cellulose acetate and mixed esters........	115,094	112,396
Sheets, under 0.003 gage..............	17,472	17,785
Sheets, 0.003 gage and over...........	14,058	12,239
All other sheets, rods, tubes..........	5,809	5,343
Molding and extrusion materials.......	77,695	76,563
Nitro-cellulose sheets, rods, tubes........	7,597	5,266
All other cellulose plastics[b]..............	6,272	5,562

[a] "Synthetic Organic Chemicals," (published annually), U.S. Tariff Commission
[b] Includes ethyl cellulose and other cellulosic material.

TABLE 6. ESTIMATED CONSUMPTION OF MAJOR RESINS[a]

(Millions of pounds)

Resin	1947	1953	1957
Acrylics.....................	30	80	120
Alkyds (molding)[b]............	...	5	15
Cellulose ethers..............	100	113	125
Ethyl cellulose...............	...	5	7
Epoxy resins.................	...	10	45
Fluorocarbons................	...	4	10
Melamines...................	17	55	130
Petroleum resins..............	...	173	200
Phenolics....................	294	403	650
Polyesters...................	4	27	60
Polyethylene.................	15	120	500
Polystyrene..................	99	451	700
Silicones....................	...	5	15
Ureas.......................	80	180	280
Vinyls......................	161	480	700

[a] John Walsh, Arthur D. Little, Inc., and *Chem. Eng. News*, **32**, 4614 (1954).
[b] Alkyds for paints not included but approximate 360,000,000 lb. a year.

fields. The coal mines and petroleum supply the basic needs for phenol, formaldehyde, dyes, solvents, maleic and phthalic anhydrides, and many other organic chemicals. The forests supply the lumber for wood-flour fillers and for some few chemicals. The farms are the basis for lactic acid from milk or corn sugar, bean meal from soy plants, glycerine from fatty oils, and the like. The quarries supply asbestos and other mineral fillers, limestone for calcium carbide, and ultimately for acetylene and vinyl resins. The paper and textile mills provide paper products and fabrics for laminated plastics. The cotton plantations grow cotton and linters for cellulose esters and ethers. The natural gas and petroleum fields furnish hydrocarbons and other chemicals for resins, solvents, asphalts, and very many industries.

Plastics are made from molding compositions which are prepared from two or more of the following raw-material groups:

Binder. This is usually a resin or cellulose derivative.

TABLE 7. CLASSIFICATION OF FILLERS

Organic origin	*Inorganic origin*
Cellulosic:	Mineral fillers:
Wood flour	Asbestos
Cotton	Powdered mica
α-Cellulose	Silicate clays, talc, kieselguhr
Paper pulp	Barites
Shredded textiles	Whiting
Bagasse, corn husks, seed hulls, etc.	Pumice, emery
	Zinc and lead oxides
	Cadmium and barium sulfides
Carbonaceous:	
Graphite	Powdered metals:
Carbon black	Iron
	Lead
Miscellaneous:	Copper
Powdered rubber	Aluminum
Plasticizers	

Filler. Cellulose, wood flour, cotton fiber, asbestos, mica, glass fibers, or fabrics may be added to increase strength. These are classified in Table 7.

Plasticizer. Plasticizers are added to vary the properties of the cellulose derivatives and certain other thermoplastic resins to produce tough and resilient products. These plasticizers may be camphor, esters of phthalic, adipic, phosphoric, lauric, oleic, ricinoleic, sebacic, stearic and other stable and low-volatility acids. The phosphate esters are fire retardants. Table 8 presents statistics for the principal plasticizers. The average percentage of plasticizers used was over 10 per cent of the weight of finished products. In certain plastics the percentage of plasticizers greatly exceeds this average.

Dyes and Pigments. The dyes used vary in resistance to sunlight and to the plastic binder.

Catalyst. The thermosetting resins may use either an acid or basic catalyst depending upon the desired properties, while the resins of the vinyl group may use peroxides to initiate the polymerization of the monomers.

Lubricants. Lubricants, such as stearates and other metallic soaps, are used particularly in cold-molding compounds to facilitate the molding operation.

TABLE 8. PLASTICIZERS, UNITED STATES PRODUCTION[a]

Chemical	Production		Sales
	1953 1,000 lb.	1954 1,000 lb.	1954 Value per lb.
Total......................	292,898	300,674	0.31
Tricresyl phosphate[b].............	22,109	23,847	0.32
Triphenyl phosphate............	7,418	6,426	0.36
Dibutyl phthalate...............	23,208	19,876	0.27
Diethyl phthalate...............	17,584	15,999	0.25
Dioctyl phthalates..............	84,813	88,924	0.30
Octyl-decyl phthalate...........	8,678	10,060	0.32
Di(2-ethylhexyl) adipate.........	3,497	2,710	0.43
Diisooctyl adipate..............	1,511	884	0.45
Lauric acid esters..............	113	55	0.38
Butyl oleate...................	1,372	....	
Glyceryl trioleate..............	3,214	4,054	0.27
Ricinoleic, acetylricinoleic esters...	4,572		
Di(2-ethylhexyl) sebacate........	2,498	4,076	0.64
Dibutyl sebacate...............	2,186	1,950	0.70
Butyl stearate.................	2,417	3,647	0.21

[a] "Synthetic Organic Chemicals," (published annually), U.S. Tariff Commission. See original report for many lesser production figures omitted in above tabulation but included in total.
[b] Includes motor-fuel additive.

THERMOSETTING RESINS

Phenolic Resins. Phenolic resins comprise molding resins, casting resins, and the manufacture of laminates, adhesives, and surface coatings. They may be made from almost any phenolic body and an aldehyde. Phenol-formaldehyde resins constitute by far the greatest proportion, but phenol-furfural, resorcinol-formaldehyde, and similar resins are also included in this group. The product obtained depends primarily on the concentration and chemical nature of the reactants, the nature and concentration of the catalyst used, the temperature and reaction time, and the modifying agents, fillers, and extenders.

A large proportion of phenolic resins goes into the manufacture of molding materials (see Table 4), since this process is best adapted for the large-scale production of thermosetting plastic articles of various shapes and designs. Phenolic resins may be made by either the "wet" or the "dry" process. The latter employs paraformaldehyde or similar aldehyde-producing solid products. Because of higher cost it is little used except when transparent or light-colored resins are desired. The "wet" process is generally carried out in two stages as it gives more uniform results and is more easily controlled than the one-stage process.

The molding-type phenolic resins are of the "two-step" variety.[1] An acid catalyst is used for the reaction of a formaldehyde with excess phenol.

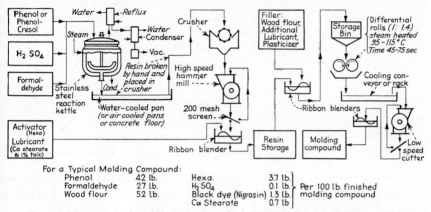

For a Typical Molding Compound:

Phenol	42 lb.	Hexa.	3.7 lb.	
Formaldehyde	27 lb.	H_2SO_4	0.1 lb.	Per 100 lb. finished
Wood flour	52 lb.	Black dye (Nigrosin)	1.3 lb.	molding compound
		Ca Stearate	0.7 lb	

FIG. 1. Flow sheet of molding compound of the phenol-formaldehyde type.

The resulting thermoplastic resin is later mixed with more aldehyde in the presence of a basic catalyst such as hexamethylenetetramine, known in this industry as *hexa*. Figure 1 and the following description show the coordinated sequences of *unit operations* (Op.) and *unit processes* (Pr.) for the production of this type of resin.

The phenol and formaldehyde are placed in the reaction kettle with the catalyst (sulfuric acid) and heated 3 or 4 hr. at a temperature of 285 to 325°F. (Pr.).

During the *condensation*, reaction water is eliminated and forms the upper of two layers. This water of reaction is removed under vacuum without the addition of heat (Op.).

The warm, dehydrated, viscous resin is run out of the kettle into shallow trays and allowed to cool and harden. The cooled, brittle resin is crushed, finely ground, and becomes the resin binder for molding phenolic resins (Op.).

The crushed and ground resin is blended with the catalyst or activator (hexamethylenetetramine, "hexa") (Op.).

[1] CALLAHAM, Modern Plant Makes Phenolic Resins at Springfield, *Chem. & Met. Eng.*, **48** (6), 88 (1941); *Chem. & Met. Eng.*, **46**, 519 (1939), pictured flow sheet; ANON., Spray Drying Speeds Resin Production, *Chem. Inds.*, **54**, 54 (1944); CARSWELL, "Phenoplasts, Their Structure, Properties, and Chemical Technology," Interscience Publishers, Inc., New York, 1947.

Phenolic molding compounds are molded primarily in compression and transfer molds. The powder, mixed with fillers, lubricant, and plasticizers, is further reacted on steam-heated rolls, cooled, and ground (Pr.). In *compression molding* the powder is placed in hardened steel molds under a temperature of 270 to 360°F. and at pressures from 2,000 to 5,000 lb. per sq. in. (Op. and Pr.).

In *transfer molding* the thermosetting material is subject to heat and pressure in an outside chamber from where it is forced by means of a plunger into a closed mold where curing takes place (Op. and Pr.). Electronic preheating (high-frequency electrostatic field outside the process) of the molding powders as such or in the form of pellets, prior to mold loading, helps achieve a more rapid cure with less pressure as it promotes the flow of material in the mold cavity (Op.).

The final chemical polymerization reaction, or cure, which takes place in the mold to transform the powder into a rigid, infusible shape, requires 30 sec. to 10 or 12 min. depending on the class of the molding powder and the size and shape of the finished article.

The probable reaction and constitution of the resin by Bender and reported in an article by Butler[1] are given on page 781.

Cast phenolics differ from phenolic molding compositions in the fact that no pressure is required to make the composition flow. Cast phenolic

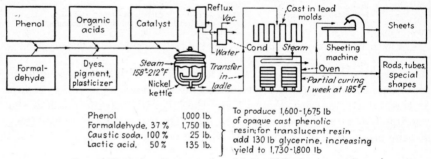

Phenol	1,000 lb.	To produce 1,600–1,675 lb of opaque cast phenolic resin; for translucent resin add 130 lb glycerine, increasing yield to 1,730–1,800 lb
Formaldehyde, 37%	1,750 lb.	
Caustic soda, 100%	25 lb.	
Lactic acid, 50%	135 lb.	

FIG. 2. Flow sheet for cast phenol-formaldehyde type resin.

products are generally more costly than the molded varieties which are susceptible to large-scale production methods. Cast phenolics are easily machined. They are usually produced in the form of rods, sheets, and tubes, and are used particularly where a relatively small quantity of articles possessing different shapes is required such as specialty buttons, buckles, jewelry, and art objects. The phenol and formaldehyde with a basic catalyst (usually sodium or potassium hydroxide) are placed in a nickel or stainless-steel reaction kettle and heated from the boiling point to as low as 160°F. for a period of 10 min. to 3 hr. The longer time at the lower temperature permits better control (see Fig. 2). The heat of

[1] BUTLER, Phenol Resins and Resin Emulsions, *Am. Dyestuff Reptr.*, **32**, 128 (1943); cf. KIRK and OTHMER, *op. cit.*, for more detailed information; CARSWELL, *op. cit.*, pp. 17–44.

reaction liberates 159 B.t.u. per lb. of reactants.[1] Hence it is necessary at certain phases of the reaction to cool by means of water in the jacket. During the reaction, water separates as the upper layer, and the mixture

PHENOL-FORMALDEHYDE

REACTIONS: CONDENSATIONS AND POLYMERIZATIONS

Phenol > 1:formaldehyde 1
Any catalyst but generally acid
A fusible resin (two-step)
Formula: a chain polyphenol

Formaldehyde > 1:phenol 1
Any catalyst but generally alkaline
Makes first a fusible resin
Formula: a chain polyphenol-alcohol

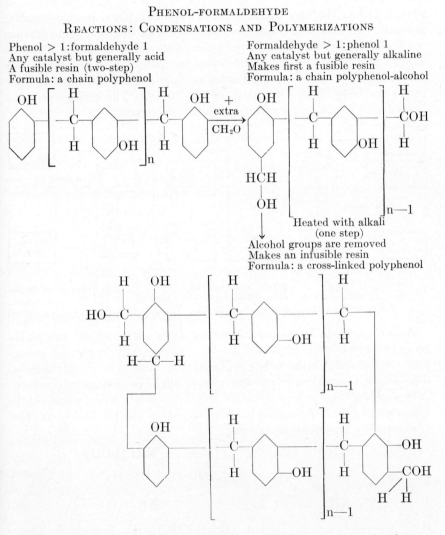

Heated with alkali
(one step)
Alcohol groups are removed
Makes an infusible resin
Formula: a cross-linked polyphenol

darkens slightly and increases in viscosity. The degree of reaction is controlled by means of time, temperature, pH readings, and viscosity determinations. During the removal of about 75 per cent of the water under vacuum, the resin becomes sirupy. At the proper time while the resin is still hydrophilic, an organic acid (lactic acid, phthalic anhydride, or maleic acid) is added to neutralize the resin and to clarify the color. If

[1] "Plastics Catalog," p. 95 (1943).

the resin is still hydrophilic, after neutralization the now four-component resin should not separate from the remaining water when cooled to 75°F. If a translucent resin is desired, glycerine is added to the four-component resin after the lactic acid addition on the basis of 130 lb. per 1,000 lb. of phenol. Before the final dehydration of the resin, plasticizers, pigments, and colors are added to the kettle and mixed with the resin. Dehydration is effected under vacuum at a resin temperature not in excess of 165 to 175°F., and the hot resin is withdrawn and poured into preheated lead molds. The final reaction and hardening take place by curing the resin in the molds at 185°F. for periods of 3 to 10 days. The curing ovens are heated with steam under precise temperature control.

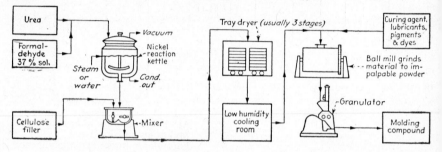

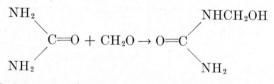

Fig. 3. Flow sheet of molding compound of the urea-formaldehyde type.

Amino-aldehyde Resins and Plastics.[1] Urea-formaldehyde and melamine-formaldehyde condensates are the commercially important amino resins. Other resins in this family utilize sulfonamides, aniline, and thiourea. The simplest condensates are the methylolureas or methylolmelamines. A typical low-stage resin is formed when *urea* is mixed with formaldehyde as shown in Fig. 3. Ammonia is added to control the pH (7.6 to 8). The reaction may be written as follows:

$$\begin{array}{c} NH_2 \\ \diagdown \\ C{=}O + CH_2O \rightarrow O{=}C \\ \diagup \\ NH_2 \end{array} \qquad \begin{array}{c} NHCH_2OH \\ \diagup \\ \diagdown \\ NH_2 \end{array}$$

Some dimethylol urea, $HOH_2CNH \cdot CO \cdot NHCH_2OH$, is formed. These water-soluble, water-white intermediates are employed in admixture with some form of cellulose before the final reaction and curing to an infusible, insoluble product. A suitable catalyst and a controlled temperature are also needed.

[1] Powers, Phenol, Urea- and Melamine-formaldehyde Plastics, *Ind. Eng. Chem.*, **45**, 1063 (1953); O'Connor, Highlights in Production of Melamine and Urea Resins, *Chem. Eng.*, **56** (12), 88 (1949).

Melamine-formaldehyde resins are made in much the same way, but since melamine is not readily soluble in water or formalin at room temperature, heating to about 80°C. is usually employed for methylol compounds. Adhesive resins are usually carried somewhat further than the methylol stage and are offered as sirups or dry powders. The fields of applications for these resins include paper manufacture, textile treating, in adhesives, in molding, and in enamels and lacquers.

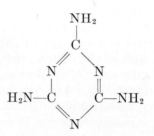

Silicone[1] resins are composed of a network of silicon and oxygen atoms with hydrocarbon radicals attached to the silicon. The excellent thermal and water-repellent properties have led to the development of silicone resins and varnishes. These resins filled with glass fibers, mica, or asbestos are employed as electrical insulation. As electric-motor insulation the silicone resins have withstood temperatures of 390 to 590°F. alternating with periods of complete saturation with moisture for thousands of hours of operation.

THERMOPLASTICS BASED ON CELLULOSE

Cellulose is generally pictured as being composed of a chain of glucosidic units represented by the formula:

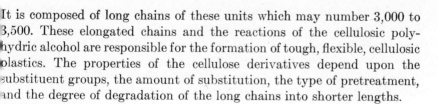

It is composed of long chains of these units which may number 3,000 to 3,500. These elongated chains and the reactions of the cellulosic polyhydric alcohol are responsible for the formation of tough, flexible, cellulosic plastics. The properties of the cellulose derivatives depend upon the substituent groups, the amount of substitution, the type of pretreatment, and the degree of degradation of the long chains into shorter lengths.

[1] Chapter 39 considers manufacture and structure.

Cellulose Ester Plastics.[1] Cellulose plastics are usually solid or colloidal solutions of esters in plasticizers. The esters are made by esterifying purified, pretreated cellulose with appropriate acids and acid anhydrides in the presence of catalysts under controlled temperature. Both inorganic and organic esters are available commercially. The most important are the nitrate, acetate, and a mixed acetate-butyrate. Flow sheets for the production of cellulose nitrates are given in Fig. 3 of Chap. 22. See Table 5 for statistics of these plastics.

Fully *nitrated cellulose* is unsuited for a plastic base because of its explosive character. Hence there is made a partly nitrated product with a nitrogen content of about 10.7 to 11.2 per cent. This cellulose nitrate is placed in large kneading mixers with solvents and plasticizers and thoroughly mixed. The standard plasticizer is camphor, first used by Hyatt in 1868. The compounded mixture is then strained under hydraulic pressure and mixed on rolls with coloring agents. The material is pressed into blocks. Finally, the plastic is made into sheets, strips, rods, or tubes, seasoned to remove the residual solvent, and polished by pressing under low heat. Some of the outstanding properties of cellulose nitrate include toughness, water resistance, ease of fabrication, ease of cementing, clarity, and colorability. Typical uses include drawing instruments, covering for airplane propellers, wet-cell battery cases, fountain-pen barrels, buttons, handles, and dresser sets.

Cellulose Acetate. Fully acetylated cellulose is partly hydrolyzed to give an acetone-soluble product, which is usually between the di- and tri-ester. This hydrolysis takes place in aqueous organic acids in the presence of a catalyst under controlled time and temperature. These cellulose organic esters are precipitated in a large volume of water, washed, filtered, and dried under controlled conditions of temperature and humidity. The esters are mixed with plasticizers, dyes, and pigments and processed in various ways depending upon the form of plastic desired (see Fig. 8, Chap. 34).

These plastics may be fabricated by compression molding, injection molding, or continuous extrusion. Compression molding involves a temperature of 290 to 350°F. and a pressure of 2,000 to 5,000 lb. per sq. in. The material is cooled in the mold under pressure so that it can be handled without deformation when it is discharged from the mold. In injection molding, the material is heated to the temperature at which it will flow easily under a high applied pressure. The hot plastic is forced into a cold mold and the finished piece may be discharged from the mold immediately without further cooling.

The important properties of cellulose acetate include mechanical strength, impact resistance, transparency, colorability, fabricating versatility, moldability, and high dielectric strength. Some of its uses are as

[1] See "Modern Plastics Encyclopedia," Breskin Publications, Inc., New York, 1954.

automobile steering wheels, airplane cockpit closures, electrical appliances, protective goggles, dials, control boards, and musical instruments.

Some of the noteworthy properties of *cellulose acetate-butyrate* are low moisture absorption, high dimensional stability, excellent weathering resistance, high impact strength, availability in colors, and improved finish. This plastic is used for telephones, automobile steering wheels, knife handles, and whistles.

Ethyl Cellulose Plastics. The base of these plastics is ethyl cellulose, a cellulose ether in which ethyl groups have replaced the hydrogen of the hydroxyl group. Commercial ethyl cellulose contains between 2.4 and 2.5 ethoxy groups per glucoside unit of the cellulose chain. The ethers are made by treating cellulose, such as wood pulp or cotton linters, with a concentrated solution of sodium hydroxide. The alkali cellulose formed is alkylated with such agents as ethyl chloride or ethyl sulfate. The alkylation must be carried out under carefully controlled conditions to prevent degradation of the cellulose chain and destruction of the alkylating agent. After the reaction is complete, the excess reagents are easily washed out. The ether is purified by washing it free from soluble materials. Ethyl cellulose plastics may be molded in any manner or machined. Some of the outstanding properties are unusually good low-temperature flexibility and toughness, wide range of compatibility, stability to heat, thermoplasticity, and electrical resistance. It is often used for communication and flashlight housings, tool cabinets, molded covers for bowling pins, and refrigerator breaker strips.

THERMOPLASTIC RESINS

Acrylic Resins and Plastics.[1] Methyl and ethyl acrylate and methyl, ethyl, and butyl methacrylate monomers are manufactured in large tonnages (Table 4). The procedures and reactions for methyl acrylate and methyl methacrylate are shown in Fig. 4. These esters are polymerized under the influence of heat, light, or peroxides. The polymerization reaction is exothermic (8 cal. per gram for methyl ester). The polymerization may be carried out en masse as in castings, in suspension as in molding powders, in emulsion, and in solution. The molecular weights of the polymeric esters vary with the conditions of manufacture, such as temperature, catalyst, catalyst concentration, and monomer concentration. The molecular weight decreases as temperature and catalyst concentration are increased. The polymers become less brittle, tougher, and more extensible as the molecular weight increases.

Cast and molded acrylic parts are widely used because of their clarity, brilliance, ease of forming, strength, and light weight (about half that of plate glass). Among their applications are cockpit canopies, gun turrets,

[1] PORTER, New Process for Acrylic Resins, *Chem. Eng.*, **54** (4), 102 (1945).

spray shields for boats, signs, wall partitions, and decorative items of many sorts. Emulsions are widely applied as textile finishes, leather finishes, and base coats for rubberized surfaces. Solution polymers in volatile solvents find use as special adhesives.

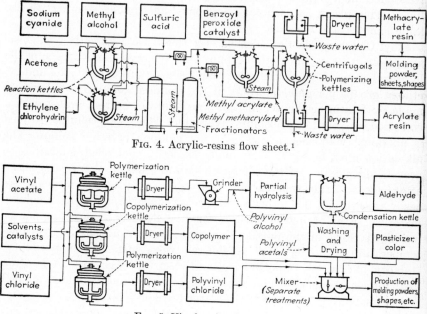

FIG. 4. Acrylic-resins flow sheet.[1]

FIG. 5. Vinyl-resins flow sheet.

Vinyl Resins.[2] The polyvinyl resins are synthetic materials made from compounds having the vinyl ($-CH=CH_2$) group. The most important members of this class are polyvinyl acetate, polyvinyl chloride, and the copolymer of the acetate and the chloride that combines the best properties of each one. Figure 5 illustrates the methods for preparing polyvinyl resins.

Vinyl acetate is a clear liquid the formation of which may be expressed:

$$\begin{matrix} CH \\ \| \\ CH \end{matrix} + HO \cdot OCCH_3 \xrightarrow[\text{salt}]{Hg} \begin{matrix} CH=CH_2 \\ | \\ O \cdot OCCH_3 \end{matrix}$$

A flow sheet for this reaction is given in Chap. 39, Fig. 2. A copper salt is added to the monomer to prevent premature polymerization. This may

[1] LEE, "Materials of Construction for Chemical Process Industries," McGraw-Hill Book Company, Inc., New York, 1950, p. 292, flow sheet using molding powder.

[2] ATLAS and ARIES, Vinyl Resins as Consumers of C_2H_2 and C_2H_4, *Chem. Eng.,* **54** (3), 101 (1947); RUEBENSAAL, Vinyl Resins, *Chem. Eng.,* **57** (12), 102 (1950); LEE, Vinyl Resins, *Chem. Eng.,* **53** (8), 120 (1946); *Chem. Eng.,* **56** (8), 100 (1949); SCHILDKNECHT, Vinyl Type Polymers, *Chem. Eng. News,* **31,** 4516 (1953).

be left behind by distillation. The monomer, a catalyst such as acetyl peroxide, and a solvent are placed in an autoclave, and some heat is applied. After a short induction period the polymerization begins and is allowed to proceed to a predetermined limit. Then the unreacted monomer and the solvent are removed. The polymer is a linear-chain compound which can be formulated in part as follows:

$$-CH-CH_2-CH-CH_2-CH-CH_2-$$
$$\quad | \qquad\qquad | \qquad\qquad |$$
$$OOCCH_3 \quad OOCCH_3 \quad OOCCH_3$$

The dried polymer is ground and becomes the resin binder for molding compositions or a base for adhesives.

Under normal conditions, vinyl chloride is a gas that boils at $-14°C$. It may be made by the following reactions:

$$HC\equiv CH + HCl \xrightarrow[100-200°C.]{HgCl_2} ClCH=CH_2;$$

$$\Delta H = -23,000 \text{ cal. per mole} \quad (1)$$

$$CH_2=CH_2 + Cl_2 \rightarrow ClCH_2CH_2Cl \xrightarrow[300-600°C.]{Alkali} ClCH=CH_2 \quad (2)$$

The monomeric vinyl chloride, like the vinyl acetate, is polymerized in an autoclave using a peroxide catalyst to give a polymer with a linear-chain molecule as follows:

$$-CH-CH_2-CH-CH_2-CH-CH_2-$$
$$\quad | \qquad\qquad | \qquad\qquad |$$
$$Cl \qquad\quad Cl \qquad\quad Cl$$

Usually but not always this resin is plasticized for use, whereas the polyvinyl acetate may or may not be plasticized.

A resin of more importance and wider use than either of the preceding is the copolymer of vinyl acetate and vinyl chloride. The monomers of both acetate and chloride are mixed with a solvent and catalyst and polymerized in an autoclave to yield a copolymer which might be represented in part as follows:

$$-CH-CH_2-CH-CH_2-CH-CH_2-CH-CH_2-$$
$$\quad | \qquad\qquad | \qquad\qquad | \qquad\qquad |$$
$$Cl \qquad\quad Cl \qquad\quad O·OCCH_3 \quad Cl$$

Although the acetate to chloride ratio can be varied over wide limits to give resinous products suitable for a great variety of applications, the more important copolymers at present contain a preponderance of the chloride.

Hard resins are those containing 95 per cent or more of polyvinyl chloride. Soft resins contain 92 per cent or less of polyvinyl chloride and are used principally in the coating industry. Hard resins are used for almost every plastic use.

The properties of the preceding resins are closely associated with their average molecular weight and with the relative quantities of the polymers that make up the resin. For each ester type, the tensile and impact strengths, abrasion resistance, and viscosity in solution increase with higher molecular weights. The water absorption, refractive index, hardness, and electrical properties remain almost constant.

Examples of copolymerized vinyl acetate–vinyl chloride to show how the average molecular weight is varied to suit a particular application are listed as follows:

TABLE 9. MOLECULAR WEIGHTS OF VINYL COPOLYMERS

Average molecular weight	Use
9,000	Surface-coating resin
10,000	Resin for calendar-coating paper or injection molding
12,500	Compression molding
15,500	Stiff sheet stock
21,000	Highly plasticized sheet and extruded wire coatings
22,000	Textile fiber

Some outstanding properties and uses of these vinyl resins may be listed as follows:

1. *Vinyl acetate*—clear, adhesive, nontoxic, zero acid number, odorless and tasteless; used for molding compounds, adhesives, and plastic woods. Largest use is for production of polyvinyl alcohol.

2. *Vinyl chloride*—resistant to water and chemicals, tough, nontoxic, odorless and tasteless; used for cable coverings, coated fabrics, tank linings, and as a rubber substitute.

3. *Copolymerized acetate-chloride*—nonwarping, nonshrinking, tough, strong, rigid, resistant to chemicals, nontoxic, odorless and tasteless, available in colors; used for sound records, floor tile, pen parts, cable covering, belts and suspenders, raincoats, watch straps, and radio dials.

Vinyl Alcohol and Acetal Resins. These resins are made from polyvinyl acetate which is first reacted with alcohol to yield polyvinyl alcohol and then condensed with aldehydes to give a group of resins (or acetals), as shown in Fig. 5. The polyvinyl acetate is reacted with alcohol under controlled conditions by a trace of either acid or alkali which replaces the acetyl groups with hydroxyl groups to yield polyvinyl alcohol.

$$-CH-CH_2-CH-CH_2- \xrightarrow{+2ROH} -CH-CH_2-CH-CH_2- + 2CH_3CO_2R$$
$$\quad\; | \qquad\qquad\; | \qquad\qquad\qquad\qquad\quad | \qquad\qquad\; |$$
$$O{\cdot}OCCH_3 \quad O{\cdot}OCCH_3 \qquad\qquad OH \qquad\quad OH$$

This method of preparation is used because polyvinyl alcohol cannot be prepared by direct polymerization as the monomer is an unknown compound. Vinyl alcohol, $CH_2=CHOH$, is the enol form of acetaldehyde, CH_3CHO, and is not stable. Polyvinyl alcohol is a unique plastic because it is plasticized by water and is completely soluble in an excess of water.[1] Polyvinyl alcohol reacts with an aldehyde under the influence of heat and in the presence of an acid catalyst, such as sulfuric or hydrochloric acid, and the result is a typical acetal. The polyvinyl butyral is shown as follows:

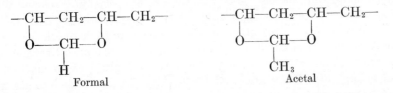

In like manner, the corresponding formal and acetal are illustrated:

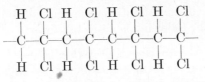

In actual commercial production, the hydrolysis and condensation reactions are never carried to completion because it has been found that the presence of residual acetyl and hydroxyl groups gives the resins some better properties.

The polyvinyl butyral[2] is usually extruded as a sheet for the interlayer for safety glass. Some of the polyvinyl acetals can be compression-molded at temperatures from 100 to 130°C. and injection-molded at temperatures from 170 to 190°C. The polyvinyl formals can be molded by either compression or injection, depending on the softening point.

Vinylidene Chloride Resins.[3] This class of resins was introduced in 1940 and may be formed by the polymerization of the monomeric vinylidene chloride, $CH_2=CCl_2$. These resins may be represented in part as

$$
\begin{array}{cccccccc}
H & Cl & H & Cl & H & Cl & H & Cl \\
| & | & | & | & | & | & | & | \\
-C & -C & -C & -C & -C & -C & -C & -C- \\
| & | & | & | & | & | & | & | \\
H & Cl & H & Cl & H & Cl & H & Cl
\end{array}
$$

[1] PEIERLS, Polyvinyl Alcohol Plastics, *Modern Plastics*, **18** (6), 53 (1941).

[2] ANON., Shawnigan Ups Polyvinyl Butyral, *Chem. Eng.*, **61** (2), 122 (1954), a pictured flow sheet on p. 346.

[3] *Cf.* KIRK and OTHMER, *op. cit.*

or, the monomer may be copolymerized with vinyl chloride to give a new product represented as follows:

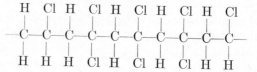

The resins formed by copolymerization range from a flexible material having a softening point of about 70°C. to a hard, thermoplastic solid with a softening point of 180°C. Their higher softening point indicates a greater degree of crystalline character. If the fibrous crystals are not oriented, the vinylidene chloride resin has a tensile strength of 8,000 lb. per sq. in., which is an ordinary value. However, if the crystals are oriented by drawing, the tensile strength may be increased to about 60,000 lb. per sq. in. These resins may be fabricated by compression or injection molding or extrusion with the use of specially developed techniques and equipment to get accurate control of properties and shapes.

Some noteworthy properties of these resins are high tensile strength, high fatigue and abrasion resistance, toughness, resistance to water and chemicals, nonflammability, high dielectric strength, ease of machining, and colorability. They are used for subway car seats, chair seats, fish leaders, and corrosion-resistant pipe.

Styrene Resins. Monomeric styrene is made by the pyrolysis of ethylbenzene, which is synthesized from ethylene and benzene.[1] The factors that affect the polymerization of the monomer are the temperature and the purity of the styrene. Polymerization at moderate temperatures without catalysts produces resins which are of high average molecular weight and which impart high viscosity to their solutions. If the temperature is increased and catalysts such as benzoyl peroxide, oxygen, or stannic chloride are added, the average molecular weight and viscosity tend to decrease.

It appears highly probable that the mechanism of the polymerization of styrene and other monomeric vinyl derivatives may occur in at least three steps: chain initiation, chain propagation, and chain termination, and that the second step is very rapid compared to the first and the last. In the light of recent investigations the configuration of the polymer is thought to be in the following head-to-tail form:

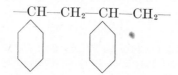

[1] For flow sheets for ethyl benzene and styrene, see Chap. 36, Figs. 5 and 6.

The molecular weight of commercial styrene resin is around 100,000, much higher than usual commercial resins. Some of the outstanding properties which make this the most popular resin of all are low specific gravity, high index of refraction, lack of color, excellent chemical and water resistance, dimensional stability, good molded finish and electrical properties, and transparency.

Polyethylene.[1] It is estimated that around 120,000,000 lb. of polyethylene are made annually (Table 6). It is most difficult to manufacture, although the equation for its polymerization looks simple:

$$n\text{CH}_2 = \text{CH}_2 \xrightarrow[\text{Oxygen and/or peroxides}]{\text{2,000 atm., 200°C.}} -(\text{CH}_2\text{---CH}_2)_n\text{---}$$

The polymer is not a perfectly linear product. About every fifty carbon atoms there is a branched carbon atom; much less frequently there is a branched ethyl group. The small amount of oxygen present, necessary but critical, can act as a cross-linking agent. At room temperature or lower, polyethylene is about two-thirds crystalline and one-third amorphous. The branching and occasional cross linkage are believed to be responsible for the amorphous properties which help account for the inherent flexibility of the product. Polyethylene is not compatible with conventional plasticizers. The conditions for polymerizing ethylene are not at all typical. Gaseous ethylene of high purity but containing a small amount of catalyst may be passed at high velocity through a high-pressure tube at from 1,000 to 2,000 atm. and at about 200°C. Conversion per pass is low, from 15 to 25 per cent, and polymer formed may dissolve in the compressed, unreacted ethylene gas.

Polyethylene is the fastest-growing polymer currently produced. Because of its excellent electrical properties, low power loss, and low moisture absorption it is used for coaxial cables. Film uses are advantageous because of low density, high flexibility without plasticizers, high resilience, high tear strength, and good chemical resistance. It is very suitable for squeeze bottles (150,000,000 in 1953), strips, and coatings.

In Germany a new low-pressure catalytic process for ethylene high polymers has been developed by Karl Ziegler. This process gives promise of producing these extremely interesting and fast-growing polymers at perhaps half the price of the present high-pressure procedure. The low-pressure process probably operates at atmospheric pressure and at around 60 to 70°C. and employs a metal alkyl catalyst, which may be triethylenealuminum. Furthermore, low-purity ethylene can be polymerized to straight-chain macromolecules that may also be useful in fiber form.

In polyfluoroethylene polymers such as Teflon and Fluorothene or Kel-F, the hydrogen atoms of polyethylene are replaced by halogen and

[1] GOLDING, BRAGE, *private communication;* SCHILDKNECHT, *op. cit.;* U.S. Pat. 2153553(1939).

there is little if any branching. At least 25 different halogenated compounds have been homopolymerized or copolymerized, but these are the only two of present commercial importance. Teflon, *polytetrafluoroethylene,* is prepared from a monomer with a boiling point of $-76°C$. and this polymer is the least thermoplastic of all the vinyl-type polymers and has no melting point or stage when the polymer is liquid. It is comparatively expensive and difficult to fabricate; thus it finds use where its superior inertness and temperature resistance preclude use of less expensive products. Kel-F and Fluorothene are obtained from chlorotrifluoroethylene by a very slow polymerization.

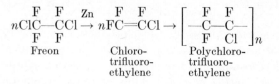

$$n\text{ClC---CCl} \xrightarrow{\text{Zn}} n\text{FC}{=}\text{CCl} \rightarrow \left[\text{---C---C---} \right]_n$$

Freon   Chloro-   Polychloro-
               trifluoro-   trifluoro-
               ethylene   ethylene

In resistance to solvents and extremes of temperature, these polymers are second only to Teflon.

Coumarone-Indene Resins. Coumarone and indene occur in the 150 to 200°C. fraction which is obtained from coal-tar light oils recovered from by-product coking operations. These compounds are polymerized with concentrated sulfuric acid. The formulas of the two monomers are as follows:

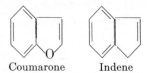

Coumarone   Indene

The polymerization is assumed to be a chain reaction to give polymers of the following general patterns:

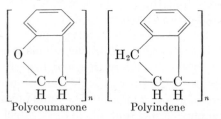

Polycoumarone   Polyindene

Regulation of the polymerization conditions produces resins from a viscous semifluid state to a hard, brittle solid. When these resins are hydrogenated in the presence of catalysts, a series of so-called *cycloparaffin resins* are obtained which are more compatible with waxes and aliphatic hydrocarbons than are the regular coumarone-indene polymers. These hydrogenated resins are much lighter in color than the regular resins, varying from a pale straw to water white. Some important properties of these resins are acid, alcohol, alkali, brine, and water resistance, high electrical breakdown, low power factor, neutral reaction, thermoplasticity, nonsaponifiability, low specific gravity, low viscosity in solution, and compatability with waxes, natural resins and derivatives, synthetic resins, rubber, and bitumens. They are used for rubber compounding, mastic floor tile, protective coatings, and transcription records.

MISCELLANEOUS PLASTICS

Shellac Compositions.[1] Shellac is obtained from a resinous material secreted by an insect, *Laccifer lacca Kerr*, which is native to India. The insect produces the raw lac from glands located in its skin. The resin is a solid solution of several chemical compounds having similar structures. The lac consists of two materials: a hard and a soft resin. Shellac is a unique plastic resin because it shows properties of both thermoplastic and thermosetting resins. Heat curing increases the mechanical and electrical strength. The resin is compatible with phenolic resins so that a wide variety of molding compositions can be made.

Compositions are softened on steam tables at 225 to 250°F. They are molded by compression molding at temperatures from 250 to 275°F. and pressures from 1,000 to 3,500 lb. per sq. in. The molds must be cooled to 90 to 120°F. before the pressure is released. Injection molding at 230°F. can be carried out on a 1- or 2-min. cycle for many pieces. Some noteworthy properties of shellac compositions are low dielectric constant, high dielectric strength, arcing resistance, adhesion, hardness, high gloss, resilience, low thermal conductivity, ease of molding, ability to wet fillers, and oil resistance when cured. These compositions find use in phonograph records, protective coatings, adhesives, and electrical insulation.

Lignin Plastics. Lignin plastics[2] are made from woody materials. Lignin is the binding material for the cellulose in live plants and in a few plastics. The lignin bond of the woody material is released by the action of high-pressure steam which so activates the lignin that it can be used as a plastic binder. Wood chips are charged into suitable containers and treated with steam up to 1,200 lb. per sq. in. for a period of seconds. Normally the time cycle, including the filling and emptying of these containers, is about 1 min. In this time the lignin is softened by the sudden high temperature. When the chips are suddenly released to atmospheric pressure, they are exploded by the high internal pressure into a mass of fibers and fiber bundles which still contain the natural coating of lignin. These fibers are formed into mats under pressures from 50 to 300 lb. per

[1] "Plastics Catalog," p. 168 (1943).
[2] "Plastics Catalog," pp. 190, 300 (1943), pictured flow sheet.

sq. in. and at a temperature of about 180°C. The product is usually cured at a pressure of 1,500 lb. per sq. in. and a temperature of 175°C. The only plasticizer needed is about 4 per cent moisture which is present at the usual humidities. The curing is very rapid.

MANUFACTURE OF LAMINATES

Laminated plastics[1] are made largely from the thermosetting class of resins with fibrous fillers such as paper, cotton fabric, and asbestos. The resins and fillers may be consolidated by heat and pressure into dense, infusible, insoluble materials in the form of flat sheets, rods, angles, and piping. The resins are applied in the form of solutions in solvents such as alcohol or water. The phenol-formaldehyde type is dissolved in alcohol, and the urea-formaldehyde type is dissolved in water.

The resins are employed as varnishes with the fillers dipped or passed continuously through the solution so that all fibers are impregnated with resin and solvent. Gentle heat removes the solvent as the sheet is dried to the proper degree for partial polymerization to take place. The degree of drying is carefully controlled because too dry a material is brittle and an insufficiently dried material flows too readily during pressing.

Laminated products can be made in a variety of colors with or without printed designs and inlays. For plain effects a colored sheet is used with a backing. If designs or inlays are desired, the top sheet has the designs printed on with special urea inks. This printed sheet is dipped in the varnish solution and dried to the proper degree, and the various layers are consolidated under heat and pressure to form infusible, insoluble products. In making decorative inlays of metal or colored laminated plastics, the cut and designs are laid out on the surface of a sheet and pressed down into it to a point where they are level with the surface. The surface of a laminated sheet is determined by that of the steel press plate. For a glossy finish on the sheet the steel plate has a mirror surface. For a satin finish, the plate has a satin surface. Leather finishes or special raised designs are made with the use of carefully engraved plates.

The laminated sheets should be cured and cooled in the mold. If the laminated sheets were removed from the mold while hot, the residual solvent in the varnish on the partly dried sheets would flash and cause blisters and surface irregularities. The curing time varies with the thickness of the material and its type. Urea laminates require about 2 hr. of curing time while the phenolic laminates require less time. The maximum temperature is about 270°F.

Decorative laminates[1] are harder than marble and will stand a great deal of wear. They are chemically inert and will not spot with fruit acids,

[1] Pictured flow sheet, *Chem. & Met. Eng.*, **47**, 183 (1940).

alcohol or other solvents, or mild alkalies. The decorative laminates with the best and most stable colors are made with urea varnishes as pigment carriers. As the phenolic resins have a greater tendency to yellow with age, delicate colors cannot be used. Outstanding properties of decorative laminates are depth of color, durability, resistance to stains and cigarette burns, beauty of surface, chemical inertness, and resistance to discolorations.

Typical uses are for furniture tops, wall coverings, doors, elevator cab interiors, inlaid mural designs, telephone booths, counter tops and paneling, refrigerator door backs, translucent lighting fixtures, signs and displays, instruments and dials, translucent Venetian blinds, and architectural lights. Industrial laminates include gears, cams, bearings, rayon buckets, gaskets, coils, bushings, etc., where laminated plastics have several predominant characteristics that make them the ideal materials to be used. Such advantages are a high ratio of strength to weight, resilience or low modulus of elasticity, lightness in weight, resistance to corrosion, and low heat conductivity and machinability. These properties are permanent at normal humidities and temperatures.

SELECTED REFERENCES

Nauth, Raymond, "The Chemistry and Technology of Plastics," Reinhold Publishing Corporation, New York, 1947.

Meyer, K. H., translated by L. E. R. Picken, "Natural and Synthetic High Polymers," 2d ed., Interscience Publishers, Inc., New York, 1950.

Simonds, H. R., A. J. Weith, and M. H. Bigelow, "Handbook of Plastics," 2d ed., D. Van Nostrand Company, Inc., New York, 1949.

Blout, E. R., H. Mark, and W. P. Hohenstein, "Monomers," Interscience Publishers, Inc., New York, 1949.

Clapp, W. H., and D. S. Clark, "Engineering Materials and Processes," 2d ed., International Textbook Company, Scranton, Pa., 1949.

Engel, H. C., C. B. Hemming, and H. R. Merriman, "Structural Plastics," McGraw-Hill Book Company, Inc., New York, 1950.

Perry, T. D., "Modern Plywood," 2d ed., Pitman Publishing Corporation, New York, 1948.

Houwink, R., "Fundamentals of Synthetic Polymer Technology," Elsevier Press, Inc., Houston, Tex., 1952.

Morrell, R. S., and H. M. Langton, editors, "Synthetic Resins and Allied Plastics," Oxford University Press, New York, 1951.

Vale, C. P., "Aminoplastics," Cleaver-Hume Press, Ltd., London, 1950.

Robitschek, P., and A. Lewin, "Phenolic Resins," British Book Centre, New York, 1950.

Carswell, T. S., "Phenoplasts, Their Structure, Properties, and Chemical Technology," Interscience Publishers, Inc., New York, 1947.

Buttrey, D. N., "Cellulose Plastics," Interscience Publishers, Inc., New York, 1947.

Schildknecht, C. E., "Vinyl and Related Polymers," John Wiley & Sons, Inc., New York, 1952.

Buttrey, D. N., "Plasticizers," Interscience Publishers, Inc., New York, 1950.

Doolittle, A. K., "The Technology of Solvents and Plasticizers," John Wiley & Sons, Inc., New York, 1954.

Kirk, R. E., and D. F. Othmer, "Encyclopedia of Chemical Technology," Vol. 10, The Interscience Encyclopedia, Inc., New York, 1953.

Modern Plastics, monthly trade journal, Breskin Publications, Inc., New York.

"Modern Plastics Encyclopedia and Engineer's Handbook," Breskin Publications, Inc., New York, 1954.

"Technical Data on Plastics," 4th ed., Manufacturing Chemists Association, Washington, 1952.

"Plastics Engineering Handbook of the Society of the Plastics Industry," Reinhold Publishing Corporation, New York, 1955.

CHAPTER 36

NATURAL AND SYNTHETIC RUBBER

Rubber is one of the most useful substances in the world today. Were it or allied substances removed entirely from our lives, technical civilization would be plunged into another Dark Age. The modern systems of communication and transportation would be greatly restricted and whole branches of business would disappear. Yet this product has not always been with us, for it was only in 1839 that the process of vulcanization was discovered, which made possible the successful manufacture and application of rubber.

In its real sense rubber is the product of the tree *Hevea brasiliensis* which originated in Brazil, whence it was transplanted to Malaya, Indonesia, Ceylon, and other places. A number of other plants yield rubbery products. Chemical evidence indicates that the structure unit of the rubber univalent molecule is the C_5H_8 group which is able to add two univalent groups:

$$-CH_2-\underset{\underset{CH_3}{|}}{C}=CH-CH_2-$$

The synthetic resilient materials are polymerized from different base chemical or chemicals and consequently are *not* rubber in the narrow conventional sense. However, these products are popularly called *synthetic* rubber. This chapter will be divided into two divisions: natural and synthetic rubber.

NATURAL RUBBER

Historical.[1] Although at an early date the natives of southeastern Asia knew of rubber prepared from the juice of a tree, it was from the New World that Europeans received their knowledge of rubber. As early as 1736 an effort to introduce rubber into Europe failed. Joseph Priestley, the noted chemist, is credited with giving rubber its name. In 1770 he wrote of a curious substance which had the ability "to rub from paper the marks of a black lead pencil." Until Charles Goodyear perfected the

[1] DINSMORE, Rubber Chemistry, *Ind. Eng. Chem.*, **43**, 795 (1951).

process of vulcanization, rubber goods were very unsatisfactory. Vulcanization is the process of combining rubber and sulfur under the influence of heat and pressure to change the rubber to an elastic, strong, nonplastic, and nontacky material. As a result of this, demand grew as did the need for a good, economical supply. The original source was from many wild species, but practically all the rubber used today comes from the tree *Hevea brasiliensis* which originated in the Amazon section of South America.

Uses and Economics. In 1954 the United States consumed approximately 597,000 tons of natural rubber and 619,000 tons of synthetic rubber. World consumption was 2,440,000 tons of which 1,580,000 tons was natural. The rubber industry with sales in excess of 5 billion dollars is a large consumer of raw materials. One year's consumption of a few of the raw materials amounts to:

Material	Short tons	Material	Short tons
Asphalt	33,288	Mica, ground	5,126
Barytes	14,000	Sulfur	75,000
Carbon black	537,273	Talc	64,476
Clay, kaolin	240,982	Zinc oxide	72,774

In addition to these raw materials sizable quantities of lime, litharge, lithopone, antioxidants, accelerators, carbon dioxide, colors, mold lubricants, and deodorants are consumed.

MANUFACTURE

Rubber is a coherent, elastic solid obtained from a milky liquid known as *latex*, which, not to be confused with sap, occurs in a wide variety of tropical plants. The rubber is usually coagulated to remove the excess water in the latex before shipment to the consuming countries, where the vulcanization and fabrication take place.

Chemically, rubber, or coagulated latex, is a polymerized hydrocarbon, of which the structural unit is the isoprene radical which is able to add two univalent groups. The molecular weight of raw rubber is lower than that of fresh latex, but may be as high as 460,000.[1] Though resistant to a great many chemicals, rubber is soluble in certain hydrocarbon solvents and in some of their derivatives, examples of both being pentane, benzene, chloroform, ether, carbon disulfide, gasoline, and lubricating oils. Ordinary crude rubber is insoluble in water but, with prolonged contact, it takes up large quantities of this substance. Rubber is practically incompressible, but its shape is easily changed under pressure. The practical importance

[1] Kirk and Othmer, *op. cit.*, **11**, pp. 810*ff.*

of rubber is due to its physical properties—primarily its ability to return to its original shape when distorted plus abrasion resistance, softness, toughness, elasticity, impermeability, adhesion, and electric resistance. The word elastic does not fully describe the most important property of rubber since thermoplastics also have elasticity but do not have the ability to return to practically the original shape or dimension.

Raw Materials. The rubber of commerce is almost entirely the product of the tropical tree *Hevea brasiliensis.* The latex from this tree is a milky fluid which, without the addition of preservatives, soon becomes putrid and partly solidifies, *i.e.,* coagulates. Many other plants also produce latex, but latex-bearing plants of the cold and temperate zones are characterized by their small rubber content and only a few of those of the tropics contain sufficient quantities to warrant their commercial exploitation. On the whole, rubber is produced in a belt limited to within 15 degrees of the equator.

The latex[1] is obtained from the trees and sent to a plantation factory for treatment before shipment. It is diluted with water and the foreign matter allowed to settle. The diluted latex is coagulated with formic acid or sometimes acetic acid whereupon the coagulum rises to the surface as a white, doughy material. This is milled to remove most of the moisture. Milled rubber may be smoked before shipment, or it may be milled very thin in creping machines and shipped as crepe sheets. Some products (rubber adhesives, rubber yarns and threads, surgical gloves, foam rubber, etc.) require the use of uncoagulated latex. Caustic soda, formaldehyde, or ammonia, usually the latter, is added to the raw latex to prevent coagulation during the period of transportation to the factory.

Manufacturing Procedures.[2] Rubber, in the natural state, is much too plastic and not sufficiently elastic to be very useful. Thus, essentially, the manufacture consists of vulcanization to impart elasticity and reduce plasticity. Other ingredients are added for various purposes: to prevent oxidation, to impart abrasion resistance, and the like.

Methods for *rubber fabrication* utilize appropriate sequences from the following procedures: (1) mastication of the rubber by mechanical action, (2) addition of compounding ingredients by further mechanical working, (3) sheeting out the rubber compound or extruding it in some special cross-sectional shape, (4) impregnation of fabric with rubber compound by calendering or by dipping of forms into rubber solution, (5) assembly of these unvulcanized materials into the approximate shape of the finished article, (6) vulcanization by means of heat and pressure or at room temperature in the presence of chemicals for a controlled and definite period of time.

[1] MURPHY, Recent Progress in Latex Technology, *Ind. Eng. Chem.,* **44,** 756 (1952).

[2] See KIRK and OTHMER, *op. cit.,* Vol. 11, pp. 927*ff.*

The making of *automobile tires*[1] illustrates the general principles of rubber manufacture. Figure 1 gives the essential features and may be divided into the following *unit operations* (Op.) and *unit processes* (Pr.):

The crude rubber is broken down in the masticating and mixing mill (Op.), which consists of two rolls revolving at different speeds and heated or cooled as desired (see Fig. 2). Crude rubber as received from the plantation is high in viscosity. This operation lowers the viscosity by breaking up of the long rubber molecules into shorter ones. GR-S is normally made to an appreciably lower viscosity than natural and some manufacturers do not premasticate it. After premastication, compounding takes place with further milling. In natural-rubber

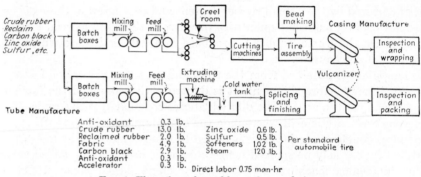

Anti-oxidant	0.3 lb.		
Crude rubber	13.0 lb.		
Reclaimed rubber	2.0 lb.	Zinc oxide	0.6 lb.
Fabric	4.9 lb.	Sulfur	0.5 lb.
Carbon black	2.9 lb.	Softeners	1.02 lb.	Per standard automobile tire
Anti-oxidant	0.3 lb.	Steam	120 lb.
Accelerator	0.3 lb.	Direct labor 0.75 man-hr	

FIG. 1. Flow sheet for rubber tubes and tires.

compounding, the ingredients which all rubber compounds must have are zinc oxide, stearic acid, and the vulcanizing agent, sulfur or sulfur-bearing complex organic compounds together with accelerators. The addition of carbon black, mineral fillers, softeners, antioxidants, etc., are primarily aimed at the end-product service requirements (Op.). The carbon black imparts toughness.

From the milling machines the rubber is run through calenders (Op.), which consist of three hollow rolls set one above the other. The rubber is forced into thin sheets, and cords (rayon, nylon, or cotton) are also introduced between the rolls so that the product is a thin sheet of rubber adhering to the fabric.

The rubberized fabric is cut on the bias (approximately 40 deg) into strips (Op.). Thus the cords in the tire will be at an angle and give added strength.

The strips are formed over an iron core to produce the tire carcass. The tread, a heavy strip of masticated and compounded rubber, is shaped around the carcass and finally the bead is applied (Op.). The bead is a strip of very hard rubber containing wire threads embedded in it and forms the edge of the tire that is in contact with the rim of the wheel.

The assembled tire is placed in a mold into which the tread design has been cut. Heat, supplied by steam, and pressure for a very definitely controlled time cause the sulfur to vulcanize the rubber (Op. and Pr.).

The vulcanized tire is inspected and wrapped (Op.).

[1] LEE, Modern Methods Make 1948 Tires, *Chem. Eng.*, **55** (5), 139 (1948), a pictured flow sheet on pp. 146–149.

The manufacture of inner tubes is somewhat similar up to the calendering operation.[1] They are made by extruding a continuous tube of compounded butyl rubber, cutting this into proper lengths, applying a prefabricated valve, and splicing the tube ends together to form a ring. After the tube is inflated to stretch it into a doughnut shape, it is vulcanized in a curing mold.

Rubber Compounding. Raw rubber, as such, has few commercial applications. The few exceptions would include crepe-rubber shoe soles,

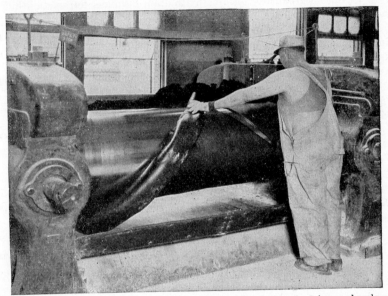

FIG. 2. Milling or mixing rolls for compounding rubber before forming and vulcanization. (*Courtesy of The Goodyear Tire & Rubber Company.*)

rubber cements, adhesives, and masking tapes. By far the greatest part of rubber must be modified, usually by vulcanization with other additions. Each rubber article[2] requires individual compounding formulas, ingredients, and handling. Successful compounding is very complicated and depends mainly upon two considerations: (1) the use requirements of the item to be made and (2) the processing methods which can, or must, be used to make the article, namely, calendering, mixing, extruding, coating, building, metal adhesion. The following list (by no means complete) of materials that are in *general use* gives some idea of the complexity of the rubber-compounding problem.

[1] BUCKLEY, et al., Utilization of Butyl Rubber in Automotive Inner Tubes, *Ind. Eng. Chem.*, **42**, 2407 (1950).

[2] GARVEY, The Compounder in the Rubber Industry, *Ind. Eng. Chem.*, **44**, 796 (1952); KIRK and OTHMER, *op. cit.*, Vol. 11, pp. 892–945.

Elastomers. Cold GR-S (usually designated as GR-S-1500), natural rubber, GR-S-1000, GR-S-1002, GR-I or butyl, reclaim, nitrile rubbers, neoprenes, Thiokols, polyacrylate rubbers, silicone rubbers. Of these elastomers, the polymers and copolymers of butadiene have a general similarity to natural rubber in compounding. Since these elastomers are by far the most used, the rest of this list will be limited to the rubber chemicals commonly needed for their compounding.

Vulcanizing Agents. Sulfur, sulfur monochloride, selenium, tellurium, thiuram disulfides, *p*-quinone dioximes, polysulfide polymers.

Vulcanization Accelerators. 2-Mercaptobenzothiazole, benzothizolyl disulfide, zinc diethyldithiocarbamate, tetramethylthiuram disulfide, tetramethylthiuram monosulfide, 1,3-diphenyl-guanidine.

Accelerator Activators. Zinc oxide, stearic acid, litharge, magnesium oxide, amines, amine soaps.

Retarders. Salicylic acid, benzoic acid, phthalic anhydride.

Antioxidants. *N*-Phenyl-2-naphthylamine, alkylated diphenylamine, an acetone-diphenylamine reaction product (B-L-E).

Pigments. Carbon black, zinc oxide, certain clays, calcium carbonate, titanium dioxide, color pigments.

Softeners and Extenders. Petroleum products, pine tars and resins, coal-tar fractions.

Waxes. Certain petroleum waxes.

Blowing Agents. Sodium or ammonium bicarbonate, diazoaminobenzene, dinitrosopentamethylenetetramine.

Chemical Plasticizers. 2-Naphthalenethiol, bis(*o*-benzaminophenyl)-disulfide, mixed xylenethiols, zinc salt of xylenethiols.

The simplest compound for vulcanizing would be natural rubber with the essential sulfur added. The amount of sulfur used for soft-rubber goods is generally from 0.5 to 4 per cent. For semihard stocks, such as are used in tire beads, 25 to 35 per cent sulfur is common. Hard-rubber (ebonite) articles are made by vulcanizing rubber with 40 to 50 per cent of sulfur. The inclusion of certain metal oxides (zinc oxide is most used) increases the vulcanization rate with slight improvement in the physical properties. However, better aging properties, production of nonblooming compounds, and better physical properties in general result from lower sulfur ratios. To achieve this, organic *accelerators* plus metal oxides are used to increase the rate of cure. Most accelerators require *fatty acids* for their efficient functioning. Sometimes the naturally occurring fatty acids in rubber suffice, but generally stearic acid must be added especially in those formulas containing part or all GR-S. In addition *antioxidants* are employed which still further retard the deterioration of natural rubber due to oxidation. Many antioxidants are also effective in stabilizing synthetic rubbers (principally the butadiene polymers) at the time of preparation and when thus used are called *stabilizers*. *Pigments* are finely divided powders which are often loosely classified as reinforcing agents or fillers. The most important pigment is carbon black (see Chap. 9), which imparts toughness and improves the vulcanization. With certain exceptions, *i.e.*, fine-particle zinc oxides, fine precipitated calcium carbonates, certain clays, and fine magnesium carbonates, most nonblacks function primarily as fillers or diluents. Color pigments are those employed in small amounts solely for color.

Softeners is the term formerly given to those materials which were used principally to get better processing through improved softness and tack. The term now includes a great number of materials which are primarily used for six main purposes: processing aids for uncured stock, softeners for cured stock, elasticizers, freezing-point depressants, organic reinforcing agents, and extenders. Softeners which are processing aids for uncured stock may be classified as plasticizers for softness, for retentivity or flatness, and for thermoplasticity; lubricants; tackifiers; and dispersing aids. The important development in synthetic rubber of oil extending is discussed later in this chapter.

In addition to the classes of materials in general use, there are a number of materials used for special effects such as antiseptics, blowing agents for sponge rubber, peptizing agents, and retarders. A typical recipe[1] of the materials used in compounding follows. The figures in parentheses show the variations sometimes used.

	Parts		Parts
Rubber	100	Stearic acid	1 (0–4.0)
Sulfur	3 (0.5–50.0)	Antioxidant	1 (0–3.0)
Accelerator	1 (0.3–3.0)	Softener	5 (2–50.0)
Zinc oxide	5 (2.0–10.0)	Pigment	50 (20–300)

Energy Requirements. As the mastication of rubber generates a large quantity of heat, the rolls of the compounding mill must be cooled to dissipate this heat. Energy must be supplied in the form of power to operate the mill and to run the calender and the extruding machines. Vulcanization requires external energy to supply both heat and pressure.

Latex.[2] Latices, natural and synthetic, are increasing rapidly in consumption. Over half the natural latex imported (75,000 tons in 1954) is converted into foam rubber. In 1954, 62,794 tons of latices were manufactured. This figure includes the sizable quantities of neoprene and other specialty latices.[3] Here technology is expanding so rapidly that tailor-made latices may be developed for practically any use.

[1] GARVEY, *op. cit.*, p. 797.

[2] Symposium, Latex, *Ind. Eng. Chem.*, **44**, 756 (1952).

[3] *Cf.* ZWICKER, Latices of Flexible Synthetic Polymers, *Ind. Eng. Chem.*, **44**, 774 (1952); HOWLAND, *et al.*, Synthetic Rubber Latex Developments, *Ind. Eng. Chem.*, **44**, 762; D'IANNI, *et al.*, Butadiene-styrene Resinous Copolymers, *Ind. Eng. Chem.*, **43**, 319 (1951).

In latex fabrication, whether it be natural or synthetic, the compounding ingredients must be brought into aqueous solution or dispersion for the water-insoluble materials. Liquid emulsions are made through the addition of emulsifying agents followed by high-speed agitation or the employment of a colloid mill or homogenizer. Solids may be dispersed in various kinds of ball, pebble, and colloid mills. *Foams* are mostly produced by mechanical means, although chemical sponge may be made by incorporating heat-sensitive blowing agents in the latex. In making cushions and mattresses, the compounded latex is frothed by air and a gelling agent (*i.e.*, sodium fluosilicate) is introduced. The mixture is poured into a mold where it gels, then is cured, washed, and dried. Electrodeposition, which was used for forming items such as gloves and toys, has been replaced by *coagulant deposition*. In the Anode process, a coagulant, such as solutions of polyvalent metal salts, is placed on the form. This is dipped in the compounded latex for a dwell time which determines the thickness of the deposit. In the other process the form is first dipped into the compounded latex and next into the chemical coagulant for gelling. *Drying*, where the compound is spread on a surface or poured into a mold, is limited to fabric coating, films, and adhesives where the water can be readily and quickly removed by evaporation. Drying can be accelerated by the use of a porous form whereby the water is absorbed.

Reclaimed Rubber.[1] To illustrate the importance of reclaimed rubber, for years the proportion of reclaimed rubber consumed to the total new rubber employed has run around 20 per cent. In 1954, reclaimed-rubber consumption, both natural and synthetic, was 249,049 long tons. About two-thirds of all reclaim produced is used in automobiles in tires, tubes, floor mats, battery boxes, tire-repair materials, and radiator hose. Around 85 per cent of the scrap rubber reclaimed is automotive tires.

The fundamental chemistry of rubber reclaiming is very complex because of the composition of the scrap. According to Hader and le Beau, "The reclaiming process causes the predominant scission of the rubber hydrocarbon molecule, followed by a smaller amount of recombination of chain fragments as the time of reclaiming progresses. The net result is a considerable increase in plasticity. However, the structure of GR-S causes at first much scission of its molecules which, as the time of reclaiming proceeds, is soon overshadowed by extensive recombination, resulting in a progressive and extraordinary hardening of this polymer." Since it is practically and economically impossible to segregate the natural from the synthetics, either the reclaiming must be interrupted after a short time while scission predominates in the GR-S, or reclaiming agents must be used which prevent heat hardening of the GR-S. Not only does the elastomer content of the scrap vary but likewise does the large number of compounding ingredients originally used.

[1] HADER and LE BEAU, Rubber Reclaiming, *Ind. Eng. Chem.*, **43**, 250 (1951); BALL, "Reclaimed Rubber," Rubber Reclaimers Association, Inc., New York, 1947.

The two principal reclaiming processes[1] are the *digester* process and the *heater* process. The digester process is depicted in Fig. 3. The scrap is prepared by mechanical shredding. Bead wires are removed by an operator; ferrous tramp metal by a magnetic pulley. The scrap may be reground before it is charged into a steam-heated digester. A normal charge may consist of about 5,000 lb. of scrap and about 10,000 lb. of heated 4 to 6 per cent caustic soda solution or dilute zinc chloride solution. Reclaiming (softener) oils and chemicals are blended into the solution during the warming process. Other chemicals are employed for synthetic rubber and in general include alkylated-phenol sulfides, aromatic mercaptans, and amino compounds. For natural rubber, the reclaiming

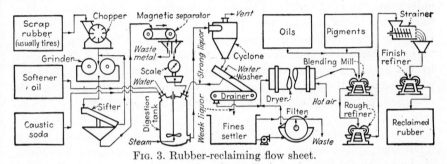

FIG. 3. Rubber-reclaiming flow sheet.

"oils" may be crude solvent naphtha, dipentene, coal tars, and pine tar oil. After 9 to 12 hr. at elevated temperature and pressure, the batch is discharged and washed for removal of water-soluble impurities. The stock is dewatered, dried, and compounded. Any natural rubber is defibered, desulfurized, and devulcanized by a single heating with dilute caustic soda.

The much less used heater process produces a reclaim more suitable for certain applications such as inner tubes and mechanical goods. Small lots of finely ground scrap are blended with reclaiming agents by means of a ribbon mixer. The mixture is placed in shallow pans. These are stacked on small flatcars on rails and pushed into a pressure vessel. Live steam at 185 lb. per sq. in. is maintained for 5 to 6 hr., after which the scrap is taken to the mill room for final working and compounding.

Resins from Rubber. Although natural rubber is commonly considered to be a relatively inert material, it may be made to react with a wide variety of chemicals. From the many possible reactions only three have achieved appreciable commercial importance: chlorinated rubber, cyclorubber (cyclized rubber), and rubber hydrochloride. Some similar derivatives are also obtainable from certain synthetic rubbers.

Chlorinated rubber (Parlon) is much employed for the manufacture of various kinds of paints and finishes, inks, paper coatings, textile finishes, and adhesives. The rubber is chlorinated in solution, usually with carbon

[1] HADER and LE BEAU, *op. cit.*, detailed flow sheets, statistics, prices, and pictures.

tetrachloride or a mixture of hexachloroethane and carbon tetrachloride as the solvent. The reaction takes place in a vessel provided with a reflux condenser at a temperature of 80 to 100°C.[1] When approximately 65 per cent chlorine has been absorbed, further addition is cut off and heating continued until no more hydrogen chloride is evolved. The final product is isolated by precipitation in ethyl alcohol and is highly resistant to a wide variety of chemicals.

Cyclorubbers (Pliolite) require a very high grade of low-protein-content rubber which is milled on a cold mill for increased solubility. The milled rubber is dissolved in benzene or chloroform and the viscous cement is charged to a jacketed reactor provided with reflux. A catalyst, such as anhydrous stannic chloride or titanium chloride, is added which yields a molecular addition compound. The degree of cyclization is controlled by the time and conditions of reaction; therefore, products representing various degrees of cyclization are available. The reaction is terminated by the action of alcohol or water which decomposes the addition compound to yield the final cyclorubber. It is employed in the manufacture of adhesives, paper coatings, wax modifiers, printing inks, rubber products, and paints.

Rubber hydrochloride is made by passing dry hydrogen chloride into a 6 per cent rubber cement until the required degree (about 30 per cent) of hydrochlorination has been achieved. After neutralization with ammonia or soda ash, the product is steam-distilled to remove volatiles (benzene). The product is then broken into small pieces, washed with water, and vacuum-dried at about 160°F. Film, the only available form, is made by dissolving the reaction mass in chloroform (5 per cent solution). Photochemical inhibitor, plasticizers, colors, and modifiers are added to the solution. The compound is filtered and cast onto a suitable surface to form the film, known as Pliofilm. It is used for packaging a wide variety of products including textile items, paper products, and foodstuffs, particularly red meats.

SYNTHETIC RUBBER

The term synthetic rubber applies to that group of high polymers which possess, to a greater or lesser extent, the physical properties of natural rubber (Table 1). None of the synthetics produced to date is identical with natural rubber. Hence, some prefer to call these polymers elastomers, but the term synthetic rubber continues in popular usage. These materials are employed by the rubber industry both as substitutes for and to supplement natural rubber. Certain properties of the synthetics, such as oil and gas resistance, dictate their use in many applications for which natural rubber is not suitable.

[1] Cf. LEE, How Rubber Is Chlorinated, Chem. & Met. Eng., **46**, 456 (1939).

Historical.[1] As early as 1860 investigations for rubber substitutes began. The Germans manufactured a poor-quality "methyl rubber" from 2,3-dimethylbutadiene during the First World War. Between the wars research in the United States was directed more toward synthetics with special properties than for a natural-rubber replacement as was the case in Europe. The first rubberlike materials (early 1920's) to be used on a commercial scale here were the reaction products of ethylene dichloride

TABLE 1. UNITED STATES CONSUMPTION OF SYNTHETIC RUBBER[a]

Year	GR-S	Butyl	Neoprene	N type	Total
1941	227	. . . . . .	5,692	2,464	8,383
1943	182,259	1,373	33,603	14,487	231,722
1945	719,404	47,426	45,672	7,871	820,373
1947	408,858	31,495	68,824	6,618	515,795
1949	295,166	52,237	35,215	11,072	392,690
1952	666,420	71,229	55,522	13,866	807,037
1953	624,181	77,826	64,150	15,929	782,086
1954	498,835	60,644	57,203	17,115	635,977

[a] U.S. Department of Commerce, Industry Reports, Rubber.

and sodium polysulfide known as Thiokols. Neoprene, butyl rubber, and the nitrile rubbers were all introduced in the 1930's. In May, 1941, the government synthetic rubber program began by pooling technical information and experience. The general-purpose polymer decided upon was a copolymer prepared from a charge ratio of 75 per cent butadiene and 25 per cent styrene, now known as GR-S.[2] The growth of this industry was phenomenal, as is illustrated by Table 1. Since the war, the new developments have been "cold" rubber, oil master-batched polymers, high-abrasion furnace blacks, and various new elastomers and high polymers.

MANUFACTURE

The manufacture of synthetic rubbers involves three problems: the economical production of the raw materials, the actual polymerization, and the compounding. The manufacture of the various types of GR-S requires tonnages of butadiene and styrene that before were unavailable. Table 2 gives the more important types of rubbers with their polymer-building units.

Raw Materials. About 90 per cent of the *butadiene*[3] produced is used in GR-S. Nitrile rubbers are the next largest consumer (2 per cent). The

[1] DINSMORE, *op. cit.*, p. 800.

[2] GR-S is the abbreviation for government rubber from styrene.

[3] TRACY, Butadiene, *Chem. Eng. News*, **31**, 2666 (1953); FROLICH and MORRELL, Butadiene, *Chem. Eng. News*, **21**, 1138 (1943); ANON., How to Make Butadiene, *Chem. Eng.*, **61** (9), 306 (1954), a pictured flow sheet.

remainder is consumed as an alternate raw material for nylon, for latex paints and other protective coatings, and for resins. Total installed butadiene capacity in 1954 was 852,000 short tons a year, of which 215,000 tons were from alcohol, the rest based on the cheaper petroleum. Actual

TABLE 2. CLASSIFICATION OF RUBBER AND RUBBERLIKE PRODUCTS

Raw materials	Polymer unit	Trade names
Latex from Hevea tree	$-CH_2-C=CH-CH_2-$ with CH_3 substituent	Natural rubber
Butadiene + styrene	$-CH_2-CH=CH-CH_2-CH_2-CH-$ with C_6H_5	GR-S Buna S (Ger.)
Isobutylene + isoprene	CH_3, CH_3 on $-CH_2-C-CH_2-C=CH-CH_2-$ with CH_3	Butyl
Chloroprene	$-CH_2-C=CH-CH_2-$ with Cl	Neoprene
Butadiene + acrylonitrile	$-CH_2-CH=CH-CH_2-CH_2-CH-$ with CN	N type Buna N (Ger.) Butaprene (Firestone) Hycar (Goodrich) Chemigum (Goodyear) Paracril (U.S. Rubber)
Sodium polysulfide + organic dichloride	$-CH_2-CH_2-S-S-$ with S S	Thiokols (polymer unit depicted is Type A made from sodium tetrasulfide and ethylene dichloride)
Dimethylsiloxane	CH_3, CH_3, CH_3 on $-Si-O-Si-O-Si-O-$ with CH_3, CH_3, CH_3	Silicone rubbers

NOTE: In the case of copolymers, the polymer unit as given above is only approximate as it is usual to have a smaller amount of the second constituent than the molecular equivalent structurally depicted above. There are several varieties of each of the representative synthetics depicted above.

Second World War plants for butadiene were constructed for the following processes: (1) catalytic dehydrogenation of butenes, (2) thermal cracking, (3) dehydrogenation of n-butane, (4) production from ethyl alcohol, (5) chlorination of butenes (minor, wartime only), and (6) production from acetaldehyde by aldol condensation (never commercial). Production of butadiene from ethyl alcohol is not competitive costwise with butadiene from hydrocarbon-conversion processes, although alcohol-conversion plants require less capital. The alcohol plants are in stand-by condition for an emergency. Primary feed was a mixture of acetaldehyde and ethyl alcohol, the former having been produced by the dehydrogenation of the latter over copper- or silver-containing catalyst.

The *catalytic dehydrogenation of butenes* from cracking, to butadiene is the largest source and is described in this chapter in connection with dehydrogenation of n-butane.

Thermal cracking[1] may be done either in tubular furnaces with steam as the diluent or in regenerative stoves or furnaces. Preferred feedstocks are heavy naphthas and gas oils. Contact times in the cracking zone (temperature above 1200°F.) must be a few seconds or less to prevent decomposition of butadiene and other unsaturated compounds. The steam helps to maintain low partial pressures of the reactive hydrocarbons produced, thereby minimizing their conversion, largely by polymerization reactions, to less valuable materials. The operation may be conducted in a cyclic manner, cracking for 3 min., followed by a 3-min. reheat period during which fuel is burned within the cracking zone. The butadiene yield amounts to about 3.5 weight per cent on naphtha cracked. By-product recovery of benzene, naphthalene, and isoprene is necessary for the thermal-cracking processes to compete economically.

The *dehydrogenation of n-butane* to butenes is endothermic, the heat of reaction amounting to about 32.2 kg.-cal. per mole of butane.

$$C_4H_{10} \rightleftarrows CH_2{=}CHCH_2CH_3 + CH_3CH{=}CHCH_3$$
$$\rightleftarrows CH_2{=}CH{-}CH{=}CH_2({+}H_2)$$

The best catalysts are compositions containing alumina and chromia, although these are very sensitive to steam. The thermodynamics of this reversible dehydrogenation reaction indicate that, at pressures close to atmospheric, temperatures above 1000°F. are necessary to obtain commercially practical conversions. A successful process[2] includes (see Fig. 4): (1) Dehydrogenation of n-butane to 1 butene and *cis-* and *trans-*2-butene. (2) Separation of butenes from unconverted n-butane and other conversion products by a combination of fractionation and extractive distillation with acetone or aqueous furfural. n-Butane is recycled to (1). (3) Dehydrogenation of mixed butenes from (2) to butadiene using an iron oxide catalyst and regenerating or removing carbon by water-gas reaction. (4) Separation and purification of butadiene from (3) by extractive distillation with cuprous ammonium acetate (Fig. 4) or aqueous furfural, the unconverted butenes being recycled to (3).

---

[1] BUELL and BOATRIGHT, Furfural Extractive Distillation for Separation and Purification of C₄ Hydrocarbons, *Ind. Eng. Chem.*, **39**, 695 (1947).

[2] ANON., Butadiene, Pictured flow sheet, *Chem. Eng.*, **61** (9), 306 (1954); ANON., Petrochemical Processes, *Petroleum Refiner*, **32** (11), 148–151; HACHMUTH and HANSON, Butane Dehydrogenation, *Chem. Eng. Progr.*, **44** (6), 421 (1948); HANSON and HAYS, *Chem. Eng. Progr.*, **44** (6), 431 (1948); pilot-plant yields of 80 per cent of butenes from butane.

Superheated steam is employed to obtain low butene partial pressure and to supply necessary heat for reaction. All the hydrocarbon-conversion processes yield products in which butadiene is mixed with other closely boiling hydrocarbons. Ordinary fractionation alone is incapable of separating butadiene of the necessary purity (98 per cent) from these mixtures. The most useful method is an extractive distillation with aqueous cuprous ammonium acetate or furfural as the selective solvent. Here the slightly polar solvent markedly alters the relative volatilities of the hydrocarbon constituents. The solubility of hydrocarbon in this

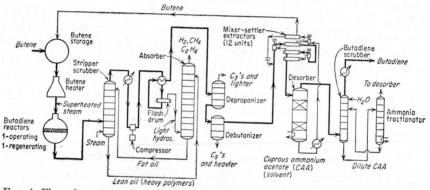

FIG. 4. Flow sheet for butadiene from purified butenes (acetone used for extractive removal of butane, and sulfuric acid for polymerizing and withdrawing isobutenes, prior to butene dehydrogenation to butadiene). See *Chem. Eng.*, **61** (9), 306 (1954) for further details and a pictured flow sheet.

type of solution increases with degree of unsaturation; for example, butadiene is one to five times more soluble than the closely boiling butenes. With this degree of selectivity, it is possible to design concentration units operating under a wide variety of conditions.

In 1954, 352,000 tons of *styrene*[1] were produced making it the most important cyclic intermediate in quantity of output. Styrene is employed as an ingredient of GR-S rubber and as a polymer and copolymer plastic material. Another use is in synthetic coatings and in styrenated drying oils and resins. A generalized flow sheet of the Dow process is illustrated by Figs. 5 and 6. It may be divided into three parts: (1) alkylating with ethylene and benzene to ethylbenzene, (2) dehydrogenating the purified ethylbenzene to crude styrene, and (3) separating

[1] MITCHELL, The Dow Process for Styrene Production, *Trans. Am. Inst. Chem. Engrs.*, **42**, 293 (1946); ANON., Styrene by Dow Process, *Chem. Eng.*, **51** (2), 160 (1944); SMITH, Los Angeles Styrene Plant, *Chem. Eng. Progr.*, **43** (4), 152 (1947); GROGGINS, "Unit Processes in Organic Synthesis," 4th ed., p. 889, McGraw-Hill Book Company, Inc., New York, 1952, for more elaborate process for ethylbenzene; BUNDY, R. H., and R. F. BOYER, "Styrene, Its Polymers, Copolymers and Derivatives," Reinhold Publishing Corporation, New York, 1952.

and recovering the styrene monomer from unreacted ethylbenzene and by-product benzene-toluene by vacuum distillation.

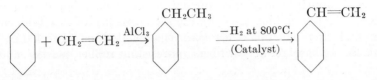

In the first step ethyl chloride provides hydrogen chloride which acts as a catalyst activator for the aluminum chloride. All the reactants

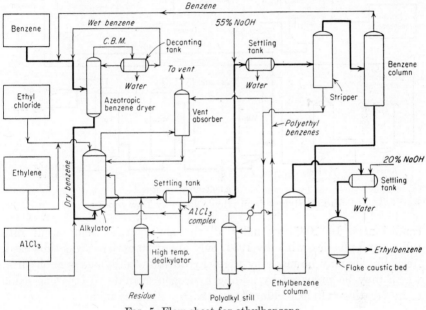

Fig. 5. Flow sheet for ethylbenzene.

must be dry and of high purity. The alkylation by-products, polyalkyl benzenes, are removed to avoid formation of polyfunctional, highly reactive products during dehydrogenation.

In the dehydrogenation reaction, the addition of superheated steam forces the reaction to the right because it: (1) reduces partial pressure of components to about 0.1 atm.; (2) supplies heat for the endothermic reaction; (3) minimizes undesirable side reactions; (4) removes carbon deposits from the catalyst by the water-gas reaction; and (5) controls the temperature, thus removing the necessity of heating the ethylbenzene with attendant possibility of coking. Vacuum distillation is employed for product purification. A small amount of elemental sulfur acts as an inhibitor. The temperature must not exceed 190°F. for the concentrated monomer. Seventy actual plates are used for separation; the pressure drop is about 4 mm. per plate. *p*-Tert-butyl-catechol (20 p.p.m.) is added to the purified styrene (99.9 per cent) as an inhibitor. The presence of trace impurities may give premature polymerization or too much inhibition. After chilling to 68°F., the styrene is loaded into tank cars.

In 1954 the production of *acrylonitrile* amounted to 63,107,000 lb. This chemical is a base[1] for acrylic fibers, oil-resistant rubber, plastics, and soil

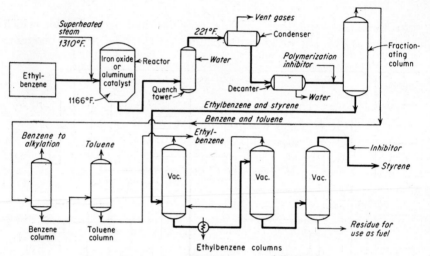

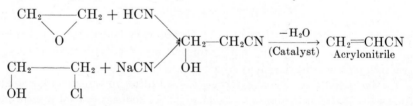

FIG. 6. Styrene from ethylbenzene by Dow process.

conditioners. In 1945, virtually all the acrylonitrile made went into rubber and plastics, while by 1954, only about 20 per cent was thus used. Acrylonitrile may be made by the dehydration of ethylene cyanohydrin, which may be prepared by adding hydrogen cyanide to ethylene oxide or by treating ethylene chlorohydrin with sodium cyanide.

$$CH_2\text{———}CH_2 + HCN$$
$$\diagdown O \diagup$$

$$CH_2\text{———}CH_2 + NaCN$$
$$| \qquad |$$
$$OH \qquad Cl$$

$$CH_2\text{—}CH_2CN \xrightarrow[\text{(Catalyst)}]{-H_2O} CH_2\text{=}CHCN$$
$$| \qquad\qquad\qquad\qquad \text{Acrylonitrile}$$
$$OH$$

Acrylonitrile may also be prepared by what is known as the natural-gas route. Natural gas is partially oxidized to acetylene which is reacted with hydrogen cyanide to form acrylonitrile. The hydrogen cyanide is also prepared from methane by reacting it with ammonia.

Chloroprene, 2-chloro-1,3-butadiene, is made in the following manner:[2]

[1] WEITH, Acrylonitrile, *Chem. Eng. News*, **31**, 2763 (1953).

[2] NIEUWLAND and VOGT, "The Chemistry of Acetylene" pp. 160*ff.*, Reinhold Publishing Corporation, New York, 1945.

Acetylene is polymerized to vinyl-acetylene in a horizontally agitated copper vessel at 55 to 65°C. The catalyst is a weak ammonium chloride solution of cuprous and potassium chlorides. The reactor gas is passed through a condenser to remove the water and fractionated into reaction products. The vinyl-acetylene is treated with cold, aqueous hydrochloric acid at 35 to 45°C. The catalyst is an aqueous solution of cuprous chloride.

$$2CH \equiv CH \xrightarrow{\text{Cat-}\atop\text{alyst}} CH \equiv C - CH = CH_2 \xrightarrow{\text{HCl}} CH_2 = CCl - CH = CH_2$$
$$\underset{\text{Acetylene}}{} \qquad \underset{\text{Vinyl-acetylene}}{} \qquad \underset{\text{Chloroprene}}{}$$

$n CH_2 = CCl - CH = CH_2$ polymerizes to $(-CH_2 - CCl = CH - CH_2 -)_n$
Chloroprene   Neoprene

Isobutylene is obtained from petroleum (see Chap. 37).

Polymerization. The synthetic rubbers made from chloroprene and silicone are *true polymers*, *i.e.*, the final molecule is composed of many small molecules added together with none of the original atoms of the monomer eliminated in the process. The various types of GR-S and nitrile rubbers are *copolymers* from two raw materials. An example of *condensation polymers* is the polysulfide rubbers. Here the chlorine of the hydrocarbon and the sodium of the sulfide complex do not appear in the polymer. Polymerizations of the butadiene-styrene type may be carried out by one of two methods: bulk and emulsion. The bulk method, which consists of combining the monomers with a suitable catalyst (such as sodium) and with or without a diluent, was used by the Germans for the Buna varieties.[1] Emulsion polymerization, described below, is used in the United States.

GR-S. During the years 1942 to 1945, almost all the GR-S produced was based on the following recipe:

	Parts		Parts
Butadiene......	75	Potassium persulfate (initiator of polymerization)..	0.3
Styrene........	25	Dodecyl mercaptan (modifier regulating molecular	
Water.........	180	weight of polymer).........................	0.3
Soap flakes.....	5.0	Hydroquinone (stopper)......................	0.1
		Phenyl-2-naphthylamine (stabilizer)............	1.25

A detailed description of the layout and operations is given by Soday.[2] The polymerization reaction took place principally as a batch process in autoclaves at a temperature of 50°C. (122°F.), though later continuous processing was introduced. A 75 per cent conversion was obtained in 12

[1] REBB, *et al.*, Synthetic Rubber Polymerization Practices, *Ind. Eng. Chem.*, **44**, 724 (1952).

[2] Preparation and Properties of GR-S, *Trans. Am. Inst. Chem. Engrs.*, **42**, 647 (1942); *cf.* 1st ed. of this book, pp. 789–792.

to 15 hr. when the polymerization was stopped by adding hydroquinone. Unreacted monomers were removed; the butadiene by flash stripping, the styrene by steam stripping under reduced pressure. The stabilizer was added to the stripped latex. Isolation of the polymer was effected by first creaming with brine and then coagulating with aqueous sulfuric acid or aluminum sulfate. The polymer crumbs, after drying, were compressed into bales. Polymerization times were reduced by improving monomer purity and the soap emulsifiers.

An important development in synthetic rubber was the discovery that lower polymerization temperatures improved the quality of the product. *Cold-rubber* production was made possible by the discovery of redox initiation, which permits practical polymerization rates at low temperatures. Redox polymerization can be described as the chemically controlled production of free radicals in the presence of the monomers by action between a reducing agent and an oxidizing agent. Most present production processes utilize an organic hydroperoxide, which is decomposed by a ferrous iron complex, producing free radicals and ferric iron. The free radicals initiate chain polymerization of the butadiene and styrene. Reducing sugars or certain other reducing agents may be used to regenerate the ferrous iron. Beginning in 1948 when 30,000 long tons of "cold" rubber were made commercially, production has increased until now over 75 per cent of the GR-S is made in this way.

Figure 7 illustrates the main steps for the continuous manufacture[1] of low-temperature GR-S. This flow sheet may be broken down into the following coordinated sequences of *unit operations* (Op.) and *unit processes* (Pr.):

Butadiene, received by tank car or pipe line, is given a dilute caustic wash to remove the polymerization inhibitor of the raw monomer (Pr.). No attempt is made to remove the inhibitor from styrene prior to use.

The emulsifier is prepared by making a 6 per cent potassium rosin soap-water solution plus small amounts of caustic and sodium phosphate (Op.).

The activator solution is prepared in a 2,500-gal. glass-lined steel tank. Dextrose and potassium pyrophosphate are dissolved in 10 parts of water at about 90°F. After heating and aging, ferrous sulfate solution is added (Pr.).

Butadiene, styrene, emulsifier, part of the charge water, activator solution, and tertiary mercaptans (chain modifying agents) are charged to the first of the 12 glass-lined reactors at the same time after passing through a cooler (Op.).

The initiator (cumene hydroperoxide or diisopropylbenzene monohydroperoxide or *p*-menthane hydroperoxide) is added last along with the rest of the

[1] SHEARON, *et al.*, Low Temperature Manufacture of Chemical Rubber, *Ind. Eng. Chem.*, **40**, 769 (1948); quantities, flow sheets, and 47 references; HOWLAND, *et al.*, Polymerization of GR-S at Low Temperatures, *Ind. Eng. Chem.*, **45**, 1304 (1953), new formulas; PRYOR, *et al.*, Reaction Times for Polymerization of Cold GR-S, *Ind. Eng. Chem.*, **45**, 1311 (1953). ANON., Cold Rubber, *Chem. Eng.*, **57** (4), 176 (1950), pictured flow sheet.

charge water to ensure that the reaction does not begin at a temperature above 41°F. (Op.).

Isopropanol, cooled by ammonia or Freon refrigerating plants to 15°F., is forced through a header to the feedstock cooler, reactor jackets, and surge tank. The amount of coolant necessary to maintain each reactor at 41°F. is controlled separately (Op.).

Copolymerization to attain a 60 per cent conversion is carried on under controlled conditions for approximately 5 to 14 hr. (Pr.).

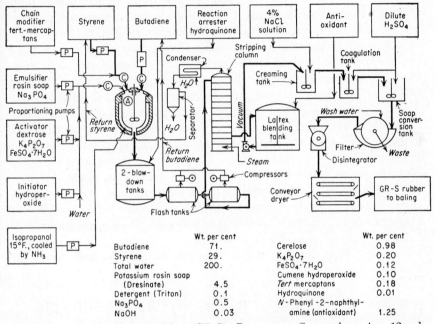

	Wt. per cent		Wt. per cent
Butadiene	71.	Cerelose	0.98
Styrene	29.	$K_4P_2O_7$	0.20
Total water	200.	$FeSO_4 \cdot 7H_2O$	0.12
Potassium rosin soap		Cumene hydroperoxide	0.10
(Dresinate)	4.5	*Tert* mercaptans	0.18
Detergent (Triton)	0.1	Hydroquinone	0.01
Na_3PO_4	0.5	*N*-Phenyl-2-naphthyl-	
NaOH	0.03	amine (antioxidant)	1.25

FIG. 7. Flow sheet for cold rubber (GR-S). P = pump, C = coolers, A = 12 polymerization kettles in series, kept at 41°F. by cork insulation and by cold isopropanol in jacket.

The copolymerization mass with the excess of reactants is dropped into a cold blowdown tank and the shortstop agent (reaction arrester) is added simultaneously (Op.). The glass-lined, steel blowdown tanks have a 7,500-gal. capacity. The primary blowdowns are not jacketed, but the secondary blowdowns are jacketed so that warm water can be circulated to warm the latex and generate sufficient pressure (20 lb. per sq. in.) to transfer the contents to the recovery system. Heat is supplied by circulating styrene water from the recovery-system stripping column plus additional steam (Op.).

Unreacted butadiene is removed in two successive horizontal flash tanks (Op.).

Excess styrene is steam-stripped under vacuum (Op.).

Antioxidant is added to the stripped latex which is pumped to the finishing area (Op.).

The stripped latex is creamed with a saturated solution of rock salt (Ca and

Mg salts removed) and coagulated with H_2SO_4. All three ingredients are fed through a pump into the coagulating tank (Op.).

The coagulum passes through an automatic overflow to a holding tank and then to a vibrating screen for dewatering (Op.). Sulfuric acid is added to the serum from the screen to bring the pH to 1.8 to 2.0 and recycled to the coagulating tank (Op.).

The crumb rubber is reslurried with fresh water, filtered, shredded, dried, weighed, and baled (Op.).

Oil-extended[1] GR-S represents another new development, where more rubber hydrocarbon can be made from a given amount of base polymer at lower cost. Commercially available in 1951, by 1953 oil-extended GR-S accounted for 18 per cent of the market. Practically all of it is used for tires. In the unvulcanized state regular GR-S is considered to be composed of long, zigzag polymer chains with relatively few cross linkages. Soft lower polymers between the chains act as internal lubricants for successful processing. When "cold" rubber is polymerized to high molecular weights, very small amounts of lower polymers are present. Oil, emulsified with soap and water, is added to the stripped latex to cut the viscosity back to a workable range. In effect, the oil replaces the lower polymers as an internal lubricant. This is known as *master batching*. After coagulation, the material is dried and baled as usual. The two GR-S oil master batches currently produced are: 25 parts of oil to 100 of polymer or 37.5 parts of oil to 100 of polymer. The oils are special cuts of standard petroleum-refinery feedstocks.

Neoprene.[2] Reactions by which this first of the successful synthetic rubbers is made are as follows:

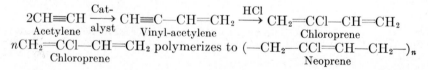

$$2CH{\equiv}CH \xrightarrow[\text{alyst}]{\text{Cat-}} CH{\equiv}C{-}CH{=}CH_2 \xrightarrow{\text{HCl}} CH_2{=}CCl{-}CH{=}CH_2$$

Acetylene   Vinyl-acetylene   Chloroprene

$nCH_2{=}CCl{-}CH{=}CH_2$ polymerizes to $({-}CH_2{-}CCl{=}CH{-}CH_2{-})_n$

Chloroprene   Neoprene

The chloroprene is emulsified in water with a sodium rosin soap and is polymerized by the action of potassium persulfate. A modifying agent is used to make the polymer more plastic. Dry neoprene is isolated from the latex by the continuous coagulation of a polymer film on a freeze drum followed by washing and drying. The dry polymer is cut into rope-like sections and bagged. Neoprene is supplied in both dry polymer (nine kinds) and latex (seven kinds). It is vulcanized with metallic oxides, MgO and ZnO, and is compounded with special accelerators, antioxidants, softeners, and fillers. The uses for neoprene parallel those for natural and GR-S rubber, but neoprene costs more. Therefore, it is used where there is need for resistance to deterioration by oils, solvents,

[1] ANON., Do Oil and Rubber Mix? *Chem. Eng. News*, **32**, 1553 (1954).

[2] ANON., Neoprene, *Chem. & Met. Eng.*, **51** (1), 130 (1944), a pictured flow sheet.

and many chemicals, and to degradation by sunlight, ozone, weather, or heat. Typical applications include protective jackets over electric wire and cable, hoses, and conveyer belting. The latices are employed as adhesives, in coated fabrics, in foam sponge, and as a wet-strength additive to paper.

Butyl Rubber.[1] Butyl rubber is the best for automobile inner tubes. It also has many industrial applications because of its excellent physical and chemical properties and also because of its low price as compared with other types of synthetic rubber. Butyl rubber is a copolymer of isobutylene and isoprene (1 to 3 per cent). Butyl has less than 3 per cent of the unsaturation of natural rubber with consequent high chemical and heat resistance. The proper ratios of isobutylene and isoprene are dissolved in methyl chloride and cooled to the reaction temperature ($-95°$C.). The Friedel-Crafts catalyst, also dissolved in methyl chloride, is added and the polymerization takes place. The reaction is continuous and crumbs of the product are filtered and dried to obtain the crude butyl polymer. Butyl is compounded and vulcanized by the same general method as natural rubber except for special precautions required by its low unsaturation. Unlike natural rubber additional sulfur will not increase the hardness of butyl. Carbon black and softeners are used to adjust hardness.

Nitrile Rubbers. Another important class of special synthetic rubbers consists of copolymers of butadiene and acrylonitrile. Nitrile rubbers exhibit exceptional solvent resistance with minimum loss of low-temperature flexibility. Properties of these copolymers can be varied at will by changing the monomer ratio. Almost all the commercial polymers contain from 20 to 40 per cent acrylonitrile. In recent years the cold-rubber process has been carried over to the nitrile rubbers. Polymerization at 5°C. results in polymers with improved tensile strength and increased solubility in aromatic hydrocarbons which leads to improved compounding. Nitrile rubbers are used in the manufacture of hose and belting, wire insulation, automobile parts, and textile equipment.

Polysulfide Rubbers.[2] Thiokols are prepared by the condensation polymerization of an alkaline polysulfide with a suitable dihalide:

$$x\text{NaS}_4\text{Na} \quad + \quad x\text{ClCH}_2\text{CH}_2\text{Cl} \rightarrow (\text{CH}_2\text{CH}_2\text{S}_4)_x + 2x\text{NaCl}$$
Sodium tetrasulfide   Ethylene dichloride   Thiokol Type A

Other sodium polysulfides are also reacted with other dihalides; methylene, ethylene, and propylene dichloride, glycerol dichlorohydrin, dichloroethyl ether, dichloroethyl formal, and triglycol dichloride. Poly-

[1] LEE, Butyl Rubber, *Chem. & Met. Eng.*, **50** (7), 102 (1943), a pictured flow sheet; McNAMEE, Butyl Rubber, *Chem. Eng.*, **61** (10), 238 (1954).

[2] FETTES and JORCZAK, Polysulfide Polymers, *Ind. Eng. Chem.*, **42**, 2217 (1950); Polysulfide Liquid Polymers, *Ind. Eng. Chem.*, **43**, 324 (1951).

sulfide polymers are supplied as crude rubbers, water dispersions, and liquid polymers. They are much used for tank linings for petroleum storage, building and calking putties, solid cements and special sealants, to name but a few of their specialized applications.

Silicone Rubbers and Other Special Synthetics.[1] *Silicone rubbers* constitute one of the newest classes of rubberlike polymers. These exhibit unique physical and chemical properties. Chemically they are specially prepared polymers of purified dimethyl siloxane in which the reaction is controlled to give linear chains of several thousand units. The unique properties of silicone polymers are partially explained by the fact that the bond energy of the silicone-oxygen linkage is about 1.5 times as strong as the C—C linkage in hydrocarbon polymers. Although the polymer is saturated it can be vulcanized by heating with a source of free radicals such as benzoyl peroxide. It is assumed the free radicals derived from benzoyl peroxide remove H_2 atoms from the polymer molecules. The unsatisfied valences on the polymer molecules then give rise to cross linkage which results in a vulcanized product. The outstanding characteristic of silicone rubbers is their very broad useful temperature range (from -100 to $+500°$F.). In this range flexibility, resilience, and tensile strength are retained to an amazing degree. Because of their expense, silicone polymers are normally employed where their unique properties justify. They are of great value in many aircraft applications such as jet-engine components, ducting, gaskets, seals, and diaphragms.

Polymers of acrylic acid esters may vary from hard plastics to soft, waxy polymers, depending upon the specific ester employed. Esters from alcohols of intermediate molecular weight, such as the ethyl and butyl esters, yield rubbery products known as *acrylic rubbers*. As a class these possess good flex resistance, resistance to hot oils and air up to $350°$F., unlimited oxygen resistance, and low permeability to gases. *Polyester rubbers* are a new type of condensation polymer of interest as a vulcanizable polymeric plasticizer for coatings and proofing in admixture with other materials such as polyvinyl formal, nitro-cellulose, and cellulose acetate. An example is Chemigum SL, a polyester-diisocyanate polymer. *Hypalon S-2* is prepared by the chlorination of polyethylene to 25 to 30 per cent chlorine content. This is reacted with sulfur dioxide to introduce a number of sulfonyl chloride groups along the polymer chain:

$$(-CH_2-CH_2-)_n + Cl_2 + SO_2 \rightarrow -CH_2-CH_2-\underset{\underset{Cl}{|}}{CH}-CH_2-CH_2-\underset{\underset{SO_2Cl}{|}}{CH}-$$

This material has special properties for mechanical goods. *Saran* is probably an internally plasticized copolymer of vinylidene chloride. It is vulcanized with amines in the absence of sulfur compounds. Saran

[1] KIRK and OTHMER, *op. cit.*, Vol. 12, p. 393.

possesses outstanding chemical resistance, excellent abrasion resistance, and fair electrical properties. Tank linings are an important outlet.

SELECTED REFERENCES

Barron, Harry, "Modern Rubber Chemistry," D. Van Nostrand Company, Inc., New York, 1948.

Moakes, R. C. W., and W. C. Wake, "Rubber Technology," Butterworths Scientific Publications, London, 1951.

Barron, Harry, "Modern Synthetic Rubbers," 3d ed., Chapman & Hall, Ltd., London, 1949.

Whitley, G. S., editor, C. C. Davis, and R. F. Dunbrook, "Synthetic Rubber," John Wiley & Sons, Inc., New York, 1954.

Marchionna, Frederick, "Butalastic Polymers," Reinhold Publishing Corporation, New York, 1946.

Marchionna, Frederick, "Latex and Rubber Derivatives," Vols. II, III, Abstracts through January, 1937, Rubber Age, New York.

Houwink, R., editor, "Elastomers and Plastomers," 3 vols., Elsevier Press, Inc., Houston, Tex., 1948–1950.

Burton, W. E., "Engineering with Rubber," McGraw-Hill Book Company, Inc., New York, 1949.

Rogers, S. S., editor, "The Vanderbilt Rubber Handbook," 9th ed., R. T. Vanderbilt Company, New York, 1948.

Ball, J. M., "Reclaimed Rubber," Rubber Reclaimers Association, Inc., New York, 1947.

Kirk, R. E., and D. F. Othmer, "Encyclopedia of Chemical Technology," The Interscience Encyclopedia, Inc., New York, 1947–1956.

Dawson, T. R., and B. D. Porritt, "Rubber: Physical and Chemical Properties," Research Association of British Rubber Manufacturers, Croydon, England, 1935; compiled from 300,000 references.

Boundy, R. H., and R. F. Boyer, "Styrene," Reinhold Publishing Corporation, New York, 1952.

India Rubber World, monthly periodical, Bill Brothers Publishing Corporation, New York.

Rubber Age, monthly periodical, Palmerton Publishing Company, Inc., East Stroudsburg, Pa.

Rubber Chemistry & Technology, quarterly. Division of Rubber Chemistry, American Chemical Society, Lancaster, Pa.

Davis, Carroll C., and John T. Blake, "Chemistry and Technology of Rubber," Reinhold Publishing Corporation, New York, 1937. Contains 3,000 references.

Symposium, Rubber, Ind. Eng. Chem., **43**, 315 (1951). Symposium, Low Temperature Rubber, Ind. Eng. Chem., **41**, 1553 (1949). Symposium, Elastomers, Ind. Eng. Chem., **44**, 696 (1952).

Rubber Statistical Bulletin, monthly, Rubber Age, New York.

CHAPTER 37

THE PETROLEUM INDUSTRY

America is indeed fortunate in her petroleum situation. She stands at the head of other nations in her resources of crude petroleum, in her transportation of petroleum products, and in her refineries for processing crude petroleum into products of greater usefulness. If we except the primary production of food and clothing from our soils, there is no organic industry more important to modern technical civilization than the petroleum industry.

Initially, the refining of petroleum involved the simple fractionation of the constituents already present in the crude oil. This was the easiest approach, and it was lucky that the first crude oil discovered in Pennsylvania was adapted to such an operation. However, as markets were developed for more specialized products and as new fields supplying more varied crude oil were discovered, it was necessary and economical to use chemical reactions to change the molecular structure of the compounds initially present in the crude, thus opening up greatly enlarged and more adaptable markets to the petroleum industry.

For the manufacture of very many chemicals from carbon black and ammonia through ethyl alcohol and glycol to synthetic rubber, man-made fibers and plastics, the petroleum industry is providing the cheapest raw materials. Although the petroleum industry is finding it economical to import more and more crude oil, it is not at all likely that the use of petroleum products as chemical raw materials will be curtailed. Rather, when in the many decades ahead, the cost of petroleum products as liquid fuels for heat and power become comparatively enhanced, shale oil and coal can be processed.

The petroleum industry in its design, operation, development, sales, and executive branches has become the largest employer of chemical engineers. This has been particularly true recently because the simple distillations of the earlier years have been generally replaced by complicated refining procedures which involve numerous unit physical operations and unit chemical processes, frequently of great complexity and large size. This industry is so interrelated and so technical in all its branches that the trained engineer is a necessity. He should not become too narrow in his view as the petroleum industry is reaching out into many other chemical fields, supplying raw materials, or using other chemicals. Thus chemical engineers within the petroleum industry should know something of other fields to be most efficient whether in operating, constructing, or designing work.

Historical.[1] It seems hardly believable that the petroleum industry has grown so rapidly and so extensively from the first skimming of petroleum seepages by the Indians for a medicinal or rubbing oil or the first modern petroleum well drilled near Titusville, Pa., by Colonel Drake in 1859 to the tremendous industry now flourishing, not only in the United States but throughout the world. This development has gone through a great many market changes. At first, the chief petroleum product sold was kerosene for illuminating purposes. Now kerosene is of secondary importance in comparison with the tremendous consumption of gasoline occasioned by the growth of the internal-combustion engine and its application to transportation or to power, in the air, on our roads, in our factories, and on our farms. The synthesis of many chemicals out of petroleum raw materials is the outstanding characteristic of the broad chemical and allied industries.

Chemical engineering owes a great deal to the discovery and application of engineering principles in distillation, heat transfer, fluid flow, and the like by the petroleum engineers in the designing, building, and operating of their refineries. At first their almost universally used equipment was a batch still. Here a relatively small amount, or batch, of crude petroleum was pumped into a horizontal direct-fired cylindrical vessel provided with a condenser. The various constituents of the petroleum were distilled and condensed, the lightest coming over first and leaving behind in the still a residuum of tar or heavy lubricating oil. This has been supplanted almost entirely by the modern *continuous* pipe still, as will be exemplified by the flow sheets presented in this chapter.

Origin.[2] There have been many organic theories of the origin of petroleum, some emphasizing a vegetable or animal background, others a close relationship to coal, while certain of these theories lay stress on how any organic matter of either background could be transformed into petroleum products. There seems to be general agreement that petroleum has been formed from organic matter of near-shore *marine* deposits in an environment deficient in oxygen; and associated with the sediments later on solidified into the rocks: limestones, dolomites, shales, or sandstones.

[1] EGLOFF and ALEXANDER, Petroleum Chemistry, *Ind. Eng. Chem.*, **43**, 809 (1951), excellent historical article.

[2] *Cf.* ILLING, LIND, TRASK, BROOKS, and HOBSON, in DUNSTAN, NASH, BROOKS, and TIZARD, "Science of Petroleum," Vol. 1, pp. 32–56, Oxford University Press, New York, 1938. This large many-volume publication on petroleum is a monumental work and should be freely consulted by anyone interested in petroleum; Petroleum Symposium, *Ind. Eng. Chem.*, **44**, 2556–2577 (1952), 4 articles on origin.

The concentration of the organic matter may not have been high in the original deposition, but petroleum has migrated and gathered in places most favorable to its retention, such as porous sandstone in domes protected by oil-impervious strata or against sealed faults in the sediments. Brooks[1] points out, referring to this organic matter, that "the proteins and soluble carbohydrates are undoubtedly quickly destroyed in the initial processes of decay or bacterial action . . . . Fatty oils are relatively resistant to bacterial action . . . . Fatty oils (or acids) are probably the chief source material from which petroleum has been derived."

Exploration. At one time the drilling for petroleum was a hit-or-miss affair and in such cases about 1 out of 300 of the "wildcat"[2] wells struck oil. However, by employing skilled geologists who have studied the origin and occurrence of petroleum, as well as geophysicists, who are expert in the use of very delicate instruments to determine something about the geological conditions under the earth's surface, the drilling of wells has become so vastly improved that in 1951, 1 out of 5.3 of the new wells yields oil or gas. The geologist early recognized that petroleum occurred in oil pools caught in the anticlinal folds of sedimentary rocks. The success of the oil geologist[3] has been due to the correlation of a great deal of experience and data. This includes the study of cores from all types of wells and the accurate observation of surface indication, coupled with newer geophysical exploratory procedures, many of which have been developed and perfected by the scientific staffs of the oil companies.

By the use of very sensitive instruments, the geophysicists can determine the likelihood of the occurrence of domes and deposits at considerable distances in the earth. The top of the arch of an anticline, or a dome, has, by virtue of compression, a greater specific gravity than the surrounding rocks, as shown by Fig. 1, which depicts the various strata surrounding oil-bearing rock or sand. Oil and salt deposits also have a different (lower) specific gravity than the accompanying rocks. These variations are measured by very delicate gravity instruments which record changes in the gravity constant g. The plotting of these results gives us a *gravimetric survey*. Other methods of forecasting such anticlines include the exploding of dynamite charges at selected intervals with special instruments located at various points to measure and time the

[1] "Science of Petroleum," Vol. 1, p. 52; KIRK and OTHMER, *op. cit.*, Vol. 10, pp. 97–109, 52 references and detailed discussion.

[2] A "wildcat" is a well whose location is determined without resorting to scientific exploration of any kind, especially in a previously untested area.

[3] See "Science of Petroleum," particularly pp. 270–397, for numerous articles by experts in this field. See also HAGER, "Practical Oil Geology," 6th ed., McGraw-Hill Book Company, Inc., New York, 1951; and SCHNACKE and DRAKE, "Oil for the World," Harper & Brothers, New York, 1950.

reflected wave initiated by the explosion. This results in a *seismic survey*. Other methods are also used, such as a determination of the electrical conductivity of the earth or the magnetic conditions. These two methods do not seem to be so successful as the gravimetric and seismic surveys. All these studies lead to the drilling of a test well which, if successful, frequently opens up a new oil field.

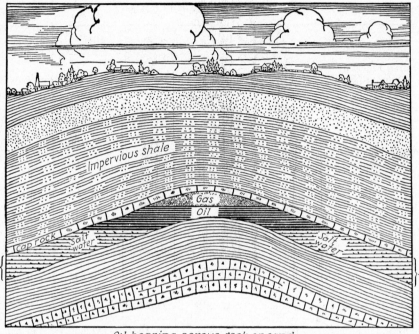

FIG. 1. Oil trapped in nature's reservoir. (*Courtesy of American Petroleum Institute.*)

Production Statistics. The world's production of petroleum from 1857 to January, 1952, aggregated about 74 billion barrels,[1] of which the fields in the United States are producing now approximately 51 per cent, as shown in Table 1. There is no industry that publishes more extensive statistical data than the petroleum industry,[2] through the American Petroleum Institute wherein the refiners, producers, and marketers have banded themselves together for presenting such data to the public. Table 2 gives a comparison of the total quantities of important refined products in the United States for the years 1945–1953.

[1] In the petroleum field a barrel holds 42 gal.

[2] "Petroleum Facts and Figures," American Petroleum Institute, New York, published every few years, 11th ed., 322 pp., 1955. This is a most unusual volume on statistics presenting the industry from the point of view of utilization, production, refining, transportation, marketing, prices, and taxation. The facts are shown in tables. The U.S. Bureau of Mines also publishes generalized statistics on this industry.

Reserves and Raw Materials. Estimates of oil reserves are only of an approximate nature. However, it should be apparent that some idea, although far from exact, of the available reserves of essential minerals—petroleum included—is of vital importance in mapping their development

TABLE 1. WORLD CRUDE-OIL PRODUCTION, BY REGIONS AND COUNTRIES,
BY YEARS[a]
(Thousands of barrels of 42 U.S. gal.)

Country	1953	1952	1947	1945
North America:				
United States...............	2,359,998	2,291,997	1,856,987	1,713,655
Canada...................	80,862	61,103	7,692	8,483
Mexico...................	73,178	77,275	56,284	43,547
Others...................	22,361	21,294	20,821	21,244
Total.................	2,536,399	2,451,669	1,941,784	1,786,929
South America:				
Venezuela................	644,244	660,254	434,905	323,156
Others...................	89,972	84,883	62,160	62,199
Total.................	734,216	745,137	497,065	385,355
Europe:				
U.S.S.R. (Russia)...........	364,900	322,400	187,463	148,953
Others...................	87,822	82,188	48,853	49,038
Total.................	452,722	404,588	236,316	197,991
Africa:				
Egypt...................	16,499	16,464	8,627	9,406
Other...................	875	1,106	21	26
Total.................	17,374	17,570	8,648	9,432
Asia:				
Iran.....................	9,390	10,100	154,998	130,526
Iraq.....................	210,672	140,799	35,834	35,112
Kuwait..................	314,593	273,433	16,225	
Indonesia................	76,898	62,495	8,020	7,600
Sarawak.................	36,855	38,300	12,970	2,100
Saudi Arabia.............	308,295	301,861	89,852	21,311
Others...................	49,793	50,378	20,361	18,439
Total.................	1,006,496	877,366	338,260	215,088
World total..............	4,747,207	4,498,057	3,022,075	2,594,798
Per cent United States........	50	51	64.45	66.04

[a] "Minerals Yearbook."

and the future trend of the related industries. The following statements apply only to proved[1] oil reserves and leave out of consideration the volume of alternate total oil reserves. It should be noted that up to 80 per cent of the petroleum stored underground can be economically

[1] By proved reserves is meant the oil that is in known and proved fields and recoverable by present production methods.

brought to the surface, that although practically all the natural gas can be recovered and utilized, in actual practice some oil is wasted. Proved reserves of the world in January, 1951, were estimated at somewhat under 104 billion barrels, of which the proved reserves in the United States amounted to 27½ billion barrels.[1,2]

In discussing oil reserves, emphasis should be placed on improved technique in the operation of oil wells. The concern of early operators with efficient methods of extraction and with the quantity of oil that ultimately would be left unrecovered in the reservoir sands, after the wells

TABLE 2. PRODUCTION OF PETROLEUM PRODUCTS IN UNITED STATES
REFINERIES, BY YEARS[a]
(Thousands of barrels)

Product	1953	1952	1951	1945
Finished gasoline...............	1,259,040	1,189,781	1,140,843	774,460
Kerosene......................	129,751	132,300	135,742	81,024
Distillate fuel oil...............	532,221	521,264	475,801	249,224
Residual fuel oil................	449,979	454,784	469,377	469,492
Lubricants.....................	52,545	55,600	61,489	41,867
Wax, thousands of lb...........	1,393,840	1,212,680	1,347,920	817,880
Coke, thousands of short tons.....	4,310	3,622	3,795	2,023
Asphalt, thousands of short tons..	13,170	12,780	12,055	7,127
Still gas, million cu. ft..........	368,400	342,990	346,658	372,449
All other finished products.......	42,397	45,224	46,346	21,766

[a] "Minerals Yearbook."

no longer could be operated profitably, was noticeably secondary. Ashburner, in 1887, estimated that wasteful producing operations in Pennsylvania and New York oil fields would leave ultimately eight to nine times as much of the original oil in the sands as would be recovered.[3] Laboratory experiments indicate that if early New York and Pennsylvania operators had been able to produce their oil in an economical manner, by methods now considered efficient, 2 to 2½ times more oil than was withdrawn from the sands might have been recovered by natural flow and pumping.[4]

The key to the problem is proper conservation and use of reservoir

[1] Details are given in "Petroleum Facts and Figures," op. cit., especially p. 236.

[2] Western Hemisphere Oil Study Committee, "Petroleum in the Western Hemisphere," 183 pp., Independent Petroleum Association of America, Tulsa, Okla., 1952. This is an optimistic report with many tables and charts.

[3] ASHBURNER, Petroleum and Natural Gas in New York, Trans. Am. Inst. Mining Met. Engrs., **16**, 1915 (1887).

[4] MUSKAT, WYCHOFF, BOTSET, and MERES, Flow of Gas-liquid Mixtures through Sands, Trans. Am. Inst. Mining Met. Engrs., **123**, 69 (1937).

energy.[1] Oil is underlain by water under high head in the extraneous parts of the reservoir systems of most oil fields and overlain with gas, as diagrammatically shown by Fig. 1. The energy available to produce oil is represented by the head of water and the pressure of the gas acting on the oil. If the withdrawal of oil from the reservoir is at a *sufficiently low rate*,[2] entrance of meteoric water at the outcrops and expansion of large water supplies already present tends to maintain the pressure head and supply the necessary energy.

An extremely important method of conservation is the return of natural gas to the oil wells. As an example, in the Sugarland, Tex., field, reintroduction of or cycling with gas at a pressure of 1,400 lb. per sq. in. and a slower rate of production are expected to recover twice as much as would have been recovered under older methods of producing oil (a net recovery of 70 per cent of the original store).[3] Air mixed with the gas has certain disadvantages because it tends to deteriorate slightly the quality of the oil produced.

Water-flooding methods are responsible for the recovery of millions of barrels of oil that former production practices left in the reservoir sands. Water is usually introduced in a central well and allowed to extend gradually outward as an expanding circle to drive oil to surrounding wells. "Water flooding is estimated to have established a recoverable reserve of approximately 600,000,000 bbl. of oil in the Bradford-Allegheny district that never could have been obtained by customary methods of production."[4]

For years oil wells drilled into hard limestone formations have been "shot" with nitro-glycerine because the resulting fissures and fractures increased the drainage of oil and gas into the well. Today, almost every well drilled into a limestone formation has the drainage channels enlarged by treatment with inhibited hydrochloric acid; sometimes in dense limestone the action of the nitro-glycerine is followed by acid treatment. This acid treatment has transformed many apparently nonproductive wells into rich producers. In the Illinois basin,[5] frequently wells drilled into oölitic limestone failed to show any oil until acid treatment was

[1] MILLER and SHEA, Gains in Oil and Gas Production Refining and Utilization Technology, pp. 5ff., *Tech. Paper* 3, National Resources Planning Board, 1941.

[2] SCHNACKE and DRAKE, *op. cit.*, p. 50.

[3] MILLER and LINDSLY, Report on Petroleum Development and Production, Hearing on H.R. 441, 73d Cong., Recess, 1934, pt. II, p. 1207.

[4] MILLER and SHEA, *op. cit.;* STEIDLE, Some Basic Problems in the Conservation and Future Production of Pennsylvania Grade Crude Oil, *Oil Weekly*, p. 22, June 18, 1934.

[5] MILLER and SHEA, Report on Recent Progress in Petroleum Development and Production, p. 369, Petroleum Investigation (U.S. Congress, House of Representatives), Hearings on H.R. 290 and H.R. 7372 R, 76th Cong., 1939.

used. This acid treatment has become so important that it has now been given to about 10,000 wells in the carbonate rock (limestone and dolomite) regions of Michigan, Ohio, Illinois, Kentucky, Kansas, Oklahoma, Texas, and Louisiana. For this purpose more than 25,000,000 gal.[1] of hydrochloric acid, containing an inhibitor to prevent corrosive action on iron, are consumed yearly.

The movement of oil in underground reservoirs is closely connected to the viscosity and surface tension of the oil. These in turn are related to the amount of gas dissolved in the oil. All this is a very practical application of Henry's law,[2] which states that at constant temperature, a liquid will dissolve the weight of a gas that is proportional to its pressure.

Transportation. In the United States a great pipe-line transportation system moves a tremendous tonnage of petroleum and natural gas. The pipe line has reached its maximum application east of the Rocky Mountains, where trunk lines, branch lines, and pumping stations form an extremely complex system. The pipe line is the only economical method yet discovered of transporting natural gas. At regular intervals pressure-booster stations are located, using a small part of the gas to drive gas engines connected to compressors.

In 1950,[3] the United States possessed 128,589 miles of petroleum pipe lines, and 314,480 miles of natural-gas lines. Of this latter total, 172,270 miles were employed in distributing the gas with the remainder or 142,210 miles in gathering and transmitting.

Tank ships are the "water pipe lines" that connect remote oil fields with the refineries and markets. As an efficient and cheap means of bulk transportation, particularly over long distances, they are cheaper than the pipe line on land. The refined products of the industry are transported by an occasional special pipe line and by thousands of tank cars and motor tank trucks. Huge steel or concrete reservoirs holding 100,000 bbl. or more are employed for the storage of petroleum and its products. Despite a tremendous potential fire hazard, the loss through fire is among the smallest of industrial fire losses, owing to care, forethought, and many automatic protective devices.

Earnings and Investment. Contrary to the popular conception of petroleum as "liquid gold," the total income of the industry has been moderate. Such profits as have accrued have been more the reward of

---

[1] KIESSLING, ROGERS, et al., "Technology, Employment and Output per Man in Petroleum and Natural Gas Production," p. 150, Work Projects Administration, National Research Project in cooperation with U.S. Bureau of Mines, Report E-10, July, 1939.

[2] This matter is well treated with references to the original literature on pp. 17–25 of MILLER and SHEA, Gains in Oil and Gas Production, etc.

[3] Petroleum Facts and Figures," pp. 160, 166.

business enterprise and sound research than of good fortune. In the 5 years from 1946 to 1950, the annual rate of return on net worth averaged 15.8 per cent,[1] in comparison with 15.94 per cent from the manufacturing industries. The large investment in the petroleum field is summarized in Table 3. The subdivisions of this tabulation show the varied nature of this extensive business.

TABLE 3. SUMMARY OF CAPITAL EXPENDITURES BY UNITED STATES
OIL INDUSTRY[a]
(Millions of dollars)

	1955[b]	1951	Yearly average 1946–1950
Production.............................	2,350	1,913	1,220
Transportation........................	315	390	283
Refining..............................	846	303	359
Fertilizers, chemicals.................	66	25	23
Marketing............................	370	268	218
Other................................	66	149	43
Total............................	4,014	2,948	2,147
Facilities outside the United States.........	605	323	328
Grand total........................	4,619	3,271	2,475

[a] "Petroleum Facts and Figures."
[b] Estimated.

CONSTITUENTS OF PETROLEUM, INCLUDING PETROLEUM GASES

Crude petroleum is made up of hundreds of different individual chemicals from methane to asphalt. Although most of the constituents are hydrocarbons (83 to 87 per cent of carbon and 11 to 15 per cent hydrogen), the ultimate analyses indicate the presence in small quantities of nitrogen (0 to 0.5 per cent), sulfur (0 to 6 per cent), and oxygen (0 to 3.5 per cent).[2]

In recent decades, much detailed work has been carried out by M. R. Fenske at Pennsylvania State College and by F. D. Rossini and coworkers cooperating with American Petroleum Institute[3] to determine the actual constituents of petroleum. The results have been published in the current

[1] "Petroleum Facts and Figures," p. 233; cf. COQUERON, "Financial Analysis of 30 Oil Companies for 1952," Chase National Bank, New York, 1953.

[2] See NELSON, "Petroleum Refinery Engineering," 3d ed., p. 11 et seq., McGraw-Hill Book Company, Inc., New York, 1949, for tables and many references.

[3] ROSSINI, Hydrocarbons in Petroleum, Chem. Eng. News, 25, 231 (1947); ROSSINI and MAIR, Composition of Petroleum, "Progress in Petroleum Technology," p. 334, American Chemical Society, Washington, D.C., 1951.

literature but have been excellently summarized by Sweeney,[1] Sachanen,[2] and Nelson.[3]

The hydrocarbons may be divided into two chemical classes:

1. **Open-chain or Aliphatic Compounds,** comprising:

n-Paraffin Series, C_nH_{2n+2}. This series of hydrocarbons comprises a larger fraction of most petroleums than any of the other individual classes. Important members are, with volume percentage occurrence in crudes from Ponca, Okla., East Texas, and Bradford: *n*-hexane (2 ± per cent) and *n*-heptane (2.5, 1.7, 2.5 per cent). The *n*-paraffins predominate in most straight-run gasolines.

Isoparaffin Series, C_nH_{2n+2}. The branched-chain compounds are very desirable and are frequently manufactured by hydroforming, alkylation, and isomerization (see page 843). Naturally occurring members are: 2- and 3-methylpentanes (0.8, 1.5, 0.9 per cent), 2,3-dimethylpentane, and 2-methylhexane (1.2, 1.3, 1.3 per cent), in crudes from Ponca, East Texas, and Bradford.

Olefin Series, C_nH_{2n}. This series is not present or exists in very small quantities. Cracking processes produce large amounts of olefins. Olefins are very useful because of their excellent antiknock properties and chemical reactivity. The olefins are the most important class of compounds *chemically derived* from petroleum for the making of other products also by chemical processing or conversion. Examples of pure lower members are: ethylene, propylene, and butylene. In cracked gasolines and in residual products are many of the higher members of the series.

2. **Ring Compounds,** comprising:

Naphthene Series, C_nH_{2n}. This series, which has the same type formula as the olefin series, differs in that its members are completely saturated. It is the second most abundantly occurring series of compounds in most crudes. Members are: methylcyclopentane (0.95, 1.3, 0.5 per cent), cyclohexane (0.78, 0.66, 0.64 per cent), dimethyl cyclopentanes (1.75, 2.0, 1.0 per cent), methylcyclohexane (1.8, 2.4, 2.0 per cent) in crudes from Ponca, East Texas, and Bradford. These naphthenes predominate in most gas oils and lubricating oils from all types of crudes. These are also present in residual products.

Aromatic or Benzene Series, C_nH_{2n-6}. Although only small amounts of aromatic compounds are present in most petroleums, the Borneo and Sumatra crudes contain relatively large amounts. These compounds are produced by chemical processing and, like the olefins, have high anti-

---

[1] Sweeney, Petroleum and Its Products, 24th Annual Priestley Lecture, Pennsylvania State College, 1950, splendid charts and tables.

[2] Sachanen, "The Chemical Constituents of Petroleum," Reinhold Publishing Company, New York, 1945; Kirk and Othmer, *op. cit.*, Vol. 10, p. 93.

[3] Nelson, *op. cit.*, p. 11 *et seq.*

knock qualities. Members are benzene (0.15, 0.07, 0.06 per cent), toluene (0.5, 0.6, 0.5 per cent), ethylbenzene (0.18, 0.2, 0.9 per cent), xylenes (0.9, 1.1, 1.0 per cent) in crudes from Ponca, East Texas, and Bradford. Petroleum crudes are characterized by *variability* in composition. Yet these must be evaluated[1] before they can be refined. Over the years it has become usual to divide the crudes into three "bases":

1. *Paraffin Base*. These crudes consist primarily of open-chain compounds, and furnish low-octane-number straight-run gasoline and excellent but waxy lubricating-oil stocks.

2. *Intermediate Base*. These crudes contain large quantities of both paraffinic and naphthenic compounds and furnish medium-grade straight-run gasolines and lubricating oils. Both wax and asphalt are found in these oils.

3. *Naphthene Base*. These crudes contain a high percentage of cyclic (naphthenic) compounds and furnish relatively high octane-number straight-run gasoline. The lubricating-oil fractions must be solvent-refined. Asphalt is present.

Petroleum products[2] have long been divided into salable cuts by fractionation in the refining operations. This is a separation by boiling ranges. Indeed, the natural separation that takes place when the petroleum leaves its underground reservoirs, into natural gas and ordinary crude, is based on the same principle. Such refinery fractions may be classified roughly as follows:

Natural (or casing-head) gasoline and natural gas.
Light distillates.
  Motor gasolines.
  Solvent naphthas.
  Kerosene.
  Light heating oils.
Intermediate distillates.
  Heavy fuel oils.
  Diesel oils.
  Gas oils.

Heavy distillates.
  Heavy mineral oils (medicinal).
  Heavy flotation oils.
  Waxes (candles, sealing, paper treating, insulating).
  Lubricating oils (large range).
Residues.
  Lubricating oils.
  Fuel oils.
  Petrolatum.
  Road oils.
  Asphalts.
  Coke.

Natural gas occurs as accumulations in underground, porous reservoirs either with or without petroleum oil. Though natural gas has been known for centuries, not until the early 1800's was it first discovered in

[1] NELSON and BUTHOD in KIRK and OTHMER, *op. cit.*, Vol. 10, 114 (1953). See this reference to the more exact "characterization factor," NELSON, *op. cit.*, p. 86.

[2] *Cf.* Table III, Summary of Petroleum Products—Their Composition, Properties and Uses, in KIRK and OTHMER, *op. cit.*, Vol. 10, pp. 164–175, excellent details with references.

the United States; since that time it has become one of this country's great industries. While some natural gas was early wasted, it is now being conserved and legislation has been enacted prohibiting the stripping of "wet" gas for its small gasoline content and then wasting the gas. The total marketed production of natural gas in the United States is over 5 thousand billion cubic feet. The present annual consumption of natural gas in the United States is valued at more than $350,000,000 at the wells. Natural gas is composed chiefly of hydrocarbons of the paraffin series from methane up to pentane, carbon dioxide, nitrogen, sometimes helium, but few if any unsaturated hydrocarbons. The most important products obtained from natural gas are fuel, natural gasoline, liquefied petroleum gas, carbon black, helium, hydrogen, and petrochemicals.

Natural Gasoline. Gasoline extracted from natural gas is differentiated from straight-run or refinery gasoline (which is distilled from crude oil) by the term *natural* or *casing-head* gasoline. The recovery of natural gasoline from natural gas has given us a highly volatile gasoline for blending into a motor fuel, particularly for easy starting in cold weather. In 1953, the United States produced 239,000,000 bbl. of natural-gas liquids of which 111,000,000 bbl. represented liquefied petroleum gases.

When crude oil is forced from a well by the pressure of the natural gas, some of its lighter components are vaporized into the gas. Consequently, the composition and characteristics of the recovered natural gasoline are determined by the composition of the oil. The first commercial process for the recovery of natural gasoline was by means of *compression cooling*. Later, the natural gas was passed through adsorption towers containing *activated carbon*, but today the natural gasoline is *absorbed* by a low-boiling *gas oil* which is then heated and stripped of the gasoline by steam. Some of the recent plants combine compression and absorption. The recovered gasoline is "stabilized" or fractionated under pressure to remove the light, high-vapor-pressure components which comprise usually 10 to 30 per cent of the raw gasoline, as shown in Fig. 2.[1] The primary use of natural gasoline is for blending with refinery products to make motor fuel. Natural gasoline plants are now producing by isomerization large quantities of pure isobutane and isopentane for alkylation with light olefins as ethylene, propylene, or butylene to furnish aviation gasoline. Similarly, from natural gasoline stabilizers, propane and butane are available. See Petrochemicals, this chapter.

Cracked or Refinery Gases. Natural gas is particularly devoid of unsaturated hydrocarbons and hydrogen; these compounds are, however, present in the cracked gases of refineries.[2] Because of the large quantities of unsaturated and hence chemically reactive hydrocarbons produced by cracking processes, the oil industry is now developing along the line of

[1] NELSON, *op. cit.*, pp. 361, 717, analyses.
[2] Analyses are given in PERRY, *op. cit.*, p. 2366.

synthesis. The olefin hydrocarbons of these cracked gases are used in the manufacture of polymerized and alkylated gasoline, antifreezes, explosives, solvents, medicinals, fumigants, resins, synthetic rubber, and many other products. When olefins are not available in sufficient amounts, they are made by dehydrogenation of paraffins.

Liquefied Petroleum Gases[1] (L.P.G.). Light hydrocarbons such as propane and butane, which are produced as a by-product from natural gasoline are now finding wide use as "bottled" or liquefied petroleum gas for domestic gas and heating, for city gas, as well as for direct motor

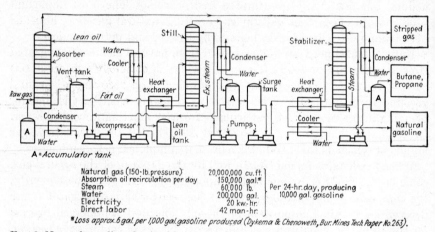

Natural gas (150-lb. pressure)	20,000,000 cu. ft.	
Absorption oil recirculation per day	150,000 gal.*	
Steam	60,000 lb.	Per 24-hr. day, producing
Water	200,000 gal.	10,000 gal. gasoline
Electricity	20 kw-hr.	
Direct labor	42 man-hr.	

Loss approx. 6 gal. per 1,000 gal. gasoline produced (Dykema & Chenoweth, Bur. Mines Tech. Paper No. 263).

Fig. 2. Natural gasoline obtained by absorption and compression. (*Courtesy of Burrell-Mase Engineering Company.*)

fuel in special services (farm and other tractors, trucks, buses). There are now 7,500,000 domestic and rural customers for these products. An increasing amount, probably now around 20 per cent, is used for manufacture of petroleum chemicals. Some of the gas is for transportation. Since the heating value of the pure gas is so high, it is often mixed with an inert gas before using. Liquefied petroleum gases are competitive with many types of fuel in present use. Bottled gas is used by many rural dwellers, who are too far from any gas mains, for cooking, lighting, heating water, and gas refrigeration.

PRODUCTS OF REFINING

Light Distillates. These embrace naphthas and refined oils, aviation gasoline, motor gasoline, petroleum solvents, and kerosene. Gasoline is the most important of these; it is *the most important petroleum product.*

[1] NELSON, *op. cit.*, p. 708, CARNEY, Natural Gas Liquids, in "Progress in Petroleum Technology," pp. 251–261, American Chemical Society, Washington, D.C., 1951, references.

With the advent of high-compression motors, the tendency of a fuel to knock, or detonate violently (thought to be due to autoignition of part of the compressed charge in front of the flame), has become increasingly important. Certain substances such as lead tetraethyl[1] and iron carbonyl[2] tend to prevent knocking. *Octane number* is the percentage of isooctane (2,2,4-trimethylpentane) in a mixture with normal heptane, which as a sample fuel will give the same knocking characteristics as the gasoline in question. *Aviation gasoline* with an octane number of 100 or even higher is composed of about one-third alkylate derived from isobutane and gaseous olefins, blended with catalytical cracked gasoline and suitable crude distillate to which several cubic centimeters of tetraethyl lead per gallon are added to reduce knocking tendency. The amount of sulfur that can be safely allowed in gasoline is a controversial question. Quantities as high as 0.2 per cent will not cause serious corrosion; the quantity of sulfur is usually limited by state regulation to 0.1 per cent. Sulfur in low percentage markedly reduces the effect of tetraethyl lead in increasing the octane number. The color of a gasoline indicates little about its quality. Dyes[3] are required in leaded gasoline. Then oil-soluble dyes also mask the off-white color of cracked gasoline. The term *naphtha* refers to any light oil product having properties intermediate between gasoline and kerosene. Naphthas are extensively used as commercial solvents in paints and for dry cleaning. Kerosene is commonly consumed as a fuel and for illuminating purposes. Light heating oils are employed as fuel in home furnaces.

Intermediate Distillates. These include gas oil, heavy furnace oil (domestic), cracking stock, Diesel fuel oil, absorber oil, and distillates cracked and reformed to produce needed gasoline of adequate quality. Often distillates are blended with heavy tar to reduce the viscosity of the tar so that it can be marketed as a fuel oil. Certain special heavy naphthas are used to reduce the viscosity of asphalt so that it can be readily applied as road oil; such material is known as *cutback asphalt*. Originally, gas oil was widely used for enriching artificial gas, but today most of it is used as a fuel or cracked into gasoline. Diesel fuel is a special grade of gas oil which has become a most important specialty in recent years. The proper viscosity of Diesel fuel is very essential and should be held within rigid limits. Distillates may also be used as vehicles for insecticides.

Heavy distillates furnish lubricating oils (also from residues), heavy oils for various purposes, and waxes. Of the 2,469 million barrels of crude

[1] MIDGLEY, Tetraethyl Lead, *Ind. Eng. Chem.*, **17**, 827 (1925), EDGAR, Tetraethyl Lead, in "Progress in Petroleum Technology," pp. 221–234, American Chemical Society, Washington, D.C., 1951, tables and properties.

[2] Used in Germany.

[3] EGLOFF, *et al.*, Dyes to Reduce Loss in Acid Treatment, *Oil Gas J.*, **29** (42), 133 (1931).

oil run to stills in 1951, there were produced 61 million barrels of lubricating oils. The field of *lubricating oils*[1] is too broad to permit a complete discussion of it here. The S.A.E.[2] has greatly assisted in classifying oils by introducing a number system based on viscosity and change in viscosity with temperature (viscosity index). Such tests as flash point, viscosity, pour point, emulsibility, and resistance to sludging are useful in determining the application to which an oil may be put. Solvent extraction (Figs. 5 to 7) and chemical treatment have long been important operations to upgrade lubricants. The performance of most lubricants has been improved by use of *additives* (0.001 to 25 per cent or more) such as antioxidants, detergents, extreme-pressure agents, and antifoam compounds.

Paraffin wax is first obtained as crude scale wax. This may be refined by separating into several narrow-melting fractions by "sweating" and progressive crystallizations. Refined wax is finished by acid (sulfuric) treatment and percolation through an absorbent clay such as the Attapulgus variety.

Residues include asphalt, fuel-oil residual, greases, coke, petrolatum. These are merely by-products or residues from the regular refining processes. Petroleum coke is used commercially for electrodes, in the manufacture of calcium carbide, in paints, and in the ceramics industry. *Asphalt*,[3] also of great importance, finds employment as a paving or roofing material or for waterproofing structures. The properties of asphalt may be markedly altered by heating it to a high temperature and partly oxidizing it by blowing air through it. Such material is more viscous and less resilient than ordinary asphalt, is known as *oxidized* asphalt, and is widely used in the manufacture of roofing and for grouting. Very hard asphalt finds some use as a briquetting binder.

Greases constitute a large group of different materials and may be grouped into three classes:

1. Mixtures of mineral oil and solid lubricants.
2. Blends of waxes, fats, resin oils, and pitches.
3. Soap-thickened mineral oils.

PETROLEUM CHEMICALS, OR PETROCHEMICALS

Petroleum chemicals are derived from petroleum products and natural gas in increasing amounts. Examples of these are ammonia (Chap. 20), carbon black (Chap. 9), butadiene and styrene (Chap. 36) and over a

[1] NELSON, *op. cit.*, very many tables and references, fine presentation, see index, PIGOTT and AMBROSE, Petroleum Lubricants, in "Progress in Petroleum Technology," pp. 235–245, American Chemical Society, Washington, D.C., 1951, 35 references.

[2] Society of Automotive Engineers.

[3] HUGHES and HARDMAN, Asphalts and Waxes, in "Progress in Petroleum Technology," pp. 262–277, American Chemical Society, Washington, D.C., 1951, with 128 references.

thousand inorganic and organic chemicals.[1] While these petrochemicals amount now to only between 1 and 2 per cent of the total products of the petroleum industry, they are an increasingly important proportion of the raw materials throughout the chemical process industries. Already it has been estimated that petroleum products, including refinery and natural gas, supply over 25 per cent of the raw materials for the entire

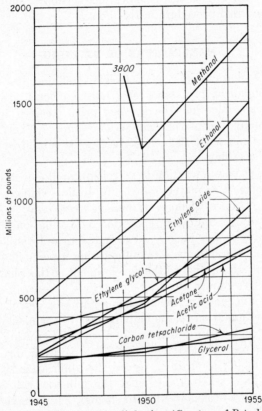

Fig. 3. Total production of major aliphatics. (*Courtesy of Petroleum Refiner.*)

chemical industry and 50 per cent of organic chemicals. As petrochemicals are growing at the rate of 14 per cent a year in comparison with 10 per cent for the other divisions of the chemical industry, it has been predicted that in the not too distant future petroleum will furnish about 50 per cent of the raw materials for the entire chemical industry. In this case, there will be required up to 5 per cent of the products of the petroleum industry, including herein the necessary fuel.

Figure 3 indicates the production of the major aliphatic chemicals of which all or a substantial part are based on petroleum. As is well known,

[1] KIRK and OTHMER, *op. cit.*, Vol. 10, p. 177 (1953), see Table III, pp. 202–209, where over 250 most important commercial petroleum chemicals are listed with process for manufacture and chief use.

the basic paraffins are not very reactive chemically. These are converted by various chemical reactions: (1) pyrolysis and dehydrogenation into unsaturated compounds such as olefins or even acetylene; (2) isomerization into isobutane and the like; (3) nitration into nitroparaffins; (4) chlorination into chloro-derivatives; and (5) oxidation into aldehydes, alcohols, and acids, etc. To better present these petrochemicals, they are classified according to this chemical conversion or unit process, thus following the normal procedure in this book.

MANUFACTURE OR REFINING

The general characteristic of petroleum refining has been a most unusually economical processing of crudes to consumer products. It seems hardly possible that the average price received by refiners for gasoline is around 12 cents per gallon. The difference between what the consumer pays and what the refiner receives is caused by taxation and the expense of retailing.

The refining or manufacturing of petroleum products and of petroleum chemicals involves two major branches—physical changes or *separation operations* and chemical changes or *conversion processes*.[1]

The initial refining embraced separation by distillation, which involves the unit operations of fluid flow, heat transfer, and distillation. Indeed the necessity of studying these manufacturing aspects in the petroleum field was a great stimulation to the development of this phase of chemical engineering. These purely physical separations were early supplemented by chemical conversions in the further *refining* of petroleum products. But the great stimulation to the employment of chemical change in the manufacture of petroleum products came with the growing consumption of gasoline in excess of that supplied by separation distillation. This situation, developing after 1912, forced the application of pyrolysis to petroleum products wherein, by what the industry calls *cracking*, the long molecules were broken down into smaller ones suitable for gasoline. Although cracking, thermal and catalytic, is still the most important chemical change taking place in the petroleum industry, yet in recent years, to meet the demands for better gasoline, or for alcohol, acetone, or various chemicals from petroleum, other chemical changes have been applied on a large scale. Among these we may list alkylation, isomerization, polymerization, hydrogenation, hydroforming, and dehydrogenation (see Unit Processes).

---

[1] *Cf.* SWEENEY, "Petroleum and Its Products," *op. cit.*, Chap. 3, p. 1. Sweeney calls both branches "processes" but it seemed better to name one "operations" and the other "processes"; NELSON, *op. cit.*, Chaps. 20, 21, 22, classifies these conversion processes under thermal cracking and decomposition processes, rebuilding hydrocarbons and catalytic cracking. These might also be called unit processes.

It is a long step from the initial shell-still topping[1] gasoline and other like products from the crude, to the modern *continuous* complicated refinery wherein 200,000 bbl. or more per day of crude, day in and day out, enter the manufacturing equipment by way of the pipe stills and are separated in the continuous bubble-cap towers into the various constituents from gas through petrochemicals, gasoline, kerosene, gas oil, lubricating oil, down to fuel oil, residuums, or tars. Such refineries are also equipped to carry on most of the secondary treatments in a continuous manner. Naturally each individual treatment depends on the type of crude oil processed. Furthermore, procedures vary with market demand. With modern increased demand for gasoline, manufacturing procedures naturally are adapted to obtain a maximum yield of gasoline.

Energy Changes. The energy changes involved in petroleum refining are both mechanical and chemical. Some of the unit processes are exothermic reactions though most are endothermic. In addition to the heat[2] that must be supplied for cracking, distillation, and the other processes, large amounts of mechanical energy are needed for pumping, compressing gases, and the like.

Separation Operations. In theory, the unit operations of oil refining are fairly simple; in actual practice they are quite complicated. The typical refinery consists of one or more units called *stills* which include a furnace, an oil heater of the tube type, a bubble tower, steam strippers, heat-exchange equipment, coolers and condensers; working storage tanks at the unit; batch agitators or continuous closed-tank units for treating the products to remove deleterious compounds of sulfur and give acceptable color; filters; blending and mixing tanks for loading; a piping system for the receipt of crude oil; pumps for the transfer of oils and for loading and shipping products; storage tanks for crude-oil supply and finished product; a vapor-recovery system and many auxiliaries. A power plant for generation of steam and perhaps electric power and light should also be included. In the operation of this large entity, heat, energy, and material balances are of utmost importance in keeping a rigid control upon all steps in the processing of the oil.

In presenting the separation branch of refining, this can be broken down into the ordinary unit operations, as follows:

---

[1] Topping involves the simple distillation of the more highly volatile materials, or what may be called *tops*, from the crude oil.

[2] The following references bear on this subject: NELSON, *op. cit.*, pp. 573–576, for heats of cracking; p. 686, for typical calculations of heat balances; GRUSE and STEVENS, "The Chemical Technology of Petroleum," 2d ed., pp. 432*ff.*, for thermodynamic data for petroleum hydrocarbons; pp. 210*ff.*, for latent heats of evaporation and specific heats, McGraw-Hill Book Company, Inc., New York, 1942; PERRY, *op. cit.*, pp. 567–576, 225–227, for distillation data and specific heats; "Science of Petroleum," Vol. 2, p. 1256.

Fluid Flow.[1] The petroleum engineer has turned to the comprehensive literature on fluid flow of water and suitably revised this information for petroleum. Two important differences between oil and water should be recognized: oils exhibit wide change of viscosity with temperature and wide range of viscosity, and they are sensitive to heat.

Heat Transfer.[2] The solution of this problem is somewhat complicated because of lack of complete data. In general, the use of empirical results will be desirable. Equipment should be cleaned regularly to maintain satisfactory heat transfer and to remove fouling which frequently greatly reduces the transfer rates. The large quantities of cooling water used generally make cooling towers and water-treating equipment essential.

Distillation.[3] This ranks with heat transfer as being among the more important of unit operations. The older operations of batch distillation have now been almost entirely superseded by continuous ones. The present system involves heating the crude by pumping it through tubes placed inside a furnace (tube still) and then allowing it to vaporize in a fractionating column, which is tapped at several points allowing continuous side draw of the various boiling "fractions" or products. The residuum withdrawn from the bottom of the column may be subjected to a vacuum or steam distillation. Figure 4 is a schematic drawing of a modern refining group showing the separation of the crude into the various fractions and the subsequent treatment of each fraction. Several products are removed from the crude tower as shown. The kerosene and naphtha fractions contain small amounts of imperfectly separated straight-run gasoline of higher volatility than the main fraction. These are removed in strippers (short columns containing only a few plates) by blowing in steam. The gasoline vaporizes out the top of the stripper and is returned to the crude tower.

Absorption.[4] Absorption is generally used to separate a higher-boiling constituent from other components of a system of vapors and gases. Usually the absorption medium is a special gas-oil cut. Absorption is widely employed for the recovery of natural gasoline from well gas and for the recovery of vapors given off from storage tanks. The absorbed products are recovered by fractionating or steam stripping.

---

[1] PERRY, *op. cit.*, pp. 369–412; NELSON, *op. cit.*, pp. 339–357.

[2] PERRY, *op. cit.*, pp. 455–498; NELSON, *op. cit.*, pp. 471–565, 489–495, for fouling factors.

[3] PERRY, *op. cit.*, has an entire section on distillation, pp. 561–660. This should be consulted for many references to literature, presentation of fundamental principles, and applications. NELSON, *op. cit.*, pp. 377–470; BRADLEY and LAKE, Petroleum Distillation, in "Progress in Petroleum Technology," pp. 199–209, American Chemical Society, Washington, D.C., 1951, diagrams, azeotropic and extraction distillation, 59 references.

[4] PERRY, *op. cit.*, pp. 667–711; NELSON, *op. cit.*, pp. 711–750.

Adsorption.[1] Adsorption is employed for about the same purpose as absorption; in the process just mentioned natural gasoline may be separated from the natural gas by adsorption on charcoal. Adsorption is also used to remove undesirable colors from lubricating oil, usually with activated clay.

Filtration.[2] Filtration after chilling is the usual method for removal of wax from wax distillate. The mixture of wax and adhering oil obtained

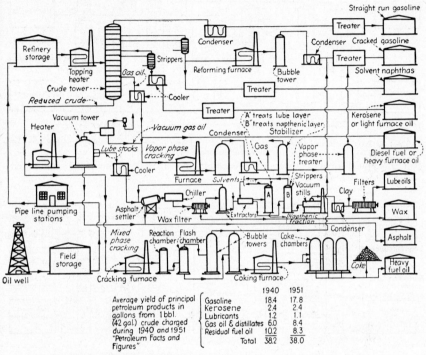

		1940	1951
Average yield of principal petroleum products in gallons from 1 bbl. (42 gal.) crude charged during 1940 and 1951 "Petroleum Facts and Figures"	Gasoline	18.4	17.8
	Kerosene	2.4	2.4
	Lubricants	1.2	1.1
	Gas oil & distillates	6.0	8.4
	Residual fuel oil	10.2	8.3
	Total	38.2	38.0

Fig. 4. Generalized over-all flow sheet from oil well to salable products.

from the press is frozen and allowed to warm slowly so the oil drains (sweats) from the cake, thus further purifying the wax. "Contact" filtration, involving the use of clay, is the common method of purification of oils; decolorization takes place at the same time. (This is an adsorption phenomenon.)

Extraction. This involves the removal of a component from a liquid by means of the solvent action of another liquid. The procedure of selective extraction by means of solvents is important in the further refining of lubricating oils. An example is the production of toluene by extraction from a specially processed petroleum. Low viscosity-index

[1] PERRY, *op. cit.*, pp. 886–916, especially pp. 889–896 (clays), 906–907 (natural gasoline); NELSON, *op. cit.*, pp. 265–267, 288–293.

[2] PERRY, *op. cit.*, pp. 964–992, especially p. 987; NELSON, *op. cit.*, pp. 288–290.

hydrocarbons, unstable sludges, and some colored materials may be removed in this way from lubricating oil. Usually the extraction is countercurrent. Two problems are involved: obtainment of solution equilibriums and separation of the two immiscible phases.

Figure 5 shows a typical solvent refining process for lubricating oil. The oil is mixed with the solvent or solvents in an extractor or column.

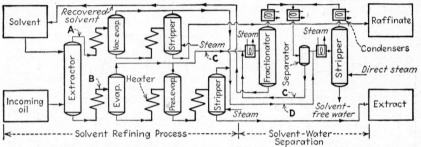

Key: A = Raffinate and solvent; B = Solvent extract and water; C = Solvent saturated with water
D = Water saturated with solvent

Fig. 5. Typical solvent-refining process employing furfural and provided with solvent-water separation and recovery.

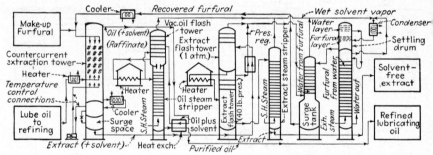

Fig. 6. Flow sheet for lube oil refining by furfural extraction.

If a proper solvent[1] has been chosen, the mixture separates into two layers: one rich in solvent and containing the dissolved impurities (extract); the other containing little solvent and most of the desirable high-viscosity oil (raffinate). This latter consists largely of naphthenic-type compounds and wax. Dewaxing by propane or methyl ethyl ketone (MEK) follows the selective solvent separation of Fig. 5. Sometimes deasphalting is in the sequence (Fig. 7).

The procedure as shown in Figs. 5 or 6 involves the following *unit operations* when furfural is the solvent:

[1] NELSON, *op. cit.*, pp. 298–318; GESTER, Solvent Extraction in the Petroleum Industry, in "Progress in Petroleum Technology," pp. 177–198, American Chemical Society, Washington, D.C., 1951, excellent; TREYBAL, "Liquid Extraction," McGraw-Hill Book Company, Inc., New York, 1951.

Continuous countercurrent extraction of the lubricating stock with furfural at temperatures between 130 and 280°F., depending on the oil used; provided with suitable heat exchangers.

Continuous separation of raffinate fraction from extract fraction.

Recovery of solvent (furfural) by vacuum evaporation from raffinate or refined oil.

Stripping by steam distillation of small amounts of remaining solvent from refined oil, giving wet furfural or water solution of furfural.

Recovery of solvent (furfural) from extract by atmospheric and by pressure distillations, this wet solvent (furfural) being the main recovery; fractionation leaves dry solvent behind and ready for reuse.

Stripping by steam of small amounts of solvent left in extract, furnishing wet solvent or water solution of solvent.

Final stripping of solvent from combined aqueous solutions. The overhead is chilled, and the solvent is conducted to fractionator.

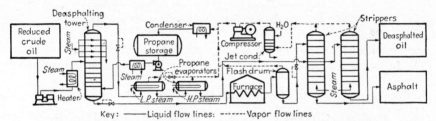

Key: ——— Liquid flow lines; ------ Vapor flow lines

FIG. 7. Flow sheet for lube oil deasphalting—Kellogg tower process.

When furfural is used, the solvent is recirculated through the system as many as fifteen times each day and with the very small solvent loss of less than 0.03 per cent of solvent circulation.

Other solvents frequently used are liquid sulfur dioxide, propane and cresylic acid, dichloro-ethyl ether, phenol, and nitro-benzene.[1] Solvents are also widely employed for removing the wax from lubricants and thus lowering the pour point.[2] Figures 6, 7, and 8 present typical lubricating-oil purifications.

Conversion Processes. Petroleum offers such a fertile field for chemical synthesis both for gasoline and for petrochemicals that it is difficult to list all the conversion or unit processes that may be applied to this raw material. Even now "about 70% of U.S. crude is subjected to conversion processing."[3] Much study has been given to the fundamentals of these chemical[4] changes as applied to petroleum raw materials. Schmerling

[1] NELSON, op. cit., pp. 298–318, 756, 760.

[2] ANON., Solvent Dewaxing of Lubricants, Chem. & Met. Eng., **48** (10), 106 (1941), pictured flow sheet employing methylethylketone and benzene.

[3] SWEENEY, op. cit., Chap. 3, p. 2.

[4] SCHMERLING, LOUIS, The Mechanism of the Reactions of Aliphatic Hydrocarbons, J. Chem. Educ., **28**, 562 (1951), 48 references; "Progress in Petroleum Technology," American Chemical Society, Washington, D.C., 1951.

makes a division into reactions in "presence of acid type catalysts," and "those which occur thermally or are induced by peroxides." The former

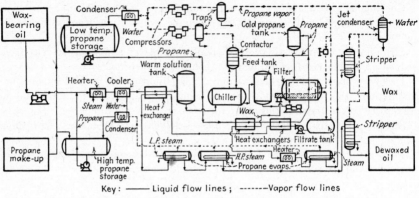

Key: —— Liquid flow lines; ------Vapor flow lines

Fig. 8. Lube oil dewaxing—Kellogg propane process.

are explained by a carbonium mechanism and the latter by free radicals. The following examples are a few of the more important basic reactions:[1]

1. Cracking or Pyrolysis (see Figs. 9 to 14):

$$C_7H_{15}\cdot C_{15}H_{30}\cdot C_7H_{15} \rightarrow C_7H_{16} + C_6H_{12}:CH_2 + C_{14}H_{28}:CH_2$$

<table>
<tr><td>Heavy gas oil</td><td>Gasoline</td><td>Gasoline
(antiknock)</td><td>Recycle stock</td></tr>
</table>

2. Polymerization (see Figs. 15 and 16):

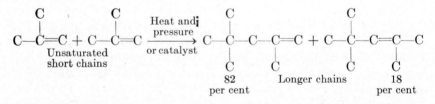

3. Alkylation[2] (see Fig. 17):

Unsaturated + isosaturated $\xrightarrow{\text{catalyst}}$ saturated branched chain, *for example:*

---

[1] GRUSE and STEVENS, *op. cit.*, Chap. 3, Group Reactions in Petroleum Oils and Derived By-products, p. 646; "Progress in Petroleum Technology," American Chemical Society, Washington, D.C., 1951, excellent collection of papers and various authors.

[2] MURPHREE, War Developments in the Petroleum Industry, *Ind. Eng. Chem.*, **35**, 626 (1943).

Catalytic alkylation.

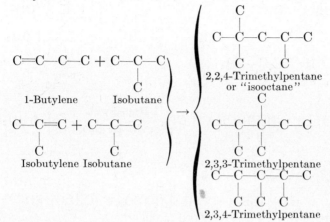

C=C—C—C + C—C—C\
                 |
                 C
1-Butylene   Isobutane

C—C=C + C—C—C
| |
C   C
Isobutylene Isobutane

2,2,4-Trimethylpentane or "isooctane"

2,3,3-Trimethylpentane

2,3,4-Trimethylpentane

Thermal alkylation.

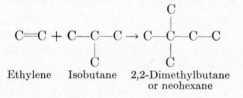

$$C{=}C + C{-}C{-}C \rightarrow C{-}C{-}C{-}C$$

Ethylene   Isobutane   2,2-Dimethylbutane or neohexane

4. *Hydrogenation:*

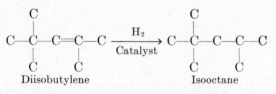

$$C{-}C{-}C{=}C{-}C \xrightarrow[\text{Catalyst}]{H_2} C{-}C{-}C{-}C{-}C$$

Diisobutylene   Isooctane

5. *Chlorination:*

$$C_5H_{12} + Cl_2 \rightarrow C_5H_{11}Cl + HCl$$

Pentanes   Chloro-pentanes

6. *Isomerization:*

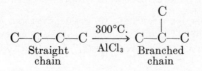

$$C{-}C{-}C{-}C \xrightarrow[\text{AlCl}_3]{300°C.} C{-}C{-}C$$

Straight chain   Branched chain

7. *Hydroforming or Aromatization:*

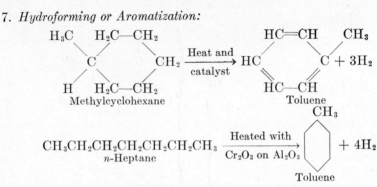

Methylcyclohexane   Toluene

$$CH_3CH_2CH_2CH_2CH_2CH_2CH_3 \xrightarrow[\text{Cr}_2\text{O}_3 \text{ on Al}_2\text{O}_3]{\text{Heated with}} + 4H_2$$
n-Heptane

Toluene

8. *Esterification and Hydration:*

$$C_2H_4 + H_2SO_4 \rightarrow C_2H_5O\cdot HO\cdot SO_2 + (C_2H_5O)_2\cdot SO_2$$
$$C_2H_5O\cdot HO\cdot SO_2 + (C_2H_5)_2O\cdot SO_2 + \text{aqua}$$
$$\rightarrow H_2SO_4 \text{ dil.} + C_2H_5OH + C_2H_5OC_2H_5$$

Cracking or Pyrolysis. Cracking[1] (pyrolysis) is the process of converting large molecules into smaller ones by the application of heat and/or catalysts. Olefins always are formed. A significant amount of polymerization of these smaller molecules occurs, and some carbon is formed. Nelson summarizes the reactions:

Charge stock. . . . . $C_7H_{15}\cdot C_{15}H_{30}\cdot C_7H_{15}$
↓   *Heavy gas oil*
Cracked stock. . . . . C_7H_{16} + $C_{14}H_{28}$:CH_2 + C_6H_{12}:CH_2
| *Gasoline* +   *Recycle*   + *Gasoline (antiknock)*
↓   *stock*
More cracking. . . . . C_2H_6 + $(C_4H_8$:CH_2 + C_8H_{18} + C_6H_{12}:$CH_2)$ +
| *Gas* +   *Gasoline*
| CH_2:$CH\cdot CH$:$CH\cdot CH_3$ + C_2H_4
| *Gum-forming materials*   *Gas*
↓
Polymerization. . . . . C_2H_6 + $(C_4H_8$:CH_2 + $C_8H_{18})$ + $C_{12}H_{22}$ + C_2H_4
        Gas   *Gasoline*   *Tar or*   *Gas*
                                       recycle

These equations are highly simplified examples of this process, for the original molecule may be broken at any one of the carbon-carbon bonds and usually with carbon formation. Thus, in cracking one pure compound, such as tetradecane, several products (heptane, heptene, hexane, octane,

---

[1] GRUSE and STEVENS, *op. cit.*, Chap. 10, p. 354; NELSON, *op. cit.*, Chap. 20, pp. 566*ff.*; Chap. 22, pp. 667*ff.*, many references, tables, flow sheets; many important articles in "Progress in Petroleum Technology," American Chemical Society, Washington, D.C., 1951.

butane, butenes, carbon, etc.) are formed. In cracking the mixture of compounds occurring in petroleum the number of possible products is so great that the representation of the process by simple equations is impossible.

The *heat of decomposition*[1] of petroleum is difficult, if not impossible, to calculate accurately, owing to the lack of necessary data. In the cracking reaction, if large amounts of gas are produced, the heat of decomposition is endothermic and relatively high. Also, the heat of reaction is often lower than theoretical owing to the exothermic reforming of some of the cracked products.

"The cracking process," according to Egloff,[2] "is the greatest force for conservation that has been developed in the oil industry." Cracking is of two kinds: thermal and catalytic. In the early days of *thermal cracking*, gas oil was used as the charging stock. More recent technological developments have advanced the technique of cracking, making possible its adaptation to a wide range of materials from naphthas to heavy crude residuums. In the combination distillation-cracking unit, crude oil from the storage tanks is separated into various fractions directly and the resulting fractions are cracked in continuous operations. Selective cracking operations with a high degree of flexibility have been made possible by catalytic cracking and by thermal cracking, this latter using multiple heating coils and cracking under temperatures ranging from 900 to 1100°F. and pressures from 600 to over 1,000 lb. per sq. in. Today, total gasoline yields of 70 to 85 per cent[3] are obtained from the crude oil with approximately one-half of the country's gasoline produced by cracking. See Fig. 4 for generalized relationships of cracking in the petroleum industry.

Catalytic cracking has the advantage of being able to produce gasoline of high quality from almost any crude oil in equipment subject to careful control and operated at low pressure and hence at comparatively lower cost. Catalytic gasolines also have these desirable characteristics: excellent response to tetraethyl lead, low in gum formers and in corrosive sulfur compounds with uniform octane rating over the boiling range of the gasoline. Marshall Sittig writes,[4] "Catalytic cracking represents the largest single stride in the development of refining processes that the

---

[1] NELSON, *op. cit.*, p. 573, discusses this subject and gives examples of typical calculations.

[2] EGLOFF, 300 Years of Oil, *Ind. Eng. Chem.*, **27**, 648 (1935).

[3] NELSON, *op. cit.*, pp. 96, 97, 99, presents a tabulation of the gasoline content of many domestic crudes, pp. 576*ff.*, p. 595 for cracking yields.

[4] SITTIG, Catalytic Cracking Techniques, in Review Reprint of Petroleum Refiner, Gulf Publishing Co., Houston, Tex., 1952, 545 references and many diagrams and tables. See this excellent summary for *all* phases of catalytic cracking.

petroleum industry has ever made." Sachanen[1] states that catalytic cracking has these advantages over thermal cracking:

1. More selective cracking and less light end products.
2. More olefin isomerization—both of olefin bonds and carbon skeletons.
3. More controllable saturation of double bonds.
4. Greater production of aromatics.
5. Less diolefin production.
6. Relatively more coke.
7. Greater ability to tolerate high sulfur feed stocks.

The *fluidized catalytic cracking* process employs a finely divided solid catalyst made by aerating the ground powder of an alumina-silica gel.

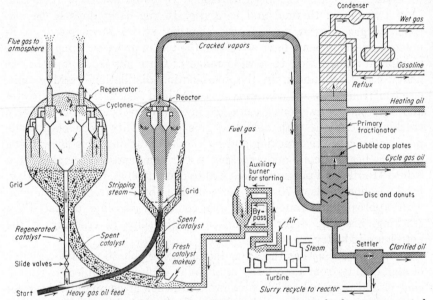

FIG. 9. Fluid catalytic-cracking unit. White areas represent fresh or regenerated catalyst. [*Courtesy Standard Oil Company (N.J.).*]

This is maintained at all times as a simulated fluid by suspension in the reacting vapors or in the regenerating air. A high degree of turbulence is necessary throughout the system to ensure a uniform suspension. Under these conditions the solid catalyst flows similarly to a liquid and exerts a like pressure. Because of the even distribution of the catalyst and because of its high specific heat in relation to the vapors reacting, the entire cracking reaction can be maintained at a remarkably exact temperature. Separation of the catalyst from gases or vapors after the reaction and regeneration processes is largely by means of cyclone separators. Coke

[1] SACHANEN, "Conversion of Petroleum," 2d ed., Reinhold Publishing Corporation, New York, 1948 (as summarized by Sittig).

and tar are formed on the catalyst by the cracking. These are burned from the catalyst with air during the regeneration part of the cycle. Both cracking and regenerative cycles are continuous.

The fluid catalytic cracking process has been put into operation by the Esso Standard Oil Company on a very large scale. This procedure operates

FIG. 10. Recent "cat" cracker at Linden, N.J. The two vessels at right are catalyst hoppers (storage) and the large vessel in the center is the regenerator. The reaction and the fractionating tower are behind the visible elements. [*Courtesy of Standard Oil Co. (N.J.).*]

at a pressure of about 20 lb. gage and at a temperature of from 850 to 1000°F. It produces a high-octane gasoline. This fluid catalytic cracking is illustrated by the flow diagram of Fig. 9 and the picture of Fig. 10. The flow diagram of Fig. 9 includes the cracking or pyrolysis under the control of the fluid catalyst of the heavy gas oil and may be broken down into the following coordinated series of *unit physical operations* (Op.) and *unit chemical conversions* or *processes* (Pr.):

The heavy gas oil feed is preheated in a conventional tube furnace (Op.).
This preheated oil is vaporized by injection into the stream of the hot (1100°F.) regenerated finely divided catalyst (Op.).

The mixture of the vapors and catalyst (1 to 7) flows up into the reactor where the cracking reactions take place (Pr.). The oil vapors rise through the "boiling" bed of catalyst.

The cracked vapors are carried overhead through cyclones to remove the catalyst, on to the primary fractionator (Op.).

From the primary fractionator, the products as listed in Fig. 9 are separated in the conventional way, with the slurry recycle returned to reactor (Op.).

In the reactor the spent catalyst, deactivated by a carbonaceous coating ("coke"), falls to the bottom and flows to the regenerator aided by air (Op.).

In the regenerator the carbon and tar are burned off, with the flue gases passing out through cyclones (Pr. and Op.). The heat from the combustion of the carbonaceous matter raises the temperature of the regenerated catalyst to over 1000°F.

The regenerated catalyst falls through appropriate pipe to enter at the start of the continuous cycle (Op.).

This fluid catalytic process is contributing a valuable principle to the chemical industry. The use of a large amount of turbulent solid capable

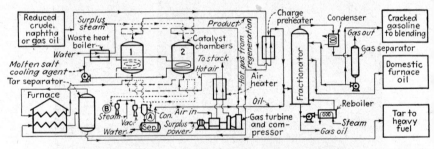

Notes and Key: Three catalyst chambers used instead of two as shown. No.1 is shown on run and No.2 being regenerated by burning off coke with compressed hot air. Dashed lines indicate open connections during phase shown. Dotted lines show purge connections. Ⓐ is system for purging oil vapor from chambers prior to regeneration. Ⓑ is system for purging waste gas from chambers after regeneration.

FIG. 11. Flow sheet for catalytic cracking—Houdry process.

of absorbing much heat in the reaction mass greatly aids in the elimination of temperature variations and hot spots. If no catalytic action is desired, an inert, powdered solid[1] may be used.

Other catalytic cracking[2] processes should be mentioned: the *Houdry* (see Fig. 11), using a fixed base catalyst and the *Thermofor catalytic*

[1] This principle may be applied to the control of organic oxidations that are inclined to proceed to where the oxidation is a combustion. SITTIG, *op. cit.*, p. 139 with 30 references.

[2] SITTIG, *op. cit.*, p. 111 *et seq.;* flow sheets in "Process Handbook," Gulf Publishing Co., Houston, Tex., 1952; ANON., Packaged TCC Unit, *Chem. Eng.*, **59** (1), 210 (1952), pictured flow sheet.

cracking (T.C.C.) (Fig. 12), employing a flowing bead-type catalyst. The catalysts are aluminum silicates, either clay or artificial. Both produce high-quality gasoline or base stock for blending with alkylate, toluene, or cumene to aviation gasoline. The Thermofor units are economical in small sizes (1,000 bbl. per day). In many instances where the Thermofor units are installed for first-pass cracking to produce butylenes and gasoline, this gasoline is recracked over Houdry units for producing

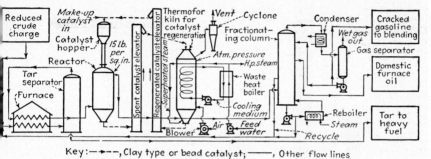

Key:—►—, Clay type or bead catalyst;———, Other flow lines

FIG. 12. Flow sheet for catalytic cracking—Thermofor continuous cracking or T.C.C. process.

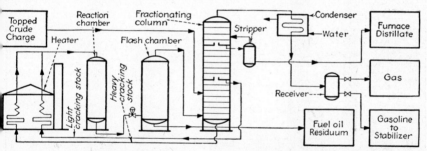

FIG. 13. Universal Oil Products two-coil selective cracking unit.

final aviation or high-octane base stock. The *Houdriflow*[1] has versatile application to furnish high-octane gasoline by catalytic cracking in moving bed with regenerator below reactors and provided with mechanical lift. *Cycloversion* is also detailed by Sittig. The estimate is made by Sittig that by 1960 the catalytic cracking capacity of the United States will be 5,100,000 bbl. per day.

Figures 13 and 14 show the *Universal Oil Products two-coil selective thermal cracking* process. The charging stock is topped or reduced crude crude from which the lighter fractions down to gas oil have been removed by distillation (see Fig. 4)]. The topped crude is charged to a fractionating tower which is heated by vapors from the flash chamber. The lighter part of the charge is thus vaporized but not enough heat is present to carry

[1] Description and flow sheet in "Process Handbook," Gulf Publishing Co., Houston, Tex., 1952; flow sheet, p. 10; SITTIG, p. 91 *et seq.*, p. 111 for cycloversion.

it out of the top of the column. These vapors of light oil are condensed above the trap tray and are sent to the heating furnace. The heavy oil fraction of the charge is removed from the bottom of the tower and also sent to the heating furnace.

FIG. 14. Universal Oil Products two-coil selective cracking unit.

The furnace has two coils: one to heat the light oil and the other to heat the heavy oil. The heavy oil is easier to crack but, because it has not been vaporized, it contains tars and other materials that tend to form coke and clog the furnace. Thus the heavy-oil coil of the furnace is not operated at so high a temperature as the light-oil coil and it is so constructed as to permit easier cleaning.

The heated and partly cracked material from both coils is combined and sent to a downflow reaction chamber for the completion of the cracking or pyrolysis. This is simply a large tower and most of the coke produced by the cracking operation is deposited in it. Several chambers are used in practice, though Fig. 13 shows only one. When a chamber becomes filled with coke, the heated material is sent from the furnace to another tower while the first one is being cleaned.

The cracked material, which has lost most of its coke, is piped to the flash chamber where the pressure is reduced. This reduction in pressure causes the lighter portions to vaporize from the residuum which is removed at the bottom. The vapors next flow to the bottom of the fractionating tower where their heat is used to separate the charging stock. The vapors that reach the top of the column are condensed and consist of gasoline containing dissolved gas. Part of the vapor is heavier than gasoline and condenses near the top of the column. This is called *furnace distillate*. Any material too heavy to reach either of these levels in the column is sent back to the cracking furnace.

Reforming. Reforming involves both cracking and isomerization. Straight-run gasoline and light naphthas usually have very low octane numbers. By sending these fractions to a reforming unit and giving them a light "crack" their octane number may be increased. This upgrading is probably due primarily to the production of olefins and the formation of lower-molecular-weight compounds, which, as a general rule, have higher octane numbers. Some isomerization (conversion of straight-chain compounds to branched-chain compounds) also takes place.

Polymerization.[1] Rapid progress has been made in the development of polymerization processes for converting by-product hydrocarbon gases produced in cracking into liquid hydrocarbons suitable for use as high-octane motor and aviation fuels and for petrochemicals, *e.g.*, C_{12} tetramer for detergents. To combine gases or highly volatile liquids by polymerization to form heavier fractions, the combining fractions must be unsaturated. The hydrocarbon gases from cracking stills, particularly the olefins, have been the foundation of polymerization. The following equation is typical of polymerization reactions. Propylene, normal butylene, and isobutylene are the olefins usually polymerized.

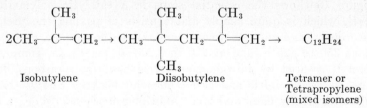

$$2CH_3{-}\overset{\overset{\displaystyle CH_3}{|}}{C}{=}CH_2 \rightarrow CH_3{-}\overset{\overset{\displaystyle CH_3}{|}}{\underset{\underset{\displaystyle CH_3}{|}}{C}}{-}CH_2{-}\overset{\overset{\displaystyle CH_3}{|}}{C}{=}CH_2 \rightarrow \quad C_{12}H_{24}$$

Isobutylene   Diisobutylene   Tetramer or
                                            Tetrapropylene
                                            (mixed isomers)

---

[1] MASCHWITZ and HENDERSON, Polymerization of Hydrocarbon Gases to Motor Fuels, in "Progress in Petroleum Technology," p. 83, American Chemical Society, Washington, D.C., 1951.

Vapor-phase cracking produces considerable quantities of unsaturated gases; hence polymerization units are often operated in conjunction with this type of cracking. *Thermal* polymerization is practical only for large-scale operations because of the difficulty of obtaining good heat control in small-sized units, whereas *catalytic* polymerization is practical on both

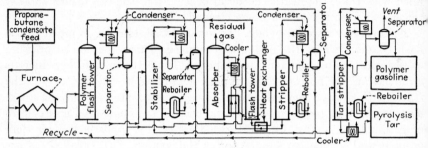

FIG. 15. Flow sheet for polymer gasoline—Pure Oil thermal process.

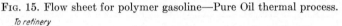

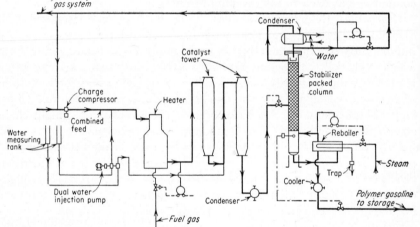

FIG. 16. Catalytic polymerization process—chamber type. (*Courtesy of Universal Oil Products Co.*)

a large and a small scale and is furthermore adaptable to combination with reforming to increase the quality of the gasoline (see Fig. 15).

Figure 16 shows the essential steps in a catalytic polymerization process, which is quite simple and consists of passing the preheated unsaturated gases through towers containing the granular catalyst in beds at 350 to 425°F. and at 250 to 1,200 lb. per sq. in. Temperature control is secured by introducing recycle light hydrocarbons, low in olefins, to reactor inlets and as a "quench" between catalyst beds. A catalyst frequently employed is a "solid phosphoric acid," *i.e.*, a silico-phosphate. Until recently the catalyst had to be regenerated at frequent intervals by burning off the carbonaceous deposits, but new developments have greatly increased the active life of the catalyst and now regeneration is seldom necessary.

Alkylation. Alkylation[1] processes are exothermic and are fundamentally similar to polymerization but differ in that only part of the charging stock need be unsaturated. It is based on the reactivity of the tertiary carbon of the isobutane with olefins such as propylene, butylenes, and amylenes. The product "alkylate" is a mixture of saturated, stable isoparaffins

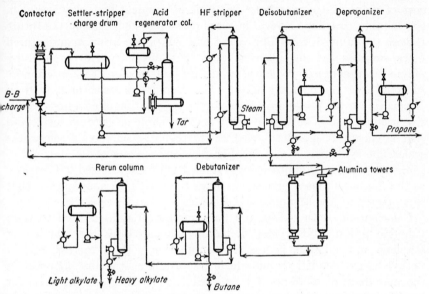

Contactor Settler-stripper Acid HF stripper Deisobutanizer Depropanizer
charge drum regenerator col.

B-B charge

Steam

Tar

Propane

Rerun column Debutanizer Alumina towers

Light alkylate Heavy alkylate Butane

FIG. 17. Flow sheet for "HF" alkylation. (*Courtesy of Universal Oil Products Co.*)

distilling in the gasoline range, which becomes the principal component of many high-octane gasolines.

Alkylation with liquid hydrogen fluoride is illustrated by the flow sheet of Fig. 17. Here the acid can be used repeatedly and offers no acid-disposal problem. Ratio of acid to hydrocarbon in the contactor is 2 to 1. The temperature range is cheaply maintained as no refrigeration is necessary, being from 60 to 100°F. The simplified reaction is as given under the unit process of alkylation with a 5- to 10-fold excess of isobutane over the butylenes to minimize realkylation of the primary alkylate. The anhydrous hydrofluoric acid, when dirty, is easily regenerated by distillation from heavy alkylate. Sufficient pressure is required on the system to keep the reactants in the liquid phase. Corrosion is low. The separated isobutane is recycled.

---

[1] For ethylbenzene flow sheet see Chap. 36; MRSTIK, SMITH, and PINKERTON, Alkylation of Isobutane, in "Progress in Petroleum Technology," p. 97, American Chemical Society, Washington, D.C., 1951. ANON., Sulfuric Acid Alkylation, *Chem. Eng.*, **58** (9), 212 (1951).

Hydrogenation.[1] Hydrogen is added to an unsaturated hydrocarbon under high pressure and temperature in the presence of a catalyst to produce a more fully saturated product. Exceedingly high yields of gasoline or of lubricating oils with a high viscosity index, low carbon residue, and high resistance to oxidation can be obtained by hydrogenating heavy oils. The entire result is an upgrading of the products. The adoption of hydrogenation has not been too general owing to high initial cost of plant and equipment,[2] but it is economical and very useful in specialized procedures. It will be employed more and more in the future though probably not for lubricating oils, which are being manufactured more suitably by solvent extraction. The diisobutylene obtained by polymerization of isobutylene is frequently hydrogenated to secure a more suitable aviation blending agent. The Bergius process, originated in Germany, for the production of oils by hydrogenation of coal finds extensive use in Europe, where petroleum is unavailable or very expensive and coal is cheap. It has been tried in this country only on a semiworks scale. The synthesis of a motor fuel from carbon monoxide and hydrogen is a hydrogenation process which has been industrialized in Germany as the Fischer-Tropsch process[3] to make Synthol. It is not expected that this process will be economical in America for many years.

Chlorination. Both olefins and paraffins may be chlorinated to yield valuable products. Ethylene dichloride, prepared by the reaction of ethylene and chlorine, is used in conjunction with tetraethyl lead in "ethyl" gasoline. Ethyl chloride is important as the raw material in the manufacture of tetraethyl lead. Chloro-pentanes are the basis for the Sharples process for synthetic amyl alcohols.

Isomerization.[4] This unit or conversion process has become of the utmost importance to furnish the isobutane need for making "alkylate" as a basis for aviation gasoline (see Alkylation). The reaction may be formulated:

$$CH_3 \cdot CH_2 \cdot CH_2 \cdot CH_2 \rightarrow CH_3 \cdot \overset{\displaystyle CH_3}{CH} \cdot CH_3$$

$$\quad n\text{-Butane} \qquad\qquad\qquad \text{Isobutane}$$

[1] Dehydrogenation to furnish styrene and butadiene are presented with flow sheets in Chap. 36.

[2] MURPHREE, BROWN, and GOHR, Hydrogenation of Petroleum, *Ind. Eng. Chem.*, **32**, 1203 (1940); **31**, 1083 (1939).

[3] FISCHER, ROELEN, and FEIST, Synthesis of Gasoline by the Fischer-Tropsch Process, *Petroleum Refiner*, **22** (12), 97 (1943); **23** (2), 112 (1944). This presents a good review with many references; GROGGINS, "Unit Processes in Organic Synthesis," 4th ed., p. 587, McGraw-Hill Book Company, Inc., New York, 1952.

[4] EGLOFF, HULLA, and KOMAREWSKY, "Isomerization of Pure Hydrocarbons," Reinhold Publishing Corporation, New York, 1942; ANON., Liquid-phase Isomerization, *Petroleum Refiner*, **23** (2), 61 (1944); GUNNERS, Isomerization, "Progress in Petroleum Technology," p. 109, American Chemical Society, Washington, D.C., 1951.

This equilibrium reaction is accelerated by $AlCl_3$ promoted by HCl, both in the anhydrous form. At 250°F. and under about 300 lb. pressure, a conversion of 45 to 55 per cent is attained commercially. Ninety-eight per cent of the butane charged is recovered as such or as isobutane. Being in the anhydrous state, the reaction can be carried out in steel equipment. The tertiary carbon atom formed by the isomerization is very reactive (see Fig. 18).

Hydration to Alcohols.[1] When 35 to 95 per cent ethylene is passed into concentrated (98 per cent) sulfuric acid, the latter retains the hydrocarbon as the esters, ethyl and diethyl sulfuric acid, which by dilution

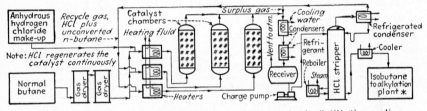

* Product contains some n-butane which is normally segregated in distillation section of the alkylation plant and returned for further isomerization

FIG. 18. Flow sheet for isomerization of butane—Shell catalytic process.

and heat can be hydrolyzed to ethyl alcohol with varying amounts of ether. The alcohol may then be distilled off and the acid concentrated and reused. See Fig. 19 and also Chap. 31 where comparison is made for fermentation alcohol.

$$C_2H_4 + H_2SO_4 \rightarrow C_2H_5HSO_4 + (C_2H_5)_2SO_4$$
$$C_2H_5HSO_4 + (C_2H_5)_2SO_4 + (aqua) \rightarrow C_2H_5OH + H_2SO_4 \ (aqua)$$
$$+ \ C_2H_5OC_2H_5$$

Virtually all the isopropyl alcohol used is made in this fashion from propylene. Recently the catalytic hydration of ethylene in the vapor phase has become of increasing significance.

Hydroforming or Aromatization. Aromatization may be linked with cyclization and is accompanied by much coke formation on the catalyst. If carried out under partial hydrogen pressure, this coke making is much decreased. This process involving catalytic dehydrogenation in presence of hydrogen is known as *hydroforming*. The reactions given under this subhead under Unit Processes are probably more complicated. This process was of vital importance during the Second World War for

---

[1] "Science of Petroleum," p. 2803; ANON., Spirit of the Times, *Petroleum Refiner,* **23** (1), 101 (1944), pictured flow diagram; ANON., "Petrochemical Process Handbook," Gulf Publishing Co., Houston, Tex., 1953; *cf. Petroleum Refiner,* **32** (11), 126 (1953).

the making of toluene for explosives, a very large amount being produced in this fashion.[1]

The best example of hydroforming and aromatization is the *Platforming* process[2] depicted in Fig. 20. It was developed by Universal Oil Products Company as an "economical commercial method of upgrading the octane ratings of straight run, natural and thermally cracked gasolines, and for producing large quantities of benzene, toluene, xylenes and other aromatic

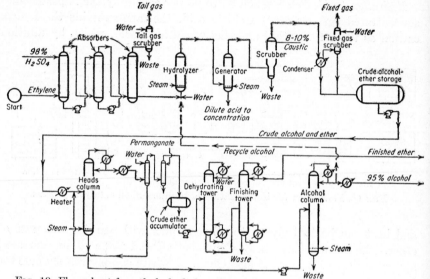

FIG. 19. Flow sheet for ethyl alcohol and ether. (*Courtesy of Petroleum Refiner.*)

hydrocarbons for use in chemical manufacture and in aviation fuel." The name comes from the fact that this process uses fixed-bed Al_2O_3 catalyst containing 0.25 per cent platinum. This catalyst has a long life without regeneration. The process operates as an example of a specialized hydroforming process whereby the reactions take place in the presence of recirculated hydrogen. The feed must be carefully prepared to get the best results and is usually a naphtha cut. The steps depicted in Fig. 20 may be resolved into the following *unit physical operations* and *unit chemical conversions* or *processes:*

The naphtha feed is prepared in a prefractionator (Op.).

The charge is mixed with the hydrogen and introduced into the feed preheater where the temperature is raised (Op.).

[1] SMITH and MOORE, Hydroforming; A New Refining Process, *Chem. & Met. Eng.*, **48** (4), 77 (1941); TRUSTY, Petroleum as a Source of the Aromatic Hydrocarbons, *Petroleum Refiner*, **22** (4), 95 (1943); MURPHREE, *op. cit.*, p. 625, flow sheet; SITTIG, *op. cit.*, p. 116.

[2] SITTIG, *op. cit.*, p. 116, references; HAENSEL and STERBA, Comparison of Platforming and Thermal Reforming, in "Progress in Petroleum Technology," p. 60, American Chemical Society, Washington, D.C., 1951; ANON., Platforming, *Chem. Eng.*, **59** (5), 242 (1952), pictured flow sheet.

The hot-feed naphtha vapors with recycle hydrogen are conducted through the four catalyst-containing reactors in series with an interheating for each reactor (Op. and Pr.). The temperature is 850 to 950°F. at from 200 to 1,000 lb. per sq. in. gage.

The reactions that take place are essentially as follows (Pr.):

1. Isomerization of alkyl cyclopentanes to cyclohexanes.
2. Dehydrogenation of cyclohexanes to aromatics.
3. Dehydrocyclization of paraffins to aromatics.
4. Hydrocracking of paraffins and naphthenes.
5. Hydrogenation of olefins.
6. Isomerization of paraffins.
7. Desulfurization (quoted from Universal Oil Products Company).

From the reactor the products are cooled in heat interchangers (Op.) (not shown in Fig. 20).

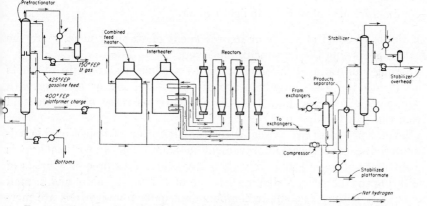

FIG. 20. Flow sheet for platforming. (*Courtesy of Universal Oil Products Co.*)

From the exchanger a 90 per cent hydrogen is obtained, compressed, and recycled (Op.). The main product is fractionated or stabilized after having the temperature reduced to the proper point in heat exchangers and conducted into a bubble-cap column (Op.), or stabilizer from which the overhead may be used as fuel.

The product is the stabilized "platformate" which may be used as a high-octane gasoline or further fractionated into its constituents, *e.g.*, to furnish benzene, toluene, and xylenes.

Oxidation.[1] The oxidation reaction in petroleum gives more troubles than useful products, forming as it does gums and resins that interfere with the employment of gasolines, particularly those which contain unsaturated bodies. However, some serviceable products are obtained from petroleum by oxidation, *e.g.*, formaldehyde by restricted oxidation of natural gas. Much study is also being directed toward making fatty acids[2] from paraffins.

[1] GRUSE and STEVENS, *op. cit.*, pp. 119–138, 653.

[2] PARDUN and KUCHINKA, Reaction Rates in the Liquid-phase Oxidation of Paraffins, *Petroleum Refiner*, **22** (11), 140 (1943).

The Celanese Corporation has installed several plants for the controlled oxidation[1] of propane and butane to a number of organic acids, aldehydes, and alcohols, such as acetic acid, acetic anhydride (about 1,500,000 lb. per week), vinyl acetate (about 600,000 lb. per week), acetaldehyde, acetone, methanol, propionic, and butyric acids.

Chemical Treatment. Some type of chemical treatment to remove or alter the constitution of impurities in petroleum products is usually necessary to produce marketable material.[2] Depending upon the particular treatment used, one or more of the following purposes are achieved:

1. Improvement of color.
2. Improvement of odor.
3. Removal of sulfur.
4. Removal of gums.
5. Improvement of stability to light and air.

Of these, removal of sulfur or improvement of stability usually are the factors governing the treatment employed.

Strong sulfuric acid is widely used to produce water-white products but it has the great disadvantage of also dissolving or reacting with valuable olefins. (See Fig. 2 of Chap. 19 for recovery of sulfuric acid from the spent sludge acid.)

Several processes are available for the alteration of objectionable sulfur and the consequent improvement in odor.[3] The *doctor treatment* is probably used more extensively than any other. This process consists of agitating the oil with an alkaline solution of sodium plumbite and a small amount of sulfur. The sulfur compounds usually found in oils are mercaptans. These give the material a disagreeable odor and cause corrosion. *Doctor* converts mercaptans to lead sulfide and comparatively harmless disulfides.

$$2RSH + Na_2PbO_2 \rightarrow (RS)_2Pb + 2NaOH$$
$$(RS)_2Pb + S \rightarrow R_2S_2 + PbS$$

Catalytic methods for desulfurization are modern developments and are becoming increasingly important.

[1] For flow sheets and outlines, see "Petrochemicals Process Handbook," p. 144, Gulf Publishing Co., Houston, Tex., 1953; for earlier pictured flow sheet (McCarthy Oil Co.), ANON., Organics from Natural Gas, *Chem. Eng.*, **56** (1), 132 (1949).

[2] MASON, BENT, and McCULLOUGH, Naphtha Treating "Pays Its Way," *Petroleum Refiner*, **20**, 432 (1941); for a fundamental presentation of this subject, see Chap. 8 in GRUSE and STEVENS, *op. cit.*

[3] HAPPEL, CAULEY, and KELLY, Critical Analysis of Sweetening Processes and Mercaptan Removal, *Petroleum Refiner*, **21**, 406 (1942); RYAN, Influence of Sulfur Compounds on Octane Number and Lead Susceptibility of Gasoline, *Ind. Eng. Chem.*, **34**, 824 (1942); NELSON, *op. cit.*, p. 257; TAIT, Desulfurization, in "Progress in Petroleum Technology," p. 151, American Chemical Society, Washington, D.C., 1951.

It is now common practice to add antioxidants[1] to prevent formation of gums rather than to remove them chemically. Among the antigumming materials used are α-naphthol, substituted catechols, cresols, benzyl-p-aminophenols, and certain wood-tar and coal-tar fractions.

Research. The petroleum industry has been characterized by continuous improvement based upon research[2] and a willingness to replace antiquated equipment or old processes by more modern ones. This development went through two phases—the first, wherein the *unit operations* of distillation, heat transfer, fluid flow, and the like, were subjected to accurate study and experimentation, resulting in the carrying through of these operations with greater efficiency and consequently less cost. Investigations of these unit operations are naturally being continued. However, the second phase[3] of research in this field applies to the study of chemical changes involving petroleum raw materials or petroleum products. The industrial application of these we recognize as *unit processes or conversion processes.* We are right in the midst of this aspect of the development of the petroleum industry. It has yielded rich returns and is certain to yield even more products of greater usefulness in the future. Synthetic rubber is an example.

No longer can petroleum companies be satisfied simply to separate into salable fractions the various products as they occur in petroleum. To maintain a competitive and well-rounded position many petroleum compounds must be chemically altered to obtain products of greater usefulness or value. Each year is showing a higher percentage of petroleum sales arising from the action of chemical change on petroleum raw materials. Indeed the petroleum industry has become one of the most important sources for cheap raw materials for the entire chemical industry. Such chemical change will be more marked in the future than it has been in the past.

The present sound technical position has all come about through the wise dependence of the petroleum executives upon research in the very broadest meaning of this term, *protected by patents covering the public disclosure of new discoveries.* Robert E. Wilson states,[4] "Oil industry research expenditures are now well over $100,000,000 a year—about five times the amount spent on petroleum research in 1940."

[1] GRUSE and STEVENS, *op. cit.*, p. 132.

[2] BROOKS, Petroleum Research and Wars, *Ind. Eng. Chem.*, **34**, 798 (1942); FITZGERALD, Mobilizing Petroleum Hydrocarbons, *Chem. & Met. Eng.*, **49** (3), 83 (1942).

[3] Many divide petroleum development into three phases: the first pertaining largely to the physical operation of distillation, the second characterized by cracking, and the third distinguished by the many other chemical processes or reactions that are being applied industrially in this field.

[4] Scope of Symposium, in "Progress in Petroleum Technology," p. 1, American Chemical Society, Washington, D.C., 1951. Covers many phases of results of petroleum research.

SELECTED REFERENCES

Dunstan, A. E., A. W. Nash, B. T. Brooks, and Henry Tizard, "Science of Petroleum," Oxford University Press, New York, 1938. This large work of five volumes and supplements is the most thorough covering of this field.

Wilson, R. E., Chairman Symposium "Progress in Petroleum Technology," 35 excellent articles, American Chemical Society, Washington, D.C., 1951.

Nelson, W. L., "Petroleum Refinery Engineering," 3d ed., McGraw-Hill Book Company, Inc., New York, 1949.

Van Winkle, Matthew, "Aviation Gasoline Manufacture," McGraw-Hill Book Company, Inc., New York, 1944.

Gruse, W. A., and D. R. Stevens, "The Chemical Technology of Petroleum," 2d ed., McGraw-Hill Book Company, Inc., New York, 1942.

Ellis, Carleton, "Chemistry of Petroleum Derivatives," 2 vols., Reinhold Publishing Corporation, New York, 1937.

Uren, L. C., "Petroleum Production Engineering," McGraw-Hill Book Company, Inc., New York, 1950.

Huntington, R. L., "Natural Gas and Natural Gasoline," McGraw-Hill Book Company, Inc., New York, 1950.

Bell, H. S., "Oil Shales and Shale Oils," D. Van Nostrand Company, Inc., New York, 1948.

Sachanen, A. N., "Conversion of Petroleum," 2d ed., Reinhold Publishing Corporation, New York, 1948.

Egloff, Gustav, and George Hulla, "Alkylation of Alkanes," Reinhold Publishing Corporation, New York, 1948.

Goldstein, R. F., "The Petroleum Chemicals Industry," E. & F. N. Spon, Ltd., London, 1949.

Weil, B. H., and J. C. Lane, "Synthetic Petroleum from the Synthine Process," Chemical Publishing Company, Inc., New York, 1948.

Sage, B. H., and W. N. Lacey, "Thermodynamic Properties of the Lighter Paraffin Hydrocarbons and Nitrogen," American Petroleum Institute, New York, 1950.

Brooks, B. T., C. E. Boord, S. S. Kurtz, and L. Schmerling, "The Chemistry of Petroleum Hydrocarbons," 3 vols., Reinhold Publishing Corporation, New York, 1954.

Garner, F. H., and E. B. Evans, edited by George Sell, "Reviews of Petroleum Technology," 13th vol., 1951, Institute of Petroleum, London, 1953.

Jones, P. J., "Petroleum Production," 5 vols., Reinhold Publishing Corporation, New York, 1946-1948.

Hart, W. B., "Industrial Waste Disposal for Petroleum Refineries and Allied Plants," Petroleum Processing, Cleveland, Ohio, 1947.

"Petroleum Facts and Figures," 11th ed., American Petroleum Institute, 1954, biyearly statistical report.

Petroleum Processing, monthly periodical, National Petroleum Publishing Company, Cleveland, Ohio.

Petroleum Engineer, monthly periodical, The Petroleum Engineer Publishing Company, Dallas, Tex.

Petroleum Refiner, monthly periodical, The Gulf Publishing Co., Houston, Tex.

"Process Handbook Section" and "The Refinery Catalog"; these yearly publications are indispensable in this industry, the first including about 80 flow sheets with diagrams, pictures, and descriptions; and the second presenting the various types of equipment used, Gulf Publishing Co., Houston, Tex.

Industrial and Engineering Chemistry, American Chemical Society, Washington, D.C. This monthly periodical contains much of the fundamental work in petroleum.

CHAPTER 38

INTERMEDIATES, DYES, AND THEIR APPLICATION

Coal has been called the *black diamond*. The analogy is true not only because both consist of carbon but because from both we get a rainbow of colors, one from the effect of light and the other from the action of various chemicals. The purpose of this chapter is to follow through the manifold chemical and engineering changes that transform coal and even petroleum by the action of many other chemicals into literally a coat of a thousand hues. The 1,000-odd commercial dyes that we use bring grace and variety in what would otherwise be a drab world. Furthermore, the entire dye industry throws a protective mantle over many another industry and even over a wise scheme of national preparedness.

Because of the way in which dyes are connected with or enter into so many other phases of our industrial life we have learned to view the industry as an essential one. It took the First World War to convince America and some other nations of this fact. Prior to 1914, Germany made a very large proportion of the dyes used throughout the world; indeed, propaganda insisted that only on the banks of the Rhine could dyes be made economically and of a high quality. However, since the derangement of industrial life by the cutting off of German dyes beginning in 1914 and since the realization of the connection between the raw materials of the dye industry and a wise program of national preparedness, many of the important nations have endeavored to build up within their own borders and from their own basic materials a self-contained dye industry. If we run our mind's eye across a portion of our industrial life, we shall see how the dyes enter in. Consider clothing, drapes and wall coverings, paints and varnishes, and many other industries. In these, dyes act to make a great many products salable. We *could* go around in gray homespun, live in unpainted houses, and keep the sun out with unbleached or undyed curtains, but much of the attractiveness of our modern civilization would disappear. We would live literally in a colorless world. One dollar's worth of dyes makes salable about $100 worth of other products, such as textiles, hats, carpets, leathers, paints, varnishes, inks, paper, feathers, furs, and many others. Hence the 137 million dollars' worth of dyes sold in 1954 are essential to the sale of about

15 billion dollars from these various industries, giving employment to around 2 million men and women.

This is not the whole story. The First World War demonstrated how closely the chemical industry and, in particular, the dye industry were connected with the system of national preparedness. The raw materials, which in times of peace enter into the making of intermediates that are changed into dyes, in many instances are the basis of our high explosives in time of war. This is true of benzene and toluene which furnish dyes or such explosives as picric acid, tetryl, and T.N.T. Likewise the acids that are used in times of peace to make dyes are absolutely essential to make the nitro-derivatives which are such an important division of explosives. And finally, much of the plant and many of the trained personnel who in times of peace make dyes, can be transferred in any emergency to the making of explosives or to serve as the nucleus for rapid expansion of such materials.

In 1914 we imported 90 per cent of our dyes. Our position then could be represented as in the accompanying table.

TABLE 1. SUMMARY OF DYES, 1914

	Employees	Firms manufacturing	Pounds
Dyes made.........................	528	7	6,619,729
Dyes imported....................	...	..	45,950,895

This does not represent the real picture for, while not belittling the excellent work that the 7 American firms accomplished, it is a fact that many of the necessary intermediates were being imported from Germany, Switzerland, or even from England. The dye industry had been struggling for 50 years to establish itself here in the United States. Many courageous souls had tried to break in and a few succeeded. When importations were stopped in the summer of 1914, the country became panicky over the dye shortage. The dark corners of warehouses were searched for abandoned kegs of dyes; even the floors were scraped and extracted. Simultaneously, the chemical industry took up the challenge.

Thanks to the skill of American chemists, the versatility of American engineers, and the confidence of American businessmen, the establishment of a permanent dye industry in America rapidly took shape. Indeed, before the ending of the war in 1918, a good start had been made. The country had learned its lesson and both parties in Congress supported a wise temporary tariff to encourage the further development leading to the independence of America in dyes and intermediates. In 1920 the scales had been reversed; America was then manufacturing over 90 per cent of the dyes needed for domestic consumption out of American intermediates and American raw materials. This accomplishment was not the complete story for, although some products were still being imported, certain largely consumed dyes, as sulfur black and indigo, were being made on such a large scale and so cheaply that they entered world markets in competition with products made in Germany and Switzerland. These exports in value and in tonnage exceeded the imports. The present situation regarding intermediate and dye production in America is summarized in Table 2, which includes medicinals, flavors, perfumes, and plastics-resins, etc., for the reason that these, as well as dyes, are frequently based on the same or analogous intermediates. More details about dyes are included in Tables 6 and 7.

The question may well be asked, what do American-made dyes cost? Ordinary competition based on improved and cheaper manufacture has brought the price down so that the consumer pays less for his dyes than he once did. This is a real and lasting accomplishment.

But, although the dyestuff industry is now an American one and dyes are more economical to the consumer, what about quality? Are American dyes as good as those that were imported from Germany? The answer is an emphatic yes. Most of the dyes made in America are chemical compounds identical to those that were made years ago and are still being made on the banks of the Rhine. Competition in America has in certain instances increased the purity and the strength of the commercially sold dyes. The American dye industry has not been content simply to copy what the rest of the world has done but has pioneered in bringing out new processes for old dyes and intermediates and improved equipment for the cheaper manufacture of both. Indeed many *new* processes for old products have been developed, together with much *new* machinery for carrying out the reactions, and also *new* intermediates and many *new* dyes with numerous improved properties.

Following the Second World War, much information has become available regarding recent German dye accomplishments, largely through FIAT and BIOS reports and German microfilms (see Literature References at end of this chapter). This has stimulated considerable imitative investigations, particularly in the field of new anthraquinone vat dyes, which supplements the usual adaptation to American needs of the many textile dyes discovered in Germany, Switzerland, and England, both after the First World War and before.

This satisfactory state has been accomplished only by continuous research both in the fundamental chemistry involved and in the chemical engineering necessary to commercialize these reactions on an economic scale. Such research has been and is still being carried on. All our large dye factories have well-equipped laboratories and pilot plants either for improving old processes or for developing new. There is no chemical

TABLE 2. SYNTHETIC ORGANIC CHEMICALS: SUMMARY OF UNITED STATES
PRODUCTION OF INTERMEDIATES AND FINISHED PRODUCTS, WITH SALES
FOR MAIN GROUPS[a]
(Production and sales in thousands of pounds; sales value in thousands of dollars)

Product	1934–1938 average	1948–1952 average	1953	1954
Production, grand total............	....	22,390,675	29,128,545	28,444,749
Sales, grand total.................	....	11,930,716	15,636,993	15,732,303
Sales value, grand total...........	....	2,943,868	4,030,357	3,977,444
Organic chemicals, cyclic:				
Production, total...............	....	7,070,171	9,637,093	9,173,954
Sales, total...................		4,462,820	6,072,460	5,764,463
Sales value, total..............		1,552,971	2,011,311	1,970,452
Organic chemicals, acyclic:				
Production, total...............	....	15,320,504	19,491,452	19,270,793
Sales, total...................	....	7,467,896	9,564,533	9,967,840
Sales value, total..............	....	1,390,897	2,019,046	2,006,992
Intermediates:				
Production....................	462,614	3,494,976	4,698,585	4,613,869
Dyes:				
Production....................	102,528	166,640	165,806	142,982
Toners and lakes:				
Production....................	....	42,271	44,056	39,840
Medicinals:				
Production, cyclic.............	11,596	44,444	53,003	49,262
Production, acyclic............	....	8,520	15,582	16,662
Flavor and perfume materials:				
Production, cyclic.............	4,041	16,801	18,458	21,663
Production, acyclic............	....	8,520	13,147	13,437
Plastic and resin materials:				
Production, cyclic.............	102,644	1,175,713	1,605,447	1,588,180
Production, acyclic............	....	804,664	1,171,180	1,239,623
Rubber-processing chemicals:				
Production, cyclic.............	....	94,569	121,532	109,865
Production, acyclic............	....	16,673	23,252	20,057
Elastomers or synthetic rubbers:				
Production, cyclic.............	....	1,060,050	1,414,944	973,249
Production, acyclic............	....	376,520	543,406	461,713
Plasticizers:				
Production, cyclic.............	....	162,100	223,810	227,618
Production, acyclic............	....	58,955	69,088	73,056
Surface-active agents:				
Production, cyclic.............	....	344,002	594,089	640,222
Production, acyclic............	....	239,002	327,505	385,614
Pesticides and other agricultural chemicals:				
Production, cyclic.............	....	256,679	297,054	357,533
Production, acyclic............	....	33,085	58,899	61,741
Miscellaneous:				
Production, cyclic.............	....	202,812	402,309	409,157
Production, acyclic............	....	13,773,525	17,267,127	16,998,930

[a] "Synthetic Organic Chemicals," U.S. Tariff Commission (published annually). This reference gives many more details pertaining to production, sales, and sales values.

industry other than that making synthetic organic chemicals that plows back into research such a large proportion of its sales. The actual expenditure for such research is shown in Table 3.

TABLE 3. RESEARCH IN THE SYNTHETIC ORGANIC CHEMICAL INDUSTRY—
COSTS, SALARIES, NUMBER[a,b]

				Total reported cost of research		
Year	Companies reporting, number	Technically trained research workers, number	Salaries paid research workers, 1,000	Within the plant		Outside the plant 1,000
				Gross 1,000	Net[c] 1,000	
1946	313	7,527	35,791	73,376	69,412	4,249
1947	301	8,707	41,571	90,640	87,825	4,600
1948	303	9,114	46,346	98,729	95,417	4,594
1949	338	8,916	51,521	105,333	106,580	4,996
1950	335	10,529	56,619	115,191	111,374	6,648
1951	353	9,984	67,376	149,607	144,784	6,724
1952	381	12,203	76,701	194,993	186,503	9,603
1953	363	12,208	83,694	210,035	199,829	7,951
1954	388	13,474	94,432	236,524	221,842	9,238

[a] "Synthetic Organic Chemicals," 1955, p. 171, U.S. Tariff Commission.
[b] See this book, 1st ed., p. 840, for costs in coal-tar products 1928–1940.
[c] The net cost figure is obtained by deducting from gross cost the credits for salable products obtained in course of research.

Raw Materials. The dye industry draws upon every division of the chemical industry for the multiplicity of raw materials needed to make its finished products. However, the backbone of the raw material sequence may be represented in one line:

Coal → coal tar → crudes → intermediates → dyes

Figures 2 and 7 in Chap. 6 illustrate the making of the main initial products out of coal and coal tar. The so-called *crudes* are really not crude materials. They *were* 50 years ago, but the skill of the modern chemical engineer has made them, even though sold in large quantities at low prices, almost chemically pure. The name *crude* still persists and applies to the five hydrocarbons obtained by distillation and crystallization from coal tar. We might better call them the *coal-tar dye hydrocarbons*.

COAL-TAR DYE HYDROCARBONS

Benzene   Naphthalene
Toluene   Anthracene
Xylene

In developing the dye industry, America had to manufacture these various hydrocarbons not only of sufficient purity but also in adequate tonnage. This enhanced demand was a tremendous incentive to increasing the installation of co-product coke ovens and the disappearing of the old wasteful beehive ovens. The obtaining of coke in this manner not only provided basic raw materials for the dye and other industries but also increased greatly the value of the products derived from coal. In recent years, the production of aromatic hydrocarbons from petroleum has been increasing at a very rapid rate, as the following tabulation indicates:

Aromatic hydrocarbon	Production from petroleum, millions of lb.		Increased per cent
	1953	1954	
Benzene..........	462	674	46
Toluene..........	836	890	6
Xylene..........	749	726	−3

These large amounts are mostly produced by cyclization and/or dehydrogenation reactions in catalytic reforming or hydroforming plants.

Inorganic Chemicals. Dyes and intermediates are very heavy consumers of inorganic as well as organic chemicals. The use of these chemicals in the making of dyes and intermediates has frequently been the stimulus for improved processes by virtue of greatly increased demand. This is well exemplified in the development of the contact process for the manufacture of oleum, which came as a further extension of the catalytic oxidation of SO_2 to SO_3, brought about by the need for SO_3 as an oxidizing agent in the old process for converting naphthalene to phthalic anhydride, giving as a by-product sulfur dioxide. Similarly, there is a great demand for chloro-derivatives such as chloro-benzene requiring large tonnages of chlorine. A surprising quantity of inorganic chemicals is frequently required to make 1 lb. of the finished dye, it being estimated that, for some of the anthraquinone dyes, up to 75 lb. of such chemicals are required to make 1 lb. of the finished product. Dyes and intermediates consume in general the following chemicals on a large scale:

Acids: Nitric, sulfuric, mixed, hydrochloric, acetic, formic, etc.

Alkalies: Caustic soda, soda ash, ammonia, slaked lime, quicklime, limestone (calcium carbonate), caustic potash, and alkylamines.

Salts: Salt (NaCl), sodium sulfate (various forms), sodium nitrite, sodium sulfide, sodium cyanide, copper sulfate, potassium chloride, aluminum chloride, sodium hydrosulfite, etc.

Miscellaneous: Chlorine, bromine, iodine, hydrogen, alcohol, methanol, formaldehyde, iron, sulfur, etc.

INTERMEDIATES

The intermediates are the building stones out of which dyes are directly constructed, just as our houses are made out of brick, wood, mortar, plaster, or steel, except that chemical reactions are used to connect one intermediate with another in manufacturing a dye. Thus we find the producing of intermediates, economically and in a pure form, to be the very foundation of the dye industry, and the reduction that has come in the last 10 or 15 years in the cost of dyes is due very largely to the lowering of the cost of making pure intermediates. In America this has been achieved through research leading to higher yields in the chemical reactions and to improved chemical engineering when commercializing these reactions. The wise management of our dye factories, stimulated by competition, has directed the study of all the important phases of our factory procedures from which have come lowered labor charges, increased yields, and more uniformity of product, together with enlarged production. This has required the development of improved apparatus in many cases and the courageous discarding of any outmoded plant.

The census of intermediates, taken by the U.S. Tariff Commission, shows that in 1954 there were produced in the United States 4,614,000,000 lb. of cyclic intermediates or 2 per cent more than for 1953. Table 4 lists the important intermediates. Some intermediates such as β-naphthol are made in a preponderating quantity by one company and hence cannot have the quantity manufactured disclosed. However, many of the cyclic intermediates in Table 4 are not used at all, or to only a minor degree, to build dyes. For instance, part of the acetanilide, aniline, phenol, and salicylic acid enter the medicinal field. But most of the phenol is consumed by plastics and resins, while practically all the dodecyl-benzene becomes a raw material for detergents. Much chlorobenzene and o- and p-dichlorobenzenes are used for insecticides. Cyclohexane is a raw material for nylon. Phthalic anhydride is much consumed in the plastics and surface coating fields. Styrene enters plastics and rubber. The dye industry used the intermediates first, but these are now also the building stones for much of the organic chemicals consumed by the public and summarized in Table 2.

Unit Operations, Unit Processes, Energy Changes. These factors for the intermediate and dye industry are so important that, particularly for the intermediates, a presentation under each main unit process will be made as a logical and technical one. Thereunder will be described[1] the energy changes and any particular unit operation involved in the manufacture, such as special mixing or filtration.

---

[1] A more detailed presentation, particularly of the chemical and thermal aspects of unit processes as applied to intermediates and many other similar compounds, is given in GROGGINS, "Unit Processes in Organic Synthesis," 4th ed., McGraw-Hill Book Company, Inc., New York, 1952.

TABLE 4. PRODUCTION OF IMPORTANT CYCLIC INTERMEDIATES[a]

Intermediate	1953, 1,000 lb.	1954, 1,000 lb.
Acetanilide, tech.	4,468	3,140
N-Acetylsulfanilyl chloride.	3,775	2,868
1-Amino-anthraquinone and salt.	1,174	621
2-Amino-anthraquinone and salt.	1,095	857
6-Amino-1,3-naphthalene-disulfonic acid (Amino I acid).	1,152	1,263
2-Amino-1-naphthalene-sulfonic acid (Tobias acid).	3,286	3,825
8-Amino-1-naphthol-3,6-disulfonic acid (H acid) Na salt.	2,437	2,227
Aniline.	113,487	97,349
1-Anthraquinone-sulfonic acid.	3,011	1,636
7-Benz(de)anthracen-7-one (Benzanthrone).	1,900	1,450
Benzidine hydrochloride and sulfate.	1,413	1,277
o-Benzoyl-benzoic acid.	6,970	5,180
m-Chloro-aniline.	1,065	
Chloro-benzene.	377,184	367,947
1-Chloro-2,4-dinitro-benzene (Dinitro-chloro-benzene).	4,695	4,150
α-Chloro-toluene (Benzyl chloride).	10,491	11,545
Cresols, total.	18,757	22,036
Cresylic acid, refined, total.	50,647	47,894
Cyclohexane.	299,578	216,619
o-Dichloro-benzene.	26,230	23,890
p-Dichloro-benzene.	59,289	51,871
3,3'-Dichloro-benzidine base and salts.	1,086	923
2,4-Dichloro-phenol.	15,436	17,215
4,4'-Dinitro-2,2'-stilbene-disulfonic acid.	1,147	861
Dodecyl-benzenes.	297,286	357,781
3-Hydroxy-2-naphthoic acid (B.O.N.).	3,571	3,428
Metanilic acid (m-amino-benzene-sulfonic acid).	1,114	780
Naphthionic acid Na salt.	1,222	1,133
2-Naphthol-3,6-disulfonic acid	1,198	1,119
2-Naphthol-6,8-disulfonic acid (G acid).	1,075	1,508
Nitro-benzene.	148,048	122,545
m- and p-Nitro-benzoic acids.	1,178	
5-Nitro-o-toluene-sulfonic acid.	2,025	1,582
2-Nitro-p-toluidine (NH₂ = 1).	1,963	2,170
Nonyl-phenol.	4,448	9,196
Phenol.	382,423	417,503
Phenyl-acetic acid (α-Toluic acid), potassium salt.	2,306	2,041
Phenyl-acetonitrile (α-Tolunitrile).	1,030	1,513
o- and p-Phenylene-diamines.	1,058	
Phenyl-glycine, K and Na salts.	5,545	3,625
Phthalic anhydride.	226,646	253,847
Picolines.	1,264	963
Quinizarin.	1,408	1,198
Salicylic acid, tech. *sales*.		15,053
Styrene.	798,433	703,169
1,2,4,5-Tetrachloro-benzene.	8,948	5,124
Toluene-2,4-diamine.	1,217	1,627

[a] "Synthetic Organic Chemicals," U.S. Tariff Commission (published annually).

Nitration

Nitration is one of the most important of the unit processes operated for the manufacture of intermediates and dyes. In the industry very few nitro-groups appear in the final product, the nitro-radical being usually reduced to the very reactive amine or subjected to other changes. However, the nitration is frequently the initial side entrance into the aromatic ring whether of benzene or more complicated rings.

A typical nitration may be expressed conventionally as follows:

$$R \cdot H + HNO_3(H_2SO_4) \rightarrow R \cdot NO_2 + H_2O + (H_2SO_4);$$
$$\Delta H = -15,000 \text{ to } -35,000 \text{ cal.}$$

Although the usual nitrating acids are nitric or mixed acid, the actual nitrating *agent* is believed to be the *nitronium ion*, NO_2^+ which is formed as follows:

In mixed acid:

$$HNO_3 + 2H_2SO_4 \rightleftarrows NO_2^+ + 2HSO_4^- + H_3O^+$$

In nitric acid:

$$2HNO_3 \rightleftarrows H_2NO_3^+ + NO_3^-$$
$$H_2NO_3^+ \rightleftarrows NO_2^+ + H_2O$$

Removal of the water favors the nitration reaction by shifting the equilibrium to the right. In case of mixed acid the sulfuric effects this removal by what is expressed as the dehydrating value of the sulfuric acid (D.V.S.). Following Groggins (*op. cit.*), the following equation is used:

$$D.V.S. = \frac{\text{actual 100 per cent sulfuric acid}}{\text{water present in reactants} + \text{water formed by nitration}}$$

Experiments have indicated what D.V.S. is needed for a given nitration but it varies from 2.0 to as high as 12 for technical nitrations. Much *heat* is evolved by the nitration itself as well as by the absorption by the sulfuric acid of the water split out, but the specific heat of the sulfuric acid enables some of this heat to be absorbed. As the higher nitro-compounds may be explosive, a certain amount of precaution is necessary in handling this reaction so as to keep it always under control. Nitric acid is also a powerful oxidizing agent, and this action must be minimized as much as possible by keeping temperatures as low as possible.

The *equipment* used varies from acidproof stoneware, or large nitrators constructed of acidproof brick when using 40° or 42° nitric acid, to cast-iron or stainless-steel nitrators when employing mixed acid; but in every case the unit operations of heat transfer and of mixing should be most carefully considered. The nitration unit process is applied to the making of a number of intermediates among which those in the following list are important.

Chloro-2,4-dinitro-benzene, from chloro-benzene through o- and p-chloro-nitro-benzene, by strong mixed acid

o- and p-Chloro-nitro-benzene, from chloro-benzene by mixed acid. Separate by distillation and crystallization

m-Dinitro-benzene, from benzene through nitro-benzene by strong mixed acid

1,4-Dichloro-2-nitro-benzene from p-dichloro-benzene by mixed acid

p-Nitro-acetanilide and p-nitro-aniline, from acetanilide by cold mixed acid nitration. Hydrolysis furnishes p-nitro-aniline

Nitro-benzene, from benzene by mixed acid

α-Nitro-naphthalene,[a] from naphthalene by mixed acid

o- and p-Nitro-phenol, from phenol by nitric acid or mixed acid. Separate by steam distillation

o- and p-Nitro-toluene, from toluene by mixed acid at moderate temperature to lessen oxidation. Separate by distillation and crystallization

m-Nitro-p-toluidine, from acyl-p-toluidine by mixed acid at low temperature

[a] For further consideration of α-nitro-naphthalene, see Chap. 39.

Example of Technical Nitration. *Nitro-benzene* is and has been one of the most important intermediates in the dye field, and between 25,000

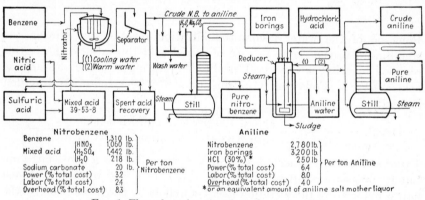

FIG. 1. Flow sheet for nitro-benzene and aniline.

and 30,000 tons are manufactured yearly. Out of it are made aniline, benzidine, metanilic acid (sulfonation and reduction), as well as dinitro-benzene and many dyes such as nigrosines and magenta. Nitro-benzene is also consumed in large amounts as an industrial solvent. As the flow sheet in Fig. 1 indicates, nitro-benzene is made by the direct nitration of benzene, using mixed acid, according to the following reaction:

$$C_6H_6 + HNO_3(H_2SO_4) \rightarrow C_6H_5NO_2 + H_2O(H_2SO_4);$$

$$\Delta H = -27,000 \text{ cal.}[1]$$

[1] For mononitration of benzene, and particularly for a continuous process, *cf.* GROGGINS, *op. cit.*, pp. 59–67.

This procedure is carried out in cast-iron nitrators arranged with efficient cooling devices to remove the heat of reaction and to keep the procedure under control. In the smaller nitrators a jacket of cooling water will suffice, but for the modern large nitrator taking, for instance, over 1,000 gal. of benzene, it is necessary to supplement the jacket by other means of cooling.[1]

These additional devices consist of the insertion in the body of the nitrator of water-cooled cast-iron tubes, as indicated in Fig. 1, or the use of steel coils, as in the Hough or Buffalo nitrator. When employing steel coils, because of the greater chance of leakage through a weld, or by reason of corrosion, the water should be sucked through the cooling coils. In case of leakage the acid will enter into the coils and will not do the harm that water would cause if introduced into the nitration mixture under pressure. An electric conductivity automatic indicating device can be easily installed on the exit line of the cooling water to ring an alarm and to light a red lamp whenever any acid is in the exit cooling water. Much of the nitro-benzene is used for further synthesis and can usually be separated from the spent acid and simply given several water washes. If it is to be sold in the pure form, for instance, as oil of myrbane as a cheap perfume in the soap industry, it should be distilled.

Amination by Reduction

The amino group is an exceedingly important one for dyes as it is the one changed to the azo chromophore or alkylated. This amino radical is also one of the chief auxochromes. It is made by the reduction of a nitro-derivative or recently, in special cases, by ammonolysis (page 874).

The *agents* employed are iron and an acid catalyst, zinc and an alkali, sodium sulfide or polysulfide, with a scattering of less important reagents. The list on page 873 presents some of the aminations particularly pertaining to intermediates. In this and similar lists in this section, a bare indication is given of the process for manufacture. Amines also are made by catalytic hydrogenation and by ammonolysis. Liquid and vapor-phase catalytic hydrogenations have become quite important large-scale industrial methods[2] for production of naphthylamines and of aniline, and of reduction of nitro-benzene to hydrazo-benzene, and of p-nitro-phenol to p-amino-phenol. More details for those intermediates, not fully treated here, can be found in the books on intermediates in the references at the

---

[1] As the size of a given equipment increases, a jacket becomes proportionately less effective, owing to the increase in the contents according to the cube of the corresponding dimension, while the jacket area increases by only the square of the corresponding dimension.

[2] U.S. Pats. 2194938(1940), 2233128(1941), 2233139(1941), FIAT Rept. 649; U.S. Pat. 2105321(1938).

end of this chapter. The generalized reaction is

$$RNO_2 + 6H \rightarrow RNH_2 + 2H_2O$$

However, for many of our technical aminations by reduction, a better expression would be

$$4RNO_2 + 9Fe + 4H_2O \xrightarrow{\text{Catalyst}} 4RNH_2 + 3Fe_3O_4$$

The *energy* of these reactions is exothermic and so large (see Aniline) that much thought must be given to efficient heat transfer.

The *equipment* to commercialize these chemical changes is frequently a highly specialized apparatus, as the reducer for aniline. In other cases, particularly when dealing with nonvolatile products like *m*-phenylenediamine, a simple well-ventilated wooden vat performs satisfactorily. However, it should have an efficient sweep stirrer located near the bottom to keep the iron in suspension.

Example of Technical Amination by Reduction. *Aniline.*[1] This intermediate has been of such great importance that frequently we hear the dyes spoken of as *aniline dyes*.[2] Aniline itself is made by iron reduction of nitro-benzene, by ammonolysis (page 875) of chloro-benzene, or by vapor-phase hydrogenation of nitro-benzene.[3] A flow sheet exemplifying the iron reduction is included in Fig. 1. The reduction can be summarized:

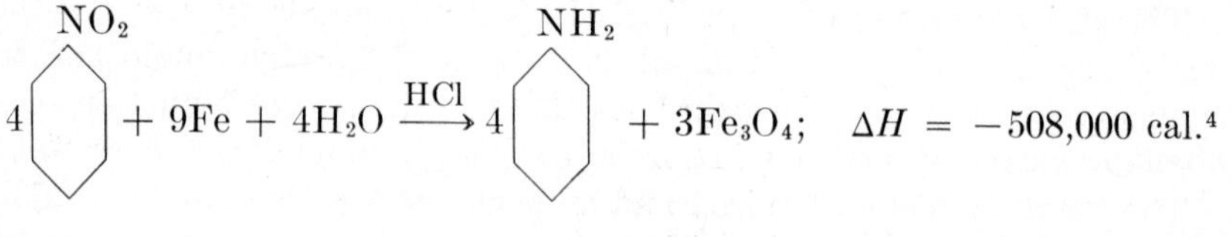

In the reduction, as in many other processes, the chemical reactions are much more complicated. These changes can probably be formulated with the sequences listed as follows:

[1] For further details in making aniline see GROGGINS, "Aniline and Its Derivatives," D. Van Nostrand Company, Inc., New York, 1921; GROGGINS, "Unit Processes in Organic Synthesis," Chaps. 1 and 2.

[2] It is essential from a manufacturing or research viewpoint to know just how many and what dyes are derived from aniline, or any other intermediate. To supply this information the following book was written: SHREVE, "Dyes Classified by Intermediates," Reinhold Publishing Corporation, New York, 1922. The book also serves as a dictionary for the various names of the intermediates, as both their chemical and trivial names are arranged alphabetically.

[3] Flow sheet, GROGGINS, "Unit Processes in Organic Synthesis," p. 133.

[4] Further consideration of the heat of reaction of aniline manufacture is given in GROGGINS, *op. cit.*, pp. 94, 120.

$$Fe + 2H_2O \xrightarrow{FeCl_2} Fe(OH)_2 + H_2$$

$$C_6H_5NO_2 + 3Fe + 4H_2O \xrightarrow{FeCl_2} C_6H_5NH_2 + 3Fe(OH)_2$$

$$C_6H_5NH_2 + H_2O \rightarrow C_6H_5NH_3OH \rightarrow C_6H_5NH_3^+ + OH^-$$

$$FeCl_2 \rightarrow Fe^{++} + 2Cl^-$$

$$2C_6H_5NH_3^+ + 2OH^- + Fe^{++} + 2Cl^- \rightarrow 2C_6H_5NH_3Cl + Fe(OH)_2$$

$$C_6H_5NH_3Cl \rightarrow C_6H_5NH_3^+ + Cl^-$$

$$2C_6H_5NH_3^+ + 2Cl^- + 2Fe(OH)_2 + 2Fe \rightarrow 2C_6H_5NH_2 + FeCl_2$$
$$+ Fe_3O_4 + 3H_2$$

Note that the iron ends up as the ferroso-ferric oxide. If too little iron is used, the analysis indicates a greater proportion of ferrous iron present, probably as ferrous hydroxide. In actually conducting this reduction on a technical and hence a large scale, it is easy to observe that the chemical change proceeds in stages, for instance, where hydrogen is evolved and when the iron swells owing to hydroxide formation. Such a breakdown into steps is frequently observed when running chemical reactions on a large scale. The iron used for reduction should be cast-iron turnings (or powdered iron) free from oil and nonferrous metals.

AMINATION BY REDUCTION AS UNIT PROCESS IN MANUFACTURE OF INTERMEDIATES

p-Amino-acetanilide (Acetyl-p-phenylene-diamine), from p-nitro-acetanilide by iron and acetic acid under 60°C.

α-Amino-anthraquinone, from α-nitro-anthraquinone by Na$_2$S solution; or by ammonolysis of α-anthraquinone-sulfonic acid

p-Amino-phenol, from nitroso-phenol by aqueous Na$_2$S; or from p-nitro-phenol from p-nitro-chloro-benzene

o-Amino-phenol-p-sulfonic acid, from o-nitro-phenol-p-sulfonic acid by Na$_2$S following sulfonation, nitration, and hydrolysis of chloro-benzene

Aniline, from nitro-benzene by iron and a little dilute HCl

Chloro-toluidine-sulfonic acids, from chloro-toluene-sulfonic acids by nitration and subsequent iron reduction[1]

Diamino-stilbene-disulfonic acid, from dinitro-stilbene-disulfonate by alkaline zinc reduction

Diamino-anthraquinone, from corresponding dinitro- or aminonitro-anthraquinone by reduction, or from corresponding dichloro-, disulfo-, or dihydroxy-anthraquinone by ammonolysis

2,5-Dichloro-aniline and sulfonic acid, from 1,4-dichloro-2-nitro-benzene by iron and a little aqueous HCl. Sulfonation

Dianisidine by rearrangement of hydrazoanisole, from o-nitro-anisole by alkaline zinc reduction in alcoholic solution, followed by acid rearrangement

Benzidine by rearrangement of hydrazobenzene, from nitro-benzene by alkaline reduction by Fe or Zn, followed by acid rearrangement

Tolidine by rearrangement of hydrazotoluene, from o-nitro-toluene by alkaline reduction by Zn followed by acid rearrangement

[1] For chloro-toluidine-sulfonic acids, cf. VENKATARAMAN, "The Chemistry of Synthetic Dyes," p. 175, 2 vols., Academic Press, Inc., New York, 1952.

Metanilic acid, from nitro-benzene-*m*-sulfonic acid, following oleum sulfonation of nitro-benzene

α-Naphthylamine, from α-nitro-naphthalene by iron and a little dilute HCl

m-Nitro-aniline, from dinitro-benzene by hot aqueous sodium polysulfide

m-Phenylenediamine, from dinitro-benzene by iron and a little dilute HCl

n-Phenylenediamine, from *p*-nitro-aniline by iron and a little dilute HCl, boiling at the end

Picramic acid, from picric acid by hot sodium polysulfide solution

Toluidines, from nitro-toluenes by iron and a little dilute HCl

m-Tolylenediamine (or Toluene-2,4-diamine), from 2,4-dinitro-toluene by iron and a little dilute HCl

Xylidines, from nitro-xylenes by iron and a little dilute HCl

Amination by Ammonolysis

This unit process has been used for a long time to make β-naphthylamine but its extension to aniline and *p*-nitro-aniline is fairly recent. It functions by reacting, usually at elevated temperatures and in autoclaves, with large excess of aqueous ammonia sometimes in the presence of sulfites (Bucherer[1] reaction). With the present low cost of ammonia this method of amination has a much more favorable position. The *agent* used is ammonia or a substituted ammonia which replaces a number of different groups: —Cl, —OH, or —SO₃H. This unit process is particularly useful when *labilizing* groups are present in the ortho or para positions in respect to the halogen as in the following ammonolysis reactions:

$$Cl_2C_6H_3NO_2 \xrightarrow{\text{NH}_3 \text{ (aqua)}} ClNO_2C_6H_3NH_2$$

1,4-Dichloro-2-nitro-benzene   4-Chloro-2-nitro-aniline

$$Cl_2C_6H_4NO_2 \xrightarrow{\text{NH}_3 \text{ (aqua)}} NH_2C_6H_4NH_2$$

1-Chloro-4-nitro-benzene   *p*-Nitro-aniline

The ammonia is used as aqua-ammonia in large excess, four to ten times theory. Frequently catalysts help speed up the chemical change. As such a large excess of ammonia is necessary for good yields, an efficient recovery system is required to keep costs low. Here then is an excellent example of the unit operation of distillation.

The *equipment* required to commercialize this unit process is almost always some type of agitated pressure vessel made out of ammonia-resisting metal, such as all iron even to the valves. Fortunately the all-iron valves, fittings, pumps, and other equipment previously developed for ammonia ice machines are available at low cost for amination by ammonolysis.[2]

Technical Example. *Aniline.* The reactions involved in the making of aniline through ammonolysis may be expressed as follows:

[1] VENKATARAMAN, *op. cit.*, pp. 80–81, 89.

[2] For all these unit processes, reference should be made to GROGGINS, *op. cit.*, in which are specific chapters covering the details of each unit process,

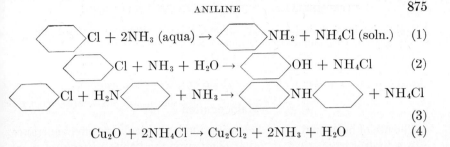

$$Cu_2O + 2NH_4Cl \rightarrow Cu_2Cl_2 + 2NH_3 + H_2O \qquad (4)$$

These reactions[1] are carried out using about 4 moles of aqueous 28 to 30 per cent ammonia, first at 180°C. and then for a few hours at 210 to 220°C. under constant agitation. The pressure rises to about 750 lb. Reaction (1) is the desired one, and with the 4 or 5 moles of 28 to 30 per cent NH_3 the formation of phenol [reaction (2)] is to aniline as 1:20. By the use of higher concentrations of ammonia this ratio can be reduced to 1:50, but this larger excess is too costly. The active catalyst is cuprous chloride but by introduction of cuprous oxide (about 1/10 mole) the cuprous chloride is formed and the disadvantageous concentration of NH_4Cl reduced simultaneously. Agitation is secured in a clever manner by the use of horizontal rotating autoclaves.[2] Conversion is about 90 per cent to aniline which can be raised by greatly prolonging the time of reaction, but this is uneconomical.

The products are recovered by blowing off the free ammonia through the recovery and condensing system and separating the oily layer from the aqueous one. The oily layer contains some ammonia, chloro-benzene, aniline, phenol, and diphenylamine, and these are separated by distillation, using normally an alkali, CaO, to hold back the phenol. The aqueous layer is treated with lime to liberate the ammonia and then distilled to recover ammonia and small amounts of chloro-benzene, aniline, and phenol. The copper compound is filtered off and used again. This process gives an excellent grade of aniline.

AMINATION BY AMMONOLYSIS IN MANUFACTURE OF INTERMEDIATES

β-Amino-anthraquinone, from chloro-anthraquinone by excess of 28 per cent aqueous ammonia at 200°C. in a stirred autoclave, or from β-anthraquinone-sulfonate by excess ammonia water

Aniline, from chloro-benzene by excess 28 per cent aqueous ammonia at 200°C. and 900 lb. pressure, in presence of Cu_2O

β-Naphthylamine, from β-naphthol by excess of 28 per cent ammonia aided by ammonium sulfite, at 150°C. in a stirred autoclave

2-Naphthylamine-1-sulfonic acid (Tobias acid) from 2-naphthol-1-sulfonic acid by excess ammonia water and ammonium sulfite at 150°C. in an autoclave

2-Naphthylamine-6-sulfonic acid (Broenner's acid), from sodium salt of 2-naphthol-6-sulfonic acid (Schaeffer's acid) by 28 per cent NH_3 at 180°C. in an autoclave

---

[1] Cf. GROGGINS, op. cit., p. 392.
[2] These are pictured in Chem. Inds., **46**, 690 (1940).

2-Naphthylamine-6, 8-disulfonic acid (amino-G acid) from 2-naphthol-6, 8-disulfonate by heating with ammonia and sodium bisulfite in an autoclave

p-Nitro-aniline from p-chloro-nitro-benzene by excess of 28 per cent aqueous ammonia at 170°C. and 500 lb. pressure

Phthalimide, from molten phthalic anhydride by gaseous NH_3 at 240°C.

Halogenation

The use of halogenation and chlorination in particular to effect entrance into a hydrocarbon ring, or other compound, and thus to make a more reactive derivative, is becoming of increasing importance in the field of intermediates as well as in all organic chemistry. The *agent* used is generally dried chlorine gas with or without a catalyst, though other agents like HCl may be necessary for a specific reaction. The chlorination proceeds (1) by *addition* to an unsaturated bond, (2) by *substitution* for hydrogen, or (3) by *replacement* of another group such as —OH or —SO_3H. Examples are

$$CH_2{=}CH_2 + HCl \xrightarrow{\text{Anhydrous}} CH_3CH_2Cl \tag{1}$$

$$C_6H_6 + Cl_2 \xrightarrow[\text{Anhydrous}]{FeCl_3} C_6H_5Cl + HCl \tag{2}$$

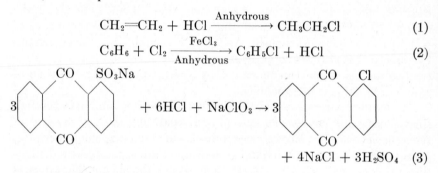

$$+ 4NaCl + 3H_2SO_4 \tag{3}$$

Reaction (3) proceeds in hot dilute aqueous solution. In certain of halogenation reactions much *heat* is liberated and must be removed (*cf.* chloro-benzene).

The *equipment* necessary is much simplified if anhydrous conditions are called for, as frequently happens. Under these circumstances steel is very satisfactory unless iron and iron compounds exert a disadvantageous effect, when enameled steel or earthenware is used. Nickel is also employed in some special cases.

Technical Example. *Chloro-benzene* is a very important intermediate particularly for sulfur colors. It is also employed as a solvent and to make many other products such as aniline, phenol, chloro-nitro-benzene and chloro-dinitro-benzene, and *o*-aminophenol-*p*-sulfonic acid. Table 4 indicates production of 184,000 tons in 1954.

Chloro-benzene is manufactured by passing dry chlorine through benzene in iron or lead-lined iron vessels, using ferric chloride as a catalyst. The reaction is as follows:

$$C_6H_6 + Cl_2 \xrightarrow{FeCl_3} C_6H_5Cl + HCl$$

The reaction rate of monochlorination is approximately 8.5 times[1] that of dichlorination, so some dichloro-benzene is always formed. Much heat is generated and, if monochloro-benzene is the preferred product, the temperature should be kept at not over 40 to 60°C., by circulating and cooling the benzene–chloro-benzene mixture. The hydrochloric acid escaping is washed free of chlorine by benzene and absorbed in water for sale. The products of chlorination are distilled to separate the benzene and chloro-benzene, leaving the dichloro-benzenes (ortho and para) in the still residue.

HALOGENATION AS A UNIT PROCESS IN MANUFACTURE OF INTERMEDIATES

Chloro-acetic acid, from glacial acetic acid by passing in chlorine at 100°C. in presence of red phosphorus

Chloro-benzene, from benzene by action of Cl_2 in presence of iron at 50–60°C.

p-Dichloro-benzene, from benzene or chloro-benzene by action of Cl_2 in presence of iron at 50–60°C.

2,6-Dichloro-benzaldehyde, from o-nitro-toluene through ring chlorination by Cl_2 furnishing 2-chloro-6-nitro-toluene (40 per cent) and 4-chloro-6-nitro-toluene (60 per cent). These are separated and the 2,6-isomer is subjected to reduction, diazotization, and the Sandmeyer reaction giving 2,6-dichloro-toluene, which upon side-chain chlorination furnishes 2,6-dichloro-benzal chloride which hydrolyzes to 2,6-dichloro-benzaldehyde

Sulfonation

This is one of the most widely employed of the chemical changes to effect variation in properties such as to introduce greater solubility or to make a hydrocarbon more reactive for the purpose of further synthesis. The fundamental chemistry has been carefully studied[2] and many data are available in the literature. Frequently isomers are formed and the cost of a process will be high unless application can be found for the principal isomers produced. The *agents* employed are various strengths of SO_3 in water from 66°Bé. sulfuric acid or even weaker, to the strongest oleums. However, for special cases, sulfite and chloro-sulfonic acid are very useful. As in nitrations, care should be taken to avoid oxidations by not having temperatures or concentrations too high. Excessive concentrations also form sulfones.

The reaction may be expressed as follows:

$$R \cdot H + \begin{matrix} HO \\ HO \end{matrix} \!\!\!> SO_2 \rightarrow R \cdot SO_2 \cdot OH + H_2O$$

However, recent studies[3] indicate that an ion such as HO_3S^+ is the

[1] BOURION, *Compt. rend.*, **170**, 1309 (1920).

[2] See volumes by VENKATARAMAN, DAVIDSON, GROGGINS, REVERDIN and FULDA, SCHWALBE, and WICHELHAUS in the references at end of this chapter.

[3] GROGGINS, *op. cit.*, p. 313.

active sulfonating agent when sulfuric acid is used:

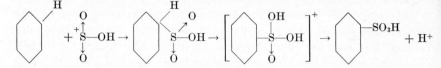

Depending on what product is being sulfonated there is a critical concentration of sulfuric acid below which sulfonation ceases.[1] Therefore, the removal of the water formed is important. The *energy* of the reaction is exothermic but its removal is often not required, since many sulfonations proceed best at elevated temperatures.

The *equipment*[2] for most sulfonations is fairly simple, consisting of cast-iron vessels provided with an efficient agitator, vent, condenser, and usually a jacket for heating by steam or circulating hot oil. The list on page 880 outlines some of the important industrial sulfonations.

Technical Examples. *Benzene-sulfonate* is a step in the manufacture of phenol by the sulfonation process. Improvements in this procedure have kept this process competitive with the making of phenol through chloro-benzene. The reaction is as follows:

$$\text{C}_6\text{H}_6 + \text{H}_2\text{SO}_4 \rightarrow \text{C}_6\text{H}_5\text{SO}_3\text{H} + \text{H}_2\text{O}$$

When the concentration of the sulfuric acid drops below 78 per cent H_2SO_4 (the rest being water), the sulfonating action ceases. At one time, sufficient strong sulfuric acid was used to absorb the water and keep up the concentration. This, however, was a costly procedure, not only wasting sulfuric acid but causing expensive separation of the benzene-sulfonic acid. At present, the water formed is removed by passing benzene vapor through the sulfonation product, thus removing the water by a reverse steam distillation. The ratio of benzene required may be calculated from the formula:[3]

Weight of benzene = weight of water $\times$

$$\frac{\text{molecular weight of benzene} \times \text{vapor pressure of benzene}}{\text{molecular weight of water} \times \text{vapor pressure of water}}$$

The vapor pressure of the benzene and the water (in presence of sulfuric

[1] *Ibid.*, pp. 302, 313, 320–324.

[2] SHREVE, Equipment for Nitration and Sulfonation, *Ind. Eng. Chem.*, **24**, 1344 (1932).

[3] Derived from Avogadro's law which states that, under the same conditions of temperature and pressure, equal volumes of perfect gases contain the same number of molecules. *Cf.* GROGGINS, "Aniline and Its Derivatives," p. 24.

acid) must be at that temperature at which the sum of the two vapor pressures equals the pressure on the system.[1]

When the water is removed from the sulfonation to keep the acid concentration above 78 per cent H_2SO_4, the sulfonation proceeds until only a few per cent of free sulfuric acid is present which is then directly neutralized to form the sodium salt in conformance with the flow sheet of Fig. 2. The rest of this flow sheet is commented upon under Hydrolysis (page 881).

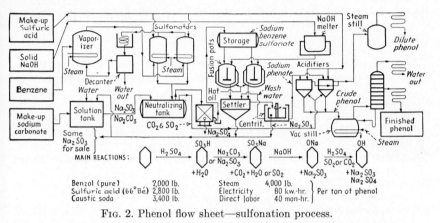

FIG. 2. Phenol flow sheet—sulfonation process.

The 1- and 2-*naphthalene-sulfonic acids* are formed simultaneously by the sulfonation of naphthalene. They must be separated if they are to be used for the preparation of pure naphthols. This is a difficult procedure. However, the alpha acid can be hydrolyzed[2] to naphthalene and this is distilled out by passing dry steam into the mixed sulfonation mass at around 160°C., leaving behind pure beta acid suitable for hydrolysis or fusion to make β-naphthol.

The usual sulfonation products[3] are more complicated to handle than those just cited, and are illustrated by the examples listed on page 880. The various sulfonic derivatives are frequently difficult to separate from their isomers. The following tabulation gives some of the properties employed for separations or isolations:

[1] Cf. TYRER, U.S. Pat. 1210725(1917); GUYOT, Chimie & industrie, 2, 879 (1919); ZAKHAROV, J. Chem. Ind., U.S.S.R., 6, 1648 (1929).

[2] SHREVE, β-Naphthol, Color Trade J., 14, 42 (1924); cf. MASTERS, U.S. Pat. 1922813(1933); GROGGINS, op. cit., pp. 271–273, 330, 691; 1-Naphthalene-sulfonic acid is the principal isomer formed when the sulfonation is carried out at around 60°C.

[3] For more details regarding sulfonation see the chapter under this heading in GROGGINS, op. cit., and the books in the Selected References by FIERZ-DAVID and BLANGEY, REVERDIN and FULDA, and WICHELHAUS. Also see ULLMANN, "Enzyklopaedie der technischen Chemie," 3d ed., Urban & Schwarzenberg, Berlin and Vienna, 1951.

1. Variation in the solubilities of the potassium salts.

2. Variation in the solubilities of the calcium or barium or metal salts.

3. Differences in the solubilities of the sulfonic acids themselves in water or acids or other media.

4. Differences in solubilities of the sodium sulfonic salts in presence of a sodium salt such as sodium chloride, sulfate, nitrate, or acetate.

5. Difference in properties of derivatives such as sulfonchlorides or amides.

SULFONATION UNIT PROCESS IN MANUFACTURE OF INTERMEDIATES

1-Amino-2-naphthol-4-sulfonic acid (1,2,4 acid), from 1-nitroso-2-naphthol by joint reducing and sulfonating action of sodium bisulfite

Benzene-sulfonic acid, by passing hot benzene vapor through sulfuric acid until all sulfuric acid reacted

β-Naphthalene-sulfonic acid, from naphthalene and 66°Bé. sulfuric acid at 160°C.; the α-isomer simultaneously formed is hydrolyzed to naphthalene and removed by passing in steam

Naphthionic acid, from α-naphthylamine sulfate by baking at 170–180°C.

2-Naphthol-6-sulfonic acid (Shaeffer's acid), from β-naphthol by 98 per cent sulfuric acid at 100°C., and separation from the 2:8 acid (Croceine acid) formed simultaneously

2-Naphthol-3,6-disulfonic acid (R acid), from β-naphthol by excess sulfuric acid at low temperatures and separation from G acid

2-Naphthol-6,8-disulfonic acid (G acid), from β-naphthol by excess sulfuric acid at elevated temperature and separation from R acid

1-Naphthylamine-5-sulfonic acid (Laurent's acid) and 1-naphthylamine-8-sulfonic acid from naphthalene by low-temperature sulfonation to the alpha acid, followed by nitration to the two isomers, reduction by iron, and separation

2-Naphthylamine-5,7-disulfonic acid, from β-naphthylamine by oleum sulfonation

2-Naphthylamine-6,8-disulfonic and 2-naphthylamine-5,7-disulfonic acids by sulfonation of β-naphthylamine, first with monohydrate followed by 60 per cent oleum. These acids are separated and fused with NaOH to give, respectively, gamma acid (NOS:286) and J acid (NOS:257)

1-Naphthylamine-3,6,8-trisulfonic acid (Koch acid), from naphthalene by trisulfonation with oleum, followed by nitration and iron reduction

p-Nitro-toluene-o-sulfonic acid, from p-nitro-toluene by oleum

Hydrolysis

In the manufacture of intermediates the phase of hydrolysis employed is usually alkaline fusion to replace an —SO_3H group by —OH. However, this unit process is also operated to replace —Cl, particularly in making phenol. The *agent* generally used is caustic soda, though other alkalies, acids, or plain water are of industrial importance. The reaction may be formulated as follows:

$$ArSO_3Na \text{ (or ArCl)} + 2NaOH \rightarrow ArONa + Na_2SO_3 + H_2O$$
$$\text{(or } NaCl + H_2O)$$

The *energy* involved is exothermic in many instances. In phenol from chloro-benzene, the heat evolved maintains the reaction temperature.

The *equipment* required is generally either open cast-iron fusion pots heated by gas or closed cast-iron or welded steel autoclaves. Especially in alkaline fusions some loss is experienced from oxidation to tars at the temperatures employed, 300 to 325°C.

Technical Examples. *Phenol* is manufactured[1] by the following reactions:

Sulfonation Process:

$$C_6H_5SO_3Na + 2NaOH \xrightarrow{300°C.} C_6H_5ONa + Na_2SO_3 + H_2O$$
$$C_6H_5ONa + CO_2 \text{ (or } SO_2) + H_2O \longrightarrow C_6H_5OH + NaHCO_3 \text{ (or}$$
$$NaHSO_3)$$

Chloro-benzene Process (Liquid Phase):

$$C_6H_5Cl + 2NaOH \xrightarrow{360°C.} C_6H_5ONa + NaCl + H_2O$$
$$C_6H_5ONa + HCl \longrightarrow C_6H_5OH + NaCl$$
$$2C_6H_5OH \rightleftharpoons C_6H_5OC_6H_5 + H_2O$$

Catalytic Vapor Phase (or Regenerative Process):

$$C_6H_6 + HCl + \tfrac{1}{2}O_2 \xrightarrow{230°C.} C_6H_5Cl + H_2O \text{ (exothermic)}$$

$$C_6H_5Cl + HOH \xrightarrow{425°C.} C_6H_5OH + HCl \text{ (endothermic)}$$

The older or sulfonation process has held its own competitively, largely because of improvements in procedure such as described under Sulfonation (page 879). Figure 2 outlines the technical steps. It should be noted that either Na_2CO_3 or Na_2SO_3 is used to make the $C_6H_5SO_3Na$, and that either the CO_2 or SO_2 is employed in the acidifiers to liberate or "spring" the phenol. Generally a little diluted H_2SO_4 is necessary to finish the acidification. The fusion is frequently carried out in open cast-iron fusion pots or those with sheet-iron removable covers.

The chloro-benzene hydrolysis[2] proceeds according to Fig. 3 by pumping a mixture of chloro-benzene and dilute caustic soda through a steel pipe heat exchanger, a reactor, and then through the heat exchanger for cooling. The reactor temperature is about 360°C. and the pressure 5,000 lb. per sq. in. The heat of reaction after the initial start is sufficient to maintain the desired temperature by the use of an efficient heat exchanger. This process affords an excellent application of the unit operations of high pressure, pumping, and heat transfer at high pressure.

[1] See Oxidation for the new cumene hydroperoxide process.
[2] HALE and BRITTON, Development of Synthetic Phenol from Benzene Halides, *Ind. Eng. Chem.*, **20**, 114 (1928); HALE and BRITTON, U.S. Pat. 1607618(1926); BRITTON, U.S. Pat. 1824867(1937); GRISWOLD, U.S. Pat. 1833485(1931); BRITTON, U.S. Pat. 1959283(1934); GROGGINS, *op. cit.*, pp. 693–701.

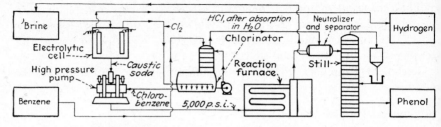

Note · Small quantities of copper and sodium oleate are used as catalysts

Caustic Soda 120 lb. ⎫ To produce 100 lb. Phenol
Chlorobenzene 132 lb. ⎭ and some Diphenyl oxide*

*If no D.P.O. is desired, add 0.1 mole with reactants

FIG. 3. Phenol flow sheet—chloro-benzene process.

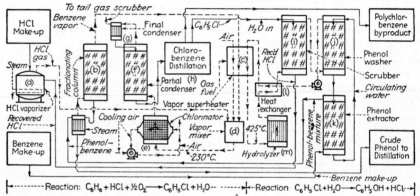

⊢--------Reaction: C₆H₆ + HCl + ½O₂──►C₆H₅Cl + H₂O-- ------⊣⊢--Reaction C₆H₅Cl + H₂O──►C₆H₅OH + HCl--⊣

Solid lines represent liquids, dashed lines, vapors and gases. HCl gas from (a) plus benzene vapor from column (b) and air are heated in vapor superheater (c) and mixed in (d), then passed through air-cooled chlorinator (e) (Cu-Fe catalyst). The resulting chlorobenzene mixture is condensed in (f) and (g) (and benzene recovered in the tail gas scrubber), distilled in (h) and the C₆H₅Cl sent, with make-up water, to scrubber (i) where the mixture extracts the phenol from the hydrolysis step and recovers HCl for return to (a). The vapor mixture of C₆H₅Cl, C₆H₅OH and H₂O from (i) passes to washer (j) where the phenol is extracted in water, flowing to extractor (k), and a mixture of C₆H₅Cl and H₂O is vaporized for hydrolysis. The phenol in the water solution is extracted in make-up benzene in (k), the water recirculating to (j) and the benzene-phenol mixture flowing to fractionating column (b) for separation of the crude phenol. The C₆H₅Cl and H₂O vapor from (j) pass through heat exchanger (l), vapor superheater (c), and hydrolyzer (m) (SiO₂ catalyst) for conversion to C₆H₅OH, the product returning through exchanger (l) to scrubber (i), thus completing the cycle.

FIG. 4. Phenol flow sheet—vapor-phase regenerative process.

In order to repress the accumulation of diphenyloxide, about 1/10 mole is added with the reactants.

The regenerative or catalytic vapor-phase process is based on the patents assigned to Raschig.[1] This procedure has been described and pictured in the literature.[2] It presents some very interesting engineering problems, particularly as to the handling of hot HCl in the presence of steam and air.

[1] RASCHIG, U.S. Pats. 1963761, 2009023, and 2035917 (1935).

[2] ANON., New Synthetic Phenol Plant, Ind. Eng. Chem., News Ed., 18, 921 (1940); OLIVE, Chem. & Met. Eng., 47, 770 (1940); 47, 789, pictured flow sheet; 46, 222 (1939); GROGGINS, op. cit., pp. 697–700, detailed description.

The conversions are low and require much recirculation. Figure 4 shows the sequences of unit operations and unit processes that represent the commercialization of the basic chemical changes.

TABLE 5. PHENOL PRODUCTION, SYNTHETIC AND NATURAL[a]

Year	Thousand lb.	Year	Thousand lb.
1941	115,047	1948	297,338
1942	146,125	1949	224,544
1943	194,967	1950	312,107
1944	202,000	1951	338,429
1945	205,100	1952	337,761
1946	203,829	1953	382,433
1947	265,269	1954	417,503

[a] "Synthetic Organic Chemicals," U.S. Tariff Commission. In 1953, 25,596,000 lb. were natural phenol, from coal tar, and petroleum.

Phenol is used for a great variety of products: dyes, plastics, explosives, medicines, and perfumes. Its economic position is shown by the production figures of Table 5.

β-Naphthol is made somewhat similarly to the phenol sulfonation process. The conditions for the hydrolysis (alkali fusion) of the 2-naphthalenesulfonate are given in the references under Sulfonation.

HYDROLYSIS (OR IN MANY INSTANCES "ALKALI FUSION") IN MANUFACTURE OF INTERMEDIATES

1-Amino-8-naphthol-3,6-disulfonic acid (H acid), from 1-naphthylamine-3,6,8-trisulfonic acid by caustic-soda fusion in an autoclave

2-Amino-5-naphthol-7-sulfonic acid (J acid), from 2-naphthylamine-5,7-disulfonic acid by caustic-soda fusion in an autoclave

2-Amino-8-naphthol-6-sulfonic acid (gamma acid), from 2-naphthylamine-6,8-disulfonic acid by caustic-soda fusion in an autoclave

1,5-Dihydroxyanthraquinone (anthrarufin), from anthraquinone-1,5-disulfonic acid by milk of lime under pressure

1,8-Dihydroxynaphthalene-3,6-disulfonic acid (chromotropic acid), from 1-naphthol-3,6,8-trisulfonic acid by caustic-soda fusion at 200°C.

2,4-Dinitro-phenol, from chloro-2,4-dinitro-benzene by boiling with soda-ash solution

β-Naphthol, from purified β-naphthalenesulfonate (naphthalene and hot sulfuric acid) by caustic-soda fusion

α-Naphthol, from purified α-naphthalenesulfonate (naphthalene and cold sulfuric acid) by caustic-soda fusion, or from α-naphthylamine

1-Naphthol-4-sulfonic acid (Nevile-Winther's acid) from sodium naphthionate by heating with NH_4HSO_3 (Bucherer reaction)

p-Nitro-aniline, from p-nitro-acetanilide, by boiling with caustic-soda solution

o- or p-Nitro-phenol, from o- or p-chloro-nitro-benzene by hot dilute NaOH solution

Phenol from benzene-sulfonate by caustic-soda fusion at 320°C.

Phenol from chloro-benzene by caustic-soda solution at 360°C., 5,000 lb. pressure

Phenol from chloro-benzene by H_2O at 425°C.

Oxidation

Oxidation is controlled or tempered combustion and is one of the very useful unit processes for the entire organic technology. The cheapest *agent* is air, but oxygen is sometimes employed. For liquid-phase reactions a great many oxidizing agents are in industrial use, such as nitric acid permanganates, pyrolusite dichromates, chromic anhydrides, hypochlorites, chlorates, lead peroxide, and hydrogen peroxide. Water and carbon dioxide and many other oxidized substances are the by-products of the main oxidation.

When charcoal or carbon (amorphous) changes to carbon dioxide, $\Delta H = -96{,}500$ cal.[1] per g.-mole and when hydrogen burns to H_2O (gaseous), $\Delta H = -57{,}800$ cal. per g.-mole. These *energy changes*, although the basis of combustion, frequently accompany our controlled oxidation, as in the making of phthalic anhydride (page 885) and maleic acid. In most oxidations, even when the formation of CO_2 and H_2O can be repressed, the energy change is exothermic and large. This entails particular care in the design and construction of the *equipment* so as to ensure efficient heat transfer and to prevent the controlled oxidation from becoming a combustion.

Technical Example. *Phthalic anhydride* has become one of our most important intermediates. It is used in making directly a number of dyes such as eosin, rhodamines, erythrosin, quinoline yellow, copper phthalocyanine, and phenolphthalein, but it is of more value as a step in manufacturing anthraquinone and anthraquinone derivatives by condensation (Friedel-Crafts) procedure (page 890), where it has opened up the entire anthraquinone vat dyes to the American market at reasonable prices. Figure 5 presents the production and price trends. These products are consumed also in industries other than dyes, as in making resins and plasticizers. Phthalic anhydride and phenol are two among many intermediates whose consumption has expanded far beyond dyes.

The present process for phthalic anhydride[2] is a controlled catalytic air oxidation of naphthalene.

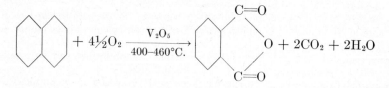

[1] For carbon, the equivalent in B.t.u. per pound = 14,400; for hydrogen, 52,000 B.t.u. from 1 lb.

[2] Downs, Oxidation of Aromatic Hydrocarbons, *Ind. Eng. Chem.*, **32**, 1294 (1940), bibliography; Conover, Economics of Catalytic Oxidation in the Vapor Phase, *Ind. Eng. Chem.*, **32**, 1298 (1940), flow sheet; Anon., *Petroleum Refiner*, **32** (10), 162–163 (1953).

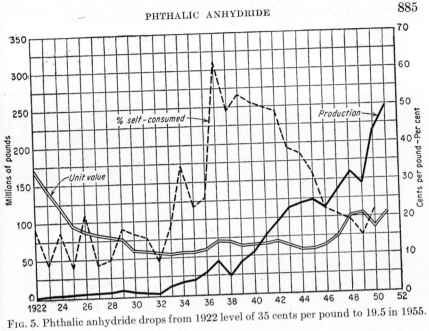

FIG. 5. Phthalic anhydride drops from 1922 level of 35 cents per pound to 19.5 in 1955.

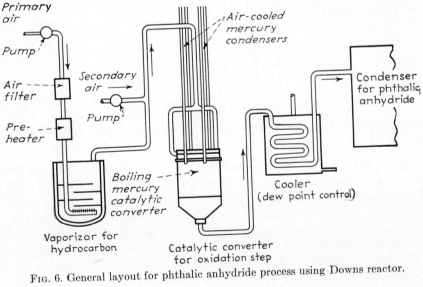

FIG. 6. General layout for phthalic anhydride process using Downs reactor.

Here $\Delta H = -5,460$ B.t.u. per lb. naphthalene oxidized. If naphthalene is burned completely to CO_2 and H_2O, 18,000 B.t.u. per lb. of naphthalene are liberated. Actually, when manufacturing phthalic anhydride by this process, an exothermic reaction of from 6,000 to more than 10,000 B.t.u. per lb. of naphthalene is observed, owing to a certain amount of complete combustion that always occurs.

This process, with a suitable catalyst, was discovered by Gibbs and Conover.[1] It was also necessary to work out efficient equipment to remove the great amount of heat liberated and to keep the temperature within the favorable narrow limits. One of the successful devices is that patented by Downs[2] and depicted in principle in Figs. 6 and 7. It consists of square tubes (to increase surface in relation to volume) carrying the V_2O_5 catalyst, surrounded by mercury. This mercury by its boiling

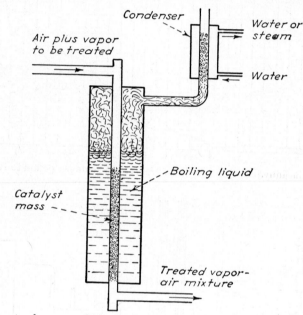

Fig. 7. Apparatus for removal of reaction heat by boiling of a liquid. (*After Marek and Hahn.*)

removes the heat of reaction, and the hot mercury vapor preheats the entering naphthalene vapor and then passes on to the condenser. In the Downs reactor the temperature is nicely controlled by raising or lowering the boiling point of mercury by the raising and lowering of the pressure of an inert gas (nitrogen) on the mercury boiling and condensing system. Other heat-transfer media have been proposed, such as sulfur, diphenyl, diphenyl oxide, mercury amalgams, and mixed nitrate-nitrite.[3] The products from the reaction are rapidly cooled to about 125°C. (approximately the dew point of phthalic anhydride) and are then sublimed[4] into

[1] U.S. Pat. 1285217(1918).

[2] U.S. Pat. 1604739(1926). Also Downs, U.S. Pats. 1374020, 1373021(1921); 1789809(1931); and 1873876(1932).

[3] Kirst, Nagle, and Castner, A New Heat Transfer Medium for High Temperatures, *Trans. Am. Inst. Chem. Engrs.*, **36**, 371 (1940).

[4] *Cf.* Perry, *op. cit.*, pp. 1474–1476.

large chambers or towers in which the phthalic anhydride condenses in needle crystals. The contact time is 0.6 sec.

Phenol is also being made by *oxidizing* cumene[1] as shown in the following reactions:

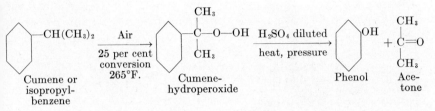

Cumene or isopropyl-benzene → Air, 25 per cent conversion 265°F. → Cumene-hydroperoxide → H_2SO_4 diluted, heat, pressure → Phenol + Acetone

OXIDATION UNIT PROCESS IN MANUFACTURE OF INTERMEDIATES

Anthranilic acid, from phthalimide by alkaline hypochlorite

Anthraquinone, from anthracene by chromic acid

1,4-Dihydroxy-anthraquinone (quinizarin), from anthraquinone by sulfuric acid oxidation in presence of boric acid

Dinitro-stilbene-disulfonic acid, from *p*-nitro-toluene by sulfonation and alkaline NaOCl oxidation

Phthalic anhydride, from naphthalene by air oxidation at 425°C. in presence of vanadium pentoxide

Dihydroxy-dibenzanthrone from dibenzanthrone by MnO_2 in concentrated H_2SO_4 (anthraquinone vat dyes)

Alkylation

Although alkylation of a hydroxyl is used occasionally in the dye field to reduce solubility of phenol derivatives, its most extensive application in commercial dyes is that of producing, with oxygen alkylated products, dyeings that do not change their shade when exposed to dilute alkalies or acids. An outstanding example is the conversion of dihydroxy-dibenzanthrone to anthraquinone Vat Jade Green (C.I. 1101) by alkylation[2] with dimethyl sulfate or the methyl ester of β-toluene-sulfonic acid. Alkylation is also used in alkylating amines. The *agents*[3] employed are exceedingly varied but an alcohol such as methanol, or an alkyl halide, or a dialkyl sulfate or the methyl ester of *p*-toluene-sulfonic acid is frequently employed.

The *equipment* used quite often requires pressure to keep the reactants in the desired liquid state. Such an autoclave is depicted in Fig. 8. For autoclaves of small size, jackets are frequently convenient for heating; in the larger sizes an interior coil, such as shown in this figure, enables more heating surface to be available than would be possible from a jacket.

---

[1] ANON., Phenol from Cumene, *Petroleum Refiner*, **32** (11), 154 (1953); "Petrochemical Process Handbook," p. 154, Gulf Publishing Co., Houston, Tex., flow sheet and description.

[2] VENKATARAMAN, *op. cit.*, p. 969; see footnote, p. 873.

[3] See GROGGINS, *op. cit.*, pp. 796ff., on Alkylation by Shreve.

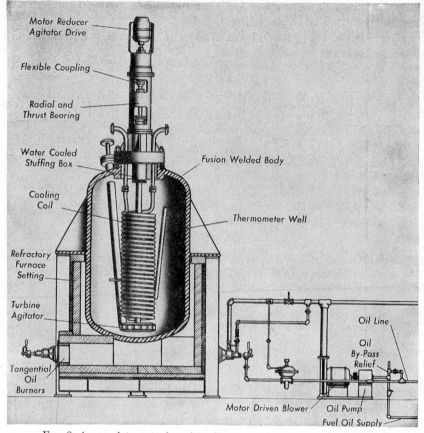

FIG. 8. A complete autoclave installation engineered by Blaw-Knox.

Furthermore, it is advantageous to have the corrosion concentrated on the more easily replaceable coil than on the more expensive shell.

Technical Example. *Dimethyl-aniline* is employed extensively in the manufacture of a number of triarylmethane dyes. It is prepared according to the following reaction:

$$C_6H_5NH_2 + 2CH_3OH \xrightarrow{H_2SO_4} C_6H_5N(CH_3)_2 + 2H_2O$$

Aniline, with a considerable excess of methanol and a little sulfuric acid, is heated in an autoclave, such as shown in Fig. 8, at around 200°C. for 5 or 6 hr., the pressure rising to 525 or 550 lb. The product can be tested by noting any rise in temperature when mixed with acetic anhydride, to ascertain if any monomethylaniline is still present. If monomethyl is low or absent, the alkylation product can be discharged under its own pressure through a cooling coil, neutralized, and vacuum-distilled.

FIG. 9. Dyestuffs intermediate still, showing gage and chart controls, at the dye works of E. I. du Pont de Nemours and Co., Deepwater Point, N. J. (*Courtesy of Du Pont.*)

ALKYLATION UNIT PROCESS IN MANUFACTURE OF INTERMEDIATES

Benzyl-ethyl-aniline (and sulfonic acid), from ethyl-aniline and benzyl chloride

Diethyl-aniline, from aniline, ethyl alcohol, and a little HCl in an autoclave, or from aniline and diethyl sulfate

Dimethyl-aniline, from aniline, methanol, and a little sulfuric acid at 200°C. in an autoclave

o-Nitro-anisole, from o-chloro-nitro-benzene by methanol and caustic soda

Condensation and Addition Reactions (Friedel-Crafts)

The list on the next page gives only a few products that are manufactured in any considerable tonnage, but these unit processes are used in the making of a great many different chemicals. Three of the intermediates listed in the table are, however, the basis of some of our most useful vat dyes. The *agent* employed in this reaction is usually an acid anhydride or an acid chloride, catalyzed by aluminum chloride. Typical examples involve the making of p-chloro-benzoyl-benzoic acid and β-chloro-anthraquinone according to the following reactions:

Addition to Furnish p-Chloro-benzoyl-benzoic Acid:

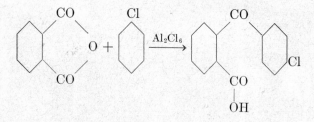

Condensation or Ring Closure to Furnish β-Chloro-anthraquinone:

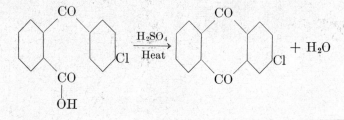

Typical *equipment* necessary to carry out these reactions and that of the following ring closure is sketched in Fig. 14, page 919, where are listed the approximate conditions and proportions. The industrial significance of these reactions coupled with the ring closure to make anthraquinone or anthraquinone derivatives as the basis for the fast vat dyes for cotton cannot be overestimated. Without these processes the manufacture of vat dyes would be much more costly, as the American tar distillers do not produce cheap anthracene.

ADDITION AND CONDENSATION UNIT PROCESSES IN MANUFACTURE OF INTERMEDIATES

Benzanthrone, from naphthalene, benzoyl chloride, and AlCl₃ to α-benzoyl-naphthalene to benzanthrone (benzanthrone is also condensed from anthranol and glycerine by aid of sulfuric acid—preferred commercial procedure)

Benzoylbenzoic acid, from phthalic anhydride, benzene, and aluminum chloride

p-Chloro-benzoylbenzoic acid, from phthalic anhydride, chloro-benzene, and aluminum chloride

p-Methyl-benzoylbenzoic acid (for 2-methyl-anthraquinone), from phthalic anhydride, toluene, and aluminum chloride

3-Hydroxy-2-naphthoic acid anilide, from 3-hydroxy-2-naphthoic acid and aniline

Phenyl-glycine, from aniline and chloro-acetic acid

Phenyl-1-naphthylamine-8-sulfonic acid, from 1-naphthylamine-8-sulfonic acid, aniline, and aniline hydrochloride by heating in an autoclave

Tetramethyldiamino-benzophenone (Michler's ketone), from dimethyl-aniline (2 moles) and phosgene

Tetramethyldiamino-diphenylmethane, from dimethyl-aniline (2 moles) and formaldehyde in presence of hydrochloric acid

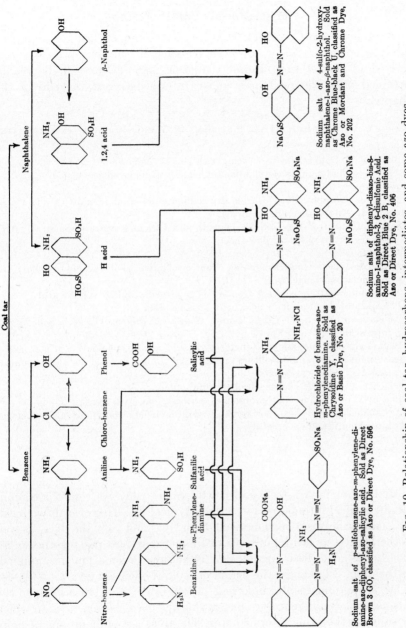

FIG. 10. Relationship of coal tar, hydrocarbons, intermediates, and some azo dyes.

891

Miscellaneous Unit Processes

The following list presents, in outline, a selection of the most important intermediates that have not been included in the unit processes considered in this section. Details on their manufacture can be readily obtained from the references under Intermediates at the end of this chapter.

VARIOUS MISCELLANEOUS UNIT PROCESSES IN MANUFACTURE OF INTERMEDIATES

Acylation:
   Acetanilide, from aniline by heating with glacial acetic acid
   Acetyl-*p*-toluidine, from *p*-toluidine by heating with glacial acetic acid
Carboxylation:
   3-Hydroxy-2-naphthoic acid, from dry sodium β-naphtholate and CO_2 under pressure at 200°C. (see Salicylic Acid)
   Salicylic acid, from dry sodium phenate and CO_2 under pressure and at 140°C. See Fig. 8, Chap. 39 for flow sheet
Miscellaneous:
   Aminoazo-toluene (and sulfonate), from *o*-toluidine to diazoamino-toluene, and molecular rearrangement
   Anthraquinone (ring closure), from *o*-benzoylbenzoic acid by sulfuric acid
   Benzoic acid, from phthalic acid by decarboxylation
   2-Chloro-anthraquinone (ring closure), from *p*-chloro-benzoylbenzoic acid by sulfuric acid
   Phenyl-glycine from aniline, formaldehyde, and sodium cyanide[1]
   Anthrimides from amino-anthraquinones containing halogen in alpha position (anthraquinone vat dyes)
   Dibenzanthrone from benzanthrone (anthraquinone vat dyes)
   Benzoylation of amino-anthraquinones (anthraquinone vat dyes)
   Arylamination of chloro- (or bromo-) anthraquinones containing alpha halogen atoms (anthraquinone vat dyes)

DYES

Many of us have a feeling of bewilderment when we view the complicated chemical formula representing a typical dye. However, if we recall the analogy between our houses and our dyes and view the dyes, as well as the houses, as being built out of simpler materials put together in an orderly fashion, these complicated structures become much simplified. As the architect changes the period or style of a house by varying the use of the same fundamental materials, wood, brick, stone, and steel, so the chemist makes different dyes by varying the chemical reactions to which he subjects the same intermediates. The dyes are built up out of more than 500 intermediates by a dozen or so important unit processes that unite one or more of these intermediates into a new chemical individual which, if it has the right structure, becomes a dye.

[1] VENKATARAMAN, *op. cit.*, p. 1014.

Figures 10 to 12 present a tabular outline of the sequences in the procedures from the basic coal-tar hydrocarbons through the intermediates to a number of characteristic dyes, all by subjecting first the hydrocarbons and then the intermediates to the chemical changes (unit processes when commercially applied). This chapter includes a number of typical intermediates and dyes, and in their presentation the chemical changes necessary for their fabrication are given.[1] Attention is called to the names of the dyes in Figs. 10 to 12 as being both chemical and the most used commercial designations. The dyes are classified both chemically (by structure) and by application (by use).

Cause of Color. A certain amount of unsaturation in the dye molecule with part of it at least in the form of aromatic rings combined with the quinoid structure of a minimum complexity usually lays the foundation of the molecules that we recognize as dyes. Much has been correlated between chemical structure and color,[2] and the earlier conceptions promulgated by the dye chemists in this field are still helpful. We may write the equation

$$\text{Dye} = \text{chromogen} + \text{auxochrome}$$

The *chromogen* is an aromatic body containing a group called a *chromophore*. By derivation, chromophore means *color-giver* and is represented by such chemical radicals as the following:

1. The nitroso group: —NO (or =N—OH)
2. The nitro group: —NO₂ (or =NO·OH)
3. The azo group: —N=N—
4. The ethylene group: >C=C<
5. The carbonyl group: >C=O
6. The carbon-nitrogen groups: >C=NH and —CH=N—
7. The sulfur groups: >C=S and >C—S—S—C<

---

[1] From the selected references at the end of this chapter further details can be obtained, particularly for the intermediates from the volumes by GROGGINS, DAVIDSON, or CAIN, and for the dyes from the books by VENKATARAMAN, LUBS, ROWE, SCHULTZ, and GEORGIEVICS. NOTE: When this book is used as a college text, an excellent assignment would be to have the students fill in the necessary chemical changes in Figs. 10 to 12. "C.I." followed by a number refers to ROWE, "Color Index and Supplement," Society of Dyers and Colourists, Bradford, Yorkshire, 1924, 1928; here dyes are numbered serially.

[2] WATSON, "Colour and Its Relation to Chemical Constitution," Longmans, Green & Co., Inc., New York, 1918. For the various theories of color see the introduction to GEORGIEVICS and GRANDMOUGIN, "A Textbook of Dye Chemistry," Scott, Greenwood and Son, London, 1920; and Chap. 8 of VENKATARAMAN (many references); KIRK and OTHMER, *op. cit.*, Vol. 4.

Such groups add color to the simpler aromatic bodies by causing displacement of, or an appearance of, absorbent bands in the visible spectrum. These chromophores are so important that we chemically classify many of our dyes by the chief chromophore that they contain. These chromophore groups are capable of reduction and, if this is carried out, the color frequently disappears, probably owing to the removal of electron resonance. Close packing of unsaturation, as conjugation, also tends toward color. Thus even the hydrocarbon dimethylfulvene:

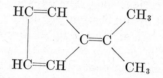

has an orange color. Although it may be colored, a chromogen may lack the chemical affinities necessary to make the color adhere to the textile fiber. Thus assistant groups, or *auxochromes*, are needed, which are usually salt-forming groups such as —NH$_2$, —OH, their derivatives, or the solubilizing radicals —COOH or —SO$_3$H. These auxochromes, chromophores, and chromogens will be very apparent by following the classification of dyes, but the assisting radicals such as —OH, —NH$_2$, —SO$_3$H, and —COOH have usually more influence on placing a dye in a given use group directed toward dyeing a certain fiber, rather than in a chemical structural classification.

None of these color theories fully satisfies all the facts, but the above have been exceedingly useful in working out new dyes and giving some understanding of the entire color picture. Probably resonating energy is of great importance in explaining why chromophores, auxochromes, and unsaturation cause color. See references on bottom page 893 for adequate treatment of color theories.

Testing of Dyes. In the use of dyes it is of the utmost importance to know such properties as fastness, solubility, and method of dyeing.[1] There are various types of fastness for dyes, all relative to one another. It is essential to know, in properly evaluating and applying a dye, its fastness not only to light and washing but also to bleaching, perspiration, acids, and alkalies, rubbing, sea water, and carbonizing. American-made dyes are as fast as any others in the world, being the same chemical compounds here as abroad.

Classification of Dyes. Dyes are classified from both the chemical and the application viewpoints. The manufacturers look at dyes from

---

[1] The books herein referred to, particularly those by ROWE ("Colour Index and Supplement,") and by KNECHT, RAWSON, and LOWENTHAL give such properties. However, the yearbooks of the American Association of Textile Chemists and Colorists present each year the latest methods for testing fastness of dyes together with recent references to the literature.

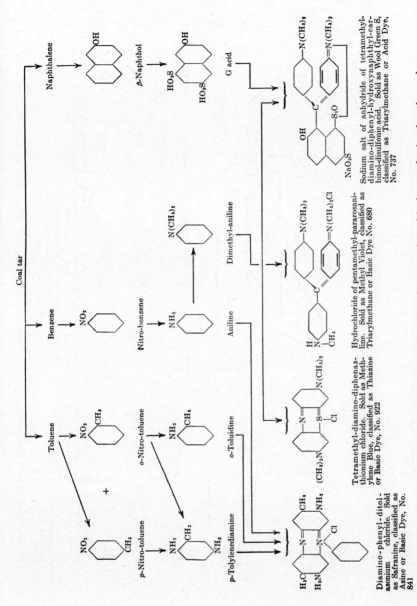

FIG. 11. Relationship of coal tar, hydrocarbons, and some azine, thiazine, and triarylmethane dyes.

895

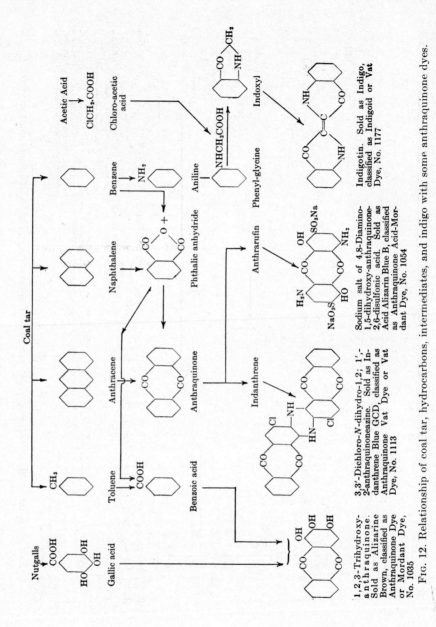

FIG. 12. Relationship of coal tar, hydrocarbons, intermediates, and indigo with some anthraquinone dyes.

1,2,3'-Trihydroxy-anthraquinone. Sold as Alizarine Brown, classified as Anthraquinone Dye or Mordant Dye, No. 1035

3,3'-Dichloro-N-dihydro-1,2; 1',2'anthraquinoneazine. Sold as Indanthrene Blue GCD, classified as Anthraquinone Vat Dye or Vat Dye, No. 1113

Sodium salt of 4,8-Diamino-1,5-dihydroxy-anthraquinone-2,6-disulfonic acid. Sold as Acid Alizarin Blue B, classified as Anthraquinone Acid-Mordant Dye, No. 1054

Indigotin. Sold as Indigo, classified as Indigoid or Vat Dye, No. 1177

the *chemical* aspect and arrange and manufacture them in groups usually of like unit processes; this frequently brings similar chromophores together. Thus, dyes that contain the azo chromophore are found manufactured in a building that may be called the *azo building*. On the other hand, a similarity in grouping of those that contain the indigoid radical is found. This very largely parallels the modern unit process way of classifying and looking at applied organic reactions. Not only do the factories arrange dyes in this way but the books presenting the properties of dyes so classify them, among which we may particularly cite the volumes by Schultz and by Rowe.[1]

In this chapter the various dyes are presented under this chemical classification. On the other hand, the users of dyes group them according to the methods of *application*. A dyer engaged in coloring silk is particularly interested in the type of dye that gives good results on this fiber and not specially in dyes that color cotton only. We do not always have this sharp differentiation in application; indeed, we have certain dyes that are union dyes and will color more than one fiber. There are three broad divisions that we wish to color: those products of vegetable origin, those from animals, and those made artificially. Cotton, linen, and paper are of a vegetable nature and essentially consist of cellulose. On the other hand, the products of animal origin that we wish to dye are much more reactive and consist of such substances as silk, wool, feathers, fur, and leather. The artificial fibers consist principally of nylon,[2] Dacron, Orlon, dynel, Acrilan, and of viscose rayon which latter dyes quite similarly to cotton, it being also essentially cellulose, and acetate rayon which is an ester and requires special dyes. The following are the main types of dyes in our *application* classification:

Acetate rayon	Lake or pigment	Food
Acid	Mordant or chrome	Photographic
Azoic	Sulfur or sulfide	Medicinal
Basic	Spirit-soluble	Bacteriological
Direct cotton	Vat	Indicator

The U.S. Tariff Commission presents dyes by both the use and the chemical classification. Table 6 gives the production of the different dyes by their use.

The *acetate*[3] *rayon* dyes are those which have been specially developed

---

[1] See Selected References at the end of this chapter.

[2] See Chap. 34.

[3] VENKATAMARAN, *op. cit.*, Chap. 6; THORPE, "Dictionary of Applied Chemistry," 4th ed., Longmans, Green & Co., Inc., New York, 1937; Vol. 1, 1939. For an excellent generalized presentation of dyeing, *cf. ibid.*, Vol. 4, pp. 120–188; "Rogers' Manual of Industrial Chemistry," 6th ed., D. Van Nostrand Company, Inc., New York, 1942. However, the standard text in the field of dyeing or dye application is KNECHT, RAWSON, and LOWENTHAL, "Manual of Dyeing," 8th ed., 2 vols., Charles Griffin & Co.,

to dye cellulose acetate and some of the new synthetic fibers. They may be broadly divided into two general groups embracing insoluble simple azo dyes and insoluble amino-anthraquinone[1] colors, both in a highly dispersed type and consequently capable of penetrating or dyeing the fiber. Both of these general groups of dyes usually contain the ethanol-amine

TABLE 6. COMPARISON OF UNITED STATES PRODUCTION OF DYES, BY CLASSES OF APPLICATION[a]

Class of application	Production, 1,000 lb.			
	Average 1934–1938	Average 1947–1951	1953	1954
Total.....................	102,527	187,173	165,806	142,982
Acetate rayon.................	1,961	7,435	6,263	5,326
Acid.......................	13,849	21,103	15,510	15,783
Azoic......................	1,077	8,083	6,713	10,336
Basic......................	5,149	8,654	7,981	6,995
Direct......................	25,780	40,717	31,495	26,142
Lake and spirit soluble.........	2,765	5,825	6,270	6,091
Mordant and chrome..........	5,262	6,776	3,844	4,150
Sulfur......................	16,619	24,999	22,489	22,608
Vat, total....................	29,234	60,280	60,957	45,200
Indigo....................	15,378	21,614	17,839	11,129
All other..................	13,856	38,666	43,118	34,071
All other coal-tar dyes........	831	3,301	2,284	2,351

[a] "Synthetic Organic Chemicals," U.S. Tariff Commission, Washington (published annually).

(—NHCH$_2$CH$_2$OH) or a similar radical which renders these dyes more readily dispersible in water and more easily absorbed. Early examples of the dispersed dyes are the S.R.A. wherein the dispersing agent is sulforicinoleic acid (hence the designation S.R.A.). Until these and similar special dyes for acetate were developed, the selling of acetate rayon was much handicapped. See basic dyes for the Astrazones.

The *acid* dyes are used to color animal fibers from acidified solutions, probably by combining with the amphoteric proteins of such fibers.

Ltd., London, 1925. See ROSE, The Mechanism of Dyeing, *Am. Dyestuff Reptr.*, **31**, 204–211 (1942). For a very good summary of dyeing embracing the principal application classes as well as a consideration of the kinetics of dyeing, see LEWIS, SQUIRES, and BROUGHTON, "Industrial Chemistry of Colloidal and Amorphous Materials," pp. 505–518, The Macmillan Company, New York, 1942.

[1] ROWE and CHAMBERLAIN, Dyeings on Cellulose Acetate Rayon, *J. Soc. Dyers Colourists*, **53**, 268 (1937); KARTASCHOFF and FARINE, The Dyeing Phenomena of Acetate Artificial Silk, *Helv. Chim. Acta*, **11**, 813 (1928).

The acid auxochromic or solubilizing groups, $-NO_2$, $-SO_3H$, and $-COOH$ frequently aided by $-OH$, are usually present in the acid dye, whether the fundamental chemical structure be that of the azo, triarylmethane, or anthraquinone complex. These acid dyes are of importance in wool and silk dyeing. Such dyes are somewhat deficient in fastness to alkalies and soap, though usually possessed of good color resistance. Examples are Orange II, 151,[1] and Acid Black 10B, 246 (the azos), and Acid Alizarine Blue B, 1054 (the anthraquinone) dyes.

Azoic dyes are direct and developed dyes, applied especially on cotton. These azoic dyes are essentially *colorless azo dye intermediates* that are marketed in four different groups of products: (1) Simple arylamines or their mineral acid salts ("Color Bases"). These need ice, sodium nitrite, and mineral acid for diazotization before coupling. (2) Stabilized diazonium compounds ("Fast Salts") which are made by combining diazotized arylamines with a precipitant, such as zinc chloride. These are stable products soluble in water and which can be coupled on the fiber with a selected component. Either the "Color Base" after diazotization or the already diazotized "Fast Salt" can be reacted by the user *in situ* with the same coupling constituent to produce the same dye. (3) The "Naphtol" group (Du Pont's "Naphthanil") dye by first impregnating the fiber with a selected coupling component to which the diazotized arylamine is coupled *in situ*. (4) This group comprises mixtures of one selected triazene (made by combining a diazotized arylamine with a special type of secondary amine) and one selected "Naphtol," resulting in a *stabilized* specific insoluble azo dye produced *in situ* by special printing and acid aging technique. These are marketed as "Rapidogens" (Du Pont "Diagen" brand) and are exclusively used for printing.

The azoics are next in importance to the vat dyes which they surpass in brilliance of shade, particularly in the bright reds.

Basic dyes are mostly amino, or substituted amino, derivatives frequently from the triarylmethane or xanthene class but they are applied mostly to paper. Practically all the Auramine, 655, manufactured in America is consumed in paper dyeing. Some basic dyes, Bismarck Brown, 332 and Chrysoidine, 20, are used for leather. Crystal Violet, 681, and Methyl Violet, 680, are mainly employed in typewriter ribbons, carbon papers, and duplicating inks where also some other basic dyes find application. A significant use of spirit-soluble basic dyes is in writing and printing inks. In the sulfonated form some special types of basic dyes still find a limited application in the dyeing of silk and wool but a more important utility of these sulfonated forms is their conversion to lakes for printing inks. The special types of basic dyes, the Astrazones,[2] are of interest for dyeing some of the newer synthetic fibers and for

[1] Colour Index number, see ROWE, footnote page 893.
[2] VENKATARAMAN, *op. cit.*, pp. 713, 1174, table.

cellulose acetate printing. These have better fastness to light and to washing than is true of the ordinary basic dyes.

The *direct* dyes are frequently from the azo class and are used to dye cotton or the vegetable fibers. Some of them are also employed for dyeing union goods (cotton and wool, or cotton and silk). As this dyeing is usually aided by the addition of common salt, or Glauber's salt, to the dye bath, such dyes have been called *salt dyes*. The salt decreases the solubility of the dye and hence causes better exhaustion of it from the dyeing solution. They are also called *substantive* colors. Examples are Direct Blue 2B, 406, Direct Black EW, 581, Direct Brown 3GO, 596, and many others. A number of direct dyes possessed of free NH_2 groups can be *developed* on the fiber thus increasing their insolubility and hence their fastness to washing. This developing is by the processes of *diazotizing* the free amino group and then *coupling* with the developer which may be β-naphthol (*cf.* azo dyes, page 904).

Lake or *pigment* dyes form insoluble compounds or lakes with salts of Ca, Ba, Cr, Al, or phosphomolybdic acid. The dye molecule frequently contains —OH or —SO_3H groups. Such lakes, when ground in oil or other media, form the pigments of many of our paints and inks. In this use class fall such dyes as Lithol Red R, 189, Ponceau 2R, 79, Orange II, 151, and the splendid phthalocyanines (pigments). Some basic dyes are used for the tinting of paper in a water-dispersed form of phosphomolybdic (or tungstic) acid lakes. Wallpapers are frequently colored with lakes from basic dyes containing a sulfonic group.

Certain insoluble dyes are widely used in a pure form known as toners or pigment toners in paints, printing inks, and wallpapers and especially for the *pigment printing* method for textiles, employing pigments of the metal phthalocyanone and other types. The Aridye[1] (Interchemical Corp.) products are printing pastes or emulsions containing a modern heat-hardening resin for anchoring the pigment to the fabric. It has been estimated that 50 per cent of all textile printing, especially for inexpensive women's dresses, is being carried on by this method.

The use of pigments in the "dope" before spinning rayon, acetate, and synthetic fibers, is growing rapidly and is resulting in excellent colors of outstanding all-round fastness.

The *mordant* or *chrome* dyes are applied principally to wool wherein by the use of a mordant which may be chromium or less frequently aluminum or iron, the fastness to light and washing is much increased. Such dyes contain —OH or —COOH radicals frequently attached to azo or anthracene (anthraquinone) complexes. The mordant dyeing is really a metallic salt or lake formed in the fiber. Examples are Alizarin, 1027, Chrome Blue Black U, 202, Gallocyanine, 883, and many others.

The *sulfur* or *sulfide* dyes contain a chromophore with sulfur and are

[1] VENKATARAMAN, *op. cit.*, p. 293; *Milliand Textilberichte*, **1951**, 634–638.

also dyed from a sodium sulfide bath, wherein the sulfur color is reduced to a colorless or light-colored leuco[1] derivative. Sulfur dyes are usually applied on cotton and form a large, low-priced, and useful group, among which we find Sulfur Black, 978, as the most extensively sold single dye (basis dry weight). These dyes furnish dull shades of good fastness to light, washing, and acids. However, they are very sensitive to bleach or chlorine.

The *vat* dyes, including the long-used indigo, are those whose chemical structure is such that reduction furnishes an alkali-soluble, "leuco vat" with which the fiber, generally of vegetable origin such as cotton, is impregnated. This, upon exposure to air, oxidizes back to the insoluble color. Such dyes are of complicated chemical structure such as indan-threnes but furnish dyes of exceptional fastness to light, alkaline washing, perspiration, and even chlorine. The vat dyes provide the fast-dyed cotton shirtings and dress goods and, although relatively expensive, are rapidly increasing in use. The vat dyes are likewise made in a paste with alkaline hydrosulfite-aldehyde reducing agent, printed on the cloth and passed through an oxidizing bath of sodium bichromate or perborate. Examples are Indigo, 1177, Indanthrene Blue GCD, 1113, and Anthra-quinone Vat Yellow GC, 1095, Anthraquinone Vat Jade Green, 1101, and Anthraquinone Vat Khaki 2G. Indigo has a unique and very important use for dyeing wool in extremely heavy (navy blue) shades where it shows surprisingly good fastness properties. Quite important also is the use of several thioindigo dyes for the printing of rayon fabric (mainly for women's dresses) in very bright shades with good fastness properties.

The *spirit-soluble* or oil-soluble dyes are frequently simple azos or triarylmethane bases or anthraquinones used to color oils, waxes, var-nishes, shoe dressings, lipsticks, and gasoline. *Food* dyes are of various structures, selected and tested for harmlessness and employed in coloring foods, candies, and confections. The *photographic, medicinal, bacterio-logical,* and *indicator* dyes are highly specialized products of relatively small sales volume but of fundamental importance in the maintenance of our national economy.

Manufacture of Dyes

The very distinguished and pioneering English chemist, Sir William Henry Perkin, is the father of the synthetic organic chemical dyes.[2] Not

---

[1] ZERWECK, *Angew. Chem.*, **60**, 141–147 (1948), for discussion of constitution of sulfur dyes and chemical reactions.

[2] An authoritative, logical, and readable presentation of this industry is in the booklet by ROWE, "Two Lectures on the Development of the Chemistry of Commer-cial Synthetic Dyes (1856–1938)," Institute of Chemistry, London, 1939.

only did he discover[1] the first practical synthetic aniline dye, *Mauve*, which is made of toluidine, containing aniline, by oxidation, but he organized with his father and brother a company to make synthetic dyes, designed and built the equipment to manufacture Mauve and other dyes, and went out into the dyeing establishments to show how to apply his products. In the early years, from 1856 on, Perkin *was* the dye industry. After 17 years of success, he sold out to enjoy a life of research and investigation. In the meanwhile the Germans took up the dye industry and rapidly became the leaders in the field until 1914, when the Americans, English, and other nations intensively cultivated this line of manufacture as an essential industry.

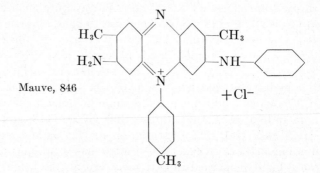

Mauve, 846

Industrially there are used now in the United States over 1,000 different dyes of which 500 are made in appreciable tonnage,[2] some, such as Sulfur Black, Sulfur Blue, Sulfur Brown, Indigo, Direct Black EW, and Developed Black BH, amounting in production to more than 1,000 tons annually for each.

To present some of the outstanding dyes we shall arrange them by the chemical (or chromophore) classification, such as nitro, nitroso, azo dyes, but include also the application designation. Dyes have entered the markets of the world with a *variety of names for the same chemical individual*. Such are listed in the indexes and tabulations of a number of books.[3] The usual name adopted here is that appearing in the annual

[1] Perkin's first patent for a synthetic dye was taken out Aug. 26, 1856, English Pat. 1984(1856). Initially his yields on Mauve, or as he early called it, *Aniline Purple*, were only 5 per cent.

[2] "Synthetic Organic Chemicals, U.S. Production and Sales," U.S. Tariff Commission, Government Printing Office, Washington, yearly. This report of production and sales of dyes, intermediates, and other organic chemicals should be in the hands of everyone interested in this field, as it supplies most up-to-date statistics on the entire organic field. Not only are current tonnages available, but trends are seen by comparison of different years. This pamphlet for 1953 contains (Table C, p. 116) a very useful "Glossary of Synonymous Names of Cyclic Intermediates."

[3] ROWE, *op. cit.;* SCHULTZ, "Farbstofftabellen," 7th ed., Akademische Verlagsgesellschaft m.b.H., Leipzig, 1936. These two volumes have the commercial dyes numbered

reports of the U.S. Tariff Commission to which is added the C.I. number definitely to distinguish a specific chemical compound among the many names under which it may be marketed.

The commercial names are frequently followed by letters, some of which have special designations, among which may be listed:

B   bluish, BB or 2B, more bluish.
G   yellowish (gelblich), occasionally greenish.
R   reddish.
S   bisulfite compound or sulfonic derivative or dye for silk.
W   for wool, HW for part wool, WS for wool and silk.
L   easily soluble (löslich), lake forming, or for linen.

From a manufacturing aspect, dyes fall naturally into their chemical classification, which also is identical with that in the tabulations by Rowe and Schultz (page 902). The presentation will follow this long-accepted arrangement. See Table 7 for production summary by chemical classification.

Nitroso or Quinone Oxime Dyes. Chromophore: —NO (or ═N— OH). Only two members of this class are listed as produced in America by the U.S. Tariff Commission: *Fast Printing Green*, C.I. 2, and *Naphthol Green B*, C.I. 5. The latter is an acid dye, is used in wool and pigment dyeing, and is made by the action of nitrous acid on 2-naphthol-6-sulfonic acid and conversion to the ferric sodium salt.

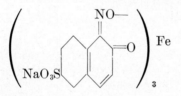

Nitro Dyes. Chromophore: —NO₂. The only nitro dye that is reported as made in the United States is *Naphthol Yellow S*, C.I. 10, which is a cheap acid dye for clear yellow shades on wool and silk, now little used because of low light stability. It is a dye permitted in foods. Its chemical name is sodium 2,4-dinitro-1-naphthol-7-sulfonate, and it is manufactured by sulfonating α-naphthol to 1-naphthol-2,7-disulfonic acid or 1-naphthol-2,4,7-trisulfonic acid, and then nitrating, thus replacing one or two sulfonic groups.

---

and arranged under the chemical classification with references to patents and other literature, together with data on properties both chemical and dyeing, and with directions for making. SHREVE, "Dyes Classified by Intermediates," Reinhold Publishing Corporation, New York, 1922, also lists the multitudinous names under which dyes are sold. The yearbook of the American Association of Textile Chemists and Colorists, Howes Publishing Co., New York, presents such names particularly for the American manufacture. The list is very extensive, embracing over 150 pages.

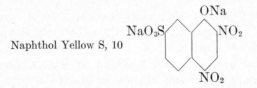

Naphthol Yellow S, 10

Azo Dyes. Chromophore:[1] —N=N—. This class exemplifies the application of the unit process of diazotization and coupling. Over half of the dyes of commerce fall within this classification, of various degrees of

TABLE 7. COMPARISON OF UNITED STATES PRODUCTION AND SALES OF DYES, BY CHEMICAL CLASSIFICATION, 1954[a]

		Sales		
Chemical class	Production, 1,000 lb.	Quantity, 1,000 lb.	Value, $1,000	Unit value per lb.
Total..................................	142,982	137,463	160,302	$1.17
Azo.....................................	52,388	50,342	67,274	1.34
Anthraquinone vat[b].........................	31,128	30,058	40,387	1.34
Indigoid and thioindigoid...................	14,041	13,253	6,451	0.49
Sulfur or sulfide...........................	22,608	22,801	6,573	0.29
Triphenylmethane and diphenylnaphthyl-methane..............................	5,599	3,938	7,925	2.01
Anthraquinone.............................	5,040	4,961	11,069	2.23
Stilbene.................................	2,935	3,057	6,276	2.05
Ketonimine...............................	984	973	1,681	1.73
Pyrazolone...............................	1,190	1,155	2,550	2.21
Xanthene.................................	869	678	2,387	3.52
Thiazole.................................	434	454	804	1.77
Thiazine.................................	298	315	508	1.61
Quinoline.................................	258	248	762	3.07
Acridine.................................	130	90	140	1.56
All other[c]	5,080	5,140	5,515	1.07

[a] "Synthetic Organic Chemicals," U.S. Tariff Commission, Washington (published annually).

[b] Includes carbazole vat dyes.

[c] Includes naphthalimide, nitro, nitroso, azine, oxazine, phthalocyanine, and aniline black and allied dyes; also includes rubber colors and miscellaneous mixtures. Statistics for these groups cannot be published separately without disclosing information received in confidence.

complexity according to the number of azo groups contained or of the assisting or auxochrome groups. Table 7 exhibits the production figures, indicating that of azo dyes to be 35 per cent of the total. Pursuing the

[1] VENKATARAMAN, op. cit., Chaps. 11–15.

chemical classification, we name subgroups under the azo dyes as mono-azo, disazo, trisazo, or tetrakisazo dyes, depending upon whether there are present one, two, three, or four azo groups. And, as we may vary the chemical skeleton and the number and nature of the auxochrome groups, we obtain basic or mordant, acid or direct dyes, or indeed members of all the use classes except vat and sulfur dyes. After the fundamental principles of the reactions were worked out, following the basic discovery by Peter Griess[1] in 1858, literally thousands of azo dyes were made and their properties investigated. Those which survived are the azo dyes that possess suitable properties of fastness or ease of dyeing.

Azo dyes can be made soluble or insoluble as the central rings, or the auxochromes, are changed. They *can* be made actually on or in the fiber,[2] or another azo group can be added to an azo dye already on the fiber (developed colors), or a stabilized diazo derivative can be coupled with a suitable intermediate, both being on the fiber (stabilized azoics). This flexibility of formation leads to useful dyes of a great variety of properties.

The fundamental reactions may be expressed as follows:

$$RNH_2 + HNO_2 + HCl(NaNO_2 + 2HCl) \rightarrow R\!-\!N_2^+ Cl^- + 2H_2O$$
Diazonium
chloride

$$R\!-\!N_2^+ Cl^- + HR'OH \text{ (or } HR'NH_2) \rightarrow RN\!\!=\!\!NR'OH + HCl$$

These two reactions are known as *diazotization* and *coupling*. Specifically, the energy change in diazotizing in aqueous solution and thus forming diazobenzene hydrochloride may be expressed:[3]

$$C_6H_5\!\cdot\!NH_2\!\cdot\!HCl + HNO_2 \rightarrow 2H_2O + C_6H_5N_2Cl; \qquad \Delta H = -22,800 \text{ cal.}$$

For α-naphthylamine subjected to the same reaction, $\Delta H = -24,820$ cal. Fortunately for their wide industrial application these reactions can usually be carried out almost quantitatively,[4] if the temperature is kept low: this is done by the use of ice.

There are specific rules for the coupling of an amine or of a phenol to a diazo body.[5] Generally the diazo solution is to be run into the aryl-amine, phenol, naphthol, or derivative, though there are some exceptions, as *Chrome Blue Black U* exemplified in Fig. 13. With phenols and naph-

[1] GRIESS, *Ann.*, **106**, 123 (1858).

[2] Ice or ingrain or developed colors, now called *azoics*.

[3] CAIN, "Chemistry and Technology of the Diazo Compounds," p. 32, Edward Arnold & Co., London, 1920; *cf.* SAUNDERS, "Aromatic Diazo Compounds and Their Technical Applications," 2d. ed., Edward Arnold & Co., London, 1949.

[4] There are a number of books that present these reactions in various aspects. Particularly pertinent is the chapter on Diazotization and Coupling by Woodward in Groggins "Unit Processes in Organic Synthesis." *Cf.* O'BRIEN, "Factory Practice in the Manufacture of Azo Dyes," Chemical Publishing Company, Inc., New York, 1924. See also references at the end of this chapter.

[5] SAUNDERS, *op. cit.*, Chap. VI; VENKATARAMAN, *op. cit.*, pp. 411*ff*.

thols the coupling is usually *para* to the hydroxyl group or, if this position is occupied, then the *ortho* place is taken. However, the very important β-naphthol couples only once and in the *one* position. Amines couple less readily than do phenols; the coupling takes place only in the *para* position. Of the diamines the *meta* derivatives react most easily, the coupling taking place *para* to one —NH₂ group and *ortho* to the other. This is frequently called the *Chrysoidine law* and is exemplified in the making of *Chrysoidine G*, C.I. 20.

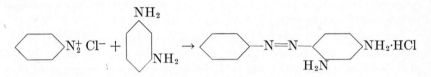

Substituents and pH influence coupling. For instance, H acid,

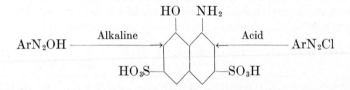

has the position *ortho* to the —NH₂ group activated in acid solutions, and the coupling takes place there, while the activation in alkaline solutions is *ortho* to the —OH with coupling in this position; thus H acid can couple twice. The important amino-naphthol-sulfonic acids, gamma acid and J acid, can couple only once but the position is influenced also by the pH. This property is of very great technical importance in governing the formation of azo derivatives of proper shade and of desired fastness.

Table 8 lists important azo dyes under the azo subclasses and the application class. This table also gives the intermediates from which the dye is derived.[1] Following the rules of coupling just enumerated, the structure of these dyes can be determined.

The equipment in which azo dyes are manufactured by diazotization and coupling is quite simple in comparison to that used for most other unit processes. It is exemplified in Fig. 13 depicting the making of *Chrome Blue Black U*, C.I. 202, and consists largely of wooden stirred tanks of various sizes, wooden plate-and-frame filter presses, drying boxes wherein on steel carts the dye, previously placed on trays, is dried by circulating hot air. Sometimes sensitive dyes are dried in vacuum shelf driers. The milling, mixing, and standardizing of dyes end the manufacturing sequence. The mills must be so chosen as not to ignite the sensitive dyes. As customers require absolute uniformity in dyes, the

---

[1] *Cf.* SHREVE, "Dyes Classified by Intermediates," for extensive tables of dyes under each constituent intermediate.

mixing and standardizing are of utmost importance. The double-cone dye mixer and blender, sometimes used, has no internal parts to hold up a dye and performs the mixing and blending in an unusually satisfactory manner.

Among the monoazo dyes, *Chrome Blue Black U*[1] ranks as one of the important chrome colors on wool for men's wear, particularly as its various qualities of fastness are very good (fastness to light, acids, alkalies, carbonizing, ironing, washing, perspiration, etc.). The U.S.

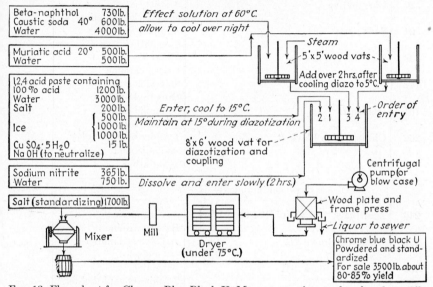

FIG. 13. Flow sheet for Chrome Blue Black U. Monoazo or chrome dye; batch = 5 lb. moles.

Tariff Commission reports annual sales of over 700,000 lb. It is sold for a low price because of the cheapness of the raw materials and the skill of the dyemakers. The two intermediates are 1,2,4 acid (1-amino-2-naphthol-4-sulfonic acid) and β-naphthol. It might seem easy to make but in this case the nitrous acid not only diazotizes the —NH₂ group but tends to oxidize the 1,2,4 acid to tars and thus throw off the shade of the finished dye and decrease the yield. This can be avoided by diazotizing 1-amino-naphthalene-2,4-disulfonic acid and then replacing the 2-sulfonic acid by —OH through caustic soda, or by diazotizing in the presence of a zinc salt.[2] However, the oxidizing influence of the nitrous acid is

[1] This is C.I. 202 and, like most other dyes, is sold under many names, frequently one for each manufacturer: Eriochrome Blue Black R (Gy), Calcochrome Blue Black (CCC), Pontochrome Blue Black R (DuP), Superchrome Blue B Ex (NAC). The initials in parentheses are those of the manufacturer, *e.g.*, DuP stands for Du Pont. See also dye lists in the yearbooks of the American Association of Textile Chemists and Colorists.

[2] *Cf.*, ROWE, *op. cit.*, C.I. 202, where methods and references are given.

TABLE 8. IMPORTANT AZO DYES

Color Index No.	Name and class of dye	Intermediates from which dye is made	Dye application class
	Monoazo dyes: containing R—N=N—R'		
20	Chrysoidine Y	Aniline m-Phenylenediamine	B
24	Sudan I	Aniline β-Naphthol	SS
138	Metanil Yellow	Metanilic acid Diphenylamine	A
142	Methyl Orange	Sulfanilic acid Dimethyl-aniline	A[1]
151	Orange II	Sulfanilic acid β-Naphthol	A
202	Chrome Blue Black R	1-Amino-2-naphthol-4-sulfonic acid β-Naphthol	M
	Disazo dyes: containing R—N=N—X—N=N—R'		
246	Acid Black 10B (Naphthol Blue Black)	p-Nitro-aniline H acid, Aniline	A
332	Bismarck Brown 2R	m-Tolylenediamine (3 moles)	B
401	Developed Black BH	Benzidine 2-Amino-8-naphthol-6-sulfonic acid (alk.) 1-Amino-8-naphthol-3,6-disulfonic acid (alk.)	D
406	Direct Blue 2B	Benzidine 1-Amino-8-naphthol-3,6-disulfonic acid (alk.) (2 moles)	D
518	Direct Sky Blue FF	Dianisidine 1-Amino-8-naphthol-2,4-disulfonic acid (alk.) (2 moles)	D
	Trisazo dyes: containing R—N=N—X—N=N—Y—N=N—R'		
593	Direct Green B	Benzidine Phenol 1-Amino-8-naphthol-3,6-disulfonic acid p-Nitro-aniline	D

[1] Indicator. NOTE: In this table A stands for acid dye, B for basic dye, D for direct dye, M for mordant dye, and SS for spirit-soluble dye.

diminished in the presence of a small amount of a copper salt.[1] The flow sheet, Fig. 13, follows this procedure[2] and carries out the reaction:

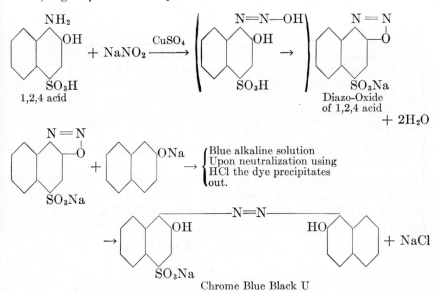

1,2,4 acid

Diazo-Oxide of 1,2,4 acid

+ 2H₂O

Blue alkaline solution Upon neutralization using HCl the dye precipitates out.

Chrome Blue Black U

As in all diazotizations and couplings, tests must be made toward the end of the reaction. In this case, after stirring for a while, a sample diluted with an equal volume of distilled water should dissolve and show only a slight excess of nitrous acid when tested with starch iodide paper.[3] The diazo oxide of the 1,2,4 acid is a suspension of bronze crystals which can be filtered off. However, this is not usually considered necessary, and the coupling is carried out next morning after reducing the temperature to 5°C. by adding about 1,000 lb. of ice. The coupling is then effected by running in the sodium naphthol solution slowly over 2 hr. The blue alkaline solution of the dye is precipitated the next day with diluted muriatic acid, testing toward the end so as to leave the mother liquor faintly acid to Congo red test paper. The usual product sold, except for the higher-priced concentrates, contains salt about equal to the dye contents.[4]

From the flow sheet and current material prices, the cost of the ma-

---

[1] SAUNDERS, op. cit., p. 7; GEIGY, U.S. Pat. 793743 and English Pat. 10234(1904).

[2] SAUNDERS, op. cit., p. 7; O'BRIEN, op. cit., pp. 151–154.

[3] U.S. Pat. 2160882(1939) by Lubs describes a new method for removal of excess nitrous acid, using sulfamic acid and thus avoiding side reactions which adversely affect the purity of the color of the dye.

[4] Most dyes contain salt or sodium sulfate to standardize, since batches will not come from the plant in exactly the same strength. This is adjusted by a harmless diluent. Very pure dyes are such products as the food, medicinal, or bacteriological dyes, which are costly compared with the low-priced textile dyes.

terials[1] for Chrome Blue Black can be calculated, to which should be added:

Per 100 lb. of
standardized dye

Productive labor.......................................	$2.50
Nonproductive labor..................................	1.00
Power and steam......................................	1.25
Maintenance and repairs.............................	1.55
Supplies...	0.55
Plant overhead.......................................	1.50
	$8.35

This figure should be increased by pro rata charges for depreciation, taxes, insurance, and sales expense.

Directions for making other dyes can be found in the references at the end of this chapter.[2] The apparently complicated trisazo dye, *Direct Green B*, C.I. 593, is made from four intermediates according to the scheme:

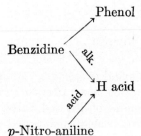

The arrows indicate coupling from diazo body to a hydroxy or amino derivative. The resulting dye formula is

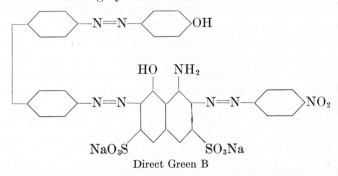

Direct Green B

---

[1] A flow sheet with costs for 1,2,4 acid is given on pp. 1111 and 1114 in the chapter on dyes, by Shreve, in "Rogers' Manual of Industrial Chemistry." This dye is sold so cheaply that even the 1,2,4 acid would have to be manufactured to compete.

[2] Particularly in Rowe, "Colour Index and Supplement." A flow sheet for C.I. 518, Direct Pure Blue 6B or Diamine Sky Blue FF, is given by Woodward, in Groggins, *op. cit.*, p. 170; *cf.* O'Brien, *op. cit.*

In 1880, the making of an azo dye, *Para Red*, C.I. 44, right on the fiber was undertaken. This was done by padding the cotton cloth with an alkaline β-naphthol solution, followed by an acid solution of diazotized *p*-nitro-aniline. Later the β-naphthol was replaced by 3-hydroxy-2-naphthoic acid or its anilide (Naphtol AS), to attain more substantivity and brighter shades of superior fastness. This generalized process enabled the more soluble constituents to penetrate into the fiber and there to form the insoluble azo dye. Such procedures are still very important and comprise a good share[1] of those made-on fiber dyes, now known as azoics (see under Classification of Dyes). Azoic prints from diazonium pastes on "Naphtolated" goods are of wide utility.

This and other azoic procedures require the dyer to be also a dyemaker. To simplify and to give the dyer an improved line, particularly for printing on cotton, the *stabilized* azoics (class 4) have been made. These are azo dyes and may be defined as "a mixture of a soluble stabilized aromatic diazo compound and a secondary component with which it can couple under suitable conditions to form an insoluble colored pigment."[2] Among stabilized azoics[3] the Diagens of the Du Pont Company and the Rapidogens of the General Dyestuffs Corporation are outstanding developments for printing on cotton goods with results of good fastness and at a reasonable price. The diazo is stabilized by combination with a secondary amine containing a solubilizing group. This gives a perfectly stable mixture with a coupling component, usually an arylamide of 3-hydroxy-2-naphthoic acid, as long as in alkaline condition. The constituents react and form the insoluble azo dye when acidified, as exemplified in the reactions shown on page 912.

For years, metallic[4] salts, particularly of chromium and of aluminum, have been used in making lakes and as mordants, having been initiated by the *Neolin* of the Swiss. Crossley and Shafer[5] of the Calco Chemical Division of the American Cyanamid Company, have brought out a class of colors, the *metallized dyes*, sold under the name *Calcofast*. These dye wool from acid baths with excellent fastness to washing, milling, and light. Examples[6] are Calcofast Olive Brown G, Calcofast Orange 4R, and Calcofast Orange YF made by coupling nitro-diazo-phenols with

---

[1] The U.S. Tariff Commission reported production of Naphtol AS as over 900,000 lb. out of over 6,000,000 for the total azoic group.

[2] LUBS, Stabilized Azoic Colors, *Am. Dyestuff Reptr.*, **26**, 101 (1937); *cf.* DORMAN, Naphtol AS Type Dyes, *Am. Dyestuff Reptr.*, **28**, 79 (1939); for nitrosamines, *cf.* C.I. 70; WOODWARD, in GROGGINS, *op. cit.*, pp. 136–137.

[3] LUBS, *op. cit.*; DORMAN, *op. cit.*; DAHLEN, U.S. Pats. 1968878(1934) and 2008750 (1935); DAHLEN and ZWILGMEYER, U.S. Pat. 2021911(1935).

[4] VENKATARAMAN, *op. cit.*, Metal-dye complexes, pp. 534*ff.*, 551*ff.*

[5] CROSSLEY and SHAFER, U.S. Pats. 2034390(1936), 2086854(1937), 2120799(1938), 2136650(1938), 2213647(1940), 2220396(1940), 2220397(1940).

[6] U.S. Pat. 2120799(1938). Specific examples are given.

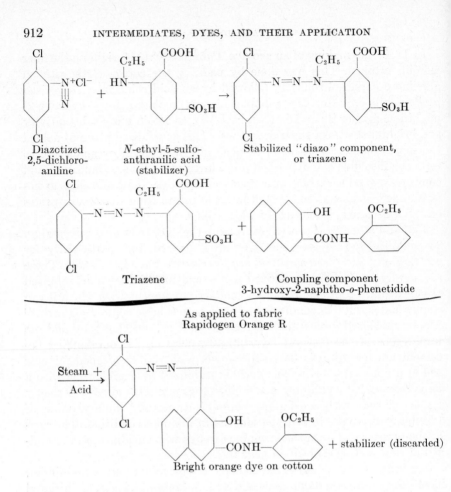

Diazotized 2,5-dichloro-aniline

N-ethyl-5-sulfo-anthranilic acid (stabilizer)

Stabilized "diazo" component, or triazene

Triazene

Coupling component
3-hydroxy-2-naphtho-o-phenetidide

As applied to fabric
Rapidogen Orange R

Steam + Acid →

+ stabilizer (discarded)

Bright orange dye on cotton

phenyl-methyl-pyrazolones in weakly metallic salt. The metal used may vary over a wide range, or a combination of metals may be employed yielding different colors. The metal derivatives are soluble and are a part of the molecule. The metallized dye is obtained by salting out the reaction liquor using common salt up to 25 per cent of the aqueous solution.

Stilbene Dyes. Chromophores: —N=N— and =C=C=. These dyes are sometimes classed with the azo group to which they are closely related. Although this class of dyes contains an azo chromophore, it is not made by the diazotization and coupling reactions. These are *direct* cotton dyes and the most used example is Direct Yellow R, C.I. 620, which is made by the action of heat and caustic soda on *p*-nitro-toluene-*o*-sulfonic acid (4 moles). These stilbene dyes (C.I. 620–635) are now held to be mixtures of azo dyes of unknown constitution.[1]

[1] ZIEGLER, K., *FIAT Rev. Ger. Sci.*, 1939–1946, Part II, p. 27; KNIGHT, A. H., *J. Soc. Dyers Colourists*, **66** (8), 417.

Pyrazolone Dyes. Chromophores: —N=N— and =C=C=. These are also sometimes classed with the azo group. The members are acid dyes and are usually used on silk and wool, though to some extent for lakes. The chief member is *Tartrazine*, C.I. 640, which is made from dioxytartaric acid and phenylhydrazine-*p*-sulfonic acid (2 moles). Its formula is

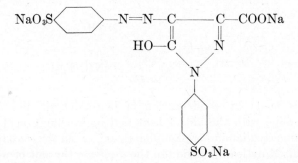

Ketonimine Dyes. Chromophore: NH=C=. This small class (2 members) is so close to the next, or triarylmethane dyes, that these two dyes are frequently grouped with the triarylmethane ones. The members are Auramine, C.I. 655, and its homolog. Auramine is used primarily for paper dyeing. It is manufactured from dimethyl-aniline (2 moles) and formaldehyde furnishing 4,4'-bis(dimethylamino)-diphenylmethane. This intermediate upon heating with sulfur, ammonium chloride, and salt to about 200°C. in a current of NH₃ yields auramine base which is converted to the hydrochloride:

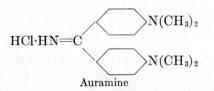

Auramine

Triarylmethane Dyes. Chromophores: =C=NH and =C=N—. However, the cause of color in this class with this complex as the charac-

teristic chemical group, is due to more than the presence of a simple chromophore. Conjugated bonds, unsaturation, and quinoid arrangement are all important, but it is the possibility of more than one resonating form of the entire molecule (including generally the amino auxochromes) that is now held to be responsible for the color.[1] These dyes are basic ones, dyeing cotton with tannin mordant, or when sulfonated, acid dyes for wool and silk. They furnish very beautiful shades but, for the most part, they are not very fast to light.

Malachite Green, C.I. 657, is the chloride of p,p'-tetramethyldiamino-triphenylcarbinol,[2] sold usually as zinc chloride complex. Its formula is

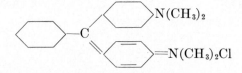

This dye is made by condensation of benzaldehyde and 2 moles of dimethyl-aniline with the aid of heat and hydrochloric acid. This furnishes tetramethyldiamino-triphenylmethane, called the *leuco* base, which is then oxidized by lead peroxide to the *dye base*, the salt of which is the commercial dye (either oxalate or zinc double chloride).

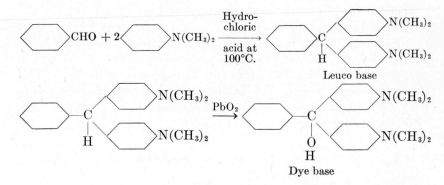

Many of the triarylmethane dyes are carried through this same sequence.

Methyl Violet, C.I. 680, is a basic dye, produced in about 1,400,000 lb. per year and for a wide variety of uses, *e.g.*, on cotton, silk, and paper as a self color, in calico and silk printing, in the dyeing of jute, coco fiber, wood, linen, straw, leather, and in the manufacture of marking and stamping inks, carbon papers, copying pencils, and lacquers. This dye is the hydrochloride of pentamethyltriamino-triphenyl-carbinol. It is made by the oxidation of dimethyl-aniline (3 moles) using cupric chloride in the presence of phenol. One methyl group goes to formaldehyde which

---

[1] LEWIS and CALVIN, Color, *Chem. Rev.*, **25**, 273 (1939). The influence of alkylation in color change is tabulated by SHREVE in 3d ed., p. 508, in GROGGINS, "Unit Processes in Organic Synthesis."

[2] This is the nomenclature found in the dye books. Chemical Abstracts names these dyes by the more logical I.U.C. system and would call the dye base of which commercial Malachite Green is a salt, bis(p-dimethyl-aminophenyl)-phenylmethanol.

supplies the central carbon.[1] The function of the phenol in this reaction is unknown. The Methyl Violet has the formula:

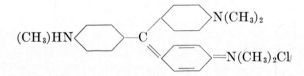

Xanthene Dyes. These dyes usually are derivatives of xanthene.

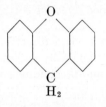

It is difficult to say what the chromophore is, but the remarks as to the cause of color in the triaryl group are of value here. These dyes are quite closely related to the aryl methane ones, and the oxygen bridge can be viewed as made by the elimination of water from two hydroxyl groups, ortho to the carbon bridge. The presence of conjugation is characteristic of such chromophores as $=C=O$ or $=C=N-$. The most widely sold of these dyes is *Eosin*, C.I. 768, which is tetrabromofluorescein. Fluorescein is made by condensation of resorcinol (2 moles) and phthalic anhydride in presence of a dehydrating agent such as zinc chloride. The formula of Eosin is given below. Eosin is an acid dye for wool and silk, and also for cotton with a tin or alum mordant. However, its chief application is to make lakes and for the preparation of ordinary red writing and stamping inks.

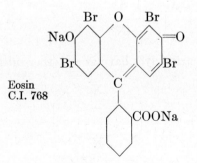

Eosin
C.I. 768

---

[1] Details of these various processes and the merchandising of the reactions as far as they are published can be obtained from the references at the end of this chapter. The "Colour Index and Supplement" and the book by VENKATARAMAN, *op. cit.* are the best general references.

Thiazole Dyes, or Primuline Dyes. These contain sulfur in the thiazole ring:

The chromophores are $\diagup$C=N— as well as the —S—C≡ etc., but the arrangement in conjugated double bonds is of importance. These dyes are chiefly direct or developed dyes for cotton, though some of them are union dyes.

Direct Fast Yellow, C.I. 814, is a direct color of excellent properties; it is also a union dye. It is made by sodium hypochlorite oxidation of the sodium salt of dehydrothio-*p*-toluidine-sulfonic acid.

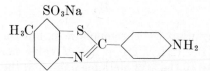

This latter is prepared by heating *p*-toluidine and sulfur followed by sulfonation. Direct Fast Yellow has also an azo chromophore, as is shown by the following structure:

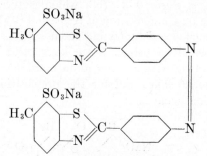

Azine Dyes. The azine dyes have as a mother substance phenazine:

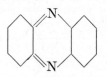

and we may assume as chromophores $\diagup$C=N—; but here, as in many other of these complicated ring systems, resonance is being more and more looked upon as the basis of color. Indeed in these simpler chromophores like $\diagup$C=N— the structure contains a "fairly loosely bound chromophoric electron."[1] The azine dyes are quite varied in their application. The *Nigrosines*, C.I. 864 and 865, have annual sales of over 2,600,000 lb. and are used, after jetting with suitable yellow dyes, for blue-black and black polishes for leather shoes and other leather goods. Their ultimate constitution is unknown. The nigrosines are also employed for silk dyeing. They are such good dyes at such reasonable prices, that a welcome addition is *Microsol Black*,[2] a black pigment insoluble in water and substantially insoluble in acetone, alcohols, and hydrocarbons. This black pigment, which gives a gray upon dilution, is useful for coloring lacquers, plastics, paints, inks, and emulsions for textile printing. It is made by treating spirit-soluble or unsulfonated nigrosine (or induline) with an oxidizing agent such as manganese dioxide or nitric acid.

Although Safranine, C.I. 841, is not sold so largely as the nigrosines, its constitution is simple and it may be formulated:

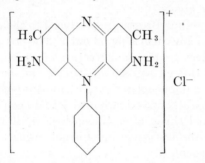

It is made by oxidation by CrO_3 in acetic acid of equimolecular proportions of *p*-tolylenediamine and *o*-toluidine to the indamine:

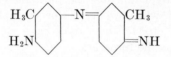

This is then condensed with aniline (or *o*-toluidine) in the presence of an oxidant. Safranine is a basic dye and is used largely on cotton mordanted with tannin and fixed with tartar emetic.

Thiazine Dyes. These have the important member, *Methylene Blue*, C.I. 922, which has the formula:

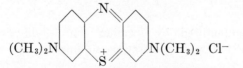

This is a basic dye and is made from dimethyl-aniline.

[1] GLASSTONE, "Textbook of Physical Chemistry," p. 573, D. Van Nostrand Company, Inc., New York, 1940.

[2] FRIESE (American Cyanamid Company). U.S. Pat. 2194423(1940).

Sulfur or Sulfide Dyes.[1] These dyes are so complex that very little is known of their chemical structure. The chromophores present are $\equiv$C—S—C$\equiv$ and $\equiv$C—S—S—C$\equiv$ as bridges in complicated molecules.[2] These sulfur dyes are used to dye cotton from a sodium sulfide bath in dull but full shades of excellent fastness.

Sulfur Black, C.I. 978, is the most widely sold of all dyes figuring on a dry basis, the sales amounting to over 11,000 tons annually. It is also a very low priced product. Sulfur black is made from either 2,4-dinitro-chloro-benzene or 2,4-dinitro-phenol by refluxing with a polysulfide solution for many hours followed by precipitation of the dye by air oxidation. The demand for sulfur black was responsible for the first plant in America to produce chloro-benzene, installed about 1915. The time for thionation in some of these sulfur colors can be much shortened—from days to hours—by changing the solvent from alcohol or water to a monoalkyl ether of diethylene glycol.[3]

Sulfur Blue and Sulfur Brown are produced to the extent of more than 4,000 tons per year for each while about 2,000 tons of Sulfur Green are produced. These dyes are also manufactured from a large variety of pure intermediates by thionation, among which can be named: diphenyl-amine derivatives, indophenol derivatives, dinitro-naphthalenes, tolylene-diamines, and many others. Oxidation with hydrogen peroxide sometimes brings out a desired shade after thionation. Hydron Blue, C.I. 969, is the product from the carbazole indophenol, using alcoholic polysulfide as the thionation agent.

Anthraquinone Dyes. Chromophores: $=$C$=$O and $=$C$=$C$=$ arranged in the anthraquinone complex. The auxochromes are frequently (1) —OH when the dyes fall into the mordant class like Alizarin, C.I. 1027, or (2) —SO$_3$H when we have, for example, the acid dye *Acid Alizarin Blue B*, C.I. 1054. These dyes have very fast characteristics. Acid Alizarin Blue has the formula:

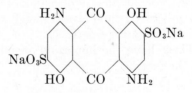

and is manufactured by forming the 1,5-dihydroxy-anthraquinone (anthrarufin) followed by nitration, sulfonation, and reduction.

---

[1] VENKATARAMAN, *op. cit.*, Chap. 35, pp. 1059*ff.*; *BIOS*, **983**; *BIOS*, **1155**; *FIAT*, **1313**, II, III.

[2] Empirical formulas are variously given as $C_{24}H_{16}N_6O_8S_7$ or $C_{24}H_{16}N_6O_8S_8$ for typical sulfur dyes.

[3] LUBS and STROUSE, U.S. Pat. 1944250(1934).

Anthraquinone Vat Dyes. These are also based on anthraquinone like the preceding class and have many of the chromophore and the fastness characteristics of that class, only accentuated in many instances. However, these dyes are capable of being reduced to an alkaline soluble derivative which is called a *vat* and which oxidizes to the color (thus resembling the next class or indigo dyes). To make a commercial dye the reduced or leuco compound must have affinity for the fiber, and the insoluble dye must adhere firmly.[1] These necessities are met with in so many of the members of this class that we have in the vat dyes a rapidly

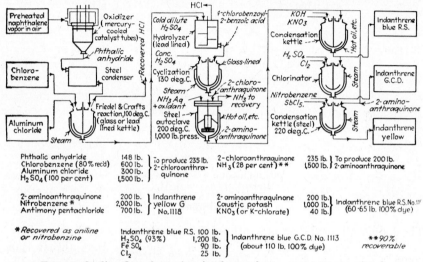

Phthalic anhydride	148 lb.	To produce 235 lb.	2-chloroanthraquinone	235 lb.	To produce 200 lb.
Chlorobenzene (80% rec'd)	600 lb.	2-chloroanthra-	NH_3 (28 per cent)**	1,500 lb.	2-aminoanthraquinone
Aluminum chloride	300 lb.	quinone			
H_2SO_4 (100 per cent)	1,500 lb.				

2-aminoanthraquinone	200 lb.	Indanthrene	2-aminoanthraquinone	200 lb.	Indanthrene blue R.S. No.1¹'
Nitrobenzene *	2,000 lb.	yellow G	Caustic potash	1,000 lb.	(60·65 lb. 100% dye)
Antimony pentachloride	700 lb.	No.1118	KNO_3 (or K-chlorate)	40 lb.	

*Recovered as aniline or nitrobenzine	Indanthrene blue R.S.	100 lb.	Indanthrene blue G.C.D. No. 1113	**90% recoverable
	H_2SO_4 (93%)	1,200 lb.	(about 110 lb. 100% dye)	
	$FeSO_4$	90 lb.		
	Cl_2	25 lb.		

FIG. 14. Outline flow sheets for simple vat dyes—many steps omitted.

growing class of colors of remarkable properties of fastness and permanency. Their growth has been greatly stimulated, indeed made possible, by the American discovery or commercialization of synthetic phthalic anhydride from air oxidation of naphthalene, from which synthetic anthraquinone is manufactured. These vat dyes are employed largely on cotton and rayon and, to a limited extent, on silk; indeed they furnish us some of our finest and *fastest* colored fabrics. Figure 14 summarizes the flow sheets depicting in outline the sequences from main raw materials to the following three vat dyes:

[1] The basic chemical structure that gives to an anthraquinone or indigoid dye the vat dyeing characteristics is usually the presence of two CO groups which on reduction give alkali-soluble C(OH) groups.

The almost invariably used reducing agent is sodium hydrosulfite, $Na_2S_2O_4$, employed for solutions; or the formaldehyde compound, formaldehyde sulfoxalate employed for printing. The reaction may be expressed:

$$Na_2S_2O_4 + 2NaOH + H_2O = Na_2SO_4 + Na_2SO_3 + 2H_2 \text{ (on the dye)}$$

Recently Lubs has patented in U.S. Pat. 2164930(1939) the use of the hydrogen peroxide oxidation product of thiourea for the same purpose.

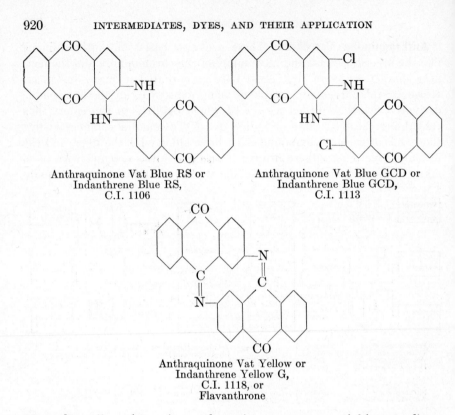

Anthraquinone Vat Blue RS or
Indanthrene Blue RS,
C.I. 1106

Anthraquinone Vat Blue GCD or
Indanthrene Blue GCD,
C.I. 1113

Anthraquinone Vat Yellow or
Indanthrene Yellow G,
C.I. 1118, or
Flavanthrone

These dyes all need β-amino-anthraquinone as an essential intermediate, proceeding by an oxidizing condensation to the dyes. Indanthrene Blue GCD is a chlorination product, and has superior fastness properties because of this.

Another example of these very fast and stable vat dyes is *Anthraquinone Vat Dark Blue BO*, C.I. 1099 (also sold as Hydroform Deep Blue BOA as well as under other names), which has the structure:

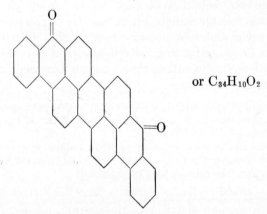

or $C_{34}H_{10}O_2$

This is a very compact molecule, consisting very largely of carbon (nearly 90 per cent) and possessing great stability. It is made by caustic-potash fusion from benzanthrone.

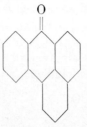

The benzanthrone is manufactured by condensation from anthranol and glycerine under the influence of sulfuric acid, and the anthranol in turn from anthraquinone by reduction with sulfuric acid and iron (or copper).

The anthraquinone vat dyes because of their superior fastness, especially on cotton, are becoming both relatively and tonnagewise more important every year. They are gradually supplanting dyes of less superior qualities; for example, in the Second World War most of the khaki uniforms were vat-dyed and exhibited practically no fading against light and washing in striking contrast to the bad fading of the sulfur-dyed cotton uniforms of the First World War. At present the anthraquinone vats of Table 7 are produced to more than 31,000,000 lb. To these should be added 4,000,000 lb. of anthraquinone vats of "ungrouped" dyes, i.e., those not classified. This makes a total for these dyes of 35,000,000 lb., or 25 per cent of the total yearly dye production.

The 18,000,000-lb. plant of Ciba States, Ltd., at Toms River, N.J., with a normal producing capacity of 4,000,000 lb. of anthraquinone vat dyes, has been pictured and described.[1] The reference gives the fullest details ever published of any vat dye, including diagrammatic flow sheet material requirements, yields, reactions, and chemical engineering details to produce anthraquinone Vat Brown BR;[2] from 1,4-diamino-anthraquinone and 1-chloro-anthraquinone through the trianthrimide.

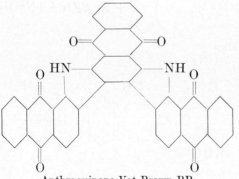

Anthraquinone Vat Brown BR

[1] BRADLEY and KRONOWETT, Anthraquinone Vat Dyes, *Ind. Eng. Chem.*, **46**, 1146 (1954).

[2] VENKATARAMAN, *op. cit.*, p. 906; see this reference for other such dyes, e.g., Anthraquinone Khaki 2G.

Anthraquinone Vat Jade Green, C.I. 1101, was produced in the largest amount in 1953 of any anthraquinone vat dye, this amounting to 6,000,000 lb. of 6 per cent paste at an average value of $.89 per lb.

Indigoid Dyes. The remarks that headed the vat-dyes section pertain largely to this chemical class also, except that the members of this class are derivatives of indigo or thioindigo.

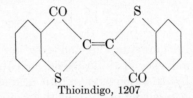

Thioindigo, 1207

These dyes fall in the vat use classification and are applied principally on cotton. A very large tonnage of indigo is manufactured each year. Recently this has amounted to about 11,000 tons annually of 20 per cent paste. When the Oriental export business was flourishing, production up to 15,000 tons was made. Indigo was first a naturally cultivated dye, but the German chemists worked out a profitable synthesis for indigo, though only after spending over $6,000,000 in research and development. However, this was a profitable venture for them as their synthetic indigo was more uniform and much cheaper than that previously grown on 1,500,000 acres, principally in India.

Indigo,[1] C.I. 1177, itself is a water-insoluble blue dye of good properties, largely used on cotton and rayon, but sometimes on silk. Indigo has become quite important in dyeing full shades of navy blue on wool for uniform cloth of good fastness. When dyeing, it is reduced by hydrosulfite to make the alkali-soluble leuco derivative or to make indigo white.

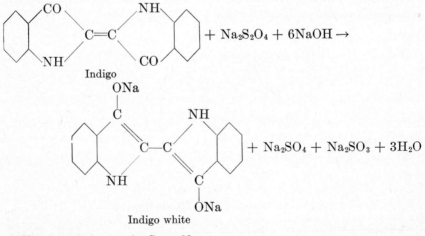

Indigo

$+ Na_2S_2O_4 + 6NaOH \rightarrow$

Indigo white

$+ Na_2SO_4 + Na_2SO_3 + 3H_2O$

[1] VENKATARAMAN, *op. cit.*, CHAP. 33.

Figure 15 gives an outline flow sheet for the manufacture of indigo by several sequences from aniline, which is the present commercial starting

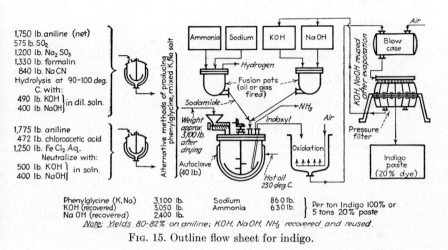

Phenylglycine (K,Na)	3,100 lb.	Sodium	860 lb.	Per ton Indigo 100% or
KOH (recovered)	3,050 lb.	Ammonia	630 lb.	5 tons 20% paste
Na OH (recovered)	2,400 lb.			

Note: Yields 80-82% on aniline; KOH, NaOH, NH₃ recovered and reused.

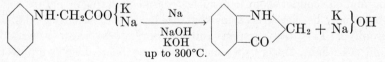

FIG. 15. Outline flow sheet for indigo.

point for the intermediate product, phenyl-glycine. The following reactions summarize the chemical changes involved in this flow sheet (*cf.* also Fig. 12).

Indoxyl Using Sodium Amide:

$$\text{NH·CH}_2\text{COO}\left\{{K \atop Na}\right. \xrightarrow[\substack{NaOH \\ KOH \\ 220\text{-}240°C.}]{NaNH_2} \text{—NH} \diagdown \text{CH}_2 + \left. {K \atop Na}\right\}\text{OH}$$
$$\text{—CO} \diagup$$

(+ NH₃ from NaNH₂)

Indoxyl Using Metallic Sodium:

$$\text{NH·CH}_2\text{COO}\left\{{K \atop Na}\right. \xrightarrow[\substack{NaOH \\ KOH \\ up\ to\ 300°C.}]{Na} \text{—NH} \diagdown \text{CH}_2 + \left. {K \atop Na}\right\}\text{OH}$$
$$\text{—CO} \diagup$$

Although, apparently, the sodium amide or the metallic sodium does not enter into the reaction, these two reagents and the mixed NaOH and ꞏKOH maintain the necessary fluxing and anhydrous condition for the dehydrating ring closure to proceed with good yields. The use of the *mixed* Na, K salt of phenyl-glycine and of *mixed* NaOH, KOH gives lower fusion points with consequent lower temperatures and enhanced yields.

Phenyl-glycine by Chloro-acetic Acid:

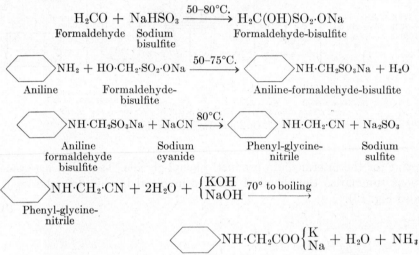

Phenyl-glycine by Formaldehyde and Sodium Cyanide:

$$H_2CO + NaHSO_3 \xrightarrow{50\text{–}80°C.} H_2C(OH)SO_2{\cdot}ONa$$

Formaldehyde   Sodium   Formaldehyde-bisulfite
                bisulfite

Mixed Na, K salt of phenyl-glycine

Phthalocyanine[1] Dyes and Pigments. Figure 17 represents the structure of copper phthalocyanine. This group contains a new chromophore of great complexity, or more likely a new arrangement of the simpler chromophores: $=C=N-$ and $=C=C=$. Here again, it may be that resonance will be shown to be the fundamental cause of the color. In copper phthalocyanine four isoindole units are linked by four nitrogen atoms and one copper atom to furnish a complicated ring structure which, however, may be viewed as somewhat similar to the basic ring system of chlorophyll. This ring system and its derivatives show remarkable stability[2] to light, water, chemicals, and even heat. They sublime unchanged at 550°C. Because of this stability, their insolubility in water, and the intensity and beauty of their color, these phthalocyanines are

[1] DAHLEN, The Phthalocyanines, *Ind. Eng. Chem.*, **31**, 839 (1939). This article includes a bibliography of the work, gives patents, and describes the fundamental and enlightening studies of R. P. Linstead of England. For more details (107 references) *cf.* VENKATARAMAN, *op. cit.*, Chap. 37.

[2] SCHWARZ, The Phthalocyanines Are Faster Than Anything in Color Produced So Far, *Am. Dyestuff Reptr.*, **29**, 7 (1940).

FIG. 16. A dye worker at Du Pont's Chamber Works, Deepwater Point, N.J., is shown placing dye cake in trays for drying, after the cake has been removed from a filter press. After grinding, testing, and standardizing, the product is ready for shipping. (*Courtesy of Du Pont.*)

of particular applicability to the pigment and paint fields. Three of these blue-green pigments have become important commercially: The metal-free phthalocyanine is sold as *Monastral Fast Blue GS* powder (Du Pont) and also as aqueous pastes and dispersions. The copper derivative is merchandised as a practically pure powder as *Monastral Fast Blue BSN* powder.

The copper phthalocyanine is highly chlorinated and is then sold as *Monastral Fast Green GS* powder and modifications. It has about 14 chlorine atoms per phthalocyanine unit. These dyes are only of the blue and green shades, but they supply a long-felt want for pigments of their excellent properties. They were discovered accidentally as an impurity in the manufacture of phthalimide. They are sold as pigments, or insoluble but highly dispersed colors, in printing inks, artists' colors,

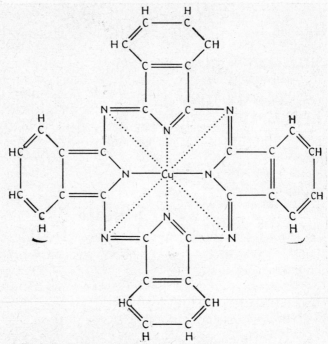

FIG. 17. Copper phthalocyanine structure. (*After Dahlen.*)

paints, lacquers, enamels, coated textiles, paper, linoleum, and rubber. We may summarize[1] their manufacture according to the following equation:

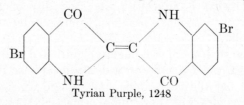

$$4 \quad \begin{array}{c} \text{—CN} \\ \text{—CN} \end{array} + Cu \xrightarrow{180\text{–}250°} \text{Structure as in Fig. 17}$$

Phthalonitrile   Copper   Phthalocyanine (Copper)

Natural Organic Dyes. For centuries these have been of the utmost importance. We have all heard of *Tyrian purple* of the ancients. It was extracted from mollusks growing on the shore of the Mediterranean. It is, however, a dye, 6,6′-dibromo-indigo, of the following formulation:

Tyrian Purple, 1248

[1] Other procedures are available, such as heating the phthalonitrile with cuprous chloride, or probably better by reacting phthalic anhydride and urea in presence of cupric chloride. The crude reaction product is not suitable for dye use and must be dissolved in concentrated sulfuric acid and reprecipitated by dilution with water to obtain the physical and chemical form suitable for dyes. *Cf.* DAHLEN, *op. cit.*

It could be made synthetically but we have other and better products to take its place.

This replacement of the natural, or, as they have been called, *vegetable*, dyes, by their duplicates synthetically made in our factories or by better and more cheaply made products is quite the usual thing. However, *logwood*,[1] C.I. 1246, in the form of chips and extract of the wood of the tree growing in Central America, has survived competition and is used extensively to give black and blue-black colors on wool and silk, mordanted with chromium or other metals. To a lesser extent fustic, cutch, and cochineal are also employed.

Inorganic Coloring Matters. There are a great many inorganic chemicals that are used as pigments. These were considered under paints (Chap. 24). However, khaki shades are prepared on ducks, drills, canvas, particularly for tents, cots, and such out-of-door use by soaking the cotton cloth in a solution of ferrous sulfate or ferrous acetate. The iron is converted into the hydroxide, either by an alkali or by drying, and is then oxidized by a bleaching powder solution to the darker ferric condition.

SELECTED REFERENCES

The following list, mostly of books, embraces the most pertinent references to dyes and intermediates. As this is an old industry, books published a number of years ago are still of much value.

Intermediates:

Barnett, E. deB., "Anthracene and Anthraquinone," D. Van Nostrand Company, Inc., New York, 1921.

Cain, J. C., "Manufacture of Intermediate Products for Dyes," The Macmillan Company, New York, 1919.

Davidson, A., "Intermediates for Dyestuffs," Ernest Benn, Ltd., London, 1926.

Frank, G. H., "The Manufacture of Intermediates and Dyes, An Introduction to Works Practice," Chemical Publishing Company, Inc., New York, 1952.

Groggins, P. H., "Aniline and Its Derivatives," D. Van Nostrand Company, Inc. New York, 1924.

————, editor, "Unit Processes in Organic Synthesis," 4th ed., McGraw-Hill Book Company, Inc., New York, 1952.

Houben, J., and W. Fischer, "Das Anthracen und die Anthrachinone," Georg Thieme Verlag, Leipzig, 1929.

Reverdin, F., and H. Fulda, "Tabellarische Uebersicht der Naphthalinderivate," Basel, 1894.

Schwalbe, C., "Benzol-tabellen," Verlagsbuchhandlung Gebrüder Borntraeger, Berlin, 1903.

Shreve, R. Norris, "Dyes Classified by Intermediates," Reinhold Publishing Corporation, New York, 1922.

Wichelhaus, H., "Sulfurieren, Alkalischmelze der Sulfosäuren," Otto Spamer, Leipzig, 1911.

[1] TISDALE, Natural Dyewoods, *Chem. Inds.*, **49**, 784–786 (1942).

Dyes:

Lubs, H. A., *et al.*, "The Chemistry of Synthetic Dyes and Pigments," Reinhold Publishing Corporation, New York, 1955.

Venkataraman, K., "The Chemistry of Synthetic Dyes," Academic Press, Inc., New York, 1952.

Kirk, R. E., and D. F. Othmer, "Encyclopedia of Chemical Technology," Vol. 5, etc., The Interscience Encyclopedia, Inc., New York, 1950.

BIOS (British Intelligence Objectives Subcommittee) Reports, British Information Services, 30 Rockefeller Plaza, New York,

FIAT (Field Information Agency, Technical) Reports, Office of Technical Services, U.S. Dept. of Commerce, Washington. (Write for list, but Lubs, *et al.*, includes discussion of both BIOS and FIAT reports).

Bucherer, H. T., "Lehrbuch der Farbenchemie," Otto Spamer, Leipzig, 1914.

Cain, J. C., "Chemistry and Technology of the Diazo Compounds," Edward Arnold & Co., London, 1920.

———, "The Manufacture of Dyes," Edward Arnold & Co., London, 1922.

Fierz-David, H. E., and L. Blangey, "The Fundamental Processes of Dye Chemistry," from 5th Austrian ed., Interscience Publishers, Inc., New York, 1949.

Georgievics, G. von, and E. Grandmougin, "A Textbook of Dye Chemistry," Scott, Greenwood and Son, London, 1920.

Green, A. G., "Landmarks in Evolution of the Dye Industry," Jubilee Issue of Society of Dyers & Colourists, Bradford, Yorkshire, 1934.

Hantsch, A., and G. Reddelien, "Die Diazoverbindungen," Springer-Verlag OHG, Berlin, 1921.

Heumann, K., "Die Anilinfarben und ihre Fabrikation," Vieweg-Verlag, Brunswick, Germany, 1906.

Hewitt, J. T., "Synthetic Coloring Matters: Dyestuffs Derived from Pyridine, Quinoline, Acridine and Xanthene," Longmans, Green and Company, New York, 1922.

———, "Synthetic Coloring Matters: Azine and Oxazine Dyestuffs," Longmans, Green & Co., Inc., New York, 1918.

Lange, Otto, "Die Schwefelfarbstoffe, ihre Herstellung und Verwendung," Otto Spamer, Leipzig, 1925.

Mayer, Fritz, "Chemie der organischen Farbstoffe," Springer-Verlag OHG, Berlin, 1934.

O'Brien, W. B., "Factory Practice in the Manufacture of Azo Dyes," Chemical Publishing Company, Inc., New York, 1924.

Rose, R. E., Growth of the Dyestuffs Industry, *J. Chem. Educ.*, **3** (9), 973 (1926).

Rowe, F. M., "Colour Index and Supplement," Society of Dyers and Colourists, Bradford, Yorkshire, 1924 and 1928.

———, Two lectures on the development of chemistry of commercial synthetic dyes (1856–1938), Institute of Chemistry, London, 1938.

Saunders, K. H., "Aromatic Diazo Compounds and Their Technical Applications," 2d ed., Edward Arnold & Co., London, 1949.

Thorpe, J. F., "Dictionary of Applied Chemistry," 4th ed., Longmans, Green & Co., Inc., New York, 1937–.

Truttwin, H., "Enzyklopädie der Kupenfarbstoffe," Springer-Verlag OHG, Berlin, 1920.

Ullmann, Fritz, "Enzyklopaedie der technischen Chemie," 3d ed., Urban & Schwarzenberg, Berlin and Vienna, 1951.

Patents:

Doyle, Aida M., "Digest of Patents, Coal Tar Dyes and Allied Compounds," Chemical Publishing Company, Inc., New York, 1925.

Fierz-David, H. E., and Max Dorn, "Fortschritte der Teerfarbenfabrikation und verwandter Industriezweige," Springer-Verlag OHG, Berlin, 1927.

Friedlander, P., "Fortschritte der Teerfarbenfabrikation," Springer-Verlag OHG, Berlin, 1910.

Lange, Otto, "Die Zwischenprodukte der Teerfarbenfabrikation," Otto Spamer, Leipzig, 1920.

Winther, Adolf, "Zusammenstellung der Patents auf dem Gebiete der organischen Chemie," Alfred Topelmann, Giessen, 1908 and 1910, 3 vols.

Miscellaneous:

Knecht, E., C. Rawson, and R. Lowenthal, "Manual of Dyeing," 8th ed., Charles Griffin & Co., Ltd., London, 1925.

Whittaker, C. M., "Testing of Dyestuffs in the Laboratory," Heywood and Co., Ltd., London, 1920.

———, and C. C. Wilcock, "Dyeing with Coal Tar Dyestuffs," 5th ed., Baillière, Tindall, & Cox, London, 1950.

Technical Manual and Yearbook, American Association of Textile Chemists and Colorists, Howes Publishing Co., New York. This is a very excellent *annual* classified listing of articles and books pertaining to textiles and dyes.

CHAPTER 39

ORGANIC CHEMICALS, NOT OTHERWISE CLASSIFIED

All in all, the manufacture of the various synthetic organic chemicals is the fastest growing and the most complex of all of the divisions of the chemical industry. Special phases of organic chemicals are presented under the respective industries as, for instance, in Chap. 38 pertaining to intermediates and dyes, in Chap. 37 including many organics based upon petroleum, and in Chap. 27 embracing perfumes and the flavoring industries. This chapter includes those organic chemicals which do not fall more specifically under one of the above or other headings in this book.

Historical. The beginnings of the organic chemical industry in the United States started with the manufacture of certain medicinal compounds during the Civil War. In 1879, a small dye works was built, and by 1917 there were seven companies engaged in the manufacture of dyes and intermediates. The medicinal field had also increased. Up to 1914 many organic chemicals had been imported from Germany. The start of the First World War not only eliminated German and Swiss imports but increased the market for organic chemicals within the United States and forced a general realization of the importance of this field. The use of refinery and natural gases as raw materials for the making of organic chemicals dates back to 1922, when isopropyl alcohol was manufactured commercially from propylene gas from a petroleum refinery.

Uses and Economics. The production of synthetic organic compounds has been and is increasing rapidly. The rate varies with the industry and with the individual compound within an industry, depending on the lowering of the cost and the extent of the consumption. Summaries for acyclic and for cyclic (coal tar) chemicals are in Tables 1 and 2. These tables give some comparative data.[1] Individual statistics appear where the compound itself is presented. The usage of these organic compounds covers a wide range. A partial classification includes the following: dyes, medicinals, perfumes and flavors, rubber accelerators, rubber antioxidants, synthetic resins, solvents, refrigerants, detergents, antiknock and antifreeze compounds, insecticides, flotation agents, photographic chemicals, war gases, tanning agents, dry-cleaning fluids, synthetic rubbers, humectants, and vitamins. The intricate relationships among

[1] Compare Table 2, Chap. 38, particularly for 1954 production figures.

TABLE 1. PRODUCTION OF ACYCLIC SYNTHETIC ORGANIC CHEMICALS IN THE
UNITED STATES[a]
(In thousands of pounds)

	1937	1939	Average 1948–1952	1954
Medicinals................	1,314	1,668	8,520	16,662
Flavors and perfumes.......	1,803	2,137	9,560	13,437
Plastics and resins..........	....	....	804,664	1,239,623
Rubber chemicals..........	....	13,122	16,673	20,037
Synthetic rubbers.........	....	....	376,520	461,713
Plasticizers................	....	....	58,955	73,056
Surface-active agents.......	....	....	239,002	385,614
Pesticides, etc..............	....	....	33,085	61,741
Miscellaneous and other.....	2,505,027	2,984,037	13,773,525	16,998,930
Total................	....	4,000,000[b]	15,320,504	19,270,793

[a] "Synthetic Organic Chemicals," U.S. Tariff Commission (published annually).
[b] Approximate.

TABLE 2. PRODUCTION OF CYCLIC SYNTHETIC ORGANIC CHEMICALS IN THE
UNITED STATES[a]
(In thousands of pounds)

	1920	1940	Average 1948–1952	1954
Intermediates....................	257,727	805,801	3,494,976	4,613,869
Finished products................	....	....	3,575,195	4,560,085
Dyes...........................	88,264	127,834	173,754	142,982
Toners and lakes...............	....	....	42,271	39,840
Medicinals.....................	5,185	18,208	46,444	49,262
Flavors and perfumes...........	266	4,490	16,801	21,663
Plastics and resins..............	4,660	222,943	1,175,713	1,588,180
Rubber chemicals...............	....	....	94,569	109,865
Synthetic rubbers...............	....	....	1,060,050	933,249
Plasticizers.....................	....	....	162,100	227,618
Surface-active agents...........	....	....	334,002	640,222
Pesticides, etc..................	....	....	256,679	257,533
Miscellaneous or other..........	14,567	148,385	202,812	409,157
Total......................	....	....	7,070,071	9,173,954

[a] "Synthetic Organic Chemicals," U.S. Tariff Commission (published annually).

these products has been shown in the literature[1] by means of various
charts. Figure 1 illustrates some of the chemicals that may be prepared
from coal, air, and water.

[1] ANON., Opportunities in the Synthetic Organic Chemical Industry, *Chem. &
Met. Eng.* **48** (10), 94 (1941).

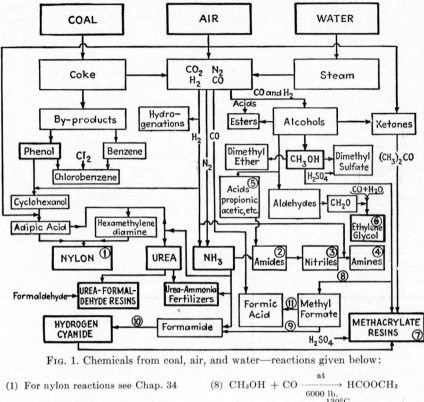

FIG. 1. Chemicals from coal, air, and water—reactions given below:

(1) For nylon reactions see Chap. 34

(2) $RCO_2H + NH_3 \rightarrow RCONH_2 + H_2O$

(3) $RCONH_2 \rightarrow RCN + H_2O$

(4) $RCN + H_2 \rightarrow RCH_2NH_2$

(5) $CH_3OH + CO \rightarrow CH_3COOH$

(6) $CH_2O + CO + H_2O \xrightarrow[\text{pressure}]{\text{high}} COOH \cdot CH_2OH \xrightarrow{H_2} CH_2OH \cdot CH_2OH + H_2O$

(7) $CH_3COCH_3 + HCN \rightarrow CH_3C(OH)(CH_3)CN \xrightarrow[CH_3OH]{H_2SO_4} CH_2 = C(CH_3)CO_2CH_3 \rightarrow$
Acetone cyanohydrin   Methyl methacrylate
Methacrylate resin (Fig. 4, Chap. 35).

(8) $CH_3OH + CO \xrightarrow[\substack{6000 \text{ lb.}}]{\text{at}} HCOOCH_3$

(9) $HCOOCH_3 + NH_3 \xrightarrow[\substack{100 \text{ psi}}]{130°C} HCONH_2$
$+ CH_3OH$

(10) $HCONH_2 \rightarrow HCN + H_2O$

(11) $HCOOCH_3 + H_2O \rightarrow HCOOH$
$+ CH_3OH$

The classification of such a large number of products is naturally difficult. They might be arranged according to their origin as (1) coal-tar derivatives, (2) petroleum and natural-gas derivatives, and (3) miscellaneous (such as methanol from CO and H_2). Perhaps a more modern method would be according to their manufacturing procedure, namely, according to *unit chemical processes*. As adopted here, this results in the following divisions for arranging the various miscellaneous organic chemicals: products resulting from nitration, esterification, amination by reduction, amination by ammonolysis, halogenation, sulfonation, hydrolysis, oxidation, hydrogenation, alkylation, and condensation. These parallel the arrangement for intermediates in Chap. 38. Since, in the preceding chapter, each unit process is broadly defined and described as to its basic chemistry, agents, and equipment, these aspects will not be repeated here. Chapter 2 introduces the unit processes as well as the unit operations.

NITRATION

Nitration is one of the important means for introducing nitrogen into hydrocarbons. Except for explosives and an occasional solvent, the nitro group is usually changed as by amination reduction before the product is used. Nitric acid is a powerful oxidizing agent as well as a nitrating one. Especially in difficult nitrations is much oxidation met with. Here the exact conditions for the maximum yield of nitrobodies and the minimum of oxidation products should be determined and closely adhered to.

Probably nitro-benzene is the most important technical nitration product (Chap. 38) except for the wartime explosives such as trinitro-toluene, tetryl, picric acid, and cyclonite (Chap. 22). The so-called *nitro-glycerine* and *nitro-cellulose* are nitrate esters (Chap. 22).

α-Nitro-naphthalene. In nitrating naphthalene,[1] a mixed acid of the following composition has been used: H_2SO_4, 60 per cent; HNO_3, 16 per cent. The acid is run into a jacketed cast-iron nitrator, and the finely powdered naphthalene is added while holding the temperature at 25 to 30°C. The reaction is carried out at 50°C. for 6 hr. and at 60°C. for 1 hr. At the end of this period the mass is run into a separator where the nitro-naphthalene, which floats on the surface, is removed from the spent acid. The product is washed twice with boiling water to remove acid and to steam-distill any unnitrated naphthalene. The molten product is run under agitation into cold water, producing fine pellets. If necessary, the product can be purified by recrystallization from solvent naphtha. The yield under these conditions is 95 per cent. The product is a yellow crystalline solid melting at 61°C. and is used as a dye intermediate and in further syntheses to make α-naphthylamine and dinitro-naphthalene. However, much α-naphthylamine is changed by ammonolysis into phenyl-α-naphthylamine for an antioxidant in rubber or gasoline.

Nitro-paraffins. A basic development in the field of nitration has been the vapor-phase low-pressure nitration of aliphatic hydrocarbons.[2] The hydrocarbon, propane for example, is vaporized and mixed with

---

[1] *Cf.* GROGGINS, "Unit Processes in Organic Synthesis," 4th ed., p. 75, McGraw-Hill Book Company, Inc., New York, 1952; FIERZ-DAVID and BLANGEY, "Dye Chemistry," Interscience Publishers, Inc., New York, 1949.

[2] HASS, HODGE, and VANDERBILT, Nitration of Gaseous Paraffins, *Ind. Eng. Chem.*, **28**, 339 (1936); HASS and RILEY, The Nitroparaffins, *Chem. Rev.*, **32**, 373 (1943), an excellent bibliography and summary.

vaporized nitric acid to give at least a 2 to 1 ratio of hydrocarbon to acid. The reactions, nitrations, and oxidations take place very quickly and at around 400°C. The vapors are condensed rapidly to give liquids of nitro-paraffins and nitric acid, with the vapors of excess propane and the products of oxidation passing on. Various paraffins may be nitrated with similar procedures. It is characteristic of these nitrations that the original carbon chain may be reacted at any point to yield a variety of products.

$$
\begin{array}{ll}
\text{Propane (in excess)} \\
+ \\
\text{Nitric acid}
\end{array}
\rightarrow
\left\{
\begin{array}{ll}
CH_3CH_2CH_2NO_2 & CO_2 \\
CH_3CHNO_2CH_3 & H_2O \\
CH_3CH_2NO_2 & + NO \\
CH_3NO_2 & \text{etc.}
\end{array}
\right.
$$

These reactions have been described,[1] and the equipment has been pictured. The material of construction is essentially stainless steel arranged in a continuous series of heaters, reactors, condensers, distillation columns with the necessary pumps, and control instruments.

The nitro-paraffins are so very reactive and offer raw materials that can be employed in so many useful syntheses that they promise to become the basis of an important branch of chemical industry. Typical syntheses from the nitro-paraffins are as follows:

1. *Reduction to Amines:*

$$CH_3CHNO_2CH_3 + 3H_2 \rightarrow CH_3CHNH_2CH_3 + 2H_2O$$

2-Nitro-propane   Hydrogen   Isopropylamine   Water

2. *Addition of an Aliphatic Aldehyde:*

$$CH_3NO_2 + 3CH_2O \xrightarrow[\text{Catalyst}]{\text{Basic}} CH_2OH\text{---}\underset{\underset{CH_2OH}{|}}{\overset{\overset{NO_2}{|}}{C}}\text{---}CH_2OH$$

Nitro-methane   Formalde-   Tris (hydroxymethyl)-
hyde   nitro-methane

3. *Addition of an Aromatic Aldehyde:*

$$CH_3CHNO_2CH_3 + C_6H_5CHO \xrightarrow{KOH} C_6H_5CHOHC(CH_3)NO_2CH_3$$

2-Nitro-propane   Benzaldehyde   2-Nitro-2-methyl-1-phenyl-1-propanol

4. *Formation of Hydroxylamine or Salts:*

$$CH_3CH_2CH_2NO_2 + H_2SO_4 + H_2O \rightarrow NH_2OH \cdot H_2SO_4 + CH_3CH_2COOH$$

1-Nitro-propane   Hydroxylammonium   Propionic
acid sulfate   acid

[1] GABRIEL, The Nitro-paraffins and Their Derivatives, *Chem. Inds.*, **45**, 664 (1939); GABRIEL, The Nitro-paraffins, New Synthetics for Synthesis, *Ind. Eng. Chem.*, **32**, 887 (1940).

ESTERIFICATION

The making of esters is important for solvents, plasticizers, medicines, and perfumes. Also certain nitrate esters such as nitro-glycerine and nitro-cellulose are among the most powerful explosives (Chap. 22). The acids used may be either organic like acetic and salicylic, or inorganic like nitric and phosphoric.

Ethyl Acetate.[1] This is an important solvent particularly in lacquers. It is manufactured by the following reaction:

$$CH_3CH_2OH + CH_3COOH \underset{\longleftarrow}{\overset{H_2SO_4}{\rightleftharpoons}} CH_3COOC_2H_5 + H_2O$$

Reactions such as this must be forced to completion by applying the law of mass action. In other words, one or more of the products must be removed as they are formed, and an excess of one reagent employed. Such reactions are also accelerated by using a catalyst such as sulfuric acid. The raw materials are acetic acid, ethyl alcohol in excess, and a little sulfuric acid. They are mixed, conducted through heat exchangers, and passed through an esterification column, the overhead of which is the ternary (boiling point 70.2°C.) having the composition: 82.6 per cent ethyl acetate, 8.4 per cent ethyl alcohol, and 9 per cent water. Frequently some water is added to the condensate to remove most of the alcohol which is returned to the system. The ester carrying about 4 per cent of water is rectified through a column, the water going overhead as a constant boiling mixture. It should be noted that all of the acetic acid reacts by virtue of the mass action of the excess alcohol. Ethyl acetate is consumed in such large quantities that this esterification is frequently conducted in a continuous manner. The equipment is almost invariably constructed from copper.

Amyl, butyl, and isopropyl acetates are all obtained from the respective alcohol and acetic acid. The total production of these esters in 1954 was around 100,000,000 lb. of which three-quarters was butyl acetate. All are important lacquer solvents and as such impart good "blush"-resisting qualities to the dried lacquer film. Butyl acetate is the most important nitro-cellulose lacquer solvent. Other esters made similarly are methyl salicylate, methyl anthranilate, diethyl phthalate, and dibutyl phthalate.

Esterification of Olefins. Another important type of esterification is carried out by the addition of an acid to an unsaturate such as ethylene.

$$CH_2:CH_2 + H_2SO_4 \rightarrow C_2H_5OSO_2OH$$

The acid ester is then hydrolyzed by dilution and heat.

$$C_2H_5OSO_2OH + H_2O \rightarrow C_2H_5OH + H_2SO_4$$

[1] Details of various procedures and the physical chemistry involved, are presented by GROGGINS, *op. cit.*, pp. 596–620, 632–635.

This is an alternative procedure for the manufacture of ethyl alcohol in competition with the fermentation procedure described in Chap. 31 (see also Chap. 37). Propylene can be similarly reacted:

$$CH_3 \cdot CH{:}CH_2 + H_2SO_4 \rightarrow CH_3CH(OSO_3H)CH_3$$
$$CH_3CH(OSO_3H)CH_3 + H_2O \rightarrow CH_3CHOHCH_3 + H_2SO_4$$

The propylene from petroleum cracking-still gases is passed up through packed towers at 75 to 80°F. countercurrent to 97 per cent sulfuric acid, the acid absorbing approximately 50 per cent by weight of the propylene. The reaction mixture is taken to a lead-lined dilution tank where the concentration of isopropyl sulfuric acid is reduced to 20 per cent. Heating now hydrolyzes this ester and the isopropyl alcohol distills over. Isopropyl alcohol is used extensively as a solvent and as a rubbing alcohol, but its most important consumption is in the preparation of acetone.

$$CH_3CHOHCH_3 \rightarrow CH_3COCH_3 + H_2$$

This reaction is carried out by passing the isopropyl alcohol over a copper-gauze catalyst at 300°C. Acetone is also prepared by fermentation as presented in Chap. 31 and as a by-product from phenol, from cumene (Chap. 38).

Vinyl Esters. The addition of acids to acetylene furnishes valuable esters.

$$CH{:}CH + CH_3COOH \rightarrow CH_3COOCH{:}CH_2 \tag{1}$$
$$\text{Vinyl acetate}$$
$$CH{:}CH + HCl \rightarrow CH_2{:}CHCl \tag{2}$$
$$\text{Vinyl chloride[1]}$$

If two molecules of acid react, a compound such as ethylidene diacetate is formed.

$$CH{:}CH + 2CH_3COOH \rightarrow (CH_3COO)_2CHCH_3 \tag{3}$$

Reactions (1) and (3) are carried out together[2] as shown in Fig. 2. Oleum, acetic acid, and mercuric oxide are mixed to give a mercury sulfate–mercury acetate catalyst. This, plus acetylene gas and acetic acid, goes into a continuous-reaction kettle which can be heated by steam. The products leave the reactor as vapors, are condensed, and led to a column still. The vapors from the top of the column, containing chiefly vinyl acetate, are condensed and sent to a rectification system to give the refined vinyl acetate, recovered acetic acid, and by-product acetaldehyde. This entire process must be carried on in an anhydrous state. The sludge coming off the bottom of the kettle goes to a settler. Here the

---

[1] Flow sheets and conditions for making vinyl chloride are given in "Petrochemical Process Handbook," Gulf Publishing Co., Houston, Tex., 1953, or *Petroleum Refiner*, **32** (11), 134–137 (1953).

[2] ANON., Vinyl Acetate, *Chem. & Met. Eng.*, **42**, 596 (1935); MORRISON and SHAW, Vinyl Plastics from Carbide, *Chem. & Met. Eng.*, **40**, 293 (1933).

solids are separated and returned to the mercury recovery system, while the liquids are treated in a rectification column to give the ethylidene diacetate. The reaction kettle may be constructed of Duriron. The vinyl acetate plus vinyl chloride produced according to the reactions above is consumed in the making of vinylite resins (*cf.* Chap. 35). The ethylidene

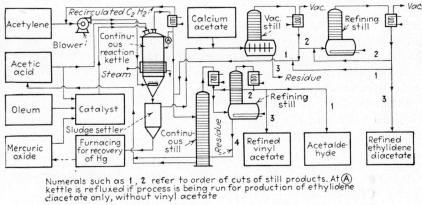

Numerals such as 1, 2 refer to order of cuts of still products. At Ⓐ kettle is refluxed if process is being run for production of ethylidene diacetate only, without vinyl acetate

Fig. 2. Vinyl acetate and ethylidene diacetate.

diacetate is distilled with sodium pyrophosphate or zinc chloride to give acetic anhydride and acetaldehyde.

$$(CH_3COO)_2CHCH_3 \rightarrow (CH_3CO)_2O + CH_3CHO$$

Miscellaneous Esters. Cellulose acetate and cellulose xanthate are extensively manufactured for the synthetic fibers industry as described in Chap. 34. An important series of compounds, the Gardinols or long-chain sodium alkyl sulfates, finds extensive use as wetting agents and detergents (*cf.* Chap. 29). In Fig. 1 the making of some additional esters, methyl formate for example, is shown in outline.

AMINATION BY REDUCTION

These reactions are widely used for the production of dye intermediates and a more complete discussion of them may be found in Chap. 38. However, nitro-paraffins and nitriles are being reduced more extensively each year to meet the demands for amines as emulsifying agents, for absorption of gases, and for many other purposes.

AMINATION BY AMMONOLYSIS

Amination by ammonolysis[1] relates to those reactions in which an amino compound is formed using ammonia or a substituted ammonia as the agent.

[1] GROGGINS, *op. cit.*, Chap. 6, pp. 340*ff*.

Ethylenediamines. An important application of this unit process is in the manufacture of ethylenediamine from ethylene dichloride. This latter compound is treated in a pressure autoclave with aqueous ammonia at 100 to 180°C.

$$CH_2ClCH_2Cl + 4NH_3 \rightarrow CH_2NH_2CH_2NH_2 + 2NH_4Cl$$

A large excess of ammonia is used in order to favor the formation of the primary amine over the various secondary products; even then only a 40 per cent yield of the desired product is obtained. It is used as a corrosion inhibitor, a solvent for vat dyes, a latex stabilizer, and its fatty acid derivatives are employed as detergents.

Ethanolamines. A mixture of mono-, di- and triethanolamines is obtained when ethylene oxide is bubbled through 28 per cent aqueous ammonia at 50 to 60°C. as shown by the following equations:

$$CH_2\underset{O}{\diagdown\diagup}CH_2 + NH_3 \text{ (Excess)} \rightarrow \begin{cases} HOCH_2CH_2NH_2 \\ \text{monoethanolamine} \\ (HOCH_2CH_2)_2NH \\ \text{diethanolamine} \\ (HOCH_2CH_2)_3N \\ \text{triethanolamine} \end{cases}$$

These compounds, usually sold as a mixture, find extensive use in cosmetics as emulsifying agents and as ingredients for dry-cleaning soaps.

Methylamines. Ammonia under pressure may be used to replace an —OH group as well as a halogen atom. An example of this is the preparation of methylamines from methanol. This reaction is carried out in the vapor phase by passing a mixture of methanol and ammonia in the ratio of 1 to 5 over an alumina gel catalyst held at 450°C. The pressure is 200 lb. per sq. in. About 13.5 per cent monomethylamine, CH_3NH_2; 7.5 per cent dimethylamine, $(CH_3)_2NH$; and 10.5 per cent trimethylamine, $(CH_3)_3N$, are obtained on the basis of the ammonia. The recirculation of monoamine raises the yield of the diamine.

Hexamethylenediamine. This is a striking example of a chemical that is now in large-scale production where only a few years ago it was a laboratory curiosity. It is prepared by a two-step amination of adipic acid. The adipic acid is first treated with ammonia and a dehydrating catalyst at 320 to 400°C. in the vapor phase to produce adiponitrile.

$$HO_2C(CH_2)_4CO_2H + 2NH_3 \rightarrow NC(CH_2)_4CN + 4H_2O$$

The adiponitrile is reacted with hydrogen in the presence of ammonia in the liquid phase under pressure below 200°C. to produce hexamethylenediamine (1,6-hexanediamine).

$$NC(CH_2)_4CN + NH_3 + 4H_2 \rightarrow H_2N(CH_2)_6NH_2 + NH_3$$

This compound finds extensive consumption in the making of nylon (Chap. 34).

Hexamethylenetetramine. Evaporation of the reaction product of formaldehyde and ammonia produces hexamethylenetetramine. This compound finds use as a

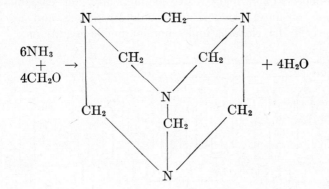

$$6NH_3 + 4CH_2O \rightarrow \qquad + 4H_2O$$

urinary antiseptic (Urotropine), in the rubber industry, and in the preparation of the explosive, cyclonite (Chap. 22). It is also consumed in the making of phenol-formaldehyde resins where it is known as *hexa*.

Sulfanilamide. This compound is made by the following series of reactions:

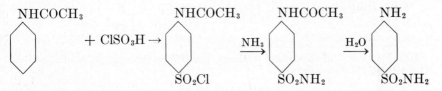

Sulfanilamide is used widely as a specific cure for infections caused by streptococcus and some other organisms. Many similar compounds have also been prepared that possess excellent bactericidal properties. Of these the more important are sulfapyridine, sulfathiazole, and sulfadiazine.[1]

HALOGENATION

Halogenation is the process of introducing halogen atoms into an organic molecule. This may be carried out by substitution for hydrogen, addition to an unsaturated bond, or replacement for an —OH or a —SO₃H group.

[1] FURNAS, editor, "Rogers' Manual of Industrial Chemistry," 6th ed., D. Van Nostrand Company, Inc., New York 1942. See Chap. 34 by Shonle, particularly p. 1312.

Chlorination of Aliphatics. The direct chlorination of aliphatic hydrocarbons has been studied by Hass[1] and coworkers at Purdue University. The various products are obtained through both liquid- and vapor-phase reactions, using various temperatures and pressures, and with or without catalysts. The mixtures of products are separated by rectification. These chloro-aliphatics find many uses commercially; for example, for the production of amyl alcohols from chloro-pentanes and as solvents, particularly in dry cleaning under nonflammable conditions.

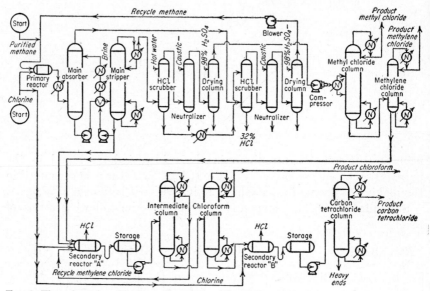

FIG. 3. Flow sheet for chlorinated methane. The HCl scrubbers are of Karbate carbon (*Courtesy of Petroleum Refiner.*)

Chloro-methane (methyl chloride), *dichloro-methane* (methylene chloride), and chloroform are produced in large quantities, the three totaling about 100,000,000 lb. annually. All are obtained by chlorinating methane, although methyl chloride has been made from methanol and hydrogen chloride and chloroform from the decarboxylation of trichlor-acetic acid with lime. Methyl chloride is used as an alkylating agent and refrigerant, methylene chloride as a dewaxing solvent for oils, and chloroform finds employment as a solvent, intermediate, and medicinal.

In chlorinating methane[2] according to the flow sheet of Fig. 3, the Cl_2 and CH_4 (including recycle) are charged in the ratio of 0.6 to 1.0.

[1] HASS, et al., Syntheses from Natural Gas Hydrocarbons, *Ind. Eng. Chem.*, **23,** 352 (1931); HASS, McBEE, and WEBER, *Ind. Eng. Chem.*, **28**, 333 (1936); HASS and WEBER, *Ind. Eng. Chem., Anal. Ed.*, **7**, 231 (1935); HASS, McBEE, and HATCH, *Ind. Eng. Chem.*, **29**, 1335 (1937).

[2] ANON., Chlorinated Methanes, *Petroleum Refiner*, **32** (11), 124 (1953), or "Petrochemical Process Handbook," Gulf Publishing Co., Houston, Tex., 1953.

The temperature in the primary reactor is maintained at 650 to 700°F. using the products to preheat the reactants. The Cl_2 conversion is essentially 100 per cent with the CH_4 conversion about 65 per cent. High velocities are maintained through narrow channels to avoid ignition. The effluent gases contain in the following ratio:

Methyl chloride	6
Methylene chloride	3
Chloroform	1
Carbon tetrachloride	¼

Besides these are the unreacted CH_4 and the HCl together with traces of Cl_2 and heavy chlorinated products.

The secondary chlorination is in liquid phase at ambient temperature, and is light (mercury-arc) catalyzed, in reactor A, converting CH_2Cl_2 to CCl_3H, and in reactor B, CCl_3H to CCl_4. Products can be varied somewhat to satisfy market demands.

Trichloro-ethylene and *tetrachloro-ethylene* (perchloro-ethylene) are cheap, important solvents, dry-cleaning fluids, and degreasing agents. Tetrachloro-ethylene is often preferred for the latter use because of its greater resistance to alkaline attack. Almost half a billion pounds of these two chemicals were produced in 1954. Trichloro-ethylene is made chiefly by dehydrohalogenation of acetylene tetrachloride with lime. Tetrachloro-ethylene is made by exhaustive thermal chlorination of ethane, by dehydrohalogenation of pentachloro-ethane, or by pyrolysis of carbon tetrachloride.

Benzyl Chloride. To produce benzyl chloride, toluene and chlorine are reacted under conditions different from those employed for the ring chlorination yielding chloro-benzene as described in Chap. 38. This reaction is carried out in the *absence* of iron, the temperature being at

$$C_6H_5CH_3 + Cl_2 \rightarrow C_6H_5CH_2Cl + HCl$$

130 to 140°C. and with the reaction mixture circulating through a glass arm in the autoclave where *light catalyzes* the reaction. This product is used in making benzyl alcohol and other chemicals incorporated in perfumes as well as benzyl derivatives.

Ethylene Dichloride. The addition of halogen to unsaturates serves to give many valuable derivatives such as ethylene dichloride, ethylene dibromide, dichloro-ethylene, trichloro-ethylene, and tetrachloro-ethane. The preparation of ethylene dichloride is a typical example.

$$CH_2{:}CH_2 + Cl_2 \xrightarrow{C_2H_4Br} ClCH_2CH_2Cl$$

The chlorine gas is bubbled through a tank of ethylene dibromide and the mixed vapors sent to a chlorinating tower where they meet a stream of ethylene. Here reaction takes place at a temperature of 40 to 50°C.

The products from the tower pass through a partial condenser followed by a separator, the crude ethylene dichloride passing off as a gas and the liquid ethylene dibromide being returned to the process. The product enters into further synthesis as in the preparation of ethylenediamine and Thiokol. It is also used as a solvent and as an additive to tetraethyl lead.

Ethylene Dibromide. This compound, commonly known as *ethylene bromide*, is prepared by the direct addition of bromine to ethylene. It is used in very large quantities as an additive reagent to tetraethyl lead in gasoline. It serves to prevent the deposition of lead oxide on the valves of the gasoline engine.

Carbon Tetrachloride.[1] A typical example of a replacement reaction is found in the preparation of carbon tetrachloride. Carbon disulfide is treated with chlorine in the presence of iron in a lead-lined still with a reflux condenser and heating coils.

$$CS_2 + 3Cl_2 \xrightarrow{Fe} S_2Cl_2 + CCl_4$$

These products are separated by distillation and the sulfur monochloride is treated with CS_2 to give more carbon tetrachloride.

$$CS_2 + 2S_2Cl_2 \rightarrow CCl_4 + 6S$$

When the reaction mixture from the latter step is cooled, the sulfur precipitates, and the carbon tetrachloride is separated and further purified by rectification. The sulfur is converted back to carbon disulfide. The solvent properties of carbon tetrachloride direct its use as a degreasing agent and dry-cleaning fluid. It is also employed in fire extinguishers.

Ethyl Chloride. Halogen acids also may be used to give halogenated derivatives. HCl reacts with ethylene both being in the liquid phase, in the presence of a catalyst such as aluminum chloride, to give ethyl chloride.

$$CH_2:CH_2 + HCl \xrightarrow{AlCl_3} CH_3CH_2Cl$$

Such a reaction may be carried out as a batch process by bringing the reagents together in a pressure vessel. A low temperature is used. HCl may also be made to react with ethyl alcohol to give ethyl chloride according to the equation:

$$CH_3CH_2OH + HCl \rightarrow CH_3CH_2Cl + H_2O$$

This reaction will probably not compete with cheap ethylene from petroleum cracking. The use of ethyl chloride in the making of tetraethyl lead is its most important consumption. It is also employed as a refrigerant, solvent, and anesthetic.

[1] FURNAS, *op. cit.*, p. 467; see also Chlorination of Aliphatics.

Ethylene Chlorohydrin. Hypohalogen acids also add to unsaturates, ethylene chlorohydrin being made according to the equations:

$$CaO + H_2O + 2Cl_2 \rightarrow CaCl_2 + 2HOCl$$
$$HOCl + CH_2{:}CH_2 \rightarrow CH_2OHCH_2Cl$$

In commercial operation, a hydrated lime suspension is passed down a tower countercurrent to a stream of ethylene at 200 atm. and 20°C., thus giving a solution of ethylene in lime water. Chlorine is introduced and the reactants are passed to a chamber where the hypochlorous acid reacts with the ethylene. The ethylene chlorohydrin-calcium chloride solution coming from the reactor may be treated to give ethylene glycol (page 944). This latter is highly valued as an antifreeze.

SULFONATION

Since the sulfonation unit process is applied principally to intermediates and dyes, see Chap. 38 for description and examples. At present, certain detergents employ sulfonation in building up their molecules though usually sulfate esterification is the chosen process.

HYDROLYSIS AND HYDRATION

Hydrolysis,[1] as the name implies, involves the reaction of water, usually in a double decomposition. In almost every case, an accelerating agent is necessary to carry out the process commercially. The hydrolysis of starch to dextrose is presented in Chap. 30, of fats to soaps in Chap. 29, of sulfonates and halides to hydroxy derivatives in Chap. 38, and of ethyl alcohol from ethylene under esterification in this chapter.

Amyl Alcohols. The manufacture of amyl alcohols from the chloropentanes[2] is a typical hydrolysis reaction and is shown in Fig. 4 together with the preceding chlorination. n-Pentane and isopentane are separated from natural gasoline and chlorinated in the vapor phase at 250 to 300°C. The products pass through a heat exchanger to the rectification unit where the hydrogen chloride and the dichlorides (5 per cent) are removed. The hydrolysis of the monochlorides is carried out in a system of digesters, pumps, and heaters through which a hot emulsion of amyl alcohol, water, and sodium oleate circulates. The amyl chlorides and sodium hydroxide solution are continuously added to the system, and a spent brine and crude amyl alcohol vapors are continuously withdrawn. The salt solu-

---

[1] LLOYD and HAMNER, in Chap. 11 of GROGGINS, *op. cit.*, discuss the various aspects of this unit process.

[4] ANON., Synthetic Amyl Alcohol and Acetate, *Chem. & Met. Eng.*, **47**, 493 (1940), pictured flow sheet; ANON., Amyl Alcohol Flow Sheet, *Petroleum Refiner*, **32** (11), 152–153 (1953).

tion is scrubbed to remove alcohol vapors and then returns to the electrolytic cells where the necessary chlorine and caustic for the process are made. The crude amyl alcohol vapors are condensed and rectified to give the following products as shown in Fig. 4: (1) amylene which is hydrated to amyl alcohol, (2) unchanged amyl chlorides to be returned to process, (3) diamyl ether, (4) special amyl alcohol fractions, (5) the mixture of amyl alcohols sold under the name Pentasol and used as lacquer solvents.

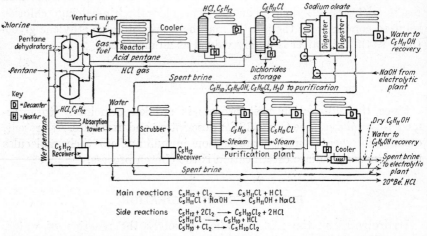

Main reactions $C_5H_{12} + Cl_2 \longrightarrow C_5H_{11}Cl + HCl$
$C_5H_{11}Cl + NaOH \longrightarrow C_5H_{11}OH + NaCl$

Side reactions $C_5H_{12} + 2Cl_2 \longrightarrow C_5H_{10}Cl_2 + 2HCl$
$C_5H_{11}Cl \longrightarrow C_5H_{10} + HCl$
$C_5H_{10} + Cl_2 \longrightarrow C_5H_{10}Cl_2$

Reacting quantities not known ; weight of 100% HCl produced approx. 50% of chlorine charged

FIG. 4. Flow chart for production of amyl alcohols (Pentasol) from pentanes—Sharples procedures.

Ethylene Glycol. The important permanent antifreeze, ethylene glycol, is made by several processes, involving hydrolysis. In the first, ethylene chlorohydrin is treated with sodium bicarbonate solution.

$$CH_2OHCH_2Cl + NaHCO_3 \rightarrow CH_2OHCH_2OH + NaCl + CO_2$$

The chlorohydrin solution is concentrated to 35 to 40 per cent and reacted with the theoretical amount of sodium bicarbonate solution in a closed, stirred, steam-jacketed kettle. At a temperature of 70 to 80°C., the hydrolysis proceeds smoothly with the evolution of CO_2 and is complete in 4 to 6 hr. The glycol solution is concentrated by distillation. As the high-boiling ethylene glycol can be separated only with difficulty from the salt, it is presumably better engineering to make ethylene oxide out of the ethylene chlorohydrin by heating with caustic soda or hydrated lime. This would then be hydrated to the glycol by treating with weakly acidulated water under low pressure.

Diethylene glycol is obtained as a by-product in about 10 per cent yields from the manufacture of ethylene glycol. Its principal use is as a humectant for tobaccos. It is also used as an emulsifying agent for oils and in throwing and soaking operations in the textile industry. Nearly 40,000,000 lb. were produced in 1954.

Another method for making glycol is by the reaction of ethylene, oxygen, and water in the presence of a silver catalyst. The reaction is probably stepwise, involving oxidation and subsequent hydrolysis.

$$CH_2{:}CH_2 + O_2 \rightarrow CH_2\underset{O}{\overset{}{\diagdown\diagup}}CH_2 \xrightarrow{H_2O} \begin{array}{c} CH_2OH \\ | \\ CH_2OH \end{array}$$

A recent high-pressure process for ethylene glycol involves the following reactions:

$$CH_2O + CO + H_2O \rightarrow CH_2OH{\cdot}COOH$$
$$CH_2OH{\cdot}COOH + 2H_2 \rightarrow CH_2OH{\cdot}CH_2OH + H_2O$$

Propylene oxide and *propylene glycol* are produced by reactions analogous to those for ethylene oxide and glycol. Approximately 100,000,000 lb. of propylene glycol are manufactured annually, which is used as an antifreeze, humectant, or hydraulic-fluid additive.

Gallic Acid. Gallic acid, 3,4,5-trihydroxy-benzoic acid, is obtained by the hydrolysis of the glucoside, tannic acid, found in nutgalls and sumac. The process consists of an alkaline or acid autoclaving of the water extracts of the nutgalls. It may also be prepared by fermentation of an extract with *Aspergillus niger* or *Aspergillus gallomyces*. The gallic acid is purified by several recrystallizations from water using nonferrous equipment. The chief uses of gallic acid are in the manufacture of dyes and as a raw material for the production of pyrogallol and bismuth subgallate. It is also a constituent of many inks where the ferric gallate formed on oxidation is the permanent pigment.

OXIDATION

Oxidation is one of the most valuable tools to the synthetic chemist. The possibilities of this process are so varied that a type reaction is impossible. However, it may be said that it involves the addition of oxygen to a molecule or the removal of hydrogen from it. The cheapest reagent, and the one always employed when possible, is air. The reactions are carried out in both the liquid and vapor phases, using a variety of catalysts, V_2O_5 for example. In the latter case, fairly high temperatures (about 400°C.) are employed and, since the reactions are highly exothermic, the problem of heat removal is a large one. This is described under Phthalic Anhydride in Chap. 38, page 884.

Camphor. An organic chemical produced by oxidation is camphor. The raw material for this process is turpentine and the following steps are involved: (1) distillation of turpentine to obtain pinene, (2) saturation with HCl gas giving bornyl chloride, (3) hydrolyzing this to obtain camphene, (4) esterifying to give isoborneol acetate, (5) saponification to isoborneol, and (6) oxidation to camphor. The last reaction is carried out in the liquid phase using nitric acid as the reagent. Twenty parts of isoborneol are dissolved in 100 parts of 1.32 sp. gr. nitric acid plus 5 parts

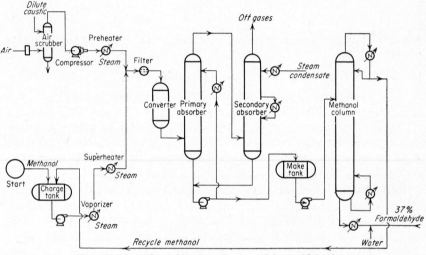

Fig. 5. Flow sheet for manufacture of formaldehyde.

of 50 per cent sulfuric acid. The mixture is heated to 80 to 90°C. and stirred well for 10 hr. The largest use of camphor is as a plasticizer in various resins. It is also consumed in many pharmaceutical preparations.[1]

Formaldehyde. The oxidation of methanol to formaldehyde is an important commercial process.

$$CH_3OH + \tfrac{1}{2}O_2 \overset{Ag}{\rightarrow} H_2CO + H_2O; \qquad \Delta H = -38,000 \text{ cal.}$$
$$CH_3OH \rightarrow H_2CO + H_2; \qquad \Delta H = +20,000 \text{ cal.}$$

The oxidation requires 26.7 cu. ft. of air per pound of methanol reacted, a ratio that is maintained when passing separate streams of these two materials forward. Fresh and recycle methanol are vaporized, super-heated, and passed into the methanol-air mixer. Atmospheric air is purified as shown in the flow diagram of Fig. 5, compressed and preheated to 130°F. in a finned heat exchanger. The products leave the converter at around 1150°F. and at 5 to 10 lb. per sq. in. The converter is a small

[1] GUBELMANN and ELLEY, Production of Synthetic Camphor from Turpentine, *Ind. Eng. Chem.*, **26**, 589 (1934); GROGGINS, *op. cit.*, p. 378.

water-jacketed vessel containing several layers of silver gauze catalyst. About 65 per cent of the CH_3OH is converted per pass.

The reactor effluent contains about 25 per cent formaldehyde which is absorbed with the excess CH_3OH and piped to the make tank. This latter feeds the methanol column for separation of recycle methanol overhead, with the bottom stream containing the formaldehyde and a few per cent of CH_3OH. The water intake adjusts the formaldehyde to 37 per cent strength. The yield in the reaction is 85 to 90 per cent, the formaldehyde being marketed as a 37 per cent solution sometimes called Formalin.[1]

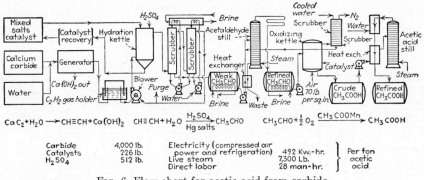

$$CaC_2 + H_2O \rightarrow CH{\equiv}CH + Ca(OH)_2 \qquad CH{\equiv}CH + H_2O \xrightarrow[Hg\ salts]{H_2SO_4} CH_3CHO \qquad CH_3CHO + \tfrac{1}{2}O_2 \xrightarrow{CH_3COOMn} CH_3COOH$$

		Electricity (compressed air		
Carbide	4,000 lb.	power and refrigeration)	492 Kw.-hr.	Per ton
Catalysts	226 lb.	Live steam	7,300 Lb.	acetic
H_2SO_4	512 lb.	Direct labor	28 man-hr.	acid

Fig. 6. Flow chart for acetic acid from carbide.

Much of the equipment is made of stainless steel. Formaldehyde is competitively manufactured by controlled oxidation of natural gas or methane.[2]

Acetic Acid. Various methods for the manufacture of acetic acid involve oxidation. Thus, the production from acetylene goes through the following reactions:

$$C_2H_2 + H_2O \rightarrow CH_3CHO \qquad (1)$$
$$CH_3CHO + \tfrac{1}{2}O_2 \rightarrow CH_3COOH \qquad (2)$$

Reaction (1) is carried out by passing acetylene into a suspension of mercurous sulfate in 25 per cent sulfuric acid in a Duriron kettle under a pressure of 15 lb. per sq. in., as shown in Fig. 6. The temperature is maintained between 70 and 100°C. by the heat of reaction. As a result of side reactions the catalyst is reduced to metallic mercury, necessitating the addition of make-up catalyst every 15 min. and complete change every 8 hr. A series of scrubbers and condensers removes the acetaldehyde from the effluent gases, the yield being 95 per cent. The oxidation of acetaldehyde is carried out in a series of two aluminum-lined steel

[1] HOMER, Formaldehyde, Properties, Analysis and Manufacture, *J. Soc. Chem. Ind.*, **60**, 213 (1941); ANON., Formaldehyde, *Petroleum Refiner*, **32** (11), 120 (1953).

[2] ANON., Formaldehyde from Natural Gas, *Chem. & Met. Eng.*, **49** (9), 154 (1942), pictured flow sheet.

vessels. Here, at a temperature of 55°C. and a pressure of 70 lb. per sq. in., air is used to carry out the reaction, 0.1 per cent of manganese acetate being used to hold down the concentrations of the explosive intermediate, peracetic acid. The crude acetic acid of 94 per cent strength is taken off from the second reactor and rectified.

Acetaldehyde for oxidation is also made from ethyl alcohol according to the following reactions which occur simultaneously:

$$C_2H_5OH + \tfrac{1}{2}O \rightarrow CH_3CHO + H_2O$$
$$C_2H_5OH \rightarrow CH_3CHO + H_2$$

The reaction is exothermic, taking place at 540°C. upon passing through a silver-gauze catalyst with the alcohol vapors entering at 160°C. and

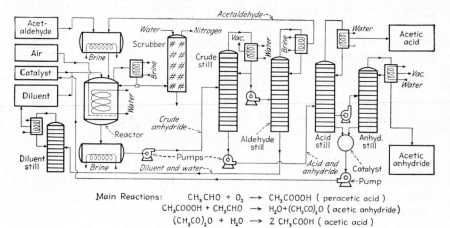

Main Reactions:
$$CH_3CHO + O_2 \rightarrow CH_3COOH \text{ (peracetic acid)}$$
$$CH_3COOH + CH_3CHO \rightarrow H_2O + (CH_3CO)_2O \text{ (acetic anhydride)}$$
$$(CH_3CO)_2O + H_2O \rightarrow 2\,CH_3COOH \text{ (acetic acid)}$$

FIG. 7. Flow chart for acetic anhydride from acetaldehyde.

the air at 200°C. The yield is 85 to 95 per cent, the conversion 50 to 55 per cent, and the product is recovered by scrubbing the vapors from the reactor with ethyl alcohol and then rectifying to give 99 per cent acetaldehyde; this product can be made in the plant of Fig. 5. Acetic acid is also made from CH_3OH and CO as shown in Fig. 1.

Acetic Anhydride. Acetaldehyde, produced by either of the methods discussed above under Acetic Acid, may be oxidized to acetic anhydride according to the process shown in Fig. 7. The acetaldehyde is oxidized by air in the main reactor with methyl acetate diluent and with manganese acetate catalyst present to prevent the formation of explosive amounts of peracetic acid.[1] The pressure is around 60 lb. per sq. in. and the temperature at 50 to 70°C. The products, acetic anhydride and acetic acid, are purified in a series of bubble-cap columns, with the crude still and the anhydride still operating under vacuum. The most impor-

[1] BENSON, New Acetic Anhydride Process, *Chem. & Met. Eng.*, **47**, 150 (1940).

tant use of acetic anhydride is in the making of cellulose acetate. It is also employed in various other acetylations.

Adipic Acid. Vigorous HNO_3 oxidation of cyclohexanol and cyclohexanone produces adipic acid, $HO_2C(CH_2)_4CO_2H$. This compound is extensively used in the preparation of nylon in combination with hexamethylenediamine.

HYDROGENATION

Hydrogenation is employed in the chemical industries today to give many useful products. The various methods for the production of hydrogen are discussed fully in Chap. 8. Besides the addition of hydrogen to double bonds, this reaction may be used to eliminate other elements from a molecule, as is done in petroleum hydrogenations. These include mainly oxygen, nitrogen, sulfur, carbon, and halogens. Hydrogenation is carried on under pressure and usually at elevated temperatures with a suitable catalyst. The temperatures are ordinarily below 400°C. but may extend up to 500°C. in some cases. The catalysts vary with temperature, the noble metals such as platinum or palladium being used up to 150°C., nickel and copper from 150 to 250°C., and various combinations of metals and metal oxides for the higher temperatures. Pressure not only increases the rate of reaction but, in the cases where there is a decrease in volume as the reaction proceeds, causes a desirable shift in the equilibrium according to Le Châtelier's principle. The equipment generally used consists either of a pressure autoclave or a tubular pressure system, built to withstand pressures up to 3,000 lb. per sq. in. or more. Since most hydrogenations are exothermic, the equipment should be designed to facilitate the removal of heat, especially from the catalyst chamber.

Hydrogenation of Fatty Oils. Some of the most familiar hydrogenated products in use today are the solid cooking fats made from various oils. This procedure is fully presented in Chap. 28.

Hydrogenation of Petroleum. The hydrogenation of petroleum is one of the most useful reactions employed in the refinery today. It serves to upgrade heavy oils and residues giving increased yields of gasoline, to produce higher octane gasoline, and to furnish improved lubricating oils. A discussion of this process is given in Chap. 37.

Methanol Synthesis. One of the most important of the high-pressure syntheses in use today is the production of methanol and various higher alcohols from carbon monoxide and hydrogen. The essential reaction is

$$CO + 2H_2 \rightarrow CH_3OH; \qquad \Delta H = -24,620 \text{ cal.}$$

The catalyst most commonly employed is copper mixed with oxides of zinc, chromium, manganese, or aluminum. For the synthesis of methanol, contact of the gases with hot iron must be avoided and so copper-lined reactors are used. The theoretical proportions of the gases are mixed and compressed to 4,500 lb. per sq. in. After oil purification, the gases go to the reactors where, at 300°C., the equilibrium yield is better than 60 per cent. The gaseous products then pass through the heat exchangers to high-pressure condensers where the methanol is condensed at 3,500 to 4,000 lb. per sq. in. with the gases being sent back to the process. Very pure (99 per cent) methanol is furnished by this process. The higher alcohols are produced at higher temperatures, 350 to 475°C., using a catalyst containing alkali (see Fig. 1).[1]

Methanol finds a wide variety of direct industrial uses such as a denaturant, antifreeze, fuel, and solvent. In addition, it is the starting material in such reactions as the preparation of methylamines, formaldehyde, and dimethyl-aniline.

High-molecular-weight Aliphatic Amines.[2] These compounds are made by catalytically hydrogenating the corresponding nitriles prepared by dehydration at elevated temperatures of the ammonium salts of the fatty acids.

$$RCO_2NH_4 \rightarrow RCONH_2 \rightarrow RCN \xrightarrow{H_2} RCH_2NH_2$$

These are essentially new industrial compounds of the "cationic" active class and are finding employment as flotation agents, in water treatment, and in textile finishing. They also possess bactericidal properties, and some of them are insecticides or insect repellents. These are commercially available with the alkyl chain in the above reaction having from 6 to 18 carbon atoms, some being shipped in carload lots.

ALKYLATION

A wide variety of reactions[3] may be employed to introduce an alkyl radical into the various organic compounds such as are classified under Alkylation in Chap. 2 and exemplified here and in Chap. 38.

Ethyl Ether. Ethyl ether and other aliphatic ethers are made by the dehydrating action of sulfuric acid on an alcohol.

$$C_2H_5OH + H_2SO_4 \rightarrow C_2H_5 \cdot HSO_4 + H_2O \tag{1}$$
$$C_2H_5OH + C_2H_5 \cdot HSO_4 \rightarrow C_2H_5OC_2H_5 + H_2SO_4 \tag{2}$$

The alcohol and sulfuric acid are heated to 140°C. in a lead-lined vessel. After the reaction is started, the process is continuous. A mixture of ether, alcohol, and water is constantly vaporized and rectified to furnish a pure product. The yield for the reaction is 94 per cent. Ethyl ether

---

[1] Anon., Methanol, *Petroleum Refiner*, **32** (11), 122 (1953), flow sheet and description.
[2] Ralston, Chemicals from Fats, *Chem. Eng. News*, **21**, 3 (1943).
[3] See Chap. 13 on Alkylation by Shreve in Groggins, *op. cit.*

is also produced in the hydration of ethylene to ethyl alcohol. The first step in the process gives ethyl sulfate as above from which the second reaction proceeds. The uses of ethyl ether are many and varied. Some important ones are as a solvent, an anesthetic, and for further synthesis of organic compounds.

Glycol Ethers. A very practical series of ethers is obtained by the use of ethylene oxide as an alkylating agent. Two of these, ethylene glycol ethyl ether (Cellosolve) and diethylene glycol ethyl ether (Carbitol), are obtained by the reaction of ethylene oxide with ethyl alcohol.

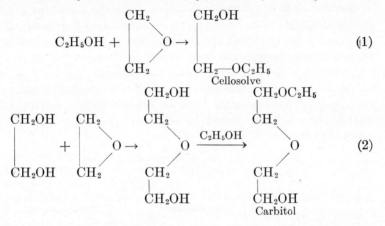

(1)

Cellosolve

(2)

Carbitol

Isomers are made by varying the reactants from those given. Absolute ethyl alcohol and liquid ethylene oxide under pressure are introduced into an autoclave, the alcohol being present in 15 per cent excess. The autoclave is heated at 150°C. for 12 hr., the pressure changing from 250 lb. per sq. in. at the start, to 125 at the end. The reaction mass is fractionated, and the Cellosolve is taken off at 134°C. It is obtained in yields of 70 per cent based on the alcohol. Further distillation of the residue gives the Carbitol which boils at 201.9°C. The latter results from any ethylene glycol present in the reagents or formed by action of ethylene oxide on any water present or made. Carbitol is also manufactured directly. Both of these substances find widespread usage as specialized solvents in textiles, cosmetics, dyeing, and in sealing cellophane packages.

Tetraethyl Lead. A very important alkylated product is tetraethyl lead, the universal antiknock compound for gasolines. It is prepared commercially by the action of ethyl chloride on a lead-sodium alloy.

$$4PbNa + 4C_2H_5Cl \rightarrow Pb(C_2H_5)_4 + 3Pb + 4NaCl$$

The autoclave for the reaction must have a heating jacket, a heavy-duty stirrer to agitate the lead alloy, and a reflux condenser. The alloy should be finely divided, and the temperature should be below 70°C. The reaction is heated at the start and then must be cooled to maintain the temperature at 40 to 60°C. After 2 to 6 hr., the excess ethyl chloride is distilled off and tetraethyl lead steam distilled from the reaction mixture.

Silicones.[1] Like tetraethyl lead, silicones are examples of important compounds of mixed organic-inorganic nature. The silicones and derivatives are remarkable in the variety and unusualness of their properties, such as solubility in organic solvents, insolubility in water and alcohols, heat stability, chemical inertness, high dielectric properties, relative low flammability, solutions low in viscosity at high resin content and with low viscosity change with temperature, and nontoxicity.

Because of these properties, the silicones are useful for (1) fluids for hydraulics and heat transfer, (2) lubricants and greases, (3) sealing compounds for electrical applications, (4) resins for lamination and for high-temperature-resistant varnishes and enamels, (5) silicone rubber, (6) water repellents, and (7) waxes and polishes, etc.

The silicones are made either through the Grignard reaction or more economically by alkylating with an organic halide, usually CH_3Cl (or C_6H_5Cl or mixtures thereof) a silicon-copper alloy, according to the following reaction:

$$Si(10 \text{ per cent Cu}) + nCH_3Cl \xrightarrow[\text{48 hr.}]{200°C., 1–2 \text{ atm.}} (CH_3)_nSiCl_{(4-n)}$$

Principal products: $\underbrace{(CH_3)_2SiCl_2, (CH_3)_3SiCl, CH_3SiCl_3}_{\text{Chloro-silanes}}$

The silicon or copper may absorb any excess chlorine. The further reactions to silanols, siloxanes, and polymers may be expressed:

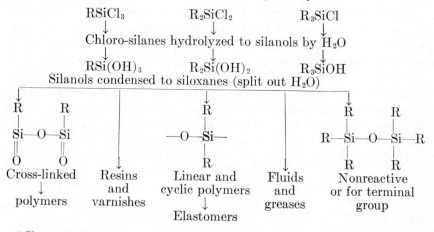

[1] Chapter 35 for plastic and insulation use; KIRK and OTHMER, *op. cit.*, Vol. 10, p. 808; ROCHOW, "An Introduction to the Chemistry of the Silicones," 2d ed., John Wiley & Sons, Inc., New York, 1947; MCGREGOR, R. R., "Silicones and Their Uses," McGraw-Hill Book Co., Inc., New York, 1954.

Chain length varied by percentage of R_3SiCl which provides end groups. Lower polymers are oils; higher polymers are solids.

Barbital. Barbital (diethyl-barbituric acid) is prepared by a series of reactions starting with the ethyl ester of malonic acid.

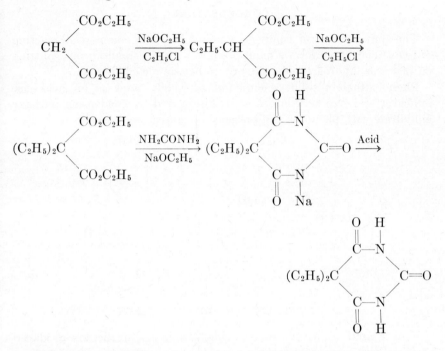

A whole series of similar compounds may be prepared in a like manner by using alkylating agents other than ethyl chloride. For example, phenyl-ethyl-barbituric acid is known as *phenobarbital*. These compounds find extensive pharmaceutical use as hypnotics and soporifics.

Procaine (Novocaine). The production of the important local anesthetic, procaine, involves not only the unit process of alkylation but also halogenation and reduction.

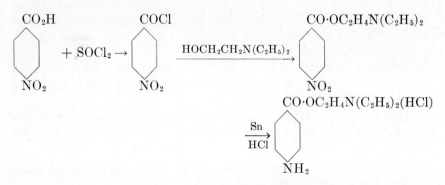

The hydroxy tertiary amine that is used to condense with the *p*-nitro-benzoyl chloride is prepared by treating ethylene chlorohydrin with diethylamine.

CONDENSATION

The unit process of condensation involves the commercial reacting of two chemicals to form a main product with the simultaneous splitting off of water, hydrogen chloride, or another simple compound.

Phenolphthalein.[1] This compound is widely used as an acid-base indicator and also as a laxative. It is prepared by condensing phthalic anhydride with phenol in the presence of sulfuric acid.

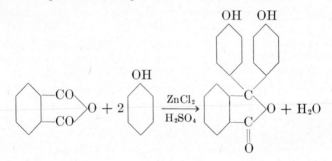

MISCELLANEOUS UNIT PROCESSES

Formic Acid. Two very useful acids, formic and oxalic, are produced starting with sodium hydroxide solution and carbon monoxide. Sodium hydroxide (97 to 98 per cent) is reacted with the carbon monoxide at 200°C. and under a pressure of 8 to 10 atm. in a jacketed autoclave.

$$CO + NaOH \rightarrow HCOONa$$

The carbon monoxide is usually produced by the incomplete combustion of coke, followed by removal of CO_2 with an amine solvent, or by scrubbing with caustic soda. After the reaction is complete, the solution is acidified and the formic acid distilled off. The product is 90 per cent formic acid and the yield is 95 per cent. Formic acid serves for the preparation of formate esters and oxalic acid. In the anhydrous state it is employed as a solvent for certain reactions and as a reducing agent (see Fig. 1) for conversion of methanol and carbon monoxide into methyl formate and then into formic acid.

Oxalic Acid. If, after the sodium formate is made according to the foregoing equation, the pressure is reduced in the autoclave and the temperature is raised to 375°C., sodium oxalate will be formed.

[1] ROWE, "Colour Index and Supplement," Society of Dyers and Colourists, Bradford, Yorkshire, 1924; GROGGINS, *op. cit.*, p. 648.

$$2\text{HCOONa} \rightarrow \underset{\underset{\text{COONa}}{|}}{\text{COONa}} + \text{H}_2$$

The hydrogen is exhausted from the autoclave, and the reaction is complete when no more hydrogen is evolved. Milk of lime is added to the solution and the mixture thoroughly agitated. The calcium oxalate formed is filtered off and the caustic solution is concentrated and reused.

$$\text{Na}_2\text{C}_2\text{O}_4 + \text{Ca(OH)}_2 \rightarrow \text{CaC}_2\text{O}_4 + 2\text{NaOH}$$

The calcium oxalate, plus some calcium carbonate that is present, is reacted with dilute sulfuric acid. Much of the calcium precipitates as $\text{CaSO}_4\cdot2\text{H}_2\text{O}$ while on concentration the remaining calcium sulfate

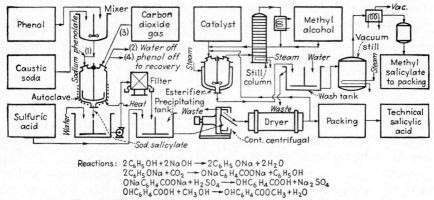

Reactions: $2\text{C}_6\text{H}_5\text{OH} + 2\text{NaOH} \rightarrow 2\text{C}_6\text{H}_5\text{ONa} + 2\text{H}_2\text{O}$
$2\text{C}_6\text{H}_5\text{ONa} + \text{CO}_2 \rightarrow \text{ONaC}_6\text{H}_4\text{COONa} + \text{C}_6\text{H}_5\text{OH}$
$\text{ONaC}_6\text{H}_4\text{COONa} + \text{H}_2\text{SO}_4 \rightarrow \text{OHC}_6\text{H}_4\text{COOH} + \text{Na}_2\text{SO}_4$
$\text{OHC}_6\text{H}_4\text{COOH} + \text{CH}_3\text{OH} \rightarrow \text{OHC}_6\text{H}_4\text{COOCH}_3 + \text{H}_2\text{O}$

FIG. 8. Flow sheet for salicylic acid and methyl salicylate.

present precipitates out and is filtered off. Further concentration to 30°Bé., followed by cooling, causes the oxalic acid to crystallize. These crystals are removed and washed in a centrifuge while the mother liquor is employed for make-up in subsequent runs.

The uses of oxalic acid are many and varied. Some of the important ones are as a germicide, a bleaching agent, a solvent, and as a starting material in the manufacture of various other chemicals, especially many simple and complex oxalates.

Salicylic Acid. Salicylic acid[1] is made by the Kolbe reaction from CO_2 (see Fig. 8). The starting material is phenol, which is run into hot aqueous caustic soda to give sodium phenate. This step is carried out in a heated iron tank.

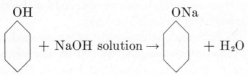

[1] SHONLE, p. 1305, in FURNAS, op. cit.; pictured flow sheet in Chem. & Met. Eng., **50** (8), 132–135 (1943).

The resulting solution is evaporated to dryness in stirred autoclaves under vacuum at 130°C. The sodium phenate must be absolutely dry; to ensure this, certain manufacturers conduct this unit operation in a heated ball mill so that the material being dried is simultaneously ground up. The temperature is reduced to 100°C., and dry CO_2 gas is introduced under 6 atm. pressure. The following reactions occur:

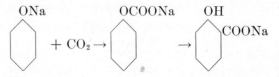

The sodium salicylate is dissolved in water and decolorized by passing through activated carbon containing some Zn powder. The solution is acidified with excess hydrochloric acid, precipitating the salicylic acid.

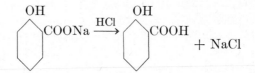

Salicylic acid is used as a medicinal and an intermediate in the production of other medicinals, but the largest consumption is in the making of aspirin, acetyl salicylic acid. It also finds use as an antiseptic.

Aspirin. Aspirin, acetyl salicylic acid, is prepared by acylating salicylic acid with acetic anhydride. It is widely used as a pain-relieving drug.

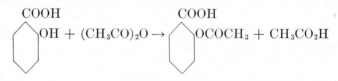

Tartaric Acid. Tartaric acid,[1] dihydroxysuccinic acid, has the formula:

$$HOOCCHOHCHOHCOOH$$

This occurs as its dextro-rotary isomer and as its crude acid potassium salt with some calcium salt in argols and wine lees—the solid deposits left in a wine vat after fermentation. The pure acid potassium salt, $KHC_4H_4O_6$, cream of tartar, is obtained by leaching with water, precipitation of the calcium and other impurities, evaporation, and crystallization, followed by recrystallization if necessary. It is dried and powdered for use as an ingredient of baking powders.

Tannic Acid. Tannic acid, a glucoside of gallic acid, is obtained by countercurrent extraction of nutgalls by water. The extract as obtained

---

[1] ULLMANN, "Enzyklopaedie der technischen Chemie," 3d ed., Urban & Schwarzenberg, Berlin and Vienna, 1951.

is 10 to 11°Bé. The equipment is constructed either of copper or of wood. It is imperative that no iron be present as iron reacts with tannic acid to form black iron tannate. Even traces of iron are sufficient to discolor the product. The water extract is concentrated in volume and, on drying, yields technical tannin which is used as a mordant in dyeing and as a source of gallic acid. Extraction of nutgalls with alcohol or ether, bleaching of the extract with mild reducing agents, such as sodium bisulfite, and evaporation of the extract yield medicinal grade tannin. This is used for burns, as an astringent, in gargles, and to precipitate proteins in wineries and breweries.

Pyrogallol. Pyrogallol, 1,2,3-trihydroxybenzene, is obtained by decarboxylating gallic acid. The gallic acid is autoclaved with water at 12 atm. and 200°C. with copper equipment. The reaction is complete when no more carbon dioxide is evolved, and the water solution is then evaporated to dryness. The solid pyrogallol is purified by sublimation *in vacuo* or in superheated carbon dioxide. It is used in photography, for dyeing, medicinally to treat skin diseases, and as an oxygen absorbent in analytical chemistry.

Alkaloids. Alkaloids[1] are generally defined as complex organic bases of plant origin. A few of the more important alkaloids are morphine, cocaine, caffeine, quinine, strychnine, and atropine. They are widely employed as medicinals and are obtained by extraction from the plant source and purified by various precipitations and crystallizations.

Vitamins.[2] Certain organic compounds have been found to be essential in the diet of man. Absence of these compounds produces scurvy, beriberi, and many other disorders. It is interesting to note that, important as the presence of these substances is in the diet, only very small quantities are needed by man. The supply must be maintained daily either from food or special means. At present, a number of these essential compounds or vitamins have been synthesized, but others are known whose exact chemical structure has not been established. Although vitamins A and D are obtained economically from natural sources (chiefly fish-liver oils), their structures are known. Vitamin C, present in citrus fruits, is manufactured more cheaply by synthetical processes. Vitamin B has been found to consist of a complex mixture of compounds, part of which can be synthesized economically and some of which, with unknown or known chemical structure, are extracted from natural sources.

Chemicals from Milk. There are available, throughout the United States, some billions of pounds of whey, resulting from the making of cream and of cheese. Much of this whey is wasted each year or used as

---

[1] SHONLE, p. 1284, in "Rogers' Manual of Industrial Chemistry."
[2] SHONLE, p. 1298, *op. cit.;* ROSENBERG, "Chemistry and Physiology of the Vitamins," Interscience Publishers, Inc., New York, 1942.

a cheap animal food. A great deal of study has been given to the exploitation of this raw material and now about 5,000,000 lb. of lactic acid is made annually by fermentation as described in Chap. 31. In addition, this country manufactures about 5,000,000 lb. of lactose and 50,000,000 lb. of casein. The lactose has a certain limited consumption, almost entirely in infant foods and pharmaceutical preparations. Casein is a phosphoprotein of high molecular weight (probably near 100,000) with many and varied applications. About three-quarters of the casein now manufactured is consumed as a binder in high-grade coated paper for

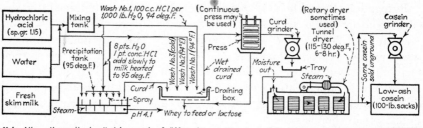

Note: Alternative methods, all giving casein of different properties, include precipitation with sulfuric or lactic acids (sour whey or allowing milk to sour), or by enzyme action with rennet

Skim milk	3,333 lb.	Water	Variable	
Hydrochloric acid (sp.gr.1.15)	19.93 lb.	Electricity	12 Kw.-hr.	Per 100 lb.
Steam*	1,200 lb.	Direct labor	3 man-hr.	casein

* Average present practice; can be much reduced

Fig. 9. Flow sheet for casein—grain-curd process using hydrochloric acid.

printing and stationery. Most of the remainder is used in glues, cold-water paints, and plastics.

Casein[1] is precipitated from skim milk by the use of an acid such as hydrochloric, sulfuric, or lactic acid, or by rennet. The casein resulting from these different methods has somewhat varying properties, and there seems to be more demand for the lactic casein among consumers. This is made by allowing the skim milk to sour naturally or, better, to use a starter fermentation to develop the lactic acid necessary to precipitate the casein. The manufacture through hydrochloric acid is depicted in the flow sheet of Fig. 9 where the casein is carefully precipitated as a grainy curd in a continuous spiral trough reactor, washed, pressed, disintegrated, dried, and pulverized.[2] Whey resulting from this separation

[1] CORWIN, Chap. 44 in "Rogers' Manual of Industrial Chemistry," many references and many data. TRIMBLE and BELL, Methods for Manufacturing Acid Precipitated Casein from Milk, *U.S. Dept. Agr. Circ.* 279, 1938; SUTERMEISTER and BROWNE, "Casein and Its Industrial Applications," Reinhold Publishing Corporation, New York, 1939; ANON., Lactic Acid and Casein from Skim Milk, *Chem. & Met. Eng.*, **43**, 480–483 (1936).

[2] Fuller details of this process are given by a pictured flow sheet, *Chem. & Met. Eng.*, **47**, 427 (1940); TRIMBLE and BELL, *op. cit.*, p. 25; CHRISMAN, Success in By-Production Demands Quality Control, *Food Inds.*, **12**, 45 (1940).

seems most suitable for concentration to lactose (Fig. 10) or for fermentation to lactic acid (page 692 of Chap. 31).

Lactose or milk sugar is much less sweet than sucrose. It has been consumed[1] chiefly in infant feeding. The only commercial source of any importance in the United States is the whey of cheese and casein plants.

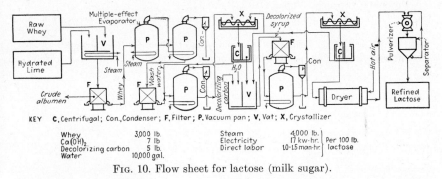

KEY **C**, Centrifugal; **Con.**, Condenser; **F**, Filter; **P**, Vacuum pan; **V**, Vat; **X**, Crystallizer

Whey	3,000 lb
Ca(OH)₂	7 lb
Decolorizing carbon	5 lb
Water	10,000 gal.

Steam	4,000 lb.
Electricity	17 kw-hr.
Direct labor	1.0-1.5 man-hr.

Per 100 lb. lactose

FIG. 10. Flow sheet for lactose (milk sugar).

Figure 10 shows the *unit operations* (Op.) and *unit processes* (Pr.) involved in the manufacture of lactose.

The raw whey is mixed with hydrated lime in a vat heated with steam coils (Pr.).

The precipitated albumin is removed by filtration (Op.).

The mother liquor, containing the lactose, is evaporated in multiple-effect vacuum evaporators (Op.).

The concentrated sirup is filtered to remove any foreign matter and concentrated further in a vacuum pan (Op.).

The sirup from this evaporator is crystallized and centrifuged. The mother liquor is sent back to the vacuum pan to be further concentrated to obtain another crop of lactose crystals. The mother liquor from this second crop of crystals is concentrated and sold as a by-product for its riboflavin content (Op.).

The crude lactose crystals are treated with water and activated carbon to remove coloring impurities (Op.).

Filtration removes the carbon and the decolorized sirup is concentrated, crystallized, and centrifuged (Op.).

The mother liquor is returned to the vat containing the decolorizing carbon and the crystals are dried, pulverized, and made ready for the market (Op.).

SELECTED REFERENCES

Groggins, P. H., editor, "Unit Processes in Organic Synthesis," 4th ed., McGraw-Hill Book Company, Inc., New York, 1952.

Ellis, Carleton, "Hydrogenation of Organic Substances," D. Van Nostrand Company, Inc., New York, 1930.

———, "Chemistry of Petroleum Derivatives," Reinhold Publishing Corporation, New York, 1937.

[1] HORNE, Sugar Industries of the United States, *Ind. Eng. Chem.*, **27**, 989 (1935).

Schotz, S. P., "Synthetic Organic Compounds," Ernest Benn, Ltd., London, 1925.

Ullmann, Fritz, "Enzyklopaedie der technischen Chemie," 3d ed., 10 vols., Urban & Schwarzenberg, Berlin and Vienna, 1951.

Furnas, C. C., editor, "Rogers' Manual of Industrial Chemistry," 6th ed., D. Van Nostrand Company, Inc., New York, 1942.

Schwyzer, Julius, "Die Fabrikation pharmazeutischer und chemischtechnischer Produkte," Springer-Verlag OHG, Berlin, 1931.

Curme, G. O., and F. Johnston, "Glycols," Reinhold Publishing Corporation, New York, 1952.

Kirk, R. E., and D. F. Othmer, "Encyclopedia of Chemical Technology," 15 vols., Interscience Publishers, Inc., New York, 1947–1956.

PROBLEMS

Problems should be an important part of any chemical engineering textbook. The instructor should make up some new problems each year, or modify ones used in a previous year. Also, a mixture of simple and comprehensive problems should be given to the class. The best comprehensive problems are the ones published annually and called the Student Contest Problems of the American Institute of Chemical Engineers'.[1]

Recently a new and enlarged edition of the problem book by Lewis, Radasch, and Lewis[2] has appeared. Some of these problems are of the comprehensive type. All of the problems and the text of this book will be helpful in causing the student to apply through problems many of the principles presented in this volume.

The following pages give, under the chapter numbers and titles used in this volume, a number of simple problems for about half the chapters followed by reference to chapters in Lewis, Radasch, and Lewis, *op. cit.*, for additional problems.

CHAPTER 3. GENERAL FUNDAMENTALS

Cf. Lewis, Radasch, and Lewis, Chapter 1.

CHAPTER 4. WATER CONDITIONING AND WASTE-WATER TREATMENT

1. A water contains the following metals, expressed in milligrams per liter: Ca^{++}, 30; Mg^{++}, 10; Fe^{++}, 0.5.

   a. Calculate the total hardness expressed in milligrams of equivalent $CaCO_3$ per liter.

   b. Assuming that 95 per cent CaO costs $11 per ton, calculate the cost of softening 1,000 gal. of this water.

2. A water has the following analysis expressed in grains per gallon (7,000 grains per lb.): $Ca(HCO_3)_2$, 7.00; $Mg(HCO_3)_2$, 2.92; $MgCO_3$, 1.00; $CaSO_4$, 1.36; $MgSo_4$, 2.16. Assuming 100 per cent CaO, Na_2CO_3, and NaCl cost $11, $20, and $4.50 per ton, respectively, calculate

   a. The cost of softening 1,000,000 gal. a day by the lime-soda process.

   b. The cost of salt per day for regeneration of zeolite if 0.5 lb. of salt is required for each 1,000 grains of hardness (as $CaCO_3$) removed from the water.

3. A water has the following ions present, p.p.m.: Ca^{++}, 75; Mg^{++}, 10; HCO_3^-, 190; CO_2, 11. If lime costs 68 cents and Na_2CO_3 costs $1.30 per 100 lb. what is the total cost for softening 800,000 cu. ft. of water?

[1] "A.I.Ch.E. Student Contest Problems, and the Prize Winning Solutions," American Institute of Chemical Engineers, New York, 1950.

[2] LEWIS, RADASCH, and LEWIS, "Industrial Stoichiometry," 2d ed., McGraw-Hill Book Company, Inc., New York, 1954.

CHAPTER 5. FUELS, POWER, AND AIR CONDITIONING

1. From the following data calculate the heat balance for a certain boiler plant: Coal fired, 5,000 lb. per hr.; water fed to boiler, 40,000 lb. per hr. at 200°F.; steam, 580°F. at 250 lb. per sq. in. abs.; flue gas, 650°F. The coal had the following analysis: C, 76.3; H_2, 4.8; O_2, 4.0; N_2, 0.7; S, 1.1; ash, 9.7; moisture, 3.4; 12,800 B.t.u. per lb. The cinder analysis was ash, 71.5; combustible, 28.5. The flue gas analysis was CO_2, 13.1; O_2, 5.7; CO, 0.6; N_2, 80.6. Assume 1 hr. and 60°F. as the datum line for the basis of calculations.

2. A roasting oven is fired with coal containing 8 per cent moisture, 21.0 per cent volatile combustible, 62 per cent fixed carbon, and 9.0 per cent ash with a heating value of 13,200 B.t.u. per lb. Refuse taken from the ashpit contains 10.0 per cent moisture, 9.0 per cent volatile combustible, 26.6 per cent fixed carbon, and 54.4 per cent ash. Calculate the percentage of the heating value of the coal that is lost by the presence of unburned combustible matter in the refuse.

3. Explain exactly how each of the following factors affects the efficiency, furnace temperature, and stack temperature of a steam boiler:

a. Insufficient air.

b. Excess air.

c. Leaky furnace settings.

d. Tube deposits.

4. A furnace fired with a hydrocarbon fuel oil has a dry stack gas analysis of 12.1 per cent CO_2, 6.1 per cent O_2, and 81.8 per cent N_2. Calculate

a. Composition of original fuel oil.

b. Percentage of excess air used.

c. Cubic feet of air (s.t.p.) per pound of fuel.

Cf. Lewis, Radasch, and Lewis, Chapters 1, 2, and 4.

CHAPTER 6. COAL CHEMICALS

Cf. Lewis, Radasch, and Lewis, Chapter 12, problems 3 and 4.

CHAPTER 7. FUEL GASES

1. A large three-lift water-sealed gas holder used for the storage of city gas is to be removed from service for internal inspection. State the principal precautions you would observe to ensure safety.

2. A producer gas has the following composition: CO, 24.0 per cent; CO_2, 4.0 per cent; O_2, 2.0 per cent; N_2, 70 per cent. Calculate

a. The cubic feet of gas at 70°F. and 750 mm. Hg pressure, per pound of carbon present.

b. The volume of air at the conditions of part (*a*), required for the combustion of 100 cu. ft. of the gas at the same conditions if it is desired that the total O_2 content present before combustion shall be 20 per cent in excess of that theoretically required.

c. The percentage composition by volume of the gases leaving the burner of part (*b*), assuming complete combustion.

d. The volume of the gases leaving the combustion of parts (*b*) and (*c*) at a temperature of 600°F. and a pressure of 750 mm. Hg per 100 cu. ft. of gas burned.

3. Using van der Waals' equation of state, calculate the density of methane at 500 lb. per sq. in. abs. and 80°F.

4. The reaction for the production of blue water gas containing 48 per cent H_2, 42 per cent CO, 5 per cent CO_2, and 5 per cent N_2 is presumed to be

$$C + H_2O \rightarrow CO + H_2$$

   a. Using handbook data, compute the heat absorbed in the production of the actual blue water gas, per pound of carbon consumed. Assume that the reaction takes place at 20°C.
   b. How much heat would be absorbed per pound of carbon consumed if the reaction took place at 1000°C?

5. A natural gas has the composition CH_4, 93 per cent; N_2, 4 per cent; H_2, 2 per cent; O_2, 1 per cent. The gas is piped from the well at a temperature of 16°C. and a pressure of 40 lb. per sq. in. abs. Assuming that the simple gas law is applicable, calculate

   a. The partial pressure of the O_2.
   b. The partial volume of N_2 per 20 cu. ft. of gas.
   c. The density of the mixture in pounds per cubic foot at the existing conditions.

6. A gas with a heating value of 1950 B.t.u. per cu. ft. has the following composition: C_2H_4 and C_6H_6, 55.1 per cent; O_2, 1.3 per cent; CH_4, 15.5 per cent; C_2H_6, 25.0 per cent; N_2, 3.1 per cent. Calculate the percentage of C_2H_4 and C_6H_6.

7. Calculate the theoretical flame temperature of the following gas when burned with theoretical amount of air. Combustion is only 75 per cent complete. Air and gas are initially at a temperature of 18°C.

   CO, 20 per cent; N_2, 74 per cent; CO_2, 6 per cent.

8. Calculate the number of calories required to heat, from 373 to 2000°C., 10,000 cu. ft. (s.t.p.) of a gas having the following composition (by volume): CO_2, 19 per cent; O_2, 2 per cent; N_2, 79 per cent.

9. A producer gas (8 per cent CO_2, 17 per cent H_2, 26 per cent CO, 1 per cent CH_4, 48 per cent N_2) is made from a coal containing 72 per cent C, 4 per cent H_2O, 7 per cent ash, 17 per cent volatile combustibles. Assuming that all steam and water are decomposed and the volatile combustibles contain only C and H, calculate

   a. Cubic feet of producer gas (dry s.t.p.) per pound of coal fired.
   b. Cubic feet of air used (dry s.t.p.) per pound of coal fired.
   c. Pounds of steam decomposed per pound of coal fired.
   d. Ultimate analysis of the fuel.
   e. Pounds of steam decomposed per pound of coal fired in excess of that brought in by the fuel itself.

10. A producer gas analyzing 3.6 per cent CO_2, 0.8 per cent C_2H_4, 2.7 per cent CH_4, 11.6 per cent H_2, 29.7 per cent CO_2, and 51.6 per cent N_2 under a positive pressure of 1.5 in. of water and saturated with water vapor at 100°F. is burned in a furnace with air which enters at 70°F. and 60 per cent saturated with water vapor. The flue gas, which is at 460°F., analyzes 8.1 per cent CO_2, 1.7 per cent CO, 7.9 per cent O_2, and 82.3 per cent N_2. The barometer is 747 mm. Calculate

   a. Percentage of excess air.
   b. Cubic feet of gas formed per cubic foot of fuel gas entering.
   c. Cubic feet of air supplied per cubic foot of fuel gas entering.

   Cf. Lewis, Radasch, and Lewis, Chapters 2, 3, and 5.

CHAPTER 8. INDUSTRIAL GASES

1. Hydrogen by the steam-iron process is being produced at the rate of 3,500 cu. ft. per hr. If 2.5 times the necessary steam is used, what is the weight of steam used per day?

2. It is desired to market O_2 in small cylinders having volumes of 0.8 cu. ft., each containing 1.5 lb. of oxygen. If the cylinders are subjected to a maximum temperature of 110°F., calculate the pressure for which they must be designed. Assume the applicability of the simple gas law.

3. Calculate the number of hours of service that can be derived from 5 lb. of carbide in an acetylene lamp burning 5 cu. ft. of gas per hour at a temperature of 70°F. and a pressure of 755 mm. of Hg.

4. Calculate the molecular heat of combustion of acetylene from the following data (basis C as *graphite*):

$$2H_2 + O_2 \rightarrow 2H_2O; \quad \Delta H = -2(68,375) \text{ cal.}$$
$$2C + O_2 \rightarrow 2CO; \quad \Delta H = -2(26,390) \text{ cal.}$$
$$C + O_2 \rightarrow CO_2; \quad \Delta H = -94,030 \text{ cal.}$$
$$2Ca + O_2 \rightarrow 2CaO; \quad \Delta H = -2(151,700) \text{ cal.}$$
$$Ca, O_2, H_2 \rightarrow Ca(OH)_2; \quad \Delta H = -236,000 \text{ cal.}$$
$$Ca, 2C \rightarrow CaC_2; \quad \Delta H = -14,500 \text{ cal.}$$
$$2C, H_2 \rightarrow C_2H_2; \quad \Delta H = +54,800 \text{ cal.}$$

5. *a.* How much coke, air, water, and limestone are necessary for the production of 500,000,000 B.t.u. from acetylene?

b. How much of each is necessary if the CO is to be burned also?

6. CO_2 is being absorbed in alkaline solution and heated to recover the pure CO_2. The average CO_2 content in the flue gases entering the absorbing towers is 18 per cent and the gases leaving the towers contain 10 per cent. Of the recovered CO_2 12 per cent is lost in various ways and 88 per cent is recovered as the pure CO_2 product. Calculate

a. The percentage of the entering CO_2 absorbed in the towers.

b. The percentage of the original CO_2 recovered as a final product.

7. By passing a clean purified flue gas up an absorption tower fed with a so-called *lye* solution, made up originally with Na_2CO_3, the CO_2 content of the gas is reduced from 17.1 to 12.1 per cent. The lye solution at entrance and exit is analyzed with 0.2303N HCl, using in each case 10-cc. samples of lye. For the incoming lye 28.21 cc. of acid are required to decolorize phenol-phthalein and a total of 72.30 cc. to get an end point with methyl orange. For the exit liquor these values are 18.41 and 73.16 cc., respectively. 185 gal. of lye per hour are supplied to the tower, which operates at a substantially constant temperature of 150°F.

a. What percentage of the alkali in the two solutions is in the form of bicarbonate?

b. How many pounds of CO_2 are absorbed per hour?

c. What is the volume in cubic feet per hour of the gas entering the tower?

8. By treating dolomitic limestone with sulfuric acid, pure CO_2 can be prepared. The limestone used in such a process contained $CaCO_3$ and $MgCO_3$, the remainder being inert, insoluble materials. The acid used contained 10 per cent H_2SO_4 by weight. The residue from the process had the following composition:

Per cent

Water............	85.00
$CaSO_4$............	8.30
$MgSO_4$............	5.00
H_2SO_4............	1.00
Inerts............	0.60
CO_2............	0.10

During the process the mass was warmed and CO_2 and water vapor removed.

a. Calculate the analysis of the limestone used.

b. Calculate the percentage of excess acid used.

c. Calculate the weight and analysis of the material removed from the reaction mass per 100 lb. of limestone treated.

Cf. Lewis, Radasch, and Lewis, Figs. 10-4; 10-5.

CHAPTER 9. INDUSTRIAL CARBON

A plant is designed to manufacture charcoal from walnut shells which cost $1 per ton. The gas required for charring the shells costs $1 per ton of shells. Electricity is 6 cents per kilowatt-hour and $4\frac{1}{4}$ hp. of electricity is used continuously per 24-hr. day. Water costs $1.50 per day. Nine tons of shells are used per day to manufacture 3 tons of charcoal. Three men working 10 hr. per day and one man working 8 hr. a day are paid at the rate of $1.50 per hour. Sacking expenses are $4 per ton of charcoal. What is the profit per ton of charcoal selling at $50 per ton?

CHAPTER 10. THE CERAMIC INDUSTRIES

1. A pottery kiln is made up of a 4-in. layer of firebrick and an 8-in. layer of building brick, the latter being on the outside where the temperature is 125°F. The temperature within the kiln is 2500°F. The thermal conductivities for firebrick and brick are 0.62 and 0.42 B.t.u. per hr.-ft.² per °F. per ft., respectively. Assuming perfect contact between the layers, calculate

a. The rate of heat flow through the wall B.t.u. per hr.-ft.²

b. The temperature at the junction of the two layers.

2. A test run is being made on a tunnel kiln used for firing bricks. The kiln is coal-fired, and all ash is removed by allowing it to drop into a pit filled with water. Evaporated water enters the stack with other gases. The tunnel holds 36 cars. One car is removed every 2 hr. and each car carries 900 bricks. Calculate the amount of heat and percentage loss due to

a. Sensible heat in dry flue gas.

b. Sensible heat in refuse.

c. Heat carried out by clay and clay structure of the kiln.

d. Unburned CO in flue gas.

e. Heat loss due to C in refuse.

Use the following data:

Analysis of Coal:

	Per cent
H_2	5.22
C	76.17
N_2	1.50
O_2	7.65
S	1.92
Ash	7.54
Calorific value	13,830 B.t.u. per lb.
Total coal fired	1,937 lb.

Analysis of Refuse:

	Per cent
H₂O	0.15
Volatile	1.65
Fixed C	28.66
Ash	69.54

H_2O ... 0.15
Volatile ... 1.65
Fixed C ... 28.66
Ash ... 69.54

Temperatures:

Atmosphere ... 79°F.
Flue gas ... 340°F.

Specific Heat (at 209.5°F.):

B.t.u. per lb. °F.

Clay ... 0.23
CO_2 ... 0.2095
O_2 ... 0.2167
N_2, CO ... 0.2471
Steam ... 0.491 (between 212° and 340°)

(Latent heat of vaporization of water = 967 B.t.u. per lb.)
Ashpit holds 566 lb. H_2O.
4.735 lb. wet ash as removed weighed 2.71 lb. after drying.
Boiling point H_2O = 212°F.

Flue Gas Analysis:

	Per cent
CO₂	3.29
CO	0.16
N₂	79.88
O₂	16.67

CO_2 ... 3.29
CO ... 0.16
N_2 ... 79.88
O_2 ... 16.67

Removable percentage of water in bricks = 4.55.
Green ware = 17,100 lb.
Clay structure in kiln = 7,100 lb.
Assume heat content of all other parts of structure as negligible, heat content of moisture as a product of combustion and is driven out of the clay ware as negligible.
The cars containing the clay came out at a temperature of 900°F.
Heat of combustion of CO = 4,380 B.t.u. per lb.
Cf. Lewis, Radasch, and Lewis, Chapters 11 and 12 (design of a tunnel kiln).

CHAPTER 11. CEMENTS, CALCIUM AND MAGNESIUM COMPOUNDS

1. Draw a flow sheet for a plant manufacturing portland cement by the wet process. All units should be numbered or otherwise designated and a concise, accurate description of each type of unit given in an appendix.

2. A portland cement contains 4 moles of tricalcium silicate to 3 moles of dicalcium silicate. If there are 23.03 lb. of SiO_2 per 100 lb. of cement, what are the absolute amounts of the silicates present? How much CaO should be added to change the ratio to 8 moles of tricalcium silicate to 1 mole of dicalcium silicate?

3. A limestone containing 48 per cent CO_2 (dry basis) and no other volatile material is burned with a coal containing 78.1 per cent C, 6.2 per cent H, 6.2 per cent ash, and 9.5 per cent O_2. The air is dry. Barometric pressure is 757 mm. The stack gases, leaving at 650°F. and 757 mm., contain 26.3 per cent CO_2, 2.9 per cent O_2, and 70.8 per cent N_2. Calculate

    a. Pounds of lime produced per pound of coal fired.

    b. Percentage of excess air.

    c. Cubic feet of stack gas per pound of lime produced.

    4. In the calcination of pure $CaCO_3$, the CO_2 leaves the kiln at 400°C. The CaO is withdrawn at 1500°C. If the charge enters at 70°C., how many B.t.u. are necessary for complete calcination of 500 lb. of $CaCO_3$? Specific heat of CaO is 0.22 cal. per gram-°C.

    5. The gases from a shaft limekiln, externally fired, are 20.0 per cent CO_2, 5.0 per cent O_2, and 75.0 per cent N_2, and leave at 400°F. The coal fired has a heating value of 13,000 B.t.u. per lb. and contains 79.0 per cent C, 6.0 per cent H, 7.5 per cent O, and 7.5 per cent ash. The limestone enters at 70°F. and its analysis is 81.0 per cent $CaCO_3$, 6.0 per cent $MgCO_3$, and 13.0 per cent inert. The burnt lime leaves at 500°F. The entering air is at 70°F. with a water vapor pressure of 12 mm. The barometric pressure is 755 mm. Calculate

    a. Pounds of burnt lime produced per pound of coal fired.

    b. Percentage of excess air.

    c. Sensible heat in waste gases (as percentage of heating value of coal burned).

    d. Latent heat in waste gases (as percentage of heating value of coal burned).

    e. Heat of decomposition of lime (as percentage of heating value of coal burned).

    f. Sensible heat in the lime (as percentage of heating value of coal burned).

    g. Radiation and other losses (as percentage of heating value of coal burned).

Heat of formation of $MgCo_3$ from MgO and CO_2 at 70°F.

$$= 47,300 \text{ B.t.u. per lb.-mole}$$

Heat of formation of $CaCO_3$ from CaO and CO_2 at 70°F.

$$= 76,500 \text{ B.t.u. per lb.-mole}$$

Specific heat of burnt lime = 0.18 B.t.u. per lb. per °F.

Cf. Lewis, Radasch, and Lewis, Chapters 1 and 8.

CHAPTER 12. GLASS INDUSTRIES

    1. A glass for the manufacture of chemical ware is composed of the silicates and borates of several basic metals. Its composition is as follows:

	Per cent		Per cent
SiO_2	65.0	ZnO	10.8
B_2O_3	8.5	MgO	7.0
Al_2O_3	1.0	Na_2O	7.7

Al_2O_3 acts as a base and B_2O_3 as an acid, HBO_2. Determine whether the acid or basic constituents are in excess in this glass and the percentage of excess reacting value above that theoretically required for a neutral glass.

    2. A glass company is producing single-strength (⅛ in. thick) window panes 2½ by 1½ ft. in size. The glass drawn from a débiteuse is 65 in. wide and has a specific gravity of 2.60. What is the largest number of window panes that can be made from a batch of glass of the following weights:

Tons

Sand (pure SiO_2)................................... 50
Na_2CO_3.. 16
CaO.. 7
Na_2SO_4... 6
Coal.. $\frac{1}{4}$

3. Calculate the percentage of the total charge in the previous problem which disappears from the melt as CO_2 and SO_3.

CHAPTER 13. POTASSIUM SALTS AND MIXED FERTILIZERS

1. Five hundred metric tons of fixed nitrogen are needed. Assuming 95 per cent purity, what weight of urea should be ordered? Assuming 95 per cent purity, repeat the calculations for ammonium sulfate and Chilean nitrate. (One metric ton = 2,205 lb.)

2. A fertilizer is to have a 2-16-4 ratio and is to be made from KNO_3 and a Peruvian guano which contains 1.95 per cent N_2, 19 per cent P_2O_5, and $3\frac{1}{3}$ per cent K_2O. Calculate the amounts of each per ton of fertilizer.

3. It is desired to make a 4-14-2 fertilizer by mixing ammonium dihydrogen phosphate and ammonia with a 2-11-3 fertilizer already on hand. How much of each of these three materials will be necessary to make 100 lb. of the 4-14-2 fertilizer? Is a filler necessary? If so, how much?

4. Make a fertilizer with the composition:

N_2...................................... 4 per cent
P_2O_5.................................... 8 per cent
K_2O..................................... 10 per cent

from

a. $NaNO_3$ containing 16 per cent N_2.
b. Acid phosphate containing 15 per cent available P_2O_5.
c. KCl containing 50 per cent K_2O.
d. Inert filler.

How many pounds of each of these materials will be required per ton of fertilizer?

CHAPTER 14. SALT AND MISCELLANEOUS SODIUM COMPOUNDS

1. 1,000 lb. of rasorite containing 85 per cent $Na_2B_4O_7 \cdot 4H_2O$ is redissolved, filtered, and run to the crystallizer as a 20 per cent solution of borax, $Na_2B_4O_7 \cdot 10H_2O$ at 175°F. After cooling to 110°F. the crystals are centrifuged and go to the drier carrying 6 per cent moisture. The mother liquor contains 10 per cent borax. What yield of dry crystals is obtained?

2. In the evaporation of salt brines a certain manufacturer uses a triple-effect evaporator with parallel feed. Fifty per cent of the feed sent into each effect is evaporated. Eight thousand pounds of saturated steam per hour at 230°F. is sent into the first effect. Brine is sent into first effect at 70°F.

	Effect		
	I	II	III
Boiling point, °F................................	210	180	125
Area, sq. ft....................................	500	500	500

Calculate

a. Capacity of the evaporator.

b. Steam economy.

c. Over-all coefficient for each effect.

Cf. Lewis, Radasch, and Lewis, Chapter 1.

CHAPTER 15. SODA ASH, CAUSTIC SODA, AND CHLORINE

1. A plant is to manufacture 500,000 lb. of Solvay ammonia soda per day, containing 96.7 per cent Na_2CO_3. How much salt will be required for the actual conversion if it is 98.5 per cent NaCl? If the carbonating towers consume only 66 per cent of the salt, how much salt is actually required?

2. A plant is making soda with a 98.1 per cent purity; 50,000 lb. of salt is actually converted. The reaction $NH_4HCO_3 + NaCl \rightarrow NaHCO_3 + NH_4Cl$ goes 80 per cent to completion while the conversion of bicarbonate to carbonate is done without loss. How many pounds of $NaHCO_3$ (dry) are produced? How many pounds of dry soda ash are made? How much salt is originally used?

3. Calculate the weight of NaCl and of $CaCO_3$ to make 1 ton of soda ash containing the equivalent of 58 per cent Na_2O. Assume that 25 per cent excess NaCl is necessary in the first step and 7 per cent $NaHCO_3$ lost in washing.

4. 3,000 lb. of NaCl is to be converted into Na_2CO_3 per cycle by the Solvay process. Assume all reactions go 100 per cent and that 19 per cent of the salt put in is lost. 920 lb. of CO_2 is recirculated with losses of CO_2 amounting to 5 per cent of the total CO_2 present each cycle plus 10 per cent of the recycled CO_2. Ammonia losses are 0.5 per cent and the rest of the ammonia is recycled. Calculate the amounts of $CaCO_3$ and NH_3 that must be supplied initially for conversion of 3,000 lb. NaCl per cycle and that which must be supplied for each subsequent 3,000-lb. cycle.

5. A single-effect evaporator is to be designed to concentrate 250 gal. of 10 per cent NaOH solution (sp. gr. = 1.116) per hour to 50 per cent (sp. gr. = 1.540). Feed is to enter at 70°F. (steam pressure = 5 lb. per sq. in. gage). Vacuum is 27 in. referred to a 30-in. barometer. The specific heat of feed is 0.95; of finished liquor, 0.85.

Boiling point rise (50 per cent NaOH solution) = 30°F.
Over-all heat transfer coefficient = 225.

The finished liquor will leave the evaporator at the boiling temperature and condensate will leave the basket at equilibrium temperature for 5 lb. steam. Calculate,

a. Area of heating surface to be supplied (sq. ft.).

b. Steam consumption in pounds per hour.

c. Expected steam economy.

6. Sodium carbonate crystals (decahydrate) are dissolved in 103 lb. of water. This is treated with a $Ca(OH)_2$ slurry giving 200 lb. of 9 per cent NaOH solution with a 92 per cent conversion. Calculate

a. Weight of $Ca(OH)_2$ slurry.

b. Weight of $Na_2CO_3 \cdot 10H_2O$ used.

c. Percentage of Na_2CO_3 in NaOH solution.

d. Percentage of Na_2CO_3 solution.

7. A soda ash solution containing 22 per cent Na_2CO_3 is to be treated with lime (83 per cent conversion) to form a caustic solution containing 14 per cent NaOH. If there were 9.8 lb. of lime in the original suspension, what percentage of the total suspension is lime?

8. A caustic soda solution is to be made by adding a 16 per cent Na_2CO_3 solution in the proper stoichiometric proportions to a slurry containing 30 per cent $Ca(OH)_2$. If the conversion is 90 per cent complete, what is the concentration of the resulting solution?

9. A plant causticizes 300 tons of 95 per cent soda ash per day obtaining a 96 per cent yield. The lime is 96 per cent CaO and is used in theoretical amount. If 42 per cent NaOH liquor is to be made, how much lime is to be used and how much caustic soda will be produced daily?

10. The liquor from a diaphragm cell contains 10 per cent NaOH and 13 per cent NaCl. 15,000 lb. of caustic containing 2.3 per cent NaCl is produced per day by evaporation of the liquors. Calculate the pounds of salt that precipitate per day in the evaporators and the decomposition efficiency of the cell.

11. Chlorine gas and caustic are being made in Hooker-type cells. The chlorine contains 0.9 per cent oxygen and, for the purpose of measuring the rate of generation, more O_2 gas is added to the chlorine at a rate of 2 lb. O_2 per min. The gas now analyzes 3.0 per cent O_2. How much caustic (100 per cent) will be produced in one hour? (Temperature is 25°C., barometer normal.)

12. An alkali chlorine manufacturer has an excess of moist cell gas (97 per cent chlorine) which he proposes to liquefy.

a. Draw a schematic diagram of the equipment required.

b. Describe the function of each unit and specify the material from which it may be constructed.

c. Describe the type of compression and liquefaction equipment you would select.

13. A battery of 50 Nelson cells produces 8 tons of Cl_2 per day. Cathodic current efficiency is 94 per cent. Anodic current efficiency is the same.

Calculate,

a. Amount of caustic soda produced in the cell per day.

b. Assuming 100 per cent current efficiency, calculate current in ampere-hours that passes through the cell if 1 amp.-hr. is required for 0.0033 lb. of NaOH.

Cf. Lewis, Radasch, and Lewis, Chapters 9 and 12, Design of sodium hypochlorite process.

CHAPTER 16. ELECTROLYTIC INDUSTRIES

1. If finely pulverized iron costs 10 cents per pound, 30 per cent muriatic acid 1.05 cents per pound, and electricity 1 cent per kilowatt-hour, what is the comparative price for a pound atom of active reducing hydrogen produced (1) from iron and hydrochloric acid and (2) by the passage of the electric current if 2 volts are required to release the hydrogen?

2. "10 volume" hydrogen peroxide will liberate upon acidification at 60°F. and under normal barometric pressure oxygen whose volume is ten times the volume of the original solution. What is the percentage of hydrogen peroxide in the original water solution?

3. A bauxite sample runs 61 per cent Al_2O_3 and 8 per cent SiO_2. This material is roasted, dissolved in caustic soda to form a solution from which the iron present is precipitated by dilution and oxidation, then removed by filtration. By suitable treatment hydrated Al_2O_3 is precipitated in a very pure form with a recovery of 80 per cent of the original Al_2O_3. The SiO_2 remains behind as Na_2SiO_3. The precipitated hydrated Al_2O_3 is dehydrated and forms the charge to an aluminum furnace. If caustic soda is purchased as a solution in water containing NaOH equivalent to 38.8 per cent Na_2O at a cost of 1.3 cents per pound of solution, what will be the cost of the caustic soda used in producing 100 lb. of pure Al_2O_3 assuming that there is used 10 per cent more than the theoretical amount of NaOH required to react with the silica and Al_2O_3 present in the original bauxite? Note that most of this caustic soda is concentrated and reused.

Cf. Lewis, Radasch, and Lewis, Chapter 12, Problem 1.

CHAPTER 18. PHOSPHORUS INDUSTRIES

Cf. Lewis, Radasch, and Lewis, Chapter 12, Problem 5.

CHAPTER 19. SULFUR AND SULFURIC ACID

1. An iron pyrite has the following composition: Fe, 40.0 per cent; S, 43.6 per cent. This pyrite is burned with air 100 per cent in excess of that required to burn all the iron to Fe_2O_3 and all the sulfur to SO_2. Assume that no SO_3 is formed in the furnace. After the gases formed have passed through the converter, 95 per cent of the SO_2 is oxidized to SO_3. What will be the composition of the gases entering and leaving the converter?

2. Oxides of nitrogen may be produced by treating crude $NaNO_3$ with sulfuric acid or by the oxidation of ammonia. How many pounds of 66°Bé. sulfuric acid and 95 per cent sodium nitrate must be used to yield the equivalent of the oxides of nitrogen produced by oxidizing 1 lb. of anhydrous ammonia?

3. A typical analysis of an Illinois coal shows it to contain 2.99 per cent S, 66.5 per cent C, 4.26 per cent H, and the remainder noncombustibles. A large power plant burns 500 tons of this coal per day with 40 per cent excess air. What will be the composition of the stack gas in percentage SO_2? If a plant was installed to recover this sulfur dioxide, how many cubic feet of gas (at 300°F. and 750 mm.) would have to be scrubbed per minute? Assuming a recovery of 50 per cent of the sulfur fired in the form of SO_2, how many tons of sulfuric acid (66°Bé.) could be produced as a by-product of this plant in a year?

CHAPTER 20. NITROGEN INDUSTRIES

Where the presence of nitrogen is not objectionable, hydrogen for reductions may be produced by cracking ammonia at high temperature. A cylinder of hydrogen under high pressure contains 1 lb. of hydrogen and weighs approximately 100 lb. An ammonia cylinder containing 100 lb. of ammonia weighs approximately 150 lb. A plant wishes to reduce 1 ton of Fe_2O_3 to metallic iron per day with hydrogen. If freight is 20 cents per 100 lb. hauled and it costs 3 cents per pound to crack ammonia, calculate and compare the costs of cylinder hydrogen and hydrogen from ammonia. Ammonia costs 5 cents per pound and cylinder hydrogen $1 per pound.

Cf. Lewis, Radasch, and Lewis, Chapter 7.

CHAPTER 22. EXPLOSIVES, PYROTECHNICS, AND CHEMICAL WARFARE

1. The spent acid from a nitration process has the composition 43 per cent sulfuric acid, 36 per cent nitric acid, and 21 per cent water by weight. This acid is to be fortified by the addition of concentrated sulfuric acid containing 91 per cent H_2SO_4 and strong nitric acid containing 88 per cent HNO_3. The fortified mixed acid is to contain 40 per cent H_2SO_4 and 43 per cent HNO_3. Calculate the quantities of spent and concentrated acids that should be mixed together to yield 1,000 lb. of the desired acid.

2. Four hundred pounds of toluene is agitated with 4,000 lb. of mixed acid having the following composition: 7.5 per cent HNO_3, 80 per cent H_2SO_4, 12.5 per cent H_2O. If the nitration proceeds until all of the toluene is changed to mononitro-toluene, what will be the composition of the spent acid when the mononitro-toluene is separated from it?

3. Nitro-glycerine decomposes on explosion according to the following empirical formula:

$$C_3H_5(NO_3)_3 \rightarrow 3CO_2 + 2.5H_2O + 1.5N_2 + 0.25O_2$$

The temperature of the gases has been determined to be 3360°C. at the instant of explosion. If 5 grams of nitro-glycerine are exploded in a 1-liter bomb, what pressure should be exerted at the instant of explosion if the walls are not to rupture?

CHAPTER 24. PAINT, VARNISH, LACQUER, AND ALLIED INDUSTRIES

Cf. Lewis, Radasch, and Lewis, Chapter 10, Problem 6.

CHAPTER 29. SOAP AND OTHER SURFACE-ACTIVE AGENTS

A washing compound is to be made by drying a solution containing 15 per cent soap and 25 per cent sodium carbonate. During the course of the drying the sodium carbonate is converted to the decahydrate and appears in the finished product in this form. The finished washing compound contains 8 per cent free moisture. How many pounds of solution should be taken to produce 100 lb. of finished washing compound?

CHAPTER 33. PULP AND PAPER INDUSTRIES

Cf. Lewis, Radasch, and Lewis, Chapter 9 (particularly Ill. 6 and Problem 11); Chapter 12 (Problem 2).

CHAPTER 35. PLASTICS

Plastics as a whole are made of a very limited number of raw materials of which petroleum, lime, salt, coal, water, air, and naval stores are the most fundamental. Starting with those raw materials, prepare a chart showing all the intermediates involved in the manufacture of the following plastics: acrylate resins, vinyl resins, synthetic rubber (several types), phenolic resins, alkyd resins, and melamine resins.

CHAPTER 36. NATURAL AND SYNTHETIC RUBBER

1. Certain ingredients are generally added to rubber in very small quantities. To aid in the rapid incorporation of these materials and in the accuracy of the measured quantity used, the chemical to be added is often blended into a "master batch" of rubber separately, and small known weights of the master batch are added to the rubber as it is worked on the rolls. A certain rubber formula is to contain, among other things, in the finished product 0.56 per cent Captax, 0.49 per cent phenyl-β-naphthylamine, and 65 per cent smoked sheet, the entire batch weighing 150 lb. The chemist uses 100 lb. of smoked sheet to make up a master batch of Captax containing 5 per cent Captax. Later, by error, he incorporates 6 lb. of phenyl-β-naphthylamine into this batch. In order to avoid discarding the master batch, he adjusts its components to a fixed ratio between Captax and phenyl-β-naphthylamine. What will be the composition of the master batch and how much master batch should be added to the batch on the mill to give the proper proportions of Captax and phenyl-β-naphthylamine in the finished product?

2. Butyl rubber is polymerized at an extremely low temperature, frequently as low as $-100°F$. At these temperatures extreme care should be taken to provide absolutely dry ingredients to avoid formation of ice on the heat-transfer surfaces and to avoid the loss of heat. After polymerization the charge must be heated to $+150°F$. Describe the precautions necessary to make this process feasible from the standpoint of heat consumption and freedom from icing troubles.

3. Tennis balls are made by curing two halves around a pill of ammonium nitrite, then decomposing the nitrite by heat to inflate the interior.

$$NH_4NO_2 \rightarrow N_2 + 2H_2O$$

If the ball is a 2-in. diameter sphere, how much ammonium nitrite must be added to give an internal pressure of 50 lb. per sq. in. gage at 70°F. after it is decomposed according to the above formula? Assume the ball to be at a temperature of 30°C. at the time the pill is inserted.

CHAPTER 37. THE PETROLEUM INDUSTRY

1. A certain gasoline has an A.P.I. gravity of 62° at 60°F./60°F. What is its specific gravity? What is its gravity in degrees Baumé? How much will a 50-gal. barrel of it weigh?

2. Gasoline is sweetened to remove odor. The primary reaction involved may be assumed to be

$$2RSH + (O) \rightarrow RSSR + H_2O$$

If a straight-run gasoline (A.P.I. gravity = 51.2° at 60°F./60°F.), containing 0.06 per cent sulfur all of which is assumed to be present as mercaptans, could be sweetened catalytically by the use of the cheapest known oxidizing agent, air, how many cubic feet of dry air at 60°F. would be required to sweeten 1,000 bbl. (42 gal. each) of this gasoline if 60 per cent of the oxygen fed took part in the reaction?

3. A gas has the following composition by volume: H_2, 5.4 per cent; CH_4, 9.9 per cent; C_2H_6, 6.1 per cent; C_3H_8, 26.9 per cent; C_4H_{10}, 51.7 per cent. If this gas is compressed to 60 lb. per sq. in., how many pounds per hour will pass through an 8-in. inside diameter pipe line if the gas flows at a temperature of 60°F. and a velocity of 6 ft. per sec.?

CHAPTER 38. INTERMEDIATES, DYES, AND THEIR APPLICATIONS

Cf. Lewis, Radasch, and Lewis, Chapter 12, Problem 6.

NAME INDEX

SUBJECT INDEX

Page references in **boldface** type indicate main discussions